Mathematical Applications

for the Management, Life, and Social Sciences

12th Edition

Ronald J. Harshbarger

University of South Carolina

James J. Reynolds

Clarion University of Pennsylvania

⁂ CENGAGE

Australia • Brazil • Mexico • Singapore • United Kingdom • United States

CENGAGE

Mathematic Applications for the Management, Life, and Social Sciences, Twelfth Edition

Ronald J. Harshbarger, James J. Reynolds

Senior Vice President: Erin Joyner

Product Director: Mark Santee

Product Manager: Rita Lombard

Content Developer: Morgan Mendoza

Product Assistant: Abby DeVeuve

Marketing Manager: Ana Albinson and Giana Manzi

Senior Content Project Manager: John Fuller

Art Director: Vernon Boes

Manufacturing Planner: Douglas Bertke

IP Analyst: Ann Hoffman

IP Project Manager: Erika Mugavin

Production Service and Compositor: Lumina Datamatics

Text and Cover Design: Hespenheide Design

Cover Image: Times Square from helicopter at night. Image courtesy of WIN-Initiative/ Getty Images.

For product information and technology assistance, contact us at **Cengage Learning Customer & Sales Support, 1-800-354-9706.**
For permission to use material from this text or product, submit all requests online at **www.cengage.com/permissions.**
Further permissions questions can be emailed to **permissionrequest@cengage.com.**

Library of Congress Control Number: 2017953697

Student Edition:

978-1-337-62534-0

Loose-leaf Edition:

978-1-337-63053-5

Instructor's Edition:

978-1-337-63045-0

Cengage Learning

20 Channel Center Street

Boston, MA 02210

USA

Cengage is a leading provider of customized learning solutions with employees residing in nearly 40 different countries and sales in more than 125 countries around the world. Find your local representative at **www.cengage.com.**

Cengage products are represented in Canada by Nelson Education, Ltd.

To learn more about Cengage platforms and services, visit **www.cengage.com.**

To register or access your online learning solution or purchase materials for your course, visit **www.cengagebrain.com.**

Printed at CLDPC, USA, 08-21

Contents

Preface

To paraphrase English mathematician, philosopher, and educator Alfred North Whitehead, the purpose of education is not to fill a vessel but to kindle a fire. In particular, Whitehead encouraged students to be creative and imaginative in their learning and to continually form ideas into new and more exciting combinations. This desirable goal is not always an easy one to realize in mathematics with students whose primary interests are in areas other than mathematics. The purpose of this text, then, is to present mathematical skills and concepts and to apply them to ideas that are important to students in the management, life, and social sciences. We hope that this look at the relevance of mathematical ideas to a broad range of fields will help inspire the imaginative thinking and excitement for learning about which Whitehead spoke. The applications included allow students to view mathematics in a practical setting relevant to their intended careers. Almost every chapter of this book includes a section or two devoted to the applications of mathematical topics, and every section contains a number of application examples and problems. An index of these applications on the front and back inside covers demonstrates the wide variety used in examples and exercises. Although intended for students who have completed two years of high school algebra or its equivalent, this text begins with a brief review of algebra that, if covered, will aid in preparing students for the work ahead.

Pedagogical Features

In this new edition, we have incorporated many suggestions that reflect the needs and wishes of our users, including effective pedagogical features from previous editions.

Intuitive Viewpoint.   The book is written from an intuitive viewpoint, with emphasis on concepts and problem solving rather than on mathematical theory. Yet each topic is carefully developed and explained, and examples illustrate the techniques involved.

Flexibility.   At different colleges and universities, the coverage and sequencing of topics may vary according to the purpose of the course and the nature of the student audience. To accommodate alternative approaches, the text has a great deal of flexibility in the order in which topics may be presented and the degree to which they may be emphasized.

Applications.   We have found that integrating applied topics into the discussions and exercises helps provide motivation within the sections and demonstrates the relevance of each topic. Numerous real-life application examples and exercises represent the applicability of the mathematics, and each application problem is identified so that the instructor or student can select applications that are of special interest. In addition, we have found that offering separate lessons on applied topics such as cost, revenue, and profit functions brings the preceding mathematical discussions into clear, concise focus and provides a thread of continuity as mathematical sophistication increases. There are 10 such sections throughout the book and two application-focused chapters: Chapter 4, devoted to linear programming, and Chapter 6, devoted to financial applications. Of the more than 5500 exercises in the book, more than 2000 are applied.

Chapter Warm-ups.   With the exception of Chapter 0, a Warm-up appears at the beginning of each chapter and invites students to test themselves on the skills needed for that chapter. The Warm-up sections present many prerequisite problem types that are keyed to the appropriate sections in the upcoming chapter where those skills are needed. Students who have difficulty with any particular skill are directed to specific sections of the text for review. Instructors may also find the Warm-ups useful in creating a course syllabus that includes an appropriate scope and sequence of topics.

CHAPTER WARM-UP

Prerequisite Problem Type	For Section
Evaluate:	**1.1–1.3, 1.5, 1.6**

(a) $2(-1)^3 - 3(-1)^2 + 1$

(b) $3(-3) - 1$

(c) $14(10) - 0.02(10^2)$

Application Previews and Associated Examples.   Each section begins with an Application Preview that establishes the context and direction for the concepts that will be presented. Each of these Previews presents the mathematics in the section and references a completely worked Application Preview Example appearing later in the section.

SECTION 1.1

OBJECTIVES

- To solve linear equations in one variable
- To solve applied problems using linear equations
- To solve linear inequalities in one variable

Solutions of Linear Equations and Inequalities in One Variable

APPLICATION PREVIEW

Using data from 1980 and projected to 2050, the number of Hispanics i civilian non-institutional population can be approximated by

$$y = 0.876x + 6.084$$

million, where x is the number of years after 1980 (*Source:* U.S. Census B find the year when this we solve $36.74 = 0.876$ linear equations and in

EXAMPLE   2   U.S. Hispanic Population | APPLICATION PREVIEW |

Using data from 1980 and projected to 2050, the number of Hispanics non-institutional population can be approximated by $y = 0.876x + 6.0$ is the number of years after 1980 (*Source:* U.S. Census Bureau). Accordi in what year will the Hispanic population equal 36.74 million?

Solution

To answer this question, we solve

$$36.74 = 0.876x + 6.084$$
$$30.656 = 0.876x$$
$$34.995 \approx x$$

Recall that x is the number of years past 1980, so we use $x = 35$ when c to which this corresponds: $1980 + 35 = 2015$.

Checking reveals that $36.74 \approx 0.876(34.995) + 6.084$. ✔

Thus the number of Hispanics in the United States is estimated to 36.74 million in 2015

Comprehensive Exercise Sets.   The overall variety and grading of drill and application exercises offer problems for different skill levels, and there are enough challenging problems to stimulate students in thoughtful investigations. Many exercise sets contain critical-thinking and thought-provoking multistep problems that extend students' knowledge and skills.

Extended Applications and Group Projects.   Starting with Chapter 1, each chapter ends with at least two case studies, which further illustrate how mathematics can be used in business and personal decision making. In addition, many applications are cumulative in that solutions require students to combine the mathematical concepts and techniques they learned in some of the preceding chapters.

EXTENDED APPLICATIONS & GROUP PROJECTS

I. Hospital Administration

Southwest Hospital has an operating room used only for laser eye surgery. The annual cost of rent, heat, and electricity for the operating room and its equipment is $1.08 million, and the annual salaries of the people who staff this room total $1.6 million.

The cost for each surgery is $2395, which includes all medical supplies and drugs and a complimentary bouquet of flowers for each patient. In addition, one-quarter of the patients require dark glasses that the hospital provides at no additional charge but cost $20 per pair.

The hospital receives a payment of $6000 for each eye operation performed.

learned about a machine that would reduce by $100 per patient the amount of medical supplies needed. It can be leased for $100,000 annually. Keeping in mind the financial cost and benefits, advise the hospital on whether it should lease this machine.

4. An advertising agency has proposed to the hospital's president that she spend $20,000 per month on television and radio advertising to persuade people that Southwest Hospital is the best place to have laser eye surgery performed. Advertising account executives estimate that such publicity would increase business by 40 operations per month. If they are correct and if this increase is not big enough to affect fixed costs, what impact would this advertising have on the hospital's profits?

Graphical, Numerical, and Symbolic Methods.   A large number of real data modeling applications are included in the examples and exercises throughout the text and are denoted by the header *Modeling.* Many sections include problems with functions that are modeled from real data, and some problems ask students to model functions from the data given. These problems are solved by using one or more graphical, numerical, or symbolic methods.

 Graphing Calculators and Excel.   Instructors differ on how they use technology in their course. The icon on the left denotes the many examples, applications, Technology Notes, Calculator Notes, and Spreadsheet Notes throughout the text where technology use is featured or appropriate. Many of these notes reference detailed step-by-step instructions in Appendix A (Graphing Calculator Guide) and Appendix B (Excel Guide) and in the Online Guide for Excel. Discussions of the use of technology are placed in subsections and examples in many sections so that they can be emphasized or de-emphasized at the option of the instructor.

The discussions of graphing calculator technology highlight its most common features and uses, such as graphing, window setting, Trace, Zoom, Solver, tables, finding points of intersection, numerical derivatives, numerical integration, matrices, solving inequalities, and modeling (curve fitting). While technology never replaces the mathematics, it does supplement and extend the mathematics by providing opportunities for generalization and alternative ways of understanding, doing, and checking. Some exercises that are better worked with the use of technology—including graphing calculators and Excel—are highlighted with the technology icon. Of course, many additional exercises can benefit from the use of technology, at the option of the instructor. Technology can be used to graph functions and to discuss the generalizations, applications, and implications of problems being studied.

Excel is useful in solving problems involving linear equations; systems of equations; quadratic equations; matrices; linear programming; output comparisons of $f(x)$, $f'(x)$, and $f''(x)$; and maxima and minima of functions subject to constraints. Excel is also a useful problem-solving tool when studying the mathematics of finance in Chapter 6.

Checkpoints.   The Checkpoints ask questions and pose problems within each section's discussion, allowing students to check their understanding of the skills and concepts under discussion before they proceed. Answers to these Checkpoints appear before the section exercises. Complete solutions are available on the textbook's companion web site (www.cengagebrain.com).

EXAMPLE 4   **Solving an Equation for One of Two Variables**

Solve $4x + 3y = 12$ for y.

Solution
No fractions or parentheses are present, so we subtract $4x$ from both sides to get only term that contains y on one side.

$$3y = -4x + 12$$

Dividing both sides by 3 gives the solution.

$$y = -\frac{4}{3}x + 4$$

Check: $4x + 3\left(\dfrac{-4}{3}x + 4\right) \overset{?}{=} 12$

$$4x + (-4x + 12) = 12 \checkmark$$

CHECKPOINT   2. Solve for y: $y - 4 = -4(x + 2)$

CHECKPOINT   1. Solve the following for x.

(a) $4(x - 3) = 10x - 12$ (b) $\dfrac{5(x - 3)}{6} - x = 1 - \dfrac{x}{9}$

Objective Lists.   Every section begins with a brief list of objectives that outlines the goals of that section for the student.

SECTION 1.1

OBJECTIVES

- To solve linear equations in one variable
- To solve applied problems using

Solutions of Linear Equations and Inequalities in One Variable

APPLICATION PREVIEW

Using data from 1980 and projected to 2050, the number of Hispan civilian non-institutional population can be approximated by

---

Procedure/Example and Property/Example Tables.   Appearing throughout the text, these tables aid student understanding by giving step-by-step descriptions of important procedures and properties with illustrative examples worked out beside them.

SOLVING A LINEAR EQUATION

Procedure	Example
To solve a linear equation in one variable:	Solve $\dfrac{3x}{4} + 3 = \dfrac{x - 1}{3}$.
1. If the equation contains fractions, multiply both sides by the least common denominator (LCD) the fractions.	1. LCD is 12.
2. Remove any parentheses in the equation.	

PROPERTIES OF EQUALITY

Properties	Examples
Substitution Property	
The equation formed by substituting one expression for an equal expression is equivalent to the original equation.	$3(x - 3) - \frac{1}{2}(4x - 18) = 4$ is equivalen and to $x = 4$. We say that the solution se

Boxed Information.   All important information is boxed for easy reference, and key terms are highlighted in boldface.

Key Terms and Formulas.   At the end of each chapter, just before the Chapter Review Exercises, there is a section-by-section listing of that chapter's key terms and formulas, including their page references. This provides a well-organized core from which a student can build a review, both to consult while working the Review Exercises and to identify quickly any section needing additional study.

---

1   CHAPTER SUMMARY & REVIEW

KEY TERMS AND FORMULAS

Section 1.1

Equation; variable; solution (p. 53)   Fractional equation (p. 55)
Identities; conditional equations (p. 53)   Linear equation in two variables (p. 56)
Properties of equality (p. 53)   Linear inequalities (p. 57)
Solving a linear equation (p. 54)   Properties
Aligning the data (p. 54)   Solutions

Section 1.2

Relation (p. 63)   Graph (p. 65)

Review Exercises and Chapter Tests.   At the end of each chapter, a set of Review Exercises offers students extra practice on topics in that chapter. These reviews cover each chapter's topics in their section order, with section references, so that students get a thorough, structured review and can readily find a section for further review if difficulties occur. A Chapter Test follows each set of Review Exercises. All Chapter Tests provide a mixture of problems that do not directly mirror the order of topics found within the chapter. This organization of the Chapter Test ensures that students have a firm grasp of material in the chapter. All answers to both the Review Exercises and Chapter Tests appear in the Answers section.

Changes in the Twelfth Edition

In the twelfth edition, the text continues to be characterized by complete and accurate pedagogy, mathematical precision, excellent exercise sets, numerous real and varied applications in the examples and exercises, and student-friendly exposition. The most significant changes to this edition follow.

1. More than 250 application examples and exercises that had become outdated have been updated or replaced with new applications.
2. A number of new Calculator Notes were added or expanded in the text.
3. Normal Distributions discussions were expanded to include more calculator usage and reduce reliance on tables. The number of examples and problems using inverse normal operations was increased.
4. Discussion and instruction were streamlined and clarified where appropriate.
5. Some skill exercise sets were reorganized and rewritten to improve variety, coverage, and grading.
6. More problems were added to exercises asking students to explain their answers.
7. Numerous new Spreadsheet Notes were added throughout the text, including in the discussion of statistical measures and binomial and normal distributions.
8. Many Spreadsheet Notes have been expanded to include specific Excel steps, along with references to Appendix B and the Online Excel Guide.
9. Appendix B has been updated by eliminating Part 1, Excel 2003, and replacing Part 2 with a new Appendix B discussing Excel 2010 and Excel 2016.
10. New Excel topics have been added in Appendix B.

Chapter Changes

Chapter 1:

- Difference Quotient definition was added, and its discussion was expanded.
- Calculator Note and Spreadsheet Note discussions for graphing equations and for solving linear equations were expanded throughout the chapter.
- "Solving Linear Equations" was added as a topic in Appendix B and referenced in the Section 1.4 Spreadsheet Note.
- The discussion of domains of function that result from function operations was expanded.

Chapter 2:

- Detailed Excel instructions for modeling data with functions were added to the Spreadsheet Notes.
- Section 2.3 now defines a monopoly market in the discussion of break-even points.
- More variety was added to the skill problems in Section 2.1.

Chapter 3:

- Detailed Excel instructions involving performing matrix operations and solving systems of equations with matrices were added to Spreadsheet Notes throughout the chapter.
- The Calculator Note with instructions for finding the inverse of a matrix was rewritten for clarity. A new Spreadsheet Note with instructions for finding the inverse of a matrix was added.
- The general solution of the matrix equation $AX = B$ by using A^{-1} was shortened.

Chapter 4:

- The introduction of the simplex method for solving linear programming problems was streamlined for clarity and efficiency.

Chapter 5:

- Section 5.1 was reorganized to improve the flow from general exponential functions to exponential functions with base e.
- The discussion of graphing exponential functions with Excel in the Spreadsheet Notes was expanded.

Chapter 6:

- The definition and discussion of Return on Investment was added to Section 6.1, and the return on investment was compared to the simple interest rate.
- Updated interest rates to bring them in line with the current financial community.
- Updated payment amounts to be more realistic.

Chapter 7:

- The exposition about use of probability trees to solve problems was clarified.
- Additional application problems that use Bayes theorem were added.
- Both the drill and application exercise sets were revised to improve balance, variety, and quality.

Chapter 8:

- Section 8.4 was rewritten to include more calculator usage and reduce the reliance on tables. Discussion of using Inverse Normal commands to solve normal probability problems, and an example were added. Calculator discussion of InvNorm was added along with problems using this skill.

- New Calculator Notes were added with detailed instructions for finding binomial probabilities and cumulative binomial probabilities.
- A new Spreadsheet Note with instructions for constructing bar graphs with Excel was added. The Calculator Note with instructions for graphing histograms was revised to provide detailed steps.
- The introduction to variance was revised. A Spreadsheet Note using the Excel formulas for mean, standard deviation was added.
- Applications of expected value were expanded to include $E(f(x))$.
- New Calculator Notes and Spreadsheet Notes with instructions for finding normal probabilities and for solving normal probability problems were added to Section 8.4.
- In the introduction to normal distribution, the relationship between areas under curve and percent of population between 2 scores was clarified.
- The Powerball Project was updated.
- A number of skills exercises were revised to improve variety.

Chapter 9:

- A new Spreadsheet Note with instructions for finding limits with Excel was added.
- The Calculator Note exploring the relationship between secant lines and tangent lines was rewritten for clarity.

Chapter 10:

- Details were added to the solution steps in applied max-min examples.
- An example to illustrate all possible cases for horizontal asymptotes of rational functions was added.
- A new Spreadsheet Note discussing the use of Excel in finding relative maxima and relative minima was added.
- Quantities and values were updated in various applications.

Chapter 11:

- The drill exercises in the Chapter Review were rebalanced to improve grading and variety.
- A new Spreadsheet Note has been added with instructions for finding relative maxima and minima for functions involving logarithms.

Chapter 12:

- The drill exercises were improved and expanded.
- Objectives for Section 12.1 and 12.2 were revised and expanded.

Chapter 13:

- Skill exercises were added and reorganized.
- Calculator Notes and Spreadsheet Notes with instructions for finding areas between two curves and finding numerical integrals with the Trapezoidal Rule were added.
- The discussion of probability calculations for continuous distributions was expanded, and more conditional probability problems were added.

Chapter 14:

- The exposition in the Test for Maximum and Minimum box as well as in examples and exercises was improved.
- The notation in the development of linear regression formulas was clarified.

Resources for the Student

Student Solutions Manual (978-1-337-63046-7)
This manual provides complete worked-out solutions to all odd-numbered exercises in the text, giving you a chance to check your answers and ensure you took the correct steps to arrive at an answer.

www.webassign.com
Printed Access Card: 978-1-337-63054-2
Instant Access Code: 978-1-337-63055-9

Prepare for class with confidence using WebAssign from Cengage Harshbarger/Reynolds' *Mathematical Applications for the Management, Life, and Social Sciences, 12th Edition*. This online learning platform, which includes an interactive eBook, fuels practice, so you truly absorb what you learn—and are better prepared come test time. Videos and tutorials walk you through concepts and deliver instant feedback and grading, so you always know where you stand in class. Focus your study time and get extra practice where you need it most. Study smarter with WebAssign!

Ask your instructor today how you can get access to WebAssign, or learn about self-study options at www.webassign.com

Online Excel and Graphing Calculator Guides
To access the Online Technology Guides referenced throughout your textbook, you must first create a Cengage account at cengage.com/login. Once you are logged in, enter the ISBN for this book in the search tab: 9781337625340. This will pull up the product page for the book. Scroll down to the tabs near the bottom of the page and click on the "Free Materials" tab. Then hit the "Save to MyHome" button. The link to the free resources associated with your textbook, including the Online Technology Guides, will now be available on your My Home page.

Resources for the Instructor

Instructor Companion Site
Everything you need for your course in one place! This collection of book-specific lecture and class tools is available online via www.cengage.com/login. Access and download PowerPoint presentations, the complete solutions manual, technology guides, and more.

Complete Solutions Manual
The Complete Solutions Manual provides worked-out solutions of all exercises in the text. In addition, it contains solutions for the special features in the text, such as Extended Applications and Group Projects. This manual can be found on the Instructor Companion Site.

Cengage Learning Testing Powered by Cognero®
This flexible, online system allows you to author, edit, and manage test bank content, create multiple test versions in an instant, and deliver tests from your LMS, your classroom, or wherever you want. This is available online via www.cengage.com/login.

www.webassign.com/cengage

Printed Access Card: 978-1-337-63054-2
Instant Access Code: 978-1-337-63055-9

WebAssign from Cengage for Harshbarger/Reynolds' *Mathematical Applications for the Management, Life, and Social Sciences, 12th Edition* is a fully customizable solution, including an interactive eBook and video lecture series for STEM disciplines that empowers you to help your students learn, not just do homework. CoursePacks make assigning homework fast and easy, and the ready-made projects make the task of collecting and grading projects easier. Insightful tools save you time and highlight exactly where your students are struggling. Decide when and what type of help students can access while working on assignments—and incentivize independent work so that help features aren't abused. Meanwhile, your students get an engaging experience, instant feedback, and better outcomes. A total win-win!

To try a sample assignment, learn about LMS integration, or connect with our digital course support visit www.webassign.com/cengage

Acknowledgments

We would like to thank the many people who helped us at various stages of revising this text. The encouragement, criticism, contributions, and suggestions that were offered were invaluable to us. We are deeply grateful to Edwin Herman for his skillful and thorough accuracy checking of the entire text and answer section.

For their reviews of this textbook and the many helpful comments that were offered, we would like to thank

Annie M. Stith-Willis, PhD	*Virginia Commonwealth University*
Elsie M. Campbell	*Angelo State University*
Dr. Helen Burn	*Highline Community College*
Barbara B. Hunter	*Highline Community College*
Gina P. Dunn	*Lander University*
Dr. Joseph McCollum	*Siena College*
Micah Chrisman, PhD	*Monmouth University*
Bracha Silverstone	*Wharton County Junior College*
John C. Esenwa	*Howard Community College*
Dr. William J. Arbuckle	*University Of Central Oklahoma*

Ronald J. Harshbarger
James J. Reynolds

Algebraic Concepts

0

This chapter provides a brief review of the algebraic concepts that will be used throughout the text. You may be familiar with these topics, but it may be helpful to spend some time reviewing them. In addition, beginning with the next chapter, each chapter opens with a warm-up page that identifies prerequisite skills needed for that chapter. If algebraic skills are required, the warm-up cites their coverage in this chapter. Thus you will find that this chapter is a useful reference as you study later chapters.

The topics and some representative applications studied in this chapter include the following.

Sets

A **set** is a well-defined collection of objects. We may talk about a set of books, a set of dishes, a set of students, or a set of individuals with a certain blood type. There are two ways to tell what a given set contains. One way is by listing the **elements** (or **members**) of the set, in any order and usually between braces. We may say that a set A contains 1, 2, 3, and 4 by writing $A = \{1, 2, 3, 4\}$. To say that 4 is an element of set A, we write $4 \in A$. Similarly, we write $5 \notin A$ to denote that 5 is not an element of set A.

If all the elements of the set can be listed, the set is said to be a **finite set.** $A = \{1, 2, 3, 4\}$ and $B = \{x, y, z\}$ are examples of finite sets. When we do not want to list all the elements of a finite set, we can use three dots to indicate the unlisted elements of the set. For example, the set of even integers from 8 to 8952, inclusive, can be written as

$$\{8, 10, 12, 14, \ldots, 8952\}$$

Since we cannot list all the elements of an **infinite set**, we use the three dots to indicate that the list continues. For example, $N = \{1, 2, 3, 4, \ldots\}$ is an infinite set. This set N is called the set of **natural numbers.**

Another way to specify the elements of a given set is by description. For example, we may write $D = \{x: x \text{ is a Ford automobile}\}$ to describe the set of all Ford automobiles. Furthermore, $F = \{y: y \text{ is an odd natural number}\}$ is read "F is the set of all y such that y is an odd natural number."

EXAMPLE 1	**Describing Sets**

Write the following sets in two ways.
(a)   The set A of natural numbers less than 6
(b)   The set B of natural numbers greater than 10
(c)   The set C containing only 3

Solution
(a) $A = \{1, 2, 3, 4, 5\}$ or $A = \{x: x \text{ is a natural number less than 6}\}$
(b) $B = \{11, 12, 13, 14, \ldots\}$ or $B = \{x: x \text{ is a natural number greater than 10}\}$
(c) $C = \{3\}$ or $C = \{x: x = 3\}$

A set that contains no elements is called the **empty set** or the **null set,** and it is denoted by $\varnothing$ or by $\{\ \}$. The set of living veterans of the War of 1812 is empty because there are no living veterans of that war. Thus

$$\{x: x \text{ is a living veteran of the War of 1812}\} = \varnothing$$

Special relations that may exist between two sets are defined as follows.

RELATIONS BETWEEN SETS

Definition	Example
1. Sets X and Y are **equal** if they contain the same elements.	1. If $X = \{1, 2, 3, 4\}$ and $Y = \{4, 3, 2, 1\}$, then $X = Y$.
2. A is called a **subset** of B, which is written $A \subseteq B$ if every element of A is an element of B. The empty set is a subset of every set. Each set A is a subset of itself.	2. If $A = \{1, 2, c, f\}$ and $B = \{1, 2, 3, a, b, c, f\}$, then $A \subseteq B$. Also, $\varnothing \subseteq A, \varnothing \subseteq B, A \subseteq A$, and $B \subseteq B$.
3. If C and D have no elements in common, they are called **disjoint.**	3. If $C = \{1, 2, a, b\}$ and $D = \{3, e, 5, c\}$, then C and D are disjoint.

In the discussion of particular sets, the assumption is always made that the sets under discussion are all subsets of some larger set, called the **universal set** U. The choice of the universal set depends on the problem under consideration. For example, in discussing the set of all students and the set of all female students, we may use the set of all humans as the universal set.

We may use **Venn diagrams** to illustrate the various relationships among sets. A rectangle represents the universal set, and closed figures inside the rectangle represent the sets under consideration. Figures 0.1–0.3 show such Venn diagrams.

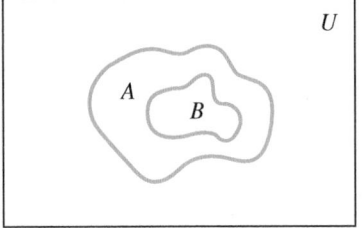

Figure 0.1
B is a subset of A; $B \subseteq A$.

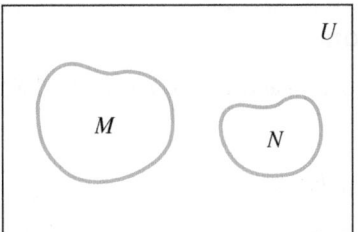

Figure 0.2
M and N are disjoint.

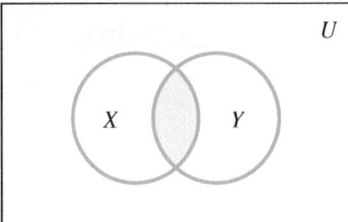

Figure 0.3
X and Y are not disjoint.

CHECKPOINT

Let $A = \{2, 3, 5, 7, 11\}$, $B = \{2, 4, 6, 8, 10\}$, and $C = \{6, 10, 14, 18, 22\}$. Use these sets to answer the following.

1. (a) Of which sets is 6 an element?
    (b) Of which sets is $\{2\}$ a subset?
2. Which of the following are true?
    (a) $2 \in A$
    (b) $\{2\} \in B$
    (c) $2 \in C$
    (d) $5 \notin A$
    (e) $5 \notin B$
3. Which pair of A, B, and C is disjoint?
4. Which of $\varnothing$, A, B, and C are subsets of
    (a) the set P of all prime numbers?
    (b) the set M of all multiples of 2?
5. Which of A, B, and C is equal to $D = \{x: x = 4n + 2 \text{ for natural numbers } 1 \le n \le 5\}$?

Set Operations

The set containing the members that are common to two sets is said to be the **intersection** of the two sets.

Set Intersection

The intersection of A and B, written $A \cap B$, is defined by

$$A \cap B = \{x: x \in A \text{ and } x \in B\}$$

EXAMPLE 2

Set Intersection

(a) If $A = \{2, 3, 4, 5\}$ and $B = \{3, 5, 7, 9, 11\}$, find $A \cap B$.
(b) Which of A, B, and $A \cap B$ is a subset of A?

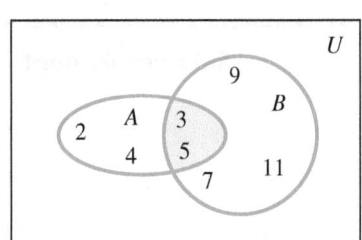

Figure 0.4

Solution

(a) $A \cap B = \{3, 5\}$ because 3 and 5 are the common elements of A and B. Figure 0.4 shows the sets and their intersection.
(b) $A \cap B$ and A are subsets of A.

The **union** of two sets is the set that contains all members of the two sets.

Set Union

The union of A and B, written $A \cup B$, is defined by

$$A \cup B = \{x : x \in A \text{ or } x \in B \text{ (or both)}\}^*$$

EXAMPLE **3** **Set Union**

If $X = \{a, b, c, f\}$ and $Y = \{e, f, a, b\}$, find $X \cup Y$.

Solution
$X \cup Y = \{a, b, c, e, f\}$

We can illustrate the intersection and union of two sets by the use of Venn diagrams. The shaded region in Figure 0.5 represents $A \cap B$, the intersection of A and B, and the shaded region in Figure 0.6—which consists of all parts of both circles—represents $A \cup B$.

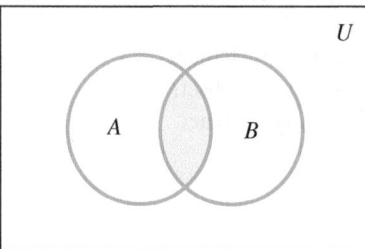

Figure 0.5
Intersection of A and B.

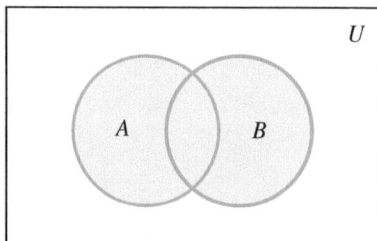

Figure 0.6
Union of A and B.

EXAMPLE **4** **Set Intersection and Union**

Let $A = \{x : x \text{ is a natural number less than 6}\}$ and $B = \{1, 3, 5, 7, 9, 11\}$.
(a) Find $A \cap B$.
(b) Find $A \cup B$.

Solution
Note that $A = \{1, 2, 3, 4, 5\}$.
(a) $A \cap B = \{1, 3, 5\}$
(b) $A \cup B = \{1, 2, 3, 4, 5, 7, 9, 11\}$

All elements of the universal set that are not contained in a set A form a set called the **complement** of A.

Set Complement

The complement of A, written A', is defined by

$$A' = \{x : x \in U \text{ and } x \notin A\}$$

We can use a Venn diagram to illustrate the complement of a set. The shaded region of Figure 0.7 represents A', and the *unshaded* region of Figure 0.5 represents $(A \cap B)'$.

* In mathematics, the word *or* means "one or the other or both."

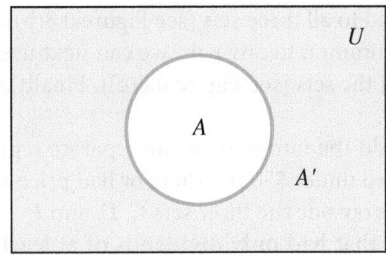

Figure 0.7

EXAMPLE 5 Operations with Sets

If U is the set of natural numbers less than 10, $A = \{1, 3, 6\}$, and $B = \{1, 6, 8, 9\}$, find the following.
(a) A'
(b) B'
(c) $(A \cap B)'$
(d) $A' \cup B'$

Solution
(a) $U = \{1, 2, 3, 4, 5, 6, 7, 8, 9\}$, so $A' = \{2, 4, 5, 7, 8, 9\}$
(b) $B' = \{2, 3, 4, 5, 7\}$
(c) $A \cap B = \{1, 6\}$, so $(A \cap B)' = \{2, 3, 4, 5, 7, 8, 9\}$
(d) $A' \cup B' = \{2, 4, 5, 7, 8, 9\} \cup \{2, 3, 4, 5, 7\} = \{2, 3, 4, 5, 7, 8, 9\}$

CHECKPOINT

Given the sets $U = \{1, 2, 3, 4, 5, 6, 7, 8, 9, 10\}$, $A = \{1, 3, 5, 7, 9\}$, $B = \{2, 3, 5, 7\}$, and $C = \{4, 5, 6, 7, 8, 9, 10\}$, find the following.
6. $A \cup B$
7. $B \cap C$
8. A'

EXAMPLE 6 Stocks

Suppose an investment adviser monitored several stocks for clients and on a certain day categorized 23 stocks according to whether

- their closing price on the previous day was less than $50/share (set C)
- their price-to-earnings ratio was less than 20 (set P)
- their dividend per share was at least $1.50 (set D).

Of these 23 stocks,

16 belonged to set P	10 belonged to both C and P
12 belonged to set C	7 belonged to both D and P
8 belonged to set D	2 belonged to all three sets.
3 belonged to both C and D	

(a) How many stocks had closing prices of less than $50 per share or price-to-earnings ratios of less than 20?
(b) How many stocks had none of the characteristics of set C, P, or D?
(c) How many stocks had only dividends per share of at least $1.50?

Solution
We use a Venn diagram to organize the information. Note that the Venn diagram for three sets has eight separate regions [see Figure 0.8(a) on the next page]. To assign numbers from our data, we must begin with some information that refers to a single region—namely, that

two stocks belonged to all three sets [see Figure 0.8(b)]. Because the region common to all three sets also is common to any pair, we can next use the information about stocks that belonged to two of the sets [see Figure 0.8(c)]. Finally, we can complete the Venn diagram [see Figure 0.8(d)].

(a) We need to add the numbers in the separate regions that lie within $C \cup P$. That is, 18 stocks closed under $50 per share or had price-to-earnings ratios of less than 20.

(b) Five stocks are outside the three sets C, D, and P.

(c) Those stocks that had only dividends of at least $1.50 per share are inside D but outside both C and P. There are no such stocks.

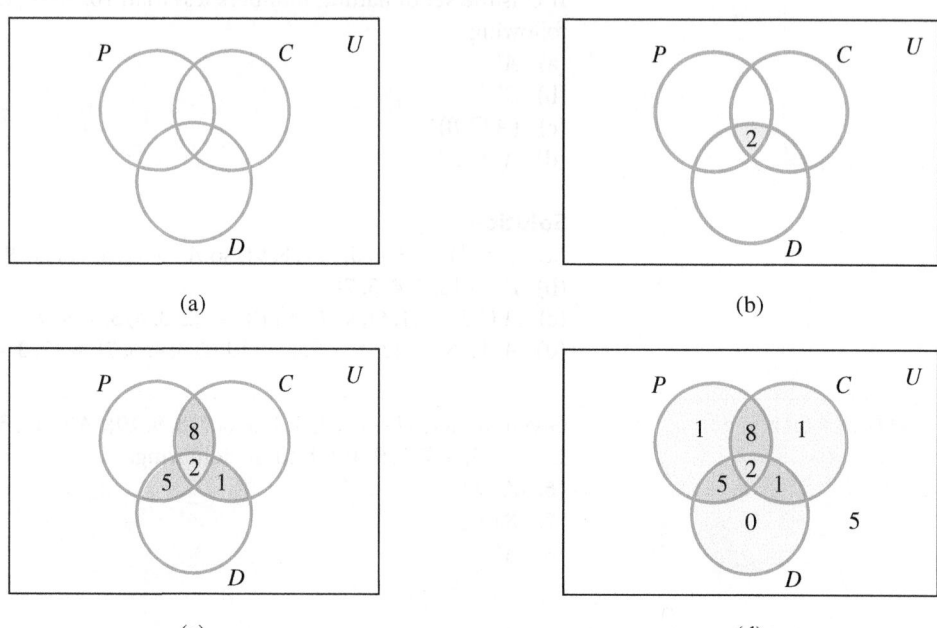

Figure 0.8

EXERCISES 0.1

In Problems 1–4, use ∈ or ∉ to indicate whether the given object is an element of the given set.

1. 12 {1, 2, 3, 4, …}
2. 5 {x: x is a natural number greater than 5}
3. 6 {x: x is a natural number less than 6}
4. 3 ∅

In Problems 5–8, write the following sets a second way.

5. {x: x is a natural number less than 8}
6. {x: x is a natural number greater than 6, less than 10}
7. {3, 4, 5, 6, 7}
8. {7, 8, 9, 10, …}

In Problems 9 and 10, which of ∅, A, and B are subsets of B?

9. $A = \{1, 2, 3, 4\}$ and $B = \{1, 2, 3, 4, 5, 6\}$
10. $A = \{a, b, c, d\}$ and $B = \{c, d, a, b\}$?
11. Is $A \subseteq B$ if $A = \{a, b, c, d\}$ and $B = \{a, b, d\}$?
12. Is $A \subseteq B$ if $A = \{6, 8, 10, 12\}$ and $B = \{6, 8, 10, 14, 18\}$?

In Problems 13–16, use ⊆ notation to indicate which set is a subset of the other.

13. $C = \{a, b, 1, 2, 3\}, D = \{a, b, 1\}$
14. $E = \{x, y, a, b\}, F = \{x, 1, a, y, b, 2\}$
15. $A = \{6, 8, 7, 4\}, B = \{8, 7, 6, 4\}$
16. $D = \{a, e, 1, 3, c\}, F = \{e, a, c, 1, 3\}$

In Problems 17–20, indicate whether the two sets are equal.

17. $A = \{a, b, \pi, \sqrt{3}\}, B = \{a, \pi, \sqrt{3}, b\}$
18. $A = \{x, g, a, b\}, D = \{x, a, b, y\}$
19. $D = \{x: x \text{ is a natural number less than 4}\},$
    $E = \{1, 2, 3, 4\}$
20. $F = \{x: x \text{ is a natural number greater than 6}\},$
    $G = \{7, 8, 9, \ldots\}$
21. From the following list of sets, indicate which pairs of sets are disjoint.

    $A = \{1, 2, 3, 4\}$
    $B = \{x: x \text{ is a natural number greater than 4}\}$
    $C = \{4, 5, 6, \ldots\}$
    $D = \{1, 2, 3\}$

22. If A and B are disjoint sets, what does $A \cap B$ equal?

In Problems 23–26, find $A \cap B$.

23. $A = \{2, 3, 4, 5, 6\}$ and $B = \{4, 6, 8, 10, 12\}$
24. $A = \{a, b, c, d, e\}$ and $B = \{a, d, e, f, g, h\}$
25. $A = \varnothing$ and $B = \{x, y, a, b\}$
26. $A = \{x: x \text{ is a natural number less than 4}\}$ and
    $B = \{3, 4, 5, 6\}$

In Problems 27–30, find $A \cup B$.

27. $A = \{1, 2, 4, 5\}$ and $B = \{2, 3, 4, 5\}$
28. $A = \{a, e, i, o, u\}$ and $B = \{a, b, c, d\}$
29. $A = \varnothing$ and $B = \{1, 2, 3, 4\}$
30. $A = \{x: x \text{ is a natural number greater than 5}\}$ and
    $B = \{x: x \text{ is a natural number less than 5}\}$

In Problems 31–42, let

$$A = \{1, 3, 5, 8, 7, 2\}$$
$$B = \{4, 3, 8, 10\}$$
$$C = \{2, 4, 6, 8, 10\}$$

and U be the universal set of natural numbers less than 11. Find the following.

31. A'
32. B'
33. $A \cap B'$
34. $A' \cap B'$
35. $(A \cup B)'$
36. $(A \cap B)'$
37. $A' \cup B'$
38. $(A' \cup B)'$
39. $(A \cap B') \cup C'$
40. $A \cap (B' \cup C')$
41. $(A \cap B')' \cap C$
42. $A \cap (B \cup C)$

The difference of two sets, $A - B$, is defined as the set containing all elements of A except those in B. That is, $A - B = A \cap B'$. Find $A - B$ for each pair of sets in Problems 43–46 if $U = \{1, 2, 3, 4, 5, 6, 7, 8, 9\}$.

43. $A = \{1, 3, 7, 9\}$ and $B = \{3, 5, 8, 9\}$
44. $A = \{1, 2, 3, 6, 9\}$ and $B = \{1, 4, 5, 6, 7\}$
45. $A = \{2, 1, 5\}$ and $B = \{1, 2, 3, 4, 5, 6\}$
46. $A = \{1, 2, 3, 4, 5\}$ and $B = \{7, 8, 9\}$

APPLICATIONS

47. *Dow Jones Industrial Average* The following table shows information about each year's Dow Jones Industrial average beginning value, ending value, and annual percent change for the years from 2005 to 2016. Let B be the set of years when the beginning value was less than 13,000. Let E be the set of years when the ending value was greater than 12,000. Let P be the set of years when the annual percent change was less than 7%.
    (a) List the elements of B, E, and P.
    (b) Is any of B, E, and P a subset of one of the others (besides itself)?
    (c) Write a verbal description of P'.
    (d) Find $B' \cap P'$ and describe it in words.
    (e) Find $E' \cap P$ and describe it in words.

Dow Jones Industrial Averages

Year	Beginning value	Ending value	Percent change
2005	10,783.01	10,717.50	−0.61%
2006	10,717.50	12,463.15	16.29%
2007	12,463.15	13,264.82	6.43%
2008	13,264.82	8776.39	−33.84%
2009	8776.39	10,428.05	18.82%
2010	10,428.05	11,577.51	11.02%
2011	11,577.51	12,217.56	5.53%
2012	12,217.56	13,104.14	7.26%
2013	13,104.14	16,576.66	26.50%
2014	16,576.66	17,823.07	7.52%
2015	17,823.07	17,425.03	−2.23%
2016	17,425.03	19,726.60	13.42%

Source: Dow Jones and Company

48. *Job growth* The number of jobs in 2000, the number projected in 2025, and the projected annual growth rate for jobs in some cities are shown in the following table. Consider the following sets.

    A = set of cities with at least 2,000,000 jobs in 2000 or projected in 2025

    B = set of cities with at least 1,500,000 jobs in 2000

    C = set of cities with projected annual growth rate of at least 2.5%

    (a) List A, B, and C (using the letters to represent the cities).
    (b) Is any of A, B, or C a subset of the other?
    (c) Find $A \cap C$ and describe the set in words.
    (d) Give a verbal description of B'.

Cities	Jobs in 2000 (thousands)	Projected Jobs in 2025 (thousands)	Annual Rates of Increase (%)
O (Orlando)	1098	2207	2.83
M (Myrtle Beach)	133	256	2.64
L (Atlanta)	2715	4893	2.38
P (Phoenix)	1953	3675	2.56
B (Boulder)	233	420	2.38

Source: Based on data from NPA Data Services, Inc.

Carbon emission controls **Suppose that the following table summarizes the opinions of various groups on the issue of carbon emission controls. Use this table for Problems 49 and 50.**

Opinion	Whites Rep.	Whites Dem.	Nonwhites Rep.	Nonwhites Dem.	Total
Favor	100	250	30	200	580
Oppose	250	150	10	10	420
Total	350	400	40	210	1000

49. Identify the number of individuals in each of the following sets.
    (a) Republicans and those who favor carbon emission controls
    (b) Republicans or those who favor carbon emission controls
    (c) White Republicans or those who oppose carbon emission controls

50. Identify the number of individuals in each of the following sets.
    (a) Whites and those who oppose carbon emission controls
    (b) Whites or those who oppose carbon emission controls
    (c) Nonwhite Democrats and those who favor carbon emission controls

51. *Languages* A survey of 100 aides at the United Nations revealed that 65 could speak English, 60 could speak French, and 40 could speak both English and French.
    (a) Draw a Venn diagram representing the 100 aides. Use E to represent English-speaking aides and F to represent French-speaking aides.
    (b) How many aides are in $E \cap F$?
    (c) How many aides are in $E \cup F$?
    (d) How many aides are in $E \cap F'$?

52. *Advertising* Suppose that a survey of 100 advertisers in *U.S. News*, *These Times*, and *World* found the following.

    14 advertised in all three
    30 advertised in *These Times* and *U.S. News*
    26 advertised in *World* and *U.S. News*
    27 advertised in *World* and *These Times*
    60 advertised in *These Times*
    52 advertised in *U.S. News*
    50 advertised in *World*

    (a) Draw a Venn diagram representing the 100 advertisers.
    (b) How many advertised in none of these publications?
    (c) How many advertised only in *These Times*?
    (d) How many advertised in *U.S. News* or *These Times*?

53. *College enrollments* Records at a small college show the following about the enrollments of 100 first-year students in mathematics, fine arts, and economics.

    38 take math
    42 take fine arts
    20 take economics
    4 take economics and fine arts
    15 take math and economics
    9 take math and fine arts
    12 take math and economics but not fine arts

(a) How many take none of these three courses?

(b) How many take math or economics?

(c) How many take exactly one of these three courses?

54. *Survey analysis*   In a survey of the dining preferences of 110 dormitory students at the end of the spring semester, the following facts were discovered about Adam's Lunch (AL), Pizza Tower (PT), and the Dining Hall (DH).

> 30 liked AL but not PT
> 21 liked AL only
> 63 liked AL
> 58 liked PT
> 27 liked DH
> 25 liked PT and AL but not DH
> 18 liked PT and DH

(a) How many liked PT or DH?

(b) How many liked all three?

(c) How many liked only DH?

55. *Blood types*   Blood types are determined by the presence or absence of three antigens: A antigen, B antigen, and an antigen called the Rh factor. The resulting blood types are classified as follows:

> *type A* if the A antigen is present
> *type B* if the B antigen is present
> *type AB* if both the A and B antigens are present
> *type O* if neither the A nor the B antigen is present

These types are further classified as *Rh-positive* if the Rh-factor antigen is present and *Rh-negative* otherwise.

(a) Draw a Venn diagram that illustrates this classification scheme.

(b) Identify the blood type determined by each region of the Venn diagram (such as A^+ to indicate type A, Rh-positive).

(c) Use Google or another source to find what percentage of the U.S. population has each blood type.

SECTION 0.2   The Real Numbers

In this text, we use the set of **real numbers** as the universal set. We can represent the real numbers along a line called the **real number line.** This number line is a picture, or graph, of the real numbers. Each point on the real number line corresponds to exactly one real number, and each real number can be located at exactly one point on the real number line. Thus, two real numbers are said to be equal whenever they are represented by the same point on the real number line. The equation $a = b$ (a equals b) means that the symbols a and b represent the same real number. Thus, $3 + 4 = 7$ means that $3 + 4$ and 7 represent the same number. Table 0.1 lists special subsets of the real numbers.

TABLE 0.1

SUBSETS OF THE SET OF REAL NUMBERS

	Description	Example (some elements shown)
Natural numbers	$\{1, 2, 3, \ldots\}$ The counting numbers.	
Integers	$\{\ldots, -2, -1, 0, 1, 2, \ldots\}$ The natural numbers, 0, and the negatives of the natural numbers.	
Rational numbers	All numbers that can be written as the ratio of two integers, a/b, with $b \neq 0$. These numbers have decimal representations that either terminate or repeat.	
Irrational numbers	Those real numbers that *cannot* be written as the ratio of two integers. Irrational numbers have decimal representations that neither terminate nor repeat.	
Real numbers	The set containing all rational and irrational numbers (the entire number line).	

The following properties of the real numbers are fundamental to the study of algebra.

PROPERTIES OF THE REAL NUMBERS

Let a, b, and c denote real numbers.

1. The **Commutative Properties** for addition and multiplication.
$$a + b = b + a \qquad ab = ba$$

2. The **Associative Properties** for addition and multiplication.
$$(a + b) + c = a + (b + c) \qquad (ab)c = a(bc)$$

3. The **Additive Identity** is 0.
$$a + 0 = 0 + a = a$$

4. The **Multiplicative Identity** is 1.
$$a \cdot 1 = 1 \cdot a = a$$

5. Each real number a has an **Additive Inverse**, denoted by $-a$.
$$a + (-a) = -a + a = 0$$

6. The **Multiplicative Inverse** of the nonzero real number a is $1/a$, called the **reciprocal of a** and denoted by a^{-1}. (Note that $a^{-1} = 1/a$.)
$$a \cdot a^{-1} = a^{-1} \cdot a = 1$$

7. The **Distributive Law** for multiplication over addition.
$$a(b + c) = ab + ac \qquad (a + b)c = ac + bc$$

Note that there is a difference between a negative number and the negative of a number. For example, -5 is a negative number, but its negative is $-(-5) = 5$. Note also that Property 5 provides the means to subtract by defining $a - b = a + (-b)$ and Property 6 provides a means to divide by defining $a \div b = a \cdot (1/b)$. The number 0 has no multiplicative inverse, so division by 0 is undefined.

Inequalities and Intervals   We say that a is less than b (written $a < b$) if the point representing a is to the left of the point representing b on the real number line. For example, $4 < 7$ because 4 is to the left of 7 on the real number line. We also may say that 7 is greater than 4 (written $7 > 4$). We indicate that the number x is less than or equal to another number y by writing $x \le y$. We also indicate that p is greater than or equal to 4 by writing $p \ge 4$.

| EXAMPLE 1 | **Inequalities** |

Use $<$ or $>$ notation to write the following.
(a) 6 is greater than 5.   (b) 10 is less than 15.
(c) 3 is to the left of 8 on the real number line.   (d) x is at most 12.

Solution
(a) $6 > 5$ (b) $10 < 15$ (c) $3 < 8$
(d) "x is at most 12" means that it must be less than or equal to 12. Thus, $x \le 12$.

The subset of the real numbers consisting of all real numbers x that lie between a and b, excluding a and b, can be denoted by the *double inequality* $a < x < b$ or by the **open interval** (a, b). It is called an open interval because neither of the endpoints is included in the interval. The **closed interval** $[a, b]$ represents the set of all real numbers x satisfying $a \le x \le b$. Intervals containing one endpoint, such as $(a, b]$ and $[a, b)$, are called **half-open intervals.**

We can use $[a, \infty)$ to represent the inequality $x \geq a$ and $(-\infty, a)$ to represent $x < a$. In each of these cases, the symbols ∞ and $-\infty$ are not real numbers but represent the fact that x increases without bound (∞) or decreases without bound $(-\infty)$. Table 0.2 summarizes the three types of intervals.

TABLE 0.2

INTERVALS

Type of Interval	Inequality Notation	Interval Notation	Graph
Open interval	$x > a$	(a, ∞)	
	$x < b$	$(-\infty, b)$	
	$a < x < b$	(a, b)	
Half-open interval	$x \geq a$	$[a, \infty)$	
	$x \leq b$	$(-\infty, b]$	
	$a \leq x < b$	$[a, b)$	
	$a < x \leq b$	$(a, b]$	
Closed interval	$a \leq x \leq b$	$[a, b]$	

Note that the interval $(-\infty, \infty)$, representing $-\infty < x < \infty$, is an open interval containing all real numbers (that is, the entire real number line).

CHECKPOINT

1. Decide which of the following are undefined.

   (a) $\dfrac{4}{0}$ (b) $\dfrac{0}{4}$

   (c) $\dfrac{4}{4}$ (d) $\dfrac{4 - 4}{4 - 4}$

2. For parts (a)–(d), write the inequality corresponding to the given interval and sketch its graph on a real number line.
   (a) $(1, 3)$ (b) $(0, 3]$
   (c) $[-1, \infty)$ (d) $(-\infty, 2)$

3. Express the following inequalities in interval notation and name the type of interval.
   (a) $3 \leq x \leq 6$ (b) $-6 \leq x < 4$

Absolute Value Sometimes we are interested in the *distance* a number is from the origin (0) of the real number line, without regard to direction. The distance a number a is from 0 on the number line is the **absolute value** of a, denoted $|a|$. The absolute value of any nonzero number is positive, and the absolute value of 0 is 0.

EXAMPLE 2   **Absolute Value**

Evaluate the following.
(a) $|-4|$ (b) $|+2|$
(c) $|0|$ (d) $|-5-|-3||$

Solution
(a) $|-4| = +4 = 4$ (b) $|+2| = +2 = 2$
(c) $|0| = 0$ (d) $|-5-|-3|| = |-5-3| = |-8| = 8$

Note that if a is a nonnegative number, then $|a| = a$, *but if a is negative, then* $|a|$ *is the positive number* $(-a)$. Thus

Absolute Value	
	$|a| = \begin{cases} a & \text{if } a \geq 0 \\ -a & \text{if } a < 0 \end{cases}$

In performing computations with real numbers, it is important to remember the following rules for computations.

OPERATIONS WITH REAL (SIGNED) NUMBERS

Procedure	Example
1. (a) To add two real numbers with the same sign, add their absolute values and affix their common sign.	1. (a) $(5) + (6) = 11$ $\left(-\dfrac{1}{6}\right) + \left(-\dfrac{2}{6}\right) = -\dfrac{3}{6} = -\dfrac{1}{2}$
(b) To add two real numbers with unlike signs, find the difference of their absolute values and affix the sign of the number with the larger absolute value.	(b) $(5) + (-3) = 2$ $\left(-\dfrac{11}{7}\right) + (1) = -\dfrac{4}{7}$
2. To subtract one real number from another, change the sign of the number being subtracted and proceed as in addition.	2. $(-9) - (-8) = (-9) + (8) = -1$ $16 - (8) = 16 + (-8) = 8$
3. (a) The product of two real numbers with like signs is positive.	3. (a) $(-3)(-4) = 12$ $\left(\dfrac{3}{4}\right)(4) = 3$
(b) The product of two real numbers with unlike signs is negative.	(b) $5(-3) = -15$ $(-3)(4) = -12$
4. (a) The quotient of two real numbers with like signs is positive.	4. (a) $(-14) \div (-2) = 7$ $36/4 = 9$
(b) The quotient of two real numbers with unlike signs is negative.	(b) $(-28)/4 = -7$ $45 \div (-5) = -9$

When two or more operations with real numbers are indicated in an evaluation, it is important that everyone agree on the order in which the operations are performed so that a unique result is guaranteed. The following **order of operations** is universally accepted.

Order of Operations

First: Perform operations within parentheses or other symbols of grouping.
Second: Find indicated powers ($2^3 = 2 \cdot 2 \cdot 2 = 8$).
Third: Perform multiplications and divisions from left to right.
Fourth: Perform additions and subtractions from left to right.

EXAMPLE 3   Order of Operations

Evaluate the following.
(a) $-4 + 3$
(b) $4 + 3(-2)$
(c) $-4^2 + 3$
(d) $[2(3 - 4)]^2 + 3$
(e) $6 \div 2(2 + 1)$

Solution

(a) -1

(b) $4 + (-6) = -2$

(c)   Note that with -4^2, the power 2 is applied only to 4, not to -4 (which would be written $(-4)^2$). Thus $-4^2 + 3 = -(4^2) + 3 = -16 + 3 = -13$.

(d) $[2(-1)]^2 + 3 = [-2]^2 + 3 = 4 + 3 = 7$

(e) $6 \div 2(3) = (6 \div 2)(3) = 3 \cdot 3 = 9$

CHECKPOINT

True or false:

4. $-(-5)^2 = 25$

5. $|4 - 6| = |4| - |6|$

6. $9 - 2(2)(-10) = 7(2)(-10) = -140$

Often, we use letters to represent real numbers, such as in the formula for the area of a circle, $A = \pi r^2$. Formula evaluations also use the order of operations.

EXAMPLE 4   Average Annual Wage

Using Social Security Administration data from 2011 and projected to 2021, the U.S. average annual wage W (in dollars) can be approximated with the formula

$$W = 48t^2 + 1000(1.8t + 41)$$

where t is the number of years past 2010. Use the formula to approximate the U.S. average annual wage in 2020.

Solution

Note that 2020 is 10 years past 2010, so we use $t = 10$. Substituting $t = 10$ into the formula for W and using the order of operations give

$$\begin{aligned}
W &= 48(10^2) + 1000(1.8(10) + 41) \\
&= 48(100) + 1000(18 + 41) = 4800 + 1000(59) \\
&= 4800 + 59{,}000 = \$63{,}800
\end{aligned}$$

We will assume that you have a scientific or graphing calculator. Discussions of some of the capabilities of graphing calculators and Excel will be found throughout the text.

Most scientific and graphing calculators use standard algebraic order when evaluating arithmetic expressions. Working outward from inner parentheses, calculations are performed from left to right. Powers and roots are evaluated first, followed by multiplications and divisions, and then additions and subtractions.

**CHECKPOINT
ANSWERS**

1.   Parts (a) and (d) are undefined because a denominator of zero means division by zero. Parts (b) and (c) are defined, and their values are 0 and 1, respectively.

2.   (a) $1 < x < 3$

(b) $0 < x \le 3$

(c) $-1 \le x < \infty$ or $x \ge -1$

(d) $-\infty < x < 2$ or $x < 2$

3.   (a) $[3, 6]$; closed interval

(b) $[-6, 4)$; half-open interval

4.   False; $-(-5)^2 = -25$.

5.   False; $|4 - 6| = |-2| = 2$ and $|4| - |6| = 4 - 6 = -2$.

6.   False; $9 - (2)(2)(-10) = 49$

EXERCISES 0.2

In Problems 1 and 2, indicate whether the given expression is one or more of the following types of numbers: rational, irrational, integer, natural. If the expression is meaningless, so state.

1. (a) $\dfrac{-\pi}{10}$

   (b) -9

   (c) $\dfrac{9}{3}$

   (d) $\dfrac{4}{0}$

2. (a) $\dfrac{0}{6}$

   (b) -1.2916

   (c) 1.414

   (d) $\dfrac{9}{6}$

Which property of real numbers is illustrated in each part of Problems 3–6?

3. (a) $8 + 6 = 6 + 8$

   (b) $5(3 + 7) = 5(3) + 5(7)$

4. (a) $-e \cdot 1 = -e$

   (b) $4 + (-4) = 0$

5. (a) $6(4 \cdot 5) = (6 \cdot 4)(5)$

   (b) $-15 + 0 = -15$

6. (a) $\left(\dfrac{3}{2}\right)\left(\dfrac{2}{3}\right) = 1$

   (b) $(12)\left(\dfrac{3}{4}\right) = \left(\dfrac{3}{4}\right)(12)$

Insert the proper sign $<, =,$ or $>$ to replace $\square$ in Problems 7–14.

7. $-6 \square 0$

8. $2 \square -20$

9. $-14 \square -3$

10. $\pi \square 3.14$

11. $0.333 \square \dfrac{1}{3}$

12. $\dfrac{1}{3} + \dfrac{1}{2} \square \dfrac{5}{6}$

13. $|-3| + |5| \square |-3 + 5|$

14. $|-9 - 3| \square |-9| + |3|$

In Problems 15–26, evaluate each expression.

15. $-3^2 + 10 \cdot 2$

16. $(-3)^2 + 10 \cdot 2$

17. $\dfrac{4 + 2^2}{2}$

18. $\dfrac{(4 + 2)^2}{2}$

19. $\dfrac{16 - (-4)}{8 - (-2)}$

20. $\dfrac{(-5)(-3) - (-2)(3)}{-9 + 2}$

21. $\dfrac{|5 - 2| - |-7|}{|5 - 2|}$

22. $\dfrac{|3 - |4-11||}{-|5^2-3^2|}$

23. $\dfrac{(-3)^2 - 2 \cdot 3 + 6}{4 - 2^2 + 3}$

24. $\dfrac{6^2 - 4(-3)(-2)}{6 - 6^2 \div 4}$

25. $\dfrac{-4^2 + 5 - 2 \cdot 3}{5 - 4^2}$

26. $\dfrac{3 - 2(5 - 2)}{(-2)^2 - 2^2 + 3}$

27. What part of the real number line corresponds to the interval $(-\infty, \infty)$?

28. Write the interval corresponding to $x \geq 0$.

In Problems 29–32, express each inequality or graph using interval notation and name the type of interval.

29. $1 < x \leq 3$

30. $-4 \leq x \leq 3$

31.

32.

In Problems 33–36, write an inequality that describes each interval or graph.

33. $[-3, 5)$

34. $(-2, \infty)$

35.

36.

In Problems 37–44, graph the subset of the real numbers that is represented by each of the following and write your answer in interval notation.

37. $(-\infty, 4) \cap (-3, \infty)$

38. $[-4, 17) \cap [-20, 10]$

39. $x > 4$ and $x \geq 0$

40. $x < 10$ and $x < -1$

41. $[0, \infty) \cup [-1, 5]$

42. $(-\infty, 4) \cup (0, 2)$

43. $x > 7$ or $x < 0$

44. $x > 4$ and $x < 0$

In Problems 45–50, use your calculator to evaluate each of the following. List all the digits on your display in the answer.

45. $\dfrac{-1}{25{,}916.8}$

46. $\dfrac{51.412}{127.01}$

47. $(3.679)^7$

48. $(1.28)^{10}$

49. $\dfrac{2500}{(1.1)^6 - 1}$

50. $100\left[\dfrac{(1.05)^{12} - 1}{0.05}\right]$

APPLICATIONS

51. *Take-home pay* A salesclerk's take-home pay is found by subtracting all taxes and retirement contributions from gross pay (which consists of salary plus commission). Given the following information, complete parts (a)–(c).
    Salary = $300.00   Commission = $788.91
    Retirement = 5% of gross pay
    Taxes: State = 5% of gross pay
         Local = 1% of gross pay
         Federal withholding =
           25% of (gross pay less retirement)
         Federal Social Security and Medicare =
           7.65% of gross pay
    (a) Find the gross pay.
    (b) Find the amount of federal withholding.
    (c) Find the take-home pay.

52. *Crude oil production* Using data from 2010 and projected to 2030, the U.S. crude oil production, in billions of barrels, can be approximated by

$$P = -0.00105t^2 + 0.0367t + 1.94$$

where t is the number of years after 2010 (*Source:* U.S. Department of Energy).
    (a) What t-value represents 2020?
    (b) Actual production in 2014 was 2.10 billion barrels. What does the equation give as the 2014 approximation?
    (c) Estimate the production for 2020.

53. *Worldwide Internet users* Using data from 2014 and projected to 2019, the percent of people in the world who are Internet users can be approximated accurately by
    (1) $y = 2.14t + 32.2$ or by
    (2) $y = 0.00536t^2 + 2.07t + 32.4$
    with t equal to the number of years after 2010 (*Source:* statista.com).
    (a) Which equation is more accurate for 2016, when the percent was 45%?
    (b) Use both formulas to estimate the percent of users in 2025.

54. *Health statistics* Using data adapted from the National Center for Health Statistics, the height H in inches and age A in years for boys between 4 and 16 years of age are related according to

$$H = 2.31A + 31.26$$

To account for normal variability among boys, normal height for a given age is $\pm 5\%$ of the height obtained from the equation.
    (a) Find the normal height range for a boy who is 10.5 years old and write it as an inequality.
    (b) Find the normal height range for a boy who is 5.75 years old and write it as an inequality.

55. *Income taxes* Use the following federal tax table for a single person claiming one personal exemption.

Taxable Income I	Tax Due T
0–9275	10% I
9276–37,650	927.50 + 15%(I − 9275)
37,651–91,150	5183.75 + 25%(I − 37,650)
91,151–190,150	18,558.75 + 28%(I − 91,150)
190,151–413,350	46,278.75 + 33%(I − 190,150)
413,351–415,050	119,934.75 +35%(I − 413,350)
Over 415,050	120,529 + 39.6%(I − 415,050)

Source: Internal Revenue Service

    (a) Write the last three taxable income ranges as inequalities.
    (b) If an individual has a taxable income of $37,650 calculate the tax due. Repeat this calculation for a taxable income of $91,150.
    (c) Write an interval that represents the amount of tax due for a taxable income between $37,650 and $91,150.

SECTION 0.3

Integral Exponents

If $1000 is placed in a 5-year savings certificate that pays an interest rate of 10% per year, compounded annually, then the amount returned after 5 years is given by

$$1000(1.1)^5$$

The 5 in this expression is an *exponent*. Exponents provide an easier way to denote certain multiplications. For example,

$$(1.1)^5 = (1.1)(1.1)(1.1)(1.1)(1.1)$$

An understanding of the properties of exponents is fundamental to the algebra needed to study functions and solve equations. Furthermore, the definition of exponential and logarithmic functions and many of the techniques in calculus also require an understanding of the properties of exponents.

For any real number a,

$$a^2 = a \cdot a, \quad a^3 = a \cdot a \cdot a, \quad \text{and} \quad a^n = a \cdot a \cdot a \cdot \ldots \cdot a \quad (n \text{ factors})$$

for any positive integer n. The positive integer n is called the **exponent,** the number a is called the **base,** and a^n is read "a to the nth power."

Note that $4a^n$ means $4(a^n)$, which is different from $(4a)^n$. The 4 is the coefficient of a^n in $4a^n$. Note also that $-a^n$ is not equivalent to $(-a)^n$ when n is even. For example, $-3^4 = -81$, but $(-3)^4 = 81$.

Some of the rules of exponents follow.

Positive Integer Exponents

For any real numbers a and b and positive integers m and n,

1. $a^m \cdot a^n = a^{m+n}$

2. For $a \neq 0$, $\dfrac{a^m}{a^n} = \begin{cases} a^{m-n} & \text{if } m > n \\ 1 & \text{if } m = n \\ 1/a^{n-m} & \text{if } m < n \end{cases}$

3. $(ab)^m = a^m b^m$

4. $\left(\dfrac{a}{b}\right)^m = \dfrac{a^m}{b^m} \quad (b \neq 0)$

5. $(a^m)^n = a^{mn}$

EXAMPLE **1**   **Positive Integer Exponents**

Use rules of positive integer exponents to rewrite the following. Assume that all denominators are nonzero.

(a) $\dfrac{5^6}{5^4}$

(b) $\dfrac{x^2}{x^5}$

(c) $\left(\dfrac{x}{y}\right)^4$

(d) $(3x^2 y^3)^4$

(e) $3^3 \cdot 3^2$

Solution

(a) $\dfrac{5^6}{5^4} = 5^{6-4} = 5^2$

(b) $\dfrac{x^2}{x^5} = \dfrac{1}{x^{5-2}} = \dfrac{1}{x^3}$

(c) $\left(\dfrac{x}{y}\right)^4 = \dfrac{x^4}{y^4}$

(d) $(3x^2 y^3)^4 = 3^4 (x^2)^4 (y^3)^4 = 81 x^8 y^{12}$

(e) $3^3 \cdot 3^2 = 3^{3+2} = 3^5$

For certain calculus operations, use of negative exponents is necessary to write problems in the proper form. We can extend the rules for positive integer exponents to all integers by defining a^0 and a^{-n}. Clearly $a^m \cdot a^0$ should equal $a^{m+0} = a^m$, and it will if $a^0 = 1$.

Zero Exponent	For any nonzero real number a, we define $a^0 = 1$. We leave 0^0 undefined.

In Section 0.2, we defined a^{-1} as $1/a$ for $a \neq 0$, so we define a^{-n} as $(a^{-1})^n$.

Negative Exponents	$$a^{-n} = (a^{-1})^n = \left(\frac{1}{a}\right)^n = \frac{1}{a^n} \qquad (a \neq 0)$$ $$\left(\frac{a}{b}\right)^{-n} = \left[\left(\frac{a}{b}\right)^{-1}\right]^n = \left(\frac{b}{a}\right)^n \qquad (a \neq 0, \ b \neq 0)$$

EXAMPLE 2   **Negative and Zero Exponents**

Write the following without exponents.

(a) $6 \cdot 3^0$

(b) 6^{-2}

(c) $\left(\frac{1}{3}\right)^{-1}$

(d) $-\left(\frac{2}{3}\right)^{-4}$

(e) $(-4)^{-2}$

Solution

(a) $6 \cdot 3^0 = 6 \cdot 1 = 6$

(b) $6^{-2} = \dfrac{1}{6^2} = \dfrac{1}{36}$

(c) $\left(\dfrac{1}{3}\right)^{-1} = \dfrac{3}{1} = 3$

(d) $-\left(\dfrac{2}{3}\right)^{-4} = -\left(\dfrac{3}{2}\right)^4 = \dfrac{-81}{16}$

(e) $(-4)^{-2} = \dfrac{1}{(-4)^2} = \dfrac{1}{16}$

As we'll see in the chapter on the mathematics of finance (Chapter 6), negative exponents arise in financial calculations when we have a future goal for an investment and want to know how much to invest now. For example, if money can be invested at 9%, compounded annually, then the amount we must invest now (which is called the present value) to have $10,000 in the account after 7 years is given by $10,000(1.09)^{-7}$. Calculations such as this are often done directly with a calculator.

Using the definitions of zero and negative exponents enables us to extend the rules of exponents to all integers and to express them more simply.

Rules of Exponents	For real numbers a and b and *integers* m and n,

1. $a^m \cdot a^n = a^{m+n}$	2. $a^m / a^n = a^{m-n} \quad (a \neq 0)$
3. $(ab)^m = a^m b^m$	4. $(a^m)^n = a^{mn}$
5. $(a/b)^m = a^m / b^m \quad (a, b \neq 0)$	6. $a^0 = 1 \quad (a \neq 0)$
7. $a^{-n} = 1/a^n \quad (a \neq 0)$	8. $(a/b)^{-n} = (b/a)^n \quad (a, b \neq 0)$

Throughout the remainder of the text, we will assume that all variable expressions are defined.

EXAMPLE 3   Using Rules of Exponents

Use the rules of exponents and the definitions of a^0 and a^{-n} to simplify the following with positive exponents.

(a) $2(x^2)^{-2}$ (b) $x^{-2} \cdot x^{-5}$

(c) $\dfrac{x^{-8}}{x^{-4}}$ (d) $\left(\dfrac{2x^3}{3x^{-5}}\right)^{-2}$

Solution

(a) $2(x^2)^{-2} = 2x^{-4} = 2\left(\dfrac{1}{x^4}\right) = \dfrac{2}{x^4}$

(b) $x^{-2} \cdot x^{-5} = x^{-2-5} = x^{-7} = \dfrac{1}{x^7}$

(c) $\dfrac{x^{-8}}{x^{-4}} = x^{-8-(-4)} = x^{-4} = \dfrac{1}{x^4}$

(d) $\left(\dfrac{2x^3}{3x^{-5}}\right)^{-2} = \left(\dfrac{2x^8}{3}\right)^{-2} = \left(\dfrac{3}{2x^8}\right)^2 = \dfrac{9}{4x^{16}}$

CHECKPOINT

1. Complete the following.
   (a) $x^3 \cdot x^8 = x^?$ (b) $x \cdot x^4 \cdot x^{-3} = x^?$

   (c) $\dfrac{1}{x^4} = x^?$ (d) $x^{24} \div x^{-3} = x^?$

   (e) $(x^4)^2 = x^?$ (f) $(2x^4y)^3 = ?$

2. True or false:

   (a) $3x^{-2} = \dfrac{1}{9x^2}$ (b) $-x^{-4} = \dfrac{-1}{x^4}$ (c) $x^{-3} = -x^3$

3. Evaluate the following if possible. For any that are undefined, so state. Assume that $x > 0$.
   (a) 0^4 (b) 0^0 (c) x^0 (d) 0^x (e) 0^{-4} (f) -5^{-2}

EXAMPLE 4   Rewriting a Quotient

Write $(x^2y)/(9wz^3)$ with all factors in the numerator.

Solution

$$\dfrac{x^2y}{9wz^3} = x^2y\left(\dfrac{1}{9wz^3}\right) = x^2y\left(\dfrac{1}{9}\right)\left(\dfrac{1}{w}\right)\left(\dfrac{1}{z^3}\right) = x^2y \cdot 9^{-1}w^{-1}z^{-3}$$

$$= 9^{-1}x^2yw^{-1}z^{-3}$$

EXAMPLE 5   Rewriting with Positive Exponents

Simplify the following so that all exponents are positive.

(a) $(2^3x^{-4}y^5)^{-2}$

(b) $\dfrac{2x^4(x^2y)^0}{(4x^{-2}y)^2}$

Solution

(a) $(2^3x^{-4}y^5)^{-2} = 2^{-6}x^8y^{-10} = \dfrac{1}{2^6} \cdot x^8 \cdot \dfrac{1}{y^{10}} = \dfrac{x^8}{64y^{10}}$

(b) $\dfrac{2x^4(x^2y)^0}{(4x^{-2}y)^2} = \dfrac{2x^4 \cdot 1}{4^2x^{-4}y^2} = \dfrac{2}{4^2} \cdot \dfrac{x^4}{x^{-4}} \cdot \dfrac{1}{y^2} = \dfrac{2}{16} \cdot \dfrac{x^8}{1} \cdot \dfrac{1}{y^2} = \dfrac{x^8}{8y^2}$

CHECKPOINT ANSWERS

1. (a) x^{11} (b) x^2
   (c) x^{-4} (d) x^{27}
   (e) x^8 (f) $8x^{12}y^3$

2. (a) False; $3x^{-2} = \dfrac{3}{x^2}$

   (b) True.

   (c) False; $x^{-3} = \dfrac{1}{x^3}$

3. (a) $0^4 = 0$ (b) 0^0 is undefined.
   (c) $x^0 = 1$ since $x \neq 0$ (d) $0^x = 0$ because $x > 0$

   (e) 0^{-4} would be $\dfrac{1}{0^4}$, which is undefined.

   (f) $\dfrac{-1}{25}$

EXERCISES 0.3

Evaluate in Problems 1–4. Write all answers without using exponents.

1. (a) $(-4)^4$ (b) -2^6
2. (a) -5^3 (b) $(-2)^5$

3. (a) 3^{-2} (b) $-\left(\dfrac{3}{2}\right)^2$

4. (a) 6^{-1} (b) $\left(\dfrac{2}{3}\right)^3$

In Problems 5–8, use a calculator to evaluate the indicated powers.

5. 1.2^4 6. $(-3.7)^3$
7. $(1.5)^{-5}$ 8. $(-0.8)^{-9}$

In Problems 9–18, simplify the expressions with all exponents positive.

9. $6^5 \cdot 6^3$ 10. $8^4 \cdot 8^2 \cdot 8$

11. $\dfrac{10^8}{10^9}$ 12. $\dfrac{7^8}{7^3}$

13. $\dfrac{9^4 \cdot 9^{-7}}{9^{-3}}$ 14. $\dfrac{5^4}{(5^{-2} \cdot 5^3)}$

15. $(3^3)^3$ 16. $(2^{-3})^{-2}$

17. $\left(\dfrac{2}{3}\right)^{-2}$ 18. $\left(\dfrac{-2}{5}\right)^{-4}$

In Problems 19–22, rewrite the expression with positive exponents ($x, y, z \neq 0$).

19. $-x^{-3}$ 20. x^{-4}
21. $xy^{-2}z^0$ 22. $4^{-1}x^0y^{-2}$

In Problems 23–36, use the rules of exponents to simplify so that only positive exponents remain.

23. $x^3 \cdot x^4$ 24. $a^5 \cdot a$ 25. $x^{-5} \cdot x^3$

26. $y^{-5} \cdot y^{-2}$ 27. $\dfrac{x^8}{x^4}$ 28. $\dfrac{a^5}{a^{-1}}$

29. $\dfrac{y^5}{y^{-7}}$ 30. $\dfrac{y^{-3}}{y^{-4}}$ 31. $(x^4)^3$

32. $(y^3)^{-2}$ 33. $(xy)^2$ 34. $(2m)^3$

35. $\left(\dfrac{2}{x^5}\right)^4$ 36. $\left(\dfrac{8}{a^3}\right)^3$

In Problems 37–48, compute and simplify so that only positive exponents remain.

37. $(2x^{-2}y)^{-4}$ 38. $(-32x^5)^{-3}$
39. $(-8a^{-3}b^2)(2a^5b^{-4})$ 40. $(-3m^2y^{-1})(2m^{-3}y^{-1})$
41. $(2x^{-2}) \div (x^{-1}y^2)$ 42. $(-8a^{-3}b^2c) \div (2a^5b^4)$

43. $\left(\dfrac{x^3}{y^{-2}}\right)^{-3}$ 44. $\left(\dfrac{x^{-2}}{y}\right)^{-3}$

45. $\left(\dfrac{a^{-2}b^{-1}c^{-4}}{a^4b^{-3}c^0}\right)^{-3}$ 46. $\left(\dfrac{4x^{-1}y^{-40}}{2^{-2}x^4y^{-10}}\right)^{-2}$

47. (a) $\dfrac{2x^{-2}}{(2x)^2}$ (b) $\dfrac{(2x)^{-2}}{(2x)^2}$

   (c) $\dfrac{2x^{-2}}{2x^2}$ (d) $\dfrac{2x^{-2}}{(2x)^{-2}}$

48. (a) $\dfrac{2^{-1}x^{-2}}{(2x)^2}$ (b) $\dfrac{2^{-1}x^{-2}}{2x^2}$

   (c) $\dfrac{(2x^{-2})^{-1}}{(2x)^{-2}}$ (d) $\dfrac{(2x^{-2})^{-1}}{2x^2}$

In many applications, it is necessary to write expressions in the form cx^n, where c is a constant and n is an integer. In Problems 49–56, write the expressions in this form.

49. $\dfrac{1}{x}$ 50. $\dfrac{1}{x^2}$

51. $(2x)^3$ 52. $(3x)^2$

53. $\dfrac{1}{4x^2}$ 54. $\dfrac{3}{2x^4}$

55. $\left(\dfrac{-x}{2}\right)^3$ 56. $\left(\dfrac{-x}{3}\right)^2$

APPLICATIONS

Compound interest **If P is invested for n years at rate i (as a decimal), compounded annually, the future value that accrues is given by $S = P(1 + i)^n$ and the interest earned is $I = S - P$. In Problems 57–60, find S and I for the given P, n, and i.**

57. $1200 for 5 years at 12%
58. $1800 for 7 years at 10%
59. $5000 for 6 years at 11.5%
60. $800 for 20 years at 10.5%

Present value **If an investment has a goal (future value) of S after n years, invested at interest rate i (as a decimal), compounded annually, then the present value P that must be invested is given by $P = S(1 + i)^{-n}$. In Problems 61 and 62, find P for the given S, n, and i.**

61. $15,000 after 6 years at 11.5%
62. $80,000 after 20 years at 10.5%
63. *Personal income* The total U.S. personal income I (in billions of dollars) from 1960 and projected to 2024 can be approximated by

$$I = 533.6(1.065)^t$$

where t is the number of years after 1960 (*Source:* U.S. Bureau of Labor Statistics).
   (a) What t-values correspond to the years 2000, 2014, and 2024?
   (b) What does the formula estimate the total U.S. personal income to be in 2000, 2014, and 2024?
   (c) The U.S. total personal income given by the U.S. Bureau of Labor Statistics for 2018 is $19,129.6 billion. What does the formula estimate it to be in 2018?

64. *China's shale gas* For the years 2013 through 2020, the estimated annual production of shale-natural gas in China, in billions of cubic feet, can be approximated by the formula

$$y = 0.012(1.75)^t$$

where t is the number of years past 2010 (*Source:* Sanford C. Bernstein).
   (a) What t-value corresponds to 2019?
   (b) According to the formula, what is the production in 2019?
   (c) What is the production in 2022 if this formula remains accurate?

65. *Diabetes* Using data from 2010 and projected to 2050, the number of millions of U.S. adults with diabetes, y, can be approximated by the formula

$$y = \frac{120}{1 + 5.25(1.066)^{-t}}$$

where t is the number of years after 2000 (*Source:* Centers for Disease Control and Prevention).

(a) The actual numbers of millions given by the CDC for selected years are as follows.

2010	2015	2020
32.3	37.3	50.0

For each of these years, find the number of U.S. adults with diabetes predicted by the formula. Round your answer to one decimal place.
   (b) Using the number of U.S. adults with diabetes given above for 2015, how many more U.S. adults with diabetes does the formula predict will be added by 2025?
   (c) Why is it reasonable that the formula approximating the number of U.S. adults with diabetes has an upper limit that cannot be exceeded? Use large t-values to discover this formula's upper limit.

66. *U.S. population, ages 20–64* Using Social Security Administration data for selected years from 1950 and projected to 2050, the U.S. population, ages 20–64, P (in millions) can be approximated by the equation

$$P = \frac{249.6}{1 + 1.915(1.028)^{-t}}$$

where t is the number of years past 1950.
   (a) Some of the Social Security Administration data for this population (in millions) are as follows.

1980	2000	2020
134.0	169.8	198.2

For each of these years, use the equation to find the predicted U.S. population, ages 20–64.
   (b) From 2000 to 2020, this population group is predicted to change by 28.4 million individuals. Find the population change predicted by the equation for 2025 to 2045. Is this greater or less than 2000–2020?
   (c) Why is it reasonable for a formula such as this to have an upper limit that cannot be exceeded? Use large t-values to discover this formula's upper limit.

67. *Health care expenditures* The national health care expenditure H (in billions of dollars) can be modeled (that is, accurately approximated) by the formula

$$H = 738.1(1.065)^t$$

where t is the number of years past 1990 (*Source:* U.S. Department of Health and Human Services).
   (a) What t-value corresponds to 2000?
   (b) Approximate the national health care expenditure in 2000.
   (c) Approximate the national health care expenditure in 2010.
   (d) Estimate the national health care expenditure in 2018.

SECTION 0.4   Radicals and Rational Exponents

Roots   A process closely linked to raising numbers to powers is that of extracting roots. From geometry, we know that if an edge of a cube has a length of x units, its volume is x^3 cubic units. Reversing this process, we determine that if the volume of a cube is V cubic units, the length of an edge is the cube root of V, which is denoted

$$\sqrt[3]{V} \text{ units}$$

When we seek the **cube root** of a number such as 8 (written $\sqrt[3]{8}$), we are looking for a real number whose cube equals 8. Because $2^3 = 8$, we know that $\sqrt[3]{8} = 2$. Similarly, $\sqrt[3]{-27} = -3$ because $(-3)^3 = -27$. The expression $\sqrt[n]{a}$ is called a **radical,** where $\sqrt{}$ is the **radical sign,** n is the **index,** and a is the **radicand.** When no index is indicated, the index is assumed to be 2 and the expression is called a **square root;** thus $\sqrt{4}$ is the square root of 4 and represents the positive number whose square is 4.

Only one real number satisfies $\sqrt[n]{a}$ for a real number a and an odd number n; we call that number the **principal nth root** or, more simply, the **nth root.**

For an even index n, there are two possible cases:

1. If a is negative, there is no real number equal to $\sqrt[n]{a}$. For example, there are no real numbers that equal $\sqrt{-4}$ or $\sqrt[4]{-16}$ because there is no real number b such that $b^2 = -4$ or $b^4 = -16$. In this case, we say that $\sqrt[n]{a}$ is not a real number.
2. If a is positive, there are two real numbers whose nth power equals a. For example, $3^2 = 9$ and $(-3)^2 = 9$. To have a unique nth root, we define the (principal) nth root, $\sqrt[n]{a}$, as the *positive* number b that satisfies $b^n = a$.

We summarize this discussion as follows.

nth Root of a   The **(principal) nth root** of a real number is defined as

$$\sqrt[n]{a} = b \quad \text{only if} \quad a = b^n$$

subject to the following conditions:

	$a = 0$	$a > 0$	$a < 0$
n even	$\sqrt[n]{a} = 0$	$\sqrt[n]{a} > 0$	$\sqrt[n]{a}$ not real
n odd	$\sqrt[n]{a} = 0$	$\sqrt[n]{a} > 0$	$\sqrt[n]{a} < 0$

When we are asked for the root of a number, we give the principal root.

EXAMPLE 1   Roots

Find the roots if they are real numbers.
(a) $\sqrt[6]{64}$ (b) $-\sqrt{16}$ (c) $\sqrt[3]{-8}$ (d) $\sqrt{-16}$

Solution
(a) $\sqrt[6]{64} = 2$ because $2^6 = 64$ (b) $-\sqrt{16} = -\left(\sqrt{16}\right) = -4$ (c) $\sqrt[3]{-8} = -2$
(d) $\sqrt{-16}$ is not a real number because an even root of a negative number is not real.   ■

Fractional Exponents   To perform evaluations on a calculator or to perform calculus operations, it is sometimes necessary to rewrite radicals in exponential form with fractional exponents.

We have stated that for $a \geq 0$ and $b \geq 0$,

$$\sqrt{a} = b \quad \text{only if} \quad a = b^2$$

This means that $\left(\sqrt{a}\right)^2 = b^2 = a$, or $\left(\sqrt{a}\right)^2 = a$. To extend the properties of exponents to rational exponents, it is necessary to define

$$a^{1/2} = \sqrt{a} \quad \text{so that} \quad \left(a^{1/2}\right)^2 = a$$

Exponent 1/*n*

For a positive integer n, we define

$$a^{1/n} = \sqrt[n]{a} \quad \text{if} \quad \sqrt[n]{a} \text{ exists}$$

Thus $\left(a^{1/n}\right)^n = a^{(1/n)\cdot n} = a$.

Because we want the properties established for integer exponents to extend to rational exponents, we make the following definitions.

Rational Exponents

For positive integer n and any integer m (with $a \neq 0$ when $m \leq 0$, with m/n in lowest terms, and with a nonnegative when n is even),

1. $a^{m/n} = \left(a^{1/n}\right)^m = \left(\sqrt[n]{a}\right)^m$
2. $a^{m/n} = \left(a^m\right)^{1/n} = \sqrt[n]{a^m}$

Throughout the remaining discussion, we assume that all expressions are real.

EXAMPLE 2 **Radical Form**

Write the following in radical form and simplify.
(a) $16^{3/4}$ (b) $y^{-3/2}$ (c) $(6m)^{2/3}$

Solution
(a) $16^{3/4} = \sqrt[4]{16^3} = \left(\sqrt[4]{16}\right)^3 = (2)^3 = 8$

(b) $y^{-3/2} = \dfrac{1}{y^{3/2}} = \dfrac{1}{\sqrt{y^3}}$

(c) $(6m)^{2/3} = \sqrt[3]{(6m)^2} = \sqrt[3]{36m^2}$

EXAMPLE 3 **Fractional Exponents**

Write the following without radical signs.

(a) $\sqrt{x^3}$ (b) $\dfrac{1}{\sqrt[3]{b^2}}$ (c) $\sqrt[3]{(ab)^3}$

Solution
(a) $\sqrt{x^3} = x^{3/2}$ (b) $\dfrac{1}{\sqrt[3]{b^2}} = \dfrac{1}{b^{2/3}} = b^{-2/3}$ (c) $\sqrt[3]{(ab)^3} = (ab)^{3/3} = ab$

Our definition of $a^{m/n}$ guarantees that the rules for exponents will apply to fractional exponents. Thus we can perform operations with fractional exponents as we did with integer exponents.

EXAMPLE 4 **Operations with Fractional Exponents**

Simplify the following expressions.
(a) $a^{1/2} \cdot a^{1/6}$
(b) $a^{3/4}/a^{1/3}$
(c) $(a^3 b)^{2/3}$
(d) $(a^{3/2})^{1/2}$
(e) $a^{-1/2} \cdot a^{-3/2}$

Solution

(a) $a^{1/2} \cdot a^{1/6} = a^{1/2+1/6} = a^{3/6+1/6} = a^{4/6} = a^{2/3}$

(b) $a^{3/4}/a^{1/3} = a^{3/4-1/3} = a^{9/12-4/12} = a^{5/12}$

(c) $(a^3 b)^{2/3} = (a^3)^{2/3} b^{2/3} = a^2 b^{2/3}$

(d) $(a^{3/2})^{1/2} = a^{(3/2)(1/2)} = a^{3/4}$

(e) $a^{-1/2} \cdot a^{-3/2} = a^{-1/2-3/2} = a^{-2} = 1/a^2$

CHECKPOINT

1. Which of the following are *not* real numbers?

   (a) $\sqrt[3]{-64}$ (b) $\sqrt{-64}$ (c) $\sqrt{0}$ (d) $\sqrt[4]{1}$ (e) $\sqrt[5]{-1}$ (f) $\sqrt[8]{-1}$

2. (a) Write as radicals: $x^{1/3}, x^{2/5}, x^{-3/2}$

   (b) Write with fractional exponents: $\sqrt[4]{x^3} = x^?, \dfrac{1}{\sqrt{x}} = \dfrac{1}{x^?} = x^?$

3. Evaluate the following.

   (a) $8^{2/3}$ (b) $(-8)^{2/3}$ (c) $8^{-2/3}$ (d) $-8^{-2/3}$ (e) $\sqrt[15]{71}$

4. Complete the following.

   (a) $x \cdot x^{1/3} \cdot x^3 = x^?$ (b) $x^2 \div x^{1/2} = x^?$ (c) $(x^{-2/3})^{-3} = x^?$

   (d) $x^{-3/2} \cdot x^{1/2} = x^?$ (e) $x^{-3/2} \cdot x = x^?$ (f) $\left(\dfrac{x^4}{y^2}\right)^{3/2} = \;?$

5. True or false:

   (a) $\dfrac{8x^{2/3}}{x^{-1/3}} = 4x$ (b) $(16x^8 y)^{3/4} = 12x^6 y^{3/4}$

   (c) $\left(\dfrac{x^2}{y^3}\right)^{-1/3} = \left(\dfrac{y^3}{x^2}\right)^{1/3} = \dfrac{y}{x^{2/3}}$

Operations with Radicals

We can perform operations with radicals by first rewriting in exponential form, performing the operations with exponents, and then converting the answer back to radical form. Another option is to apply directly the following rules for operations with radicals.

Rules for Radicals	Example
Given that $\sqrt[n]{a}$ and $\sqrt[n]{b}$ are real,*	
1. $\sqrt[n]{a^n} = (\sqrt[n]{a})^n = a$	1. $\sqrt[5]{6^5} = (\sqrt[5]{6})^5 = 6$
2. $\sqrt[n]{a} \cdot \sqrt[n]{b} = \sqrt[n]{ab}$	2. $\sqrt[3]{2}\sqrt[3]{4} = \sqrt[3]{8} = \sqrt[3]{2^3} = 2$
3. $\dfrac{\sqrt[n]{a}}{\sqrt[n]{b}} = \sqrt[n]{\dfrac{a}{b}}$ $(b \neq 0)$	3. $\dfrac{\sqrt{18}}{\sqrt{2}} = \sqrt{\dfrac{18}{2}} = \sqrt{9} = 3$

*Note that this means that $a \geq 0$ and $b \geq 0$ if n is even.

Let us consider Rule 1 for radicals more carefully. Note that if n is even and $a < 0$, then $\sqrt[n]{a}$ is not real and Rule 1 does not apply. For example, $\sqrt{-2}$ is not a real number and

$$\sqrt{(-2)^2} \neq -2 \text{ because } \sqrt{(-2)^2} = \sqrt{4} = 2, \text{ which is not } -2$$

We can generalize this observation as follows: If $a < 0$, then $\sqrt{a^2} = -a > 0$, so

$$\sqrt{a^2} = \begin{cases} a & \text{if } a \geq 0 \\ -a & \text{if } a < 0 \end{cases}$$

This means that

$$\sqrt{a^2} = |a|$$

We can use the rules for radicals to simplify radical expressions. In general, a radical expression $\sqrt[n]{x}$ is considered simplified if x has no nth powers as factors.

EXAMPLE 5   Simplifying Radicals

Simplify the following radicals; assume that the expressions are real numbers.

(a) $\sqrt[3]{8^3}$ (b) $\left[\sqrt{(3x^2 + 4)^3}\right]^7$ (c) $\sqrt{x^2}$

(d) $\sqrt{48x^5y^6}$ $(y \geq 0)$ (e) $\sqrt[3]{72a^3b^4}$

Solution

(a) $\sqrt[3]{8^3} = 8$ by Rule 1

(b) $\left[\sqrt{(3x^2 + 4)^3}\right]^7 = (3x^2 + 4)^3$ by Rule 1

(c) $\sqrt{x^2} = |x|$ by the previous discussion

(d) To simplify $\sqrt{48x^5y^6}$, we first factor $48x^5y^6$ into perfect-square factors and other factors. Then we apply Rule 2.

$$\sqrt{48x^5y^6} = \sqrt{16 \cdot 3 \cdot x^4xy^6} = \sqrt{16}\sqrt{x^4}\sqrt{y^6}\sqrt{3x} = 4x^2y^3\sqrt{3x}$$

(e) We factor $72a^3b^4$ into factors that are perfect cubes and other factors. Then we apply Rule 2.

$$\sqrt[3]{72a^3b^4} = \sqrt[3]{8 \cdot 9a^3b^3b} = \sqrt[3]{8} \cdot \sqrt[3]{a^3} \cdot \sqrt[3]{b^3} \cdot \sqrt[3]{9b} = 2ab\sqrt[3]{9b}$$

Rule 2 for radicals also provides a procedure for multiplying two roots with the same index.

EXAMPLE 6   Multiplying Radicals

Multiply the following and simplify, assuming nonnegative variables.

(a) $\sqrt[3]{2xy} \cdot \sqrt[3]{4x^2y}$ (b) $\sqrt{8xy^3z} \cdot \sqrt{4x^2y^3z^2}$

Solution

(a) $\sqrt[3]{2xy} \cdot \sqrt[3]{4x^2y} = \sqrt[3]{2xy \cdot 4x^2y} = \sqrt[3]{8x^3y^2} = \sqrt[3]{8} \cdot \sqrt[3]{x^3} \cdot \sqrt[3]{y^2} = 2x\sqrt[3]{y^2}$

(b) $\sqrt{8xy^3z} \cdot \sqrt{4x^2y^3z^2} = \sqrt{32x^3y^6z^3} = \sqrt{16x^2y^6z^2} \cdot \sqrt{2xz} = 4xy^3z\sqrt{2xz}$

Rule 3 for radicals $(\sqrt[n]{a}/\sqrt[n]{b} = \sqrt[n]{a/b})$ indicates how to find the quotient of two roots with the same index.

EXAMPLE 7   Dividing Radicals

Find the quotients and simplify, assuming nonnegative variables.

(a) $\dfrac{\sqrt[3]{32}}{\sqrt[3]{4}}$ (b) $\dfrac{\sqrt{16a^3x}}{\sqrt{2ax}}$

Solution

(a) $\dfrac{\sqrt[3]{32}}{\sqrt[3]{4}} = \sqrt[3]{\dfrac{32}{4}} = \sqrt[3]{8} = 2$

(b) $\dfrac{\sqrt{16a^3x}}{\sqrt{2ax}} = \sqrt{\dfrac{16a^3x}{2ax}} = \sqrt{8a^2} = 2a\sqrt{2}$

Rationalizing   Occasionally, we want to express a fraction containing radicals in an equivalent form that contains no radicals in the denominator. This is accomplished by multiplying the numerator *and* the denominator by the expression that will remove the radical from the denominator. This process is called **rationalizing the denominator.**

EXAMPLE 8   **Rationalizing Denominators**

Express the following with no radicals in the denominator. (Rationalize each denominator.)

(a) $\dfrac{15}{\sqrt{x}}$ (b) $\dfrac{2x}{\sqrt{18xy}}$ $(x, y > 0)$ (c) $\dfrac{3x}{\sqrt[3]{2x^2}}$ $(x \neq 0)$

Solution

(a) We want to create a perfect square under the radical in the denominator.

$$\frac{15}{\sqrt{x}} \cdot \frac{\sqrt{x}}{\sqrt{x}} = \frac{15\sqrt{x}}{x}$$

(b) $\dfrac{2x}{\sqrt{18xy}} \cdot \dfrac{\sqrt{2xy}}{\sqrt{2xy}} = \dfrac{2x\sqrt{2xy}}{\sqrt{36x^2y^2}} = \dfrac{2x\sqrt{2xy}}{6xy} = \dfrac{\sqrt{2xy}}{3y}$

(c) We want to create a perfect cube under the radical in the denominator.

$$\frac{3x}{\sqrt[3]{2x^2}} \cdot \frac{\sqrt[3]{4x}}{\sqrt[3]{4x}} = \frac{3x\sqrt[3]{4x}}{\sqrt[3]{8x^3}} = \frac{3x\sqrt[3]{4x}}{2x} = \frac{3\sqrt[3]{4x}}{2}$$

CHECKPOINT

6. Simplify:
   (a) $\sqrt[3]{24x^3y}$
   (b) $\sqrt{12xy^2} \cdot \sqrt{3x^2y}$
   (c) $\dfrac{\sqrt{24x^4y^3}}{\sqrt{3y^2}}$

7. Rationalize the denominator of $\dfrac{x}{\sqrt{5x}}$ if $x \neq 0$.

It is sometimes useful, especially in calculus, to *rationalize the numerator* of a fraction. For example, in the following expression, we can rationalize the numerator by multiplying the numerator and denominator by $\sqrt[3]{2x}$, which creates a perfect cube under the radical:

$$\frac{\sqrt[3]{4x^2}}{3x} = \frac{\sqrt[3]{4x^2}}{3x} \cdot \frac{\sqrt[3]{2x}}{\sqrt[3]{2x}} = \frac{\sqrt[3]{8x^3}}{3x\sqrt[3]{2x}} = \frac{2x}{3x\sqrt[3]{2x}} = \frac{2}{3\sqrt[3]{2x}}$$

CHECKPOINT ANSWERS

1. Part (b) $\sqrt{-64}$ and part (f) $\sqrt[8]{-1}$ are not real numbers.

2. (a) $\sqrt[5]{x}$; $\sqrt[5]{x^2}$; $\dfrac{1}{\sqrt{x^3}}$ (b) $x^{3/4}$; $\dfrac{1}{x^{1/2}} = x^{-1/2}$

3. (a) 4   (b) 4   (c) $\dfrac{1}{4}$
   (d) $-\dfrac{1}{4}$ (e) ≈ 1.32867

4. (a) $x^{13/3}$ (b) $x^{3/2}$ (c) x^2
   (d) x^{-1} (e) $x^{-1/2}$ (f) $\dfrac{x^6}{y^3}$

5. (a) False; $8x$
   (b) False; $8x^6y^{3/4}$
   (c) True.

6. (a) $2x\sqrt[3]{3y}$
   (b) $6xy\sqrt{xy}$
   (c) $2x^2\sqrt{2y}$

7. $\dfrac{\sqrt{5x}}{5}$

EXERCISES 0.4

Unless stated otherwise, assume that all variables are non-negative and that all denominators are nonzero.

In Problems 1–4, find the powers and roots, if they are real numbers.

1. (a) $\sqrt{256/9}$ (b) $\sqrt{1.44}$
   (c) $16^{3/4}$ (d) $(-16)^{-3/2}$
2. (a) $\sqrt[5]{-32^3}$ (b) $\sqrt[4]{-16^5}$
   (c) $-27^{-1/3}$ (d) $32^{3/5}$
3. (a) $\left(\dfrac{8}{27}\right)^{-2/3}$ (b) $64^{2/3}$ (c) $(-64)^{-2/3}$
4. (a) $\left(\dfrac{4}{9}\right)^{3/2}$ (b) $64^{-2/3}$ (c) $-64^{2/3}$

In Problems 5 and 6, rewrite each radical with a fractional exponent and then approximate the value with a calculator.

5. $\sqrt[9]{(6.12)^4}$ 6. $\sqrt[12]{4.96}$

In Problems 7–10, replace each radical with a fractional exponent. Do not simplify.

7. $\sqrt{m^3}$ 8. $\sqrt[3]{x^5}$ 9. $\sqrt[4]{m^2 n^5}$ 10. $\sqrt[5]{x^3}$

In Problems 11–16, write in radical form. Do not simplify.

11. $2x^{1/2}$ 12. $12x^{1/4}$
13. $x^{7/6}$ 14. $y^{11/5}$
15. $-(1/4)x^{-5/4}$ 16. $-x^{-5/3}$

In Problems 17–30, simplify each expression so that only positive exponents remain.

17. $y^{1/4} \cdot y^{1/2}$ 18. $x^{2/3} \cdot x^{1/5}$ 19. $z^{3/4} \cdot z^4$
20. $x^{-2/3} \cdot x^2$ 21. $y^{-3/2} \cdot y^{-1}$ 22. $z^{-2} \cdot z^{5/3}$
23. $\dfrac{x^{1/3}}{x^{-2/3}}$ 24. $\dfrac{x^{-1/2}}{x^{-3/2}}$ 25. $\dfrac{y^{-5/2}}{y^{-2/5}}$
26. $\dfrac{x^{4/9}}{x^{1/12}}$ 27. $(x^{2/3})^{3/4}$ 28. $(x^{4/5})^3$
29. $(x^{-1/2})^2$ 30. $(x^{-2/3})^{-2/5}$

In Problems 31–36, simplify each expression.

31. $\sqrt{64x^4}$ 32. $\sqrt[3]{-64x^6 y^3}$
33. $\sqrt{128x^4 y^5}$ 34. $\sqrt[3]{54x^5 x^8}$
35. $\sqrt[3]{40x^8 y^5}$ 36. $\sqrt{32x^5 y}$

In Problems 37–44, perform the indicated operations and simplify.

37. $\sqrt{12x^3 y} \cdot \sqrt{3x^2 y}$ 38. $\sqrt[3]{16x^2 y} \cdot \sqrt[3]{3x^2 y}$
39. $\sqrt{63x^5 y^3} \cdot \sqrt{28x^2 y}$ 40. $\sqrt{10xz^{10}} \cdot \sqrt{30x^{17}z}$
41. $\dfrac{\sqrt{12x^3 y^{12}}}{\sqrt{27xy^2}}$ 42. $\dfrac{\sqrt{250xy^7 z^4}}{\sqrt{18x^{17}y^2}}$

43. $\dfrac{\sqrt[4]{32a^9 b^5}}{\sqrt[4]{162a^{17}}}$ 44. $\dfrac{\sqrt[3]{-16x^3 y^4}}{\sqrt[3]{128y^2}}$

In Problems 45–48, determine a value for x that makes each statement true.

45. $(A^9)^x = A$ 46. $(B^{20})^x = B$
47. $(\sqrt[3]{R})^x = R$ 48. $(\sqrt{T^3})^x = T$

In Problems 49–54, rationalize each denominator and then simplify.

49. $\sqrt{2/3}$ 50. $\sqrt{5/8}$ 51. $\dfrac{\sqrt{m^2 x}}{\sqrt{mx^2}}$

52. $\dfrac{5x^3 w}{\sqrt{4xw^2}}$ 53. $\dfrac{\sqrt[3]{m^2 x}}{\sqrt[3]{mx^5}}$ 54. $\dfrac{\sqrt[4]{mx^3}}{\sqrt[4]{y^2 z^5}}$

In calculus, it is frequently important to write an expression in the form cx^n, where c is a constant and n is a rational number. In Problems 55–58, write each expression in this form.

55. $\dfrac{-2}{3\sqrt[3]{x^2}}$ 56. $\dfrac{-2}{3\sqrt[4]{x^3}}$ 57. $3x\sqrt{x}$ 58. $\sqrt{x} \cdot \sqrt[3]{x}$

In calculus problems, the answers are frequently expected to be in a form with a radical instead of a fractional exponent. In Problems 59–62, write each expression with radicals.

59. $\dfrac{3}{2}x^{1/2}$ 60. $\dfrac{4}{3}x^{1/3}$
61. $\dfrac{1}{2}x^{-1/2}$ 62. $\dfrac{-1}{2}x^{-3/2}$

APPLICATIONS

63. *Richter scale* The Richter scale reading for an earthquake measures its intensity (as a multiple of some minimum intensity used for comparison). The intensity I corresponding to a Richter scale reading R is given by

$$I = 10^R$$

(a) A quake measuring 8.5 on the Richter scale would be severe. Express the intensity of such a quake in exponential form and in radical form.
(b) Find the intensity of a quake measuring 9.0.
(c) The San Francisco quake that occurred during the 1989 World Series measured 6.9, and the March 2011 quake that devastated Sendai, Japan, measured 9.0. Calculate the ratio of these intensities (larger to smaller).

64. *Sound intensity* The intensity of sound I (as a multiple of the average minimum threshold of hearing intensity) is related to the decibel level D (or loudness of sound) according to

$$I = 10^{D/10}$$

(a) Express $10^{D/10}$ using radical notation.
(b) The background noise level of a relatively quiet room has a decibel reading of 32. Find the intensity I_1 of this noise level.
(c) A decibel reading of 140 is at the threshold of pain. If I_2 is the intensity of this threshold and I_1 is the intensity found in part (b), express the ratio I_2/I_1 as a power of 10. Then approximate this ratio.

65. *Investment* If $1000 is invested at $r\%$ compounded annually, the future value S of the account after two and a half years is given by

$$S = 1000\left(1 + \frac{r}{100}\right)^{5/2}$$

(a) Express this equation with radical notation.
(b) Find the value of this account if the interest rate is 6.6% compounded annually.

66. *Life span* Life expectancy in the United States can be approximated with the equation

$$L = 29x^{0.22}$$

where x is the number of years the birth year is past 1900 (*Source:* National Center for Health Statistics).
(a) Express this equation with radical notation.
(b) Use the equation to estimate the life expectancy for a person born in 2015.

67. *Population* The population P of India (in billions) for 2000–2050 can be approximated by the equation

$$P = 0.924t^{0.13}$$

where $t > 0$ is the number of years past 2000 (*Source:* United Nations).
(a) Express this equation with radical notation.
(b) Does this equation predict a greater increase from 2005 to 2010 or from 2045 to 2050? What might explain this difference?

68. *Trust in government* For the years after 1965, the percent of people who say they trust the government always or most of the time can be approximated by

$$y = \frac{154}{x^{0.5}}$$

where x is the number of years after 1960.
(a) Express this equation with radical notation.
(b) For the year 2020, what does this equation estimate as the percent of people who say they trust the government always or most of the time?
(c) What does this equation estimate as the change in percentage points during the decade from 1970 to 1980?

Half-life **In Problems 69 and 70, use the fact that the quantity of a radioactive substance after t years is given by $q = q_0(2^{-t/k})$, where q_0 is the original amount of radioactive material and k is its half-life (the number of years it takes for half the radioactive substance to decay).**

69. The half-life of strontium-90 is 25 years. Find the amount of strontium-90 remaining after 10 years if $q_0 = 98$ kg.
70. The half-life of carbon-14 is 5730 years. Find the amount of carbon-14 remaining after 10,000 years if $q_0 = 40.0$ g.
71. *Population growth* Suppose the formula for the growth of the population of a city for the next 10 years is given by

$$P = P_0(2.5)^{ht}$$

where P_0 is the population of the city at the present time and P is the population t years from now. If $h = 0.03$ and $P_0 = 30,000$, find P when $t = 10$.
72. *Advertising and sales* Suppose it has been determined that the sales at Ewing Gallery decline after the end of an advertising campaign, with daily sales given by

$$S = 2000(2^{-0.1x})$$

where S is in dollars and x is the number of days after the campaign ends. What are the daily sales 10 days after the end of the campaign?
73. *Company growth* The growth of a company can be described by the equation

$$N = 500(0.02)^{0.7^t}$$

where t is the number of years the company has been in existence and N is the number of employees.
(a) What is the number of employees when $t = 0$? (This is the number of employees the company has when it starts.)
(b) What is the number of employees when $t = 5$?

SECTION 0.5   Operations with Algebraic Expressions

In algebra, we are usually dealing with combinations of real numbers (such as 3, 6/7, and $-\sqrt{2}$) and letters (such as x, a, and m). Unless otherwise specified, the letters are symbols used to represent real numbers and are sometimes called **variables.** An expression obtained by performing additions, subtractions, multiplications, divisions, or extractions of roots with one or more real numbers or variables is called an **algebraic expression.**

Unless otherwise specified, the variables represent all real numbers for which the algebraic expression is a real number. Examples of algebraic expressions include

$$3x + 2y, \quad \frac{x^3y + y}{x-1}, \quad \text{and} \quad \sqrt{x-3}$$

Note that the variable x cannot be negative in $\sqrt{x-3}$ and that $(x^3y + y)/(x - 1)$ is not a real number when $x = 1$ because division by 0 is undefined.

Any product of a real number (called the **coefficient**) and one or more variables to powers is called a **term.** The sum of a finite number of terms with nonnegative integer powers on the variables is called a **polynomial.** If a polynomial contains only one variable x, then it is called a polynomial in x.

Polynomial in x

The general form of a **polynomial in x** is

$$a_nx^n + a_{n-1}x^{n-1} + \cdots + a_1x + a_0$$

where each coefficient a_i is a real number for $i = 0, 1, 2, \ldots, n$. If $a_n \neq 0$, the **degree** of the polynomial is n and a_n is called the **leading coefficient.** The term a_0 is called the **constant term.**

Thus $4x^3 - 2x - 3$ is a third-degree polynomial in x with leading coefficient 4 and constant term -3. If a term has two or more variables, the degree of the term is the sum of the exponents of the variables. The degree of a constant term is zero. Thus the degree of $4x^2y$ is $2 + 1 = 3$, the degree of $6xy$ is $1 + 1 = 2$, and the degree of 3 is 0. The **degree of a polynomial** containing one or more variables is the degree of the term in the polynomial having the highest degree. Therefore, $2xy - 4x + 6$ is a second-degree polynomial.

A polynomial containing two terms is called a **binomial,** and a polynomial containing three terms is called a **trinomial.** A single-term polynomial is a **monomial.**

Because polynomials represent real numbers, the properties of real numbers can be used to add, subtract, multiply, divide, and simplify polynomials. For example, we can use the Distributive Law to add $3x$ and $2x$.

$$3x + 2x = (3 + 2)x = 5x$$

Similarly, $9xy - 3xy = (9 - 3)xy = 6xy$.

Terms with exactly the same variable factors are called **like terms.** We can add or subtract like terms by adding or subtracting the coefficients of the variables. Subtraction of polynomials uses the Distributive Law to remove the parentheses.

EXAMPLE 1   **Combining Polynomials**

Compute (a) $(4xy + 3x) + (5xy - 2x)$ and (b) $(3x^2 + 4xy + 5y^2 + 1) - (6x^2 - 2xy + 4)$.

Solution
(a) $(4xy + 3x) + (5xy - 2x) = 4xy + 3x + 5xy - 2x = 9xy + x$
(b) Removing the parentheses yields

$$3x^2 + 4xy + 5y^2 + 1 - 6x^2 + 2xy - 4 = -3x^2 + 6xy + 5y^2 - 3$$

Using the rules of exponents and the Commutative and Associative Laws for multiplication, we can multiply and divide monomials, as the following example shows.

EXAMPLE 2   **Products and Quotients**

Perform the indicated operations.
(a) $(8xy^3)(2x^3y)(-3xy^2)$ (b) $-15x^2y^3 \div (3xy^5)$

Solution

(a) $8 \cdot 2 \cdot (-3) \cdot x \cdot x^3 \cdot x \cdot y^3 \cdot y \cdot y^2 = -48x^5y^6$

(b) $\dfrac{-15x^2y^3}{3xy^5} = -\dfrac{15}{3} \cdot \dfrac{x^2}{x} \cdot \dfrac{y^3}{y^5} = -5 \cdot x \cdot \dfrac{1}{y^2} = -\dfrac{5x}{y^2}$

Symbols of grouping are used in algebra the same way they are used in the arithmetic of real numbers. Recall that when an expression has two or more symbols of grouping, we begin with the innermost terms and work outward.

EXAMPLE 3 Symbols of Grouping

Simplify $3x^2 - [2x - (3x^2 - 2x)]$.

Solution

$$3x^2 - [2x - (3x^2 - 2x)] = 3x^2 - [2x - 3x^2 + 2x]$$
$$= 3x^2 - [4x - 3x^2]$$
$$= 3x^2 - 4x + 3x^2 = 6x^2 - 4x$$

We can use the Distributive Law to multiply a polynomial by a monomial. For example,

$$x(2x + 3) = x \cdot 2x + x \cdot 3 = 2x^2 + 3x \qquad \text{and} \qquad 5(x + y + 2) = 5x + 5y + 10$$

EXAMPLE 4 Using the Distributive Law

Find the following products.

(a) $-4ab(3a^2b + 4ab^2 - 1)$ (b) $(4a + 5b + c)ac$

Solution

(a) $-4ab(3a^2b + 4ab^2 - 1) = -4ab(3a^2b) + (-4ab)(4ab^2) + (-4ab)(-1)$
$$= -12a^3b^2 - 16a^2b^3 + 4ab$$

(b) $(4a + 5b + c)ac = 4a \cdot ac + 5b \cdot ac + c \cdot ac = 4a^2c + 5abc + ac^2$

The Distributive Law can be used to multiply two polynomials. Consider the product of two binomials $(a + b)(c + d)$. If we begin by treating the sum $(a + b)$ as a single quantity, then two successive applications of the Distributive Law give

$$(a + b)(c + d) = (a + b) \cdot c + (a + b) \cdot d = ac + bc + ad + bd$$

Thus we see that the product can be found by multiplying $(a + b)$ by c, multiplying $(a + b)$ by d, and then adding the products.

EXAMPLE 5 The Product of Two Polynomials

Find the following products.

(a) $(x + 2)(x + 5)$ (b) $(4x^2 + 3xy + 4x)(2x - 3y)$

Solution

Notice that each part uses two successive applications of the Distributive Law.

(a) $(x + 2)(x + 5) = (x + 2)(x) + (x + 2)(5) = x^2 + 2x + 5x + 10 = x^2 + 7x + 10$

(b) $(4x^2 + 3xy + 4x)(2x - 3y) = (4x^2 + 3xy + 4x)(2x) + (4x^2 + 3xy + 4x)(-3y)$
$$= 8x^3 + 6x^2y + 8x^2 - 12x^2y - 9xy^2 - 12xy$$
$$= 8x^3 - 6x^2y + 8x^2 - 9xy^2 - 12xy$$

Note in Example 5(a) that the product of two binomials has a special structure. We can obtain these products by finding the products of the First terms, Outside terms, Inside terms, and Last terms, and then adding the results. This is called the FOIL method of multiplying two binomials.

EXAMPLE 6   **Products of Binomials**

Multiply the following.
(a) $(x - 4)(x + 3)$
(b) $(3x + 2)(2x + 5)$

Solution

$$\qquad\qquad\qquad\text{First}\quad\text{Outside}\quad\text{Inside}\quad\text{Last}$$
(a) $(x - 4)(x + 3) = (x^2) + (3x) + (-4x) + (-12) = x^2 - x - 12$
(b) $(3x + 2)(2x + 5) = (6x^2) + (15x) + (4x) + (10) = 6x^2 + 19x + 10$

While all binomial products can be found with the Distributive Law (or FOIL), some products have special forms worth remembering.

Special Products

1. $(x + a)^2 = x^2 + 2ax + a^2$ binomial squared
2. $(x - a)^2 = x^2 - 2ax + a^2$ binomial squared
3. $(x + a)(x - a) = x^2 - a^2$ difference of two squares
4. $(x + a)^3 = x^3 + 3ax^2 + 3a^2x + a^3$ binomial cubed
5. $(x - a)^3 = x^3 - 3ax^2 + 3a^2x - a^3$ binomial cubed

EXAMPLE 7   **Special Products**

Multiply the following.
(a) $(x + 5)^2$ (b) $(3x - 4y)^2$
(c) $(x - 2)(x + 2)$ (d) $(x^2 - y^3)^2$
(e) $(x + 4)^3$

Solution

(a) $(x + 5)^2 = x^2 + 2(5)x + 25 = x^2 + 10x + 25$
(b) $(3x - 4y)^2 = (3x)^2 - 2(3x)(4y) + (4y)^2 = 9x^2 - 24xy + 16y^2$
(c) $(x - 2)(x + 2) = x^2 - 4$
(d) $(x^2 - y^3)^2 = (x^2)^2 - 2(x^2)(y^3) + (y^3)^2 = x^4 - 2x^2y^3 + y^6$
(e) $(x + 4)^3 = x^3 + 3(4)(x^2) + 3(4^2)(x) + 4^3 = x^3 + 12x^2 + 48x + 64$

CHECKPOINT

1. Remove parentheses and combine like terms: $9x - 5x(x + 2) + 4x^2$
2. Find the following products.
    (a) $(2x + 1)(4x^2 - 2x + 1)$ (b) $(x + 3)^2$
    (c) $(3x + 2)(x - 5)$ (d) $(1 - 4x)(1 + 4x)$

The techniques used to perform operations on polynomials and to simplify polynomials also apply to other algebraic expressions.

EXAMPLE 8   **Operations with Algebraic Expressions**

Perform the indicated operations.
(a) $3\sqrt{3} + 4x\sqrt{y} - 5\sqrt{3} - 11x\sqrt{y} - (\sqrt{3} - x\sqrt{y})$
(b) $x^{3/2}(x^{1/2} - x^{-1/2})$
(c) $(x^{1/2} - x^{1/3})^2$
(d) $(\sqrt{x} + 2)(\sqrt{x} - 2)$

Solution

(a) We remove parentheses and then combine the terms containing $\sqrt{3}$ and the terms containing $x\sqrt{y}$.

$$(3 - 5 - 1)\sqrt{3} + (4 - 11 + 1)x\sqrt{y} = -3\sqrt{3} - 6x\sqrt{y}$$

(b) $x^{3/2}(x^{1/2} - x^{-1/2}) = x^{3/2} \cdot x^{1/2} - x^{3/2} \cdot x^{-1/2} = x^2 - x$

(c) $(x^{1/2} - x^{1/3})^2 = (x^{1/2})^2 - 2x^{1/2}x^{1/3} + (x^{1/3})^2 = x - 2x^{5/6} + x^{2/3}$

(d) $(\sqrt{x} + 2)(\sqrt{x} - 2) = (\sqrt{x})^2 - (2)^2 = x - 4$

In later chapters, we will need to write problems in a simplified form so that we can perform certain operations on them. We can often use division of one polynomial by another to obtain the simplification, as shown in the following procedure.

DIVISION OF POLYNOMIALS

Procedure	Example
To divide one polynomial by another:	Divide $4x^3 + 4x^2 + 5$ by $2x^2 + 1$.
1. Write both polynomials in descending powers of a variable. Include missing terms with coefficient 0 in the dividend.	1. $2x^2 + 1\overline{)4x^3 + 4x^2 + 0x + 5}$
2. (a) Divide the highest-power term of the divisor into the highest-power term of the dividend and write this partial quotient above the dividend. Multiply the partial quotient times the divisor, write the product under the dividend, and subtract, getting a new dividend. (b) Repeat until the degree of the new dividend is less than the degree of the divisor. Any remainder is written over the divisor and added to the quotient.	2. (a) $$\begin{array}{r} 2x \\ 2x^2 + 1\overline{)4x^3 + 4x^2 + 0x + 5} \\ \underline{4x^3 + 2x } \\ 4x^2 - 2x + 5 \end{array}$$ (b) $$\begin{array}{r} 2x + 2 \\ 2x^2 + 1\overline{)4x^3 + 4x^2 + 0x + 5} \\ \underline{4x^3 + 2x } \\ 4x^2 - 2x + 5 \\ \underline{4x^2 + 2} \\ -2x + 3 \end{array}$$ Degree $(-2x + 3) <$ degree $(2x^2 + 1)$ Quotient: $2x + 2 + \dfrac{-2x + 3}{2x^2 + 1}$

EXAMPLE   9   **Division of Polynomials**

Divide $(4x^3 - 13x - 22)$ by $(x - 3)$, $x \neq 3$.

Solution

$$\begin{array}{r} 4x^2 + 12x + 23 \\ x - 3\overline{)4x^3 + 0x^2 - 13x - 22} \\ \underline{4x^3 - 12x^2 } \\ 12x^2 - 13x - 22 \\ \underline{12x^2 - 36x } \\ 23x - 22 \\ \underline{23x - 69} \\ 47 \end{array}$$ Insert $0x^2$ so that each power of x is present.

The quotient is $4x^2 + 12x + 23$, with remainder 47, or

$$4x^2 + 12x + 23 + \frac{47}{x - 3}$$

CHECKPOINT   3. Use long division to find $(x^3 + 2x + 7) \div (x - 4)$.

CHECKPOINT
ANSWERS

1. $-x^2 - x$
2. (a) $8x^3 + 1$
   (b) $x^2 + 6x + 9$
   (c) $3x^2 - 13x - 10$
   (d) $1 - 16x^2$
3. $x^2 + 4x + 18 + \dfrac{79}{x - 4}$

EXERCISES 0.5

For each polynomial in Problems 1–4, (a) give the degree of the polynomial, (b) give the coefficient (numerical) of the highest-degree term, (c) give the constant term, and (d) decide whether it is a polynomial of one or several variables.

1. $10 - 3x - x^2$
2. $5x^4 - 2x^9 + 7$
3. $7x^2y - 14xy^3z$
4. $2x^5 + 7x^2y^3 - 5y^6$

The expressions in Problems 5 and 6 are polynomials with the form $a_nx^n + a_{n-1}x^{n-1} + \cdots + a_1x + a_0$, where n is a positive integer. Complete the following.

5. For $2x^5 - 3x^2 - 5$,
   (a) $2 = a_?$
   (b) $a_3 = ?$
   (c) $-3 = a_?$
   (d) $a_0 = ?$
6. For $5x^3 - 4x - 17$,
   (a) $a_3 = ?$
   (b) $a_1 = ?$
   (c) $a_2 = ?$
   (d) $-17 = a_?$

In Problems 7–12, evaluate each algebraic expression at the indicated values of the variables.

7. $4x - x^2$ at $x = -2$
8. $10 - 6(4 - x)^2$ at $x = -1$
9. $10xy - 4(x - y)^2$ at $x = 5$ and $y = -2$
10. $3x^2 - 4y^2 - 2xy$ at $x = 3$ and $y = -4$
11. $\dfrac{2x - y}{x^2 - 2y}$ at $x = -5$ and $y = -3$
12. $\dfrac{16y}{1 - y}$ at $y = -3$
13. Evaluate $1.98T - 1.09(1 - H)(T - 58) - 56.8$ when $T = 74.7$ and $H = 0.80$.
14. Evaluate $R\left[\dfrac{0.083i}{1 - (1 + 0.083i)^{-n}}\right]$ when $R = 100,000$, $i = 0.07$, and $n = 360$.

In Problems 15–22, simplify by combining like terms.
15. $(16pq - 7p^2) + (5pq + 5p^2)$
16. $(3x^3 + 4x^2y^2) + (3x^2y^2 - 7x^3)$
17. $(4m^2 - 3n^2 + 5) - (3m^2 + 4n^2 + 8)$

18. $(4rs - 2r^2s - 11rs^2) - (11rs^2 - 2rs + 4r^2s)$
19. $-[8 - 4(q + 5) + q]$
20. $x^3 + [3x - (x^3 - 3x)]$
21. $x^2 - [x - (x^2 - 1) + 1 - (1 - x^2)] + x$
22. $y^3 - [y^2 - (y^3 + y^2)] - [y^3 + (1 - y^2)]$

In Problems 23–58, perform the indicated operations and simplify.
23. $(5x^3)(7x^2)$
24. $(-3x^2y)(2xy^3)(4x^2y^2)$
25. $(39r^3s^2) \div (13r^2s)$
26. $(-15m^3n) \div (5mn^4)$
27. $ax^2(2x^2 + ax + ab)$
28. $-3(3 - x^2)$
29. $(3y + 4)(2y - 3)$
30. $(4x - 1)(x - 3)$
31. $6(1 - 2x^2)(2 - x^2)$
32. $2(x^3 + 3)(2x^3 - 5)$
33. $(4x + 3)^2$
34. $(2y + 5)^2$
35. $(0.1 - 4x)(0.1 + 4x)$
36. $(x^3y^3 - 0.3)^2$
37. $9(2x + 1)(2x - 1)$
38. $3(5y + 2)(5y - 2)$
39. $\left(x^2 - \dfrac{1}{2}\right)^2$
40. $\left(\dfrac{2}{3} + x\right)\left(\dfrac{2}{3} - x\right)$
41. $(0.1x - 2)(x + 0.05)$
42. $(6.2x + 4.1)(6.2x - 4.1)$
43. $(x - 2)(x^2 + 2x + 4)$
44. $(a + b)(a^2 - ab + b^2)$
45. $(x^3 + 5x)(x^5 - 2x^3 + 5)$
46. $(x^3 - 1)(x^7 - 2x^4 - 5x^2 + 5)$
47. $(18m^2n + 6m^3n + 12m^4n^2) \div (6m^2n)$
48. $(16x^2 + 4xy^2 + 8x) \div (4xy)$
49. $(24x^8y^4 + 15x^5y - 6x^7y) \div (9x^5y^2)$
50. $(27x^2y^2 - 18xy + 9xy^2) \div (6xy)$
51. $(x + 1)^3$
52. $(x - 3)^3$
53. $(2x - 3)^3$
54. $(3x + 4)^3$
55. $(x^3 + x - 1) \div (x + 2)$
56. $(x^5 + 5x - 7) \div (x + 1)$
57. $(x^4 + 3x^3 - x + 1) \div (x^2 + 1)$
58. $(x^3 + 5x^2 - 6) \div (x^2 - 2)$

In Problems 59 and 60, simplify each expression.
59. (a) $(3x - 2)^2 - 3x - 2(3x - 2) + 5$
    (b) $(3x - 2)^2 - (3x - 2)(3x - 2) + 5$
60. (a) $(2x - 3)(3x + 2) - (5x - 2)(x - 3)$
    (b) $2x - 3(3x + 2) - 5x - 2(x - 3)$

In Problems 61–68, perform the indicated operations with expressions involving fractional exponents and radicals and then simplify.

61. $x^{1/2}(x^{1/2} + 2x^{3/2})$

62. $x^{-2/3}(x^{5/3} - x^{-1/3})$

63. $(x^{1/2} + 1)(x^{1/2} - 2)$

64. $(x^{1/3} - x^{1/2})(4x^{2/3} - 3x^{3/2})$

65. $(\sqrt{x} + 3)(\sqrt{x} - 3)$

66. $(x^{1/5} + x^{1/2})(x^{1/5} - x^{1/2})$

67. $(2x + 1)^{1/2}[(2x + 1)^{3/2} - (2x + 1)^{-1/2}]$

68. $(4x - 3)^{-5/3}[(4x - 3)^{8/3} + 3(4x - 3)^{5/3}]$

APPLICATIONS

69. *Revenue* A company sells its product for $55 per unit. Write an expression for the amount of money received (revenue) from the sale of x units of the product.

70. *Profit* Suppose a company's revenue R (in dollars) from the sale of x units of its product is given by

$$R = 215x$$

Suppose further that the total costs C (in dollars) of producing those x units is given by

$$C = 65x + 15{,}000$$

(a) If profit is revenue minus cost, find an expression for the profit from the production and sale of x units.

(b) Find the profit received if 1000 units are sold.

71. *Rental* A rental truck costs $49.95 for a day plus 49¢ per mile.

(a) If x is the number of miles driven, write an expression for the total cost of renting the truck for a day.

(b) Find the total cost of the rental if it was driven 132 miles.

72. *Cell phones* Cell Pro makes cell phones and has weekly costs of $1500 for rent, utilities, and equipment plus labor and material costs of $18.50 for each phone it makes.

(a) If x represents the number of phones produced and sold, write an expression for Cell Pro's weekly total cost.

(b) If Cell Pro sells the phones to dealers for $45.50 each, write an expression for the weekly total revenue for the phones.

(c) Cell Pro's weekly profit is the total revenue minus the total cost. Write an expression for Cell Pro's weekly profit.

73. *Investments* Suppose you have $4000 to invest and you invest x dollars at 10% and the remainder at 8%. Write expressions in x that represent the

(a) amount invested at 8%,

(b) interest earned on the x dollars at 10%,

(c) interest earned on the money invested at 8%,

(d) total interest earned.

74. *Medications* Suppose a nurse needs 10 cc (cubic centimeters) of a 15.5% solution (that is, a solution that is 15.5% ingredient) of a certain medication, which must be obtained by mixing x cc of a 20% solution and y cc of a 5% solution. Write expressions involving x for

(a) y, the amount of 5% solution,

(b) the amount of ingredient in the x cc of 20% solution,

(c) the amount of ingredient in the 5% solution,

(d) the total amount of ingredient in the mixture.

75. *Package design* The volume of a rectangular box is given by $V = $ (length)(width)(height). If a rectangular piece of cardboard that is 10 in. by 15 in. has a square with sides of length x cut from each corner (see the figure) and if the sides are folded up along the dotted lines to form a box, what expression of x represents the volume?

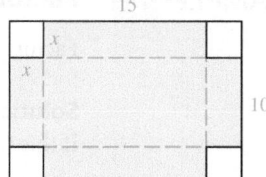

SECTION 0.6   Factoring

Common Factors We can factor monomial factors out of a polynomial by using the Distributive Law in reverse; $ab + ac = a(b + c)$ is an example showing that a is a monomial factor of the polynomial $ab + ac$. But it is also a statement of the Distributive Law (with the sides of the equation interchanged). To factor out a monomial factor, it must be a factor of each term of the polynomial, so it is frequently called a **common monomial factor.**

EXAMPLE 1   **Monomial Factor**

Factor $-3x^2t - 3x + 9xt^2$.

Solution

1. We can factor out $3x$ as follows.

$$-3x^2t - 3x + 9xt^2 = 3x \cdot (-xt) + 3x \cdot (-1) + 3x \cdot 3t^2 = 3x(-xt - 1 + 3t^2)$$

2. Or we can factor out $-3x$ (factoring out the negative will make the first term of the polynomial positive) and obtain

$$-3x^2t - 3x + 9xt^2 = -3x(xt + 1 - 3t^2)$$

We can use the Distributive Law to factor out common factors that are not monomials. For example, we can factor $(a + b)$ out of the polynomial $2x(a + b) - 3y(a + b)$ and get $(a + b)(2x - 3y)$. The following example demonstrates the **factoring by grouping** technique.

EXAMPLE 2 Factoring by Grouping

Factor $5x - 5y + bx - by$.

Solution
We can factor this polynomial using grouping. The grouping is done so that common factors (frequently binomial factors) can be removed. We see that we can factor 5 from the first two terms and b from the last two, which gives

$$5(x - y) + b(x - y)$$

This gives us two terms with the common factor $x - y$, so we get

$$(x - y)(5 + b)$$

Factoring Trinomials We can use the formula for multiplying two binomials to factor certain trinomials. The formula

$$(x + a)(x + b) = x^2 + (a + b)x + ab$$

can be used to factor trinomials such as $x^2 - 7x + 6$.

EXAMPLE 3 Factoring a Trinomial

Factor $x^2 - 7x + 6$.

Solution
If this trinomial can be factored into an expression of the form

$$(x + a)(x + b)$$

then we need to find a and b such that

$$x^2 - 7x + 6 = x^2 + (a + b)x + ab$$

That is, we need to find a and b such that $a + b = -7$ and $ab = 6$. The two numbers whose sum is -7 and whose product is 6 are -1 and -6. Thus

$$x^2 - 7x + 6 = (x - 1)(x - 6)$$

A similar method can be used to factor trinomials such as $9x^2 - 31x + 12$. However, finding the proper factors for this type of trinomial may involve a fair amount of trial and error because we must find factors $a, b, c,$ and d such that

$$(ax + b)(cx + d) = acx^2 + (ad + bc)x + bd$$

When a second-degree trinomial can be factored but many possible factors need to be tested to find the correct factorization, an alternative method that uses factoring by grouping can be used. The procedure for this method of factoring second-degree trinomials such as $9x^2 - 31x + 12$ follows.

FACTORING A TRINOMIAL

Procedure	Example
To factor a trinomial into the product of its binomial factors:	Factor $9x^2 - 31x + 12$.
1. Form the product of the second-degree term and the constant term.	1. $9x^2 \cdot 12 = 108x^2$
2. Determine whether any two factors of the product of Step 1 will sum to the middle term of the trinomial. (If the answer is no, the trinomial will not factor into two binomials.)	2. The factors $-27x$ and $-4x$ give a sum of $-31x$.
3. Use the sum of these two factors to replace the middle term of the trinomial.	3. $9x^2 - 31x + 12 = 9x^2 - 27x - 4x + 12$
4. Factor this four-term expression by grouping.	4. $9x^2 - 31x + 12 = (9x^2 - 27x) + (-4x + 12)$ $= 9x(x - 3) - 4(x - 3)$ $= (x - 3)(9x - 4)$

In the example just completed, note that writing the middle term $(-31x)$ as $-4x - 27x$ rather than $-27x - 4x$ (as we did) will also result in the correct factorization. (Try it.)

EXAMPLE 4 **Factoring a Trinomial**

Factor $9x^2 - 9x - 10$.

Solution

The product of the second-degree term and the constant is $-90x^2$. Factors of $-90x^2$ that sum to $-9x$ are $-15x$ and $6x$. Thus

$$9x^2 - 9x - 10 = 9x^2 - 15x + 6x - 10$$
$$= (9x^2 - 15x) + (6x - 10)$$
$$= 3x(3x - 5) + 2(3x - 5) = (3x - 5)(3x + 2)$$

We can check this factorization by multiplying.

$$(3x - 5)(3x + 2) = 9x^2 + 6x - 15x - 10$$
$$= 9x^2 - 9x - 10$$

Some special products that make factoring easier are as follows.

Special Factorizations   The perfect-square trinomials:

$$x^2 + 2ax + a^2 = (x + a)^2$$
$$x^2 - 2ax + a^2 = (x - a)^2$$

The difference of two squares:

$$x^2 - a^2 = (x + a)(x - a)$$

EXAMPLE 5 **Special Factorizations**

(a) Factor $25x^2 - 36y^2$.
(b) Factor $4x^2 + 12x + 9$.

Solution

(a) The binomial $25x^2 - 36y^2$ is the difference of two squares, so we get

$$25x^2 - 36y^2 = (5x)^2 - (6y)^2 = (5x - 6y)(5x + 6y)$$

These two factors are called binomial **conjugates** because they differ in only one sign.

(b) Although we can use the technique we learned to factor trinomials, the factors come quickly if we recognize that this trinomial is a perfect square. It has two square terms, and the remaining term $(12x)$ is twice the product of the square roots of the squares $4x^2$ and 9 $(12x = 2 \cdot 2x \cdot 3)$. Thus

$$4x^2 + 12x + 9 = (2x + 3)^2$$

Most of the polynomials we factored were second-degree polynomials, or **quadratic polynomials.** Some polynomials that are not quadratic are in a form that can be factored in the same manner as quadratics. For example, the polynomial $x^4 + 4x^2 + 4$ can be written as $a^2 + 4a + 4$, where $a = x^2$.

EXAMPLE 6   Polynomials in Quadratic Form

Factor (a) $x^4 + 4x^2 + 4$ and (b) $x^4 - 16$.

Solution

(a) The trinomial is in the form of a perfect square, so letting $a = x^2$ will give us

$$x^4 + 4x^2 + 4 = a^2 + 4a + 4 = (a + 2)^2$$

Thus

$$x^4 + 4x^2 + 4 = (x^2 + 2)^2$$

(b) The binomial $x^4 - 16$ can be treated as the difference of two squares, $(x^2)^2 - 4^2$, so

$$x^4 - 16 = (x^2 - 4)(x^2 + 4)$$

But $x^2 - 4$ can be factored into $(x - 2)(x + 2)$, so

$$x^4 - 16 = (x - 2)(x + 2)(x^2 + 4)$$

CHECKPOINT

1. Factor the following.
   (a) $8x^3 - 12x$ (b) $3x(x^2 + 5) - 5(x^2 + 5)$ (c) $x^2 - 10x - 24$
   (d) $x^2 - 5x + 6$ (e) $4x^2 - 20x + 25$ (f) $100 - 49x^2$
2. Consider $10x^2 - 17x - 20$ and observe that $(10x^2)(-20) = -200x^2$.
   (a) Find two expressions whose product is $-200x^2$ and whose sum is $-17x$.
   (b) Replace $-17x$ in $10x^2 - 17x - 20$ with the two expressions in (a).
   (c) Factor (b) by grouping.
3. True or false:
   (a) $4x^2 + 9 = (2x + 3)^2$ (b) $x^2 + x - 12 = (x - 4)(x + 3)$
   (c) $5x^5 - 20x^3 = 5x^3(x^2 - 4) = 5x^3(x + 2)(x - 2)$

A polynomial is said to be factored completely if all possible factorizations have been completed. For example, $(2x - 4)(x + 3)$ is not factored completely because a 2 can still be factored out of $2x - 4$. The following guidelines are used to factor polynomials completely.

Guidelines for Factoring Completely

Look for: Common monomial factors first
Then for: Difference of two squares (if the expression is a binomial)
Then for: Trinomial squares
Then for: Other methods of factoring trinomials
Then for: Factoring by grouping (for 4-term polynomials)

EXAMPLE 7   **Factoring Completely**

Factor completely (a) $12x^2 - 36x + 27$ and (b) $16x^2 - 64y^2$.

Solution

(a) $12x^2 - 36x + 27 = 3(4x^2 - 12x + 9)$ Monomial
    $\qquad\qquad\qquad\quad = 3(2x - 3)^2$ Perfect Square

(b) $16x^2 - 64y^2 = 16(x^2 - 4y^2)$
    $\qquad\qquad\quad = 16(x + 2y)(x - 2y)$

Factoring the difference of two squares immediately would give $(4x + 8y)(4x - 8y)$, which is not factored completely (because we still could factor 4 from $4x + 8y$ and 4 from $4x - 8y$).

CHECKPOINT
ANSWERS

1. (a) $4x(2x^2 - 3)$
   (b) $(x^2 + 5)(3x - 5)$
   (c) $(x - 12)(x + 2)$
   (d) $(x - 3)(x - 2)$
   (e) $(2x - 5)^2$
   (f) $(10 + 7x)(10 - 7x)$
2. (a) $(-25x)(+8x) = -200x^2$ and $-25x + 8x = -17x$
   (b) $10x^2 - 25x + 8x - 20$
   (c) $(2x - 5)(5x + 4)$
3. (a) False; $4x^2 + 9$ cannot be factored. In fact, sums of squares cannot be factored.
   (b) False; $(x + 4)(x - 3)$
   (c) True

EXERCISES 0.6

In Problems 1 and 2, factor out the common monomial factor.

1. (a) $9ab - 12a^2b + 18b^2$ (b) $4x^2 + 8xy^2 + 2xy^3$
2. (a) $8a^2b - 160x + 4bx^2$ (b) $12y^3z + 4yz^2 - 8y^2z^3$

In Problems 3–6, factor by grouping.

3. $7x^3 - 14x^2 + 2x - 4$
4. $5y - 20 - x^2y + 4x^2$
5. $6x - 6m + xy - my$
6. $x^3 - x^2 - 5x + 5$

Factor each expression in Problems 7–18 as a product of binomials.

7. $x^2 + 8x + 12$
8. $x^2 - 2x - 8$
9. $x^2 - 15x - 16$
10. $x^2 - 21x + 20$
11. $7x^2 - 10x - 8$
12. $12x^2 + 11x + 2$
13. $x^2 - 10x + 25$
14. $4y^2 + 12y + 9$
15. $49a^2 - 144b^2$
16. $16x^2 - 25y^2$

17. (a) $9x^2 + 21x - 8$ (b) $9x^2 + 22x + 8$
18. (a) $10x^2 - 99x - 63$ (b) $10x^2 - 27x - 63$
    (c) $10x^2 + 61x - 63$ (d) $10x^2 + 9x - 63$

In Problems 19–44, factor completely.

19. $4x^2 - x$
20. $2x^5 + 18x^3$
21. $x^3 + 4x^2 - 5x - 20$
22. $x^3 - 2x^2 - 3x + 6$
23. $x^2 - x - 6$
24. $x^2 + 6x + 8$
25. $2x^2 - 8x - 42$
26. $3x^2 - 21x + 36$
27. $2x^3 - 8x^2 + 8x$
28. $x^3 + 16x^2 + 64x$
29. $2x^2 + x - 6$
30. $2x^2 + 13x + 6$
31. $3x^2 + 3x - 36$
32. $4x^2 - 8x - 60$
33. $2x^3 - 8x$
34. $16z^2 - 81w^2$
35. $10x^2 + 19x + 6$
36. $6x^2 + 67x - 35$

37. $9 - 47x + 10x^2$ 38. $10x^2 + 21x - 10$
39. $y^4 - 16x^4$ 40. $x^8 - 81$
41. $x^4 - 8x^2 + 16$ 42. $81 - 18x^2 + x^4$
43. $4x^4 - 5x^2 + 1$ 44. $x^4 - 3x^2 - 4$

In Problems 45–48, determine the missing factor.

45. $x^{3/2} + x^{1/2} = x^{1/2}(?)$ 46. $2x^{1/4} + 4x^{3/4} = 2x^{1/4}(?)$
47. $x^{-3} + x^{-2} = x^{-3}(?)$ 48. $x^{-1} - x = x^{-1}(?)$

Use the following factorization formulas involving cubes to factor each expression in Problems 49–56.

Factorizations with Cubes

Perfect cube
$$a^3 + 3a^2b + 3ab^2 + b^3 = (a + b)^3$$
Perfect cube
$$a^3 - 3a^2b + 3ab^2 - b^3 = (a - b)^3$$
Difference of two cubes
$$a^3 - b^3 = (a - b)(a^2 + ab + b^2)$$
Sum of two cubes
$$a^3 + b^3 = (a + b)(a^2 - ab + b^2)$$

---

49. $x^3 + 3x^2 + 3x + 1$ 50. $x^3 + 6x^2 + 12x + 8$
51. $x^3 - 12x^2 + 48x - 64$ 52. $y^3 - 9y^2 + 27y - 27$
53. $x^3 - 64$ 54. $8x^3 - 1$
55. $27 + 8x^3$ 56. $a^3 + 216$

APPLICATIONS

57. *Simple interest* The future value of a simple-interest investment of P dollars at an annual interest rate r for t years is given by the expression $P + Prt$. Factor this expression.

58. *Reaction to medication* When medicine is administered, the reaction (measured in change of blood pressure or temperature) can be described by

$$R = \frac{cm^2}{2} - \frac{m^3}{3}$$

where c is a positive constant and m is the amount of medicine absorbed into the blood.* Factor the expression for the reaction.

*Source: R. M. Thrall et al., *Some Mathematical Models in Biology,* U.S. Department of Commerce, 1967.

59. *Sensitivity to medication* From the formula for reaction to medication given in Problem 58, an expression for sensitivity S can be obtained, where

$$S = cm - m^2$$

Factor this expression for sensitivity.

60. *Volume* Squares of side x are cut from four corners of an 8-by-8-inch piece of cardboard, and an open-top box is formed (see the figure). The volume of the box is given by $64x - 32x^2 + 4x^3$. Factor this expression.

61. *Consumer expenditure* The consumer expenditure for a commodity is the product of its market price, p, and the number of units demanded. Suppose that for a certain commodity, the consumer expenditure is given by

$$10{,}000p - 100p^2$$

   (a) Factor this to find an expression for the number of units demanded.
   (b) Use (a) to find the number of units demanded when the market price is $38.

62. *Power in a circuit* Factor the following expression for the maximum power in a certain electrical circuit.

$$(R + r)^2 - 2r(R + r)$$

63. *Revenue* Revenue R from the sale of x units of a product is found by multiplying the price by the number of items sold.
   (a) Factor the right side of $R = 300x - x^2$.
   (b) What is the expression for the price of the item?

64. *Poiseuille's law* The expression for the speed of blood through an artery of radius r at a distance x from the artery wall is given by $r^2 - (r - x)^2$. Factor and simplify this expression.

SECTION 0.7   Algebraic Fractions

Evaluating certain limits and graphing rational functions require an understanding of algebraic fractions. The fraction $6/8$ can be reduced to $3/4$ by dividing both the numerator and the denominator by 2. In the same manner, we can reduce the algebraic fraction

$$\frac{(x + 2)(x + 1)}{(x + 1)(x + 3)} \quad \text{to} \quad \frac{x + 2}{x + 3}$$

by dividing both the numerator and the denominator by $x + 1$, if $x \neq -1$.

Simplifying Fractions

We *simplify* algebraic fractions by factoring the numerator and denominator and then dividing both the numerator and the denominator by any common factors.*

EXAMPLE 1 Simplifying a Fraction

Simplify $\dfrac{3x^2 - 14x + 8}{x^2 - 16}$ if $x^2 \neq 16$.

Solution

$$\frac{3x^2 - 14x + 8}{x^2 - 16} = \frac{(3x - 2)(x - 4)}{(x - 4)(x + 4)}$$

$$= \frac{(3x - 2)\overset{1}{\cancel{(x - 4)}}}{\underset{1}{\cancel{(x - 4)}}(x + 4)} = \frac{3x - 2}{x + 4}$$

Products of Fractions

We can multiply fractions by writing the product as the product of the numerators divided by the product of the denominators and then reducing. For example,

$$\frac{4}{5} \cdot \frac{10}{12} \cdot \frac{2}{5} = \frac{80}{300} = \frac{4}{15}$$

We also can find the product by reducing the fractions before we multiply. For instance, in the example above, we can divide the first numerator and the second denominator by 4 and divide the second numerator and the first denominator by 5, which yields

$$\frac{4}{5} \cdot \frac{10}{12} \cdot \frac{2}{5} = \frac{\overset{1}{\cancel{4}}}{\underset{1}{\cancel{5}}} \cdot \frac{\overset{2}{\cancel{10}}}{\underset{3}{\cancel{12}}} \cdot \frac{2}{5} = \frac{1}{1} \cdot \frac{2}{3} \cdot \frac{2}{5} = \frac{4}{15}$$

Product of Fractions

We *multiply* algebraic fractions by writing the product of the numerators divided by the product of the denominators and then reduce to lowest terms. We also can reduce prior to finding the product.

EXAMPLE 2 Multiplying Fractions

Multiply:

(a) $\dfrac{4x^2}{5y} \cdot \dfrac{10x}{y^2} \cdot \dfrac{y}{8x^2}$

(b) $\dfrac{-4x + 8}{3x + 6} \cdot \dfrac{2x + 4}{4x + 12}$

Solution

(a) $\dfrac{4x^2}{5y} \cdot \dfrac{10x}{y^2} \cdot \dfrac{y}{8x^2} = \dfrac{\overset{1}{\cancel{4x^2}}}{\underset{1 \cdot 1}{\cancel{5y}}} \cdot \dfrac{\overset{2}{\cancel{10x}}}{y^2} \cdot \dfrac{\overset{1}{\cancel{y}}}{\underset{2}{\cancel{8x^2}}} = \dfrac{1}{1} \cdot \dfrac{2x}{y^2} \cdot \dfrac{1}{\underset{1}{\cancel{z}}} = \dfrac{x}{y^2}$

(b) $\dfrac{-4x + 8}{3x + 6} \cdot \dfrac{2x + 4}{4x + 12} = \dfrac{-4(x - 2)}{3(x + 2)} \cdot \dfrac{2(x + 2)}{4(x + 3)}$ Factor the numerators and denominators.

$$= \frac{\overset{-1}{\cancel{-4}}(x - 2)}{3\underset{1}{\cancel{(x + 2)}}} \cdot \frac{2\overset{1}{\cancel{(x + 2)}}}{\underset{1}{\cancel{4}}(x + 3)} = \frac{-2(x - 2)}{3(x + 3)}$$

*We assume that all fractions are defined.

Quotients of Fractions   In arithmetic, we learned to divide one fraction by another by inverting the divisor and multiplying. The same rule applies to division of algebraic fractions.

EXAMPLE 3   **Dividing Fractions**

(a) Divide $\dfrac{a^2 b}{c}$ by $\dfrac{ab}{c^2}$.

(b) Find $\dfrac{6x^2 - 6}{x^2 + 3x + 2} \div \dfrac{x - 1}{x^2 + 4x + 4}$.

Solution

(a) $\dfrac{a^2 b}{c} \div \dfrac{ab}{c^2} = \dfrac{a^2 b}{c} \cdot \dfrac{c^2}{ab} = \dfrac{\overset{a \cdot 1}{\cancel{a^2 b}}}{\cancel{c}} \cdot \dfrac{\overset{c}{\cancel{c^2}}}{\underset{1 \cdot 1}{\cancel{ab}}} = \dfrac{ac}{1} = ac$

(b) $\dfrac{6x^2 - 6}{x^2 + 3x + 2} \div \dfrac{x - 1}{x^2 + 4x + 4} = \dfrac{6x^2 - 6}{x^2 + 3x + 2} \cdot \dfrac{x^2 + 4x + 4}{x - 1}$

$\qquad = \dfrac{6(x - 1)(x + 1)}{(x + 2)(x + 1)} \cdot \dfrac{(x + 2)(x + 2)}{x - 1}$

$\qquad = 6(x + 2)$

CHECKPOINT

1. Simplify: $\dfrac{2x^2 - 4x}{2x}$

2. Multiply: $\dfrac{x^2}{x^2 - 9} \cdot \dfrac{x + 3}{3x}$

3. Divide: $\dfrac{5x^2(x - 1)}{2(x + 1)} \div \dfrac{10x^2}{(x + 1)(x - 1)}$

Adding and Subtracting Fractions   Recall from arithmetic that we can add or subtract two fractions when the denominators are the same. If the denominators are not the same, we can write the equivalents of each of the fractions with a common denominator—usually the least common denominator (LCD). For algebraic fractions, the **least common denominator** is the lowest-degree variable expression into which all denominators will divide. If the denominators are polynomials, then the LCD is the lowest-degree polynomial into which all denominators will divide. We can find the least common denominator as follows.

FINDING THE LEAST COMMON DENOMINATOR

Procedure	Example
To find the least common denominator of a set of fractions:	Find the LCD of $\dfrac{1}{x^2 - x}, \dfrac{1}{x^2 - 1}, \dfrac{1}{x^2}$.
1. Completely factor each denominator.	1. The factored denominators are $x(x - 1)$, $(x + 1)(x - 1)$, and $x \cdot x$.
2. Identify the different factors that appear.	2. The different factors are x, $x - 1$, and $x + 1$.
3. The LCD is the product of these different factors, with each factor used the maximum number of times it occurs in any one denominator.	3. x occurs a maximum of twice in one denominator, $x - 1$ occurs once, and $x + 1$ occurs once. Thus the LCD is $x \cdot x(x - 1)(x + 1) = x^2(x - 1)(x + 1)$.

The procedure for combining (adding or subtracting) two or more fractions follows.

COMBINING FRACTIONS

Procedure	Example
To combine fractions:	Combine $\dfrac{y-3}{y-5} + \dfrac{y-23}{y^2-y-20}$.
1. Find the LCD of the fractions.	1. $y^2 - y - 20 = (y-5)(y+4)$, so the LCD is $(y-5)(y+4)$.
2. Write the equivalent of each fraction with the LCD as its denominator.	2. The sum is $\dfrac{(y-3)(y+4)}{(y-5)(y+4)} + \dfrac{y-23}{(y-5)(y+y)}$.
3. Add or subtract, as indicated, by combining like terms in the numerator over the LCD.	3. $= \dfrac{y^2 + y - 12 + y - 23}{(y-5)(y+4)}$ $= \dfrac{y^2 + 2y - 35}{(y-5)(y+4)}$
4. Reduce the fraction if possible.	4. $= \dfrac{(y+7)(y-5)}{(y-5)(y+4)} = \dfrac{y+7}{y+4}$ if $y \neq 5$.

EXAMPLE   4   Combining Fractions

Combine:

(a) $\dfrac{3x}{a^2} + \dfrac{4}{ax}$ (b) $\dfrac{y-3}{(y-5)^2} - \dfrac{y-2}{y^2 - 4y - 5}$

Solution

(a) 1. The LCD is a^2x.

2. $\dfrac{3x}{a^2} + \dfrac{4}{ax} = \dfrac{3x}{a^2} \cdot \dfrac{x}{x} + \dfrac{4}{ax} \cdot \dfrac{a}{a} = \dfrac{3x^2}{a^2x} + \dfrac{4a}{a^2x}$

3. $\dfrac{3x^2}{a^2x} + \dfrac{4a}{a^2x} = \dfrac{3x^2 + 4a}{a^2x}$

4. The sum is in lowest terms.

(b) Since $y^2 - 4y - 5 = (y-5)(y+1)$, the LCD is $(y-5)^2(y+1)$.
Writing the equivalent fractions and then combining them, we get

$$\dfrac{y-3}{(y-5)^2} - \dfrac{y-2}{(y-5)(y+1)} = \dfrac{(y-3)(y+1)}{(y-5)^2(y+1)} - \dfrac{(y-2)(y-5)}{(y-5)(y+1)(y-5)}$$

$$= \dfrac{(y^2 - 2y - 3) - (y^2 - 7y + 10)}{(y-5)^2(y+1)}$$

$$= \dfrac{y^2 - 2y - 3 - y^2 + 7y - 10}{(y-5)^2(y+1)}$$

$$= \dfrac{5y - 13}{(y-5)^2(y+1)}$$

Complex Fractions   A fractional expression that contains one or more fractions in its numerator or denominator is called a **complex fraction.** An example of a complex fraction is

$$\dfrac{\dfrac{1}{3} + \dfrac{4}{x}}{3 - \dfrac{1}{xy}}$$

We can simplify fractions of this type using the property $\dfrac{a}{b} = \dfrac{ac}{bc}$, with c equal to the LCD of *all* the fractions contained in the numerator and denominator of the complex fraction.

For example, all fractions contained in the preceding complex fraction have LCD $3xy$. We simplify this complex fraction by multiplying the numerator and denominator as follows:

$$\frac{\dfrac{1}{3} + \dfrac{4}{x}}{3 - \dfrac{1}{xy}} = \frac{3xy\left(\dfrac{1}{3} + \dfrac{4}{x}\right)}{3xy\left(3 - \dfrac{1}{xy}\right)} = \frac{3xy\left(\dfrac{1}{3}\right) + 3xy\left(\dfrac{4}{x}\right)}{3xy(3) - 3xy\left(\dfrac{1}{xy}\right)} = \frac{xy + 12y}{9xy - 3}$$

EXAMPLE 5   Complex Fractions

Simplify $\dfrac{x^{-3} + x^2 y^{-3}}{(xy)^{-2}}$ so that only positive exponents remain.

Solution

$$\frac{x^{-3} + x^2 y^{-3}}{(xy)^{-2}} = \frac{\dfrac{1}{x^3} + \dfrac{x^2}{y^3}}{\dfrac{1}{(xy)^2}} \qquad \text{LCD} = x^3 y^3$$

$$= \frac{x^3 y^3 \left(\dfrac{1}{x^3} + \dfrac{x^2}{y^3}\right)}{x^3 y^3 \left(\dfrac{1}{x^2 y^2}\right)} = \frac{x^3 y^3 \left(\dfrac{1}{x^3}\right) + x^3 y^3 \left(\dfrac{x^2}{y^3}\right)}{x^3 y^3 \left(\dfrac{1}{x^2 y^2}\right)} = \frac{y^3 + x^5}{xy}$$

CHECKPOINT

4. Combine the following fractions.

   (a) $\dfrac{5x - 1}{2x - 5} - \dfrac{x + 9}{2x - 5}$ (b) $\dfrac{x + 1}{x} + \dfrac{x}{x - 1}$

5. Simplify $\dfrac{\dfrac{y}{x} - 1}{\dfrac{y}{x} - \dfrac{x}{y}}$.

Rationalizing Denominators   We can simplify algebraic fractions whose denominators contain sums and differences that involve square roots by rationalizing the denominators. Using the fact that $(x + y)(x - y) = x^2 - y^2$, we multiply the numerator and denominator of an algebraic fraction of this type by the conjugate of the denominator to simplify the fraction.

EXAMPLE 6   Rationalizing Denominators

Rationalize the denominators.

(a) $\dfrac{1}{\sqrt{x} - 2}$ (b) $\dfrac{3 + \sqrt{x}}{\sqrt{x} + \sqrt{5}}$

Solution

Multiplying $\sqrt{x} - 2$ by $\sqrt{x} + 2$, its conjugate, gives the difference of two squares and removes the radical from the denominator in (a). We also use the conjugate in (b).

(a) $\dfrac{1}{\sqrt{x} - 2} \cdot \dfrac{\sqrt{x} + 2}{\sqrt{x} + 2} = \dfrac{\sqrt{x} + 2}{(\sqrt{x})^2 - (2)^2} = \dfrac{\sqrt{x} + 2}{x - 4}$

(b) $\dfrac{3 + \sqrt{x}}{\sqrt{x} + \sqrt{5}} \cdot \dfrac{\sqrt{x} - \sqrt{5}}{\sqrt{x} - \sqrt{5}} = \dfrac{3\sqrt{x} - 3\sqrt{5} + x - \sqrt{5x}}{x - 5}$

CHECKPOINT

6. Rationalize the denominator: $\dfrac{\sqrt{x}}{\sqrt{x} - 3}$.

CHECKPOINT ANSWERS

1. $x - 2$

2. $\dfrac{x}{3x - 9}$

3. $\dfrac{(x - 1)^2}{4}$

4. (a) 2

   (b) $\dfrac{2x^2 - 1}{x(x - 1)}$

5. $\dfrac{y}{y + x}$

6. $\dfrac{x + 3\sqrt{x}}{x - 9}$

EXERCISES 0.7

In Problems 1–6 simplify each fraction.

1. $\dfrac{18x^3y^3}{9x^3z}$

2. $\dfrac{15a^4b^5}{30a^3b}$

3. $\dfrac{x - 3y}{3x - 9y}$

4. $\dfrac{x^2 - 6x + 8}{x^2 - 16}$

5. $\dfrac{x^2 - 2x + 1}{x^2 - 4x + 3}$

6. $\dfrac{x^2 - 5x + 6}{9 - x^2}$

In Problems 7–34, perform the indicated operations and simplify.

7. $\dfrac{6x^3}{8y^3} \cdot \dfrac{16x}{9y^2} \cdot \dfrac{15y^4}{x^3}$

8. $\dfrac{25ac^2}{15a^2c} \cdot \dfrac{4ad^4}{15abc^3}$

9. $\dfrac{8x - 16}{x - 3} \cdot \dfrac{4x - 12}{3x - 6}$

10. $(x^2 - 4) \cdot \dfrac{2x - 3}{x + 2}$

11. $\dfrac{x^2 + 7x + 12}{3x^2 + 13x + 4} \cdot (9x + 3)$

12. $\dfrac{4x + 4}{x - 4} \cdot \dfrac{x^2 - 6x + 8}{8x^2 + 8x}$

13. $\dfrac{x^2 - x - 2}{2x^2 - 8} \cdot \dfrac{18 - 2x^2}{x^2 - 5x + 4} \cdot \dfrac{x^2 - 2x - 8}{x^2 - 6x + 9}$

14. $\dfrac{x^2 - 5x - 6}{x^2 - 5x + 4} \cdot \dfrac{x^2 - x - 12}{x^3 - 6x^2} \cdot \dfrac{x - x^3}{x^2 - 2x + 1}$

15. $\dfrac{15ac^2}{7bd} \div \dfrac{4a}{14b^2d}$

16. $\dfrac{16}{x - 2} \div \dfrac{4}{3x - 6}$

17. $\dfrac{y^2 - 2y + 1}{7y^2 - 7y} \div \dfrac{y^2 - 4y + 3}{35y^2}$

18. $\dfrac{6x^2}{4x^2y - 12xy} \div \dfrac{3x^2 + 12x}{x^2 + x - 12}$

19. $(x^2 - x - 6) \div \dfrac{9 - x^2}{x^2 - 3x}$

20. $\dfrac{2x^2 + 7x + 3}{4x^2 - 1} \div (x + 3)$

21. $\dfrac{2x}{x^2 - x - 2} - \dfrac{x + 2}{x^2 - x - 2}$

22. $\dfrac{4}{9 - x^2} - \dfrac{x + 1}{9 - x^2}$

23. $\dfrac{a}{a - 2} - \dfrac{a - 2}{a}$

24. $x - \dfrac{2}{x - 1}$

25. $\dfrac{x}{x + 1} - x + 1$

26. $\dfrac{x - 1}{x + 1} - \dfrac{2}{x^2 + x}$

27. $\dfrac{4a}{3x + 6} + \dfrac{5a^2}{4x + 8}$

28. $\dfrac{b-1}{b^2+2b} + \dfrac{b}{3b+6}$

29. $\dfrac{3x-1}{2x-4} + \dfrac{4x}{3x-6} - \dfrac{x-4}{5x-10}$

30. $\dfrac{2x+1}{4x-2} + \dfrac{5}{2x} - \dfrac{x+4}{2x^2-x}$

31. $\dfrac{x}{x^2-4} + \dfrac{4}{x^2-x-2} - \dfrac{x-2}{x^2+3x+2}$

32. $\dfrac{3x^2}{x^2-4} + \dfrac{2}{x^2-4x+4} - 3$

33. $\dfrac{-x^3+x}{\sqrt{3-x^2}} + 2x\sqrt{3-x^2}$

34. $\dfrac{3x^2(x+1)}{\sqrt{x^3+1}} + \sqrt{x^3+1}$

In Problems 35–42, simplify each complex fraction.

35. $\dfrac{3-\dfrac{2}{3}}{14}$

36. $\dfrac{4}{\dfrac{1}{4}+\dfrac{1}{4}}$

37. $\dfrac{x+y}{\dfrac{1}{x}+\dfrac{1}{y}}$

38. $\dfrac{\dfrac{5}{2y}+\dfrac{3}{y}}{\dfrac{1}{4}+\dfrac{1}{3y}}$

39. $\dfrac{2-\dfrac{1}{x}}{2x-\dfrac{3x}{x+1}}$

40. $\dfrac{1-\dfrac{2}{x-2}}{x-6+\dfrac{10}{x+1}}$

41. $\dfrac{\sqrt{a}-\dfrac{b}{\sqrt{a}}}{a-b}$

42. $\dfrac{\sqrt{x-1}+\dfrac{1}{\sqrt{x-1}}}{x}$

In Problems 43–46, rewrite each of the following so that only positive exponents remain and simplify.

43. (a) $(2^{-2}-3^{-1})^{-1}$ (b) $(2^{-1}+3^{-1})^2$
44. (a) $(3^2+4^2)^{-1/2}$ (b) $(2^2+3^2)^{-1}$
45. $\dfrac{2a^{-1}-b^{-2}}{(ab^2)^{-1}}$
46. $\dfrac{x^{-2}+xy^{-2}}{(x^2y)^{-2}}$

In Problems 47–50, rationalize the denominator of each fraction and simplify.

47. $\dfrac{1-\sqrt{x}}{1+\sqrt{x}}$

48. $\dfrac{x-3}{x-\sqrt{3}}$

49. $\dfrac{x-5}{\sqrt{x}-5}$

50. $\dfrac{\sqrt{7}+x}{\sqrt{7}-x}$

In Problems 51 and 52, rationalize the numerator of each fraction and simplify.

51. $\dfrac{\sqrt{x+h}-\sqrt{x}}{h}$

52. $\dfrac{\sqrt{9+2h}-3}{h}$

APPLICATIONS

53. *Time study* Workers A, B, and C can complete a job in *a, b,* and *c* hours, respectively. Working together, they can complete

$$\frac{1}{a} + \frac{1}{b} + \frac{1}{c}$$

of the job in 1 hour. Add these fractions over a common denominator to obtain an expression for what they can do in 1 hour working together.

54. *Focal length* Two thin lenses with focal lengths *p* and *q* and separated by a distance *d* have their combined focal length given by the reciprocal of

$$\frac{1}{p} + \frac{1}{q} - \frac{d}{pq}$$

(a) Combine these fractions.
(b) Use the reciprocal of your answer in (a) to find the combined focal length.

Average cost **A company's average cost per unit when *x* units are produced is defined to be**

$$\textbf{Average cost} = \frac{\textbf{Total cost}}{\textbf{\textit{x}}}$$

Use this equation in Problems 55 and 56.

55. Suppose a company's average costs are given by

$$\text{Average cost} = \frac{4000}{x} + 55 + 0.1x$$

(a) Express the average-cost formula as a single fraction.
(b) Write the expression that gives the company's total costs.

56. Suppose a company's average costs are given by

$$\text{Average cost} = \frac{40{,}500}{x} + 190 + 0.2x$$

(a) Express the average-cost formula as a single fraction.
(b) Write the expression that gives the company's total costs.

57. *Advertising and sales* Suppose that a company's daily sales volume attributed to an advertising campaign is given by

$$\text{Sales volume} = 1 + \frac{3}{t+3} - \frac{18}{(t+3)^2}$$

where *t* is the number of days since the campaign started. Express the sales volume as a single fraction.

58. *Annuity* The formula for the future value of an annuity due involves the expression

$$\frac{(1+i)^{n+1}-1}{i} - 1$$

Write this expression over a common denominator and factor the numerator to simplify.

0 CHAPTER SUMMARY & REVIEW

KEY TERMS AND FORMULAS

Section 0.1

Sets and set membership (p. 2)
Natural numbers (p. 2)
$\quad N = \{1, 2, 3, 4 \ldots\}$
Empty set (p. 2)
$\quad \varnothing$
Set equality (p. 2)
Subset (p. 2)
$\quad A \subseteq B$
Disjoint sets (p. 2)
$\quad A \cap B = \varnothing$

Universal set (p. 3)
$\quad U$
Venn diagrams (p. 3)
Set intersection (p. 3)
$\quad A \cap B$
Set union (p. 4)
$\quad A \cup B$
Set complement (p. 4)
$\quad A'$

Section 0.2

Real numbers (p. 9)
$\quad$ Subsets
Real number line (p. 9)
Properties of real numbers (p. 10)
Inequalities (p. 10)
Intervals and interval notation (p. 10)

Closed interval (p. 10)
$\quad a \leq x \leq b$ or $[a, b]$
Open interval (p. 10)
$\quad a < x < b$ or (a, b)
Absolute value (p. 11)
Order of operations (p. 12)

Section 0.3

Exponent and base (p. 16)
$\quad a^n$ has base a, exponent n
Zero exponent (p. 17)
$\quad a^0 = 1, a \neq 0$

Negative exponent (p. 17)
$$a^{-n} = \frac{1}{a^n}$$
Rules of exponents (p. 17)

Section 0.4

Radical $\sqrt[n]{a}$ (p. 21)
$\quad$ radicand $= a$; index $= n$
Principal nth root (p. 21)
$\quad \sqrt[n]{a} = b$ only if $b^n = a$ and $a \geq 0$ and $b \geq 0$ when n
$\quad$ is even

Fractional exponents (p. 21)
$\quad a^{1/n} = \sqrt[n]{a}$
$\quad a^{m/n} = \sqrt[n]{a^m} = \left(\sqrt[n]{a}\right)^m$
Properties of radicals (p. 23)
Rationalizing the denominator (p. 24)

Section 0.5

Variable (p. 27)
Algebraic expression (p. 27)
Coefficient (p. 28)
Term (p. 28)
Polynomial in x (p. 28)
$\quad a_n x^n + \cdots + a_1 x + a_0$
Degree (p. 28)
Constant term (p. 28)
Binomial (p. 28)

Trinomial (p. 28)
Monomial (p. 28)
Like terms (p. 28)
Distributive Law (p. 29)
$\quad a(b + c) = ab + ac$
Polynomial products (p. 29)
Special binomial products (p. 30)
Division of polynomials (p. 31)

Section 0.6

Factor (p. 33)
Common factor (p. 33)
Factoring by grouping (p. 34)
Factoring trinomials (p. 34)
Special factorizations (p. 35)
    Perfect squares
        $a^2 + 2ab + b^2 = (a + b)^2$
        $a^2 - 2ab + b^2 = (a - b)^2$

Difference of squares
    $a^2 - b^2 = (a + b)(a - b)$
Conjugates (p. 35)
    $a + b; a - b$
Quadratic polynomials (p. 36)
    $ax^2 + bx + c$
Factoring completely (p. 37)

Section 0.7

Algebraic fractions (p. 38)
Numerator (p. 38)
Denominator (p. 38)
Simplifying fractions (p. 39)
Product of fractions (p. 39)
Quotient of fractions (p. 40)

Common denominator (p. 40)
Least common denominator (LCD) (p. 40)
Addition and subtraction of fractions (p. 40)
Complex fractions (p. 41)
Rationalizing the denominator (p. 42)

REVIEW EXERCISES

Section 0.1

1. Is $A \subseteq B$ if $A = \{1, 2, 5, 7\}$ and
   $B = \{x: x \text{ is a positive integer}, x \leq 8\}$?
2. Is it true that $3 \in \{x: x > 3\}$?
3. Are $A = \{1, 2, 3, 4\}$ and $B = \{x: x \leq 1\}$ disjoint?

In Problems 4–7, use sets $U = \{1, 2, 3, 4, 5, 6, 7, 8, 9, 10\}$, $A = \{1, 2, 3, 9\}$, and $B = \{1, 3, 5, 6, 7, 8, 10\}$ to find the elements of the sets described.

4. $A \cup B'$
5. $A' \cap B$
6. $(A' \cap B)'$
7. Does $(A' \cup B')' = A \cap B$?

Section 0.2

8. State the property of the real numbers that is illustrated in each case.
   (a) $6 + \dfrac{1}{3} = \dfrac{1}{3} + 6$ (b) $2(3 \cdot 4) = (2 \cdot 3)4$
   (c) $\dfrac{1}{3}(6 + 9) = 2 + 3$

9. Indicate whether each given expression is one or more of the following: rational, irrational, integer, natural, or undefined.
   (a) π (b) $0/6$ (c) $6/0$
10. Insert the proper sign ($<$, $=$, or $>$) to replace each $\square$.
   (a) $\pi \square 3.14$ (b) $-100 \square 0.1$ (c) $-3 \square -12$

For Problems 11–18, evaluate each expression.

11. $|5 - 11|$

12. $44 \div 2 \cdot 11 - 10^2$

13. $(-3)^2 - (-1)^3$

14. $\dfrac{(3)(2)(15) - (5)(8)}{(4)(10)}$

15. $2 - [3 - (2 - |-3|)] + 11$
16. $-4^2 - (-4)^2 + 3$

17. $\dfrac{4 + 3^2}{4}$

18. $\dfrac{(-2.91)^5}{\sqrt{3.29^5}}$

19. Write each inequality in interval notation, name the type of interval, and graph it on a real number line.
   (a) $0 \leq x \leq 5$
   (b) $x \geq -3$ and $x < 7$
   (c) $(-4, \infty) \cap (-\infty, 0)$
20. Write an inequality that represents each of the following.
   (a) $(-1, 16)$ (b) $[-12, 8\}$
   (c)

   $\begin{array}{ccccccc} & & & & \circ & & \\ \hline -3 & -2 & -1 & & 0 & 1 & \end{array}$

Section 0.3

21. Evaluate the following without a calculator.
   (a) $\left(\dfrac{3}{8}\right)^0$ (b) $2^3 \cdot 2^{-5}$
   (c) $\dfrac{4^9}{4^3}$ (d) $\left(\dfrac{1}{7}\right)^3 \left(\dfrac{1}{7}\right)^{-4}$

22. Rewrite each of the following with positive exponents. Assume that all variables are nonzero.
   (a) $x^5 \cdot x^{-7}$ (b) x^8/x^{-2} (c) $(x^3)^3$
   (d) $(y^4)^{-2}$ (e) $(-y^{-3})^{-2}$

For Problems 23–28, simplify each expression so that only positive exponents remain. Assume that all variables are nonzero.

23. $\dfrac{-(2xy^2)^{-2}}{(3x^{-2}y^{-3})^2}$

24. $\left(\dfrac{2}{3}x^2y^{-4}\right)^{-2}$

25. $\left(\dfrac{x^{-2}}{2y^{-1}}\right)^2$

26. $\dfrac{(-x^4y^{-2}z^2)^0}{-(x^4y^{-2}z^2)^{-2}}$

27. $\left(\dfrac{x^{-3}y^4z^{-2}}{3x^{-2}y^{-3}z^{-3}}\right)^{-1}$

28. $\left(\dfrac{x}{2y}\right)\left(\dfrac{y}{x^2}\right)^{-2}$

Section 0.4

29. Find the following roots.
   (a) $-\sqrt[3]{-64}$ (b) $\sqrt{4/49}$ (c) $\sqrt[5]{1.9487171}$

30. Write each of the following with an exponent and with the variable in the numerator.
   (a) $\sqrt{x}$ (b) $\sqrt[3]{x^2}$ (c) $1/\sqrt[4]{x}$

31. Write each of the following in radical form.
   (a) $x^{3/7}$ (b) $x^{-1/2}$ (c) $-x^{3/2}$

32. Rationalize each of the following denominators and simplify.
   (a) $\dfrac{5xy}{\sqrt{2x}}$ (b) $\dfrac{y}{x\sqrt[3]{xy^2}}$

In Problems 33–38, simplify so that only positive exponents remain. Assume that all variables are positive.

33. $x^{1/2} \cdot x^{1/3}$ 34. $y^{-3/4}/y^{-7/4}$ 35. $x^4 \cdot x^{1/4}$

36. $1/(x^{-4/3} \cdot x^{-7/3})$ 37. $(x^{4/5})^{1/2}$ 38. $(x^{1/2}y^2)^4$

In Problems 39–44, simplify each expression. Assume that all variables are positive.

39. $\sqrt{12x^3y^5}$ 40. $\sqrt{1250x^6y^9}$

41. $\sqrt[3]{24x^4y^4} \cdot \sqrt[3]{45x^4y^{10}}$ 42. $\sqrt{16a^2b^3} \cdot \sqrt{8a^3b^5}$

43. $\dfrac{\sqrt{52x^3y^6}}{\sqrt{13xy^4}}$ 44. $\dfrac{\sqrt{32x^4y^3}}{\sqrt{6xy^{10}}}$

Section 0.5

In Problems 45–62, perform the indicated operations and simplify.

45. $(3x + 5) - (4x + 7)$

46. $x(1 - x) + x[x - (2 + x)]$

47. $(3x^3 - 4xy - 3) + (5xy + x^3 + 4y - 1)$

48. $(4xy^3)(6x^4y^2)$ 49. $(3x - 4)(x - 1)$

50. $(3x - 1)(x + 2)$ 51. $(4x + 1)(x - 2)$

52. $(3x - 7)(2x + 1)$ 53. $(2x - 3)^2$

54. $(4x + 3)(4x - 3)$ 55. $(2x^2 + 1)(x^2 + x - 3)$

56. $(2x - 1)^3$ 57. $(x - y)(x^2 + xy + y^2)$

58. $\dfrac{4x^2y - 3x^3y^3 - 6x^4y^2}{2x^2y^2}$

59. $(3x^4 + 2x^3 - x + 4) \div (x^2 + 1)$

60. $(x^4 - 4x^3 + 5x^2 + x) \div (x - 3)$

61. $x^{4/3}(x^{2/3} - x^{-1/3})$

62. $(\sqrt{x} + \sqrt{a - x})(\sqrt{x} - \sqrt{a - x})$

Section 0.6

In Problems 63–73, factor each expression completely.

63. $2x^4 - x^3$ 64. $4(x^2 + 1)^2 - 2(x^2 + 1)^3$

65. $4x^2 - 4x + 1$ 66. $16 - 9x^2$

67. $2x^4 - 8x^2$ 68. $x^2 - 4x - 21$

69. $3x^2 - x - 2$ 70. $x^2 - 5x + 6$

71. $x^2 - 10x - 24$ 72. $12x^2 - 23x - 24$

73. $16x^4 - 72x^2 + 81$

74. Factor as indicated: $x^{-2/3} + x^{-4/3} = x^{-4/3}(?)$

Section 0.7

75. Simplify each of the following.
   (a) $\dfrac{2x}{2x + 4}$ (b) $\dfrac{4x^2y^3 - 6x^3y^4}{2x^2y^2 - 3xy^3}$

In Problems 76–82, perform the indicated operations and simplify.

76. $\dfrac{x^2 - 4x}{x^2 + 4} \cdot \dfrac{x^4 - 16}{x^4 - 16x^2}$

77. $\dfrac{x^2 + 6x + 9}{x^2 - 7x + 12} \div \dfrac{x^2 + 4x + 3}{x^2 - 3x - 4}$

78. $\dfrac{x^4 - 2x^3}{3x^2 - x - 2} \div \dfrac{x^3 - 4x}{9x^2 - 4}$

79. $1 + \dfrac{3}{2x} - \dfrac{1}{6x^2}$

80. $\dfrac{1}{x - 2} - \dfrac{x - 2}{4}$

81. $\dfrac{x + 2}{x^2 - x} - \dfrac{x^2 + 4}{x^2 - 2x + 1} + 1$

82. $\dfrac{x - 1}{x^2 - x - 2} - \dfrac{x}{x^2 - 2x - 3} + \dfrac{1}{x - 2}$

In Problems 83 and 84, simplify each complex fraction.

83. $\dfrac{x - 1 - \dfrac{x - 1}{x}}{\dfrac{1}{x - 1} + 1}$ 84. $\dfrac{x^{-2} - x^{-1}}{x^{-2} + x^{-1}}$

85. Rationalize the denominator of $\dfrac{3x - 3}{\sqrt{x} - 1}$ and simplify.

86. Rationalize the numerator of $\dfrac{\sqrt{x} - \sqrt{x - 4}}{2}$ and simplify.

APPLICATIONS

Section 0.1

87. *Job effectiveness factors* In an attempt to determine some off-the-job factors that might be indicators of on-the-job effectiveness, a company made a study of 200 of its employees. It was interested in whether the employees had been recognized for superior work by their supervisors within the past year, whether they were involved in community activities, and whether they followed a regular exercise plan. The company found the following.

   30 answered "yes" to all three
   50 were recognized and they exercised
   52 were recognized and were involved in the community

77 were recognized

37 were involved in the community but did not exercise

95 were recognized or were involved in the community

95 answered "no" to all three

(a) Draw a Venn diagram that represents this information.

(b) How many exercised only?

(c) How many exercised or were involved in the community?

Section 0.2

88. *Male labor force* Using data from 1950 and projected to 2050, the size of the male civilian U.S. labor force, in millions, can be approximated by the expression

$$0.587x + 43.1$$

where x is the number of years after 1950. Use this expression to project the size of this group in 2025 (*Source:* U.S. Bureau of Labor Statistics).

89. *Poiseuille's law* The expression for the speed of blood through an artery of radius r at a distance x from the artery wall is given by $r^2 - (r - x)^2$. Evaluate this expression when $r = 5$ and $x = 2$.

Section 0.3

90. *Future value* If an individual makes monthly deposits of \$100 in an account that earns 9% compounded monthly, then the future value S of the account after n months is given by the formula

$$S = \$100\left[\frac{(1.0075)^n - 1}{0.0075}\right]$$

(a) Find the future value after 36 months (3 years).

(b) Find the future value after 20 years.

91. *Health insurance cost* The per capita net cost C (in dollars) of private health insurance coverage in the United States from 2009 and projected to 2021 can be approximated by the formula

$$C = 31.9t + 310$$

where t is the number of years past 2005 (*Source:* Centers for Medicare and Medicaid Services).

(a) To estimate these per capita costs for 2021, what t-value must be used?

(b) Estimate the per capita net cost of private heath insurance coverage in 2021.

(c) What does part (b) mean for a family of 4 in 2021?

92. *Severe weather ice makers* Thunderstorms severe enough to produce hail develop when an upper-level low (a pool of cold air high in the atmosphere) moves through a region where there is warm, moist air at the surface.

These storms create an updraft that draws the moist air into subfreezing air above 10,000 feet. The strength of the updraft, as measured by its speed s (in mph), affects the diameter of the hail h (in inches) according to

$$h = 0.000595s^{1.922} \quad \text{or equivalently} \quad s = 47.7h^{0.519}$$

(*Source:* National Weather Service).

(a) What size hail is produced by an updraft of 50 mph?

(b) When a storm produces softball-sized hail (about 4.5 inches in diameter), how fast is the updraft?

Sections 0.3 and 0.7

93. *Loan payment* Suppose you borrow \$10,000 for n months to buy a car at an interest rate of 7.8% compounded monthly. The size of each month's payment R is given by the formula

$$R = 10,000\left[\frac{0.0065}{1 - (1.0065)^{-n}}\right]$$

(a) Rewrite the expression on the right-hand side of this formula as a fraction with only positive exponents.

(b) Find the monthly payment for a 48-month loan. Use both the original formula and your result from (a). (Both formulas should give the same payment.)

Section 0.4

94. *Environment* Suppose that in a study of water birds, the relationship between the number of acres of wetlands A and the number of species of birds S found in the wetlands area was given by

$$S = kA^{1/3}$$

where k is a constant.

(a) Express this formula using radical notation.

(b) If the area is expanded by a factor of 2.25 from 20,000 acres to 45,000 acres, find the expected increase in the number of species (as a multiple of the number of species on the 20,000 acres).

Section 0.5

95. *Profit* Suppose that the total cost of producing and selling x units of a product is $300 + 4x$ and the total revenue from the sale of x units is $30x - 0.001x^2$. Find the difference of these expressions (total revenue minus total cost) to find the profit from the production and sale of x units of the product.

96. *Business loss* Suppose that a commercial building costs \$1,450,000. After it is placed into service, it loses 0.25% of its original value in each of the x months it is in service. Write an expression for the value of the building after x months.

Section 0.6

97. *Revenue* The revenue for a boat tour is $600 - 13x - 0.5x^2$, where x is the number of passengers above the minimum of 50. This expression will factor into two binomials, with one representing the total number of passengers. Factor this expression.

Section 0.7

98. *Pollution: cost-benefit* Suppose that the cost C (in dollars) of removing $p\%$ of the pollution from the waste water of a manufacturing process is given by

$$C = \frac{1,200,000}{100 - p} - 12,000$$

(a) Express the right-hand side of this formula as a single fraction.
(b) Find the cost if $p = 0$. Write a sentence that explains the meaning of what you found.
(c) Find the cost of removing 98% of the pollution.
(d) What happens to this formula when $p = 100$? Explain why you think this happens.

99. *Average cost* The average cost of producing a product is given by the expression

$$1200 + 56x + \frac{8000}{x}$$

Write this expression with all terms over a common denominator.

0 CHAPTER TEST

1. Let $U = \{1, 2, 3, 4, 5, 6, 7, 8, 9\}$, $A = \{x : x \text{ is even and } x \geq 5\}$, and $B = \{1, 2, 5, 7, 8, 9\}$. Complete the following.
   (a) Find $A \cup B'$.
   (b) Find a two-element set that is disjoint from B.
   (c) Find a nonempty subset of A that is not equal to A.

2. Evaluate $(4 - 2^3)^2 - 3^4 \cdot 0^{15} + 12 \div 3 + 1$.

3. Use definitions and properties of exponents to complete the following.
   (a) $x^4 \cdot x^4 - x^?$ (b) $x^0 = ?,$ if $x \neq 0$
   (c) $\sqrt{x} = x^?$ (d) $(x^{-5})^2 = x^?$
   (e) $a^{27} \div a^{-3} = a^?$ (f) $x^{1/2} \cdot x^{1/3} = x^?$
   (g) $\dfrac{1}{\sqrt[3]{x^2}} = \dfrac{1}{x^?}$ (h) $\dfrac{1}{x^3} = x^?$

4. Write each of the following as radicals.
   (a) $x^{1/5}$ (b) $x^{-3/4}$

5. Simplify each of the following so that only positive exponents remain.
   (a) x^{-5} (b) $\left(\dfrac{x^{-8}y^2}{x^{-1}}\right)^{-3}$

6. Simplify the following radical expressions and rationalize any denominators.
   (a) $\dfrac{x}{\sqrt{5x}}$ (b) $\sqrt{24a^2b}\sqrt{a^3b^4}$ (c) $\dfrac{1 - \sqrt{x}}{1 + \sqrt{x}}$

7. Given the expression $2x^3 - 7x^5 - 5x - 8$, complete the following.
   (a) Find the degree.
   (b) Find the constant term.
   (c) Find the coefficient of x.
   (d) Find the leading coefficient.

8. Express $(-2, \infty) \cap (-\infty, 3]$ using interval notation and graph it.

9. Completely factor each of the following.
   (a) $8x^3 - 2x^2$ (b) $x^2 - 10x + 24$
   (c) $6x^2 - 13x + 6$ (d) $2x^3 - 32x^5$

10. Identify the quadratic polynomial from among (a)–(c) and evaluate it using $x = -3$.
    (a) $2x^2 - 3x^3 + 7$ (b) $x^2 + 3/x + 11$
    (c) $4 - x - x^2$

11. Find $(2x^3 + x^2 - 7) \div (x^2 - 1)$.

12. Perform the indicated operations and simplify.
    (a) $4y - 5(9 - 3y)$ (b) $-3t^2(2t^4 - 3t^7)$
    (c) $(4x - 1)(x^2 - 5x + 2)$
    (d) $(6x - 1)(2 - 3x)$
    (e) $(2m - 7)^2$ (f) $\dfrac{x^6}{x^2 - 9} \cdot \dfrac{x - 3}{3x^2}$
    (g) $\dfrac{x^4}{3^2} \div \dfrac{9x^3}{x^6}$ (h) $\dfrac{4}{x - 8} - \dfrac{x - 2}{x - 8}$
    (i) $\dfrac{x - 1}{x^2 - 2x - 3} - \dfrac{3}{x^2 - 3x}$

13. Simplify $\dfrac{\dfrac{1}{x} - \dfrac{1}{y}}{\dfrac{1}{x} + y}$.

14. In a nutrition survey of 320 students, the following information was obtained.

> 145 ate breakfast
> 270 ate lunch
> 280 ate dinner
> 125 ate breakfast and lunch
> 110 ate breakfast and dinner
> 230 ate lunch and dinner
> 90 ate all three meals

(a) Make a Venn diagram that represents this information.

(b) How many students in the survey ate only breakfast?

(c) How many students skipped breakfast?

15. If $1000 is invested for x years at 8% compounded quarterly, the future value of the investment is given by

$$S = 1000\left(1 + \frac{0.08}{4}\right)^{4x}$$

What will be the future value of this investment in 20 years?

EXTENDED APPLICATION & GROUP PROJECT

Campaign Management

A politician is trying to win election to the city council, and as his campaign manager, you need to decide how to promote the candidate. There are three ways you can do so: You can send glossy, full-color pamphlets to registered voters of the city; you can run a commercial during the television news on a local cable network; and/or you can buy a full-page ad in the newspaper.

Two hundred fifty thousand voters live in the city, and 36% of them read the newspaper. Fifty thousand voters watch the local cable network news, and 30% of them also read the newspaper.

You also know that the television commercial would cost $40,000; the newspaper ad, $27,000; and the pamphlets mailed to voters, 90 cents each, including printing and bulk-rate postage.

Suppose that the success of the candidate depends on your campaign reaching at least 125,000 voters and that because your budget is limited, you must achieve this goal at a minimum cost. What would be your plan and the cost of that plan?

If you need help devising a method of solution for this problem, try answering the following questions first.

1. How many voters in the city read the newspaper but do not watch the local cable television news?
2. How many voters read the newspaper or watch the local cable television news, or both?
3. Complete the following chart by indicating the number of voters each promotional option reached, the total cost, and the cost per voter reached.

	Number of Voters Reached	Total Cost	Cost per Voter Reached
Pamphlet			
Television			
Newspaper			

4. Now explain your plan and the cost of that plan.

Linear Equations and Functions

A wide variety of problems from business, the social sciences, and the life sciences may be solved using equations. Managers and economists use equations and their graphs to study costs, sales, national consumption, or supply and demand. Social scientists may plot demographic data or try to develop equations that predict population growth, voting behavior, or learning and retention rates. Life scientists use equations to model the flow of blood or the conduction of nerve impulses and to test theories or develop new models using experimental data.

Numerous applications of mathematics are given throughout the text, but most chapters contain special sections emphasizing business and economics applications. In particular, this chapter introduces two important applications that will be expanded and used throughout the text as increased mathematical skills permit: supply and demand as functions of price (market analysis) and total cost, total revenue, and profit as functions of the quantity produced and sold (theory of the firm).

The topics and some representative applications discussed in this chapter include the following.

Prerequisite Problem Type	For Section	Answer	Section for Review
Evaluate: (a) $2(-1)^3 - 3(-1)^2 + 1$ (b) $3(-3) - 1$ (c) $14(10) - 0.02(10^2)$ (d) $\dfrac{3-1}{4-(-2)}$ (e) $\dfrac{-1-3}{2-(-2)}$ (f) $\dfrac{3(-8)}{4}$ (g) $2\left(\dfrac{23}{9}\right) - 5\left(\dfrac{2}{9}\right)$	**1.1–1.3, 1.5, 1.6**	(a) -4 (b) -10 (c) 138 (d) $\dfrac{1}{3}$ (e) -1 (f) -6 (g) 4	0.2 Signed numbers
Graph $x \le 3$.	**1.1**		0.2 Inequalities
(a) $\dfrac{1}{x}$ is *undefined* for which real number(s)? (b) $\sqrt{x-4}$ is a real number for which values of x?	**1.1, 1.2**	(a) Undefined for $x = 0$ (b) $x \ge 4$	0.2 Real numbers 0.4 Radicals
Identify the coefficient of x and the constant term for: (a) $-9x + 2$ (b) $\dfrac{x}{2}$ (c) $x - 300$	**1.1, 1.3, 1.5, 1.6**	*Coeff.* *Const.* (a) -9 2 (b) $\dfrac{1}{2}$ 0 (c) 1 -300	0.5 Algebraic expressions
Simplify: (a) $4(-c)^2 - 3(-c) + 1$ (b) $[3(x+h) - 1] - [3x - 1]$ (c) $12\left(\dfrac{3x}{4} + 3\right)$ (d) $9x - (300 + 2x)$ (e) $-\dfrac{1}{5}[x - (-1)]$ (f) $2(2y + 3) + 3y$	**1.1–1.3, 1.5, 1.6**	(a) $4c^2 + 3c + 1$ (b) $3h$ (c) $9x + 36$ (d) $7x - 300$ (e) $-\dfrac{1}{5}x - \dfrac{1}{5}$ (f) $7y + 6$	0.5 Algebraic expressions
Find the LCD of $\dfrac{3x}{2x+10}$ and $\dfrac{1}{x+5}$.	**1.1**	$2x + 10$	0.7 Algebraic fractions

SECTION **1.1**

Solutions of Linear Equations and Inequalities in One Variable

OBJECTIVES

- To solve linear equations in one variable
- To solve applied problems using linear equations
- To solve linear inequalities in one variable

APPLICATION PREVIEW

Using data from 1980 and projected to 2050, the number of Hispanics in the U.S. civilian non-institutional population can be approximated by

$$y = 0.876x + 6.084$$

million, where x is the number of years after 1980 (*Source*: U.S. Census Bureau). To find the year when this population can be approximated to equal 36.74 million, we solve $36.74 = 0.876x + 6.084$. (See Example 2.) We will discuss solutions of linear equations and inequalities in this section.

Equations   An **equation** is a statement that two quantities or algebraic expressions are equal. An equation such as $3x - 2 = 7$ is known as an equation in one variable. The value of the variable x determines whether the equation is true. A value of the variable that makes the equation true is called a **solution** of the equation. For example, $3x - 2 = 7$ is true only for $x = 3$, so 3 is the solution of the equation. Finding the solutions of an equation is called **solving the equation.** The set of solutions of an equation is called the **solution set** of the equation.

Equations that are true for all values of the variables are called **identities.** The equation $2(x - 1) = 2x - 2$ is an example of an identity. Equations that are true only for certain values of the variables are called **conditional equations,** or simply equations.

Two equations are said to be **equivalent** if they have exactly the same solution set. We can often solve a complicated linear equation by finding an equivalent equation whose solution is easily found. We use the following properties of equality to reduce an equation to a simple equivalent equation.

PROPERTIES OF EQUALITY

Properties	Examples
Substitution Property	
The equation formed by substituting one expression for an equal expression is equivalent to the original equation.	$3(x - 3) - \frac{1}{2}(4x - 18) = 4$ is equivalent to $3x - 9 - 2x + 9 = 4$ and to $x = 4$. We say that the solution set is $\{4\}$, or the solution is 4.
Addition Property	
The equation formed by adding the same quantity to both sides of an equation is equivalent to the original equation.	$x - 4 = 6$ is equivalent to $x - 4 + 4 = 6 + 4$, or to $x = 10$. $x + 5 = 12$ is equivalent to $x + 5 + (-5) = 12 + (-5)$, or to $x = 7$. (Adding -5 to both sides is equivalent to subtracting 5 from both sides.)
Multiplication Property	
The equation formed by multiplying both sides of an equation by the same nonzero quantity is equivalent to the original equation.	$\frac{1}{3}x = 6$ is equivalent to $3(\frac{1}{3}x) = 3(6)$, or to $x = 18$. $5x = 20$ is equivalent to $(5x)/5 = 20/5$, or to $x = 4$. (Dividing both sides by 5 is equivalent to multiplying both sides by $\frac{1}{5}$.)

Solving Linear Equations   If an equation contains one variable and if the variable occurs to the first degree, the equation is called a **linear equation in one variable.** The following procedure is based on the properties of equality, and with it, we can solve any linear equation in one variable.

SOLVING A LINEAR EQUATION

Procedure	Example
To solve a linear equation in one variable:	Solve $\dfrac{3x}{4} + 3 = \dfrac{x-1}{3}$.
1. If the equation contains fractions, multiply both sides by the least common denominator (LCD) of the fractions.	1. LCD is 12. $12\left(\dfrac{3x}{4} + 3\right) = 12\left(\dfrac{x-1}{3}\right)$
2. Remove any parentheses in the equation.	2. $9x + 36 = 4x - 4$
3. Perform any additions or subtractions to get all terms containing the variable on one side and all other terms on the other side.	3. $9x + 36 - 4x = 4x - 4 - 4x$ $5x + 36 = -4$ $5x + 36 - 36 = -4 - 36$ $5x = -40$
4. Divide both sides of the equation by the coefficient of the variable.	4. $\dfrac{5x}{5} = \dfrac{-40}{5}$ gives $x = -8$
5. Check the solution by substitution in the original equation.	5. $\dfrac{3(-8)}{4} + 3 \overset{?}{=} \dfrac{-8-1}{3}$ gives $-3 = -3$ ✔

EXAMPLE   1   Solving Linear Equations

(a) Solve for z: $\dfrac{2z}{3} = -6$ (b) Solve for x: $\dfrac{3x+1}{2} = \dfrac{x}{3} - 3$

Solution

(a) $\dfrac{2z}{3} = -6$

$3\left(\dfrac{2z}{3}\right) = 3(-6)$ gives $2z = -18$ Multiply both sides by 3.

$\dfrac{2z}{2} = \dfrac{-18}{2}$ gives $z = -9$ Divide both sides by 2.

Check: $\dfrac{2(-9)}{3} \overset{?}{=} -6$ gives $-6 = -6$ ✔

(b) $\dfrac{3x+1}{2} = \dfrac{x}{3} - 3$

$6\left(\dfrac{3x+1}{2}\right) = 6\left(\dfrac{x}{3} - 3\right)$ Multiply both sides by the LCD, 6.

$3(3x+1) = 6\left(\dfrac{x}{3} - 3\right)$ Simplify the fraction on the left side.

$9x + 3 = 2x - 18$ Distribute to remove parentheses.

$7x = -21$ Add $(-2x) + (-3)$ to both sides.

$x = -3$ Divide both sides by 7.

Check: $\dfrac{3(-3)+1}{2} \overset{?}{=} \dfrac{-3}{3} - 3$ gives $-4 = -4$ ✔

When using an equation to describe a set of data, it is sometimes useful to let a variable represent the number of years past a given year. This is called **aligning the data.** Consider the following example.

EXAMPLE 2   **U.S. Hispanic Population** | APPLICATION PREVIEW |

Using data from 1980 and projected to 2050, the number of Hispanics in the U.S. civilian non-institutional population can be approximated by $y = 0.876x + 6.084$ million, where x is the number of years after 1980 (*Source:* U.S. Census Bureau). According to this equaton, in what year will the Hispanic population equal 36.74 million?

Solution
To answer this question, we solve

$$36.74 = 0.876x + 6.084$$
$$30.656 = 0.876x$$
$$34.995 \approx x$$

Recall that x is the number of years past 1980, so we use $x = 35$ when computing the year to which this corresponds: $1980 + 35 = 2015$.

Checking reveals that $36.74 \approx 0.876(34.995) + 6.084$. ✔

Thus the number of Hispanics in the United States is estimated to be approximately 36.74 million in 2015.

Notice in Example 2 that because x represents the number of years past 1980, any decimal carries into the next year, so we always round up to the next integer (year).

Fractional Equations   A **fractional equation** contains a variable in a denominator. It is solved by first multiplying both sides of the equation by the least common denominator (LCD) of the fractions in the equation. Some fractional equations lead to linear equations. Note that the solution to any fractional equation *must* be checked in the original equation, because multiplying both sides of a fractional equation by a variable expression may result in an equation that is not equivalent to the original equation. If a solution to the fraction-free linear equation makes a denominator of the original equation equal to zero, that value cannot be a solution to the original equation. Some fractional equations have no solutions.

EXAMPLE 3   **Solving Fractional Equations**

Solve for x: (a) $\dfrac{3x}{2x + 10} = 1 + \dfrac{1}{x + 5}$ (b) $\dfrac{2x - 1}{x - 3} = 4 + \dfrac{5}{x - 3}$

Solution
(a) Multiply each term on both sides by the LCD, $2x + 10$. Then simplify and solve.

$$(2x + 10)\left(\frac{3x}{2x + 10}\right) = (2x + 10)(1) + (2x + 10)\left(\frac{1}{x + 5}\right)$$
$$3x = (2x + 10) + 2 \quad \text{gives} \quad x = 12$$

Check: $\dfrac{3(12)}{2(12) + 10} \overset{?}{=} 1 + \dfrac{1}{12 + 5}$ gives $\dfrac{36}{34} = \dfrac{18}{17}$ ✔

(b) Multiply each term on both sides by the LCD, $x - 3$. Then simplify.

$$(x - 3)\left(\frac{2x - 1}{x - 3}\right) = (x - 3)(4) + (x - 3)\left(\frac{5}{x - 3}\right)$$
$$2x - 1 = (4x - 12) + 5 \quad \text{or} \quad 2x - 1 = 4x - 7$$

Add $(-4x) + 1$ to both sides.

$$-2x = -6 \quad \text{gives} \quad x = 3$$

The value $x = 3$ gives undefined expressions in the original equation because the denominators equal 0 when $x = 3$. Hence, the equation has no solution.

CHECKPOINT

1. Solve the following for x.

   (a) $4(x - 3) = 10x - 12$ (b) $\dfrac{5(x - 3)}{6} - x = 1 - \dfrac{x}{9}$

   (c) $\dfrac{x}{3x - 6} = 2 - \dfrac{2x}{x - 2}$

Linear Equations in Two Variables   The steps used to solve linear equations in one variable also can be used to solve linear equations in more than one variable for one of the variables in terms of the other. Solving an equation such as the one in the following example is important when using a graphing utility.

EXAMPLE 4   Solving an Equation for One of Two Variables

Solve $4x + 3y = 12$ for y.

Solution

No fractions or parentheses are present, so we subtract $4x$ from both sides to get only the term that contains y on one side.

$$3y = -4x + 12$$

Dividing both sides by 3 gives the solution.

$$y = -\frac{4}{3}x + 4$$

Check: $4x + 3\left(\dfrac{-4}{3}x + 4\right) \stackrel{?}{=} 12$

$$4x + (-4x + 12) = 12 ✔$$

CHECKPOINT

2. Solve for y: $y - 4 = -4(x + 2)$

EXAMPLE 5   Profit

Suppose that the relationship between a firm's profit P and the number x of items sold can be described by the equation

$$5x - 4P = 1200$$

(a) How many units must be produced and sold for the firm to make a profit of $150?
(b) Solve this equation for P in terms of x.
(c) Find the profit when 240 units are sold.

Solution

(a) $5x - 4(150) = 1200$

   $5x - 600 = 1200$

   $5x = 1800$

   $x = 360$ units

   Check: $5(360) - 4(150) = 1800 - 600 = 1200 ✔$

(b) $5x - 4P = 1200$

   $5x - 1200 = 4P$

   $P = \dfrac{5x}{4} - \dfrac{1200}{4} = \dfrac{5x}{4} - 300$

(c) $P = \dfrac{5x}{4} - 300$

   $P = \dfrac{5(240)}{4} - 300 = 0$

Because $P = 0$ when $x = 240$, we know that profit is $0 when 240 units are sold, and we say that the firm **breaks even** when 240 units are sold.

Stated Problems   With an applied problem, it is frequently necessary to convert the problem from its stated form into one or more equations from which the problem's solution can be found. The following guidelines may be useful in solving stated problems.

Guidelines for Solving Stated Problems

1. Read the problem carefully to determine what you are to find. Use variables to represent the quantities to be found.
2. Reread the problem and use your variables to translate given information into algebraic expressions. Often, drawing a figure is helpful.
3. Use the algebraic expressions and the problem statement to formulate an equation (or equations).
4. Solve the equation(s).
5. Check the solution in the problem, not just in your equation or equations. The answer should satisfy the conditions.

EXAMPLE   6   Investment Mix

Jill Ball has $90,000 to invest. She has chosen one relatively safe investment fund that has an annual yield of 10% and another riskier one that has a 15% annual yield. How much should she invest in each fund if she would like to earn $10,000 in one year from her investments?

Solution

1. We want to find the amount of each investment, so we begin as follows:

    Let $x =$ the amount invested at 10%, then
    $90,000 - x =$ the amount invested at 15% (because the two investments total $90,000)

2. If P is the amount of an investment and r is the annual rate of yield (expressed as a decimal), then the annual earnings $I = Pr$. Using this relationship, we can summarize the information about these two investments in a table.

	P	r	I
10% investment	x	0.10	0.10x
15% investment	90,000 $- x$	0.15	0.15(90,000 $- x$)
Total investment	90,000		10,000

3. The column under I shows that the sum of the earnings is

$$0.10x + 0.15(90,000 - x) = 10,000$$

4. We solve this as follows.

$$0.10x + 13,500 - 0.15x = 10,000$$
$$-0.05x = -3500 \quad \text{or} \quad x = 70,000$$

Thus the amount invested at 10% is $70,000 and the amount invested at 15% is $90,000 - 70,000 = 20,000$.

5. To check, we return to the problem and note that 10% of $70,000 plus 15% of $20,000 gives a yield of $7000 + $3000 = $10,000. ✔

Linear Inequalities   An **inequality** is a statement that one quantity is greater than (or less than) another quantity. The inequality $3x - 2 > 2x + 1$ is a first-degree (linear) inequality that states that the left side is greater than the right side. Certain values of the variable will satisfy the inequality. These values form the solution set of the inequality. For example, $x = 4$ is in the solution set of $3x - 2 > 2x + 1$ because $3 \cdot 4 - 2 > 2 \cdot 4 + 1$. On the other hand, $x = 2$ is not in the solution set because $3 \cdot 2 - 2 \not> 2 \cdot 2 + 1$. *Solving* an inequality means finding its solution set, and two inequalities are *equivalent* if they have the same solution set. As with equations, we find the solutions to inequalities by finding equivalent inequalities from which the solutions can be easily seen. We use the following properties to reduce an inequality to a simple equivalent inequality.

PROPERTIES OF INEQUALITIES

Properties	Examples	
Substitution Property		
The inequality formed by substituting one expression for an equal expression is equivalent to the original inequality.	$5x - 4x < 6$ $x < 6$ The solution set is $\{x : x < 6\}$.	
Addition Property		
The inequality formed by adding the same quantity to both sides of an inequality is equivalent to the original inequality.	$2x - 4 > x + 6$ $2x - 4 + 4 > x + 6 + 4$ $2x > x + 10$ $2x + (-x) > x + 10 + (-x)$ $x > 10$	
Multiplication Property I		
The inequality formed by multiplying both sides of an inequality by the same *positive* quantity is equivalent to the original inequality.	$\dfrac{x}{2} > 8$ $\dfrac{x}{2}(2) > 8(2)$ $x > 16$	$3x < 6$ $3x\left(\dfrac{1}{3}\right) < 6\left(\dfrac{1}{3}\right)$ $x < 2$
Multiplication Property II		
The inequality formed by multiplying both sides of an inequality by the same *negative* number and *reversing* the direction of the inequality symbol is equivalent to the original inequality.	$-x < 6$ $-x(-1) > 6(-1)$ $x > -6$	$-3x > -27$ $-3x\left(-\dfrac{1}{3}\right) < -27\left(-\dfrac{1}{3}\right)$ $x < 9$

For some inequalities, several operations are required to find their solution sets. In this case, the order in which the operations are performed is the same as that used in solving linear equations.

EXAMPLE 7 Solving an Inequality

Solve the inequality $2(x - 4) < \dfrac{x - 3}{3}$.

Solution

$$2(x - 4) < \frac{x - 3}{3}$$

$6(x - 4) < x - 3$ Multiply both sides by the LCD, 3.

$6x - 24 < x - 3$ Remove parentheses.

$5x < 21$ Subtract x from and add 24 to both sides.

$x < \dfrac{21}{5}$ Multiply both sides by $\dfrac{1}{5}$.

Check: If we want to check that this solution is a reasonable one, we can substitute the integer values around 21/5 into the original inequality. Note that $x = 4$ satisfies the inequality because

$$2[(4) - 4] < \frac{(4) - 3}{3}$$

but that $x = 5$ does not because

$$2[(5) - 4] \not< \frac{(5) - 3}{3}$$

Thus the solution $x < 21/5$ is reasonable. ✔

We may also solve inequalities of the form $a \leq b$. This means that "a is less than b or a equals b."

EXAMPLE 8   Solving an Inequality

Solve the inequality $3x - 2 \leq 7$ and graph the solution.

Solution

This inequality states that $3x - 2 = 7$ or $3x - 2 < 7$. Solving in the usual manner, we get $3x \leq 9$, or $x \leq 3$. Then $x = 3$ is the solution to $3x - 2 = 7$ and $x < 3$ is the solution to $3x - 2 < 7$, so the solution set for $3x - 2 \leq 7$ is $\{x: x \leq 3\}$.

The graph of the solution set includes the point $x = 3$ and all points $x < 3$ (see Figure 1.1).

Figure 1.1

CHECKPOINT

Solve the following inequalities for y.

3. $3y - 7 \leq 5 - y$ 4. $2y + 6 > 4y + 5$ 5. $4 - 3y \geq 4y + 5$

EXAMPLE 9   Normal Height for a Given Age

For boys between 4 and 16 years of age, height and age are linearly related. That relation can be expressed as

$$H = 2.31A + 31.26$$

where H is height in inches and A is age in years. To account for natural variation among individuals, normal is considered to be any measure falling within $\pm 5\%$ of the height obtained from the equation.* Write as an inequality the range of normal heights for a boy who is 9 years old.

Solution

For a 9-year-old boy, the height from the formula is $H = 2.31(9) + 31.26 = 52.05$ inches. To be considered of normal height, H would have to be within $\pm 5\%$ of 52.05 inches. That is, the boy's height H is considered normal if $H \geq 52.05 - (0.05)(52.05)$ and $H \leq 52.05 + (0.05)(52.05)$. We can express this range of normal heights by the compound inequality

$$52.05 - (0.05)(52.05) \leq H \leq 52.05 + (0.05)(52.05)$$

or

$$49.45 \leq H \leq 54.65$$

*Adapted from data from the National Center for Health Statistics

©iStock.com/mindundalk

EXERCISES 1.1

In Problems 1–16, solve each equation.

1. $4x - 7 = 8x + 2$
2. $3x + 22 = 7x + 2$
3. $x + 8 = 8(x + 1)$
4. $x + x + x = x$
5. $-\dfrac{3}{4}x = 24$
6. $-\dfrac{1}{6}x = 12$
7. $\dfrac{2x}{7} = \dfrac{7}{9}$
8. $\dfrac{5}{7} = \dfrac{3x}{4}$
9. $2(x - 7) = 5(x + 3) - x$
10. $3(x - 4) = 4 - 2(x + 2)$
11. $8 - 2(3x + 9) - 6x = 50$
12. $10x + 6 - 2(1 - 5x) = 9$
13. $\dfrac{5x}{2} - 4 = \dfrac{2x - 7}{6}$
14. $\dfrac{2x}{3} - 1 = \dfrac{x - 2}{2}$
15. $x + \dfrac{1}{3} = 2\left(x - \dfrac{2}{3}\right) - 6x$
16. $\dfrac{3x}{4} - \dfrac{1}{3} = 1 - \dfrac{2}{3}\left(x - \dfrac{1}{6}\right)$

In Problems 17–22, solve each fractional equation. Check your answers in the original equations.

17. $\dfrac{33 - x}{5x} = 2$
18. $\dfrac{3x + 3}{x - 3} = 7$
19. $\dfrac{2x}{2x + 5} = \dfrac{2}{3} - \dfrac{5}{4x + 10}$
20. $\dfrac{3}{x} + \dfrac{1}{4} = \dfrac{2}{3} + \dfrac{1}{x}$
21. $\dfrac{2x}{x - 1} + \dfrac{1}{3} = \dfrac{5}{6} + \dfrac{2}{x - 1}$
22. $\dfrac{2x}{x - 3} = 4 + \dfrac{6}{x - 3}$

In Problems 23–26, use a calculator to solve each equation. Round your answer to three decimal places.

23. $3.259x - 8.638 = -3.8(8.625x + 4.917)$
24. $3.319(14.1x - 5) = 9.95 - 4.6x$
25. $0.000316x + 9.18 = 2.1(3.1 - 0.0029x) - 4.68$
26. $3.814x = 2.916(4.2 - 0.06x) + 5.3$

In Problems 27–30, solve for y in terms of x.

27. $3x - 4y = 15$
28. $3x - 5y = 25$
29. $9x + \dfrac{3}{2}y = 11$
30. $\dfrac{3x}{2} + 5y = \dfrac{1}{3}$
31. Solve $S = P + Prt$ for t.
32. Solve $\dfrac{y - b}{x - a} = m$ for y.

In Problems 33–38, solve each inequality.

33. $3(x - 1) < 2x - 1$
34. $2(x + 1) > x - 1$
35. $1 - 2x > 9$
36. $17 - x < -4$
37. $\dfrac{3(x - 1)}{2} \le x - 2$
38. $\dfrac{x - 1}{2} + 1 > x + 1$

In Problems 39–44, solve each inequality and graph the solution.

39. $2(x - 1) - 3 > 4x + 1$
40. $7x + 4 \le 2(x - 1)$
41. $\dfrac{-3x}{2} > 3 - x$
42. $\dfrac{-2x}{5} \le -10 - x$
43. $\dfrac{3x}{4} - \dfrac{1}{6} < x - \dfrac{2(x - 1)}{3}$
44. $\dfrac{4x}{3} - 3 > \dfrac{1}{2} + \dfrac{5x}{12}$

APPLICATIONS

45. *Depreciation* A \$648,000 property is depreciated for tax purposes by its owner with the straight-line depreciation method. The value of the building, y, after x months of use is given by $y = 648{,}000 - 1800x$ dollars. After how many months will the value of the building be \$387,000?

46. *Depreciation* When an \$810,000 building is depreciated for tax purposes (by the straight-line method), its value, y, after x months of use is given by $y = 810{,}000 - 2250x$. How many months will it be before the building is fully depreciated (that is, its value is \$0)? How many years is this?

47. *Credit card debt* High interest rates make it difficult for people to pay off credit card debt in a reasonable period of time. The interest I (in dollars) paid on a \$10,000 debt over 3 years when the interest rate is $r\%$ can be approximated by the equation

$$\dfrac{I}{175.393} + 0.663 = r$$

(*Source:* Consumer Federation of America). If the credit card interest rate is 19.8%, find the amount of interest paid during the 3 years.

48. *Seawater pressure* In seawater, the pressure p is related to the depth d according to

$$33p - 18d = 495$$

where d is in feet and p is in pounds per square inch.
(a) Solve this equation for p in terms of d.
(b) The *Titanic* was discovered at a depth of 12,460 ft. Find the pressure at this depth.

49. *Break-even* Burnem Inc. manufactures thumb drives and sells them to a distributor. Burnem's total cost and total revenue (in dollars) for x thumb drives are given by

Total cost $= 2x + 7920$ and   Total revenue $= 20x$

How many thumb drives must Burnem sell to break even?

50. *Break-even* Dish Systems manufactures satellite systems and has its monthly profit *P* in dollars related to the number of satellite systems, *x*, by

$$4P = 81x - 29{,}970$$

Find the number of systems that Dish Systems needs to produce and sell to break even.

51. *Profit* In its second year of operation, a local Internet provider's profits were $170,500. If this amount was 576% of the company's first-year profits, find the first-year profits (to the nearest hundred dollars).

52. *Sales tax* The total price of a used car (including 6% sales tax) is $21,041. How much of this is tax?

53. *United Kingdom population* Using data from 2010 and projected to 2020, the population of the United Kingdom (*y*, in millions) can be approximated by the equation

$$10.0y - 4.55x = 581$$

where *x* is the number of years after 2000 (*Source*: statista.com).
(a) What is the projected population in 2024?
(b) In what year is the population predicted to be 67.2 million?

54. *Out-of-pocket health care expenses* Data and projections from the Centers for Medicare and Medicaid Services from 2010 to 2024 indicate that the annual per capita out-of-pocket expenses for health care can be approximated by

$$y = 39.6x + 543 \text{ (dollars)}$$

where *x* is the number of years past 2000. When are the per capita out-of-pocket expenses for health care predicted to be $1400?

55. *Course grades* To earn an A in a course, a student must get at least a 90 average on four tests and a final exam, with the final exam weighted twice that of any one test. If the four test scores are 93, 69, 89, and 97, what is the lowest score the student can earn on the final exam and still get an A in the course?

56. *Course grades* Suppose a professor counts the final exam as being equal to each of the other tests in her course, and she also will change the lowest test score to match the final exam score if the final exam score is higher. If a student's four test scores are 83, 67, 52, and 90, what is the lowest score the student can earn on the final exam and still obtain at least an 80 average for the course?

57. *Investment mix* A retired woman has $120,000 to invest. She has chosen one relatively safe investment fund that has an annual yield of 9% and another riskier fund that has a 13% annual yield. How much should

she invest in each fund if she would like to earn $12,000 per year from her investments?

58. *Investment yields* One safe investment pays 10% per year, and a riskier investment pays 18% per year. A woman who has $145,600 to invest wants to have an income of $20,000 per year from her investments. How much should she invest at each rate?

59. *Salary increases* A woman making $2000 per month has her salary reduced by 10% because of sluggish sales. One year later, after a dramatic improvement in sales, she is given a 20% raise over her reduced salary. Find her salary after the raise. What percent change is this from the $2000 per month?

60. *Wildlife management* In wildlife management, the capture-mark-recapture technique is used to estimate the populations of fish or birds in an area or to measure the infestation of insects such as Japanese beetles. Suppose 100 individuals of the species being studied are caught, marked, and released and one week later 100 more are caught. To estimate the total number of individuals, the following relationship is used:

$$\frac{\text{Total marked found in 2nd capture}}{\text{Total in 2nd capture}} = \frac{\text{Total number marked}}{\text{Total population}}$$

(a) If in the second capture of 100, it is found that 3 are marked, what is the total population?
(b) Suppose that 1000 beetles are captured, marked, and released. Suppose further that in the second capture of 1000, it is found that 63 are marked. What is the population estimate?

61. *Profit* For a certain product, the revenue is given by $R = 40x$ and the cost is given by $C = 20x + 1600$. To obtain a profit, the revenue must be greater than the cost. For what values of *x* will there be a profit? Graph the solution.

62. *Car rental* Thrift rents a compact car for $33 per day, and General rents a similar car for $20 per day plus an initial fee of $78. For how many days would it be cheaper to rent from General? Graph the solution.

63. *Purchasing* Sean can spend at most $900 for a camera and some memory sticks. He plans to buy the camera for $695 and sticks for $5.75 each. Write an inequality that could be used to find the number of sticks (*x*) that he could buy. How many sticks could he buy?

64. *Taxes* In Sweetwater, Arizona, water bills are taxed on the basis of the amount of the monthly bill to encourage conservation. If the bill is more than $0 but less than $60, the tax is 2% of the bill; if the bill is $60 or more but less than $80, the tax is 4% of the bill; and if the bill is $80 or more, the tax is 6% of the bill. Write the inequalities that represent the amounts of tax owed in these three cases.

65. *Obesity* Severely obese persons (BMI > 40) are at serious health risk, and their number is increasing. Using data from 1990 and projected to 2030, the percent of severely obese U.S. adults can be approximated by

$$S = 0.264t - 2.57$$

with *t* equal to the number of years past 1980 (*Source: American Journal of Preventive Medicine*).
   (a) What *t*-value represents 2018?
   (b) What value of *t* gives $S = 10$?
   (c) In what year does the equation predict that at least 10% of U.S. adults will be severely obese?

66. *Disposable income per capita* Disposable income, the amount left after taxes have been paid, is one measure of the health of the economy. Using U.S. Energy Information Administration data for selected years from 2015 and projected to 2040, the U.S. real disposable income per capita (in dollars) can be approximated by the equation

$$I = 707.6t + 39,090$$

where *t* is the number of years after 2015.
   (a) What *t*-value corresponds to 2023?
   (b) Find the predicted U.S. per capita real disposable income (to the nearest $10) in 2023.
   (c) In what year is the U.S. per capita real disposable income expected to exceed $55,000?

67. *Heat index* During a particular summer, Dallas, Texas, endured 29 consecutive days on which the temperature was at least 110°F. On many of those days, the combination of heat and humidity made it feel even hotter than it was. When the temperature is 100°F, the apparent temperature *A* (or heat index) depends on the humidity *h* (expressed as a decimal) according to

$$A = 90.2 + 41.3h^*$$

*Source: Bosch, W., and C. G. Cobb, "Temperature-Humidity Indices," UMAP Unit 691, *The UMAP Journal*, 10(3), Fall 1989, 237–256.

   (a) For what humidity levels is the apparent temperature at least 110°F? (Note that this answer will be a closed interval. Why?)
   (b) For what humidity levels is the apparent temperature less than 100°F?

68. *Wind chill* The combination of cold temperatures and wind speed determine what is called wind chill. The wind chill is a temperature that is the still-air equivalent of the combination of cold and wind. When the wind speed is 25 mph, the wind chill *WC* depends on the temperature *t* (in degrees Fahrenheit) according to

$$WC = 1.337t - 24.094$$

For what temperatures does it feel at least 30°F colder than the air temperature? That is, find *t* such that $WC \leq t - 30$.

McHUMOR.com by T. McCracken

"I swear it wasn't this cold before they invented the wind chill factor."

Functions

OBJECTIVES

- To determine whether a relation is a function
- To state the domains and ranges of certain functions
- To use function notation
- To perform operations with functions
- To find the composite of two functions

APPLICATION PREVIEW

Using Social Security Administration data from 2012 and projected to 2050 indicates that the average annual wage (in thousands of dollars) can be approximated by the equation

$$W = 3.94x + 26.4$$

where *x* is the number of years after 2010. In this equation, *W* depends uniquely on *x*, so we say that *W* is a function of *x*. Understanding the mathematical meaning of the phrase *function of* and learning to interpret and apply such relationships are the goals of this section. (The function here will be discussed in Example 4.)

Relations and Functions

A **relation** is defined by a set of **ordered pairs** of real numbers. These ordered pairs may be determined from a table, a graph, an equation, or an inequality. For example, the solutions to the equation $y = 4x - 3$ are pairs of numbers (one for x and one for y), so $y = 4x - 3$ expresses a relation between x and y. We write the ordered pairs in this relation in the form (x, y) so that the first number is the x-value and the second is the y-value. Because we cannot list all of the ordered pairs that define this relation, we use the equation to give its definition. Similarly, the inequality $R \le 5x$ expresses a relation between the two variables x and R.

Relation	A **relation** is defined by a set of ordered pairs or by a rule that determines how the ordered pairs are found. The relation may also be defined by a table, a graph, an equation, or an inequality.

TABLE 1.1

FEDERAL INCOME TAX

Income	Rate
$0–$9275	10%
$9276–$37,650	15%
$37,651–$91,150	25%
$91,151–$190,150	28%
$190,151–$413,350	33%
$413,351–$415,050	35%
Over $415,050	39.6%

Source: Internal Revenue Service

For example, the set of ordered pairs

$$\{(1, 3), (1, 6), (2, 6), (3, 9), (3, 12), (4, 12)\}$$

expresses a relation between the set of first components, $\{1, 2, 3, 4\}$, and the set of second components, $\{3, 6, 9, 12\}$. The set of first components is called the **domain** of the relation, and the set of second components is called the **range** of the relation. Figure 1.2(a) uses arrows to indicate how the inputs from the domain (the first components) are associated with the outputs in the range (the second components). Figure 1.2(b) shows another example of a relation. Because relations can also be defined by tables and graphs, Table 1.1 and Figure 1.3 are examples of relations.

Figure 1.2

(a)   (b)

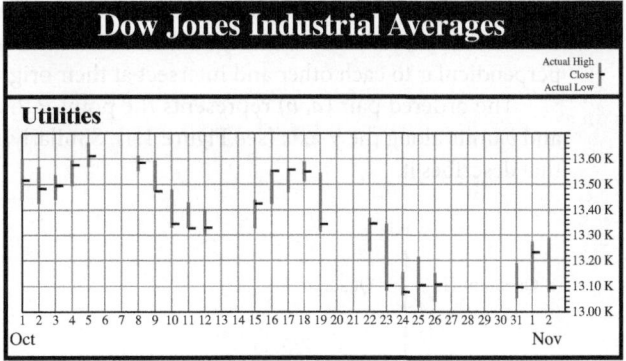

Figure 1.3   *Source:* Based on data from Yahoo Finance

An equation frequently expresses how the second component (the output) is obtained from the first component (the input). For example, the equation

$$y = 4x - 3$$

expresses how the output y results from the input x. This equation expresses a special relation between x and y called a **function** because each input x results in exactly one output y.

Definition of a Function	A **function** is a relation between two sets such that to each element of the domain (input) there corresponds exactly one element of the range (output). A function may be defined by a set of ordered pairs, a table, a graph, or an equation.

When a function is defined, the variable that represents the numbers in the domain (input) is called the **independent variable** of the function, and the variable that represents the numbers in the range (output) is called the **dependent variable** (because its values depend on the values of the independent variable). For example, in the equation $y = 4x - 3$ expresses y as a function of x, so x is the independent variable and y is the dependent variable.

We also can apply this idea to a relation defined by a table or a graph. In Figure 1.2(b) on the previous page, because each input in the domain corresponds to exactly one output in the range, the relation is a function. Similarly, the data given in Table 1.1 on the previous page (the tax brackets for U.S. income tax for single wage earners) represents the tax rate as a function of the income. Note in Table 1.1 that even though many different amounts of taxable income have the same tax rate, each amount of taxable income (input) corresponds to exactly one tax rate (output). On the other hand, the relation defined in Figure 1.3 on the previous page is not a function because the graph representing the Dow Jones Industrial Average shows that for each day there are at least three different values—the actual high, the actual low, and the closing value. This particular figure also has historical interest because it shows a break in the graph when the New York Stock Exchange closed in the wake of Hurricane Sandy, during 2012.

EXAMPLE 1 Functions

Does $y^2 = 2x$ express y as a function of x?

Solution

No, because some values of x are associated with more than one value of y. In fact, there are two y-values for each $x > 0$. For example, if $x = 8$, then $y = 4$ or $y = -4$. The equation $y^2 = 2x$ expresses a relation between x and y, but y is not a function of x.

Graphs of Functions

It is possible to picture geometrically the relations and functions that we have been discussing by sketching their graphs on a rectangular coordinate system. We construct a rectangular coordinate system by drawing two real number lines (called **coordinate axes**) that are perpendicular to each other and intersect at their origins (called the **origin** of the system).

The ordered pair (a, b) represents the point P that is located a units along the x-axis and b units along the y-axis (see Figure 1.4). Similarly, any point has a unique ordered pair that describes it.

Figure 1.4

The values a and b in the ordered pair associated with the point P are called the **rectangular** (or **Cartesian**) **coordinates** of the point, where a is the **x-coordinate** (or **abscissa**) and b is the **y-coordinate** (or **ordinate**). The ordered pairs (a, b) and (c, d) are equal if and only if $a = c$ and $b = d$.

The **graph** of an equation that defines a function (or relation) is the picture that results when we plot the points whose coordinates (x, y) satisfy the equation. To sketch the graph, we plot enough points to suggest the shape of the graph and draw a smooth curve through the points. This is called the **point-plotting method** of sketching a graph.

EXAMPLE 2   Graphing a Function

Graph the function $y = 3x^2$.

Solution

We choose some values of x and find the corresponding values of y. Placing these in a table, we have points to plot. When we have enough to determine the shape of the graph, we connect the points to complete the graph. The table and graph are shown in Figure 1.5.

x	y
-2	12
-1	3
0	0
1	3
2	12

Figure 1.5

We can determine whether a relation is a function by inspecting its graph. If the relation is a function, then no one input (x-value) has two different outputs (y-values). This means that no two points on the graph will have the same first coordinate (component). Thus no two points of the graph will lie on the same vertical line.

Vertical-Line Test	If no vertical line exists that intersects the graph at more than one point, then the graph is that of a function.

Performing this test on the graph of $y = 3x^2$ [Figure 1.6(a)], we easily see that this equation describes a function. The graph of $y^2 = 2x$ is shown in Figure 1.6(b), and we can see that the vertical-line test confirms that this is not a function (see Example 1). For example, a vertical line at $x = 2$ intersects the curve at $(2, 2)$ and $(2, -2)$.

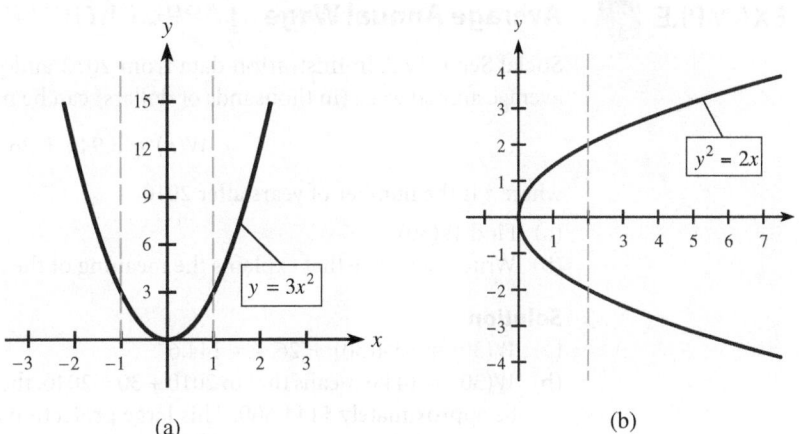

Figure 1.6   (a)   (b)

Function Notation   We can use function notation to indicate that y is a function of x. If a function is denoted by f, we write $y = f(x)$. This is read "y is a function of x" or "y equals f of x." For specific values of x, $f(x)$ represents the values of the function (that is, outputs, or y-values) at those x-values. Thus if $y = f(x) = 0.5x^2 + 3x - 3$,

$$\text{then}\quad f(2) \;\; = 0.5(2)^2 + 3(2) - 3 = 5 \qquad\qquad \text{so } y = 5 \qquad\qquad \text{when } x = 2$$

$$\text{and}\quad f(-4) = 0.5(-4)^2 + 3(-4) - 3 = -7 \quad \text{so } y = -7 \qquad\quad \text{when } x = -4$$

Figure 1.7 shows the function notation $f(x)$ as (a) a y-coordinate for a given x-value and (b) an operation on x.

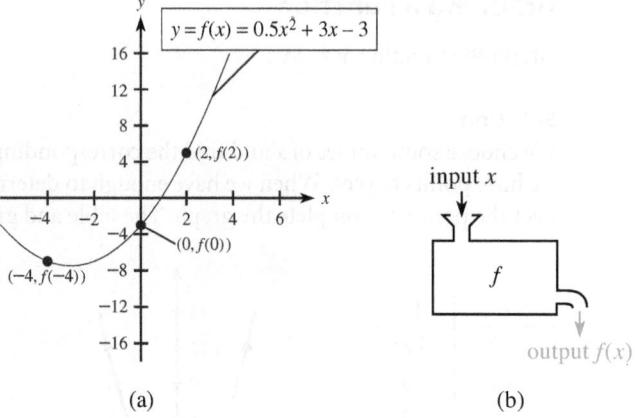

Figure 1.7   (a)   (b)

Letters other than f also may be used to denote functions. For example, $y = g(x)$ or $y = h(x)$ may be used.

EXAMPLE 3   Evaluating Functions

If $f(x) = 2x^3 - 3x^2 + 1$, find the following.
(a) $f(3)$ (b) $f(-1)$ (c) $f(-a)$

Solution

(a) $f(3) = 2(3)^3 - 3(3)^2 + 1 = 2(27) - 3(9) + 1 = 28$
(b) $f(-1) = 2(-1)^3 - 3(-1)^2 + 1 = 2(-1) - 3(1) + 1 = -4$
(c) $f(-a) = 2(-a)^3 - 3(-a)^2 + 1 = -2a^3 - 3a^2 + 1$

When a function fits a set of data exactly or approximately, we say that the function **models** the data. The model includes descriptions of all involved variables.

EXAMPLE 4   Average Annual Wage | APPLICATION PREVIEW |

Social Security Administration data from 2012 and projected to 2050 indicate that the average annual wage (in thousands of dollars) can be modeled by the function

$$W(x) = 3.94x + 26.4$$

where x is the number of years after 2010.

(a) Find $W(30)$.
(b) Write a sentence that explains the meaning of the result in part (a).

Solution

(a) $W(30) = 3.94(30) + 26.4 = 144.6$
(b) $W(30) = 144.6$ means that in $2010 + 30 = 2040$, the average annual wage is projected to be approximately \$144,600. This large projection assumes that inflation will increase wages and the cost of living. (For example, a new Corvette cost \$5472 in 1972, \$12,313 in 1979, and \$55,490 in 2017.)

TABLE 1.2

r(%)	f(r)
2.4	12
5.2	15
6.3	17
7.4	20
8.7	27

EXAMPLE 5 | **Mortgage Payment**

Table 1.2 shows the approximate number of years it will take a couple to pay off a $100,000 mortgage at several different interest rates if they pay $800 per month. If r denotes the rate (as a percent) and $f(r)$ denotes the number of years:

(a) What is $f(6.3)$ and what does it mean?
(b) If $f(r) = 20$, what is r?
(c) Does $f(2.4 + 6.3) = f(2.4) + f(6.3)$?

Solution

(a) $f(6.3) = 17$. This means that with a 6.3% interest rate, a couple can pay off the $100,000 mortgage in 17 years by paying $800 per month.
(b) The table indicates that $f(7.4) = 20$, so $r = 7.4$.
(c) $f(2.4 + 6.3) = f(8.7) = 27$ and $f(2.4) + f(6.3) = 12 + 17 = 29$, so $f(2.4 + 6.3) \neq f(2.4) + f(6.3)$.

Figure 1.8 shows the graph of a function $y = f(x)$. Notice in the figure that the change from x to $x + h$ is h units and the corresponding change in the function (y-values) is given by the difference $f(x + h) - f(x)$. The ratio of these changes is called the **difference quotient** and is given by

$$\frac{f(x + h) - f(x)}{h}$$

Difference quotient evaluations, like the one in the next example, arise in measuring rates of change of functions.

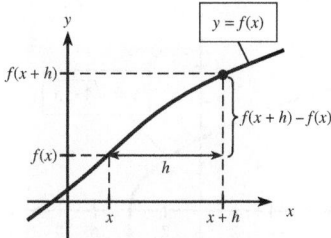

Figure 1.8

EXAMPLE 6 | **Function Notation**

Given $f(x) = x^2 - 3x + 8$, find $\dfrac{f(x + h) - f(x)}{h}$ and simplify (if $h \neq 0$).

Solution

We find $f(x + h)$ by replacing each x in $f(x)$ with the expression $x + h$.

$$\frac{f(x + h) - f(x)}{h} = \frac{[(x + h)^2 - 3(x + h) + 8] - [x^2 - 3x + 8]}{h}$$

$$= \frac{[(x^2 + 2xh + h^2) - 3x - 3h + 8] - x^2 + 3x - 8}{h}$$

$$= \frac{x^2 + 2xh + h^2 - 3x - 3h + 8 - x^2 + 3x - 8}{h}$$

$$= \frac{2xh + h^2 - 3h}{h} = \frac{h(2x + h - 3)}{h} = 2x + h - 3$$

Domains and Ranges

We will limit our discussion in this text to **real functions,** which are functions whose domains and ranges contain only real numbers. If the domain and range of a function are not specified, it is assumed that the domain consists of all real inputs (x-values) that result in real outputs (y-values), making the range a subset of the real numbers.

For the types of functions we are now studying, if the domain is unspecified, it will include all real numbers except for

1. values that result in a denominator of 0 and
2. values that result in an even root of a negative number.

EXAMPLE 7   Domain and Range

Find the domain of each of the following functions; find the range for the functions in parts (a) and (b).

(a) $y = 4x^2$ (b) $y = \sqrt{4 - x}$ (c) $y = 1 + \dfrac{1}{x - 2}$

Solution

(a) There are no restrictions on the numbers substituted for x, so the domain consists of all real numbers. Because the square of any real number is nonnegative, $4x^2$ must be nonnegative. Thus the range is $y \geq 0$. The graph shown in Figure 1.9(a) illustrates our conclusions about the domain and range.

(b) We note the restriction that $4 - x$ cannot be negative. Thus the domain consists of only numbers less than or equal to 4. That is, the domain is the set of real numbers satisfying $x \leq 4$. Because $\sqrt{4 - x}$ is always nonnegative, the range is all $y \geq 0$. Figure 1.9(b) shows the graph of $y = \sqrt{4 - x}$. Note that the graph is located only where $x \leq 4$ and on or above the x-axis (where $y \geq 0$).

(c) $y = 1 + \dfrac{1}{x - 2}$ is undefined at $x = 2$ because $\dfrac{1}{0}$ is undefined. Hence, the domain consists of all real numbers except 2. Figure 1.9(c) shows the graph of $y = 1 + \dfrac{1}{x - 2}$. The break where $x = 2$ indicates that $x = 2$ is not part of the domain.   ■

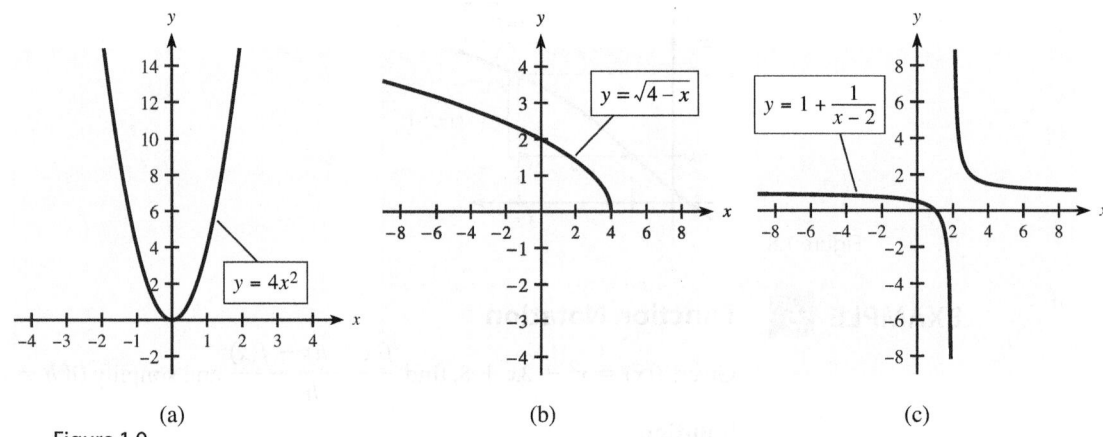

(a)   (b)   (c)

Figure 1.9

CHECKPOINT

1. If $y = f(x)$, the independent variable is _____ and the dependent variable is _____.
2. If $(1, 3)$ is on the graph of $y = f(x)$, then $f(1) = ?$
3. If $f(x) = 1 - x^3$, find $f(-2)$.
4. If $f(x) = 2x^2$, find $f(x + h)$.
5. If $f(x) = \dfrac{1}{x + 1}$, what is the domain of $f(x)$?

Operations with Functions

We can form new functions by performing algebraic operations with two or more functions. We define new functions that are the sum, difference, product, and quotient of two functions as follows.

Operations with Functions

Let f and g be functions of x and define the following.

Sum	$(f + g)(x) = f(x) + g(x)$
Difference	$(f - g)(x) = f(x) - g(x)$
Product	$(f \cdot g)(x) = f(x) \cdot g(x)$
Quotient	$\left(\dfrac{f}{g}\right)(x) = \dfrac{f(x)}{g(x)}$ if $g(x) \neq 0$

The domain of the sum, difference, and product of functions f and g consists of all real numbers of the input variable for which f and g are defined. The domain of the quotient function f/g consists of all real numbers of the input variable for which f and g are defined and $g \neq 0$.

EXAMPLE 8   **Operations with Functions**

If $f(x) = 3x + 2$ and $g(x) = x^2 - 3$, find the following functions.

(a) $(f + g)(x)$ (b) $(f - g)(x)$ (c) $(f \cdot g)(x)$ (d) $\left(\dfrac{f}{g}\right)(x)$

Solution

(a) $(f + g)(x) = f(x) + g(x) = (3x + 2) + (x^2 - 3) = x^2 + 3x - 1$
(b) $(f - g)(x) = f(x) - g(x) = (3x + 2) - (x^2 - 3) = -x^2 + 3x + 5$
(c) $(f \cdot g)(x) = f(x) \cdot g(x) = (3x + 2)(x^2 - 3) = 3x^3 + 2x^2 - 9x - 6$

(d) $\left(\dfrac{f}{g}\right)(x) = \dfrac{f(x)}{g(x)} = \dfrac{3x + 2}{x^2 - 3}$, if $x^2 - 3 \neq 0$

We now consider a new way to combine two functions. Just as we can substitute a number for the independent variable in a function, we can substitute a second function for the variable. This creates a new function called a **composite function.**

Composite Functions

Let f and g be functions. Then the **composite functions** g of f (denoted $g \circ f$) and f of g (denoted $f \circ g$) are defined as follows:

$$(g \circ f)(x) = g(f(x))$$
$$(f \circ g)(x) = f(g(x))$$

Note that the domain of $g \circ f$ is the subset of the domain of f for which $g \circ f$ is defined. Similarly, the domain of $f \circ g$ is the subset of the domain of g for which $f \circ g$ is defined.

EXAMPLE 9   **Composite Functions**

If $f(x) = 2x^3 + 1$ and $g(x) = x^2$, find the following.
(a) $(g \circ f)(x)$ (b) $(f \circ g)(x)$

Solution

(a) $(g \circ f)(x) = g(f(x))$
       $= g(2x^3 + 1)$
       $= (2x^3 + 1)^2 = 4x^6 + 4x^3 + 1$

(b) $(f \circ g)(x) = f(g(x))$
       $= f(x^2)$
       $= 2(x^2)^3 + 1$
       $= 2x^6 + 1$

Figure 1.10 illustrates both composite functions found in Example 9.

$$(g \circ f)(x) \qquad\qquad (f \circ g)(x)$$

$$f(x) = 2x^3 + 1 \qquad\qquad g(x) = x^2$$

$$g(f(x)) = (2x^3 + 1)^2 \qquad\qquad f(g(x)) = 2(x^2)^3 + 1$$
$$(g \circ f)(x) = 4x^6 + 4x^3 + 1 \qquad\qquad (f \circ g)(x) = 2x^6 + 1$$

Figure 1.10

CHECKPOINT

6. If $f(x) = 1 - 2x$ and $g(x) = 3x^2$, find the following.

   (a) $(g - f)(x)$ (b) $(f \cdot g)(x)$ (c) $(f \circ g)(x)$ (d) $(g \circ f)(x)$

   (e) $(f \circ f)(x) = f(f(x))$

CHECKPOINT
ANSWERS

1. Independent variable is x; dependent variable is y.
2. $f(1) = 3$
3. $f(-2) = 9$
4. $f(x + h) = 2(x^2 + 2xh + h^2)$
5. All real numbers except $x = -1$; $f(x)$ is undefined when $x = -1$.
6. (a) $(g - f)(x) = 3x^2 + 2x - 1$
   (b) $(f \cdot g)(x) = 3x^2 - 6x^3$
   (c) $(f \circ g)(x) = 1 - 6x^2$
   (d) $(g \circ f)(x) = 3(1 - 2x)^2$
   (e) $(f \circ f)(x) = 4x - 1$

EXERCISES 1.2

In Problems 1 and 2, use the values in the following table.

x	-7	-1	0	3	4.2	9	11	14	18	22
y	0	0	1	5	9	11	35	22	22	60

1. (a) Explain why the table defines y as a function of x.
   (b) State the domain and range of this function.
   (c) If the table expresses $y = f(x)$, find $f(0)$ and $f(11)$.
2. (a) If the function defined by the table is denoted by f, so that $y = f(x)$, is $f(9)$ an input or an output of f?
   (b) Does the table describe x as a function of y? Explain.

In Problems 3 and 4, are the relations defined by the tables functions of x? Explain why or why not and give the domain and range.

3.

x	1	2	3	8	9
y	-4	-4	5	16	5

4.

x	-1	0	1	3	1
y	0	2	4	6	9

In Problems 5 and 6, determine whether each graph represents y as a function of x. Explain your answer.

5 (a)   (b)

6 (a)   (b)

In Problems 7 and 8, determine whether the equation represents y as a function of x.

7. (a) $y = 3x^3$ (b) $y^2 = 3x$

8. (a) $y = 6x^2$ (b) $y^2 = 10x^2$

9. If $R(x) = 8x - 10$, find the following.
   (a) $R(0)$ (b) $R(2)$ (c) $R(-3)$ (d) $R(1.6)$

10. If $f(x) = 17 - 6x$, find the following.
   (a) $f(-3)$ (b) $f(1)$ (c) $f(10)$ (d) $f\left(\frac{2}{3}\right)$

11. If $C(x) = 4x^2 - 3$, find the following.
   (a) $C(0)$ (b) $C(-1)$ (c) $C(-2)$ (d) $C\left(-\frac{3}{2}\right)$

12. If $h(x) = 3x^2 - 2x$, find the following.
   (a) $h(3)$ (b) $h(-3)$ (c) $h(2)$ (d) $h\left(\frac{1}{6}\right)$

13. If $h(x) = x - 2(4 - x)^3$, find the following.
   (a) $h(-1)$ (b) $h(0)$ (c) $h(6)$ (d) $h(2.5)$

14. If $R(x) = 100x - x^3$, find the following.
   (a) $R(1)$ (b) $R(10)$ (c) $R(2)$ (d) $R(-10)$

15. If $f(x) = x^3 - 4/x$, find the following.
   (a) $f\left(-\frac{1}{2}\right)$ (b) $f(2)$ (c) $f(-2)$

16. If $C(x) = (x^2 - 1)/x$, find the following.
   (a) $C(1)$ (b) $C\left(\frac{1}{2}\right)$ (c) $C(-2)$

17. Let $f(x) = 1 + x + x^2$ and $h \neq 0$.
   (a) Does $f(2 + 1) = f(2) + f(1)$?
   (b) Find $f(x + h)$.
   (c) Does $f(x + h) = f(x) + f(h)$?
   (d) Does $f(x + h) = f(x) + h$?
   (e) Find $\dfrac{f(x + h) - f(x)}{h}$ and simplify.

18. Let $f(x) = 3x^2 - 6x$ and $h \neq 0$.
   (a) Does $f(3 + 2) = f(3) + 2$?
   (b) Find $f(x + h)$.
   (c) Does $f(x + h) = f(x) + h$?
   (d) Does $f(x + h) = f(x) + f(h)$?
   (e) Find $\dfrac{f(x + h) - f(x)}{h}$ and simplify.

19. If $f(x) = x - 2x^2$ and $h \neq 0$, find the following and simplify.
   (a) $f(x + h)$ (b) $\dfrac{f(x + h) - f(x)}{h}$

20. If $f(x) = 2x^2 - x + 3$ and $h \neq 0$, find the following and simplify.
   (a) $f(x + h)$ (b) $\dfrac{f(x + h) - f(x)}{h}$

21. If $y = f(x)$ has the graph in Problem 5(a), find the following.
   (a) $f(9)$ (b) $f(5)$

22. Suppose $y = g(x)$ has the graph in Problem 6(b).
   (a) Find $g(0)$.
   (b) How many x-values in the domain of this function satisfy $g(x) = 0$?

23. The graph of $y = x^2 - 4x$ is shown below.

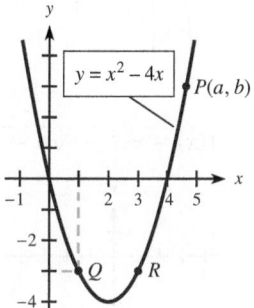

   (a) What are the coordinates of the point Q? Do they satisfy the equation?
   (b) What are the coordinates of R? Do they satisfy the equation?
   (c) If the coordinates of the point P on the graph are (a, b), how are a and b related?
   (d) What are the x-values of the points on the graph whose y-coordinates are 0? Are these x-values solutions to the equation $x^2 - 4x = 0$?

24. The graph of $y = 2x^2$ is shown below.

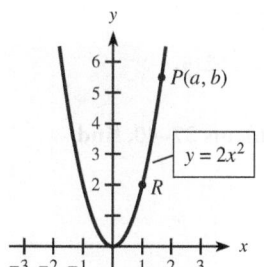

   (a) Does the point $(1, 1)$ lie on the graph? Do the coordinates satisfy the equation?
   (b) What are the coordinates of point R? Do they satisfy the equation?
   (c) If the point P, with coordinates (a, b), is on the graph, how are a and b related?
   (d) What is the x-value of the point whose y-coordinate is 0? Does this value of x satisfy the equation $0 = 2x^2$?

State the domain and range of each of the functions in Problems 25–28.

25. $y = x^2 + 4$
26. $y = x^2 - 1$
27. $y = \sqrt{x + 4}$
28. $y = \sqrt{x^2 + 1}$

In Problems 29–32, a function and its graph are given. In each problem, find the domain.

29. $f(x) = \dfrac{\sqrt{x - 1}}{x - 2}$

30. $f(x) = \dfrac{x + 1}{\sqrt{x + 3}}$

   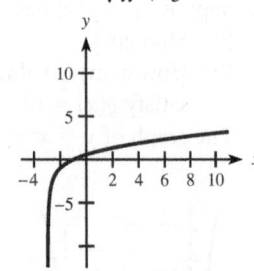

31. $f(x) = 4 + \sqrt{49 - x^2}$ 32. $f(x) = -2 - \sqrt{9 - x^2}$

   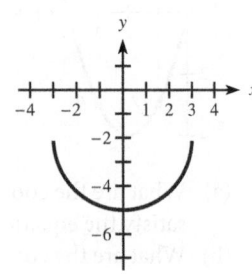

For $f(x)$ and $g(x)$ given in Problems 33–36, find
   (a) $(f + g)(x)$
   (b) $(f - g)(x)$
   (c) $(f \cdot g)(x)$
   (d) $(f/g)(x)$

33. $f(x) = 3x$ $g(x) = x^3$
34. $f(x) = \sqrt{x}$ $g(x) = 1/x$
35. $f(x) = \sqrt{2x}$ $g(x) = x^2$
36. $f(x) = (x - 1)^2$ $g(x) = 1 - 2x$

For $f(x)$ and $g(x)$ given in Problems 37–40, find
   (a) $(f \circ g)(x)$
   (b) $(g \circ f)(x)$
   (c) $f(f(x))$
   (d) $f^2(x) = (f \cdot f)(x)$

37. $f(x) = (x - 1)^3$ $g(x) = 1 - 2x$
38. $f(x) = 3x$ $g(x) = x^3 - 1$
39. $f(x) = 2\sqrt{x}$ $g(x) = x^4 + 5$
40. $f(x) = \dfrac{1}{x^3}$ $g(x) = 4x + 1$

APPLICATIONS

41. *Mortgage* A couple seeking to buy a home decides that a monthly payment of $1600 fits their budget. The amount they can borrow, A, is a function of the time t, in years, it will take to repay the debt. If we denote this function by $A = f(t)$, then the following table defines the function.

t	A	t	A
5	80,000	20	199,000
10	135,000	25	217,000
15	173,000	30	229,000

   (a) Find $f(20)$ and write a sentence that explains its meaning.
   (b) Does $f(5 + 5) = f(5) + f(5)$? Explain.
   (c) If the couple is looking at a house that requires them to finance $173,000, how long must they make payments? Write this correspondence in the form $A = f(t)$.

42. *Debt refinancing* When a debt is refinanced, sometimes the term of the loan (that is, the time it takes to repay the debt) is shortened. Suppose the current interest rate is 7% and a couple's current debt is $100,000. The monthly payment R of the refinanced debt is a function of the term of the loan, t, in years. If we represent this function by $R = f(t)$, then the following table defines the function.

t	R	t	R
5	1980.12	15	898.83
10	1161.09	20	775.30
12	1028.39	25	706.78

Source: Comprehensive Mortgage Payment Tables, Publication No. 492, Financial Publishing Co., Boston

   (a) If the couple refinances for 20 years, what is the monthly payment? Write this correspondence in the form $R = f(t)$.
   (b) Find $f(10)$ and write a sentence that explains its meaning.
   (c) Is $f(5 + 5) = f(5) + f(5)$? Explain.

43. *Social Security benefits* The following figure gives the monthly Social Security benefits for persons whose benefit would be $1000 at a full retirement age of 66 as a function of the age these beneficiaries start receiving benefits. The figure shows the benefits, $y = f(x)$, as a function of x, for $62 \le x \le 70$.
   (a) Find $f(64)$ and $f(67)$.
   (b) Find $f(68)$ and give its meaning.
   (c) Find $f(66) - f(62)$ and gives its meaning.

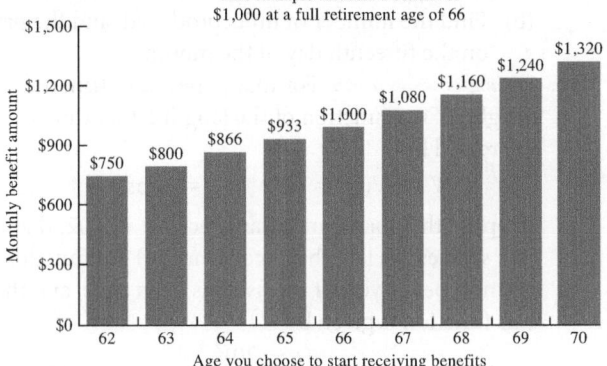

Monthly benefit amounts differ based on the
age you decide to start receiving benefits
This example assumes a benefit of
$1,000 at a full retirement age of 66

Source: Social Security Administration

44. *Dow Jones Industrial Average* The graph shows the
    Dow Jones Industrial Average on a particularly tumul-
    tuous day soon after the U.S. credit rating was down-
    graded from AAA to AA+ in 2011. If t represents the
    number of hours after 9:30 A.M., then the graph defines
    the Dow Jones Industrial Average D as a function of
    time t. If we represent this function by $D = f(t)$, use the
    graph to complete the following.
    (a) Find $f(0)$ and $f(6.5)$.
    (b) Find the domain and range for $D = f(t)$ as defined
        by the graph.
    (c) About how many t-values satisfy $f(t) = 11,000$?
        Estimate one such t-value.

Dow Jones Industrial Average

Source: Google Finance, 2011

45. *Population dynamics* As the U.S. population diversifies,
    the number of White, non-Hispanic individuals (the
    traditional "White majority") accounts for a smaller
    percent of the total. The following figure shows data from
    1980 and projected to 2050 concerning the numbers
    of White, non-Hispanics and others (non-Whites
    or Hispanics) in the U.S. civilian non-institutional
    population age 16 and older. Let $y = W(t)$ be the
    function that represents the number of White
    non-Hispanics and $y = O(t)$ be the function that
    represents the number of others, where t is the number of
    years past 1900. Use the figure to complete the following.
    (a) Estimate $W(100)$ and $O(140)$.
    (b) Find $W(120)$ and explain its meaning.
    (c) Find $O(90)$ and explain its meaning.

(d) Find $(W - O)(120)$ and explain its meaning.
(e) Find $(W + O)(150)$ and explain its meaning.
(f) Which of $(W - O)(100)$ and $(W - O)(140)$ is
    greater? Explain.

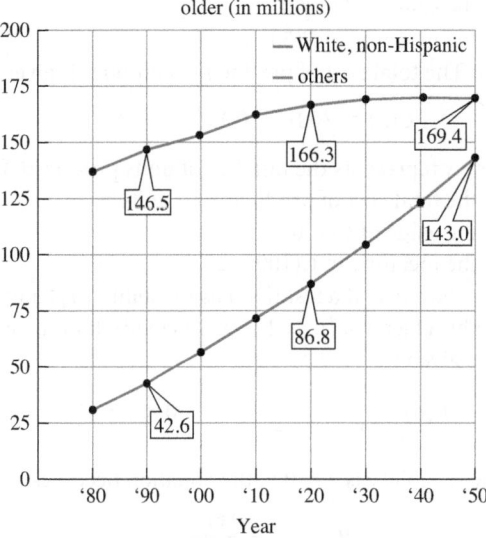

Civilian non-institutional population: 16 years and
older (in millions)

Source: U.S. Census Bureau

46. *Women in the workforce* The number (in millions) of
    women in the workforce, given as a function f of the
    year for selected years from 1920 to 2016, is shown in
    the figure.
    (a) How many women were in the labor force in 1970?
    (b) Estimate $f(1930)$ and write a sentence that explains
        its meaning.
    (c) Estimate $f(2005) - f(1990)$ and explain its meaning.

Source: U.S. Bureau of Labor Statistics

47. *Temperature measurement* The equation

$$C = \frac{5}{9}F - \frac{160}{9}$$

gives the relation between temperature readings in
Celsius and Fahrenheit.
(a) Is C a function of F?
(b) What is the mathematical domain of this function?
(c) If we consider this equation as relating tempera-
    tures of water in its liquid state, what are the
    domain and range?
(d) What is C when $F = 40°$?

48. *Profit* The profit from the production and sale of a product is $P(x) = 47x - 0.01x^2 - 8000$, where x represents the number of units produced and sold. Give
    (a) the profit from the production and sale of 2000 units
    (b) the value of $P(5000)$
    (c) the meaning of $P(5000)$.
49. *Cost* The total cost of producing a product is given by

    $$C(x) = 300x + 0.1x^2 + 1200$$

    where x represents the number of units produced. Give
    (a) the total cost of producing 10 units
    (b) the value of $C(100)$
    (c) the meaning of $C(100)$.
50. *Test reliability* If a test that has reliability r is lengthened by a factor n ($n \geq 1$), the reliability R of the new test is given by

    $$R(n) = \frac{nr}{1 + (n - 1)r} \qquad 0 < r \leq 1$$

    If the reliability is $r = 0.6$, the equation becomes

    $$R(n) = \frac{0.6n}{0.4 + 0.6n}$$

    (a) Find $R(1)$.
    (b) Find $R(2)$; that is, find R when the test length is doubled.
    (c) What percent improvement is there in the reliability when the test length is doubled?
51. *Pollution* Suppose that the cost C (in dollars) of removing p percent of the particulate pollution from the smokestacks of an industrial plant is given by

    $$C(p) = \frac{7300p}{100 - p}$$

    (a) Find the domain of this function.
    In parts (b)–(e), find the functional values and explain what each means.
    (b) $C(45)$ (c) $C(90)$
    (d) $C(99)$ (e) $C(99.6)$
52. *Shipping restrictions* If a box with a square cross section is to be sent by a delivery service, there are restrictions on its size such that its volume is given by $V = x^2(108 - 4x)$, where x is the length of each side of the cross section (in inches).
    (a) Is V a function of x?
    (b) If $V = V(x)$, find $V(10)$ and $V(20)$.
    (c) What restrictions must be placed on x (the domain) so that the problem makes physical sense?
53. *Profit* Suppose that the profit from the production and sale of x units of a product is given by

    $$P(x) = 180x - \frac{x^2}{100} - 200$$

    In addition, suppose that for a certain month, the number of units produced on day t of the month is

    $$x = q(t) = 1000 + 10t$$

    (a) Find $(P \circ q)(t)$ to express the profit as a function of the day of the month.
    (b) Find the number of units produced, and the profit, on the fifteenth day of the month.
54. *Fish species growth* For many species of fish, the weight W is a function of the length L that can be expressed by

    $$W = W(L) = kL^3 \qquad k = \text{constant}$$

    Suppose that for a particular species $k = 0.02$, that for this species the length (in centimeters) is a function of the number of years t the fish has been alive, and that this function is given by

    $$L = L(t) = 50 - \frac{(t - 20)^2}{10} \qquad 0 \leq t \leq 20$$

    Find $(W \circ L)(t)$ to express W as a function of the age t of the fish.
55. *Revenue and advertising* Suppose that a company's revenue $R = f(C)$ is a function f of the number of customers C. Suppose also that the amount spent on advertising A affects the number of customers so that $C = g(A)$ is a function g of A.
    (a) Is $f \circ g$ defined? Explain.
    (b) Is $g \circ f$ defined? Explain.
    (c) For the functions in parts (a) and (b) that are defined, identify the input (independent variable) and the output (dependent variable) and explain what the function means.
56. *Manufacturing* Two of the processes (functions) used by a manufacturer of factory-built homes are sanding (denote this as function s) and painting (denote this as function p). Write a sentence of explanation for each of the following functional expressions involving s and p applied to a door.
    (a) $s(\text{door})$ (b) $p(\text{door})$ (c) $(p \circ s)(\text{door})$
    (d) $(s \circ p)(\text{door})$ (e) $(p \circ p)(\text{door})$
57. *Fencing a lot* A farmer wants to fence the perimeter of a rectangular lot with an area of 1600 square feet. If the lot is x feet long, express the number of feet L of fence needed as a function of x.
58. *Cost* A shipping crate has a square base with sides of length x feet, and it is half as tall as it is wide. If the material for the bottom and sides of the box costs $2.00 per square foot and the material for the top costs $1.50 per square foot, express the total cost of material for the box as a function of x.
59. *Revenue* An agency charges $100 per person for a trip to a concert if 30 people travel in a group. But for each person above the 30, the amount charged each traveler will be reduced by $2. If x represents the number of people above the 30, write the agency's revenue R as a function of x.
60. *Revenue* A company handles an apartment building with 50 units. Experience has shown that if the rent for each of the units is $720 per month, all of the units will be filled, but one unit will become vacant for each $20 increase in the monthly rate. If x represents the number of $20 increases, write the revenue R from the building as a function of x.

SECTION 1.3 · Linear Functions

OBJECTIVES

- To find the intercepts of graphs
- To graph linear functions
- To find the slope of a line from its graph and from its equation
- To find the rate of change of a linear function
- To graph a line, given its slope and y-intercept or its slope and one point on the line
- To write the equation of a line, given information about its graph

APPLICATION PREVIEW

The rate of change of the population of U.S. males, y (in thousands), projected from 2015 to 2060 can be modeled by

$$y = 1125.9x + 142{,}690$$

where x is the number of years past 2000 (*Source:* U.S. Census Bureau). What does this function tell us about the population of U.S. males during this period? (See Example 7.) In this section, we find the rates of change of linear functions and the slopes and intercepts of graphs of linear functions.

The function in the Application Preview is an example of a special function, called the **linear function,** defined as follows.

Linear Function

A **linear function** is a function of the form

$$y = f(x) = ax + b$$

where a and b are constants.

As in Section 1.1 with linear equations, a linear function is also called a **first-degree function,** and the graph of such a function is a straight line.

Intercepts

The point(s) where a graph intersects the x-axis are called the x-intercept points, and the x-coordinates of these points are the **x-intercepts.** Similarly, the points where a graph intersects the y-axis are the y-intercept points, and the y-coordinates of these points are the **y-intercepts.** Because any point on the x-axis has y-coordinate 0 and any point on the y-axis has x-coordinate 0, we find intercepts as follows.

Intercepts

(a) To find the **y-intercept(s)** of the graph of an equation, set $x = 0$ in the equation and solve for y. *Note:* A function of x has at most one y-intercept.
(b) To find the **x-intercept(s),** set $y = 0$ and solve for x.

Because the graph of a linear function is a line, only two points are necessary to determine its graph. It is frequently possible to use intercepts to graph a linear function.

EXAMPLE   1   Intercepts and Graphing

Find the intercepts and graph the following.
(a) $3x + y = 9$ (b) $x = 4y$

Solution

(a) To find the y-intercept, we set $x = 0$ and solve for y:
$3(0) + y = 9$ gives $y = 9$, so the y-intercept is 9.
To find the x-intercept, we set $y = 0$ and solve for x:
$3x + 0 = 9$ gives $x = 3$, so the x-intercept is 3.
Using the intercepts gives the graph shown in Figure 1.11.

(b) Letting $x = 0$ gives $y = 0$, and letting $y = 0$ gives $x = 0$, so the only intercept of the graph of $x = 4y$ is at the point $(0, 0)$. A second point is needed to graph the line. Hence, if we let $y = 1$ in $x = 4y$, we get $x = 4$ and have a second point $(4, 1)$ on the graph. It is wise to plot a third point as a check. The graph is shown in Figure 1.12. ■

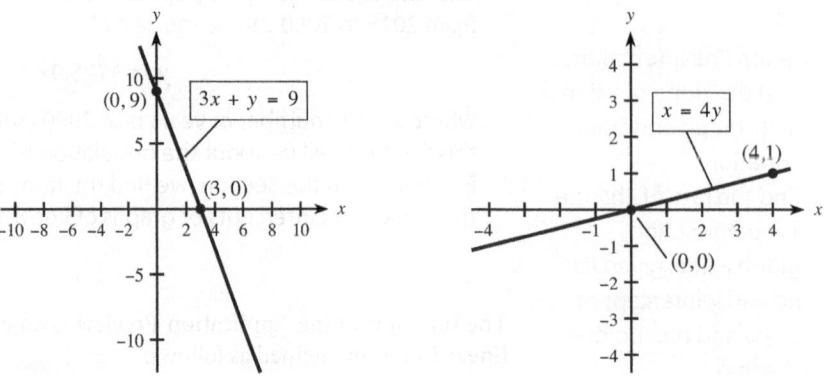

Figure 1.11   Figure 1.12

Note that the equation graphed in Figure 1.11 can be rewritten as

$$y = 9 - 3x \quad \text{or} \quad f(x) = 9 - 3x$$

We see in Figure 1.11 that the x-intercept $(3, 0)$ is the point where the function value is zero. The x-coordinate of such a point is called a **zero of the function.** Thus we see that the *x-intercepts of a function are the same as its zeros.*

EXAMPLE 2 **Depreciation**

A business property is purchased for $1,228,800 and depreciated over a period of 10 years. Its value y is related to the number of months of service x by the equation

$$40{,}960x + 4y = 4{,}915{,}200$$

Find the x-intercept and the y-intercept and use them to sketch the graph of the equation.

Solution

$$x\text{-intercept: } y = 0 \quad \text{gives} \quad 40{,}960x = 4{,}915{,}200$$
$$x = 120$$

Thus 120 is the x-intercept.

$$y\text{-intercept: } x = 0 \quad \text{gives} \quad 4y = 4{,}915{,}200$$
$$y = 1{,}228{,}800$$

Thus 1,228,800 is the y-intercept. The graph is shown in Figure 1.13 on the next page. Note that the units on the x- and y-axes are different. The y-intercept corresponds to the value of the property 0 months after purchase—that is, the purchase price. The x-intercept corresponds to the number of months that have passed before the value is 0; that is, the property is fully depreciated after 120 months, or 10 years. Note that only positive values for x and y make sense in this application, so only the Quadrant I portion of the graph is shown. ■

Despite the ease of using intercepts to graph linear equations, this method is not always the best one to use. For example, vertical lines, horizontal lines, or lines that pass through the origin may have a single intercept, and if a line has both intercepts very close to the origin, using the intercepts may lead to an inaccurate graph.

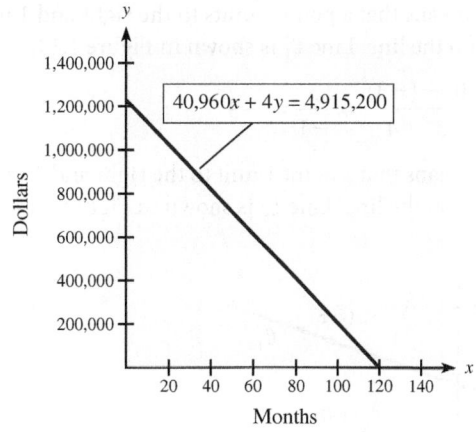

Figure 1.13

Rate of Change; Slope of a Line

Note that in Figure 1.13, as the graph moves from the y-intercept point $(0, 1{,}228{,}800)$ to the x-intercept point $(120, 0)$, the y-value on the line changes $-1{,}228{,}800$ units (from $1{,}228{,}800$ to 0), whereas the x-value changes 120 units (from 0 to 120). Thus the **rate of change** of the value of the business property is

$$\frac{-1{,}228{,}800}{120} = -10{,}240 \text{ dollars per month}$$

This means that each month the value of the property changes by $-10{,}240$ dollars, or the value decreases by \$10,240 per month. This **rate of change** of a linear function is called the **slope** of the line that is its graph (see Figure 1.13). For the graph of a linear function, the ratio of the change in y to the corresponding change in x measures the slope of the line. For any nonvertical line, the slope can be found by using any two points on the line, as follows.

Slope of a Line

If a nonvertical line passes through the points $P_1(x_1, y_1)$ and $P_2(x_2, y_2)$, its **slope,** denoted by m, is found using

$$m = \frac{y_2 - y_1}{x_2 - x_1} = \frac{\Delta y}{\Delta x}$$

where Δy, read "delta y," means "change in y" and Δx means "change in x."
The slope of a vertical line is undefined.

Note that for a given line, the slope is the same regardless of which two points are used in the calculation; this is because corresponding sides of similar triangles are in proportion.

EXAMPLE 3 Slopes

Find the slope of
(a) line ℓ_1, passing through $(-2, 1)$ and $(4, 3)$
(b) line ℓ_2, passing through $(3, 0)$ and $(4, -3)$

Solution

(a) $m = \dfrac{3 - 1}{4 - (-2)} = \dfrac{2}{6} = \dfrac{1}{3}$ or, equivalently, $m = \dfrac{1 - 3}{-2 - 4} = \dfrac{-2}{-6} = \dfrac{1}{3}$

This means that a point 3 units to the right and 1 unit up from any point on the line is also on the line. Line ℓ_1 is shown in Figure 1.14.

(b) $m = \dfrac{0 - (-3)}{3 - 4} = \dfrac{3}{-1} = -3$

This means that a point 1 unit to the right and 3 units down from any point on the line is also on the line. Line ℓ_2 is shown in Figure 1.14.

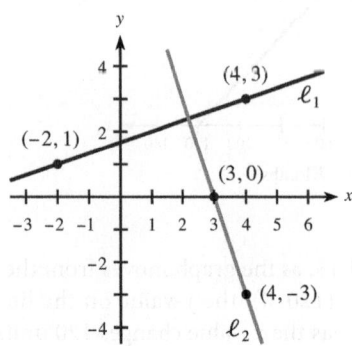

Figure 1.14

From the previous discussion, we see that the slope describes the direction of a line as follows.

ORIENTATION OF A LINE AND ITS SLOPE

1. The slope is *positive* if the line slopes upward toward the right. The function is increasing.

   $m = \dfrac{\Delta y}{\Delta x} > 0$ $m > 0$

3. The slope of a *horizontal line* is 0 because $\Delta y = 0$. The function is constant.

   $m = \dfrac{\Delta y}{\Delta x} = 0$ $m = 0$

2. The slope is *negative* if the line slopes downward toward the right. The function is decreasing.

   $m = \dfrac{\Delta y}{\Delta x} < 0$ $m < 0$

4. The slope of a *vertical line* is *undefined* because $\Delta x = 0$.

   $m = \dfrac{\Delta y}{\Delta x}$ is undefined. m undefined

Two distinct nonvertical lines that have the same slope are parallel, and conversely, two nonvertical parallel lines have the same slope.

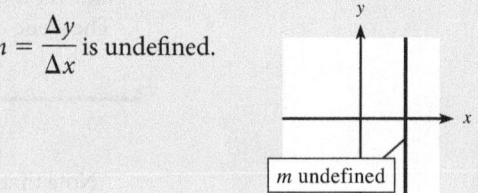

Parallel Lines   Two distinct nonvertical lines are *parallel* if and only if their slopes are *equal*.

In general, two lines are perpendicular if they intersect at right angles. However, the appearance of this perpendicularity relationship can be obscured when we graph lines unless the axes have the same scale. Note that the lines ℓ_1 and ℓ_2 in Figure 1.14 appear to be perpendicular. However, the same lines graphed with different scales on the axes will not look perpendicular. To avoid being misled by graphs with different scales, we use slopes to tell us when lines are perpendicular. Note that the slope of ℓ_1, $\frac{1}{3}$, is the negative reciprocal of the slope of ℓ_2, -3. In fact, as with lines ℓ_1 and ℓ_2, any two nonvertical lines that are perpendicular have slopes that are negative reciprocals of each other.

Slopes of Perpendicular Lines	A line ℓ_1 with slope m, where $m \neq 0$, is *perpendicular* to line ℓ_2 if and only if the slope of ℓ_2 is $-1/m$. (The slopes are *negative reciprocals*.)

Because the slope of a vertical line is undefined, we cannot use slope in discussing parallel and perpendicular relations that involve vertical lines. Two vertical lines are parallel, and any horizontal line is perpendicular to any vertical line.

CHECKPOINT

1. Find the slope of the line through $(4, 6)$ and $(28, -6)$.
2. If a line has slope $m = 0$, then the line is _____. If a line has an undefined slope, then the line is _____.
3. Suppose that line 1 has slope $m_1 = 5$ and line 2 has slope m_2.
   (a) If line 1 is perpendicular to line 2, find m_2.
   (b) If line 1 is parallel to line 2, find m_2.

Writing Equations of Lines

If the slope of a line is m, then the slope between a fixed point (x_1, y_1) and any other point (x, y) on the line is also m. That is,

$$m = \frac{y - y_1}{x - x_1}$$

Solving for $y - y_1$ gives the point-slope form of the equation of a line.

Point-Slope Form	The equation of the line passing through the point (x_1, y_1) and with slope m can be written in the **point-slope form** $$y - y_1 = m(x - x_1)$$

EXAMPLE   4   Equations of Lines

Write the equation for each line that passes through $(1, -2)$ and has
(a) slope $\frac{2}{3}$ (b) undefined slope   (c) point $(2, 3)$ also on the line

Solution
(a) Here $m = \frac{2}{3}$, $x_1 = 1$, and $y_1 = -2$. An equation of the line is

$$y - (-2) = \frac{2}{3}(x - 1)$$

$$y + 2 = \frac{2}{3}x - \frac{2}{3}$$

$$y = \frac{2}{3}x - \frac{8}{3}$$

This equation also may be written in **general form** as $2x - 3y - 8 = 0$. Figure 1.15 shows the graph of this line, the point $(1, -2)$, and the slope.

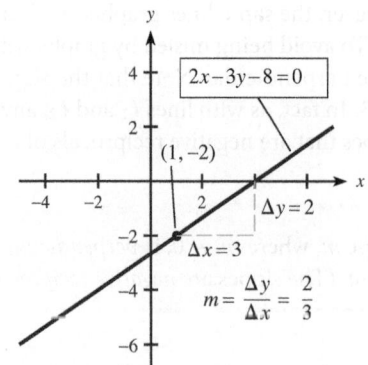

Figure 1.15

(b) Because m is undefined, we cannot use the point-slope form. This line is vertical, so every point on it has x-coordinate 1. Thus the equation is $x = 1$. Note that $x = 1$ is not a function.

(c) First use $(1, -2)$ and $(2, 3)$ to find the slope.

$$m = \frac{3 - (-2)}{2 - 1} = 5$$

Using $m = 5$ and the point $(1, -2)$ (the other point could also be used) gives

$$y - (-2) = 5(x - 1) \quad \text{or} \quad y = 5x - 7$$

Next, we consider two special lines—vertical lines and horizontal lines. The graph of $x = 1$ [from Example 4(b)] is a vertical line, as shown in Figure 1.16(a); the graph of $y = 1$ has slope 0, and its graph is a horizontal line, as shown in Figure 1.16(b).

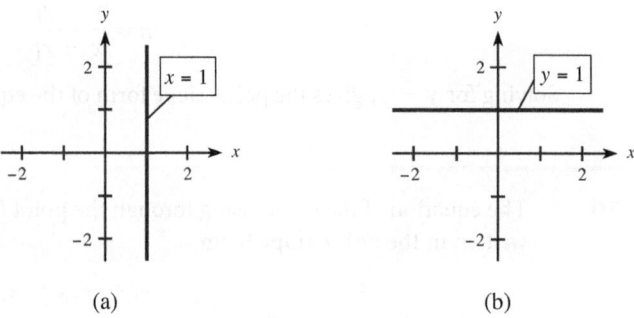

Figure 1.16   (a)   (b)

In general, **vertical lines** have undefined slope and the equation form $x = a$, where a is the x-coordinate of each point on the line. **Horizontal lines** have $m = 0$ and the equation form $y = b$, where b is the y-coordinate of each point on the line.

EXAMPLE 5 Pricing

Data from the U.S. Census Bureau indicate that the average price p of HD television sets can be expressed as a linear function of the number of sets sold N (in thousands). In addition, as N increased by 1000, p dropped by $10.40, and when 6485 (thousand) sets were sold, the average price per set was $504.39. Write the equation of the line determined by this information.

Solution
We see that price p is a function of the number of sets N (in thousands), so the slope is given by

$$m = \frac{\text{change in } p}{\text{change in } N} = \frac{-10.40}{1000} = -0.0104$$

A point on the line is $(N_1, p_1) = (6485, 504.39)$. We use the point-slope form adapted to the variables N and p.

$$p - p_1 = m(N - N_1)$$
$$p - 504.39 = -0.0104(N - 6485)$$
$$p - 504.39 = -0.0104N + 67.444$$
$$p = -0.0104N + 571.834$$

The point-slope form, with the y-intercept point $(0, b)$, can be used to derive a special form for the equation of a line, called the **slope-intercept form**.

$$y - b = m(x - 0)$$
$$y = mx + b$$

Slope-Intercept Form

The **slope-intercept form** of the equation of a line with slope m and y-intercept b is

$$y = mx + b$$

Note that if a linear equation has the form $y = mx + b$, then the coefficient of x is the slope and the constant term is the y-intercept.

EXAMPLE 6   Slope-Intercept Form

(a) Write the slope-intercept form of the equation of the line with slope $\frac{1}{2}$ and y-intercept -3.
(b) Find the slope and y-intercept of the line whose equation is $x + 2y = 8$.
(c) Graph the equation from part (b).

Solution

(a) Substituting $m = \frac{1}{2}$ and $b = -3$ in the equation $y = mx + b$ gives $y = \frac{1}{2}x + (-3)$, or $y = \frac{1}{2}x - 3$.

(b) When a linear equation is not in slope-intercept form (and does not have the form $x = a$), it can be put into slope-intercept form by solving for y. Thus to put the equation in slope-intercept form, we must solve for y.

$$2y = -x + 8 \quad \text{or} \quad y = -\frac{1}{2}x + 4$$

Thus the slope is $-\frac{1}{2}$ and the y-intercept is 4.

(c) For the line from part (b), first we plot the y-intercept point $(0, 4)$. Because the slope is $-\frac{1}{2} = \frac{-1}{2}$, moving 2 units to the right and down 1 unit from $(0, 4)$ gives the point $(2, 3)$ on the line. A third point (for a check) is plotted at $(4, 2)$. The graph is shown in Figure 1.17.

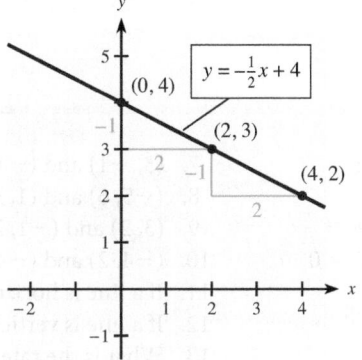

Figure 1.17

It is also possible to graph a straight line if we know its slope and any point on the line; we simply plot the point that is given and then use the slope to plot other points.

CHECKPOINT

4. Write the equation of the line that has slope $-\frac{3}{4}$ and passes through $(4, -6)$.
5. What are the slope and y-intercept of the graph of $x = -4y + 1$?

EXAMPLE   7   **Population of U.S. Males** | APPLICATION PREVIEW |

The population of U.S. males, y (in thousands), projected from 2015 to 2060 can be modeled by

$$y = 1125.9x + 142{,}690$$

where x is the number of years after 2000 (*Source:* U.S. Census Bureau).
(a) Find the slope and the y-intercept of the graph of this function.
(b) What does the y-intercept tell us about the population of U.S. males?
(c) Interpret the slope as a rate of change.

Solution
(a) The slope is $m = 1125.9$, and the y-intercept is $b = 142{,}690$.
(b) Because x is the number of years after 2000, $x = 0$ represents 2000, and the y-intercept tells us that there were approximately 142,690,000 males in the United States in 2000.
(c) The slope is 1125.9, which tells us that the population of U.S. males is predicted to increase at a rate of approximately 1,125,900 per year during this period.

The following summarizes the forms of equations of lines.

Forms of Linear Equations

General form: $ax + by + c = 0$
Point-slope form: $y - y_1 = m(x - x_1)$
Slope-intercept form: $y = mx + b$
Vertical line: $x = a$
Horizontal line: $y = b$

CHECKPOINT
ANSWERS

1. $m = -\dfrac{1}{2}$

2. If $m = 0$, then the line is horizontal. If m is undefined, then the line is vertical.

3. (a) $m_2 = -\dfrac{1}{5}$ (b) $m_2 = 5$

4. $y = -\frac{3}{4}x - 3$

5. $m = -\frac{1}{4}$; y-intercept is $\frac{1}{4}$.

EXERCISES 1.3

In Problems 1–4, find the intercepts and graph the functions.
1. $3x + 4y = 12$ 2. $6x - 5y = 90$
3. $5x - 8y = 60$ 4. $2x - y + 17 = 0$

In Problems 5–10, find the slope of the line passing through the given pair of points.
5. $(22, 11)$ and $(15, -17)$
6. $(-6, -12)$ and $(-18, -24)$

7. $(3, -1)$ and $(-1, 1)$
8. $(-5, 6)$ and $(1, -3)$
9. $(3, 2)$ and $(-1, 2)$
10. $(-4, 2)$ and $(-4, -2)$
11. If a line is horizontal, then its slope is _____.
12. If a line is vertical, then its slope is _____.
13. What is the rate of change of the function whose graph is a line passing through $(3, 2)$ and $(-1, 2)$?

14. What is the rate of change of the function whose graph is a line passing through $(11, -5)$ and $(-9, -4)$?

In Problems 15 and 16, determine whether the slope of each line is positive, negative, 0, or undefined.

15.

16.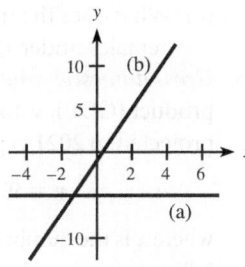

In Problems 17–24, find the slope and y-intercept and then graph each equation.

17. $y = \dfrac{7}{3}x - \dfrac{1}{4}$

18. $y = \dfrac{4}{3}x + \dfrac{1}{2}$

19. $y = 3$

20. $y = -2$

21. $x = -8$

22. $x = -1/2$

23. $2x + 3y = 6$

24. $3x - 2y = 18$

In Problems 25–28, write the slope-intercept form of the equation of the line that has the given slope and y-intercept. Then graph the line.

25. Slope $\frac{1}{2}$ and y-intercept -3

26. Slope 4 and y-intercept 2

27. Slope -2 and y-intercept $\frac{1}{2}$

28. Slope $-\frac{2}{3}$ and y-intercept -1

In Problems 29–34, write the equation of the line that passes through the given point and has the given slope. Then graph the line.

29. $(2, 0)$ with slope -5

30. $(1, 1)$ with slope $-\frac{1}{3}$

31. $(-1, 4)$ with slope $-\frac{3}{4}$

32. $(3, -1)$ with slope 1

33. $(-1, 1)$ with undefined slope

34. $(1, 1)$ with 0 slope

In Problems 35–40, write the equation of each line described or shown.

35. Through $(3, 2)$ and $(-1, -6)$

36. Through $(-4, 2)$ and $(2, 4)$

37. Through $(7, 3)$ and $(-6, 2)$

38. Through $(10, 2)$ and $(8, 7)$

39.

40.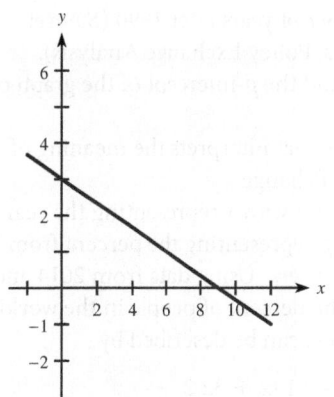

In Problems 41–44, determine whether the following pairs of equations represent parallel lines, perpendicular lines, or neither.

41. $3x + 2y = 6$; $2x - 3y = 6$

42. $5x - 2y = 8$; $10x - 4y = 8$

43. $6x - 4y = 12$; $3x - 2y = 6$

44. $5x + 4y = 7$; $y = \dfrac{4}{5}x + 7$

45. Write the equation of the line passing through $(-2, -7)$ that is parallel to $3x + 5y = 11$.

46. Write the equation of the line passing through $(6, -4)$ that is parallel to $4x - 5y = 6$.

47. Write the equation of the line passing through $(3, 1)$ that is perpendicular to $5x - 6y = 4$.

48. Write the equation of the line passing through $(-2, -8)$ that is perpendicular to $x = 4y + 3$.

APPLICATIONS

49. *Depreciation* A $360,000 building is depreciated by its owner. The value y of the building after x months of use is $y = 360,000 - 1500x$.
    (a) Graph this function for $x \geq 0$.
    (b) How long is it until the building is completely depreciated (its value is zero)?
    (c) The point $(60, 270,000)$ lies on the graph. Explain what this means.

50. *U.S population* Using Social Security Administration data for selected years from 1950 and projected to 2050, the U.S. population (in millions) can be described by

$$p(t) = 2.53t + 162.2$$

    where t is the number of years past 1950.
    (a) Find $p(0)$ and explain its meaning.
    (b) Find the slope and explain its meaning.
    (c) Graph this function for $t \geq 0$.

51. *U.S. Internet users* Using data from 2000 and projected to 2025, the percent p of the U.S. population that uses the Internet can be described by

$$p = 1.19x + 58.0$$

where x is the number of years after 1990 (*Source*: Nation and Statistics, Policy Exchange Analysis).

(a) Find the slope and the p-intercept of the graph of this equation.

(b) Write a sentence that interprets the meaning of the slope as a rate of change.

(c) Graph the function with x representing the years from 1990 and p representing the percent from 50.

52. *Worldwide Internet users* Using data from 2014 and projected to 2019, the percent of people in the world who are Internet users can be described by

$$p = 2.14x + 32.2$$

where x is the number of years after 2010 (*Source*: statista.com).

(a) Find the slope and the p-intercept of the graph of this linear function.

(b) Interpret the meaning of the slope as a rate of change.

(c) Write a sentence that interprets the meaning of the p-intercept.

53. *Heart rate* For adults, the desired heart rate to achieve weight loss during exercise is given by the linear function

$$H = -0.650t + 143$$

where t equals the person's age and H equals the heart rate in beats per minute (*Source*: paramountfitness.com).

(a) Find the slope of the graph of this function.

(b) If Jack is 20 years older than Harry, how much slower is Jack's desired heart rate to achieve weight loss during exercise?

(c) Graph this function for values of t from 20 to 60.

54. *Temperature–humidity models* Two models for measuring the effects of high temperature and humidity are the Summer Simmer Index and the Apparent Temperature.* For an outside temperature of 100°F, these indices relate the relative humidity, H (expressed as a decimal), to the perceived temperature as follows.

Summer Simmer: $S = 141.1 - 45.78(1 - H)$
Apparent Temperature: $A = 91.2 + 41.3H$

(a) For each index, find the point that corresponds to a relative humidity of 40%.

(b) For each point in part (a), write a sentence that explains its meaning.

(c) Graph both equations for $0 \leq H \leq 1$.

55. *Population of females under 18* Using projections from 2020 to 2060, the number of females in the U.S. under the age of 18, in millions, can be modeled by

$$N = 0.150x + 37.4$$

where x is the number of years after 2020 (*Source*: U.S. Census Bureau).

(a) Viewing N as a function of x, what is the slope of the graph of this function?

(b) Interpret the slope as a rate of change.

(c) What does the model predict the population of females under 18 will be in 2040?

56. *Gross domestic product* The U.S. gross domestic product (GDP), y, for the years from 2011 and projected to 2021 is given by

$$y = 977.8x + 13,643.2$$

where x is the number of years past 1990 and y is in billions of dollars (*Source*: Social Security Administration).

(a) What is the slope of the graph of this function?

(b) Interpret the slope as a rate of change.

57. *Residential electric costs* An electric utility company determines the monthly bill for a residential customer by adding an energy charge of 8.38 cents per kilowatt-hour to its base charge of $16.37 per month. Write an equation for the monthly charge y in terms of x, the number of kilowatt-hours used.

58. *Residential heating costs* Residential customers who heat their homes with natural gas have their monthly bills calculated by adding a base service charge of $9.19 per month and an energy charge of 91.91 cents per hundred cubic feet. Write an equation for the monthly charge y in terms of x, the number of hundreds of cubic feet used.

59. *Civilian workforce* The size of the U.S. civilian workforce for the years from 1950 and projected to 2050 can be approximated by a linear equation determined by the line connecting the two points $(1950, 62.2)$ and $(2050, 191.8)$, where the x-coordinate is the year and the y-coordinate is the number in the civilian workforce (in millions) in year x (*Source*: U.S. Bureau of Labour Statistics).

(a) Write the equation of the line connecting the two points.

(b) Interpret the slope of this line as a rate of change.

60. *Pension plans* According to *USA Today* most pensions for state legislators are based on the product of the legislator's years of service, compensation, and a multiplier (usually between 1% and 5%). When the multiplier is 2.5%, a state legislator's pension is calculated with a formula such as the following:
    "2.5% of average final compensation multiplied by the years of credited service"
Let p represent annual retirement pension; y, years of service; and c, average final compensation.

(a) For someone with average final compensation of $80,000, write the linear equation that gives p in terms of y.

(b) For someone intending to retire after 30 years, write the linear equation that gives p in terms of c.

*Bosch, W., and C. G. Cobb, "Temperature-Humidity Indices," UMAP Unit 691, *The UMAP Journal*, 10(3), Fall 1989, 237–256.

61. *Consumer price index* The projected consumer price index (CPI) for the years 2020 to 2050 can be approximated by a linear equation determined by the line connecting (2020, 120.56) and (2050, 276.05), where the *x*-coordinate is the year and the *y*-coordinate is the price consumers pay in year *x* for goods that cost $100 in 2012 (*Source:* Social Security Administration).
    (a) Write the equation of the line connecting these two points to find a linear model for these data.
    (b) Interpret the slope of this line as a rate of change.

62. *Drinking and driving* The following table gives the number of drinks and the resulting blood alcohol percent for a 180-pound man legally considered driving under the influence (DUI).

Number of Drinks	5	6	7	8	9	10
Blood Alcohol Percent	0.11	0.13	0.15	0.17	0.19	0.21

Source: Pennsylvania Liquor Control Board

   (a) Is the average rate of change of the blood alcohol percent with respect to the number of drinks a constant?
   (b) Use the rate of change and one point determined by a number of drinks and the resulting blood alcohol percent to write the equation of a linear model for these data.
   (c) Verify that the values in the table fit the model.

63. *Pollution effects* It has been estimated that a certain stream can support 85,000 fish if it is pollution-free. It has further been estimated that for each ton of pollutants in the stream, 1700 fewer fish can be supported. Assuming that the relationship is linear, write the equation that gives the population of fish *p* in terms of the tons of pollutants *x*.

64. *Age–sleep relationship* Each day, a young person should sleep 8 hours plus $\frac{1}{4}$ hour for each year the person is under 18 years of age. Assuming that the relation is linear, write the equation relating hours of sleep *y* and age *x*.

65. *Insulation R-values* The R-value of insulation is a measure of its ability to resist heat transfer. For fiberglass insulation, $3\frac{1}{2}$ inches is rated at R-11 and 6 inches is rated at R-19. Assuming that this relationship is linear, write the equation that gives the R-value of fiberglass insulation as a function of its thickness *t* (in inches).

66. *Depreciation* Suppose the cost of a business property is $960,000 and a company wants to use a straight-line depreciation schedule for a period of 240 months. If *y* is the value of this property after *x* months, write the linear equation of this depreciation schedule.

67. *Cholesterol and coronary heart disease risk* The Seven Countries Study, conducted by Ancel Keys, was a long-term study of the relationship of cholesterol to coronary heart disease (CHD) mortality in men. The relationship was approximated by the line shown in the accompanying figure. The line passes through the points (200, 25) and (250, 49), which means there were 25 CHD deaths per 1000 among men with 200 mg/dl (milligrams per deciliter) of cholesterol and 49 CHD deaths per 1000 among men with 250 mg/dl of cholesterol. Using *x* to represent the cholesterol and *y* to represent CHD deaths, write the equation that represents this relationship.

Graphs and Graphing Utilities

SECTION 1.4

OBJECTIVES

- To use a graphing utility to graph equations in the standard viewing window
- To use a graphing utility and a specified range to graph equations
- To use a graphing utility to evaluate functions, to find intercepts, and to find zeros of a function
- To solve linear equations with a graphing utility

APPLICATION PREVIEW

Suppose that for a certain city, the cost *C* of obtaining drinking water with *p* percent impurities (by volume) is given by

$$C = \frac{120{,}000}{p} - 1200$$

where $0 < p \le 100$. A graph of this equation would illustrate how the purity of water is related to the cost of obtaining it. Because this equation is not linear, graphing it would require many more than two points. Such a graph could be obtained efficiently with a graphing utility. (See Example 1.)

In Section 1.3, "Linear Functions," we saw that a linear equation could easily be graphed by plotting points because only two points are required. When we want the graph of an equation that is not linear, we can still use point plotting, but we must have enough points to sketch an accurate graph.

Some computer software and all graphing calculators have **graphing utilities** (also called *graphics utilities*) that can be used to generate an accurate graph. All graphing utilities use the point-plotting method to plot scores of points quickly and thereby graph an equation.

Computer monitors and calculator screens consist of a fine grid containing pixels that correspond to points on a coordinate plane. As a graphing utility plots points, the pixels corresponding to the points on the graph are lighted and then connected, revealing the graph. The graph is shown in a viewing window or viewing rectangle. The values that define the viewing window of Texas Instruments calculators (used in our discussions and graphs) can be set individually or by using ZOOM keys. The important values are

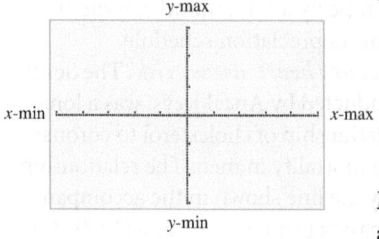

x-min: the smallest value on the x-axis (the leftmost x-value in the window)

x-max: the largest value on the x-axis (the rightmost x-value in the window)

y-min: the smallest value on the y-axis (the lowest y-value in the window)

y-max: the largest value on the y-axis (the highest y-value in the window)

Most graphing utilities have a *standard viewing window* that gives a window with x-values and y-values between -10 and 10.

x-min: -10 $\qquad\qquad\qquad\qquad$ y-min: -10

x-max: 10 $\qquad\qquad\qquad\qquad$ y-max: 10

To graph $y = \frac{1}{3}x^3 - x^2 - 3x + 2$ with the standard viewing window:

1. Under the Y = menu, enter the right side of the equation in Y_1.
2. Under ZOOM, press 6:ZStandard.

The resulting graph is shown in Figure 1.18.

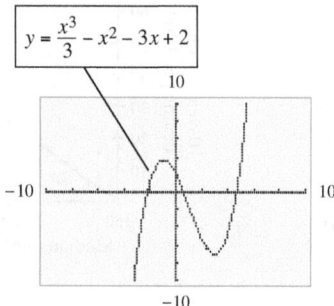

Figure 1.18

Calculator Note   With a graphing calculator, as with a graph plotted by hand, the appearance of the graph is determined by the part of the graph we are viewing, and the standard window does not always give a **complete graph**. (A complete graph shows the important parts of the graph and suggests the unseen parts.) The quality and completeness of a graph drawn with a graphing calculator are determined by the viewing window and the scales on the axes (the Xscl and Yscl settings). Details on how to enter a function, set a viewing window to see a complete graph, and set the x- and y- scales to determine the tic locations on the x- and y-axes are included in the steps for graphing a function with a graphing calculator. See Appendix A, Section 1.4. ■

EXAMPLE 1   Water Purity | APPLICATION PREVIEW |

For a certain city, the cost C of obtaining drinking water with p percent impurities (by volume) is given by

$$C = \frac{120,000}{p} - 1200$$

The equation for C requires that $p \neq 0$, and because p is the percent impurities, we know that $0 < p \leq 100$. Use the restriction on p and a graphing calculator to obtain an accurate graph of the equation.

Solution

To use a graphing calculator, we identify C with y and p with x. Thus we enter

$$y = \frac{120{,}000}{x} - 1200$$

Because $0 < p \le 100$, we set the x-range to *include* these values, with the realization that only the portion of the graph above these values applies to our equation and that $p = 0$ (that is, $x = 0$) is excluded from the domain because it makes the denominator 0. With this x-range we can determine a y-, or C-, range from the equation or by tracing; see Figure 1.19(a). We see that when p is near 0 (the value excluded from the domain), the C-coordinates of the points are very large, indicating that water free of impurities is very costly. However, Figure 1.19(a) does not accurately show what happens for large p-values. Figure 1.19(b) shows another view of the equation with the C-range (that is, the y-range) from -500 to 3500. We see that the p-intercept is $p = 100$, which indicates that water containing 100% impurities costs nothing ($C = 0$). Note that $p > 100$ has no meaning. Why?

(a)

(b)

Figure 1.19

Two views of $C = \dfrac{120{,}000}{p} - 1200$

CHECKPOINT

Use a graphing calculator and the standard viewing window to graph the following.

1. $y = -x^2/4$

2. $y = \dfrac{4(x + 1)^2}{x^2 + 1}$

We can evaluate a function $y = f(x)$ with a graphing calculator by using TABLE to find the function values corresponding to values of the independent variable. We also can use TRACE to evaluate or approximate function values. See Appendix A, Section 1.4, for instructions for using these commands.

EXAMPLE 2   Women in the Workforce

The number y (in millions) of women in the workforce is modeled by the function

$$y = -0.005x^2 + 1.38x + 0.07$$

where x is the number of years past 1940 (*Source:* Bureau of Labor Statistics).

(a) Graph this function from $x = 0$ to $x = 85$.

(b) Find the value of y when $x = 60$. Explain what this means.

(c) Use the model to estimate the number of women in the workforce in 2015.

Solution

(a) Enter the equation and set the window with x-min $= 0$ and x-max $= 85$. Using TRACE for x-values between 0 and 85 helps determine that y-values between 0 and 85 give a complete graph. These values are entered in the screen under WINDOW [see Figure 1.20(a)]. The graph is shown in Figure 1.20(b).

(b) Using TRACE or TABLE, we can find $f(60) = 64.87$ [see Figure 1.20(c) and Figure 1.20(d)]. This means that there were approximately 64.87 million, or 64,870,000, women in the workforce in $1940 + 60 = 2000$.

(c) The year 2015 corresponds to $x = 75$ and $f(75) = 75.445$ [see Figure 1.20(d)]. Thus in 2015, approximately 75,445,000 women were in the workforce.

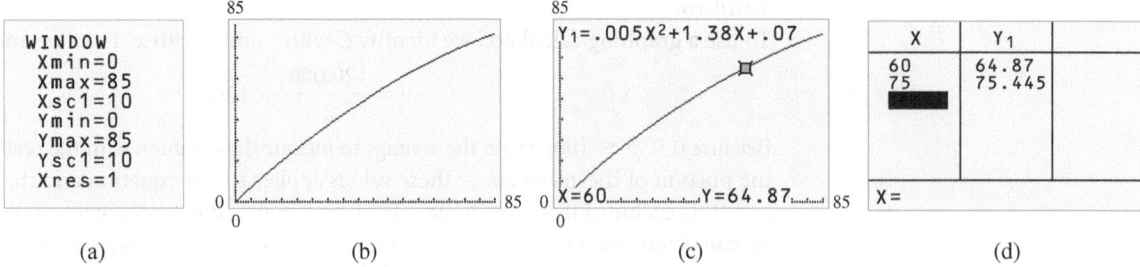

(a) (b) (c) (d)

Figure 1.20

Spreadsheet Note   Representing quantities or their interrelationships algebraically is one of the keys to using spreadsheets. Each cell in a spreadsheet has an address based on its row and column. For example, cell B3 in Figure 1.21a is the second column and the third row.

The cells can contain numbers or formulas that use numbers and cell addresses. These cell addresses act like variables in an algebraic expression. We can use "fill down" or "fill across" to find the ouputs of a function for given inputs. Figure 1.21a shows a spreadsheet for the function $f(x) = 6x - 3$ for the input set $\{-5, -2, -1, 0, 1, 3, 5\}$, with these inputs listed as entries in the first column (column A). If -5 is in cell A2, then $f(-5)$ can be found in cell B2 by typing $= 6*A2 - 3$ in cell B2. Notice that the cell B2 entry of the $f(x)$ formula begins with an equal sign and uses cell A2 in place of the variable. All Excel formulas begin with an equal sign ($=$) and use other cells (such as A2) as variables. Using the fill-down capability, we can obtain all the function values shown in column B.

We can graph the function with inputs in column A and outputs in column B of Figure 1.21a by highlighting the two columns and selecting the XY (scatter) chart type with the smooth curve option (see Figure 1.21b). See Appendix B, Section 1.4, or the Online Excel Guide for details on graphing functions.

	A	B
1	x	$f(x) = 6x - 3$
2	-5	-33
3	-2	-15
4	-1	-9
5	0	-3
6	1	3
7	3	15
8	5	27

Figure 1.21   (a)   (b)

Graphical Solutions of Linear Equations   We can use graphing calculators to determine (or approximate) the solutions of equations. TRACE can be used to approximate where the graph of the function $y = f(x)$ intersects the x-axis. This **x-intercept** is also the value of x that makes the function zero, so it is called a **zero of the function**. Because this value of x makes $f(x) = 0$, it is also a **solution** (or **root**) of the equation $0 = f(x)$. The command 2nd CALC, 2:zero also can be used to solve an equation. The following steps show how to use ZERO to find an x-intercept; this is called the **x-intercept method**.

> ### Solving an Equation Using the x-Intercept Method with a Graphing Calculator
>
> 1. Rewrite the equation to be solved with 0 (and nothing else) on one side of the equation.
> 2. Enter the nonzero side of the equation found in the previous step in the equation editor of your graphing calculator and graph the equation in an appropriate viewing window. Make sure you can see the graph cross the horizontal axis.

3. Find or approximate the *x*-intercept using ZERO. The *x*-intercept is the value of *x* that makes the equation equal to zero, so it is the solution to the equation. The value of *x* found by this method is often displayed as a decimal approximation of the exact solution rather than as the exact solution.
4. Verify the solution in the original equation.

See the following example and Appendix A, Section 1.4, for more details for using the *x*-intercept solution method with a graphing calculator.

EXAMPLE 3   Solving an Equation with a Graphing Calculator

Graphically solve $5x + \dfrac{1}{2} = 7x - 8$ for x.

Solution

To solve this equation, we rewrite the equation with 0 on one side.

$$0 = 7x - 8 - \left(5x + \frac{1}{2}\right)$$

The steps used in solving this equation are:

1. Graph $y = 7x - 8 - \left(5x + \dfrac{1}{2}\right)$. [See Figure 1.22(a) and Figure 1.22(b)].

2. Select 2nd CALC, 2:zero and find the *x*-intercept of the graph, which is approximately equal to $4.25 = \frac{17}{4}$ [see Figure 1.22(c)]. Checking $x = \frac{17}{4}$ in the original equation, or solving the equation analytically, shows that $x = \frac{17}{4}$ is the exact solution.

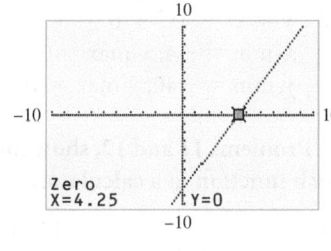

Figure 1.22   (a)   (b)   (c)

Spreadsheet Note   To solve $f(x) = 0$ by finding the zero of $f(x)$ with Excel, enter a value for the variable in cell A2 and the formula for the function in cell B2; then click the *Data* tab, select *What-If-Analysis*, and choose *Goal Seek*. Then click on B2 in the *Set Cell* box, enter 0 in *To value*, click the *By Changing cell* box, and click the A2 cell. Clicking OK will give 0 in cell B2 and the solution [zero of $f(x)$] in cell A2. The spreadsheets show the formula for $f(x) = 5x - 8$ in B2 and the solution to $0 = 5x - 8$ in cell A2 ($x = 1.6$). See Appendix B, Section 1.4, or the Online Excel Guide for details.

	A	B
1	x	$f(x) = 5x - 8$
2	1	$= 5*A2 - 8$

	A	B
1	x	$f(x) = 5x - 8$
2	1.6	0

CHECKPOINT
ANSWERS

1.

2.

$$y_1 = \frac{-x^2}{4}$$

$$y_1 = (4(x+1)^2)/(x^2+1)$$

EXERCISES 1.4

In Problems 1–8, use a graphing calculator with the standard viewing window to graph each function.

1. $y = x^2 + 4x + 1$
2. $y = 4 - 3x - x^2$
3. $y = x^3 - 3x$
4. $y = x^3 - 6x^2$
5. $y = 0.1x^3 - 0.3x^2 - 2.4x + 3$
6. $y = \frac{1}{4}x^4 - \frac{1}{3}x^3 - 3x^2 + 8$
7. $y = \frac{12x}{x^2 + 1}$
8. $y = \frac{8}{x^2 + 1}$

In Problems 9 and 10, use a graphing calculator with the specified window to graph each equation.

9. $y = x^3 - 12x - 1$
   x-min $= -5$, x-max $= 5$;
   y-min $= -20$, y-max $= 20$
10. $y = x^4 - 4x^3 + 6$
    x-min $= -4$, x-max $= 6$;
    y-min $= -40$, y-max $= 10$

In Problems 11 and 12, show the correct way to enter each function in a calculator.

11. $y = \frac{3x + 7}{x^2 + 4}$
12. $y = x^2 - \frac{4}{x - 1}$

In Problems 13–16, graph each equation with a graphing calculator using
(a) the specified window.
(b) the standard viewing window (for comparison).

13. $y = 0.01x^3 + 0.3x^2 - 72x + 150$
    x-min $= -100$, x-max $= 80$;
    y-min $= -2000$, y-max $= 4000$
14. $y = -0.0001x^3 + 0.0015x^2 + 0.6x + 7$
    x-min $= -100$, x-max $= 100$;
    y-min $= -50$, y-max $= 50$
15. $y = \frac{x + 15}{x^2 + 400}$
    x-min $= -200$, x-max $= 200$;
    y-min $= -0.02$, y-max $= 0.06$

16. $y = \frac{x - 80}{x^2 + 1700}$
    x-min $= -200$, x-max $= 400$;
    y-min $= -0.06$, y-max $= 0.01$

In Problems 17 and 18, (a) algebraically find the x- and y-intercepts of the graph and (b) graph each equation with a graphing calculator, using a window that includes the intercepts.

17. $y = 0.001x - 0.03$
18. $y = 50{,}000 - 100x$

In Problems 19–22, the graph of a function is shown in the standard viewing window. Experiment with the viewing window to obtain a complete graph.

19. $y = -0.15(x - 10.2)^2 + 10$

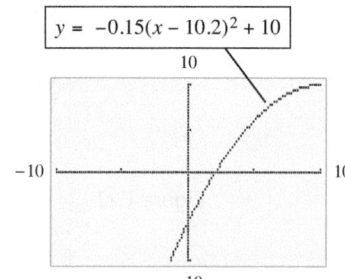

20. $y = x^2 - x - 42$

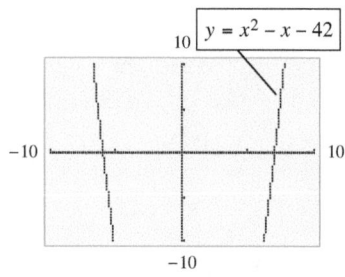

21. $y = \dfrac{x^3 + 19x^2 - 62x - 840}{20}$

22. $y = \dfrac{-x^3 + 33x^2 + 120x}{20}$

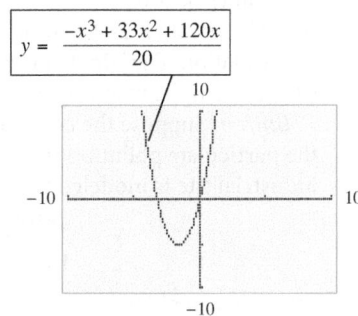

In Problems 23–28, graph the equations in the standard viewing window on a graphing calculator. Identify any linear functions.

23. $4x - y = 8$ 24. $5x + y = 8$

25. $4x^2 + 2y = 5$ 26. $6x^2 + 3y = 8$

27. $x^2 - 2y - 6 = 0$ 28. $3x^2 - 4y = 8$

In Problems 29 and 30, use TRACE or TABLE to evaluate the function.

29. If $f(x) = x^3 - 3x^2 + 2$, find $f(-2)$ and $f(3/4)$.

30. If $f(x) = \dfrac{x^2 - 2x}{x - 1}$, find $f(3)$ and $f(-4)$.

In Problems 31–34, graph each function using a window that gives a complete graph.

31. $y = \dfrac{12x^2 - 12}{x^2 + 1}$ 32. $y = \dfrac{9x^3}{4x^4 + 9}$

33. $y = \dfrac{x^2 - x - 6}{x^2 + 5x + 6}$ 34. $y = \dfrac{x^2 - 4}{x^2 - 9}$

In Problems 35–38, use the x-intercept method to find one solution of each equation.

35. $0 = 6x - 21$ 36. $12x + 28 = 0$

37. $10 = x^2 - 3x$ 38. $6x^2 + 4x = 4$

In Problems 39 and 40, use a graphing calculator to (a) approximate two x-intercepts of the graph of the function (to four decimal places) and (b) give the approximate zeros of the function.

39. $y = x^2 - 7x - 9$ 40. $y = 2x^2 - 4x - 11$

APPLICATIONS

41. *Population of females under 18* Using U.S. Census Bureau projections from 2020 to 2060, the number of U.S. females under the age of 18, in millions, can be modeled by the function

$$N = 0.150x + 37.4$$

where x is the number of years after 2020.

  (a) Use a graphing calculator to graph this equation for the range x-min = 0, x-max = 40, N-min = 35, N-max = 45.

  (b) The point (20, 40.4) lies on the graph of this equation. Explain its meaning.

  (c) What does the model predict the population of females under 18 will be in 2030?

42. *U.S. National consumption* Using U.S. Energy Information Administration data for selected years from 2012 and projected to 2040, total U.S. real consumption, C, can be expressed as a function of national disposable personal income, I, (both in billions of dollars) according to

$$C = 0.885I + 0.413$$

  (a) Use a graphing calculator to graph this equation for the range I-min = 0, I-max = 25, C-min = 0, C-max = 25.

  (b) The point (12.6, 11.6) lies on the graph of this function. Explain its meaning.

  (c) What does the function predict the total U.S. real consumption will be when national disposable personal income is $18.5 billion?

43. *Consumer expenditure* Suppose that the consumer expenditure E (in dollars) depends on the market price p per unit (in dollars) according to

$$E = 10{,}000p - 100p^2$$

  (a) Graph this equation with a graphing calculator and the window p-min = -50, p-max = 150; E-min = $-50{,}000$, E-max = 300,000.

  (b) Because E represents consumer expenditure, only values of $E \geq 0$ have meaning. For what p-values is $E \geq 0$?

44. *Rectilinear motion* The height above ground (in feet) of a ball thrown vertically into the air is given by

$$S = 112t - 16t^2$$

where t is the time in seconds since the ball was thrown.

(a) Graph this equation with a graphing calculator and the window t-min $= -2$, t-max $= 10$; S-min $= -20$, S-max $= 250$.

(b) Estimate the time at which the ball is at its highest point and estimate the height of the ball at that time.

45. *Advertising impact* An advertising agency has found that when it promotes a new product in a city of 350,000 people, the rate of change R of the number of people who are aware of the product is related to the number of people x who are aware of it and is given by

$$R = 28,000 - 0.08x$$

where $x \geq 0$ and $R \geq 0$.

(a) Use the intercepts to determine a window and then graph the equation for $x \geq 0$.

(b) Is the rate of change increasing or decreasing? Explain why your answer makes sense in the context of the problem.

46. *Learning rate* In a study using 50 foreign language vocabulary words, the learning rate L (in words per minute) was found to depend on the number of words already learned, x, according to the equation

$$L = 20 - 0.4x$$

(a) Use the intercepts to determine a window and then graph the equation for $x \geq 0$.

(b) Is the learning rate increasing or decreasing? Explain why your answer makes sense in the context of the problem.

47. *Elderly men in the workforce* Using data from 1920 and projected to 2030, the percent P of men 65 years of age or older in the labor force can be modeled by

$$P = 0.000078x^3 - 0.0107x^2 - 0.182x + 64.68$$

where x is the number of years past 1900 (*Source:* U.S. Census Bureau).

(a) What x-min and x-max should you use to view this graph for values representing 1900 to 2030?

(b) If P-min $= 0$, use a table to determine a value for P-max that would show a complete graph of the model.

(c) Graph this equation.

(d) Write a sentence that describes the percent of men 65 years of age or older in the workforce.

48. *Consumer Price Index* Using Social Security Administration data for selected years from 2012 and projected to 2050, the U.S. consumer price index (CPI) can be modeled by the function

$$y = 0.0682x^2 + 1.76x + 96.0$$

where x is the number of years past 2010 and y is the CPI in dollars. With a reference of 100 in 2012, a CPI of 120 in another year means that goods and services costing $100 in 2012 are expected to cost $120 in that other year.

(a) Use a table to determine a viewing window that shows a complete graph of this function for the years from 2010 to 2050.

(b) Graph the function.

(c) Use the graph to estimate when the CPI is predicted to reach 200.

49. *Environment* The Millcreek watershed area was heavily strip-mined for coal. Because of the resulting pollution, the streams cannot support fish. Suppose the cost C of obtaining stream water that contains p percent of the current pollution levels is modeled by

$$C = \frac{285,000}{p} - 2850$$

where $0 < p \leq 100$.

(a) Use the restriction on p and determine a range for C so that a graphing utility can be used to obtain an accurate graph. Then graph the equation.

(b) Describe what happens to the cost as p takes on values near 0.

(c) The point $(1, 282, 150)$ lies on the graph of this equation. Explain its meaning.

(d) Explain the meaning of the p-intercept.

50. *Pollution* Suppose the cost C of removing p percent of the particulate pollution from the exhaust gases at an industrial site is modeled by

$$C = \frac{8100p}{100 - p}$$

where $0 \leq p < 100$.

(a) Use the restriction on p and experiment with a C-range to obtain an accurate graph of the equation with a graphing utility.

(b) Describe what happens to C as p gets close to 100.

(c) The point $(98, 369,900)$ lies on the graph of this equation. Explain the meaning of the coordinates.

(d) Explain the meaning of the p-intercept.

51. *Tax burden* The dollars per capita of federal tax burden T can be modeled by

$$T = 2.11x^3 - 93.01x^2 + 1373.9x + 394$$

where x is the number of years past 1990 (*Source:* Internal Revenue Service).

(a) Graph this function for values of x that correspond to the years from 1990 to 2018.

(b) Is the graph increasing or decreasing over these years? What does this tell us about the per capita federal tax burden?

52. *Carbon dioxide emissions* Using U.S. Department of Energy data from 2010 and projected to 2032, the millions of metric tons of carbon dioxide emissions from biomass energy combustion, y, in the United States can be modeled by

$$y = -0.022x^3 + 0.86x^2 + 9.9x + 340$$

where x is the number of years past 2010.

(a) Graph this function for values of x that represent the years from 2010 to 2035.

(b) Does the graph in part (a) show that carbon dioxide emissions increase or decrease over this time period?

(c) Use the equation to find the change in carbon dioxide emissions from 2010 to 2011 and from 2029 to 2030.

SECTION 1.5

Solutions of Systems of Linear Equations

OBJECTIVES

- To solve systems of linear equations in two variables by graphing
- To solve systems of linear equations by substitution
- To solve systems of linear equations by elimination
- To solve systems of three linear equations in three variables

APPLICATION PREVIEW

Suppose that a person has $200,000 invested, part at 9% and part at 8%, and that the yearly income from the two investments is $17,200. If x represents the amount invested at 9% and y represents the amount invested at 8%, then to find how much is invested at each rate, we must find the values of x and y that satisfy both

$$x + y = 200{,}000 \quad \text{and} \quad 0.09x + 0.08y = 17{,}200$$

See Example 3 for the solution to this system of equations. Methods of solving systems of linear equations are discussed in this section.

Graphical Solution   In the previous sections, we graphed linear equations in two variables and observed that the graphs are straight lines. Each point on the graph represents an ordered pair of values (x, y) that satisfies the equation, so a point of intersection of two (or more) lines represents a solution to both (or all) the equations of those lines.

The equations are referred to as a **system of equations,** and the ordered pairs (x, y) that satisfy all the equations in the system are the **solutions** (or **simultaneous solutions**) of the system. Finding the solution to a system of equations is called **solving the system** or **solving simultaneously**.

We can use graphing to find the solution of a system of equations.

EXAMPLE **1**   **Graphical Solution of a System**

Use graphing to find the solution of the system

$$\begin{cases} 4x + 3y = 11 \\ 2x - 5y = -1 \end{cases}$$

Solution

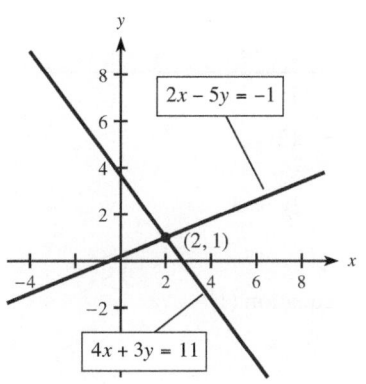

The graphs of the two equations intersect at the point $(2, 1)$. (See Figure 1.23.) The solution of the system is $x = 2$, $y = 1$. Note that these values satisfy both equations.

If the graphs of two equations are parallel lines, they have no point in common; thus the system has no solution. Such a system of equations is called **inconsistent.** For example,

$$\begin{cases} 4x + 3y = 4 \\ 8x + 6y = 18 \end{cases}$$

is an **inconsistent system** [see Figure 1.24(a) on the next page].

It also is possible that two equations describe the same line. When this happens, the equations are equivalent, and values that satisfy either equation are solutions of the system. For example,

$$\begin{cases} 4x + 3y = 4 \\ 8x + 6y = 8 \end{cases}$$

is called a **dependent system** because the equations are equivalent and all points that satisfy one equation also satisfy the other [see Figure 1.24(b) on the next page].

Figures 1.23, 1.24(a), and 1.24(b) represent the three possibilities that can occur when we are solving a system of two linear equations in two variables.

Two distinct nonparallel lines: one solution

Figure 1.23

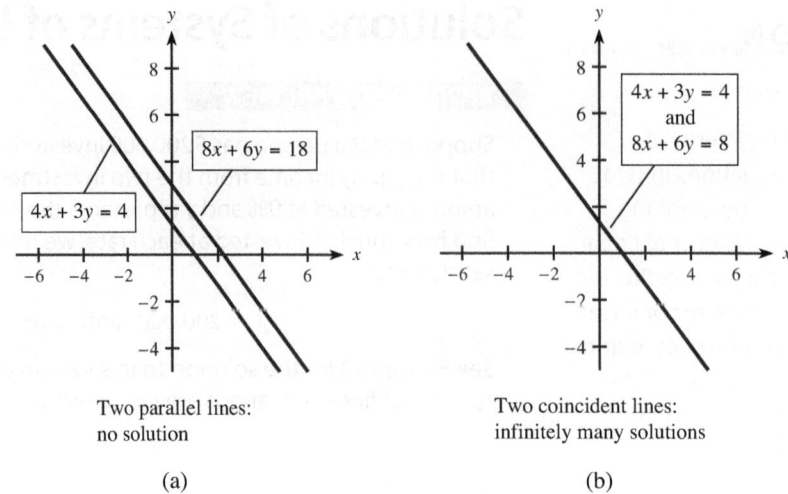

Figure 1.24   (a)   (b)

Solution by Substitution   Graphical solution methods may yield only approximate solutions to some systems. To find exact solutions, we can use algebraic methods, which are based on the fact that equivalent systems result when any of the following operations is performed.

Equivalent Systems   **Equivalent systems** result when

1. One expression is replaced by an equivalent expression.
2. Two equations are interchanged.
3. A multiple of one equation is added to another equation.
4. An equation is multiplied by a nonzero constant.

The **substitution method** is based on operation (1).

SUBSTITUTION METHOD FOR SOLVING SYSTEMS

Procedure	Example
To solve a system of two equations in two variables by substitution:	Solve the system $\begin{cases} 2x + 3y = 4 & (1) \\ x - 2y = 3 & (2) \end{cases}$
1. Solve one of the equations for either one of the variables in terms of the other.	1. Solve equation (2) for x: $x = 2y + 3$.
2. Substitute this expression into the other equation to give one equation in one unknown.	2. Substitute $2y + 3$ for x in equation (1). $2(2y + 3) + 3y = 4$.
3. Solve this linear equation for the unknown.	3. $4y + 6 + 3y = 4$ $7y = -2 \Rightarrow y = -\dfrac{2}{7}$
4. Substitute this solution into the equation in Step 1 or into one of the original equations and solve for the other variable.	4. $x = 2\left(-\dfrac{2}{7}\right) + 3 \Rightarrow x = \dfrac{17}{7}$
5. Check the solution by substituting for x and y in both original equations.	5. $2\left(\dfrac{17}{7}\right) + 3\left(-\dfrac{2}{7}\right) = 4$ ✔ $\dfrac{17}{7} - 2\left(-\dfrac{2}{7}\right) = 3$ ✔

EXAMPLE 2   **Solution by Substitution**

Solve the system

$$\begin{cases} 4x + 5y = 18 & (1) \\ 3x - 9y = -12 & (2) \end{cases}$$

Solution

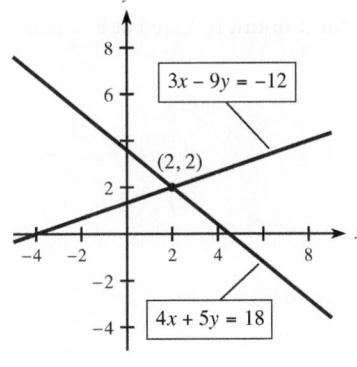

Figure 1.25

1. $x = \dfrac{9y - 12}{3} = 3y - 4$ Solve for x in equation (2).

2. $4(3y - 4) + 5y = 18$ Substitute for x in equation (1).

3. $12y - 16 + 5y = 18$ Solve for y.

        $17y = 34$

          $y = 2$

4. $x = 3(2) - 4$ Use $y = 2$ to find x.

   $x = 2$

5. $4(2) + 5(2) = 18$ and $3(2) - 9(2) = -12$ ✔   Check.

Thus the solution is $x = 2$, $y = 2$. This means that when the two equations are graphed simultaneously, their point of intersection is $(2, 2)$. See Figure 1.25. ▪

Solution by Elimination We also can eliminate one of the variables in a system by the **elimination method,** which uses addition or subtraction of equations.

ELIMINATION METHOD FOR SOLVING SYSTEMS

Procedure	Example
To solve a system of two equations in two variables by the elimination method:	Solve the system $\begin{cases} 2x - 5y = 4 & (1) \\ x + 2y = 3 & (2) \end{cases}$
1. If necessary, multiply one or both equations by a nonzero number that will make the coefficients of one of the variables identical, except perhaps for signs.	1. Multiply equation (2) by -2. $2x - 5y = 4$ $-2x - 4y = -6$
2. Add or subtract the equations to eliminate one of the variables.	2. Add the equations: $0x - 9y = -2$
3. Solve for the variable in the resulting equation.	3. $y = \dfrac{2}{9}$
4. Substitute the solution into one of the original equations and solve for the other variable.	4. $2x - 5\left(\dfrac{2}{9}\right) = 4$ $2x = 4 + \dfrac{10}{9} = \dfrac{36}{9} + \dfrac{10}{9}$ $2x = \dfrac{46}{9}$ so $x = \dfrac{23}{9}$
5. Check the solutions in both original equations.	5. $2\left(\dfrac{23}{9}\right) - 5\left(\dfrac{2}{9}\right) = 4$ ✔ $\dfrac{23}{9} + 2\left(\dfrac{2}{9}\right) = 3$ ✔

EXAMPLE 3   **Investment Mix** | APPLICATION PREVIEW |

A person has $200,000 invested, part at 9% and part at 8%. If the total yearly income from the two investments is $17,200, how much is invested at 9% and how much is invested at 8%?

Solution

Let x represent the amount invested at 9% and y represent the amount invested at 8%. Note that this means that $x + y$ is the total investment.

$$x + y = 200{,}000 \qquad (1)$$

and $0.09x + 0.08y$ is the total income earned.

$$0.09x + 0.08y = 17{,}200 \qquad (2)$$

We solve these equations simultaneously as follows:

$-8x - 8y = -1{,}600{,}000$	(3)	Multiply equation (1) by -8.
$\underline{9x + 8y = 1{,}720{,}000}$	(4)	Multiply equation (2) by 100.
$x = 120{,}000$		Add.

We find y by using $x = 120{,}000$ in equation (1).

$$120{,}000 + y = 200{,}000 \quad \text{gives} \quad y = 80{,}000$$

Thus $120,000 is invested at 9% and $80,000 is invested at 8%.
    As a check, we note that equation (1) is satisfied and that

$$0.09(120{,}000) + 0.08(80{,}000) = 10{,}800 + 6400 = 17{,}200 \checkmark$$

EXAMPLE 4   **Solution by Elimination**

Solve the systems:

(a) $\begin{cases} 4x + 3y = 4 \\ 8x + 6y = 18 \end{cases}$
    (b) $\begin{cases} 4x + 3y = 4 \\ 8x + 6y = 8 \end{cases}$

Solution

(a) $\begin{cases} 4x + 3y = 4 \\ 8x + 6y = 18 \end{cases}$

Multiply by -2 to get:	$-8x - 6y = -8$
Leave as is, which gives:	$\underline{8x + 6y = 18}$
Add the equations to get:	$0x + 0y = 10$
	$0 = 10$

The system is solved when $0 = 10$. This is impossible, so there are no solutions of the system. The equations are inconsistent. Their graphs are parallel lines; see Figure 1.24(a) earlier in this section.

(b) $\begin{cases} 4x + 3y = 4 \\ 8x + 6y = 8 \end{cases}$

Multiply by -2 to get:	$-8x - 6y = -8$
Leave as is, which gives:	$\underline{8x + 6y = 8}$
Add the equations to get:	$0x + 0y = 0$
	$0 = 0$

This is an identity, so the two equations are equivalent and share infinitely many solutions. Their graphs coincide, and each point on this graph represents a solution of the system; see Figure 1.24(b) earlier in this section.

EXAMPLE 5   **Medicine Concentrations**

A nurse has two solutions that contain different concentrations of a certain medication. One is a 12.5% concentration, and the other is a 5% concentration. How many cubic centimeters of each should she mix to obtain 20 cubic centimeters of an 8% concentration?

Solution

Let x equal the cubic centimeters of the 12.5% solution and let y equal the cubic centimeters of the 5% solution. The total amount of substance is

$$x + y = 20 \quad (1)$$

and the total amount of medication is

$$0.125x + 0.05y = (0.08)(20) = 1.6 \quad (2)$$

Solving this pair of equations simultaneously gives

$$
\begin{aligned}
50x + 50y &= 1000 && \text{Multiply equation (1) by 50.}\\
-125x - 50y &= -1600 && \text{Multiply equation (2) by 1000.}\\
\hline
-75x &= -600 && \text{Add.}\\
x &= 8 \\
8 + y = 20, \text{ so } y &= 12
\end{aligned}
$$

Thus 8 cubic centimeters of a 12.5% concentration and 12 cubic centimeters of a 5% concentration yield 20 cubic centimeters of an 8% concentration.

Checking, we see that $8 + 12 = 20$ and

$$0.125(8) + 0.05(12) = 1 + 0.6 = 1.6 \checkmark$$

CHECKPOINT

1. Solve by substitution: $\begin{cases} 3x - 4y = -24 \\ x + y = -1 \end{cases}$

2. Solve by elimination: $\begin{cases} 2x + 3y = 5 \\ 3x + 5y = -25 \end{cases}$

3. In Problems 1 and 2, the solution method is given.
   (a) In each case, explain why you think that method is appropriate.
   (b) In each case, would the other method work as well? Explain.

Calculator Note

Solutions of systems of equations, if they exist, can be found by using the intersection method. To use this method:

1. Solve both equations for y and enter each in the Y = menu.
2. Graph both equations in a window that contains their point of intersection.
3. Choose CALC (2nd TRACE) and 5:intersect; follow the prompts to find the point of intersection.

This method will give the point of intersection exactly or approximately to a large number of significant digits. Figure 1.26 shows a system and its solution, $x = 2$, $y = 3$. Details of solving systems of linear equations are shown in Appendix A, Section 1.5.

$$\begin{cases} 3x + 2y = 12 \\ 4x - 3y = -1 \end{cases}$$

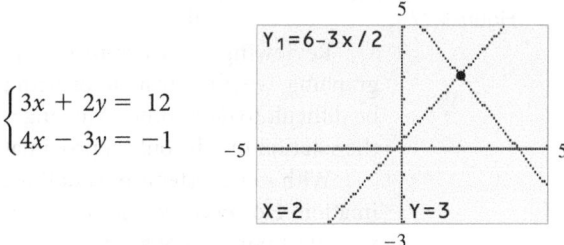

Figure 1.26

Spreadsheet Note

We can use Excel to solve the system of equations in Figure 1.26.

1. Solve both equations for y.
2. Enter an input in A2 and the formulas for the two equations in B2 and C2.
3. Enter = B2 − C2 in cell D2.
4. In the *Goal Seek* menu, under *Data > What-If-Analysis*, set D2 to 0 and select A2 as the changing cell.
5. Click OK to get the x-value of the solution in A2 and y-value in both B2 and C2.

The following spreadsheets show the input formulas and the solution ($x = 2$, $y = 3$) for the system. Details of the solution method are shown in Appendix B, Section 1.5. ∎

	A	B	C	D
1	x	= 6 − 1.5x	= 1/3 + 4x/3	= y1 − y2
2	1	= 6 − 1.5*A2	= 1/3 + 4*A2/3	= B2 − C2

	A	B	C	D
1	x	= 6 − 1.5x	= 1/3 + 4x/3	= y1 − y2
2	2	3	3	0

EXAMPLE 6 Workforce Participation

Using U.S. Bureau of Labor Statistics data for selected years from 1950 and projected to 2050, the number of men M and women W in the workforce (both in millions) can be modeled by the functions

$$M(t) = 0.591t + 37.3 \quad \text{and} \quad W(t) = 0.786t + 13.1$$

where t is the number of years past 1940. Graphically, find the year these functions predict that there will be equal numbers of men and women in the U.S. workforce.

Solution

Entering the two functions in a graphing calculator and setting the window with x-min = 0, x-max = 200, y-min = 0, and y-max = 200 give the graph in Figure 1.27(a). Using INTERSECT [see Figure 1.27(b)] gives a point of intersection at approximately $x = 124.1$ and $y = 110.6$. Thus there will be an equal number of men and women in the U.S. workforce about 124.1 years after 1940. This is just after the end of 2064, in 2065. The number of each is expected to be about 110.6 million. ∎

Figure 1.27   (a)   (b)

Reviewing our work in Example 6, we note that solving a system of equations by graphing, whether by hand or with a graphing utility, is limited by two factors. (1) It may be difficult to determine a viewing window that contains the point of intersection, and (2) the solution may be only approximate.

With *some* systems of equations, the only practical method may be graphical approximation. However, systems of *linear* equations can be consistently and accurately solved with algebraic methods.

Three Equations in Three Variables   If a, b, c, and d represent constants, then

$$ax + by + cz = d$$

is a first-degree (linear) equation in three variables. When equations of this form are graphed in a three-dimensional coordinate system, their graphs are planes. Two different planes may intersect in a line (like two walls) or may not intersect at all (like a floor and ceiling). Three different planes may intersect in a single point (as when two walls meet the ceiling), may intersect in a line (as in a paddle wheel), or may not have a common intersection. (See Figures 1.28, 1.29, and 1.30.) Thus three linear equations in three variables may have a unique solution, infinitely many solutions, or no solution. For example, the solution of the system

$$\begin{cases} 3x + 2y + z = 6 \\ x - y - z = 0 \\ x + y - z = 4 \end{cases}$$

is $x = 1$, $y = 2$, $z = -1$ because these three values satisfy all three equations and these are the only values that satisfy them. In this section, we will discuss only systems of three linear equations in three variables that have unique solutions. Additional systems will be discussed in Section 3.3, "Gauss-Jordan Elimination: Solving Systems of Equations."

We can solve three equations in three variables using a systematic procedure called the **left-to-right elimination method.**

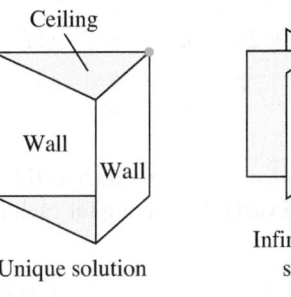

Ceiling

Wall

Wall

Unique solution

Figure 1.28

Infinitely many
solutions

Figure 1.29

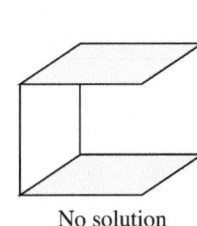

No solution

Figure 1.30

LEFT-TO-RIGHT ELIMINATION METHOD

Procedure	Example
To solve a system of three equations in three variables by the left-to-right elimination method:	Solve: $\begin{cases} 2x + 4y + 5z = 4 \\ x - 2y - 3z = 5 \\ x + 3y + 4z = 1 \end{cases}$
1. If necessary, interchange two equations or use multiplication to make the coefficient of the first variable in equation (1) a factor of the other first variable coefficients.	1. Interchange the first two equations. $\begin{aligned} x - 2y - 3z &= 5 \quad (1) \\ 2x + 4y + 5z &= 4 \quad (2) \\ x + 3y + 4z &= 1 \quad (3) \end{aligned}$
2. Add multiples of the first equation to each of the following equations so that the coefficients of the first variable in the second and third equations become zero.	2. Add $(-2) \times$ equation (1) to equation (2) and add $(-1) \times$ equation (1) to equation (3). $\begin{aligned} x - 2y - 3z &= 5 \quad (1) \\ 0x + 8y + 11z &= -6 \quad (2) \\ 0x + 5y + 7z &= -4 \quad (3) \end{aligned}$
3. Add a multiple of the second equation to the third equation so that the coefficient of the second variable in the third equation becomes zero.	3. Add $(-\frac{5}{8}) \times$ equation (2) to equation (3). $\begin{aligned} x - 2y - 3z &= 5 \quad (1) \\ 8y + 11z &= -6 \quad (2) \\ 0y + \tfrac{1}{8}z &= -\tfrac{2}{8} \quad (3) \end{aligned}$
4. Solve the third equation and *back substitute* from the bottom to find the remaining variables.	4. $z = -2$ from equation (3) $y = \tfrac{1}{8}(-6 - 11z) = 2$ from equation (2) $x = 5 + 2y + 3z = 3$ from equation (1) so $x = 3$, $y = 2$, $z = -2$

EXAMPLE 7   **Left-to-Right Elimination**

Solve: $\begin{cases} x + 2y + 3z = 6 & (1) \\ 2x + 3y + 2z = 6 & (2) \\ -x + y + z = 4 & (3) \end{cases}$

Solution

Using equation (1) to eliminate x from the other equations gives the equivalent system

$\begin{cases} x + 2y + 3z = 6 & (1) \\ -y - 4z = -6 & (2) \qquad (-2) \times \text{equation (1) added to equation (2)} \\ 3y + 4z = 10 & (3) \qquad \text{Equation (1) added to equation (3)} \end{cases}$

Using equation (2) to eliminate y from equation (3) gives

$\begin{cases} x + 2y + 3z = 6 & (1) \\ -y - 4z = -6 & (2) \\ -8z = -8 & (3) \qquad (3) \times \text{equation (2) added to equation (3)} \end{cases}$

In a system of equations such as this, the first variable appearing in each equation is called the **lead variable.** Solving for each lead variable gives

$$x = 6 - 2y - 3z$$
$$y = 6 - 4z$$
$$z = 1$$

Using **back substitution** from the bottom gives

$$z = 1$$
$$y = 6 - 4 = 2$$
$$x = 6 - 4 - 3 = -1$$

Hence, the solution is $x = -1$, $y = 2$, $z = 1$.

Although other methods for solving systems of equations in three variables may be useful, the left-to-right elimination method is important because it is systematic and can easily be extended to larger systems and to systems solved with matrices. (See Section 3.3, "Gauss-Jordan Elimination: Solving Systems of Equations.")

CHECKPOINT

4. Use left-to-right elimination to solve.

$\begin{cases} x - y - z = 0 & (1) \\ y - 2z = -18 & (2) \\ x + y + z = 6 & (3) \end{cases}$

CHECKPOINT
ANSWERS

1. $x = -4$, $y = 3$
2. $x = 100$, $y = -65$
3. (a) Substitution works well in Problem 1 because it is easy to solve for x (or for y). Substitution does not work well in Problem 2 because solving for x (or for y) introduces fractions.
    (b) Elimination would work well in Problem 1 if we multiplied the first equation by 4. As stated in (a), substitution would not be as easy in Problem 2.
4. $x = 3$, $y = -4$, $z = 7$

EXERCISES 1.5

In Problems 1 and 2, decide whether the system of equations in each problem has one solution, no solution, or an infinite number of solutions. If the system has one solution, estimate it.

1. (a)   (b)

2. (a)   (b)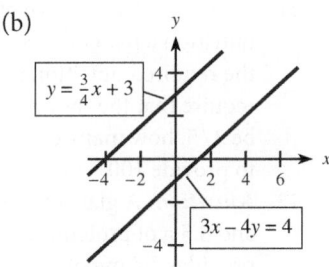

In Problems 3–6, solve the systems of equations by using graphing.

3. $\begin{cases} 4x - 2y = 4 \\ x - 2y = -2 \end{cases}$

4. $\begin{cases} x - y = -2 \\ 2x + y = -1 \end{cases}$

5. $\begin{cases} 3x - y = 10 \\ 6x - 2y = 5 \end{cases}$

6. $\begin{cases} 2x - y = 3 \\ 4x - 2y = 6 \end{cases}$

In Problems 7–10, solve the systems of equations by substitution.

7. $\begin{cases} 3x - 2y = 6 \\ \quad\ \ 4y = 8 \end{cases}$

8. $\begin{cases} 3x \quad\ \ = 6 \\ 4x - 3y = 5 \end{cases}$

9. $\begin{cases} 2x - y = 2 \\ 3x + 4y = 6 \end{cases}$

10. $\begin{cases} 4x - y = 3 \\ 2x + 3y = 19 \end{cases}$

In Problems 11–22, solve each system by elimination or by any convenient method.

11. $\begin{cases} 7x + 2y = 26 \\ 3x - 4y = 16 \end{cases}$

12. $\begin{cases} 2x + 5y = 24 \\ -6x + 2y = 30 \end{cases}$

13. $\begin{cases} 3x + 4y = 1 \\ 2x - 3y = 12 \end{cases}$

14. $\begin{cases} 5x - 2y = 4 \\ 2x - 3y = 5 \end{cases}$

15. $\begin{cases} -4x + 3y = -5 \\ \quad\ 3x - 2y = 4 \end{cases}$

16. $\begin{cases} x + 2y = 3 \\ 3x + 6y = 6 \end{cases}$

17. $\begin{cases} 0.2x - 0.3y = 4 \\ 2.3x - \quad y = 1.2 \end{cases}$

18. $\begin{cases} 0.5x + \quad y = 3 \\ 0.3x + 0.2y = 6 \end{cases}$

19. $\begin{cases} \frac{5}{2}x - \frac{7}{2}y = -1 \\ 8x + 3y = 11 \end{cases}$

20. $\begin{cases} x - \frac{1}{2}y = 1 \\ \frac{2}{3}x - \frac{1}{3}y = 1 \end{cases}$

21. $\begin{cases} 4x + 6y = 4 \\ 2x + 3y = 2 \end{cases}$

22. $\begin{cases} 6x - 4y = 16 \\ 9x - 6y = 24 \end{cases}$

Use a graphing calculator or Excel to find the solution of each system of equations in Problems 23–26.

23. $\begin{cases} y = 8 - \dfrac{3x}{2} \\ y = \dfrac{3x}{4} - 1 \end{cases}$

24. $\begin{cases} y = 9 - \dfrac{2x}{3} \\ y = 5 + \dfrac{2x}{3} \end{cases}$

25. $\begin{cases} 5x + 3y = -2 \\ 3x + 7y = 4 \end{cases}$

26. $\begin{cases} 4x - 5y = -3 \\ 2x - 7y = -6 \end{cases}$

Use the left-to-right elimination method to solve the systems in Problems 27–32.

27. $\begin{cases} x + 2y + z = 2 \\ \quad\ -y + 3z = 8 \\ \qquad\quad 2z = 10 \end{cases}$

28. $\begin{cases} x - 2y + 2z = -10 \\ \quad\ y + 4z = -10 \\ \qquad\ -3z = 9 \end{cases}$

29. $\begin{cases} x - y - 8z = 0 \\ \quad\ y + 4z = 8 \\ \quad\ 3y + 14z = 22 \end{cases}$

30. $\begin{cases} x + 3y - 8z = 20 \\ \quad\ y - 3z = 11 \\ \quad\ 2y + 7z = -4 \end{cases}$

31. $\begin{cases} x + 4y - 2z = 9 \\ x + 5y + 2z = -2 \\ x + 4y - 28z = 22 \end{cases}$

32. $\begin{cases} x - 3y - z = 0 \\ x - 2y + z = 8 \\ 2x - 6y + z = 6 \end{cases}$

APPLICATIONS

33. *Temperatures and traveling* When U.S. citizens travel abroad, they need some understanding of Celsius temperature readings—does one need mittens if the temperature will be 20°C? A quick conversion formula often used by tour guides to give a rough Fahrenheit equivalent for a Celsius reading is

$$F = 2C + 30 \qquad \text{Tourist formula}$$

The exact conversion formula relating these readings is

$$F = 1.8C + 32 \qquad \text{Scientific formula}$$

(a) At what temperatures, Fahrenheit and Celsius, do these formulas agree?

(b) As the Celsius temperature rises above the reading found in part (a), does the tourist formula overestimate or underestimate the actual Fahrenheit temperature? How can you tell this from the two given formulas?

34. *Population distribution* Using U.S. Census Bureau data (and projections to 2050), the percent of the U.S. population that is Black $B(x)$ and Hispanic $H(x)$ can be described by

$$B(x) = 0.057x + 12.3 \quad \text{and} \quad H(x) = 0.224x + 9.01$$

where x is the number of years past 1990.
   (a) In what year were the percents of these groups equal? What was the percent of each?
   (b) Do these models indicate that there were more Blacks or more Hispanics in 2012?

35. *Pricing* A concert promoter needs to make $42,000 from the sale of 1800 tickets. The promoter charges $20 for some tickets and $30 for the others. Let x represent the number of $20 tickets and y represent the number of $30 tickets.
   (a) Write an equation that states that the sum of the tickets sold is 1800.
   (b) How much money is received from the sale of $20 tickets?
   (c) How much money is received from the sale of $30 tickets?
   (d) Write an equation that states that the total amount received from the sale is $42,000.
   (e) Solve the equations simultaneously to find how many tickets of each type must be sold to yield the $42,000.

36. *Rental income* A woman has $500,000 invested in two rental properties. One yields an annual return of 10% on her investment, and the other returns 12% per year on her investment. Her total annual return from the two investments is $53,000. Let x represent the amount of the 10% investment and y represent the amount of the 12% investment.
   (a) Write an equation that states that the sum of the investments is $500,000.
   (b) What is the annual return on the 10% investment?
   (c) What is the annual return on the 12% investment?
   (d) Write an equation that states that the sum of the annual returns is $53,000.
   (e) Solve these two equations simultaneously to find how much is invested in each property.

37. *Investment yields* One safe investment pays 10% per year, and a riskier investment pays 18% per year. A woman who has $145,600 to invest would like to have an income of $20,000 per year from her investments. How much should she invest at each rate?

38. *Loans* Mr. Jackson borrowed money from his bank and on his life insurance to start a business. His interest rate on the bank loan was 10%, and his rate on the insurance loan was 12%. If the total amount borrowed was $100,000 and his total yearly interest payment was $10,900, how much did he borrow from the bank?

39. *Shipping* A freight company has shipping orders for two products. The first product has a unit volume of 10 cu ft and weighs 50 lb. The second product's unit volume is 3 cu ft, and it weighs 40 lb. If the company's trucks have 2300 cu ft of space and can carry 21,000 lb, how many units of each product can be transported in a single shipment with one truck?

40. *Manufacturing* A cake manufacturer boxes Swiss chocolate and German chocolate cakes at one site. A box of Swiss chocolate cake contains 0.55 lb of a sugar mixture and 0.45 lb of flour. A box of German chocolate cake contains 0.59 lb of the sugar mixture and 0.41 lb of flour. Each day at this site, the company has available 2300 lb of the sugar mixture and 1700 lb of flour. How many boxes of each type of cake can be made each day?

41. *Nutrition* Each ounce of substance A supplies 5% of the nutrition a patient needs. Substance B supplies 12% of the required nutrition per ounce. If digestive restrictions require that the ratio of substance A to substance B be 3/5, how many ounces of each should be in the diet to provide 100% of the required nutrition?

42. *Nutrition* A glass of skim milk supplies 0.1 mg of iron and 8.5 g of protein. A quarter pound of lean red meat provides 3.4 mg of iron and 22 g of protein. If a person on a special diet is to have 7.15 mg of iron and 73.75 g of protein, how many glasses of skim milk and how many quarter-pound servings of meat would provide this?

43. *Bacterial growth* Bacteria of species A and species B are kept in a single environment, where they are fed two nutrients. Each day the environment is supplied with 10,600 units of the first nutrient and 19,650 units of the second nutrient. Each bacterium of species A requires 2 units of the first nutrient and 3 units of the second, and each bacterium of species B requires 1 unit of the first nutrient and 4 units of the second. What populations of each species can coexist in the environment so that all the nutrients are consumed each day?

44. *Botany* A biologist has a 40% solution and a 10% solution of the same plant nutrient. How many cubic centimeters of each solution should be mixed to obtain 25 cc of a 28% solution?

45. *Medications* A nurse has two solutions that contain different concentrations of a certain medication. One is a 20% concentration, and the other is a 5% concentration. How many cubic centimeters of each should he mix to obtain 10 cc of a 15.5% solution?

46. *Medications* Medication A is given every 4 hours, and medication B is given twice each day. The total intake of the two medications is restricted to 50.6 mg per day for a certain patient. If the ratio of the dosage of A to the dosage of B is 5 to 8, find the dosage for each administration of each medication.

47. *Pricing* A concert promoter needs to take in $760,000 on the sale of 16,000 tickets. If the promoter charges $40 for some tickets and $60 for others, how many of each type must be sold to yield the $760,000?

48. *Pricing* A nut wholesaler sells a mix of peanuts and cashews. He charges $2.80 per pound for peanuts and $5.30 per pound for cashews. If the mix is to sell for $3.30 per pound, how many pounds each of peanuts and cashews should be used to make 100 pounds of the mix?

49. *Nutrient solutions* How many cubic centimeters of a 20% solution of a nutrient must be added to 100 cc of a 2% solution of the same nutrient to make a 10% solution of the nutrient?

50. *Mixtures* How many gallons of washer fluid that is 13.5% antifreeze must a manufacturer add to 200 gallons of washer fluid that is 11% antifreeze to yield washer fluid that is 13% antifreeze?

Application Problems 51–54 require systems of equations in three variables.

51. *Nutrition* Each ounce of substance A supplies 5% of the nutrition a patient needs. Substance B supplies 15% of the required nutrition per ounce, and substance C supplies 12% of the required nutrition per ounce. If digestive restrictions require that substances A and C be given in equal amounts and the amount of substance B be one-fifth of either of these other amounts, find the number of ounces of each substance that should be in the meal to provide 100% of the required nutrition.

52. *Dietary requirements* A glass of skim milk supplies 0.1 mg of iron, 8.5 g of protein, and 1 g of carbohydrates. A quarter pound of lean red meat provides 3.4 mg of iron, 22 g of protein, and 20 g of carbohydrates. Two slices of whole grain bread supply 2.2 mg of iron, 10 g of protein, and 12 g of carbohydrates. If a person on a special diet must have 10.5 mg of iron, 94.5 g of protein, and 61 g of carbohydrates, how many glasses of skim milk, how many quarter-pound servings of meat, and how many two-slice servings of whole grain bread will supply this?

53. *Social services* A social agency is charged with providing services to three types of clients: A, B, and C. A total of 500 clients are to be served, with $150,000 available for counseling and $100,000 available for emergency food and shelter. Type A clients require an average of $200 for counseling and $300 for emergencies, type B clients require an average of $500 for counseling and $200 for emergencies, and type C clients require an average of $300 for counseling and $100 for emergencies. How many of each type of client can be served?

54. *Social services* If funding for counseling is cut to $135,000 and funding for emergency food and shelter is cut to $90,000, only 450 clients can be served. How many of each type can be served in this case? (See Problem 53.)

SECTION 1.6
Applications of Functions in Business and Economics

OBJECTIVES

- To formulate and evaluate total cost, total revenue, and profit functions
- To find marginal cost, revenue, and profit, given linear total cost, total revenue, and profit functions
- To write the equations of linear total cost, total revenue, and profit functions by using information given about the functions
- To find break-even points
- To evaluate and graph supply and demand functions
- To find market equilibrium

APPLICATION PREVIEW

Suppose a firm manufactures MP3 players and sells them for $50 each, with costs incurred in the production and sale equal to $200,000 plus $10 for each unit produced and sold. Forming the total cost, total revenue, and profit as functions of the quantity x that is produced and sold (see Example 1) is called the theory of the firm. We will also discuss market analysis, in which supply and demand are found as functions of price, and market equilibrium is found.

Total Cost, Total Revenue, and Profit

The **profit** a firm makes on its product is the difference between the amount it receives from sales (its revenue) and its cost. If x units are produced and sold, we can write

$$P(x) = R(x) - C(x)$$

where

$P(x) =$ profit from sale of x units
$R(x) =$ total revenue from sale of x units
$C(x) =$ total cost of production and sale of x units*

*The symbols generally used in economics for total cost, total revenue, and profit are *TC*, *TR*, and π, respectively. To avoid confusion, especially with the use of π as a variable, we do not use these symbols.

In general, **total revenue** is found by using the equation

$$\text{Revenue} = (\text{price per unit})(\text{number of units})$$

The **total cost** is composed of two parts: fixed costs and variable costs. **Fixed costs** (*FC*), such as depreciation, rent, and utilities, remain constant regardless of the number of units produced. **Variable costs** (*VC*) are costs directly related to the number of units produced. Thus the cost is found by using the equation

$$\text{Cost} = \text{variable costs} + \text{fixed costs}$$

EXAMPLE 1   Cost, Revenue, and Profit | APPLICATION PREVIEW |

Suppose a firm manufactures MP3 players and sells them for $50 each. The costs incurred in the production and sale of the MP3 players are $200,000 plus $10 for each player produced and sold. Write the profit function for the production and sale of *x* players.

Solution

The total revenue for *x* MP3 players is $50x$, so the total revenue function is $R(x) = 50x$. The fixed costs are $200,000, so the total cost for *x* players is $10x + 200,000$. Hence, $C(x) = 10x + 200,000$. The profit function is given by $P(x) = R(x) - C(x)$. Thus,

$$P(x) = 50x - (10x + 200,000)$$
$$P(x) = 40x - 200,000$$

Figure 1.31 shows the graphs of $R(x)$, $C(x)$, and $P(x)$.

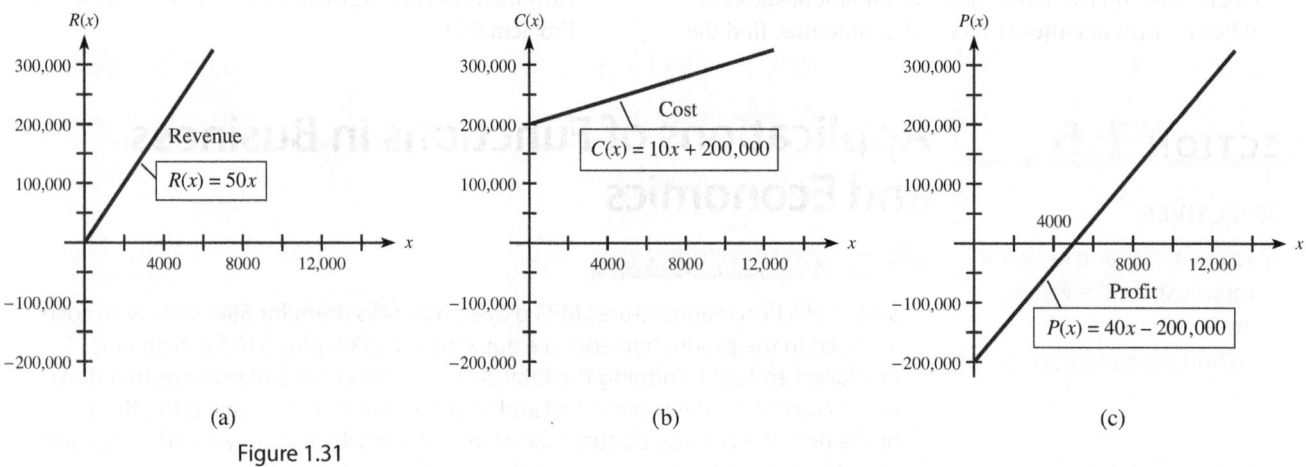

(a)   (b)   (c)

Figure 1.31

By observing the intercepts on the graphs in Figure 1.31, we note the following.

Revenue: 0 units produce 0 revenue; $R(0) = 0$.
   Cost: 0 units' costs equal fixed costs $= \$200,000$; $C(0) = FC = 200,000$.
  Profit: 0 units yield a loss equal to fixed costs $= \$200,000$;
           $P(0) = -FC = -200,000$.
           5000 units result in a profit of $0 (no loss or gain); $P(5000) = 0$.

Marginals   In Example 1, both the total revenue function and the total cost function are linear, so their difference, the profit function, is also linear. The slope of the profit function represents the rate of change in profit with respect to the number of units produced and sold. This is called the **marginal profit** ($\overline{MP}$) for the product. Thus the marginal profit for the MP3 players in Example 1 is $40. Similarly, the **marginal cost** ($\overline{MC}$) for this product is $10 (the slope of the cost function) and the **marginal revenue** $(\overline{MR})$ is \$50 (the slope of the revenue function).

EXAMPLE 2   **Marginal Cost**

Suppose that the cost (in dollars) for a product is $C = 21.75x + 4890$. What is the marginal cost for this product, and what does it mean?

Solution
The equation has the form $C = mx + b$, so the slope is 21.75. Thus the marginal cost is $\overline{MC} = 21.75$ dollars per unit.

Because the marginal cost is the slope of the cost line, production of each additional unit will cost \$21.75 more, at any level of production.

Note that when total cost functions are linear, the marginal cost is the same as the variable cost per unit. This is not the case if the functions are not linear, as we shall see later.

CHECKPOINT

1. Suppose that when a company produces its product, fixed costs are \$12,500 and variable cost per item is \$75.
   (a) Write the total cost function if x represents the number of units.
   (b) Are fixed costs equal to $C(0)$?
2. Suppose the company in Problem 1 sells its product for \$175 per item.
   (a) Write the total revenue function.
   (b) Find $R(100)$ and give its meaning.
3. (a) Give the formula for profit in terms of revenue and cost.
   (b) Find the profit function for the company in Problems 1 and 2.

Break-Even Analysis   We can solve the equations for total revenue and total cost simultaneously to find the point where cost and revenue are equal. This point is called the **break-even point.** Graphically, the break-even point is the point of intersection of the graphs of the total revenue function and the total cost function.

EXAMPLE 3   **Break-Even**

A manufacturer sells a product for \$10 per unit. The manufacturer's variable costs are \$2.50 per unit, and the total cost of 100 units is \$1450. How many units must the manufacturer produce each day to break even?

Solution
The total revenue for x units of the product is $10x$, so the equation for total revenue is $R = R(x) = 10x$. The equation for total cost is

$$C - 1450 = 2.50(x - 100) \quad \text{or} \quad C = C(x) = 2.50x + 1200$$

To find the break-even point, solve the two equations simultaneously ($R = C$ at the break-even point). By substitution,

$$10x = 2.50x + 1200$$
$$7.5x = 1200 \quad \text{so} \quad x = 160$$

Thus the manufacturer will break even if 160 units are produced per day. The manufacturer will make a profit if more than 160 units are produced. Figure 1.32 shows that for $x < 160$, $R(x) < C(x)$ (resulting in a loss) and that for $x > 160$, $R(x) > C(x)$ (resulting in a profit).

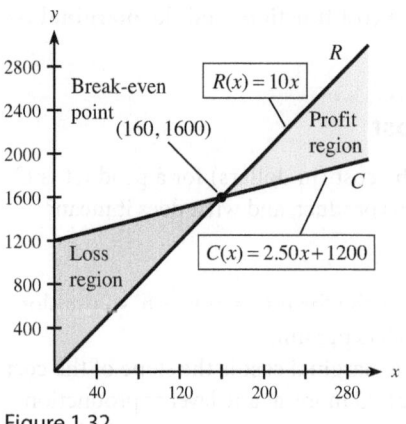

Figure 1.32

Figure 1.33

The profit function for Example 3 is given by

$$P(x) = R(x) - C(x) = 10x - (2.50x + 1200) \quad \text{or} \quad P(x) = 7.50x - 1200$$

We can find the point where the profit is zero (the break-even point) by setting $P(x) = 0$ and solving for x.

$$0 = 7.50x - 1200 \Rightarrow 1200 = 7.50x \Rightarrow x = 160$$

Note that this is the same break-even quantity that we found by solving the total revenue and total cost equations simultaneously (see Figure 1.33).

CHECKPOINT

4. Identify two ways in which break-even can be found.

Supply, Demand, and Market Equilibrium

Economists and managers also use points of intersection to determine market equilibrium. **Market equilibrium** occurs when the quantity of a commodity demanded is equal to the quantity supplied.

Demand by consumers for a commodity is related to the price of the commodity. The **law of demand** states that the quantity demanded will increase as price decreases and that the quantity demanded will decrease as price increases. The **law of supply** states that the quantity supplied for sale will increase as the price of a product increases. Note that although quantity demanded and quantity supplied are both functions of price p, economists traditionally graph these with price on the vertical axis. We will follow this tradition (see Figure 1.34).

Figure 1.34

If the supply and demand curves for a commodity are graphed on the same coordinate system, with the same units, market equilibrium occurs at the point where the curves intersect. The price at that point is the **equilibrium price,** and the quantity at that point is the **equilibrium quantity.**

For the supply and demand functions shown in Figure 1.34, we see that the curves intersect at the point (150, 20). This means that when the price is $20, consumers are willing to purchase the same number of units (150) that producers are willing to supply.

In general, the equilibrium price and the equilibrium quantity must both be positive for the market equilibrium to have meaning.

EXAMPLE 4 — Market Equilibrium

Find the market equilibrium point for the following supply and demand functions.

$$\text{Demand:} \quad p = -3q + 36$$
$$\text{Supply:} \quad p = 4q + 1$$

Solution

At market equilibrium, the demand price equals the supply price. Thus

$$-3q + 36 = 4q + 1$$
$$35 = 7q$$
$$q = 5$$
$$p = 21$$

The equilibrium point is (5, 21).
Checking, we see that

$$21 = -3(5) + 36 \checkmark \qquad \text{and} \qquad 21 = 4(5) + 1 \checkmark$$

Spreadsheet Note   We can use Goal Seek with Excel to find the market equilibrium for given supply and demand functions, as we did to find solutions of systems in Section 1.5. The following spreadsheets show the Excel setup and solution for the market equilibrium problem of Example 4.

	A	B	C	D
1	q	p: demand	p: supply	demand − supply
2	1	= −3*A2 + 36	= 4*A2 + 1	= B2 − C2

	A	B	C	D
1	q	p: demand	p: supply	demand − supply
2	5	21	21	0

EXAMPLE 5 — Market Equilibrium

A group of wholesalers will buy 50 dryers per month if the price is $200 and 30 per month if the price is $300. The manufacturer is willing to supply 20 if the price is $210 and 30 if the price is $230. Assuming that the resulting supply and demand functions are linear, find the equilibrium point for the market.

Solution

Representing price by p and quantity by q, we can write the equations for the supply and demand functions as follows.

Demand function:

$$m = \frac{300 - 200}{30 - 50} = -5$$
$$p - 200 = -5(q - 50)$$
$$p = -5q + 450$$

Supply function:

$$m = \frac{230 - 210}{30 - 20} = 2$$
$$p - 230 = 2(q - 30)$$
$$p = 2q + 170$$

Because the prices are equal at market equilibrium, we have

$$-5q + 450 = 2q + 170$$
$$280 = 7q$$
$$q = 40$$
$$p = 250$$

The equilibrium point is (40, 250). See Figure 1.35 for the graphs of these functions.

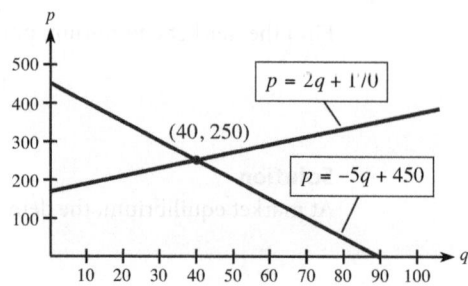

Figure 1.35

---

5. (a) Does a typical linear demand function have positive slope or negative slope? Why?
   (b) Does a typical linear supply function have positive slope or negative slope? Why?
6. (a) What do we call the point of intersection of a supply function and a demand function?
   (b) If supply is given by $p = 0.1q + 20$ and demand is given by $p = 130 - 0.1q$, find the market equilibrium point.

Supply and Demand with Taxation

Suppose a supplier is taxed \$K per unit sold, and the tax is passed on to the consumer by adding \$K to the selling price of the product. If the original supply function $p = f(q)$ gives the supply price per unit, then passing the tax on gives a new supply function, $p = f(q) + K$. Because the value of the product is not changed by the tax, the demand function is unchanged. Figure 1.36 shows the effect this has on market equilibrium.

Figure 1.36

Note that the new market equilibrium point is the point of intersection of the original demand function and the new (after-tax) supply function.

EXAMPLE   6   Taxation

In Example 5, the supply and demand functions for dryers were given as follows.

$$\text{Supply:} \quad p = 2q + 170$$
$$\text{Demand:} \quad p = -5q + 450$$

The equilibrium point was $q = 40$, $p = \$250$. If the wholesaler is taxed \$14 per unit sold, what is the new equilibrium point?

Solution

The $14 tax per unit is passed on by the wholesaler, so the new supply function is

$$p = 2q + 170 + 14$$

and the demand function is unchanged. Thus we solve the system

$$\begin{cases} p = 2q + 184 \\ p = -5q + 450 \end{cases}$$

$$2q + 184 = -5q + 450$$

$$7q = 266$$

Thus $q = 38$,   so $p = 2(38) + 184 = 260$.

The new equilibrium point is $q = 38$, $p = 260$, meaning that 38 dryers are sold per month at $260 each.

Checking: $260 = 2(38) + 184$ ✔   and $260 = -5(38) + 450$ ✔   ∎

CHECKPOINT
ANSWERS

1. (a) $C(x) = 75x + 12,500$
    (b) Yes. $C(0) = 12,500 = $ Fixed costs.
2. (a) $R(x) = 175x$
    (b) $R(100) = 17,500$; revenue is $17,500 when 100 units are sold.
3. (a) Profit $=$ Revenue $-$ Cost or $P(x) = R(x) - C(x)$
    (b) $P(x) = 100x - 12,500$
4. Break-even occurs where $R(x) = C(x)$ or where $P(x) = 0$.
5. (a) Negative slope because demand falls as price increases.
    (b) Positive slope because supply increases as price increases.
6. (a) Market equilibrium
    (b) $q = 550$, $p = 75$

EXERCISES 1.6

TOTAL COST, TOTAL REVENUE, AND PROFIT

1. Suppose a calculator manufacturer has the total cost function $C(x) = 34x + 6800$ and the total revenue function $R(x) = 68x$.
    (a) What is the equation of the profit function for the calculator?
    (b) What is the profit on 3000 units?
2. Suppose a television manufacturer has the total cost function $C(x) = 210x + 3300$ and the total revenue function $R(x) = 430x$.
    (a) What is the equation of the profit function for this commodity?
    (b) What is the profit on 500 items?
3. Suppose a ceiling fan manufacturer has the total cost function $C(x) = 43x + 1850$ and the total revenue function $R(x) = 80x$.
    (a) What is the equation of the profit function for this commodity?
    (b) What is the profit on 30 units? Interpret your result.
    (c) How many fans must be sold to avoid losing money?

4. Suppose a computer manufacturer has the total cost function $C(x) = 85x + 3300$ and the total revenue function $R(x) = 385x$.
    (a) What is the equation of the profit function for this commodity?
    (b) What is the profit on 351 items?
    (c) How many items must be sold to avoid losing money?
5. A linear cost function is $C(x) = 5x + 250$.
    (a) What are the slope and the C-intercept?
    (b) What is the marginal cost, and what does it mean?
    (c) What are the fixed costs?
    (d) How are your answers to parts (a), (b), and (c) related?
    (e) What is the cost of producing *one more* item if 50 are currently being produced? What is the cost if 100 are currently being produced?
6. A linear cost function is $C(x) = 27.55x + 5180$.
    (a) What are the slope and the C-intercept?
    (b) What is the marginal cost, and what does it mean?
    (c) What are the fixed costs?

(d) How are your answers to parts (a), (b), and (c) related?

(e) What is the cost of producing *one more* item if 50 are currently being produced? What is the cost if 100 are currently being produced?

7. A linear revenue function is $R = 27x$.
   (a) What is the slope?
   (b) What is the marginal revenue, and what does it mean?
   (c) What is the revenue received from selling *one more* item if 50 are currently being sold? If 100 are being sold?

8. A linear revenue function is $R = 38.95x$.
   (a) What is the slope?
   (b) What is the marginal revenue, and what does it mean?
   (c) What is the revenue received from selling *one more* item if 50 are currently being sold? If 100 are being sold?

9. Let $C(x) = 5x + 250$ and $R(x) = 27x$.
   (a) Write the profit function $P(x)$.
   (b) What is the slope of the profit function?
   (c) What is the marginal profit?
   (d) Interpret the marginal profit.

10. Given $C(x) = 21.95x + 1400$ and $R(x) = 20x$, find the profit function.
    (a) What is the marginal profit, and what does it mean?
    (b) What should a firm with these cost, revenue, and profit functions do? (*Hint:* Graph the profit function and see where it goes.)

11. A company charting its profits notices that the relationship between the number of units sold, x, and the profit, P, is linear. If 200 units sold results in $3100 profit and 250 units sold results in $6000 profit, write the profit function for this company. Find the marginal profit.

12. Suppose that the total cost function for a bluetooth dock is linear, that the marginal cost is $54, and that the total cost for 50 bluetooth docks is $8700. Write the equation of this cost function and then graph it.

13. Extreme Protection Inc. manufactures helmets for skiing and snow boarding. The fixed costs for one model of helmet are $6600 per month. Materials and labor for each helmet of this model are $35, and the company sells this helmet to dealers for $60 each.
    (a) For this helmet, write the function for monthly total costs.
    (b) Write the function for total revenue.
    (c) Write the function for profit.
    (d) Find $C(200)$, $R(200)$, and $P(200)$ and interpret each answer.
    (e) Find $C(300)$, $R(300)$, and $P(300)$ and interpret each answer.
    (f) Find the marginal profit and write a sentence that explains its meaning.

14. A manufacturer of DVD players has weekly fixed costs of $1540 and variable costs of $12.50 per unit for one particular model. The company sells this model to dealers for $19.50 each.
    (a) For this DVD player, write the function for weekly total costs.
    (b) Write the function for total revenue.
    (c) Write the function for profit.
    (d) Find $C(200)$, $R(200)$, and $P(200)$ and interpret each answer.
    (e) Find $C(250)$, $R(250)$, and $P(250)$ and interpret each answer.
    (f) Find the marginal profit and write a sentence that explains its meaning.

BREAK-EVEN ANALYSIS

15. The figure shows graphs of the total cost function and the total revenue function for a commodity.

    (a) Label each function correctly.
    (b) Determine the fixed costs.
    (c) Locate the break-even point and determine the number of units sold to break even.
    (d) Estimate the marginal cost and marginal revenue.

16. A manufacturer of shower surrounds has a revenue function of

$$R(x) = 81.50x$$

and a cost function of

$$C(x) = 63x + 1850$$

Find the number of units that must be sold to break even.

17. A jewelry maker incurs costs for a necklace according to

$$C(x) = 35x + 1650$$

If the revenue function for the necklaces is

$$R(x) = 85x$$

how many necklaces must be sold to break even?

18. A small business sells custom oak moldings in 12-foot lengths. One molding type has the revenue function

$$R(x) = 69x$$

and the cost function

$$C(x) = 1400 + 55x$$

Find the number of 12-foot lengths of this molding that must be sold to break even.

19. A manufacturer sells belts for $12 per unit. The fixed costs are $1600 per month, and the variable cost per unit is $8.
   (a) Write the equations of the revenue and cost functions.
   (b) Find the break-even point.

20. A manufacturer sells watches for $50 per unit. The fixed cost related to this product is $10,000 per month, and the variable cost per unit is $30.
   (a) Write the equations of the revenue and cost functions.
   (b) How many watches must be sold to break even?

21. (a) Write the profit function for Problem 19.
   (b) Set profit equal to zero and solve for x. Compare this x-value with the break-even point from Problem 19(b).

22. (a) Write the profit function for Problem 20.
   (b) Set profit equal to zero and solve for x. Compare this x-value with the break-even point from Problem 20(b).

23. Electronic equipment manufacturer Dynamo Electric Inc. makes several types of surge protectors. Their base model surge protector has monthly fixed costs of $1045. This particular model wholesales for $10 each and costs $4.50 per unit to manufacture.
   (a) Write the function for Dynamo's monthly total costs.
   (b) Write the function for Dynamo's monthly total revenue.
   (c) Write the function for Dynamo's monthly profit.
   (d) Find the number of this type of surge protector that Dynamo must produce and sell each month to break even.

24. Financial Paper Inc. is a printer of checks and forms for financial institutions. For individual accounts, boxes of 200 checks cost $0.80 per box to print and package and sell for $4.95 each. Financial Paper's monthly fixed costs for printing and packaging these checks for individuals are $1245.
   (a) Write the function for Financial Paper's monthly total costs.
   (b) Write the function for Financial Paper's monthly total revenue.
   (c) Write the function for Financial Paper's monthly profit.
   (d) Find the number of orders for boxes of checks for individual accounts that Financial Paper must receive and fill each month to break even.

25. A company manufactures and sells bookcases. The selling price is $54.90 per bookcase. The total cost function is linear, and costs amount to $50,000 for 2000 bookcases and $32,120 for 800 bookcases.
   (a) Write the equation for revenue.
   (b) Write the equation for total costs.
   (c) Find the break-even quantity.

26. A company distributes college logo sweatshirts and sells them for $50 each. The total cost function is linear, and the total cost for 100 sweatshirts is $4360, whereas the total cost for 250 sweatshirts is $7060.
   (a) Write the equation for the revenue function.
   (b) Write the equation for the total cost function.
   (c) Find the break-even quantity.

In Problems 27 and 28, *some* of the graphs of total revenue (R), total cost (C), variable cost (VC), fixed cost (FC), and profit (P) are shown as functions of the number of units, x.
   (a) Correctly label the graphs shown.
   (b) Carefully sketch and label the graphs of the other functions. Explain your method.

27. $ 28. $

SUPPLY, DEMAND, AND MARKET EQUILIBRIUM

29. As the price of a commodity increases, what happens to demand?

30. As the price of a commodity increases, what happens to supply?

The graphs of the demand function and supply function for a certain product are given below. Use these graphs to answer the questions in Problems 31 and 32.

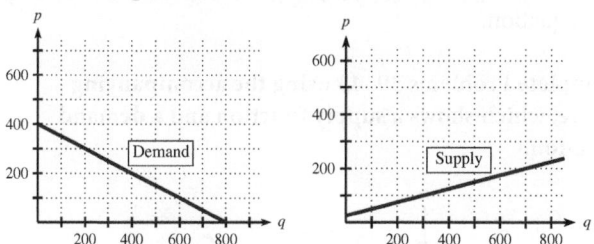

31. (a) How many units q are *demanded* when the price p is $100?
   (b) How many units q are *supplied* when the price p is $100?
   (c) Will there be a market surplus (more supplied) or shortage (more demanded) when p = $100?

32. (a) How many units q are *demanded* when the price p is $200?
    (b) How many units q are *supplied* when the price p is $200?
    (c) Will there be a market surplus or shortage when the price p is $200?

33. If the demand for a pair of shoes is given by $2p + 5q = 200$ and the supply function for it is $p - 2q = 10$, compare the quantity demanded and the quantity supplied when the price is $60. Will there be a surplus or shortfall at this price?

34. If the demand function and supply function for Z-brand juicers are $p + 2q = 100$ and $35p - 20q = 350$, respectively, compare the quantity demanded and the quantity supplied when $p = 14$. Are there surplus juicers or not enough to meet demand?

35. Suppose a certain outlet chain selling appliances has found that for one brand of home theater, the monthly demand is 240 when the price is $900. However, when the price is $850, the monthly demand is 315. Assuming that the demand function for this system is linear, write the equation for the demand function. Use p for price and q for quantity.

36. Suppose a certain home improvement outlet knows that the monthly demand for framing studs is 2500 when the price is $4.00 each but that the demand is 3500 when the price is $3.60 each. Assuming that the demand function is linear, write its equation. Use p for price and q for quantity.

37. Suppose the manufacturer of a custom board game will supply 10,000 games if the wholesale price is $15 each but will supply only 5000 if the price is $10 each. Assuming that the supply function is linear, write its equation. Use p for price and q for quantity.

38. Suppose a mining company will supply 100,000 tons of ore per month if the price is $30 per ton but will supply only 80,000 tons per month if the price is $25 per ton. Assuming that the supply function is linear, write its equation.

Complete Problems 39–43 using the accompanying figure, which shows a supply function and a demand function.

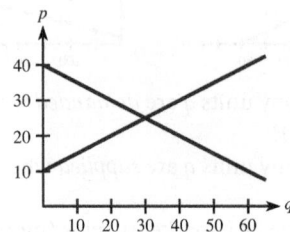

39. (a) Label each function as "demand" or "supply."
    (b) Label the equilibrium point and determine the price and quantity at which market equilibrium occurs.

40. (a) If the price is $30, what quantity is demanded?
    (b) If the price is $30, what quantity is supplied?
    (c) Is there a surplus or shortage when the price is $30? How many units is this surplus or shortage?

41. (a) If the price is $20, what quantity is supplied?
    (b) If the price is $20, what quantity is demanded?
    (c) Is there a surplus or a shortage when the price is $20? How many units is this surplus or shortage?

42. Will a price above the equilibrium price result in a market surplus or shortage?

43. Will a price below the equilibrium price result in a market surplus or shortage?

44. Find the market equilibrium point for the following demand and supply functions.

$$\text{Demand: } p = -2q + 320$$
$$\text{Supply: } p = 8q + 2$$

45. Find the market equilibrium point for the following demand and supply functions.

$$\text{Demand: } \quad 2p = -q + 56$$
$$\text{Supply: } 3p - q = 34$$

46. Find the equilibrium point for the following supply and demand functions.

$$\text{Demand: } p = 480 - 3q$$
$$\text{Supply: } p = 17q + 80$$

47. Find the equilibrium point for the following supply and demand functions.

$$\text{Demand: } p = -4q + 220$$
$$\text{Supply: } p = 15q + 30$$

48. Retailers will buy 45 Wi-Fi routers from a wholesaler if the price is $10 each but only 20 if the price is $60. The wholesaler will supply 56 routers at $42 each and 70 at $50 each. Assuming that the supply and demand functions are linear, find the market equilibrium point.

49. A group of retailers will buy 80 televisions from a wholesaler if the price is $350 and 120 if the price is $300. The wholesaler is willing to supply 60 if the price is $280 and 140 if the price is $370. Assuming that the resulting supply and demand functions are linear, find the equilibrium point for the market.

50. Stutz Department Store will buy 10 pairs of sunglasses if the price is $75 per pair and 30 pairs if the price is $25. The supplier of the sunglasses is willing to provide 35 pairs if the price is $80 per pair but only 5 pairs if the price is $20. Assuming that the supply and demand functions for the sunglasses are linear, find the market equilibrium point.

Problems 51–58 involve market equilibrium after a given tax is passed on to the consumer.
Use the following figure to answer Problems 51 and 52.

51. (a) What is the amount of the tax?
    (b) What are the original equilibrium price and quantity?
    (c) What are the new equilibrium price and quantity?
    (d) Does the supplier suffer from the tax even though it is passed on?
52. (a) If the tax is doubled, how many units will be sold?
    (b) Can a government lose money by increasing taxes?
53. If a $38 tax is placed on each unit of the product of Problem 47, what are the new equilibrium price and quantity?

54. If a $56 tax is placed on each unit of the product of Problem 46, what is the new equilibrium point?
55. Suppose that a certain product has the following demand and supply functions.

$$\text{Demand: } p = -0.05q + 65$$
$$\text{Supply: } p = 0.05q + 10$$

If a $5 tax per item is levied, find the market equilibrium point after the tax.
56. Suppose that a certain product has the following demand and supply functions.

$$\text{Demand: } p = -8q + 2800$$
$$\text{Supply: } p = 3q + 35$$

If a $15 tax per item is levied, find the market equilibrium point after the tax.
57. Suppose that in a certain market, the demand function for a product is given by $60p + q = 2100$ and the supply function is given by $120p - q = 540$. Then a tax of $0.50 per item is levied. Find the equilibrium price and quantity after the tax is levied.
58. Suppose that in a certain market, the demand function for a product is given by $10p + q = 2300$ and the supply function is given by $45p - q = 360$. If the government levies a tax of $2 per item, find the equilibrium price and quantity after the tax is levied.

CHAPTER SUMMARY & REVIEW

KEY TERMS AND FORMULAS

Section 1.1

Equation; variable; solution (p. 53)
Identities; conditional equations (p. 53)
Properties of equality (p. 53)
Solving a linear equation (p. 54)
Aligning the data (p. 54)

Fractional equation (p. 55)
Linear equation in two variables (p. 56)
Linear inequalities (p. 57)
   Properties
   Solutions

Section 1.2

Relation (p. 63)
Function (p. 64)
   Vertical-line test
   Domain, range
Coordinate system (p. 64)
   Ordered pair, origin, x-axis, y-axis

Graph (p. 65)
Function notation (p. 66)
Operations with functions (p. 68)
Composite functions (p. 69)
   $(f \circ g)(x) = f(g(x))$

Section 1.3

Linear function (p. 75)
$$y = ax + b$$
Intercepts (p. 75)
  x-intercept (zero of a function)
    where $y = 0$
  y-intercept
    where $x = 0$
Slope of a line (p. 77)
  Rate of change
$$m = \frac{y_2 - y_1}{x_2 - x_1}$$

Parallel lines (p. 78)
  $$m_1 = m_2$$
Perpendicular lines (p. 79)
  $$m_2 = -1/m_1$$
Point-slope form (p. 79)
  $$y - y_1 = m(x - x_1)$$
Vertical line (p. 80)
  $$x = a$$
Horizontal line (p. 80)
  $$y = b$$
Slope-intercept form (p. 81)
  $$y = mx + b$$

Section 1.4

Graphing utilities (p. 86)
Standard viewing window (p. 86)
Complete graph (p. 86)
Evaluating functions (p. 86)

x-intercept (p. 88)
Solutions of equations (p. 88)
  x-intercept method
Zeros of functions (p. 88)

Section 1.5

Systems of linear equations (p. 93)
Solutions (p. 93)
  Graphical solutions
Inconsistent system (p. 93)
Dependent system (p. 93)
Equivalent systems (p. 94)

Substitution method (p. 94)
Elimination method (p. 95)
Left-to-right elimination method (p. 99)
  Lead variable
  Back substitution

Section 1.6

Cost and revenue functions (p. 103)
  $C(x)$ and $R(x)$
Profit functions (p. 103)
  $$P(x) = R(x) - C(x)$$
Marginal profit (p. 104)
  Slope of linear profit function
Marginal cost (p. 104)
  Slope of linear cost function

Marginal revenue (p. 105)
  Slope of linear revenue function
Break-even point (p. 105)
  $C(x) = R(x)$ or $P(x) = 0$
Supply and demand functions (p. 106)
Market equilibrium (p. 106)

REVIEW EXERCISES

Section 1.1

Solve the equations in Problems 1–6.

1. $3x - 8 = 23$

2. $2x - 8 = 3x + 5$

3. $\dfrac{6x + 3}{6} = \dfrac{5(x - 2)}{9}$

4. $2x + \dfrac{1}{2} = \dfrac{x}{2} + \dfrac{1}{3}$

5. $\dfrac{6}{3x - 5} = \dfrac{6}{2x + 3}$

6. $\dfrac{2x + 5}{x + 7} = \dfrac{1}{3} + \dfrac{x - 11}{2x + 14}$

7. Solve for y: $3(y - 2) = -2(x + 5)$

In Problems 8–10, solve the inequality and graph the solution.

8. $3x - 9 \le 4(3 - x)$

9. $\dfrac{2x}{5} \le x + 4$

10. $5x + 1 \ge \dfrac{2}{3}(x - 6)$

Section 1.2

11. If $p = 3q^3$, is p a function of q?

12. If $y^2 = 9x$, is y a function of x?

13. If $R = \sqrt[3]{x} + 4$, is R a function of x?

14. What are the domain and range of the function $y = \sqrt{9 - x}$?

15. If $f(x) = x^2 + 4x + 5$, find the following.

    (a) $f(-3)$ (b) $f(4)$ (c) $f\left(\dfrac{1}{2}\right)$

16. If $g(x) = x^2 + 1/x$, find the following.

    (a)$g(-1)$ (b) $g\left(\dfrac{1}{2}\right)$ (c) $g(0.1)$

17. If $f(x) = 9x - x^2$, find $\dfrac{f(x+h) - f(x)}{h}$ and simplify.

In Problems 18 and 19, determine whether each graph represents y as a function of x.

18.

19.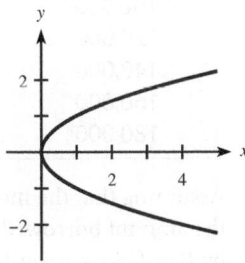

20. For the function f graphed in Exercise 18, what is $f(2)$?
21. For the function f graphed in Exercise 18, for what values of x does $f(x) = 0$?
22. The following table defines y as a function of x, denoted $y = f(x)$.

x	-2	-1	0	1	3	4
y	8	2	-3	4	2	7

    Use the table to complete the following.
    (a) Identify the domain and range of $y = f(x)$.
    (b) Find $f(4)$.
    (c) Find all x-values for which $f(x) = 2$.
    (d) Graph $y = f(x)$.
    (e) Does the table define x as a function of y? Explain.
23. If $f(x) = 3x + 5$ and $g(x) = x^2$, find
    (a) $(f + g)(x)$ (b) $(f/g)(x)$
    (c) $f(g(x))$ (d) $(f \circ f)(x)$

Section 1.3

In Problems 24–26, find the intercepts and graph.
24. $5x + 2y = 10$ 25. $6x + 5y = 9$ 26. $x = -2$

In Problems 27 and 28, find the slope of the line that passes through each pair of points.
27. $(2, -1)$ and $(-1, -4)$
28. $(-3.8, -7.16)$ and $(-3.8, 1.16)$

In Problems 29 and 30, find the slope and y-intercept of each line.
29. $2x + 5y = 10$ 30. $x = -\dfrac{3}{4}y + \dfrac{3}{2}$

In Problems 31–38, write the equation of each line described.
31. Slope 4 and y-intercept 2
32. Slope $-\frac{1}{2}$ and y-intercept 3

33. Through $(-2, 1)$ with slope $\frac{2}{5}$
34. Through $(-2, 7)$ and $(6, -4)$
35. Through $(-1, 8)$ and $(-1, -1)$
36. Through $(1, 6)$ and parallel to $y = 4x - 6$
37. Through $(-1, 2)$ and perpendicular to $3x + 4y = 12$
38. Shown in the graph

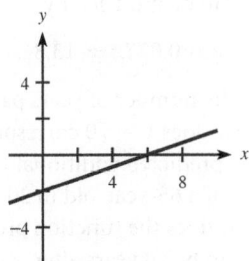

Section 1.4

In Problems 39 and 40, graph each equation with a graphing calculator and the standard viewing window.
39. $x^2 + y - 2x - 3 = 0$ 40. $y = \dfrac{x^3 - 27x + 54}{15}$

In Problems 41 and 42, use a graphing calculator and
    (a) **graph each equation in the viewing window given.**
    (b) **graph each equation in the standard viewing window.**
    (c) **explain how the two views differ and why.**
41. $y = (x + 6)(x - 3)(x - 15)$ with x-min $= -15$, x-max $= 25$; y-min $= -700$, y-max $= 500$
42. $y = x^2 - x - 42$ with x-min $= -15$, x-max $= 15$; y-min $= -50$, y-max $= 50$
43. What is the domain of $y = \dfrac{\sqrt{x + 3}}{x}$? Check with a graphing utility.
44. Use a graphing calculator and the x-intercept method to approximate the solution of $7x - 2 = 0$.

Section 1.5

In Problems 45–51, solve each system of equations.

45. $\begin{cases} 4x - 2y = 6 \\ 3x + 3y = 9 \end{cases}$ 46. $\begin{cases} 2x + y = 19 \\ x - 2y = 12 \end{cases}$

47. $\begin{cases} 3x + 2y = 5 \\ 2x - 3y = 12 \end{cases}$ 48. $\begin{cases} 6x + 3y = 1 \\ y = -2x + 1 \end{cases}$

49. $\begin{cases} 4x - 3y = 253 \\ 13x + 2y = -12 \end{cases}$ 50. $\begin{cases} x + 2y + 3z = 5 \\ y + 11z = 21 \\ 5y + 9z = 13 \end{cases}$

51. $\begin{cases} x + y - z = 12 \\ 2y - 3z = -7 \\ 3x + 3y - 7z = 0 \end{cases}$

APPLICATIONS

Section 1.1

52. *Life expectancy at age 65* Using Social Security Administration data for selected years from 1950 and projected to 2050, the additional years of life expectancy at age 65 can be modeled by

$$y = 0.077x + 13.8$$

where x equals the number of years past 1950.
(a) To what year does $x = 70$ correspond?
(b) What is the predicted additional years of life expectancy of a 65-year-old in 2050?
(c) In what year does the function predict the life expectancy to be 20 years after age 65?

53. *Course grades* In a certain course, grades are based on three tests worth 100 points each, three quizzes worth 50 points each, and a final exam worth 200 points. A student has test grades of 91, 82, and 88 and quiz grades of 50, 42, and 42. What is the lowest percent the student can get on the final and still earn an A (90% or more of the total points) in the course?

54. *Cost analysis* The owner of a small construction business needs a new truck. He can buy a diesel truck for $58,000, and it will cost him $0.76 per mile to operate. He can buy a gas engine truck for $53,200, and it will cost him $0.88 per mile to operate. Find the number of miles he must drive before the costs are equal. If he normally keeps a truck for 7 years, which is the better buy?

Section 1.2

55. *Heart disease risk* The Multiple Risk Factor Intervention Trial (MRFIT) used data from 356,222 men ages 35 to 57 to investigate the relationship between serum cholesterol and coronary heart disease (CHD) risk. The following figure shows the graph of the relationship of CHD risk and cholesterol, where a risk of 1 is assigned to 200 mg/dl of serum cholesterol and the CHD risk is 4 times as high when serum cholesterol is 300 mg/dl.

(a) Does this graph indicate that the CHD risk is a function of the serum cholesterol?
(b) Is the relationship a linear function?
(c) If CHD risk is a function f of serum cholesterol, what is $f(300)$?

56. *Mortgage loans* When a couple purchases a home, one of the first questions they face deals with the relationship between the amount borrowed and the monthly payment. In particular, if a bank offers 25-year loans at 7% interest, then the data in the following table would apply.

Amount Borrowed	Monthly Payment
$100,000	$706.78
120,000	848.14
140,000	989.49
160,000	1130.85
180,000	1272.20

Assuming that the monthly payment P is a function of the amount borrowed A (in thousands) and is denoted by $P = f(A)$, answer the following.
(a) Find $f(140)$.
(b) Find A if $f(A) = 1272.20$.
(c) Write a sentence that explains the meaning of $f(160) = 1130.85$.

57. *Profit* Suppose that the profit from the production and sale of x units of a product is given by

$$P(x) = 330x - 0.05x^2 - 5000$$

In addition, suppose that for a certain month, the number of units produced on day t of the month is

$$x = q(t) = 100 + 10t$$

(a) Find $(P \circ q)(t)$ to express the profit as a function of the day of the month.
(b) Find the number of units produced, and the profit, on the fifteenth day of the month.

58. *Fish species growth* For many species of fish, the weight W is a function of the length L that can be expressed by

$$W = W(L) = kL^3 \qquad k = \text{constant}$$

Suppose that for a particular species, $k = 0.03$ and that for this species, the length (in centimeters) is a function of the number of years t the fish has been alive and that this function is given by

$$L = L(t) = 65 - 0.1(t - 25)^2 \qquad 0 \le t \le 25$$

Find $(W \circ L)(t)$ to express W as a function of the age t of the fish.

Section 1.3

59. *Distance to a thunderstorm* The distance d (in miles) to a thunderstorm is given by

$$d = \frac{t}{4.8}$$

where t is the number of seconds that elapse between seeing the lightning and hearing the thunder.
(a) Graph this function for $0 \le t \le 20$.
(b) The point (9.6, 2) satisfies the equation. Explain its meaning.

60. *Body-heat loss* Body-heat loss due to convection depends on a number of factors. If H_c is body-heat loss due to convection, A_c is the exposed surface area of the body, $T_s - T_a$ is skin temperature minus air temperature, and K_c is the convection coefficient (determined by factors including air velocity), then we have

$$H_c = K_c A_c (T_s - T_a)$$

When $K_c = 1$, $A_c = 1$, and $T_s = 90$, the equation is

$$H_c = 90 - T_a$$

Sketch the graph.

61. *Profit* A company charting its profits notices that the relationship between the number of units sold, x, and the profit, P, is linear.
(a) If 200 units sold results in $3100 profit and 250 units sold results in $6000 profit, write the profit function for this company.
(b) Interpret the slope from part (a) as a rate of change.

62. *Health care costs* The average annual cost per consumer for health care can be modeled by

$$A = 476x + 5830$$

where x is the number of years from 2005 and projected to 2024 (*Source*: U.S. Census Bureau and U.S. Centers for Medicare and Medicaid Services).
(a) Is A a linear function of x?
(b) Find the slope and A-intercept of this function.
(c) Write a sentence that interprets the A-intercept.
(d) Write a sentence that interprets the slope of this function as a rate of change.

63. *Temperature* Write the equation of the linear relationship between temperature in Celsius (C) and Fahrenheit (F) if water freezes at 0°C and 32°F and boils at 100°C and 212°F.

Section 1.4

64. *Photosynthesis* The amount y of photosynthesis that takes place in a certain plant depends on the intensity x of the light present according to

$$y = 120x^2 - 20x^3 \qquad \text{for } x \ge 0$$

(a) Graph this function with a graphing calculator (Use y-min $= -100$ and y-max $= 700$.)
(b) The model is valid only when $f(x) \ge 0$ (that is, on or above the x-axis). For what x-values is this true?

65. *Flow rates of water* The speed at which water travels in a pipe can be measured by directing the flow through an elbow and measuring the height to which it spurts out the top. If the elbow height is 10 cm, the equation relating the height h (in centimeters) of the water above the elbow and its velocity v (in centimeters per second) is given by

$$v^2 = 1960(h + 10)$$

(a) Solve this equation for h and graph the result, using the velocity as the independent variable.
(b) If the velocity is 210 cm/sec, what is the height of the water above the elbow?

Section 1.5

66. *Investment mix* A retired couple have $600,000 to invest and want to earn $60,000 per year in interest. The safer investment yields 9.5%, but they can supplement their earnings by investing some of their money at 11%. How much should they invest at each rate to earn $60,000 per year?

67. *Botany* A botanist has a 20% solution and a 70% solution of an insecticide. How much of each must be used to make 4.0 liters of a 35% solution?

Section 1.6

68. *Supply and demand* A certain product has supply and demand functions $p = 4q + 5$ and $p = -2q + 81$, respectively.
(a) If the price is $53, how many units are supplied and how many are demanded?
(b) Does this give a shortfall or a surplus?
(c) Is the price likely to increase from $53 or decrease from it?

69. *Market analysis* Of the equations $p + 6q = 420$ and $p = 6q + 60$, one is the supply function for a product and one is the demand function for that product.
(a) Graph these equations on the same set of axes.
(b) Label the supply function and the demand function.
(c) Find the market equilibrium point.

70. *Cost, revenue, and profit* The total cost and total revenue for a certain product are given by

$$C(x) = 38.80x + 4500$$
$$R(x) = 61.30x$$

(a) Find the marginal cost.
(b) Find the marginal revenue.
(c) Find the marginal profit.
(d) Find the number of units required to break even.

71. *Cost, revenue, and profit* A certain commodity sells for $52 per unit and has the following costs for a period.

Fixed cost:	$1500
Variable cost per unit:	$22

(a) What is the total cost function?
(b) What is the total revenue function?
(c) What is the profit function?
(d) What is the marginal cost?
(e) What is the marginal revenue?
(f) What is the marginal profit?
(g) What is the break-even quantity?

72. *Market analysis* The supply function and the demand function for a product are linear and are determined by the tables that follow.
    (a) Write an equation for the supply function and an equation for the demand function.
    (b) Find the quantity and price that give market equilibrium.

Supply Function		Demand Function	
Price ($)	Quantity	Price ($)	Quantity
100	125	100	355
200	150	200	330
400	200	400	280

73. *Market analysis* Suppose that for a certain product, the supply and demand functions prior to any taxation are

$$\text{Supply:} \qquad p = \frac{q}{10} + 8$$

$$\text{Demand:} \qquad 10p + q = 1500$$

If a tax of $2 per item is levied on the supplier and is passed on to the consumer as a price increase, find the market equilibrium after the tax is levied.

1 CHAPTER TEST

In Problems 1–4, solve the equations.

1. $10 - 2(2x - 9) - 4(6 + x) = 52$

2. $4x - 3 = \dfrac{x}{2} + 6$

3. $\dfrac{3}{x} + 4 = \dfrac{4x}{x + 1}$ 4. $\dfrac{3x - 1}{4x - 9} = \dfrac{5}{7}$

5. For $f(x) = 7 + 5x - 2x^2$, find and simplify
$$\frac{f(x + h) - f(x)}{h}.$$

6. Solve $1 + \dfrac{2}{3}x \le 3x + 22$ and graph the solution.

In Problems 7 and 8, find the intercepts and graph the functions.

7. $5x - 6y = 30$ 8. $7x + 5y = 21$

9. Consider the function $f(x) = \sqrt{4x + 16}$.
   (a) Find the domain and range.
   (b) Find $f(3)$.
   (c) Find the y-coordinate on the graph of $y = f(x)$ when $x = 5$.

10. Write the equation of the line passing through $(-1, 2)$ and $(3, -4)$. Write your answer in slope-intercept form.

11. Find the slope and the y-intercept of the graph of $5x + 4y = 15$.

12. Write the equation of the line through $(-3, -1)$ that
    (a) has undefined slope
    (b) is perpendicular to $x = 4y - 8$.

13. Which of the following relations [(a), (b), (c)] are functions of x? Explain.
    (a)

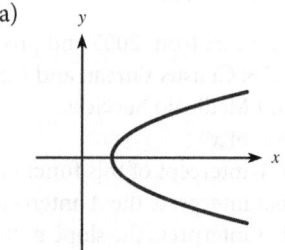

(b)

x	y
1	3
-1	3
4	2

(c) $y = \pm\sqrt{x^2 - 1}$

14. Graph $y = x^2 - 12x$
    (a) in the standard window and
    (b) in x-min $= -10$, x-max $= 30$;
        y-min $= -40$, y-max $= 40$.

15. Solve the system
$$\begin{cases} 3x + 2y = -2 \\ 4x + 5y = 2 \end{cases}$$

16. Given $f(x) = 5x^2 - 3x$ and $g(x) = x + 1$, find
    (a) $(fg)(x)$
    (b) $g(g(x))$
    (c) $(f \circ g)(x)$

17. Using U.S. Bureau of Labor Statistics data for selected years from 1950 and projected to 2050, the number of men in the U.S. workforce (in millions) can be approximated by

$$M = 0.59x + 43.2$$

where x equals the number of years past 1950.
   (a) Use a graphing calculator to graph this equation with the window x-min = 0, x-max = 100, y-min = 0, y-max = 100.
   (b) The point (80, 90.4) lies on the graph of this equation. Explain its meaning.
   (c) Find the projected number of men in the U.S. workforce in 2050 according to this model.

18. The total cost function for a product is $C(x) = 30x + 1200$, and the total revenue is $R(x) = 38x$, where x is the number of units produced and sold.
   (a) Find the marginal cost.
   (b) Find the profit function.
   (c) Find the number of units that gives the break-even point.
   (d) Find the marginal profit and explain what it means.

19. The selling price for each item of a product is $50, and the total cost is given by $C(x) = 10x + 18,000$, where x is the number of items.
   (a) Write the revenue function.
   (b) Find $C(100)$ and write a sentence that explains its meaning.
   (c) Find the number of units that gives the break-even point.

20. The supply function for a product is $p = 5q + 1500$, and the demand function is $p = -3q + 3100$. Find the quantity and price that give market equilibrium.

21. A building is depreciated by its owner, with the value y of the building after x months given by $y = 720,000 - 2000x$.
   (a) Find the y-intercept of the graph of this function and explain what it means.
   (b) Find the slope of the graph and tell what it means.

22. An airline has 360 seats on a plane for one of its flights. If 90% of the people making reservations actually buy a ticket, how many reservations should the airline accept to be confident that it will sell 360 tickets?

23. Amanda plans to invest $20,000, part of it at a 9% interest rate and part of it in a safer fund that pays 6%. How much should be invested in each fund to yield an annual return of $1560?

EXTENDED APPLICATIONS & GROUP PROJECTS

I. Hospital Administration

Southwest Hospital has an operating room used only for laser eye surgery. The annual cost of rent, heat, and electricity for the operating room and its equipment is $1.08 million, and the annual salaries of the people who staff this room total $1.6 million.

The cost for each surgery is $2395, which includes all medical supplies and drugs and a complimentary bouquet of flowers for each patient. In addition, one-quarter of the patients require dark glasses that the hospital provides at no additional charge but cost $20 per pair.

The hospital receives a payment of $6000 for each eye operation performed.

1. Write the functions for the hospital's total cost, total revenue, and profit as functions of the number of surgery cases.
2. How many laser eye operations must the hospital perform each year to break even?
3. Southwest Hospital currently averages 70 laser eye operations per month. One of the nurses has just learned about a machine that would reduce by $100 per patient the amount of medical supplies needed. It can be leased for $100,000 annually. Keeping in mind the financial cost and benefits, advise the hospital on whether it should lease this machine.
4. An advertising agency has proposed to the hospital's president that she spend $20,000 per month on television and radio advertising to persuade people that Southwest Hospital is the best place to have laser eye surgery performed. Advertising account executives estimate that such publicity would increase business by 40 operations per month. If they are correct and if this increase is not big enough to affect fixed costs, what impact would this advertising have on the hospital's profits?
5. In case the advertising agency is being overly optimistic, how many extra operations per month are needed to cover the cost of the proposed ads?
6. If the ad campaign is approved and subsequently meets its projections, should the hospital review its decision about the machine discussed in Question 3?

II. Fundraising

At most colleges and universities, student organizations conduct fundraising activities, such as selling T-shirts or candy. If a club or an organization decided to sell coupons for submarine sandwiches, it would want to find the best deal, based on the amount the club thought it could sell and how much profit it would make. In this project, you'll try to discover the best deal for this type of fundraiser conducted in your area.

1. Contact at least two different sub shops in your area from among local sub shops, a national chain, or a regional or national convenience store chain. From each contact, find the details of selling sub sandwich coupons as a fundraiser. In particular, determine the following for each sub shop and present your findings in a chart.
   (a) The selling price for each coupon and its value to the coupon holder, including any expiration date
   (b) Your cost for each coupon sold and for each one returned
   (c) The total number of coupons provided
   (d) The duration of the sale

2. For each sub shop, determine a club's total revenue and total costs as linear functions of the number of coupons sold.
3. Form the profit function for each sub shop and graph the profit functions together. For each function, determine the break-even point. Find the marginal profit for each function and interpret its meaning.
4. The shop with the best deal will be the one whose coupons provide the maximum profit for a club.

   (a) For each shop, determine a sales estimate that is based on location, local popularity, and customer value.
   (b) Use each estimate from part (a) with that shop's profit function to determine which shop gives the maximum profit.

Fully explain and support your claims; make and justify a recommendation.

Quadratic and Other Special Functions

In Chapter 1, we discussed functions in general and linear functions in particular. In this chapter, we will discuss quadratic functions and their applications, and we will also discuss other types of functions, including identity, constant, power, absolute value, piecewise defined, and reciprocal functions. Graphs of polynomial and rational functions will be introduced; they will be studied in detail in Chapter 10. We will pay particular attention to quadratic equations and to quadratic functions, and we will see that cost, revenue, profit, supply, and demand are sometimes modeled by quadratic functions. We also include, in a section on modeling, the creation of functions that approximately fit real data points.

The topics and some representative applications discussed in this chapter follow.

Prerequisite Problem Type	For Section	Answer	Section for Review
Find $b^2 - 4ac$ if (a) $a = 1, b = 2, c = -2$ (b) $a = -2, b = 3, c = -1$ (c) $a = -3, b = -3, c = -2$	2.1–2.3	(a) 12 (h) 1 (c) -15	0.2 Signed numbers
(a) Factor $6x^2 - x - 2$. (b) Factor $6x^2 - 9x$.	2.1–2.3	(a) $(3x - 2)(2x + 1)$ (b) $3x(2x - 3)$	0.6 Factoring
Is $\dfrac{1 + \sqrt{-3}}{2}$ a real number?	2.1	No	0.4 Radicals
(a) Find the y-intercept of $y = x^2 - 6x + 8$. (b) Find the x-intercept of $y = 2x - 3$.	2.2 2.3	(a) 8 (b) $\frac{3}{2}$	1.3 x- and y-intercepts
(a) If $f(x) = -x^2 + 4x$, find $f(2)$. (b) Find the domain of $f(x) = \dfrac{12x + 8}{3x - 9}$	2.2–2.4	(a) 4 (b) All $x \neq 3$	1.2 Functions
Assume that revenue is $R(x) = 500x - 2x^2$ and cost is $C(x) = 3600 + 100x + 2x^2$. (a) Find the profit function $P(x)$. (b) Find $P(50)$.	2.3	(a) $P(x) =$ $\quad -3600 + 400x - 4x^2$ (b) $P(50) = 6400$	1.6 Cost, revenue, and and profit .

Quadratic Equations

OBJECTIVES

- To solve quadratic equations with factoring methods
- To solve quadratic equations with the quadratic formula

APPLICATION PREVIEW

With fewer workers, future income from payroll taxes used to fund Social Security benefits won't keep pace with scheduled benefits. Using Social Security Administration data, the Social Security Trust Fund balance B, in billions of dollars, can be approximated by the function

$$B = -7.97t^2 + 312t - 356$$

where t is the number of years past the year 1995. For planning purposes, it is important to know when the trust fund balance will be 0. That is, for what t-value does

$$0 = -7.97t^2 + 312t - 356$$

(See Example 7 for the solution.)

In this section, we learn how to solve equations of this type using factoring methods and using the quadratic formula.

Factoring Methods

A **quadratic equation** in one variable is an equation of second degree that can be written in the *general form*

$$ax^2 + bx + c = 0 \quad (a \neq 0)$$

where a, b, and c represent constants. For example, the equations

$$3x^2 + 4x + 1 = 0 \quad \text{and} \quad 2x^2 + 1 = x^2 - x$$

are quadratic equations; the first of these is in general form, and the second can be rewritten in general form.

When solving quadratic equations, we will be interested only in real number solutions and will consider two methods of solution: factoring and the quadratic formula. We will discuss solving quadratic equations by factoring first. (For a review of factoring, see Section 0.6, "Factoring.")

Solution by factoring is based on the following property of the real numbers.

Zero Product Property

For real numbers a and b, $ab = 0$ if and only if $a = 0$ or $b = 0$ or both.

Hence, to solve by factoring, we must first write the equation with zero on one side.

EXAMPLE **1**   **Solving Quadratic Equations**

Solve: (a) $6x^2 + 3x = 4x + 2$ (b) $6x^2 = 9x$

Solution

(a)
$$6x^2 + 3x = 4x + 2$$
$$6x^2 - x - 2 = 0 \qquad \text{Proper form for factoring}$$
$$(3x - 2)(2x + 1) = 0 \qquad \text{Factored}$$
$$3x - 2 = 0 \quad \text{or} \quad 2x + 1 = 0 \qquad \text{Factors equal to zero}$$
$$3x = 2 \qquad\qquad 2x = -1$$
$$x = \frac{2}{3} \qquad\qquad x = -\frac{1}{2} \qquad \text{Solutions}$$

We now check that these values are, in fact, solutions to our original equation.

$$6\left(\frac{2}{3}\right)^2 + 3\left(\frac{2}{3}\right) \stackrel{?}{=} 4\left(\frac{2}{3}\right) + 2 \qquad 6\left(-\frac{1}{2}\right)^2 + 3\left(-\frac{1}{2}\right) \stackrel{?}{=} 4\left(-\frac{1}{2}\right) + 2$$

$$\frac{14}{3} = \frac{14}{3} \checkmark \qquad\qquad\qquad 0 = 0 \checkmark$$

(b)
$$6x^2 = 9x$$
$$6x^2 - 9x = 0$$
$$3x(2x - 3) = 0$$
$$3x = 0 \quad \text{or} \quad 2x - 3 = 0$$
$$x = 0 \qquad\qquad 2x = 3$$
$$x = \frac{3}{2}$$

Check: $6(0)^2 = 9(0)\checkmark \qquad 6\left(\frac{3}{2}\right)^2 = 9\left(\frac{3}{2}\right)\checkmark$

Thus the solutions are $x = 0$ and $x = \frac{3}{2}$.

Note that in Example 1(b), it is tempting to divide both sides of the equation by x, but this is incorrect because it results in the loss of the solution $x = 0$. Never divide both sides of an equation by an expression containing the variable.

EXAMPLE 2   Solving by Factoring

Solve: (a) $(y - 3)(y + 2) = -4$ \qquad (b) $\dfrac{x + 1}{3x + 6} = \dfrac{3}{x} + \dfrac{2x + 6}{x(3x + 6)}$

Solution

(a) Note that the left side of the equation is factored but the right member is not 0. Therefore, we must multiply the factors and rewrite the equation in general form.

$$(y - 3)(y + 2) = -4$$
$$y^2 - y - 6 = -4$$
$$y^2 - y - 2 = 0$$
$$(y - 2)(y + 1) = 0$$
$$y - 2 = 0 \quad \text{or} \quad y + 1 = 0$$
$$y = 2 \quad | \quad y = -1$$

Check: $(2 - 3)(2 + 2) = -4\checkmark \qquad (-1 - 3)(-1 + 2) = -4\checkmark$

(b) The LCD of all fractions is $x(3x + 6)$. Multiplying both sides of the equation by this LCD gives a quadratic equation that is equivalent to the original equation for $x \neq 0$ and $x \neq -2$. (The original equation is undefined for these values.)

$$\frac{x + 1}{3x + 6} = \frac{3}{x} + \frac{2x + 6}{x(3x + 6)}$$
$$x(3x + 6)\frac{x + 1}{3x + 6} = x(3x + 6)\left(\frac{3}{x} + \frac{2x + 6}{x(3x + 6)}\right) \qquad \text{Multiply both sides by } x(3x + 6).$$
$$x(x + 1) = 3(3x + 6) + (2x + 6)$$
$$x^2 + x = 9x + 18 + 2x + 6$$
$$x^2 - 10x - 24 = 0$$
$$(x - 12)(x + 2) = 0$$
$$x - 12 = 0 \text{ or } x + 2 = 0$$
$$x = 12 \text{ or } x = -2$$

Checking $x = 12$ and $x = -2$ in the original equation, we see that $x = -2$ makes the denominator equal to zero. Hence, the only solution is $x = 12$. $\checkmark$

CHECKPOINT

1. The factoring method for solving a quadratic equation is based on the _____ product property. Hence, to solve a quadratic equation by factoring, one side of the equation must equal _____.
2. Solve the following equations by factoring.
   (a) $x^2 - 19x = 20$ (b) $2x^2 = 6x$

EXAMPLE 3   **Falling Object**

A tennis ball is thrown into a swimming pool from the top of a hotel. The height of the ball from the pool is modeled by $D(t) = -16t^2 - 4t + 300$ feet, where t is the time, in seconds, after the ball was thrown. How long after the ball was thrown was it 144 feet above the pool?

Solution
To find the number of seconds until the ball is 144 feet above the pool, we solve the following equation for t.

$$144 = -16t^2 - 4t + 300$$
$$0 = -16t^2 - 4t + 156 \quad \text{Subtract 144 from both sides.}$$
$$0 = 4t^2 + t - 39 \quad\quad\quad \text{Divide both sided by (–4)}$$
$$0 = (t - 3)(4t + 13)$$
$$t - 3 = 0 \text{ or } 4t + 13 = 0$$
$$\left. \begin{array}{c} \\ 4t = -13 \end{array} \right.$$
$$t = 3 \quad \left| \quad t = -13/4 \right.$$

This indicates that the ball will be 144 feet above the pool 3 seconds after it is thrown. The negative value for t has no meaning in this application.

The Quadratic Formula   Factoring does not lend itself easily to solving quadratic equations such as

$$x^2 - 5 = 0$$

However, we can solve this equation by writing

$$x^2 = 5$$
$$x = \pm\sqrt{5}$$

In general, we can solve quadratic equations of the form $x^2 = C$ (no x-term) by taking the square root of both sides.

Square Root Property

The solution of $x^2 = C$ is

$$x = \pm\sqrt{C}$$

Note: When $C < 0$, the solutions are not real numbers.

This property also can be used to solve equations such as those in the following example.

EXAMPLE 4   **Square Root Method**

Solve the following equations.
(a) $4x^2 = 5$ (b) $(3x - 4)^2 = 9$

Solution

We can use the square root property for both parts.
(a) $4x^2 = 5$ is equivalent to $x^2 = \frac{5}{4}$. Thus

$$x = \pm\sqrt{\frac{5}{4}} = \pm\frac{\sqrt{5}}{\sqrt{4}} = \pm\frac{\sqrt{5}}{2}$$

(b) $(3x - 4)^2 = 9$ is equivalent to $3x - 4 = \pm\sqrt{9} = \pm 3$. Thus

$3x - 4 = 3$	$3x - 4 = -3$
$3x = 7$	$3x = 1$
$x = \dfrac{7}{3}$	$x = \dfrac{1}{3}$

The solution of the general quadratic equation $ax^2 + bx + c = 0$, where $a \neq 0$, is called the **quadratic formula**. It can be derived by using the square root property, as follows:

$$ax^2 + bx + c = 0 \qquad \text{Standard form}$$
$$ax^2 + bx = -c \qquad \text{Subtract } c \text{ from both sides.}$$
$$x^2 + \frac{b}{a}x = -\frac{c}{a} \qquad \text{Divide both sides by } a.$$

We would like to make the left side of the last equation a perfect square of the form $(x + k)^2 = x^2 + 2kx + k^2$. If we let $2k = b/a$, then $k = b/(2a)$ and $k^2 = b^2/(4a^2)$. Hence, we continue as follows:

$$x^2 + \frac{b}{a}x + \frac{b^2}{4a^2} = \frac{b^2}{4a^2} - \frac{c}{a} \qquad \text{Add } \frac{b^2}{4a^2} \text{ to both sides.}$$

$$\left(x + \frac{b}{2a}\right)^2 = \frac{b^2 - 4ac}{4a^2} \qquad \text{Factor and simplify.}$$

$$x + \frac{b}{2a} = \pm\sqrt{\frac{b^2 - 4ac}{4a^2}} \qquad \text{Square root property}$$

$$x = \frac{-b}{2a} \pm \frac{\sqrt{b^2 - 4ac}}{2|a|} \qquad \text{Solve for } x.$$

Because $\pm 2|a|$ represents the same numbers as $\pm 2a$, we obtain the following.

Quadratic Formula

If $ax^2 + bx + c = 0$, where $a \neq 0$, then

$$x = \frac{-b \pm \sqrt{b^2 - 4ac}}{2a}$$

We may use the quadratic formula to solve all quadratic equations, but especially those in which factorization is difficult or impossible to see. The proper identification of values for a, b, and c to be substituted into the formula requires that the equation be in general form.

EXAMPLE 5   **Quadratic Formula**

Use the quadratic formula to solve $2x^2 - 3x - 6 = 0$ for x.

Solution

The equation is already in general form, with $a = 2$, $b = -3$, and $c = -6$. Hence,

$$x = \frac{-b \pm \sqrt{b^2 - 4ac}}{2a} = \frac{-(-3) \pm \sqrt{(-3)^2 - 4(2)(-6)}}{2(2)}$$

$$= \frac{3 \pm \sqrt{9 + 48}}{4} = \frac{3 \pm \sqrt{57}}{4}$$

Thus the solutions are

$$x = \frac{3 + \sqrt{57}}{4} \quad \text{and} \quad x = \frac{3 - \sqrt{57}}{4}$$

EXAMPLE 6   **Nonreal Solution**

Using the quadratic formula, find the (real) solutions to $x^2 = x - 1$.

Solution

We must rewrite the equation in general form before we can determine the values of a, b, and c. We write $x^2 = x - 1$ as $x^2 - x + 1 = 0$. Note that $a = 1$, $b = -1$, and $c = 1$.

$$x = \frac{-(-1) \pm \sqrt{(-1)^2 - 4(1)(1)}}{2(1)} = \frac{1 \pm \sqrt{1 - 4}}{2} = \frac{1 \pm \sqrt{-3}}{2}$$

Because $\sqrt{-3}$ is not a real number, the values of x are not real. Hence, there are no real solutions to the given equation.

In Example 6, there were no real solutions to the quadratic equation because the radicand of the quadratic formula was negative. In general, when solving a quadratic equation, we can use the sign of the radicand, $b^2 - 4ac$, in the quadratic formula to determine how many real solutions there are. Thus we refer to $b^2 - 4ac$ as the **quadratic discriminant**.

Quadratic Discriminant

Given $ax^2 + bx + c = 0$ and $a \neq 0$,

If $b^2 - 4ac > 0$, the equation has two distinct real solutions.
If $b^2 - 4ac = 0$, the equation has exactly one real solution.
If $b^2 - 4ac < 0$, the equation has no real solutions.

The quadratic formula is especially useful when the coefficients of a quadratic equation are decimal values that make factorization impractical. This occurs in many applied problems.

EXAMPLE 7   **Social Security Trust Fund** | APPLICATION PREVIEW |

The Social Security Trust Fund balance B, in billions of dollars, can be described by the function

$$B = -7.97t^2 + 312t - 356$$

where t is the number of years past the year 1995 (*Source:* Social Security Administration). For planning purposes, it is important to know when the trust fund balance will be 0. To find when this occurs, solve

$$0 = -7.97t^2 + 312t - 356$$

Solution

We solve the equation with the quadratic formula using

$$a = -7.97, \quad b = 312, \quad c = -356$$

Thus

$$t = \frac{-b \pm \sqrt{b^2 - 4ac}}{2a}$$

$$= \frac{-(312) \pm \sqrt{(312)^2 - 4(-7.97)(-356)}}{2(-7.97)}$$

$$= \frac{-312 \pm \sqrt{85,994.72}}{2(-7.97)} \approx \frac{-312 \pm 293.249}{-15.94}$$

We are interested in the larger (future) positive solution, so

$$t \approx \frac{-312 - 293.249}{-15.94} \approx 37.97$$

Therefore, the trust fund balance is projected to reach zero about 37.97 years past 1995, during the year 2033.

CHECKPOINT

3. The statement of the quadratic formula says that if _____ and $a \neq 0$, then $x = $ _____.

4. Solve $2x^2 - 5x = 9$ using the quadratic formula.

Calculator Note   As we did with linear equations in Section 1.4, we can use 2nd CALC, 2:zero to solve quadratic equations of the form $f(x) = 0$ with a graphing calculator. The steps for solving quadratic equations are:

1. Graph $Y_1 = f(x)$ on a window that shows all possible x-intercepts. (Quadratic functions frequently have two x-intercepts.)
2. Under the CALC (2nd TRACE) menu, select 2:zero and follow the prompts to find each x-intercept, whose x-value is a solution.

For example, we can find the solutions of the equation $0 = -7x^2 + 16x - 4$ by graphing $Y_1 = -7x^2 + 16x - 4$, as in Figures 2.1(a) and 2.1(b). The graphs show $y = 0$ when $x = 2$ and when $x = 0.2857$ (approximately).

Figure 2.1   (a)   (b)

Solving $f(x) = 0$ algebraically gives solutions $x = 2$ and $x = \frac{2}{7} \approx 0.2857$. These values agree with those found graphically. See Appendix A, Section 2.1, for further details.

Spreadsheet Note To solve $f(x) = ax^2 + bx + c = 0$ with Excel if it has two solutions:

1. Graph $y = f(x)$ to find x-values close to the x-intercepts and enter those values in column A.
2. Use the *Goal Seek* menu under *Data > What-If-Analysis*, selecting a cell in column B containing a value at or near 0, setting it to 0, and entering the changing cell in column A that corresponds to the cell in column B.
3. Click OK; an exact or approximate solution appears in column A.
4. Repeat the process with a second function value at or near 0 to find a second solution.

For example, to solve the equation $0 = -7x^2 + 16x - 4$, we use its graph to find x-values close to the x-intercepts (use 2 and 0). The following spreadsheets illustrate how Excel works to solve the equation $0 = -7x^2 + 16x - 4$. The first spreadsheet shows how we input the formula with values near 0 and 2, and the second spreadsheet shows the approximate solutions (in column A). The solutions are $x = 0$ and $x \approx 0.2857$. See Appendix B, Section 2.1, for details.

	A	B
1	x	$7x^2 + 16x - 4$
2	2	$= -7*A2^2 + 16*A2 - 4$
3	0	$= -7*A3^2 + 16*A3 - 4$

	A	B
1	x	$-7x^2 + 16x - 4$
2	2	0
3	0.285688	-0.00032

CHECKPOINT
ANSWERS

1. Zero; zero
2. (a) $x = 20$; $x = -1$
   (b) $x = 0$; $x = 3$
3. If $ax^2 + bx + c = 0$ and $a \neq 0$, then
$$x = \frac{-b \pm \sqrt{b^2 - 4ac}}{2a}$$
4. $x = \dfrac{5 + \sqrt{97}}{4} \approx 3.712$ or $x = \dfrac{5 - \sqrt{97}}{4} \approx -1.212$

EXERCISES 2.1

In Problems 1–4, write the equations in general form.

1. $2x^2 + 3 = x^2 - 2x + 4$
2. $x^2 - 2x + 5 = 2 - 2x^2$
3. $(y + 1)(y + 2) = 4$
4. $(z - 1)(z - 3) = 1$

In Problems 5–12, solve each equation by factoring.

5. $x^2 - 4x = 12$
6. $x^2 = 11x - 10$
7. $9 - 4x^2 = 0$
8. $25x^2 - 16 = 0$
9. $x = x^2$
10. $t^2 - 4t = 3t^2$
11. $4t^2 - 4t + 1 = 0$
12. $49z^2 + 14z + 1 = 0$
13. $5x^2 + 6 = 11x$
14. $7x^2 - x = 26$

In Problems 15–20, solve each equation using the quadratic formula. Give real answers (a) exactly and (b) rounded to two decimal places.

15. $x^2 - 4x = 4$
16. $x^2 + 7 = 6x$
17. $2w^2 + w + 1 = 0$
18. $z^2 + 2z + 4 = 0$
19. $7 - 2x - x^2 = 0$
20. $6x - 2 = 3x^2$

In Problems 21–26, find the exact real solutions to each equation, if they exist.

21. $y^2 = 7$
22. $z^2 = 12$
23. $5x^2 = 80$
24. $3x^2 = 75$
25. $(x + 4)^2 = 25$
26. $(x + 1)^2 = 2$

In Problems 27–36, use any method to find the exact real solutions, if they exist.

27. $x^2 + 5x = 21 + x$
28. $x^2 + 17x = 8x - 14$
29. $\dfrac{w^2}{8} - \dfrac{w}{2} - 4 = 0$
30. $\dfrac{y^2}{2} - \dfrac{11}{6}y + 1 = 0$
31. $16z^2 + 16z - 21 = 0$
32. $10y^2 - y - 65 = 0$
33. $(x - 1)(x + 5) = 7$
34. $(x - 3)(1 - x) = 1$
35. $5x^2 = 2x + 6$
36. $3x^2 = -6x - 2$

In Problems 37–42, solve each equation using a graphing utility.

37. $21x + 70 = 7x^2$
38. $3x^2 + 6 = 11x$
39. $300 - 2x - 0.01x^2 = 0$
40. $-9.6 + 2x - 0.1x^2 = 0$
41. $25.6x^2 - 16.1x - 1.1 = 0$
42. $6.8z^2 - 4.9z - 2.6 = 0$

In Problems 43–46, multiply both sides of the equation by the LCD and solve the resulting quadratic equation.

43. $x + \dfrac{8}{x} = 9$
44. $\dfrac{x}{x - 2} - 1 = \dfrac{3}{x + 1}$

45. $\dfrac{x}{x-1} = 2x + \dfrac{1}{x-1}$ 46. $\dfrac{5}{z+4} - \dfrac{3}{z-2} = 4$

In Problems 47 and 48, solve using quadratic methods.

47. $(x+8)^2 + 3(x+8) + 2 = 0$

48. $(s-2)^2 - 5(s-2) - 24 = 0$

APPLICATIONS

49. *Profit* If the profit from the sale of x units of a product is $P = 90x - 200 - x^2$, what level(s) of production will yield a profit of $1200?

50. *Profit* If the profit from the sale of x units of a product is $P = 16x - 0.1x^2 - 100$, what level(s) of production will yield a profit of $180?

51. *Profit* Suppose the profit from the sale of x units of a product is $P = 6400x - 18x^2 - 400$.
    (a) What level(s) of production will yield a profit of $61,800?
    (b) Can a profit of more than $61,800 be made?

52. *Profit* Suppose the profit from the sale of x units of a product is $P = 50x - 300 - 0.01x^2$.
    (a) What level(s) of production will yield a profit of $250?
    (b) Can a profit of more than $250 be made?

53. *Flight of a ball* If a ball is thrown upward at 96 feet per second from the top of a building that is 100 feet high, the height of the ball is given by

$$S = 100 + 96t - 16t^2 \text{ feet}$$

where t is the number of seconds after the ball is thrown. How long after it is thrown is the height 100 feet?

54. *Flight of a ball* A tennis ball is thrown into the air from the top of a hotel that is 350 feet above the ground. The height of the ball from the ground is given by

$$D(t) = -16t^2 + 10t + 350 \text{ feet}$$

where t is the time, in seconds, after the ball is thrown. How long after the ball is thrown does it hit the ground?

55. *Wind and pollution* The amount of airborne particulate pollution p from a power plant depends on the wind speed s, among other things, with the relationship between p and s approximated by

$$p = 25 - 0.01s^2$$

   (a) Find the value(s) of s that will make $p = 0$.
   (b) What value of s from part (a) makes sense in the context of this application? What does $p = 0$ mean in this application?

56. *Drug sensitivity* The sensitivity S to a drug is related to the dosage size by

$$S = 100x - x^2$$

where x is the dosage size in milliliters.
   (a) What dosage(s) will yield 0 sensitivity?
   (b) Explain what your answer in part (a) might mean.

57. *Corvette acceleration* The time t, in seconds, it takes a Corvette to accelerate to x mph can be described by

$$t = 0.001(0.732x^2 + 15.417x + 607.738)$$

(*Source: Motor Trend*). How fast is the Corvette going after 8.99 seconds? Give your answer to the nearest tenth.

58. *Consumer Price Index* Using Social Security Administration data for selected years from 2012 and projected to 2050, the U.S. consumer price index (CPI) can be described by the equation

$$C = 0.068t^2 + 1.8t + 96$$

where t is the number of years past 2010. With 2012 as the reference year, a year in which the CPI $= 120.56$ means goods and services that cost $100.00 in 2012 are expected to cost $120.56 in that year. Find the year in which the CPI is predicted to reach 150.00

59. *Marijuana use* For the years since 2001, the percent p of high school seniors who have tried marijuana can be considered as a function of time t according to

$$p = f(t) = 0.17t^2 - 2.61t + 52.64$$

where t is the number of years past 2000 (*Source: National Institute on Drug Abuse*). In what year after 2000 is the percent predicted to reach 55% if this function remains valid?

60. *Projectile motion* Two projectiles are shot into the air over a lake. The paths of the projectiles are given by
    (a) $y = -0.0013x^2 + x + 10$ and
    (b) $y = -\dfrac{x^2}{81} + \dfrac{4}{3}x + 10$

where y is the height and x is the horizontal distance traveled (both in feet). Determine which projectile travels farther by substituting $y = 0$ in each equation and finding x.

61. *Percent profit* Ace Jewelry Store sold a necklace for $144. If the percent profit (based on cost) equals the cost of the necklace to the store, how much did the store pay for it? Use

$$P = \left(\dfrac{C}{100}\right) \cdot C$$

where P is profit and C is cost.

62. *Tourism spending* The global spending on travel and tourism (in billions of dollars) can be described by the equation

$$y = 1.48x^2 - 25.23x + 416.91$$

where x equals the number of years past 1990 (*Source: World Tourism Organization*). Find the year after 1990 in which spending is projected to reach $1968 billion.

63. *National health care* Using data from 2002 and with projections to 2024, total annual expenditures

for national health care (in billions of dollars) can be described by

$$E = 4.61x^2 + 43.4x + 1620$$

where x is the number of years past 2000 (*Source:* U.S. Centers for Medicare and Medicaid Services). If the pattern indicated by this equation remains valid, when does the model predict these expenditures will reach $7071 billion?

64. *Velocity of blood* Because of friction from the walls of an artery, the velocity of a blood corpuscle in an artery is greatest at the center of the artery and decreases as the distance r from the center increases. The velocity of the blood in the artery can be modeled by the function

$$v = k(R^2 - r^2)$$

where R is the radius of the artery and k is a constant that is determined by the pressure, the viscosity of the blood, and the length of the artery. In the case where $k = 2$ and $R = 0.1$ centimeters, the velocity is $v = 2(0.01 - r^2)$ centimeters per second.
   (a) What distance r would give a velocity of 0.02 cm/sec?
   (b) What distance r would give a velocity of 0.015 cm/sec?

   (c) What distance r would give a velocity of 0 cm/sec? Where is the blood corpuscle?

65. *Body-heat loss* The model for body-heat loss depends on the coefficient of convection K, which depends on wind speed v according to the equation

$$K^2 = 16v + 4$$

where v is in miles per hour. Find the positive coefficient of convection when the wind speed is
   (a) 20 mph
   (b) 60 mph
   (c) What is the change in K for a change in speed from 20 mph to 60 mph?

66. *Depth of a fissure* A fissure in the earth appeared after an earthquake. To measure its vertical depth, a stone was dropped into it, and the sound of the stone's impact was heard 3.9 seconds later. The distance (in feet) the stone fell is given by $s = 16t_1^2$, and the distance (in feet) the sound traveled is given by $s = 1090t_2$. In these equations, the distances traveled by the sound and the stone are the same, but their times are not. Using the fact that the total time is 3.9 seconds, find the depth of the fissure.

SECTION 2.2

Quadratic Functions: Parabolas

OBJECTIVES

- To find the vertex of the graph of a quadratic function
- To determine whether a vertex is a maximum point or a minimum point
- To find the zeros of a quadratic function
- To graph quadratic functions
- To find the average rate of change of a function

APPLICATION PREVIEW

Because additional equipment, raw materials, and labor may cause variable costs of some products to increase dramatically as more units are produced, total cost functions are not always linear functions. For example, suppose that the total cost of producing a product is given by the equation

$$C = C(x) = 300x + 0.1x^2 + 1200$$

where x represents the number of units produced. That is, the cost of this product is represented by a second-degree function, or a quadratic function. We can find the cost of producing 10 units by evaluating

$$C(10) = 300(10) + 0.1(10)^2 + 1200 = 4210$$

If the revenue function for this product is

$$R = R(x) = 600x$$

then the profit is also a quadratic function:

$$P(x) = R(x) - C(x) = 600x - (300x + 0.1x^2 + 1200)$$
$$P(x) = -0.1x^2 + 300x - 1200$$

We can use this function to find how many units give maximum profit and what that profit is. (See Example 2.) In this section, we will describe ways to find the maximum point or minimum point for a quadratic function.

Parabolas   In Chapter 1, we studied functions of the form $y = ax + b$, called linear (or first-degree) functions. We now turn our attention to **quadratic** (or second-degree) **functions.** The general equation of a quadratic function has the form

$$y = f(x) = ax^2 + bx + c$$

where a, b, and c are real numbers and $a \neq 0$.

The graph of a quadratic function

$$y = ax^2 + bx + c \qquad (a \neq 0)$$

has a distinctive shape called a **parabola**.

The basic function $y = x^2$ and a variation of it, $y = -\frac{1}{2}x^2$, are parabolas whose graphs are shown in Figure 2.2.

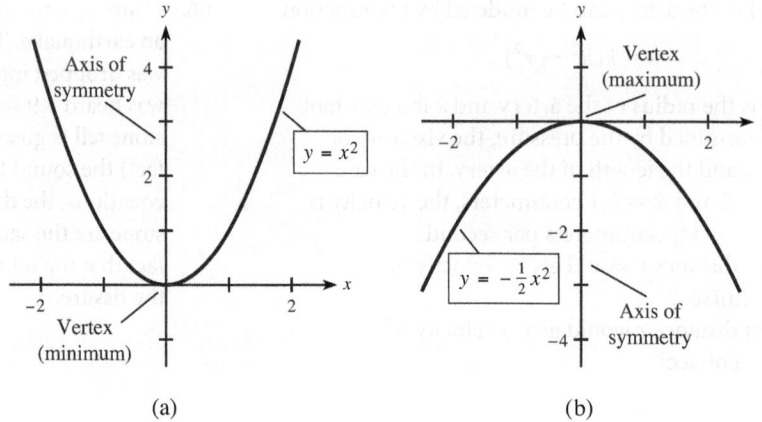

Figure 2.2

(a)   (b)

Vertex of a Parabola   As these examples illustrate, the graph of $y = ax^2$ is a parabola that opens upward if $a > 0$ and downward if $a < 0$. The **vertex,** where the parabola turns, is a **minimum point** if $a > 0$ and a **maximum point** if $a < 0$. The vertical line through the vertex of a parabola is called the **axis of symmetry** because each half of the graph is a reflection of the other half through this line.

The graph of $y = (x - 2)^2 - 1$ is the graph of $y = x^2$ shifted to a new location that is 2 units to the right and 1 unit down; its vertex is shifted from $(0, 0)$ to $(2, -1)$, and its axis of symmetry is shifted 2 units to the right. [See Figure 2.3(a).] The graph of $y = -\frac{1}{2}(x + 1)^2 + 2$ is the graph of $y = -\frac{1}{2}x^2$ shifted 1 unit to the left and 2 units up, with its vertex at $(-1, 2)$. [See Figure 2.3(b).]

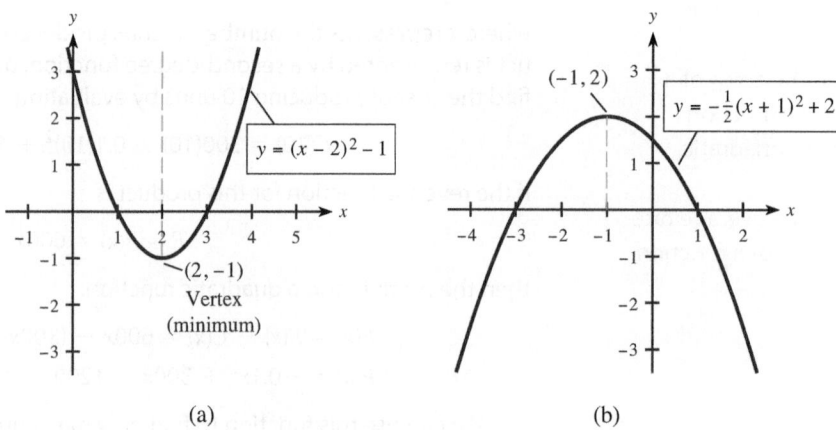

Figure 2.3

(a)   (b)

We can find the x-coordinate of the vertex of the graph of $y = ax^2 + bx + c$ using the fact that the axis of symmetry of a parabola passes through the vertex. Regardless of the location of the vertex of $y = ax^2 + bx + c$ or the direction it opens, the y-intercept of the graph of $y = ax^2 + bx + c$ is $(0, c)$ and if $b \neq 0$, then there is another point on the graph with y-coordinate c. See Figure 2.4.

Figure 2.4

The x-coordinates of the two points on this graph with y-coordinate c satisfy

$$c = ax^2 + bx + c$$

Solving this equation gives

$$0 = ax^2 + bx$$
$$0 = x(ax + b)$$
$$x = 0 \quad \text{or} \quad x = \frac{-b}{a}$$

The x-coordinate of the vertex is on the axis of symmetry, which is halfway from $x = 0$ to $x = \frac{-b}{a}$, at $x = \frac{-b}{2a}$. Thus we have the following.

Vertex of a Parabola

The quadratic function $y = f(x) = ax^2 + bx + c$ has its **vertex** at

$$\left(\frac{-b}{2a},\ f\left(\frac{-b}{2a} \right) \right)$$

The optimum value (either maximum or minimum) of the function occurs at

$$x = \frac{-b}{2a} \text{ and is } y = f\left(\frac{-b}{2a} \right). \text{ See Figure 2.5.}$$

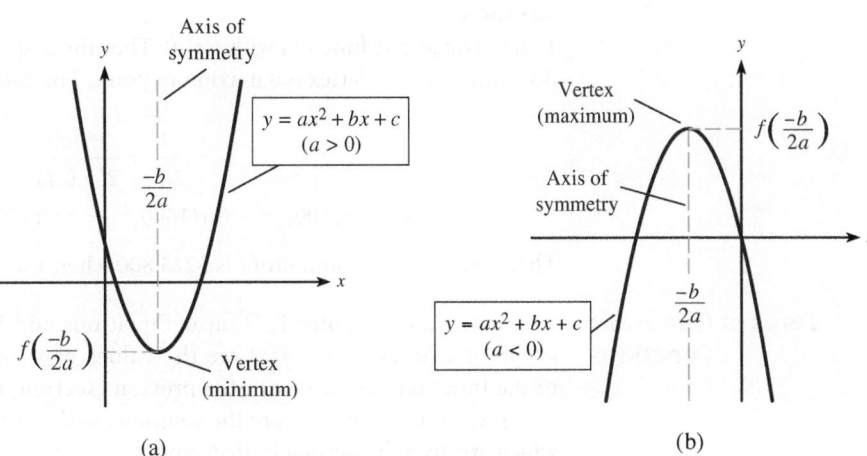

Figure 2.5   (a)   (b)

If we know the location of the vertex and the direction in which the parabola opens, we need very few other points to make a good sketch.

EXAMPLE 1   Vertex and Graph of a Parabola

Find the vertex and sketch the graph of

$$f(x) = 2x^2 - 4x + 4$$

Solution

Because $a = 2 > 0$, the graph of $f(x)$ opens upward and the vertex is the minimum point. We can calculate its coordinates as follows:

$$x = \frac{-b}{2a} = \frac{-(-4)}{2(2)} = 1$$

$$y = f(1) = 2$$

Thus the vertex is $(1, 2)$. Using x-values on either side of the vertex to plot additional points enables us to sketch the graph accurately. (See Figure 2.6.)

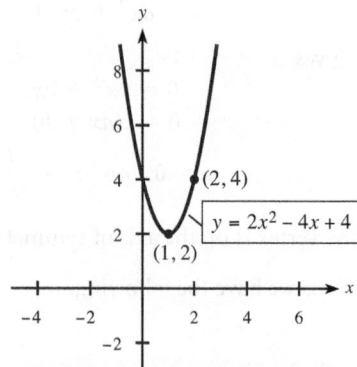

Figure 2.6

We also can use the coordinates of the vertex to find maximum or minimum values without a graph.

EXAMPLE 2   Profit Maximization | APPLICATION PREVIEW |

For the profit function

$$P(x) = -0.1x^2 + 300x - 1200$$

find the number of units that give maximum profit and find the maximum profit.

Solution

$P(x)$ is a quadratic function with $a < 0$. Thus the graph of $y = P(x)$ is a parabola that opens downward, so the vertex is a maximum point. The coordinates of the vertex are

$$x = \frac{-b}{2a} = \frac{-300}{2(-0.1)} = 1500$$

$$P = P(1500) = -0.1(1500)^2 + 300(1500) - 1200 = 223{,}800$$

Therefore, the maximum profit is \$223,800 when 1500 units are sold.

Zeros of Quadratic Functions   As we noted in Chapter 1, "Linear Equations and Functions," the x-intercepts of the graph of a function $y = f(x)$ are the values of x for which $f(x) = 0$, called the **zeros** of the function. As we saw in the previous section, the zeros of the quadratic function $y = f(x) = ax^2 + bx + c$ are the solutions of the quadratic equation $ax^2 + bx + c = 0$, which are given by the quadratic formula

$$x = \frac{-b \pm \sqrt{b^2 - 4ac}}{2a}$$

The information that is useful in graphing quadratic functions is summarized as follows.

Graphs of Quadratic Functions

Form: $y = f(x) = ax^2 + bx + c$
Graph: parabola

$a > 0$ parabola opens upward; vertex is a minimum point
$a < 0$ parabola opens downward; vertex is a maximum point

Coordinates of vertex: $x = \dfrac{-b}{2a}$, $y = f\left(\dfrac{-b}{2a}\right)$

Axis of symmetry equation: $x = \dfrac{-b}{2a}$

x-intercepts or zeros (if real*):

$$x = \frac{-b + \sqrt{b^2 - 4ac}}{2a},$$

$$x = \frac{-b - \sqrt{b^2 - 4ac}}{2a}$$

y-intercept: Let $x = 0$; then $y = c$.

EXAMPLE 3   Graph of a Quadratic Function

For the function $y = 4x - x^2$, determine whether its vertex is a maximum point or a minimum point and find the coordinates of this point, find the zeros (if any exist), find the y-intercept, and sketch the graph.

Solution

The proper form is $y = -x^2 + 4x + 0$, so $a = -1$, $b = 4$, $c = 0$. Because $a < 0$, the parabola opens downward and the vertex is the highest (maximum) point.

The vertex occurs at $x = \dfrac{-b}{2a} = \dfrac{-4}{2(-1)} = 2.$

The y-coordinate of the vertex is $f(2) = -(2)^2 + 4(2) = 4.$
The zeros of the function are solutions to

$$-x^2 + 4x = 0$$
$$x(-x + 4) = 0$$
$$\text{so } x = 0 \text{ or } x = 4$$

The y-intercept is $c = 0$ (at the origin).

The graph of this function can be found by drawing a parabola with these points [see Figure 2.7(a)].

*If the zeros are not real, the graph does not cross the x-axis.

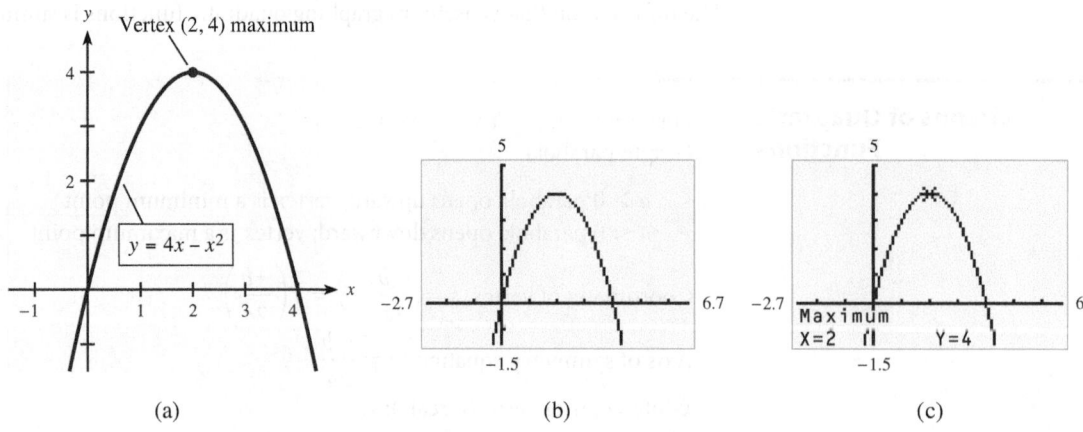

Figure 2.7

(a)   (b)   (c)

Calculator Note   We can graph the function $y = 4x - x^2$, discussed in Example 3, and other quadratic functions with a graphing calculator using the same methods as those for linear functions. Knowing the shape of a quadratic function is useful in setting a window that gives a complete graph. Figure 2.7(b) shows a graphing calculator graph of the function.

In Example 3, we used the vertex and x-intercepts to sketch the graph of a quadratic function. On the other hand, we can use a graphing calculator to graph a quadratic function and to find its vertex. For example, we can find the vertex of the quadratic function in Example 3 by choosing maximum under the CALC (2nd TRACE) menu and following the prompts. Figure 2.7(c) shows the maximum point (vertex) of the graph of $y = 4x - x^2$. ▪

Spreadsheet Note   Graphing quadratic (and other polynomial) functions with Excel requires the same steps as those for graphing linear functions. See Figure 2.8 for an Excel graph of $y = 4x - x^2$ and Appendix B, Sections 2.2 and 2.4, or the Online Excel Guide for procedural details. ▪

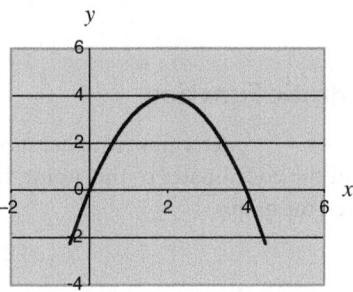

Figure 2.8

CHECKPOINT

1. Name the graph of a quadratic function.
2. (a) What is the x-coordinate of the vertex of $y = ax^2 + bx + c$?
   (b) For $y = 12x - \frac{1}{2}x^2$, what is the x-coordinate of the vertex? What is the y-coordinate of the vertex?
3. (a) How can you tell whether the vertex of $f(x) = ax^2 + bx + c$ is a maximum point or a minimum point?
   (b) In part 2(b), is the vertex a maximum point or a minimum point?
4. The zeros of a function correspond to what feature of its graph?
5. What is the y-intercept of $y = ax^2 + bx + c$?

So far, we have algebraically solved $f(x) = 0$ to find the x-intercepts of the graph of $y = f(x)$ (if they exist). Conversely, if we have the graph of $y = f(x)$ and it has x-intercepts, we can use those x-intercepts to find or approximate solutions to $f(x) = 0$.

EXAMPLE   4   **Graph Comparison**

Figure 2.9 shows the graphs of two different quadratic functions. Use the figure to complete the following.
(a) Determine the vertex of each function.
(b) Determine the real solutions of $f_1(x) = 0$ and $f_2(x) = 0$.
(c) One of the graphs in Figure 2.9 is the graph of $y = 7 + 6x - x^2$, and one is the graph of $y = x^2 - 6x + 10$. Determine which is which and why.

Solution
(a) For $y = f_1(x)$, the vertex is the maximum point, at (3, 16).
    For $y = f_2(x)$, the vertex is the minimum point, at (3, 1).
(b) For $y = f_1(x)$, the real solutions of $f_1(x) = 0$ are the zeros, or x-intercepts, at $x = -1$ and $x = 7$. For $y = f_2(x)$, the graph has no x-intercepts, so $f_2(x) = 0$ has no real solutions.
(c) Because the graph of $y = f_1(x)$ opens downward, the coefficient of x^2 must be negative. Hence, Figure 2.9(a) shows the graph of $y = f_1(x) = 7 + 6x - x^2$. Similarly, the coefficient of x^2 in $y = f_2(x)$ must be positive, so Figure 2.9(b) shows the graph of $y = f_2(x) = x^2 - 6x + 10$. Note also that for each function, the y-intercept is $f(0) = c$. Thus the constants in the functions are $c = 7$ for $f_1(x)$ and $c = 10$ for $f_2(x)$.

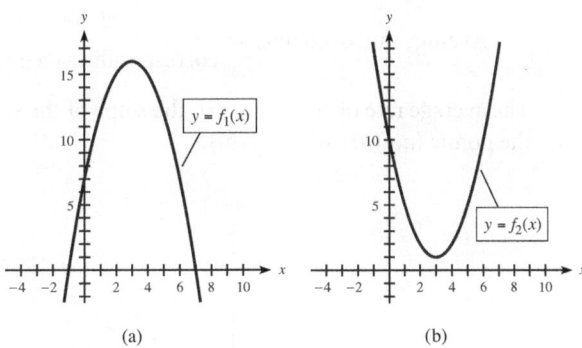

Figure 2.9   (a)   (b)

EXAMPLE   5   **Maximizing Revenue**

Ace Cruises offers a sunset cruise to a group of 50 people for a price of $30 per person, but it reduces the price per person by $0.50 for each additional person above 50.
(a) Does reducing the price per person to get more people in the group give the cruise company more revenue?
(b) How many people will provide maximum revenue for the cruise company?

Solution
(a) The revenue to the company if 50 people are in the group and each pays $30 is $50(\$30) = \$1500$. The following table shows the revenue for the addition of people to the group. The table shows that as the group size begins to increase past 50 people, the revenue also increases. However, it also shows that increasing the group size too much (to 70 people) reduces revenue.

Increase in Group Size	Number of People	Decrease in Price	New Price ($)	Revenue ($)
0	50	0	30	$50(30) = 1500$
1	51	0.50(1)	29.50	$51(29.50) = 1504.50$
2	52	0.50(2) = 1	29	$52(29) = 1508$
3	53	0.50(3) = 1.50	28.50	$53(28.50) = 1510.50$
$\vdots$	$\vdots$	$\vdots$	$\vdots$	$\vdots$
20	70	0.50(20) = 10	20	$70(20) = 1400$
$\vdots$	$\vdots$	$\vdots$	$\vdots$	$\vdots$
x	$50 + x$	0.50(x)	$30 - 0.50x$	$(50 + x)(30 - 0.50x)$

(b) The last entry in the table shows the revenue for an increase of x people in the group.

$$R(x) = (50 + x)(30 - 0.50x) = 1500 + 5x - 0.50x^2$$

From the expanded form, we see that $a = -0.50, b = 5$, and $c = 1500$. Thus, the vertex of the graph of this function is $x = \dfrac{-b}{2a} = \dfrac{-5}{2(-0.50)} = 5, R(5) = 1512.50$.

This means that the revenue will be maximized at $1512.50 when $50 + 5 = 55$ people are in the group, with each paying $30 - 0.50(5) = 27.50$ dollars.

Average Rate of Change   Because the graph of a quadratic function is not a line, the rate of change of the function is not constant. We can, however, find the **average rate of change** of a function between two input values if we know how much the function output values change between the two input values.

Average Rate of Change   The average rate of change of $f(x)$ with respect to x over the interval from $x = a$ to $x = b$ (where $a < b$) is calculated as

$$\text{Average rate of change} = \frac{\text{change of } f(x)}{\text{corresponding change in } x\text{-values}} = \frac{f(b) - f(a)}{b - a}$$

The average rate of change is also the slope of the segment (or secant line) joining the points $(a, f(a))$ and $(b, f(b))$.

EXAMPLE   6   Average Rate of Change of Revenue

We found that the revenue for the cruise in Example 5 was defined by the quadratic function

$$R(x) = 1500 + 5x - 0.50x^2$$

where x is the increase in the group size beyond 50 people. What is the average rate of change of revenue per person if the group increases from 50 to 55 persons?

Solution

The average rate of change of revenue from 50 to 55 persons is the average rate of change of the function from $x = 0$ to $x = 5$.

$$\frac{R(5) - R(0)}{5 - 0} = \frac{1512.50 - 1500}{5} = 2.50 \text{ dollars per person}$$

This average rate of change is also the slope of the **secant line** connecting the points (0, 1500) and (5, 1512.50) on the graph of the function (see Figure 2.10).

Figure 2.10

CHECKPOINT
ANSWERS

1. Parabola
2. (a) $x = \dfrac{-b}{2a}$
   (b) $x = 12$; $y = 72$
3. (a) Maximum point if $a < 0$; minimum point if $a > 0$
   (b) $(12, 72)$ is a maximum point.
4. The x-intercepts
5. y-intercept $= c$

EXERCISES 2.2

In Problems 1–6, (a) find the vertex of the graph of the equation, (b) determine whether the vertex is a maximum or minimum point, (c) determine what value of x gives the optimal value of the function, and (d) determine the optimal (maximum or minimum) value of the function.

1. $y = \dfrac{1}{2}x^2 + x$
2. $y = x^2 - 2x$
3. $y = 8 + 2x - x^2$
4. $y = 6 - 4x - 2x^2$
5. $f(x) = 6x - x^2$
6. $f(x) = x^2 + 2x - 3$

In Problems 7–12, determine whether each function's vertex is a maximum point or a minimum point and find the coordinates of this point. Find the zeros, if any exist, and the y-intercept. Then sketch the graph of the function.

7. $y = x - \dfrac{1}{4}x^2$
8. $y = -2x^2 + 18x$
9. $y = x^2 + 4x + 4$
10. $y = x^2 - 6x + 9$
11. $\dfrac{1}{2}x^2 + x - y = 3$
12. $x^2 + x + 2y = 5$

For each function in Problems 13–16, (a) tell how the graph of $y = x^2$ is shifted and (b) graph the function.

13. $y = (x - 3)^2 + 1$
14. $y = (x - 10)^2 + 1$
15. $y = (x + 2)^2 - 2$
16. $y = (x + 12)^2 - 8$

In Problems 17–20, graph each function with a graphing utility. Use the graph to find the vertex and zeros. Check your results algebraically.

17. $y = \dfrac{1}{2}x^2 - x - \dfrac{15}{2}$
18. $y = 0.1(x^2 + 4x - 32)$
19. $y = \dfrac{1}{4}x^2 + 3x + 12$
20. $y = x^2 - 2x + 5$

In Problems 21 and 22, find the average rate of change of the function between the given values of x.

21. $y = -5x - x^2$ between $x = -1$ and $x = 1$
22. $y = 8 + 3x + 0.5x^2$ between $x = 2$ and $x = 4$

In Problems 23–26, find the vertex and zeros and use them to determine a window for a graphing calculator that includes these values; graph the function with that window.

23. $y = 63 + 0.2x - 0.01x^2$
24. $y = 0.2x^2 + 16x + 140$
25. $y = 0.0001x^2 - 0.01$
26. $y = 0.01x - 0.001x^2$

In Problems 27 and 28, (a) find the vertex of each function $f(x)$. Use the vertex to set the window in which to graph $y = f(x)$ and then (b) graphically approximate the solutions to $f(x) = 0$.

27. $f(x) = 8x^2 - 16x - 16$
28. $f(x) = 3x^2 - 18x + 16$

In Problems 29 and 30, complete the following.

(a) Use the graph of $y = f(x)$ to find an integer solution to $f(x) = 0$.

(b) Use the solution from (a) to find a factor of $f(x)$.

(c) Factor $f(x)$.

(d) Solve $f(x) = 0$.

29. $f(x) = 3x^2 - 8x + 4$ 30. $f(x) = 5x^2 - 2x - 7$

APPLICATIONS

31. *Profit* The monthly profit from the sale of x units of a product is given by $P = 16x - 0.01x^2 - 900$ dollars.
    (a) What level of production maximizes profit?
    (b) What is the maximum possible profit?

32. *Profit* The monthly profit from the sale of x units of a product is $P = 80x - 0.04x^2 - 12{,}000$ dollars.
    (a) What level of production maximizes profit?
    (b) What is the maximum possible profit?

33. *Crop yield* The yield in bushels from a grove of orange trees is given by $Y = x(800 - x)$, where x is the number of orange trees per acre. How many trees will maximize the yield?

34. *Stimulus-response* One of the early results in psychology relating the magnitude of a stimulus x to the magnitude of a response y is expressed by the equation

$$y = kx^2$$

where k is an experimental constant. Sketch this graph for $k = 1$, $k = 2$, and $k = 4$.

35. *Drug sensitivity* The sensitivity S to a drug is related to the dosage x (in milligrams) by

$$S = 1000x - x^2$$

Sketch the graph of this function and determine what dosage gives maximum sensitivity. Use the graph to determine the maximum sensitivity.

36. *Maximizing an enclosed area* If 100 feet of fence is used to enclose a rectangular yard, then the resulting area is given by

$$A = x(50 - x)$$

where x feet is the width of the rectangle and $50 - x$ feet is the length. Graph this equation and determine the length and width that give maximum area.

37. *Photosynthesis* The rate of photosynthesis R for a certain plant depends on the intensity of light x, in lumens, according to

$$R = 270x - 90x^2$$

Sketch the graph of this function and determine the intensity that gives the maximum rate.

38. *Projectiles* A ball thrown vertically into the air has its height above ground given by

$$s = 112t - 16t^2$$

where t is in seconds and s is in feet. Find the maximum height of the ball.

39. *Projectiles* Two projectiles are shot into the air from the same location. The paths of the projectiles are parabolas and are given by

(a) $y = -0.0013x^2 + x + 10$ and

(b) $y = \dfrac{-x^2}{81} + \dfrac{4}{3}x + 10$

where x is the horizontal distance and y is the vertical distance, both in feet. Determine which projectile goes higher by locating the vertex of each parabola.

40. *Flow rates of water* The speed at which water travels in a pipe can be measured by directing the flow through an elbow and measuring the height to which it spurts out the top. If the elbow height is 10 cm, the equation relating the height h (in centimeters) of the water above the elbow and its velocity v (in centimeters per second) is given by

$$v^2 = 1960(h + 10)$$

Solve this equation for h and graph the result, using the velocity as the independent variable.

41. *Cost* The following figure shows the graph of a total cost function, with x equal to the number of units produced.
    (a) Is the average rate of change of cost greater from $x = a$ to $x = b$ or from $x = b$ to $x = c$? Explain.
    (b) Would the number of units d need to satisfy $d < b$ or $d > b$ for the average rate of change of cost from $x = a$ to $x = d$ to be greater than that from $x = a$ to $x = b$? Explain.

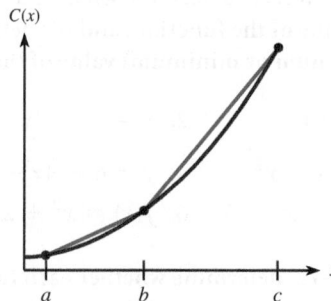

42. *Revenue* The following figure shows the graph of a total revenue function, with x equal to the number of units sold.
    (a) Is the average rate of change of revenue negative from $x = a$ to $x = b$ or from $x = b$ to $x = c$? Explain.
    (b) Would the number of units d need to satisfy $d < b$ or $d > b$ for the average rate of change of revenue from $x = a$ to $x = d$ to be greater than that from $x = a$ to $x = b$? Explain.

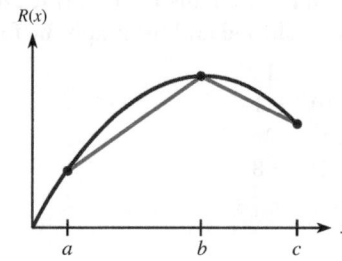

43. *Apartment rental* The owner of an apartment building can rent all 50 apartments if she charges $1800 per month, but she rents one fewer apartment for each $60 increase in monthly rent.
    (a) Construct a table that gives the revenue generated if she charges $1800, $1860, and $1920.
    (b) Does her revenue from the rental of the apartments increase or decrease as she increases the rent from $1800 to $1920?
    (c) Write an equation that gives the revenue from rental of the apartments if she makes x increases of $60 in the rent.
    (d) Find the rent she should charge to maximize her revenue.

44. *Revenue* The owner of a skating rink rents the rink for parties at $600 if 50 or fewer skaters attend, so that the cost per person is $12 if 50 attend. For each 5 skaters above 50, she reduces the price per skater by $0.50.
    (a) Construct a table that gives the revenue generated if 50, 60, and 70 skaters attend.
    (b) Does the owner's revenue from the rental of the rink increase or decrease as the number of skaters increases from 50 to 70?
    (c) Write the equation that describes the revenue for parties with x more than 50 skaters.
    (d) Find the number of skaters that will maximize the revenue.

45. *Pension resources* The Pension Benefit Guaranty Corporation is the agency that insures pensions. The figure shows one study's projection for the agency's total resources, initially rising (from taking over the assets of failing plans) but then falling (as more workers retire and payouts increase).
    (a) What kind of function might be used to model the agency's total resources?
    (b) If a function of the form $f(x) = ax^2 + bx + c$ were used to model these total resources, would $f(x)$ have $a > 0$ or $a < 0$? Explain.
    (c) If the model from part (b) used x as the number of years past 2004, explain why the model would have $b > 0$ and $c > 0$.

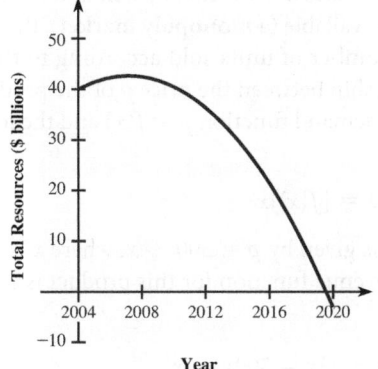

Year

46. *Projectile motion* When a stone is thrown upward, it follows a parabolic path given by a form of the equation
$$y = ax^2 + bx + c$$
If $y = 0$ represents ground level, find the equation of a stone that is thrown from ground level at $x = 0$ and lands on the ground 40 units away if the stone reaches a maximum height of 40 units. (*Hint:* Find the coordinates of the vertex of the parabola and two other points.)

47. *Health care costs per capita* Rising health care costs are a growing concern for everyone in the United States. Using U.S. Centers for Medicare and Medicaid Services data from 2006 and projected to 2021, U.S. per capita health care costs can be modeled by
$$y = 20.61x^2 - 116.4x + 7406$$
where x is the number of years past 2000. Use this equation to find, to the nearest dollar, the average rate of change of U.S. per capita health care costs from 2010 to 2015 and from 2015 to 2020.

48. *Women in the workforce* Using U.S. Census Bureau data for selected years from 1970 and projected to 2040, the percent of the total workforce that is female is given by
$$p(t) = -0.0036t^2 + 0.38t + 38.62$$
where t is the number of years past 1970.
    (a) Graph the function $y = p(t)$.
    (b) From the equation, identify the maximum point on the graph of $y = p(t)$.
    (c) In what year is the percent of women workers projected to be at its maximum, according to this model?

E-commerce **Online sales in the United States are expected to exceed $400 billion by 2017. Using data from 2000 to 2017, the revenue, in billions of dollars, can be described by**
$$y = 1.230x^2 - 22.87x + 142.9$$
where x is the number of years past 1990. Use this function in Problems 49 and 50 (*Sources*: U.S. Census Bureau, Forrester Research, Inc.).

49. Graph the function for $x = 0$ to $x = 27$.

50. The data starts in 2000, at $x = 10$, and the function may not apply before then. The graph has a minimum point; where is this point?

Business Applications Using Quadratics

OBJECTIVES

- To find break-even points
- To maximize revenue and profit functions
- To graph quadratic supply and demand functions
- To find market equilibrium

APPLICATION PREVIEW

Suppose that the supply function for a product is given by $2p - q - 38 = 0$ and the demand function is given by $p(q + 4) = 400$. Finding the market equilibrium involves solving a quadratic equation. (See Example 3.)

In this section, we graph quadratic supply and demand functions and find market equilibrium by solving supply and demand functions simultaneously using quadratic methods. We also discuss quadratic revenue, cost, and profit functions, including break-even points and profit maximization.

Break-Even Points   When we know the functions for total costs, $C(x)$, and total revenue, $R(x)$, we can find the break-even point by finding the quantity x that makes $C(x) = R(x)$.

For example, if $C(x) = 360 + 40x + 0.1x^2$ and $R(x) = 60x$, then setting $C(x) = R(x)$, we have

$$360 + 40x + 0.1x^2 = 60x$$
$$0.1x^2 - 20x + 360 = 0$$
$$x^2 - 200x + 3600 = 0$$
$$(x - 20)(x - 180) = 0$$
$$x = 20 \quad \text{or} \quad x = 180$$

Thus $C(x) = R(x)$ at $x = 20$ and at $x = 180$. If 20 items are produced and sold, $C(x)$ and $R(x)$ are both \$1200; if 180 items are sold, $C(x)$ and $R(x)$ are both \$10,800. Thus there are two break-even points. (See Figure 2.11.)

Figure 2.11

A company's total revenue from the sale of a product is the selling price times the number of units sold, where both price and sales are affected by demand for the product. When a company's product is the only one available (a **monopoly market**), then the selling price the company sets determines the number of units sold according to the product's demand function. In this case, the relationship between the price p of the product and the number of units sold x is described by the demand function $p = f(x)$ and the total revenue function for the product is given by

$$R = px = [f(x)]x$$

If, for example, the demand for a product is given by $p = 300 - x$, where x is the number of units sold and p is the price, then the revenue function for this product is the quadratic function

$$R = px = (300 - x)x = 300x - x^2$$

EXAMPLE 1   **Break-Even Point**

Suppose that in a monopoly market, the total cost per day of producing a high-tech product is given by $C = 3600 + 100x + 2x^2$. Suppose further that the daily demand function for this product is $p = 500 - 2x$. Find the number of units that will give the break-even point for the product.

Solution

The total cost function is $C(x) = 3600 + 100x + 2x^2$, and the total revenue function is $R(x) = px = (500 - 2x)x = 500x - 2x^2$.

Setting $C(x) = R(x)$ and solving for x gives

$$3600 + 100x + 2x^2 = 500x - 2x^2$$
$$4x^2 - 400x + 3600 = 0$$
$$x^2 - 100x + 900 = 0$$
$$(x - 90)(x - 10) = 0$$
$$x = 90 \quad \text{or} \quad x = 10$$

Does this mean that the firm will break even at 10 units and at 90 units? Yes. Figure 2.12 shows the graphs of $C(x)$ and $R(x)$. From the graph, we can observe that the firm makes a profit after $x = 10$ until $x = 90$ because $R(x) > C(x)$ in that interval. At $x = 90$, the profit is 0, and the firm loses money if it produces more than 90 units per day.

Figure 2.12

CHECKPOINT

1. The point of intersection of the revenue function and the cost function is called _____.
2. If $C(x) = 120x + 15{,}000$ and $R(x) = 370x - x^2$, finding the break-even points requires solution of what equation? Find the break-even points.

Revenue and Profit Maximization

Note that for Example 1, the revenue function

$$R(x) = (500 - 2x)x = 500x - 2x^2$$

is a parabola that opens downward. Thus the vertex is the point at which revenue is maximum. We can locate this vertex by using the methods discussed in the previous section.

$$\text{Vertex: } x = \frac{-b}{2a} = \frac{-500}{2(-2)} = \frac{500}{4} = 125 \text{ (units)}$$

It is interesting to note that when $x = 125$, the firm achieves its maximum revenue of

$$R(125) = 500(125) - 2(125)^2 = 31{,}250 \text{ (dollars)}$$

but the costs when $x = 125$ are

$$C(125) = 3600 + 100(125) + 2(125)^2 = 47{,}350 \text{ (dollars)}$$

which results in a loss. This illustrates that maximizing revenue is not a good goal. We should seek to maximize profit. Figure 2.12 shows that maximum profit will occur where the distance between the revenue and cost curves [that is, $R(x) - C(x)$] is largest. This appears to be near $x = 50$, which is midway between the x-values of the break-even points. This is verified in the next example.

EXAMPLE 2   Profit Maximization

For the daily total cost function $C(x) = 3600 + 100x + 2x^2$ and the daily total revenue function $R(x) = 500x - 2x^2$ (from Example 1), find the number of units that maximizes profit and find the maximum profit.

Solution
Using Profit = Revenue − Cost, we can determine the profit function:

$$P(x) = (500x - 2x^2) - (3600 + 100x + 2x^2) = -3600 + 400x - 4x^2$$

This profit function is a parabola with $a = -4$, $b = 400$, and $c = -3600$. Because $a < 0$, the graph opens downward, so the vertex will be the maximum point.

$$\text{Vertex: } x = \frac{-b}{2a} = \frac{-400}{2(-4)} = \frac{-400}{-8} = 50$$

Furthermore, when $x = 50$, we have

$$P(50) = -3600 + 400(50) - 4(50)^2 = 6400 \text{ (dollars)}$$

Thus when 50 items are produced and sold per day, a maximum profit of $6400 is made (see Figure 2.13).

Figure 2.13

Figure 2.13 shows that the break-even points are at $x = 10$ and $x = 90$ and that the maximum profit occurs at the x-value midway between these x-values. This is reasonable because the graph of the profit function is a parabola, and the x-value of any parabola's vertex occurs midway between its x-intercepts.

It is important to note that the procedures for finding maximum revenue and profit in these examples depend on the fact that these functions are parabolas. For more general functions, procedures for finding maximum or minimum values are discussed in Chapter 10, "Applications of Derivatives."

Supply, Demand, and Market Equilibrium   The first-quadrant parts of parabolas or other quadratic equations are frequently used to represent supply and demand functions. For example, the first-quadrant part of $p = q^2 + q + 2$ [Figure 2.14(a)] may represent a supply curve, whereas the first-quadrant part of $q^2 + 2q + 6p - 23 = 0$ [Figure 2.14(b)] may represent a demand curve.

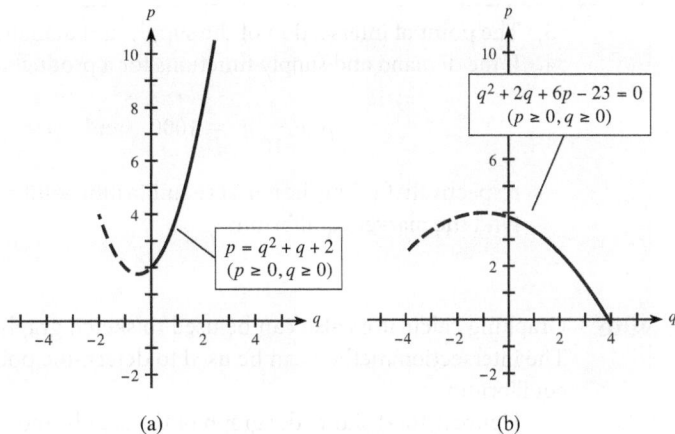

Figure 2.14   (a)   (b)

When quadratic equations are used to represent supply or demand curves, we can solve their equations simultaneously to find the market equilibrium as we did with linear supply and demand functions. As in Section 1.5, we can solve two equations in two variables by eliminating one variable and obtaining an equation in the other variable. When the functions are quadratic, the substitution method of solution may be best and the resulting equation in one unknown will usually be quadratic.

EXAMPLE 3   Market Equilibrium | APPLICATION PREVIEW |

If the demand function for a commodity is given by $p(q + 4) = 400$ and the supply function is given by $2p - q - 38 = 0$, q in thousands, find the market equilibrium.

Solution

Solving the supply equation $2p - q - 38 = 0$ for p gives $p = \frac{1}{2}q + 19$. Substituting for p in $p(q + 4) = 400$ gives

$$\left(\frac{1}{2}q + 19\right)(q + 4) = 400$$

$$\frac{1}{2}q^2 + 21q + 76 = 400$$

$$\frac{1}{2}q^2 + 21q - 324 = 0$$

Multiplying both sides of the equation by 2 yields $q^2 + 42q - 648 = 0$. Factoring gives

$$(q - 12)(q + 54) = 0$$
$$q = 12 \quad \text{or} \quad q = -54$$

Thus the market equilibrium occurs when 12 thousand items are sold, at a price of $p = \frac{1}{2}(12) + 19 = \$25$ each. The graphs of the demand and supply functions are shown in Figure 2.15.

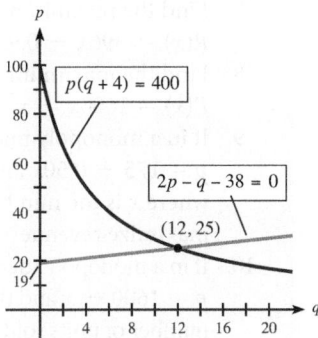

Figure 2.15

CHECKPOINT

3. The point of intersection of the supply and demand functions is called _____.
4. If the demand and supply functions for a product are

$$p + \frac{1}{10}q^2 = 1000 \quad \text{and} \quad p = \frac{1}{10}q + 10$$

respectively, finding the market equilibrium point requires solution of what equation? Find the market equilibrium.

Calculator Note   Graphing calculators also can be used to sketch graphs of supply and demand functions. The intersection method can be used to determine points of intersection that give market equilibrium.

Figure 2.16(a) shows the graph of the supply and demand functions for the commodity in Example 3. Using CALC, 5:intersect gives the same market equilibrium point determined in Example 3 [see Figure 2.16(b)]. See Appendix A, Section 2.3. ■

Figure 2.16   (a)   (b)

CHECKPOINT ANSWERS

1. The break-even point
2. Solve $120x + 15,000 = 370x - x^2$. Break-even points are at 100 units and 150 units.
3. The market equilibrium point or market equilibrium
4. Solve $-\frac{1}{10}q^2 + 1000 = \frac{1}{10}q + 10$. Market equilibrium occurs when $q = 99$ and $p = 19.90$.

EXERCISES 2.3

BREAK-EVEN POINTS AND MAXIMIZATION

1. The total costs for a company are given by

$$C(x) = 2000 + 40x + x^2$$

and the total revenues are given by

$$R(x) = 130x$$

Find the break-even points.

2. If a firm has the following cost and revenue functions, find the break-even points.

$$C(x) = 3600 + 25x + \frac{1}{2}x^2,$$

$$R(x) = \left(175 - \frac{1}{2}x\right)x$$

3. If a company has total costs $C(x) = 15,000 + 35x + 0.1x^2$ and total revenues given by $R(x) = 385x - 0.9x^2$, find the break-even points.
4. If total costs are $C(x) = 1600 + 1500x$ and total revenues are $R(x) = 1600x - x^2$, find the break-even points.

5. Given that the profit is $P(x) = 11.5x - 0.1x^2 - 150$ and that production is restricted to fewer than 75 units, find the break-even points.
6. If the profit function for a firm is given by $P(x) = -1100 + 120x - x^2$ and limitations on space require that production be less than 100 units, find the break-even points.
7. Find the maximum revenue for the revenue function $R(x) = 396x - 0.9x^2$.
8. Find the maximum revenue for the revenue function $R(x) = 1600x - x^2$.
9. If in a monopoly market the demand for a product is $p = 175 - 0.50x$ and the revenue function is $R = px$, where x is the number of units sold, what price will maximize revenue?
10. If in a monopoly market the demand for a product is $p = 1600 - x$ and the revenue is $R = px$, where x is the number of units sold, what price will maximize revenue?

11. The profit function for a certain commodity is $P(x) = 110x - x^2 - 1000$. Find the level of production that yields maximum profit and find the maximum profit.

12. The profit function for a firm making widgets is $P(x) = 88x - x^2 - 1200$. Find the number of units at which maximum profit is achieved and find the maximum profit.

13. (a) Graph the profit function $P(x) = 80x - 0.1x^2 - 7000$.
    (b) Find the vertex of the graph. Is it a maximum point or a minimum point?
    (c) Is the average rate of change of this function from $x = a < 400$ to $x = 400$ positive or negative?
    (d) Is the average rate of change of this function from $x = 400$ to $x = a > 400$ positive or negative?
    (e) Does the average rate of change of the profit get closer to or farther from 0 when a is closer to 400?

14. (a) Graph the profit function $P(x) = 50x - 0.2x^2 - 2000$.
    (b) Find the vertex of the graph. Is it a maximum point or a minimum point?
    (c) Is the average rate of change of this function from $x = a < 125$ to $x = 125$ positive or negative?
    (d) Is the average rate of change of this function from $x = 125$ to $x = a > 125$ positive or negative?
    (e) Does the average rate of change of the profit get closer to or farther from 0 when a is closer to 125?

15. (a) Form the profit function for the cost and revenue functions in Problem 3 and find the maximum profit.
    (b) Compare the level of production to maximize profit with the level to maximize revenue (see Problem 7). Do they agree?
    (c) How do the break-even points compare with the zeros of $P(x)$?

16. (a) Form the profit function for the cost and revenue functions in Problem 4 and find the maximum profit.
    (b) Compare the level of production to maximize profit with the level to maximize revenue (see Problem 8). Do they agree?
    (c) How do the break-even points compare with the zeros of $P(x)$?

17. Suppose a company has fixed costs of $28,000 and variable cost per unit of $\frac{2}{5}x + 222$ dollars, where x is the total number of units produced. Suppose further that the selling price of its product is $1250 - \frac{3}{5}x$ dollars per unit.
    (a) Find the break-even points.
    (b) Find the maximum revenue.
    (c) Form the profit function from the cost and revenue functions and find maximum profit.
    (d) What price will maximize the profit?

18. Suppose a company has fixed costs of $300 and variable cost per unit of $\frac{3}{4}x + 1460$ dollars, where x is the total number of units produced. Suppose further that the selling price of its product is $1500 - \frac{1}{4}x$ dollars per unit.
    (a) Find the break-even points.
    (b) Find the maximum revenue.

(c) Form the profit function from the cost and revenue functions and find maximum profit.
(d) What price will maximize the profit?

19. The following table gives the total revenues of Cablenet Communications for selected years.

Year	Total Revenues (millions)
2012	$63.13
2013	62.91
2014	60.53
2015	60.27
2016	61.10
2017	62.19
2018	63.09
2019	64.90
2020	67.16

Suppose the data can be modeled by the equation

$$R(t) = 0.271t^2 - 2.76t + 67.83$$

where t is the number of years past 2010.
(a) Use the function to find the year in which revenue was minimum and find the minimum predicted revenue.
(b) Check the result from part (a) against the data in the table.
(c) Graph $R(t)$ and the data points from the table.
(d) Write a sentence to describe how well the function fits the data.

The data in the table give sales revenues and costs and expenses for Continental Divide Mining for various years. Use this table in Problems 20 and 21.

Year	Sales Revenue (millions)	Costs and Expenses (millions)
2010	$2.6155	$2.4105
2011	2.7474	2.4412
2012	2.934	2.6378
2013	3.3131	2.9447
2014	3.9769	3.5344
2015	4.5494	3.8171
2016	4.8949	4.2587
2017	5.1686	4.8769
2018	4.9593	4.9088
2019	5.0913	4.6771
2020	4.7489	4.9025

20. Assume that sales revenues for Continental Divide Mining can be modeled by

$$R(t) = -0.031t^2 + 0.776t + 0.179$$

where t is the number of years past 2007.
(a) Use the function to determine the year in which maximum revenue occurs and the maximum revenue it predicts.
(b) Check the result from (a) against the data in the table.

(c) Graph $R(t)$ and the data points from the table.

(d) Write a sentence to describe how well the function fits the data.

21. Assume that costs and expenses for Continental Divide Mining can be modeled by

$$C(t) = -0.012t^2 + 0.492t + 0.725$$

where t is the number of years past 2007.

(a) Use $R(t)$ as given in Problem 20 and form the profit function (as a function of time).

(b) Use the function from (a) to find the year in which maximum profit occurs.

(c) Graph the profit function from (a) and the data points from the table.

(d) Through the decade from 2015 to 2025, does the function project increasing or decreasing profits? Do the data support this trend (as far as it goes)?

SUPPLY, DEMAND, AND MARKET EQUILIBRIUM

In Problems 22–24, a supply function and a demand function are given. (a) Sketch the first-quadrant portions of those functions on the same set of axes. (b) Label the market equilibrium point. (c) Algebraically determine the market equilibrium point.

22. Supply: $p = q^2 + 8q + 16$
     Demand: $p = 216 - 2q$

23. Supply: $p = \frac{1}{4}q^2 + 10$
     Demand: $p = 86 - 6q - 3q^2$

24. Supply: $p = q^2 + 8q + 22$
     Demand: $p = 198 - 4q - \frac{1}{4}q^2$

25. If the supply function for a commodity is $p = q^2 + 8q + 16$ and the demand function is $p = -3q^2 + 6q + 436$, find the equilibrium quantity and equilibrium price.

26. If the supply function for a commodity is $p = q^2 + 8q + 20$ and the demand function is $p = 100 - 4q - q^2$, find the equilibrium quantity and equilibrium price.

27. If the demand function for a commodity is given by the equation $p^2 + 4q = 1600$ and the supply function is given by the equation $300 - p^2 + 2q = 0$, find the equilibrium quantity and equilibrium price.

28. If the supply and demand functions for a commodity are given by $4p - q = 42$ and $(p + 2)q = 2100$, respectively, find the price and quantity that will result in market equilibrium.

29. If the supply and demand functions for a commodity are given by $p - q = 10$ and $q(2p - 10) = 2100$, what is the equilibrium price and what is the corresponding number of units supplied and demanded?

30. If the supply and demand functions for a certain product are given by the equations $2p - q + 6 = 0$ and $(p + q)(q + 10) = 3696$, respectively, find the price and quantity that give market equilibrium.

31. The supply function for a product is $2p - q - 10 = 0$, while the demand function for the same product is $(p + 10)(q + 30) = 7200$. Find the market equilibrium point.

32. The supply and demand for a product are given by $2p - q = 50$ and $pq = 100 + 20q$, respectively. Find the market equilibrium point.

33. For the product in Problem 31, if a \$22 tax is placed on production of the item, then the supplier passes this tax on by adding \$22 to his selling price. Find the new equilibrium point for this product when the tax is passed on. (The new supply function is given by $p = \frac{1}{2}q + 27$.)

34. For the product in Problem 32, if a \$12.50 tax is placed on production and passed through by the supplier, find the new equilibrium point.

SECTION 2.4

Special Functions and Their Graphs

OBJECTIVES

- To graph and apply basic functions, including constant and power functions
- To graph and apply polynomial and rational functions
- To graph and apply absolute value and piecewise defined functions

APPLICATION PREVIEW

The average cost per item for a product is calculated by dividing the total cost by the number of items. Hence, if the total cost function for x units of a product is

$$C(x) = 900 + 3x + x^2$$

and if we denote the average cost function by $\overline{C}(x)$, then

$$\overline{C}(x) = \frac{C(x)}{x} = \frac{900 + 3x + x^2}{x}$$

This average cost function is a special kind of function, called a rational function. We can use this function to find the minimum average cost. (See Example 4.)

In this section, we discuss polynomial, rational, and other special functions.

Basic Functions   The special linear function

$$y = f(x) = x$$

is called the **identity function** [see Figure 2.17(a)], and a linear function defined by

$$y = f(x) = C \qquad C \text{ a constant}$$

is called a **constant function.** Figure 2.17(b) shows the graph of the constant function $y = f(x) = 2$. (Note that the slope of the graph of any constant function is 0.)

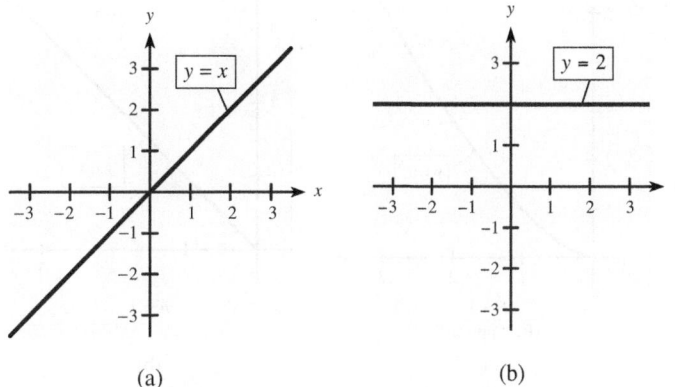

Figure 2.17   (a)   (b)

The functions of the form $y = ax^b$, where $b > 0$, are called **power functions.** Examples of power functions include $y = x^2$, $y = x^3$, $y = \sqrt{x} = x^{1/2}$, and $y = \sqrt[3]{x} = x^{1/3}$. [See Figure 2.18(a)–(d).] The functions $y = \sqrt{x}$ and $y = \sqrt[3]{x}$ are also called **root functions,** and $y = x^2$ and $y = x^3$ are also called basic **polynomial functions.**

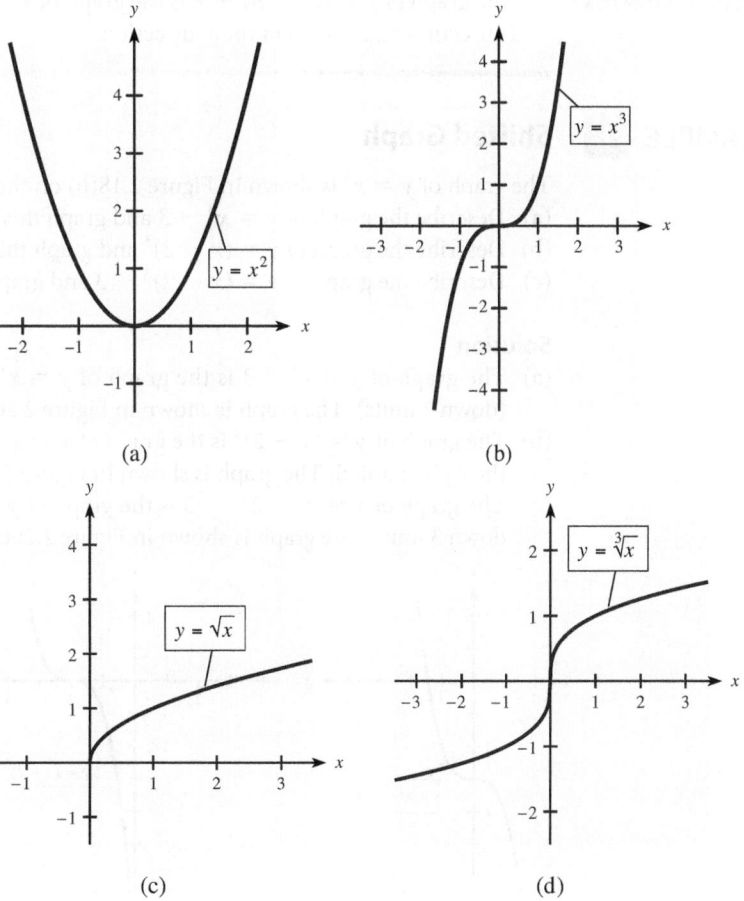

Figure 2.18   (c)   (d)

The general shape for the power function $y = ax^b$, where $a > 0$ and $b > 0$, depends on the value of b. Figure 2.19 shows the first-quadrant portions of typical graphs of $y = ax^b$ for $a > 0$ and for different values of b. (Note that Figure 2.19 shows graphs for $a = 1$, but shapes are similar for any $a > 0$.) Note how the direction in which the graph bends differs for $b > 1$ and for $0 < b < 1$. Getting accurate graphs of these functions requires plotting a number of points by hand or with a graphing utility. Our goal at this stage is to recognize the basic shapes of certain functions.

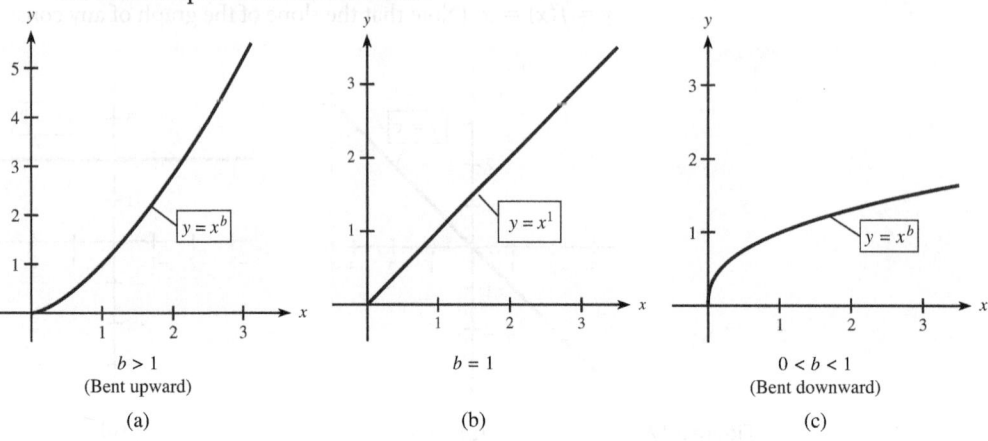

Figure 2.19

(a)   (b)   (c)

Shifts   In Section 2.2, "Quadratic Functions: Parabolas," we noted that the graph of $y = (x - h)^2 + k$ is a parabola that is shifted h units in the x-direction and k units in the y-direction. These shifts also apply to other functions.

Shifts of Graphs	The graph of $y = f(x - h) + k$ is the graph of $y = f(x)$ shifted h units in the x-direction and k units in the y-direction.

EXAMPLE   1   Shifted Graph

The graph of $y = x^3$ is shown in Figure 2.18(b) on the preceding page.
(a) Describe the graph of $y = x^3 - 3$ and graph this function.
(b) Describe the graph of $y = (x - 2)^3$ and graph this function.
(c) Describe the graph of $y = (x - 2)^3 - 3$ and graph this function.

Solution
(a) The graph of $y = x^3 - 3$ is the graph of $y = x^3$ shifted -3 units in the y-direction (down 3 units). The graph is shown in Figure 2.20(a).
(b) The graph of $y = (x - 2)^3$ is the graph of $y = x^3$ shifted 2 units in the x-direction (to the right 2 units). The graph is shown in Figure 2.20(b).
(c) The graph of $y = (x - 2)^3 - 3$ is the graph of $y = x^3$ shifted to the right 2 units and down 3 units. The graph is shown in Figure 2.20(c).

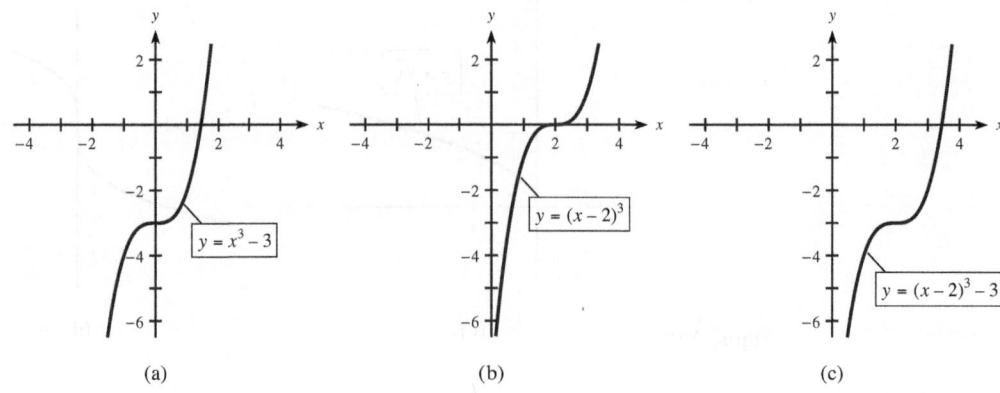

Figure 2.20   (a)   (b)   (c)

Polynomial Functions

A **polynomial function of degree** n has the form

$$y = a_n x^n + a_{n-1} x^{n-1} + \cdots + a_1 x + a_0$$

where $a_n \neq 0$ and n is an integer, $n \geq 0$.

A **linear function** is a polynomial function of degree 1, and a **quadratic function** is a polynomial function of degree 2.

Accurate graphing of a polynomial function of degree greater than 2 may require the methods of calculus; we will investigate these methods in Chapter 10, "Applications of Derivatives." For now, we will observe some characteristics of the graphs of polynomial functions of degrees 2, 3, and 4; these are summarized in Table 2.1. Using this information and point plotting or using a graphing utility yields the graphs of these functions.

TABLE 2.1

GRAPHS OF SOME POLYNOMIALS

	Degree 2	Degree 3	Degree 4
Turning points	1	0 or 2	1 or 3
x-intercepts	0, 1, or 2	1, 2, or 3	0, 1, 2, 3, or 4
Possible shapes	$\cup$ or $\cap$ (a) (b)	(a) (b) (c) (d)	(a) (b) (c) (d) (e) (f)

Calculator Note

The function $y = x^3 - 16x$ is a third-degree (cubic) polynomial function, so it has one of the four shapes shown in the "Degree 3" column in Table 2.1. Details of graphing this function are shown in Appendix A, Section 2.4 (see Figure 2.21).

(a)   (b)

Figure 2.21   Two views of $y = x^3 - 16x$

EXAMPLE 2   **Quartic Polynomial**

Graph $y = x^4 - 2x^2$.

Solution

This is a degree 4 (quartic) polynomial function. Thus it has one or three turning points and has one of the six shapes in the "Degree 4" column of Table 2.1. We begin by graphing this function with a large viewing window to obtain the graph in Figure 2.22(a). Figure 2.22(b) shows the same graph with a smaller viewing window, near $x = 0$. We now see that the graph has shape (f) from Table 2.1, with turning points at $x = -1$, $x = 0$, and $x = 1$.

(a)   (b)

Figure 2.22   Two views of $y = x^4 - 2x^2$

Spreadsheet Note   It is possible to graph additional polynomial functions with Excel by using the same methods as those for graphing linear and quadratic function. See Appendix B, Sections 2.2 and
2.4, or the Online Excel Guide.

CHECKPOINT

1. All constant functions [such as $f(x) = 8$] have graphs that are _____.
2. Which of the following are polynomial functions?
   (a) $f(x) = x^3 - x + 4$
   (b) $f(x) = \dfrac{x + 1}{4x}$
   (c) $f(x) = 1 + \sqrt{x}$
   (d) $g(x) = \dfrac{1 + \sqrt{x}}{1 + x + \sqrt{x}}$
   (e) $h(x) = 5x$
3. A third-degree polynomial can have at most _____ turning points.

Rational Functions   The function $f(x) = \dfrac{1}{x}$ is a special function called a **reciprocal function.** A table of sample
values and the graph of $y = \dfrac{1}{x}$ are shown in Figure 2.23. Because division by 0 is not possi-
ble, $x = 0$ is not in the domain of the function.

x	y
−3	−0.33
−2	−0.5
−1	−1
−0.1	−10
−0.04	−25
−0.001	−1000
3	0.33
2	0.5
1	1
0.1	10
0.04	25
0.001	1000

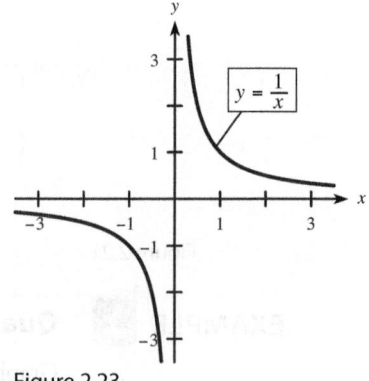

Figure 2.23

The reciprocal function $y = \dfrac{1}{x}$ is also a special **rational function,** defined below.

Rational Function   A **rational function** is a function of the form
$$y = \frac{f(x)}{g(x)} \quad \text{with } g(x) \neq 0$$
where $f(x)$ and $g(x)$ are both polynomials. Its domain is the set of all real numbers
for which $g(x) \neq 0$.

Asymptotes
The table of values and the graph in Figure 2.23 show that $|y|$ gets very large as x approaches 0 and that y is undefined at $x = 0$. In this case, we call the line $x = 0$ (that is, the y-axis) a **vertical asymptote.** On the graphs of polynomial functions, the turning points are usually the features of greatest interest. However, on graphs of rational functions, vertical asymptotes frequently are the most interesting features.

Rational functions sometimes have **horizontal asymptotes** as well as vertical asymptotes. Whenever the values of y approach some finite number b as $|x|$ becomes very large, we say that there is a horizontal asymptote at $y = b$.

Note that the graph of $y = 1/x$ appears to get close to the x-axis as $|x|$ becomes large. Testing values of x for which $|x|$ is large, we see that y is close to 0. Thus we say that the line $y = 0$ (or the x-axis) is a horizontal asymptote for the graph of $y = 1/x$. The graph in the following example has both a vertical and horizontal asymptote.

EXAMPLE 3 Rational Function

(a) Use values of x from -5 to 5 to develop a table of function values for the graph of

$$y = \frac{12x + 8}{3x - 9}$$

(b) Sketch the graph.

Solution

(a) Because $3x - 9 = 0$ when $x = 3$, it follows that $x = 3$ is not in the domain of this function. The values in the table indicate that the graph is approaching a vertical asymptote at $x = 3$.

x	−5	−4	−3	−2	−1	0	1
y	2.17	1.90	1.56	1.07	0.33	−0.89	−3.33

2	2.5	2.9	3.1	3.5	4	5
−10.7	−25.33	−142.67	150.67	33.33	18.67	11.33

To see if the function has a horizontal asymptote, we calculate y as $|x|$ becomes larger.

x	−10,000	−1000	1000	10,000
y	3.999	3.99	4.01	4.001

This table indicates that the graph is approaching $y = 4$ as $|x|$ increases, so we have a horizontal asymptote at $y = 4$.

(b) Using the information about vertical and horizontal asymptotes and plotting these points give the graph in Figure 2.24(a).

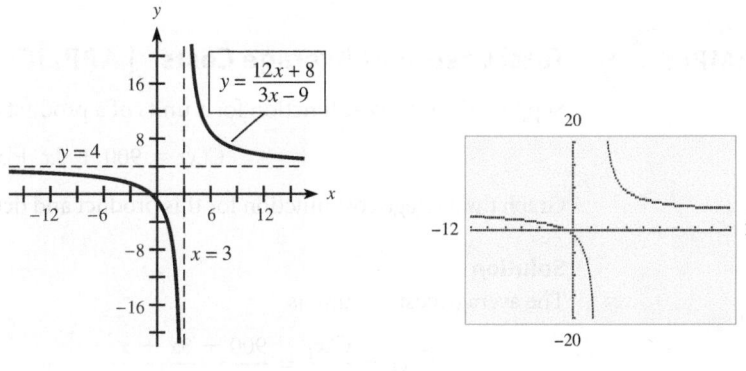

Figure 2.24   (a)   (b)

Calculator Note When a graphing calculator is used to graph a rational function, breaks in the graph will be visible at the vertical asymptotes. For example, Figure 2.24(b) shows the graph of $y = \dfrac{12x + 8}{3x - 9}$ on a graphing calculator with the window $[-12, 18]$ by $[-20, 20]$.

Note that a window centered at the x-value of the vertical asymptote ($x = 3$) shows the break. For details, see Appendix A, Section 2.4. ▪

Spreadsheet Note When graphing a function that has a break at $x = a$ with Excel, we must leave the cell corresponding to $f(a)$ blank so that Excel will not connect the values. See Appendix B, Section 2.4, or the Online Excel Guide for details. ▪

A general procedure for finding vertical and horizontal asymptotes of rational functions follows (see proof in Chapter 9).

Asymptotes

Vertical Asymptote

The graph of the rational function $y = \dfrac{f(x)}{g(x)}$ has a vertical asymptote at $x = c$ if $g(c) = 0$ and $f(c) \neq 0$.

Horizontal Asymptote

Consider the rational function $y = \dfrac{f(x)}{g(x)} = \dfrac{a_n x^n + \cdots + a_1 x + a_0}{b_m x^m + \cdots + b_1 x + b_0}$.

1. If $n < m$ (that is, if the degree of the numerator is less than that of the denominator), a horizontal asymptote occurs at $y = 0$ (the x-axis).
2. If $n = m$ (that is, if the degree of the numerator equals that of the denominator), a horizontal asymptote occurs at $y = \dfrac{a_n}{b_m}$ (the ratio of the leading coefficients).
3. If $n > m$ (that is, if the degree of the numerator is greater than that of the denominator), there is no horizontal asymptote.

Recall that the graph of the function $y = \dfrac{12x + 8}{3x - 9}$ (shown in Figure 2.24 on the previous page) has a vertical asymptote at $x = 3$, and that $x = 3$ makes the denominator 0 but does not make the numerator 0. Observe also that this graph has a horizontal asymptote at $y = 4$, and that the degree of the numerator is the same as that of the denominator with the ratio of the leading coefficients equal to $12/3 = 4$.

Determining the vertical and/or horizontal asymptotes of a rational function, if any exist, is very useful in determining a window for graphing. A rational function may or may not have turning points. The graph of the rational function in the following example has a vertical asymptote and a turning point.

EXAMPLE **4** **Total Costs and Average Costs** | APPLICATION PREVIEW |

Suppose the total cost function for x units of a product is given by

$$C(x) = 900 + 3x + x^2$$

Graph the average cost function for this product and determine the minimum average cost.

Solution

The average cost per unit is

$$\overline{C}(x) = \frac{C(x)}{x} = \frac{900 + 3x + x^2}{x} \qquad \text{or} \qquad \overline{C}(x) = \frac{900}{x} + 3 + x$$

Because x represents the number of units produced, we choose a window with $x \geq 0$ and note that $x = 0$ cannot be in the domain of the function. Figure 2.25 shows the graph of $\overline{C}(x)$. The graph appears to have a minimum near $x = 30$. Using CALC, 3:minimum on a graphing calculator or plotting points, we can verify that the minimum point occurs at $x = 30$ and $\overline{C} = 63$. Thus the minimum average cost is \$63 per unit when 30 units are produced.

Figure 2.25

$$\overline{C} = \frac{900}{x} + 3 + x$$

CHECKPOINT

4. Given $f(x) = \dfrac{3x}{x - 4}$, decide whether the following are true or false.

(a) $f(x)$ has a vertical asymptote at $x = 4$.

(b) $f(x)$ has a horizontal asymptote at $x = 3$.

Piecewise Defined Functions

Another special function comes from the definition of $|x|$. The **absolute value function** can be written as

$$f(x) = |x| \quad \text{or} \quad f(x) = \begin{cases} x & \text{if } x \geq 0 \\ -x & \text{if } x < 0 \end{cases}$$

Note that restrictions on the domain of the absolute value function specify different formulas for different parts of the domain. To graph $f(x) = |x|$, we graph the portion of the line $y = x$ for $x \geq 0$ [see Figure 2.26(a)] and the portion of the line $y = -x$ for $x < 0$ [see Figure 2.26(b)]. When we put these pieces on the same graph [Figure 2.26(c)], they give us the graph of $f(x) = |x|$. Because the absolute value function is defined by two equations, we say it is a **piecewise defined function.**

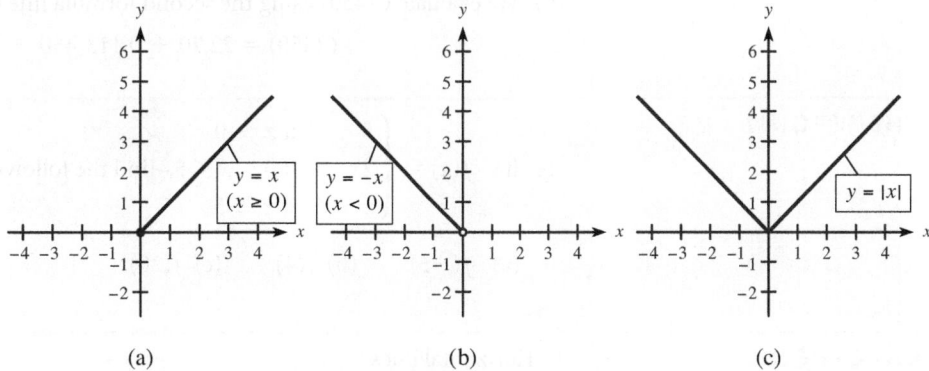

Figure 2.26   (a)   (b)   (c)

It is possible for the selling price S of a product to be defined as a piecewise function of the cost C of the product. For example, the selling price might be defined by two different equations on two different intervals, as follows:

$$S = f(C) = \begin{cases} 3C & \text{if } 0 \leq C \leq 20 \\ 1.5C + 30 & \text{if } C > 20 \end{cases}$$

Each C-value corresponds to only one piece of the formula for $S = f(C)$, so each C-value results in exactly one S-value; therefore, S is a function of C.

Note that the selling price of a product that costs $15 uses the top formula and is $f(15) = 3(15) = 45$ (dollars) and that the selling price of a product that costs $25 uses the bottom formula and is $f(25) = 1.5(25) + 30 = 67.50$ (dollars). Each of the two pieces of the graph of this function is a line and is easily graphed. It remains only to graph each in the proper interval. The graph is shown in Figure 2.27(a).

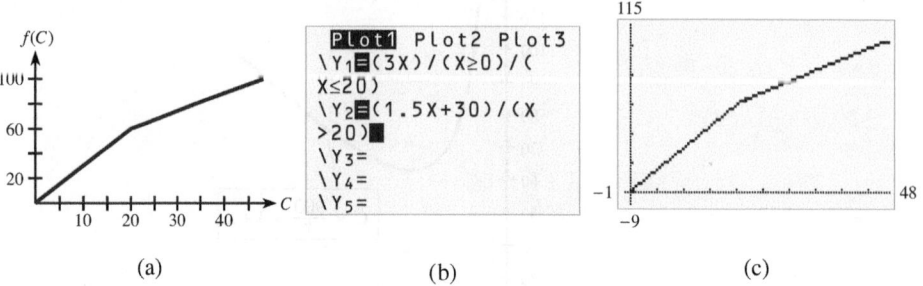

Figure 2.27   (a)   (b)   (c)

Calculator Note   Graphing calculators can be used to graph piecewise defined functions by entering each piece as a separate equation, divided by inequalities that define the interval. Figure 2.27(b) shows how the selling price function graphed in Figure 2.27(a) could be entered on a graphing calculator, using x to represent C, and Figure 2.27(c) shows the graph. Details of graphing piecewise defined functions with a graphing calculator are shown in Appendix A, Section 2.4.

EXAMPLE 5   Residential Electrical Costs

The 2018 monthly charge in dollars for x kilowatt hours (kWh) of electricity used by a residential customer of Excelsior Electric Membership Corporation during the months of November through June is given by the function

$$C(x) = \begin{cases} 10 + 0.127x & \text{if } 0 \le x \le 100 \\ 22.70 + 0.113(x - 100) & \text{if } 100 < x \le 500 \\ 67.90 + 0.119(x - 500) & \text{if } x > 500 \end{cases}$$

(a) What is the monthly charge if 1100 kWh of electricity are consumed in a month?

(b) What is the monthly charge if 450 kWh are consumed in a month?

Solution

(a) We need to find $C(1100)$. Because $1100 > 500$, we use the third formula line.

$$C(1100) = 67.90 + 0.119(1100 - 500) = \$139.30$$

(b) We evaluate $C(450)$ using the second formula line for $C(x)$.

$$C(450) = 22.70 + 0.113(450 - 100) = \$62.25$$

CHECKPOINT

5. If $f(x) = \begin{cases} 5 & \text{if } x \le 0 \\ 2x & \text{if } 0 < x < 5, \text{ find the following.} \\ x + 6 & \text{if } x \ge 5 \end{cases}$

(a) $f(-5)$ (b) $f(4)$ (c) $f(20)$

**CHECKPOINT
ANSWERS**

1. Horizontal lines
2. Polynomial functions are (a) and (e).
3. Two
4. (a) True.   (b) False; $y = 3$
5. (a) $f(-5) = 5$ (b) $f(4) = 8$ (c) $f(20) = 26$

EXERCISES 2.4

In Problems 1–12, match each of the functions with one of the graphs labeled (a)–(l) shown following these functions. Recognizing special features of certain types of functions and plotting points for the functions will be helpful.

1. $f(x) = -3$
2. $y = \sqrt{x}$
3. $y = \sqrt[3]{x}$
4. $y = (\sqrt{x})^5$
5. $y = (x + 4)^3 + 1$
6. $y = \dfrac{1}{x}$
7. $y = |x|$
8. $y = |x - 2|$
9. $f(x) = \begin{cases} x^2 & \text{if } x \le 2 \\ 4 & \text{if } x > 2 \end{cases}$
10. $f(x) = \begin{cases} 2 & \text{if } x < 0 \\ x^3 & \text{if } x \ge 0 \end{cases}$
11. $y = \begin{cases} -x & \text{if } x < -1 \\ 1 & \text{if } -1 \le x \le 1 \\ x & \text{if } x > 1 \end{cases}$
12. $y = \sqrt{x - 2}$

(a)

(b)

(c)

(d)

(e)

(f)

(g)

(h)

(i)

(j)

(k)

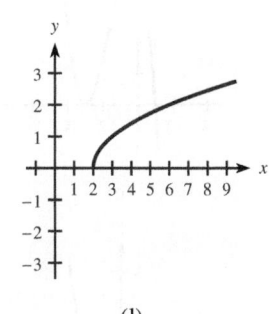

(l)

In Problems 13 and 14, decide whether each function whose graph is shown is the graph of a cubic (third-degree) or quartic (fourth-degree) function.

13.

(a)

(b)

14.

(a)

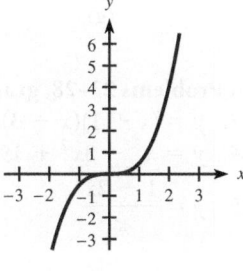

(b)

In Problems 15–22, match each equation with the correct graph among those labeled (a)–(h) by recognizing shapes and features of polynomial and rational functions. Use a graphing utility to confirm your choice.

15. $y = x^3 - x$

16. $y = (x - 3)^2(x + 1)$

17. $y = 16x^2 - x^4$

18. $y = x^4 - 3x^2 - 4$

19. $y = x^2 + 7x$

20. $y = 7x - x^2$

21. $y = \dfrac{x - 3}{x + 1}$

22. $y = \dfrac{1 - 3x}{2x + 5}$

(a)

(b)

(c)

(d)

(e)

(f)

(g)

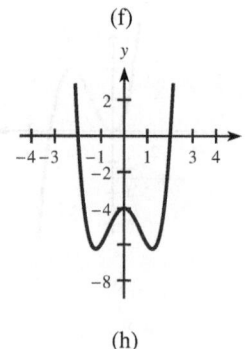
(h)

In Problems 23–28, graph the function.

23. $y = (x + 1)(x - 3)(x - 1)$

24. $y = x^3 - 8x^2 + 19x - 12$

25. $y = \dfrac{1 - 2x}{x}$

26. $y = \dfrac{x}{x - 1}$

27. $y = \begin{cases} x^3 + 2 & \text{if } x < 1 \\ \sqrt{x - 1} & \text{if } x \geq 1 \end{cases}$

28. $y = \begin{cases} x^2 & \text{if } x < 2 \\ 4 - x & \text{if } x \geq 2 \end{cases}$

29. If $F(x) = \dfrac{x^2 - 1}{x}$, find the following.

   (a) $F\left(-\frac{1}{3}\right)$ 　　　　　(b) $F(10)$
   (c) $F(0.001)$ 　　　　　(d) Is $F(0)$ defined?

30. If $H(x) = |x - 1|$, find the following.

   (a) $H(-1)$ 　　　　　(b) $H(1)$
   (c) $H(0)$ 　　　　　(d) Does $H(-x) = H(x)$?

31. If $f(x) = x^{3/2}$, find the following.

   (a) $f(16)$ 　(b) $f(1)$ 　(c) $f(100)$ 　(d) $f(0.09)$

32. If $k(x) = \begin{cases} 4 - 2x & \text{if } x < 0 \\ |x - 4| & \text{if } 0 < x < 4, \end{cases}$

   find the following.

   (a) $k(-0.1)$ 　(b) $k(0.1)$ 　(c) $k(3.9)$ 　(d) $k(4.1)$

33. If $k(x) = \begin{cases} 2 & \text{if } x < 0 \\ x + 4 & \text{if } 0 \leq x < 1, \\ 1 - x & \text{if } x \geq 1 \end{cases}$

   find the following.

   (a) $k(-5)$ 　(b) $k(0)$ 　(c) $k(1)$ 　(d) $k(-0.001)$

34. If $g(x) = \begin{cases} 0.5x + 4 & \text{if } x < 0 \\ 4 - x & \text{if } 0 \leq x < 4, \\ 0 & \text{if } x > 4 \end{cases}$

   find the following.

   (a) $g(-4)$ 　(b) $g(1)$ 　(c) $g(7)$ 　(d) $g(3.9)$

In Problems 35–40, (a) graph each function with a graphing utility; (b) classify each function as a polynomial function, a rational function, or a piecewise defined function; (c) identify any asymptotes; and (d) use the graphs to locate turning points.

35. $f(x) = 1.6x^2 - 0.1x^4$

36. $f(x) = \dfrac{x^4 - 4x^3}{3}$

37. $f(x) = \dfrac{2x + 4}{x + 1}$

38. $f(x) = \dfrac{x - 3}{x + 2}$

39. $f(x) = \begin{cases} -x & \text{if } x < 0 \\ 5x & \text{if } x \geq 0 \end{cases}$

40. $f(x) = \begin{cases} 2x - 1 & \text{if } x < 1 \\ -x & \text{if } x \geq 1 \end{cases}$

APPLICATIONS

41. *Postal restrictions* If a box with a square cross section is to be sent by the postal service, there are restrictions on its size such that its volume is limited by $V = x^2(108 - 4x)$, where x is the length of each side of the cross section (in inches).

   (a) If $V = V(x)$, find $V(10)$ and $V(20)$.
   (b) What restrictions must be placed on x (the domain) so that the problem makes physical sense?

42. *Fixed costs* Fixed costs FC are business costs that remain constant regardless of the number of units produced. Some items that might contribute to fixed costs are rent and utilities.

$$FC = 2000$$

is an equation indicating that a business has fixed costs of $2000. Graph FC = 2000 by putting x (the number of units produced) on the horizontal axis. (Note that FC does not mean the product of F and C.)

43. *Latin American Internet use* Using data from 2013 and projected to 2019, the number of Internet users (in millions) in Latin America can be modeled by

$$y = 200.8x^{0.30}$$

with x equal to the number of years after 2010 (*Source*: eMarketer).
   (a) Does the graph of this function bend upward or downward?
   (b) Graph this function on an interval representing 2010 through 2030.
   (c) In what year will the number of Internet users in Latin America reach 443,202,416, according to this model?

44. *Allometric relationships* For fiddler crabs, data gathered by Thompson show that the relationship between the weight C of the claw and the weight W of the body is given by

$$C = 0.11W^{1.54}$$

where W and C are in grams (*Source*: d'Arcy Thompson, *On Growth and Form*, Cambridge University Press, 1961).
   (a) Does the graph of this function bend upward or downward?
   (b) Graph this function.
   (c) Use this function to compute the weight of a claw if the weight of the crab's body is 10 grams.

45. *Pollution* Suppose that the cost C (in dollars) of removing p percent of the particulate pollution from the smokestacks of an industrial plant is given by

$$C(p) = \frac{7300p}{100 - p}$$

   (a) Is C(p) undefined at any p-value? If so, what value?
   (b) What is the domain of C(p) as given by the equation?
   (c) What is the domain of C(p) in the context of the application?
   (d) What happens to the cost as the percent of pollution removed approaches 100%?

46. *Average cost* If the weekly total cost of producing 42″ Toshiba television sets is given by C(x) = 50,000 + 105x, where x is the number of sets produced per week, then the average cost per unit is given by

$$\overline{C}(x) = \frac{50,000 + 105x}{x}$$

   (a) What is the average cost per set if 3000 sets are sold?
   (b) Graph this function.

(c) Does the average cost per set continue to fall as the number of sets produced increases?

47. *Area* If 100 feet of fence is to be used to enclose a rectangular yard, then the resulting area of the fenced yard is given by

$$A = x(50 - x)$$

where x is the width of the rectangle.
   (a) If A = A(x), find A(2) and A(30).
   (b) What restrictions must be placed on x (the domain) so that the problem makes physical sense?

48. *Water usage* The monthly charge for water in a small town is given by

$$f(x) = \begin{cases} 58 & \text{if } 0 \le x \le 20 \\ 58 + 0.4(x - 20) & \text{if } x > 20 \end{cases}$$

where x is water usage in hundreds of gallons and f(x) is in dollars. Find the monthly charge for each of the following usages.
   (a) 30 gallons
   (b) 3000 gallons
   (c) 4000 gallons
   (d) Graph the function for 0 ≤ x ≤ 100.

49. *Gross domestic product* Using data for selected years from 1950 and projected to 2040, the gross domestic product (GDP), in billions of dollars, of the United States is modeled by

$$y = \begin{cases} 5.59x^2 - 93.5x + 633 & \text{for } 0 \le x \le 55 \\ 6.56x^2 - 519x + 20,900 & \text{for } 55 < x \le 90 \end{cases}$$

where x is the number of years past 1950 (*Sources*: Bureau of Economic Analysis; U.S. Energy Information Administration).
   (a) Graph the function for 0 ≤ x ≤ 90.
   (b) What does the model estimate the GDP was in 2000?
   (c) What does the model predict the GDP to be in 2025?

50. *Commercial electrical usage* The monthly charge (in dollars) for x kilowatt hours (kWh) of electricity used by a commercial customer is given by the following function.

$$C(x) = \begin{cases} 7.52 + 0.1079x & \text{if } 0 \le x \le 5 \\ 19.22 + 0.1079x & \text{if } 5 < x \le 750 \\ 20.795 + 0.1058x & \text{if } 750 < x \le 1500 \\ 131.345 + 0.0321x & \text{if } x > 1500 \end{cases}$$

Find the monthly charges for the following usages.
   (a) 5 kWh   (b) 6 kWh   (c) 3000 kWh

51. *First-class postage* The postage charged for first-class mail is a function of its weight. The U.S. Postal Service uses the following table to describe the rates.

Weight Increment	Rate ($)
First ounce or fraction of an ounce	0.49
Each additional ounce or fraction	0.21

Source: United States Postal Service

(a) Convert this table to a piecewise defined function that represents postage for letters weighing between 0 and 4 ounces, using x as the weight in ounces and P as the postage in cents.

(b) Find $P(1.2)$ and explain what it means.

(c) Give the domain and range of P as it is defined above.

(d) Find the postage for a 2-ounce letter and for a 2.01-ounce letter.

52. *Income tax* In a given year, the U.S. federal income tax owed by a married couple filing jointly can be found from the following table (*Source:* Internal Revenue Service, Form 1040 Instructions).

Married Filing Jointly	
Taxable Income	Tax Rate
$0–$18,550	10%
$18,551–$75,300	$1,855 plus 15% of the amount over $18,550
$75,301–$151,900	$10,367.50 plus 25% of the amount over $75,300
$151,901–$231,450	$29,517.50 plus 28% of the amount over $151,900
$231,451–$413,350	$51,791.50 plus 33% of the amount over $231,450
$413,351–$466,950	$111,818.50 plus 35% of the amount over $413,350
$466,951 or more	$130,578.50 plus 39.6% of the amount over $466,950

(a) For incomes up to $151,900, write the piecewise defined function T with input x that models the federal tax dollars due as a function of x, the taxable income dollars earned.

(b) Use the function to find $T(70,000)$.

(c) Find the tax due on a taxable income of $100,000.

(d) A friend tells Jack Waddell not to earn any money over $75,300 because it will raise his tax rate to 25% on all of his taxable income. Test this statement by finding the tax due on $75,300 and $75,300 + $1. What do you conclude?

53. *Demand* The demand function for a product is given by

$$p = \frac{200}{2 + 0.1x}$$

where x is the number of units and p is the price in dollars.

(a) Graph this demand function for $0 \le x \le 250$, with x on the horizontal axis.

(b) Does the demand ever reach 0?

54. *Sales and training* The average monthly sales volume (in thousands of dollars) for a company depends on the number of hours of training x of its sales staff, according to

$$S = \frac{50}{x} + 10 + \frac{x}{5}, \quad 10 \le x \le 100$$

(a) Combine the terms of this function over a common denominator to create a rational function.

(b) Graph the rational function.

55. *Production costs* A manufacturer estimates that the cost of a production run for a product is

$$C(x) = 30(x - 1) + \frac{3000}{x + 10}$$

where x is the number of machines used.

(a) Graph this total cost function for values of $x \ge 0$.

(b) Interpret any turning points.

(c) Interpret the y-intercept.

SECTION 2.5   Modeling; Fitting Curves to Data with Graphing Utilities

OBJECTIVES

- To graph data points in a scatter plot
- To determine the function type that will give the best model for the data
- To use a graphing utility to create an equation that models the data
- To graph the data points and model on the same graph

APPLICATION PREVIEW

When the plot of a set of data points looks like a line, we can use a technique called linear regression (or the least-squares method) to find the equation of the line that is the best fit for the data points. The resulting equation (model) describes the data and gives a formula to plan for the future. We can use technology to fit linear and other functions to sets of data.

For selected years from 1995 and projected to 2018, the data in Table 2.2 show the amount of tax paid per capita (per person). In this section, we develop a model for these data. (See Example 3.)

Linear Regression

| TABLE 2.2 |

Year	Federal Tax per Capita
1995	$5110
2000	7177
2005	7228
2010	7005
2013	8559
2015	10,335
2018	12,029

Source: usgovernmentrevenue.com

We saw in Section 1.3, "Linear Functions," that it is possible to write the equation of a straight line if we have two points on the line. Business firms frequently like to treat demand functions as linear even when they are not exactly linear. Firms do this because linear functions are much easier to handle than other functions. If a firm has more than two points describing the demand for its product, it is likely that all the points will not lie on the same straight line. However, by using a technique called **linear regression,** the firm can determine the "best line" that fits these points.

Suppose we have the points shown in Figure 2.28 and we seek the line that is the "best fit" for the points.

The formulas that give the best-fitting line for given data are developed in Chapter 14, "Functions of Two or More Variables," but graphing calculators, computer programs, and spreadsheets have built-in formulas or programs that give the equation of the best-fitting line for a set of data.

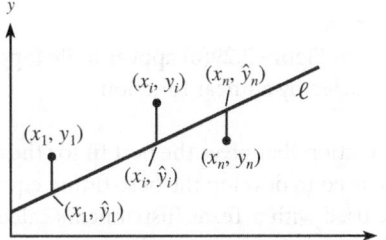

Figure 2.28

Modeling

Creating an equation, or **mathematical model,** for a set of data is a complex process that involves careful analysis of the data in accordance with a number of guidelines. Our approach to creating a model is much simplified and relies on a knowledge of the appearance of linear, quadratic, power, cubic, and quartic functions and the capabilities of computers and graphing calculators. We should note that the equations the computers and calculators provide are based on sophisticated formulas that are derived using calculus of several variables. These formulas provide the best fit for the data using the function type we choose, but we should keep the following limitations in mind.

1. The computer/calculator will give the best fit for whatever type of function we choose (even if the selected function is a bad fit for the points), so we must choose a function type carefully. To choose a function type, compare the plot of the data with the graphs of the functions discussed earlier in this chapter. The model will not fit the data if we choose a function type whose graph does not match the shape of the plotted data.
2. Some sets of data have no pattern, so they cannot be modeled by functions. Other data sets cannot be modeled by the functions we have studied.
3. Modeling provides a formula that relates the data. Even though a model may accurately fit a data set, it may not be a good predictor for values outside the data set.

To find a function that models a set of data, the first step is to plot the data and determine the shape of the curve that would best fit the data points. The plot of the data points is called a **scatter plot.** The scatter plot's shape determines the type of function that will be the best model for the data.

EXAMPLE 1   Curve Fitting

Graphs of three scatter plots are shown in Figure 2.29(a–c). Determine what type of function is your choice as the best-fitting curve for each scatter plot. If it is a polynomial function, state the degree.

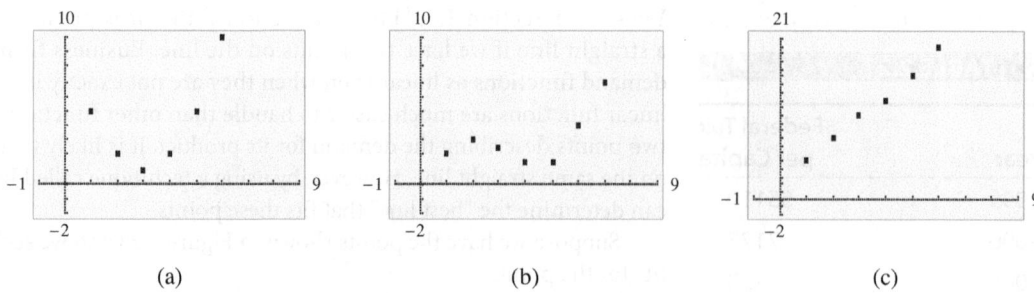

Figure 2.29   (a)   (b)   (c)

Solution

(a) It appears that a parabola will fit the data points in Figure 2.29(a), so the data points can be modeled by a second-degree (quadratic) function.

(b) The two "turns" in the scatter plot in Figure 2.29(b) suggest that it could be modeled by a cubic function.

(c) The data points in Figure 2.29(c) appear to lie (approximately) along a line, so the data can be modeled by a linear function.

After the type of function that gives the best fit for the data is chosen, a graphing utility or spreadsheet can be used to develop the best-fitting equation for the function chosen. The following steps are used with a Texas Instruments calculator to create a scatter plot of data and to find an equation that models the data.

Modeling Data with a Graphing Calculator

1. Enter the inputs (x-values) into list L1 under STAT, EDIT. Similarly, enter the outputs (y-values) into list L2 under STAT, EDIT.
2. Turn on PLOT1 in the Y = menu. Then press ZOOM and 9:ZoomStat to show a scatter plot of the data.
3. Press STAT, move to CALC, and select the function type that matches the scatter plot.
4. Press VARS, move to Y-VARS, and press ENTER twice to select Y_1. Press ENTER again to get the equation on the screen and stored as Y_1 under Y = .
5. To see how well the function models the data, press GRAPH to see the graph of the function and the data points on the same set of axes. If the graph of the equation does not fit the data points well, another type of function may model the data better.
6. After the model for a data set has been found, it can be rounded for reporting purposes. However, use the unrounded model in graphing and in calculations unless otherwise instructed. Numerical answers found using a model should be rounded in a way that agrees with the context of the problem and has no more accuracy than the original output data.

The following example illustrates modeling data with a graphing calculator.

EXAMPLE 2   World Population

World population is projected to grow to over 9 billion by 2050. The table below gives the world population, in billions, for selected years from 2000 and projected to 2050.

(a) Use a graphing calculator to create a scatter plot of the data, with x equal to the number of years after 2000.

(b) Use the graphing calculator to create an equation that models the data.

(c) Graph the function and the data on the same set of axes to see how well the function models (fits) the data.

Year	2000	2010	2020	2030	2040	2050
Population (billions)	6.08	6.82	7.52	8.18	8.72	9.19

Source: U.S. Census Bureau, International Data Base

Solution
(a) When we use x as the number of years past 2000 and use y to represent the world population, in billions, then the points representing this function are

$$(0, 6.08), (10, 6.82), (20, 7.52), (30, 8.18), (40, 8.72), (50, 9.19)$$

The scatter plot of these points is developed in Appendix A, Section 2.5, and shown in Figure 2.30(a).

(b) It appears that a line would fit close to the points in Figure 2.30(a). The points do not fit perfectly on a line because the population does not increase by exactly the same amount each year. The steps used to create the linear function that models these data are shown on page 162 and in Appendix A, Section 2.5. The line that is the best fit for the points is

$$y = 0.0626x + 6.19$$

(c) Figure 2.30(b) shows the graph of the function and the data on the same set of axes. Note that not all points lie on the graph of the function, even though this is the line that is the best fit for the data.

Figure 2.30   (a)   (b)

Notice in Example 2 that the population data all had 3 digits of accuracy (called 3 significant digits), and our reported model used this same accuracy. In general, **significant digits** are from the first nonzero digit on the left to the last digit *after* the decimal point if there is a decimal point. If there is no decimal point, any zeros to the right of the nonzero digits are not significant. Thus, 0.0126, 73,800, and 10.0 all have 3 significant digits.

EXAMPLE **3**   **Federal Tax per Capita** | APPLICATION PREVIEW |

The federal tax paid per capita (per person) has increased dramatically over the last 20 years. The following table gives the amount of federal tax paid per capita for selected years from 1995 to 2018.
(a) Create a scatter plot of these data, with x as the number of years after 1990.
(b) Find a cubic model that fits the data points.
(c) Graph the function and the scatter plot on the same axes.
(d) Use the model to predict the per capita tax for 2022.

Year	Federal Tax per Capita	Year	Federal Tax per Capita
1995	$5110	2013	$8559
2000	7177	2015	10,335
2005	7228	2018	12,029
2010	7005		

Source: usgovernmentrevenue.com

Solution
(a) The scatter plot is shown in Figure 2.31(a) on the next page. The "turns" in the graph indicate that a cubic function would be a good fit for the data.
(b) Figure 2.3(b) shows the cubic regression. The rounded model that is the best fit for the data is
$$y = 2.114x^3 - 93.01x^2 + 1374x + 393.8$$

(c) The graph of the (unrounded) function and the scatter plot are shown in Figure 2.31(c).
(d) For 2022 we use $x = 32$; the corresponding y-value [shown in Figure 2.31(d)] predicts
     $18,391 as the tax per capita in 2022. The graph's upward turn indicates an increase in
     future tax per capita, which is likely with the current government debt.

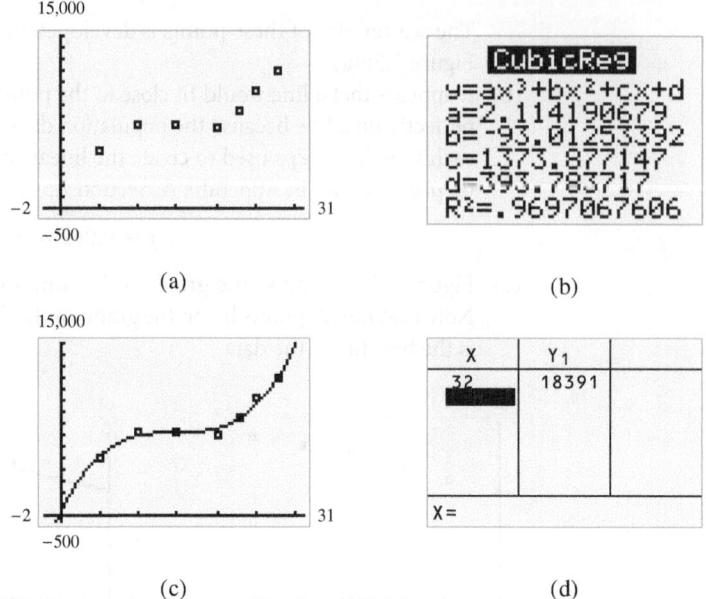

Figure 2.31

(a)   (b)

(c)   (d)

The model just found in Example 3 was reported with 4 significant digit coefficients.
If a problem does not indicate how to report the models you find, you will be expected to
report them with 3 significant digit coefficients.

CHECKPOINT

The following table gives the Social Security Trust Fund balance (in billions of dollars)
for selected years from 2000 and projected to 2030.

(1) Make a scatter plot of the data with x as the number of years past 1995.
(2) Find a model for the data. Graph the model and the data on the same axes.

Year	2000	2005	2010	2015	2020	2025	2030
Balance	1049.4	1858.7	2609.0	2682.6	2440.5	1866.5	777.3

Source: Social Security Administration

If it is not obvious what model will best fit a given set of data, several models can be
developed and compared graphically with the data.

EXAMPLE 4   Expected Life Span

Mainly because of better nutrition and health care, the number of years that Americans are
expected to live has increased and is expected to continue to increase. The table shows the
expected life span, based on the year of birth for selected years from 1920 and projected to 2050.

Year	Life Span	Year	Life Span
1920	54.1	1990	75.4
1930	59.7	2000	76.8
1940	62.9	2010	78.7
1950	68.2	2020	80.2
1960	69.7	2030	81.7
1970	70.8	2040	83.0
1980	73.7	2050	84.4

Source: National Center for Health Statistics

(a) Create linear and quadratic models that give life span as a function of birth year with x representing the number of years after 1900 and, by visual inspection, decide which model gives the better fit.
(b) Use both models to estimate the life span of a person born in the year 2000.
(c) Which model's estimation for the life span in 2050 seems better?

Solution

(a) The scatter plot for the data is shown in Figure 2.32(a). It appears that a linear function could be used to model the data. The linear equation that is the best fit for the data is

$$y = 0.213x + 54.7$$

The graph in Figure 2.32(b) shows how well the unrounded linear model fits the data points. The quadratic function that is the best fit for the data is

$$y = -0.00121x^2 + 0.418x + 47.9$$

The graph of this unrounded model is shown in Figure 2.32(c).

(a)

(b)

(c)

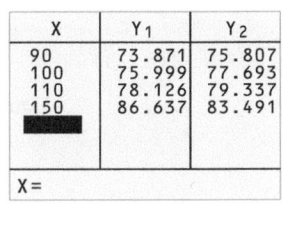

X	Y₁	Y₂
90	73.871	75.807
100	75.999	77.693
110	78.126	79.337
150	86.637	83.491

X =

(d)

Figure 2.32

The quadratic model appears to fit the data points better than the linear model. A table can be used to compare the models [see Figure 2.32(d)] with Y_1 giving values from the linear model and Y_2 giving values from the quadratic model.

(b) We can estimate the expected life span of people born in the year 2000 with either model by evaluating the unrounded functions at $x = 100$. The x-values in Figure 2.32(d) represent the years 1990, 2000, 2010, and 2050. From the linear model, the expected life span in 2000 is 76.0, and from the quadratic model, the expected life span is 77.7.

(c) Looking at Figure 2.32(d) and at Figures 2.32(b) and (c), we see that the linear model may be giving optimistic values in 2050, when $x = 150$, so the quadratic model may be better.

Spreadsheet Note   The steps used in modeling data with Excel follow:

1. Create a scatter plot of the data by highlighting the two columns containing the x- and y- values, select *Insert > Scatter*, and choose the points only option to plot the points.
2. Right-click (with a Mac, use Control-click) on one of the data points and choose *Add Trendline*.
3. Select the function type that gives the best fit, and click the box *Display Equation on chart*.
4. Close the dialog box to see the graph and the equation of the model.

See Appendix B, Section 2.5, or the Online Excel Guide for details.

EXAMPLE 5   **Corvette Acceleration**

The following table shows the times it takes a Corvette to reach speeds from 0 mph to 100 mph, in increments of 10 mph after 30 mph.

Time (sec)	Speed (mph)	Time (sec)	Speed (mph)
1.7	30	5.5	70
2.4	40	7.0	80
3.5	50	8.5	90
4.3	60	10.2	100

(a) Create a scatter plot of the data.
(b) Use a power function with Excel to model the data and graph the points and the function to see how well the function fits the points.
(c) What does the model indicate the speed is 5 seconds after the car starts to move?
(d) Use the model to determine the number of seconds until the Corvette reaches 110 mph.

Solution

(a) Using x as the time and y as the speed, the scatter plot is shown in Figure 2.33(a).
(b) The Excel power function model $y = ax^b$ [graphed in Figure 2.33(b)] is

$$y = 21.875x^{0.6663}$$

Figure 2.33   (a)   (b)

(c) Using $x = 5$ in this equation gives 64 mph as the speed of the Corvette.
(d) Excel Goal Seek (discussed in Section 2.1) with $y = 21.875x^{0.6663}$ set equal to 110 gives $x = 11.3$, so the time required to reach 110 mph is 11.3 seconds.

**CHECKPOINT
ANSWERS**

(1) The first data point is plotted as (5, 1049.4). Figure 2.34(a) shows the scatter plot.
(2) Use a quadratic function; a rounded model is $y = 7.97x^2 + 312x - 356$. Figure 2.34(b) shows a graph of the unrounded model and the data.

Figure 2.34   (a)   (b)

EXERCISES 2.5

In Problems 1–8, determine whether the scatter plot should be modeled by a linear, power, quadratic, cubic, or quartic function.

1.

2.

3.

4.

5.

6.

7.

8.

In Problems 9–16, find the equation of the function of the specified type that is the best fit for the given data. Plot the data and the equation.

9. linear

x	y
−2	−7
−1	−5
0	−3
1	−1
2	1
3	3
4	5

10. linear

x	y
−1	−5.5
0	−4
1	−2.5
2	−1
3	0.5
4	2
5	3.5

11. quadratic

x	y
−2	7
−1	−0.5
0	−4
1	−3.5
2	1
3	9.5
4	22

12. quadratic

x	y
−4	−8
−3	−4
−2	−2
−1	−2
0	−4
1	−8
2	−14

13. cubic

x	y
−4	−72
−3	−31
−2	−10
−1	−3
0	−4
1	−7
2	−6

14. cubic

x	y
−3	−22
−2	−6
−1	−2
0	−4
1	−6
2	−2
3	14

15. power

x	y
1	2
2	2.8284
3	3.4641
4	4
5	4.4721
6	4.899

16. power

x	y
1	3
2	8.4853
3	15.588
4	24
5	33.541
6	44.091

In Problems 17–24, (a) plot the given points, (b) determine what type of function best models the data, and (c) find the equation that is the best fit for the data.

17.

x	y
−1	−8
0	−3
1	2
2	7
3	12
4	17
5	22

18.

x	y
−1	−2
0	2
1	6
2	10
3	14
4	18
5	22

19.

x	y
−1	2
0	0
1	2
2	3.1748
3	4.1602
4	5.0397
5	5.848

20.

x	y
0.01	0.3
1	3
2	4.2426
3	5.1962
4	6
5	6.7082
6	7.3485

21.

x	y
−2	19
−1	8
0	1
1	−2
2	−1
3	4
4	13

22.

x	y
−4	37
−3	19
−2	7
−1	1
0	1
1	7
2	19

23.

x	y
−3	−11
−2	3
−1	5
0	1
1	−3
2	−1
3	13

24.

x	y
−3	−54
−2	−14
−1	0
0	0
1	−2
2	6
3	36

APPLICATIONS

25. *Population of females under 18* The following table gives the projected population, in thousands, of U.S. females under the age of 18.

Year	Population (1000s)	Year	Population (1000s)
2020	37,222	2045	41,067
2025	38,201	2050	41,963
2030	39,244	2055	42,855
2035	39,809	2060	43,610
2040	40,352		

Source: U.S. Census Bureau

(a) Create a linear function that models the projected population y, in thousands, as a function of the number of years past 2010.

(b) What is the projected population of females under age 18 in 2037, according to this model?

(c) When will this population reach 45,000,000 according to this model?

26. *CO_2 emissions* The following table gives the millions of metric tons of carbon dioxide emissions in the United States for selected years from 2010 and projected to 2032.

(a) Create a linear function that models these data, with x as the number of years past 2010 and y as the millions of metric tons of carbon dioxide emissions.

(b) Find the model's estimate for the 2024 data point.

(c) Find and interpret the slope of the linear model.

Year	2010	2012	2014	2016	2018	2020
CO_2 Emissions	338.5	364.5	396.1	425.8	453.1	498.4

Year	2022	2024	2026	2028	2030	2032
CO_2 Emissions	556.2	590.9	629.7	663.1	701.1	743.7

Source: U.S. Department of Energy

27. *Disposable income* Disposable income is the amount left after taxes have been paid and is one measure of the health of the economy. The following table gives the total U.S disposable income (in billions of 2005 dollars) for selected years from 2010 and projected to 2040.

(a) Use x as the number of years past 2010 and write the equation of the function that is the best fit for these data.

(b) What does the model predict for the disposable income in 2027?

(c) Interpret the slope of the model found in part (a).

28. *Diabetes* As the following table shows, projections indicate that the percent of U.S. adults with diabetes could dramatically increase.

Year	Percent	Year	Percent	Year	Percent
2010	15.7	2025	24.2	2040	31.4
2015	18.9	2030	27.2	2045	32.1
2020	21.1	2035	29.0	2050	34.3

Source: Centers for Disease Control and Prevention

(a) Find a linear model that fits the data in the table, with x as the number of years after in 2000.

(b) Use the model to predict the percent of U.S. adults with diabetes in 2018.

(c) In what year does this model predict the percent of U.S. adults with diabetes will reach 25%?

29. *Wind chill* The table gives the wind chill temperature when the outside temperature is 20°F.

Wind (mph)	Wind Chill (°F)	Wind (mph)	Wind Chill (°F)
5	13	35	0
10	9	40	−1
15	6	45	−2
20	4	50	−3
25	3	55	−3
30	1	60	−4

Source: National Weather Service

(a) Use x as the wind speed and create a quadratic model for these data.

(b) At what wind speed does the model predict that the wind chill temperature will be lowest?

(c) Do you think the model found in part (a) is valid for $x > 60$? Explain.

30. *Developing economies* The developing economies' share of the global gross domestic product (GDP) from 2003 to 2017 is shown in the following table.

(a) Find the quadratic function that best models the developing economies' share of the global GDP as a function of the number of years after 2000.

(b) Use technology to find the maximum share of GDP that the developing economies can achieve, according to this model.

Year	2010	2015	2020	2025	2030	2035	2040
Income (billions)	$10,017	$11,120	$12,655	$14,259	$15,948	$17,752	$19,785

Source: U.S. Census Bureau

Year	Share (% of GDP)	Year	Share (% of GDP)
2003	20	2011	35
2004	22	2012	38
2005	23	2013	39
2006	27	2014	40
2007	28	2015	41
2008	31	2016	42
2009	31	2017	43
2010	33		

Source: International Monetary Fund

31. *Gross domestic product* The table gives the gross domestic product (GDP), in billions of dollars, of the United States for selected years from 2000 and projected to 2070.
    (a) Create a scatter plot of the data, with y representing GDP in billions of dollars and x representing the number of years past 2000.
    (b) Find the quadratic function that best fits the data.
    (c) Find the cubic function that best fits the data.
    (d) Graph each of these functions on the same axes as the data points and visually determine which model is the better fit for the data.

Year	GDP	Year	GDP
2000	9143	2040	79,680
2005	12,145	2045	103,444
2010	16,174	2050	133,925
2015	21,270	2055	173,175
2020	27,683	2060	224,044
2025	35,919	2065	290,042
2030	46,765	2070	375,219
2035	61,100		

Source: Social Security Administration

32. *Alzheimer's disease* As the baby boomer generation ages and the proportion of the U.S. population over age 65 increases, the number of Americans with Alzheimer's disease and other dementia is projected to grow each year. The table below gives the millions of U.S. citizens age 65 or older with Alzheimer's from 2000 and projected to 2050.
    (a) Find the quadratic function that models the data, with x equal to the number of years past 2000 and y equal to the number of millions of Americans with Alzheimer's.
    (b) Find the cubic function that models the data, with x equal to the number of years past 2000 and y equal to the number of millions of Americans with Alzheimer's.
    (c) Graph each model and the data on the same axes.
    (d) Determine if one model is a better visual fit to the data.

Year	2000	2010	2020	2030	2040	2050
Millions	4.5	5.1	5.7	7.7	11.0	13.2

Source: Alzheimer's Association

33. *Crude oil* The following table gives the U.S. crude oil production, in billions of barrels, for selected years from 2010 and projected to 2030.
    (a) Find the linear function that models the data, with x equal to the number of years past 2010 and y equal to the number of billions of barrels of crude oil.
    (b) Find the quadratic function that models the data, with x and y as in part (a).
    (c) Graph each model and the data on the same axes.
    (d) Determine if one model is a better visual fit to the data.

Year	2010	2012	2014	2016	2018	2020
Billions of Barrels	1.94	2.00	2.10	2.10	2.16	2.24

Year	2022	2024	2026	2028	2030
Billions of Barrels	2.24	2.21	2.26	2.27	2.26

Source: U.S. Department of Energy

34. *Energy use* Energy use per dollar of GDP indexed to 1980 means that energy use for any year is viewed as a percent of the use per dollar of GDP in 1980. The following data show the energy use per dollar of GDP, as a percent, for selected years from 1985 and projected to 2035.
    (a) Find a linear function that models these data, with x equal to the number of years past 1980 and y equal to the energy use per dollar of GDP, as a percent.
    (b) Find a cubic function that models these data, with x equal to the number of years past 1980 and y equal to the energy use per dollar of GDP, as a percent.
    (c) Graph each model and the data on the same axes.
    (d) Which model indicates that the percent of energy use may increase after 2035?

Energy Use per Dollar of GDP

Year	1985	1990	1995	2000	2005	2010
Percent	83	79	75	67	60	56

Year	2015	2020	2025	2030	2035
Percent	51	45	41	37	34

Source: U.S. Department of Energy

35. *Income by age* The median income for workers ages 20 to 62 is shown in the following table.
    (a) Use a scatter plot of the data with x equal to the age and y equal to the median income in dollars to decide what type of function is the best model for these data. Explain your choice.
    (b) Find the best model for the data.

(c) Graph the function on the same axes as the scatter plot.
(d) At what age does the model estimate the median income to be $56,520?

Median Age	Median Income ($)	Median Age	Median Income ($)
20	25,404	47	54,260
27	37,896	52	54,405
32	45,770	57	56,427
37	50,740	62	59,222
42	51,613		

Source: U.S. Census Bureau

36. *National health care* The table shows the national expenditures for health care in the United States for selected years, with projections to 2020.

Year	National Expenditures for Health Care (billions)
1960	$28
1970	75
1980	254
1990	714
1995	1017
2000	1353
2005	1981
2010	2954
2015	3308
2020	4487

Source: U.S. Centers for Medicare and Medicaid Services

(a) Use a scatter plot with x as the number of years past 1950 and y as the total expenditures for health care (in billions) to identify what type (or types) of function(s) would make a good model for these data.
(b) Find a power model and a quadratic model for the data.
(c) Which model from part (b) approximates more accurately the data point for 2020?
(d) Use the quadratic model to predict the 2025 expenditures for national health care.

37. *E-commerce* The following table gives the online sales, in billions of dollars, from 2000 to 2017.
(a) Find the power function that models these data, with x as the number of years past 1990.
(b) Graph the data and the function on the same axes.
(c) What does the model predict the online sales revenue to be in 2020?

Year	Sales (billions)	Year	Sales (billions)
2000	$28	2009	$134
2001	34	2010	171
2002	44	2011	202
2003	56	2012	226
2004	70	2013	259
2005	87	2014	297
2006	106	2015	339
2007	126	2016	386
2008	132	2017	434

Sources: U.S. Census Bureau; Forrester Research, Inc.

38. *U.S. population* The table gives the U.S. population, in millions, for selected years from 1950 and projected to 2050.

Year	1950	1960	1970	1980	1990	2000
Population (millions)	160.1	190.2	214.8	235.1	259.6	287.9

Year	2010	2015	2020	2030	2040	2050
Population (millions)	315.2	328.4	342.9	369.5	390.8	409.1

Source: Social Security Administration

(a) Create a scatter plot for the data in the table. Use x as the number of years past 1950.
(b) Use the scatter plot to identify and determine at least two function types that could be used to model these data.
(c) Which model more accurately approximates the data point for the year 2040?
(d) Use the linear model to determine when the U.S. population is predicted to reach 425 million.

② CHAPTER SUMMARY & REVIEW

KEY TERMS AND FORMULAS

Section 2.1

Quadratic equation (p. 123)
$$ax^2 + bx + c = 0 \, (a \neq 0)$$
Factoring methods (p. 123)
Zero product property (p. 123)
Square root property (p. 125)
$$x^2 = C \Rightarrow x = \pm\sqrt{C}$$

Quadratic formula (p. 126)
$$x = \frac{-b \pm \sqrt{b^2 - 4ac}}{2a}$$
Quadratic discriminant (p. 127)
$$b^2 - 4ac$$

Section 2.2

Quadratic function; parabola (pp. 132, 135)
$$y = f(x) = ax^2 + bx + c$$
Vertex of a parabola (p. 132)
$$(-b/2a, f(-b/2a))$$
Maximum point if $a < 0$
Minimum point if $a > 0$

Axis of symmetry (p. 132)
$$x = -b/2a$$
Zeros of a quadratic function (p. 134)
Average rates of change (p. 138)
$$\frac{f(b) - f(a)}{b - a}$$

Section 2.3

Cost, revenue, and profit functions (p. 142)
$$P(x) = R(x) - C(x)$$
Break-even points (p. 142)
$$R(x) = C(x) \text{ or } P(x) = 0$$

Revenue and profit maximization (p. 143)
Supply function (p. 144)
Demand function (p. 144)
Market equilibrium (p. 144)

Section 2.4

Basic functions (p. 149)
$f(x) = ax + b$ (linear)
$f(x) = C, \quad C = $ constant
$f(x) = ax^b$ (power)
$f(x) = x$ (identity)
$f(x) = x^2, f(x) = x^3, f(x) = 1/x$
Shifts of graphs (p. 150)
$f(x - h)$ shifts $f(x)$ h units horizontally
$f(x) + k$ shifts $f(x)$ k units vertically
Polynomial function of degree n (p. 151)
$$f(x) = a_n x^n + a_{n-1} x^{n-1} + \cdots + a_1 x + a_0$$
$a_n \neq 0, n \geq 0, n$ an integer

Rational function (p. 152)
$f(x) = p(x)/q(x)$, where $p(x)$ and $q(x)$
are polynomials
Vertical asymptote (p. 154)
Horizontal asymptote (p. 154)
Absolute value function (p. 155)
$$f(x) = |x| = \begin{cases} x & \text{if } x \geq 0 \\ -x & \text{if } x < 0 \end{cases}$$
Piecewise defined functions (p. 155)

Section 2.5

Mathematical models (p. 161)
Scatter plots (p. 161)

Significant digits (p. 163)
Modeling data with a graphing calculator (p. 166)

REVIEW EXERCISES

Section 2.1

In Problems 1–10, find the real solutions to each quadratic equation.

1. $3x^2 + 10x = 5x$
2. $4x - 3x^2 = 0$
3. $x^2 + 5x + 6 = 0$
4. $11 - 10x - 2x^2 = 0$
5. $(x - 1)(x + 3) = -8$
6. $4x^2 = 3$
7. $20x^2 + 3x = 20 - 15x^2$
8. $8x^2 + 8x = 1 - 8x^2$
9. $7 = 2.07x - 0.02x^2$
10. $46.3x - 117 - 0.5x^2 = 0$

In Problems 11–14, solve each equation using a graphing utility to find the zeros of the function. Solve the equation algebraically to check your results.

11. $4z^2 + 25 = 0$
12. $z(z + 6) = 27$
13. $3x^2 - 18x - 48 = 0$
14. $3x^2 - 6x - 9 = 0$
15. Solve $x^2 + ax + b = 0$ for x.
16. Solve $xr^2 - 4ar - x^2 c = 0$ for r.

In Problems 17 and 18, approximate the real solutions to each quadratic equation to two decimal places.

17. $23.1 - 14.1x - 0.002x^2 = 0$
18. $1.03x^2 + 2.02x - 1.015 = 0$

Section 2.2

For each function in Problems 19–24, find the vertex and determine if it is a maximum or minimum point, find the y-intercept and the zeros if they exist, and sketch the graph.

19. $y = \frac{1}{2}x^2 + 2x$
20. $y = 4 - \frac{1}{4}x^2$
21. $y = 6 + x - x^2$
22. $y = x^2 - 4x + 5$
23. $y = x^2 + 6x + 9$
24. $y = 12x - 9 - 4x^2$

In Problems 25–30, use a graphing calculator to graph each function. Use the vertex and zeros to determine an appropriate window. Be sure to label the maximum or minimum point.

25. $y = \frac{1}{3}x^2 - 3$
26. $y = \frac{1}{2}x^2 + 2$
27. $y = x^2 + 2x + 5$
28. $y = -10 + 7x - x^2$
29. $y = 20x - 0.1x^2$
30. $y = 50 - 1.5x + 0.01x^2$
31. Find the average rate of change of $f(x) = 100x - x^2$ from $x = 30$ to $x = 50$.
32. Find the average rate of change of
$$f(x) = x^2 - 30x + 22$$
over the interval $[10, 50]$.

In Problems 33–36, a graph is given. Use the graph to
(a) **locate the vertex,**
(b) **determine the zeros, and**
(c) **match the graph with one of A, B, C, or D.**

    A. $y = 7x - \frac{1}{2}x^2$
    B. $y = \frac{1}{2}x^2 - x - 4$
    C. $y = 8 - 2x - x^2$
    D. $y = 49 - x^2$

33.

34.

35.

36.
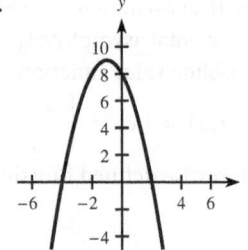

Section 2.4

37. Sketch a graph of each of the following basic functions.
    (a) $f(x) = x^2$ (b) $f(x) = 1/x$ (c) $f(x) = x^{1/4}$

38. If $f(x) = \begin{cases} -x^2 & \text{if } x \le 0 \\ 1/x & \text{if } x > 0 \end{cases}$, find the following.

    (a) $f(0)$ (b) $f(0.0001)$
    (c) $f(-5)$ (d) $f(10)$

39. If $f(x) = \begin{cases} x & \text{if } x \le 1 \\ 3x - 2 & \text{if } x > 1 \end{cases}$, find the following.

    (a) $f(-2)$ (b) $f(0)$ (c) $f(1)$ (d) $f(2)$

In Problems 40 and 41, graph each function.

40. $f(x) = \begin{cases} x & \text{if } x \le 1 \\ 3x - 2 & \text{if } x > 1 \end{cases}$

41. (a) $f(x) = (x - 2)^2$ (b) $f(x) = (x + 1)^3$

In Problems 42 and 43, use a graphing utility to graph each function. Find any turning points.

42. $y = x^3 + 3x^2 - 9x$ 43. $y = x^3 - 9x$

In Problems 44 and 45, graph each function. Find and identify any asymptotes.

44. $y = \dfrac{1}{x - 2}$ 45. $y = \dfrac{2x - 1}{x + 3}$

Section 2.5

46. *Modeling* Consider the data given in the table.
    (a) Make a scatter plot.
    (b) Fit a linear function to the data.
    (c) Try other function types and find one that fits better than a linear function.

x	0	4	8	12	16	20	24
y	153	151	147	140	128	115	102

47. *Modeling* Consider the data given in the table.
    (a) Make a scatter plot.
    (b) Fit a linear function to the data.
    (c) Try other function types and find one that fits better than a linear function.

x	3	5	10	15	20	25	30
y	100	150	200	220	250	210	190

APPLICATIONS

Section 2.1

48. *Physics* A ball is thrown into the air from a height of 96 ft above the ground, and its height is given by $S = 96 + 32t - 16t^2$, where t is the time in seconds.
    (a) Find the values of t that make $S = 0$.
    (b) Do both of the values of t have meaning for this application?
    (c) When will the ball strike the ground?

49. *Profit* The profit for a product is given by $P(x) = 82x - 0.10x^2 - 1600$, where x is the number of units produced and sold. Break-even points will occur at values of x where $P(x) = 0$. How many units will give a break-even point for the product?

Section 2.2

50. *Manufacturing employment* Using U.S. Energy Information Administration data from 2012 and projected to 2040, the total U.S. employment in manufacturing, E in millions, can be modeled by

$$E(t) = -0.0052t^2 + 0.080t + 12$$

where t is the number of years past 2010.
    (a) In what year does the model predict that manufacturing employment will be at its maximum, and what is that maximum?
    (b) When does the model predict that manufacturing employment will be 11.5 million?

51. *Maximum area* A rectangular lot is to be fenced and then divided down the middle to create two identical fenced lots (see the figure). If 1200 ft of fence is to be used, the area of each lot is given by

$$A = x\left(\frac{1200 - 3x}{4}\right)$$

(a) Find the x-value that maximizes this area.
(b) Find the maximum area.

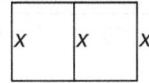

Section 2.3

52. *Supply* Graph the first-quadrant portion of the supply function

$$p = 2q^2 + 4q + 6$$

53. *Demand* Graph the first-quadrant portion of the demand function

$$p = 18 - 3q - q^2$$

54. *Market equilibrium*
(a) Suppose the supply function for a product is $p = 0.1q^2 + 1$ and the demand function is $p = 85 - 0.2q - 0.1q^2$. Sketch the first-quadrant portion of the graph of each function. Use the same set of axes for both and label the market equilibrium point.
(b) Use algebraic methods to find the equilibrium price and quantity.

55. *Market equilibrium* The supply function for a product is given by $p = q^2 + 300$, and the demand is given by $p + q = 410$. Find the equilibrium quantity and price.

56. *Market equilibrium* If the demand function for a commodity is given by the equation $p^2 + 5q = 200$ and the supply function is given by $40 - p^2 + 3q = 0$, find the equilibrium quantity and price.

57. *Break-even points* If total costs for a product are given by $C(x) = 1760 + 8x + 0.6x^2$ and total revenues are given by $R(x) = 100x - 0.4x^2$, find the break-even quantities.

58. *Break-even points* If total costs for a commodity are given by $C(x) = 900 + 25x$ and total revenues are given by $R(x) = 100x - x^2$, find the break-even quantities.

59. *Maximizing revenue and profit* Find the maximum revenue and maximum profit for the functions described in Problem 58.

60. *Break-even and profit maximization* Given profit $P(x) = 1.3x - 0.01x^2 - 30$, find maximum profit and the break-even quantities and sketch the graph.

61. *Maximum profit* Given $C(x) = 360 + 10x + 0.2x^2$ and $R(x) = 50x - 0.2x^2$, find the level of production that gives maximum profit and find the maximum profit.

62. *Break-even and profit maximization* A certain company has fixed costs of $15,000 for its product and variable costs given by $140 + 0.04x$ dollars per unit, where x is the total number of units. The selling price of the product is given by $300 - 0.06x$ dollars per unit.
(a) Formulate the functions for total cost and total revenue.

(b) Find the break-even quantities.
(c) Find the level of sales that maximizes revenue.
(d) Form the profit function and find the level of production and sales that maximizes profit.
(e) Find the profit (or loss) at the production levels found in parts (c) and (d).

Section 2.4

63. *Diabetes* The rise of adult diabetes in the United States is a growing concern for health professionals. Using Centers for Disease Control and Prevention data for selected years from 2010 and projected to 2050, the percent of U.S. adults with diabetes can be modeled by the function

$$D(t) = 4.95t^{0.495}$$

where t is the number of years past 2000.
(a) What type of function is this?
(b) What does the function predict as the percent of U.S. adults with diabetes in the year 2020?
(c) Find $D(25)$ and write a sentence that explains its meaning.

64. *Photosynthesis* The amount y of photosynthesis that takes place in a certain plant depends on the intensity x of the light present according to

$$y = 120x^2 - 20x^3 \quad \text{for } x \geq 0$$

(a) Graph this function with a graphing calculator. (Use y-min $= -100$ and y-max $= 700$.)
(b) The model is valid only when $f(x) \geq 0$ (that is, on or above the x-axis). For what x-values is this true?

65. *Cost-benefit* Suppose the weekly cost C, in dollars, of eliminating p percent of the pollution from the emissions of a factory is given by

$$C(p) = \frac{4800p}{100 - p}$$

(a) What type of function is this?
(b) Given that p represents the percent of pollution removed, what is the domain of $C(p)$?
(c) Find $C(0)$ and interpret its meaning.
(d) Find the weekly cost of removing 99% of the pollution.

66. *Municipal water costs* The Municipal Water Authority of Bella Isla used the following function to determine charges for water.

$$C(x) = \begin{cases} 10.23x & \text{if } 0 \leq x \leq 100 \\ 1023 + 8.16(x - 100) & \text{if } 100 < x \leq 1000 \\ 8367 + 6.76(x - 1000) & \text{if } x > 1000 \end{cases}$$

where $C(x)$ is the cost in dollars for x thousand gallons of water.
(a) Find the monthly charge for 12,000 gallons of water.
(b) Find the monthly charge for 825,000 gallons of water.

Section 2.5

67. *Modeling (Subaru WRX)* The table shows the times it takes a Subaru WRX to accelerate from 0 mph to speeds of 30 mph, 40 mph, etc., up to 90 mph, in increments of 10 mph.

Time (sec)	Speed (mph)	Time (sec)	Speed (mph)
1.6	30	7.8	70
2.7	40	10.2	80
4.0	50	12.9	90
5.6	60		

Source: Motor Trend

(a) Represent the times by x and the speeds by y, and name at least two function types that would be reasonable choices to model these data.
(b) Find the power function model for the data.
(c) Graph the points and the function to see how well the function fits the points.
(d) What does the model indicate the speed is 5 seconds after the car starts to move?
(e) According to the model, in how many seconds will the car reach 79.3 mph?

68. *Average annual wage* The tables below give Social Security Administration data for the U.S. average annual wage from 2011 and projected to 2021 and for selected years from 2012 and projected to 2050.
(a) Make a scatter plot of each of these data sets with x as the number of years past 2010.
(b) Decide which one function type could be used as a model for both data sets and find the two models. Let $a(x)$ be the model for the data to 2021 and $A(x)$ be the model for data to 2050. Report both models with 4 significant digit coefficients.
(c) How well do the reported models agree for the data points for 2020 and 2050?
(d) When does each reported model predict that the average annual wage will reach $150,000?

Data to 2021 (in dollars)

Year	2011	2012	2013	2014
Wage	43,009	44,644	46,496	48,595

Year	2015	2016	2017	2018
Wage	50,893	53,317	55,989	58,698

Year	2019	2020	2021	
Wage	61,179	63,676	66,161	

Data to 2050 (in thousands of dollars)

Year	2012	2014	2016	2018
Wage	44.6	48.6	53.3	58.7

Year	2020	2025	2030	2035
Wage	63.7	76.8	93.2	113.2

Year	2040	2045	2050	
Wage	137.6	167.1	202.5	

69. *Obesity* Obesity (BMI $\geq$ 30) is a serious problem in the United States and is expected to get worse. Being overweight increases the risk of diabetes, heart disease, and many other ailments, but the severely obese (BMI $\geq$ 40) are most at risk and the most expensive to treat. The percent of Americans who are obese and severely obese from 1990 and projected to 2030 are shown in the table below.
(a) Find the linear function, $O(x)$, that models obesity, with x equal to the number of years past 1980 and y the percent of obese Americans. Report the model as $y = O(x)$ with 3 significant digit coefficients.
(b) Find the linear function, $S(x)$, that models severe obesity, with x equal to the number of years past 1980 and y the percent of severely obese Americans. Report the model as $y = S(x)$ with 3 significant digit coefficients.
(c) Let $F(x) = \dfrac{S(x)}{O(x)}$. What is the mathematical name for this type of function, and what does it measure in terms of these data?
(d) Find the horizontal asymptote for $F(x)$ and explain what it means in terms of these data.

Year	1990	2000	2010	2015	2020	2025	2030
% Obese	12.7	22.1	30.9	34.5	37.4	39.9	42.2
% Severely Obese	0.8	2.2	4.9	6.4	7.9	9.5	11.1

Source: American Journal of Preventive Medicine, 42, June 2012: 563–570, ajpmonline.org

70. *U.S. population demographics* The makeup of various groups within the U.S. population may reshape the electorate in ways that could change political representation and policies. The following table shows U.S. Department of Labor data from 1980 and projected to 2050 for the civilian non-institutional population age 16 or older, in millions, according to those who are White non-Hispanic and others (non-White or Hispanic).

(a) With x as the number of years past 1970, use a scatter plot to determine which single function type could be used to model each set of data and find a model for each set. Let $W(x)$ be the function for the population of White non-Hispanic and $O(x)$ be the function for the non-Whites or Hispanics. Report both models with 3 significant digit coefficients.

(b) If these models remain valid, use them to determine the year in which these population segments are predicted to be equal.

Year	1980	1990	2000	2010	2015
White non-Hispanic	136.8	146.5	153.1	162.1	164.6
Others	30.9	42.6	56.6	71.6	79.0

Year	2020	2030	2040	2050
White non-Hispanic	166.3	168.8	169.7	169.4
Others	86.8	104.2	123.1	143.0

Source: U.S. Department of Labor

② CHAPTER TEST

1. Sketch a graph of each of the following functions.
   (a) $f(x) = x^4$
   (b) $g(x) = |x|$
   (c) $h(x) = -1$
   (d) $k(x) = \sqrt{x}$

2. The following figures show graphs of the power function $y = x^b$. Which is the graph for $b > 1$? Which is the graph for $0 < b < 1$?

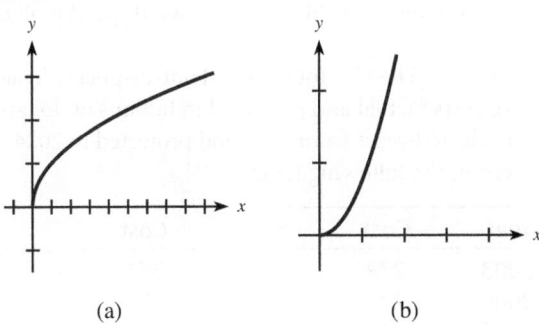

(a)   (b)

3. If $f(x) = ax^2 + bx + c$ and $a < 0$, sketch the shape of the graph of $y = f(x)$.

4. Graph:
   (a) $f(x) = (x + 1)^2 - 1$
   (b) $f(x) = (x - 2)^3 + 1$

5. Which of the following three graphs is the graph of $f(x) = x^3 - 4x^2$? Explain your choice.

(a)   (b)

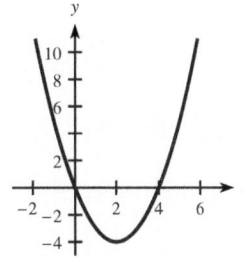

(c)

6. Let $f(x) = \begin{cases} 8x + 1/x & \text{if } x < 0 \\ 4 & \text{if } 0 \leq x \leq 2 \\ 6 - x & \text{if } x > 2 \end{cases}$

   Find the following:
   (a) the y-coordinate of the point on the graph of $y = f(x)$ where $x = 16$
   (b) $f(-2)$
   (c) $f(13)$

7. Sketch the graph of $g(x) = \begin{cases} x^2 & \text{if } x \leq 1 \\ 4-x & \text{if } x > 1 \end{cases}$

8. Find the y-intercept, vertex, and zeros (if they exist) and sketch the graph of $f(x) = 21 - 4x - x^2$.

9. Solve $3x^2 + 2 = 7x$.

10. Solve $2x^2 + 6x = 9$.

11. Solve $\dfrac{1}{x} + 2x = \dfrac{1}{3} + \dfrac{x + 1}{x}$

12. Which of the following three graphs is that of
$g(x) = \dfrac{3x - 12}{x + 2}$? Explain your choice.

(a)

(b)

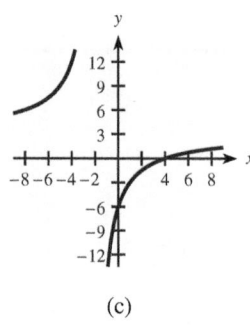

(c)

13. Find the horizontal and vertical asymptotes of the graph of

$$f(x) = \frac{8}{2x - 10}$$

14. Find the average rate of change of

$$P(x) = 92x - x^2 - 1760$$

over the interval from $x = 10$ to $x = 40$.

15. Choose the type of function that models each of the following graphs.

(a)

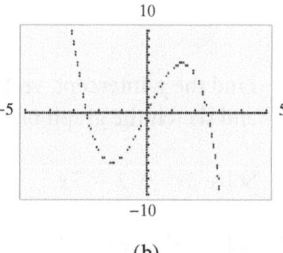

(b)

16. *Modeling*
   (a) Make a scatter plot and develop a model for the following data.
   (b) What does the model predict for $x = 40$?
   (c) When does the model predict $f(x) = 0$?

x	0	2	4	6	8	10	12	14	16	18	20
y	20.1	19.2	18.8	17.5	17.0	15.8	16.0	14.9	13.8	13.7	13.0

17. Suppose the supply and demand functions for a product are given by $6p - q = 180$ and $(p + 20)q = 30,000$, respectively. Find the equilibrium price and quantity.

18. Suppose a company's total cost for a product is given by $C(x) = 15,000 + 35x + 0.1x^2$ and the total revenue for the product is given by $R(x) = 285x - 0.9x^2$, where x is the number of units produced and sold.
   (a) Find the profit function.
   (b) Determine the number of units at which the profit for the product is maximized and find the maximum possible profit.
   (c) Find the break-even point(s) for the product.

19. The wind chill expresses the combined effects of low temperatures and wind speeds as a single temperature reading. When the outside temperature is 0°F, the wind chill WC is a function of the wind speed s (in mph) and is approximated by the following function.[*]

$$WC = f(s) = \begin{cases} 0 & \text{if } 0 \le s \le 1.13 \\ 36.23 - 35.50\sqrt[6]{s} & \text{if } 1.13 < s < 55 \\ -33 & \text{if } s \ge 55 \end{cases}$$

   (a) Find $f(15)$ and write a sentence that explains its meaning.
   (b) Find the wind chill when the wind speed is 48 mph.

20. *Modeling* The U.S. total annual out-of-pocket health care costs (actual and projected in billions of dollars) for selected years from 2003 and projected to 2024 are given in the following table.

Year	Cost	Year	Cost
2003	238	2015	351
2006	277	2018	393
2009	301	2021	463
2012	329	2024	543

Source: U.S. Department of Health and Human Services

   (a) Plot the data, with x representing the number of years after 2000 and y representing the expenses.
   (b) Find a linear and a cubic function model for the data.
   (c) Use both models to estimate the per capita expenses in 2024 (to the nearest dollar). Comment on how well the models approximate the projected data value.

*Source: National Weather Service

2   EXTENDED APPLICATIONS & GROUP PROJECTS

I. Body Mass Index (Modeling)

Obesity is a risk factor for the development of several medical problems, including high blood pressure, high cholesterol, heart disease, and diabetes. Of course, whether a person is considered obese depends not only on weight but also on height. One way of comparing weights that accounts for height is the *body mass index (BMI)*. The table below gives the BMI for a variety of heights and weights for people. Medical professionals generally agree that a BMI of 30 or greater increases the risk of developing medical problems associated with obesity.

Describe how to assist a group of people in using this information. Include the following in your description.

A. How a person uses the table to determine his or her BMI.
B. How a person determines the weight that will put him or her at medical risk.
C. How a person whose weight or height is not in the table can determine whether his or her BMI is 30 or higher. To address this particular issue, develop a formula to

find the weight that would give a BMI of 30 for a person of a given height, including how you would:

1. Pick the points from the table that correspond to a BMI of 30 and create a table of these heights and weights. Change the units of height measurement to simplify the data.
2. Determine what type of model seems to be the best fit for the data.
3. Create a model for the data.
4. Test the model with existing data.
5. Explain how to use the model to test for obesity. In particular, use the model to find the obesity threshold for someone who is 5 feet tall and someone who is 6 feet 2 inches tall (heights that are not in the table).
6. Use the Internet to find the definition of BMI and, if necessary, convert it to a formula that uses inches and pounds.
7. Make a table for heights from 61 inches to 73 inches that compares the threshold weights for a BMI of 30 from your model, from the definition of BMI, and from the table.

Body Mass Index for Specified Height (ft/in) and Weight (lb)

Height/Weight	120	130	140	150	160	170	180	190	200	210	220	230	240	250
5'1"	23	25	27	28	30	32	34	36	38	40	42	44	45	47
5'2"	22	24	26	27	29	31	33	35	37	38	40	42	44	46
5'3"	21	23	25	27	28	30	32	34	36	37	39	41	43	44
5'4"	21	22	24	26	28	29	31	33	34	36	38	40	41	43
5'5"	20	22	23	25	27	28	30	32	33	35	37	38	40	42
5'6"	19	21	23	24	26	27	29	31	32	34	36	37	39	40
5'7"	19	20	23	24	25	27	28	30	31	33	35	36	38	39
5'8"	18	20	21	23	24	26	27	29	30	32	34	35	37	38
5'9"	18	19	21	22	24	25	27	28	30	31	33	34	36	37
5'10"	17	19	20	22	23	24	25	27	28	29	31	33	35	36
5'11"	17	18	20	21	22	24	25	27	28	29	31	32	34	35
6'0"	16	18	19	20	22	23	24	26	27	29	30	31	33	34
6'1"	16	17	19	20	21	22	24	25	26	28	29	30	32	33

Source: Roche Pharmaceuticals

II. Operating Leverage and Business Risk

Once you have determined the break-even point for your product, you can use it to examine the effects of increasing or decreasing the role of fixed costs in your operating structure. The extent to which a business uses fixed costs (compared with variable costs) in its operations is referred to as **operating leverage**. The greater the use of operating leverage (fixed costs, often associated with fixed assets), the larger the increase in profit as sales rise and the larger the increase in loss as sales fall. The higher the break-even quantity for your product, the greater your **business risk**. To see how operating leverage is related to business risk, complete the following.

1. If x is the number of units of a product that is sold and the price is $\$p$ per unit, write the function that gives the revenue R for the product.
2. (a) If the fixed cost for production of this product is $\$10,000$ and the variable cost is $\$100$ per unit, find the function that gives the total cost C for the product.
   (b) What type of function is this?
3. Write an equation containing only the variables p and x that describes when the break-even point occurs.
4. (a) Solve the equation from Question 3 for x so that x is written as a function of p.
   (b) What type of function is this?
   (c) What is the domain of this function?
   (d) What is the domain of this function in the context of this application?
5. (a) Graph the function from Question 4 for the domain of the problem.
   (b) Does the function increase or decrease as p increases?
6. Suppose the company has a monopoly for this product so that it can set the price as it chooses. What are the benefit and the danger to the company of pricing its product at $\$1100$ per unit?
7. If the company has a monopoly for this product so that it can set the price, what are the benefit and the danger to the company of pricing its product at $\$101$ per unit?
8. Suppose the company currently is labor-intensive; the monthly fixed cost is $\$10,000$ and the variable cost is $\$100$ per unit, but installing modern equipment will reduce the variable cost to $\$50$ per unit while increasing the monthly fixed cost to $\$30,000$. Also suppose the selling price per unit is $p = \$200$.
   (a) Which of these operations will have the highest operating leverage? Explain.
   (b) Which of these operations will have the highest business risk? Explain.
   (c) What is the relation between high operating leverage and risk? Discuss the benefit and danger of the second operating plan to justify your answer.

Creative-Material/Shutterstock.com

Matrices

3

A wide variety of application problems can be solved using matrices. A **matrix** (plural: matrices) is a rectangular array of numbers. In addition to storing data in a matrix and making comparisons of data, we can analyze data and make business decisions by defining the operations of addition, subtraction, scalar multiplication, and matrix multiplication. Matrices can be used to solve systems of linear equations, as we will see in this chapter. Matrices and matrix operations are the basis for computer spreadsheets such as Excel, which are used extensively in education, research, and business. Matrices are also useful in linear programming, which is discussed in Chapter 4.

The topics and some representative applications discussed in this chapter include the following.

Prerequisite Problem Type	For Section	Answer	Section for Review
Evaluate: (a) $4 - (-2)$	3.1–3.5	(a) 6	0.2 Signed numbers
(b) $-4\left(\dfrac{2}{3}\right) + 3$		(b) $\dfrac{1}{3}$	
(c) $(-5)(4) + (8)(1) + (2)(5)$		(c) -2	
(d) Multiply each of the numbers $0, -3, -2, 2$ by $-\dfrac{1}{3}$.		(d) $0, 1, \dfrac{2}{3}, -\dfrac{2}{3}$	

Write the coefficients of x, y, and z and the constant term in each equation:

For Section: 3.3–3.5

	Coefficients			Const. term	0.5 Algebraic expressions
(a)	x	y	z		
	2	5	4	4	
(b)	1	-3	-2	5	
(c)	3	1	0	4	

(a) $2x + 5y + 4z = 4$
(b) $x - 3y - 2z = 5$
(c) $3x + y = 4$

Prerequisite Problem Type	For Section	Answer	Section for Review
Solve: (a) $x_1 - 2x_3 = 2$ for x_1 (b) $x_2 + x_3 = -3$ for x_2 (c) $450{,}000 - 3z \geq 0$ for z	3.3–3.5	(a) $x_1 = 2 + 2x_3$ (b) $x_2 = -3 - x_3$ (c) $z \leq 150{,}000$	1.1 Linear equations and inequalities
Solve the system: $\begin{cases} x - 0.25y = 11{,}750 \\ -0.20x + y = 10{,}000 \end{cases}$	3.3–3.5	$x = 15{,}000$ $y = 13{,}000$	1.5 Systems of linear equations

SECTION 3.1

Matrices

OBJECTIVES

- To organize and interpret data stored in matrices
- To add and subtract matrices
- To find the transpose of a matrix
- To multiply a matrix by a scalar (real number)

APPLICATION PREVIEW

The annual **balance of trade** for a country is the difference between its imports and exports for a given product or for all of its products. Table 3.1 summarizes the actual and projected U.S. dollar value (in billions) of U.S. exports and imports of pipeline natural gas with Canada and Mexico and of liquefied natural gas with other countries for selected years. Data in tabular form like this can be stored in **matrices**, which are useful for solving an assortment of problems.

TABLE 3.1

	Exports			Imports		
	2015	2020	2025	2015	2020	2025
Canada	3.15	5.76	6.53	10.13	12.05	11.39
Mexico	2.99	5.87	7.83	0.20	0.21	0.11
Other	0.10	2.25	6.64	0.63	0.89	0.92

Source: U.S. Energy Information Administration

The data in Table 3.1 can be stored in two matrices, one for exports (matrix A) and one for imports (matrix B).

$$A = \begin{bmatrix} 3.15 & 5.76 & 6.53 \\ 2.99 & 5.87 & 7.83 \\ 0.10 & 2.25 & 6.64 \end{bmatrix} \quad B = \begin{bmatrix} 10.13 & 12.05 & 11.39 \\ 0.20 & 0.21 & 0.11 \\ 0.63 & 0.89 & 0.92 \end{bmatrix}$$

Then the balance of trade in natural gas with the various countries in the selected years will be the difference of the two matrices, $A - B$. This difference is found in Example 5.

We will discuss how to find the sum and the difference of two matrices and how to multiply a matrix by a real number.

In the Application Preview's export matrix A (we generally use uppercase letters to denote matrices), the *rows* correspond to the countries and the *columns* correspond to years. In general, the rows of a matrix are numbered from the top to the bottom and the columns are numbered from left to right, as the following example matrix illustrates.

$$M = \begin{bmatrix} 20 & 25 & 22 & 18 \\ 27 & 40 & 31 & 25 \\ 16 & 16 & 19 & 16 \end{bmatrix} \begin{matrix} \text{Row 1} \\ \text{Row 2} \\ \text{Row 3} \end{matrix}$$

Column 1 Column 2 Column 3 Column 4

Matrices are classified in terms of the numbers of rows and columns they have. Matrix M has three rows and four columns, so we say that this is a 3×4 (read "three by four") matrix.

The matrix

$$A = \begin{bmatrix} a_{11} & a_{12} & a_{13} & \cdots & a_{1n} \\ a_{21} & a_{22} & a_{23} & \cdots & a_{2n} \\ & & \vdots & & \vdots \\ a_{m1} & a_{m2} & a_{m3} & \cdots & a_{mn} \end{bmatrix}$$

has m rows and n columns, so it is an $m \times n$ matrix. When we designate A as an $m \times n$ matrix, we are indicating the size of the matrix. Two matrices are said to have the same **order** (be the same size) if they have the same number of rows and the same number of columns. For example, $C = \begin{bmatrix} 1 & 3 & 2 \\ 4 & 1 & 2 \end{bmatrix}$ and $D = \begin{bmatrix} 1 & 4 \\ 2 & 1 \\ 3 & 0 \end{bmatrix}$ do not have the same order.

C is a 2×3 matrix and D is a 3×2 matrix.

The numbers in a matrix are called its **entries** or **elements.** Note that the subscripts on an entry in matrix A above correspond, respectively, to the row and column in which the entry is located. Thus a_{23} represents the entry in the second row and the third column, and we refer to it as the "two-three entry." In matrix B below, the entry denoted by b_{23} is 1.

Some matrices take special names because of their size. If the number of rows equals the number of columns, we say that the matrix is a **square matrix.** Matrix B below is a 3×3 square matrix.

$$B = \begin{bmatrix} 4 & 3 & 0 \\ 0 & 0 & 1 \\ -4 & 0 & 0 \end{bmatrix}$$

EXAMPLE 1   Population and Labor Force

Figure 3.1 shows that the U.S. labor force tends to grow as the population grows. The figure gives the U.S. civilian non-institutional population and labor force (in millions, actual and projected) for the years 2010, 2016, and 2022.

Civilian non-institutional population
and labor force

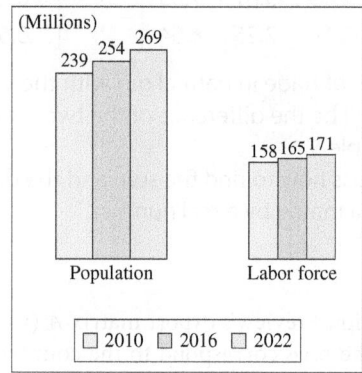

Figure 3.1

Source: U.S. Census Bureau

A partial table of values from Figure 3.1 is shown. Complete the table that summarizes these data and use it to create a 2×3 matrix describing the information.

	2010	2016	2022
Population	239		
Labor Force		165	

Solution
Reading the data from Figure 3.1 and completing the table give

	2010	2016	2022
Population	239	254	269
Labor Force	158	165	171

Writing these data in a matrix gives

$$\begin{bmatrix} 239 & 254 & 269 \\ 158 & 165 & 171 \end{bmatrix}$$

A matrix with one row, such as [9   5] or [3   2   1   6], is called a **row matrix,** and a matrix with one column, such as

$$\begin{bmatrix} 1 \\ 3 \\ 5 \end{bmatrix}$$

is called a **column matrix.** Row and column matrices are also called **vectors.**

Any matrix in which *every* entry is zero is called a **zero matrix;** examples include

$$\begin{bmatrix} 0 & 0 \\ 0 & 0 \end{bmatrix}, \quad \begin{bmatrix} 0 & 0 \\ 0 & 0 \\ 0 & 0 \end{bmatrix}, \quad \text{and} \quad \begin{bmatrix} 0 & 0 & 0 & 0 \\ 0 & 0 & 0 & 0 \\ 0 & 0 & 0 & 0 \end{bmatrix}$$

We define two matrices to be **equal** if they are of the same order and if each entry in one equals the corresponding entry in the other.

When the columns and rows of matrix A are interchanged to create a matrix B and vice versa, we say that A and B are **transposes** of each other and write $A^T = B$ and $B^T = A$. We will see valuable uses for transposes of matrices in Chapter 4, "Inequalities and Linear Programming."

EXAMPLE 2   Matrices

(a) Which element of

$$A = \begin{bmatrix} 1 & 0 & 3 \\ 3 & 4 & 2 \\ 7 & 8 & 3 \end{bmatrix} \qquad B = \begin{bmatrix} 1 & 0 & 3 \\ 3 & 4 & 2 \\ 7 & 8 & 4 \end{bmatrix}$$

is represented by a_{32}?

(b) Is A a square matrix?

(c) Find the transpose of matrix A.

(d) Does $A = B$?

Solution

(a) a_{32} represents the element in row 3 and column 2 of matrix A—that is, $a_{32} = 8$.

(b) Yes, it is a 3×3 (square) matrix.

(c)
$$A^T = \begin{bmatrix} 1 & 3 & 7 \\ 0 & 4 & 8 \\ 3 & 2 & 3 \end{bmatrix}$$

(d) No, $a_{33} \neq b_{33}$.

CHECKPOINT

1. (a) Do matrices A and B have the same order?

$$A = \begin{bmatrix} 1 & 2 & 3 \\ 4 & 5 & 6 \\ 7 & 8 & 9 \end{bmatrix} \quad \text{and} \quad B = \begin{bmatrix} 1 & 4 & 7 \\ 2 & 5 & 8 \\ 3 & 6 & 9 \end{bmatrix}$$

(b) Does matrix A equal matrix B?

(c) Does $B^T = A$?

Addition and Subtraction of Matrices   If two matrices have the same number of rows and columns, we can add the matrices by adding their corresponding entries.

Sum of Two Matrices

If matrix A and matrix B are of the same order and have elements a_{ij} and b_{ij} respectively, then their **sum** $A + B$ is a matrix C whose elements are $c_{ij} = a_{ij} + b_{ij}$ for all i and j. That is,

$$A + B = \begin{bmatrix} a_{11} & a_{12} & \cdots & a_{1n} \\ a_{21} & a_{22} & \cdots & a_{2n} \\ \vdots & \vdots & & \vdots \\ a_{m1} & a_{m2} & \cdots & a_{mn} \end{bmatrix} + \begin{bmatrix} b_{11} & b_{12} & \cdots & b_{1n} \\ b_{21} & b_{22} & \cdots & b_{2n} \\ \vdots & \vdots & & \vdots \\ b_{m1} & b_{m2} & \cdots & b_{mn} \end{bmatrix}$$

$$= \begin{bmatrix} a_{11} + b_{11} & a_{12} + b_{12} & \cdots & a_{1n} + b_{1n} \\ a_{21} + b_{21} & a_{22} + b_{22} & \cdots & a_{2n} + b_{2n} \\ \vdots & & & \vdots \\ a_{m1} + b_{m1} & a_{m2} + b_{m2} & \cdots & a_{mn} + b_{mn} \end{bmatrix} = C$$

EXAMPLE 3 Matrix Sums

Find the sum of A and B if

$$A = \begin{bmatrix} 1 & 2 & 3 \\ 4 & -1 & -2 \end{bmatrix} \quad \text{and} \quad B = \begin{bmatrix} -1 & 2 & -3 \\ -2 & 0 & 1 \end{bmatrix}$$

Solution

$$A + B = \begin{bmatrix} 1 + (-1) & 2 + 2 & 3 + (-3) \\ 4 + (-2) & -1 + 0 & -2 + 1 \end{bmatrix} = \begin{bmatrix} 0 & 4 & 0 \\ 2 & -1 & -1 \end{bmatrix}$$

Note that the sum of A and B in Example 3 could be found by adding the matrices in either order. That is, $A + B = B + A$. This is known as the **commutative law of addition** for matrices. We will see in the next section that multiplication of matrices is *not* commutative.

The matrix $-B$ is called the **negative** of the matrix B, and each element of $-B$ is the negative of the corresponding element of B. For example, if

$$B = \begin{bmatrix} -1 & 2 & -3 \\ -2 & 0 & 1 \end{bmatrix}, \quad \text{then} \quad -B = \begin{bmatrix} 1 & -2 & 3 \\ 2 & 0 & -1 \end{bmatrix}$$

Using the negative, we can define the difference $A - B$ (when A and B have the same order) by $A - B = A + (-B)$, or by subtracting corresponding elements.

EXAMPLE 4 Matrix Differences

For matrices A and B in Example 3, find $A - B$.

Solution

$A - B$ can be found by subtracting corresponding elements.

$$A - B = \begin{bmatrix} 1 - (-1) & 2 - 2 & 3 - (-3) \\ 4 - (-2) & -1 - 0 & -2 - 1 \end{bmatrix} = \begin{bmatrix} 2 & 0 & 6 \\ 6 & -1 & -3 \end{bmatrix}$$

CHECKPOINT

2. If $A = \begin{bmatrix} 1 & 2 & 0 \\ 3 & 1 & 2 \end{bmatrix}$, $B = \begin{bmatrix} 3 & 6 & 1 \\ 0 & 2 & 1 \end{bmatrix}$, and $C = \begin{bmatrix} 1 & 0 & 2 \\ 0 & 1 & 1 \end{bmatrix}$, find $A + B - C$.

3. (a) What matrix D must be added to matrix A so that their sum is matrix Z?

$$A = \begin{bmatrix} 1 & -2 & 3 \\ -5 & 1 & 2 \end{bmatrix} \quad \text{and} \quad Z = \begin{bmatrix} 0 & 0 & 0 \\ 0 & 0 & 0 \end{bmatrix}$$

(b) Does $D = -A$?

EXAMPLE 5

Balance of Trade | APPLICATION PREVIEW |

The annual **balance of trade** for a country is the difference between its imports and exports for a given product or for all of its products. Table 3.2 summarizes the actual and projected U.S. dollar value (in billions) of U.S. exports and imports of pipeline natural gas with Canada and Mexico and of liquefied natural gas with other countries for selected years. Write the matrix that describes the balance of trade in natural gas with the various countries in the selected years.

TABLE 3.2

	Exports			Imports		
	2015	2020	2025	2015	2020	2025
Canada	3.15	5.76	6.53	10.13	12.05	11.39
Mexico	2.99	5.87	7.83	0.20	0.21	0.11
Other	0.10	2.25	6.64	0.63	0.89	0.92

Source: U.S. Energy Information Administration

Solution

From Table 3.2, we represent the exports as matrix A and the imports as matrix B.

$$A = \begin{bmatrix} 3.15 & 5.76 & 6.53 \\ 2.99 & 5.87 & 7.83 \\ 0.10 & 2.25 & 6.64 \end{bmatrix} \qquad B = \begin{bmatrix} 10.13 & 12.05 & 11.39 \\ 0.20 & 0.21 & 0.11 \\ 0.63 & 0.89 & 0.92 \end{bmatrix}$$

The balance of trade we seek is given by the difference $A - B$, as follows.

$$A - B = \begin{bmatrix} 3.15 - 10.13 & 5.76 - 12.05 & 6.53 - 11.39 \\ 2.99 - 0.20 & 5.87 - 0.21 & 7.83 - 0.11 \\ 0.10 - 0.63 & 2.25 - 0.89 & 6.64 - 0.92 \end{bmatrix}$$

$$= \begin{bmatrix} -6.98 & -6.29 & -4.86 \\ 2.79 & 5.66 & 7.72 \\ -0.53 & 1.36 & 5.72 \end{bmatrix}$$

Note that any negative entry indicates an unfavorable balance of trade for the United States with the country in the year corresponding to that entry. Thus, the 1–2 entry indicates a 2020 unfavorable balance of natural gas trade with Canada of $6.29 billion. Similarly, the 2–1 entry shows a 2015 favorable balance of $2.79 billion with Mexico.

Calculator Note

Graphing calculators have the capability to perform a number of operations on matrices. To enter data into a matrix, press the MATRIX key, move to EDIT, enter the dimensions of the matrix, and enter the values. Press QUIT (2nd MODE) when finished. To view a matrix, press MATRIX, the matrix number, and ENTER.

To compute $A + B$ and $A - B$ for

$$A = \begin{bmatrix} -1 & 3 & 2 \\ 1 & 0 & 2 \\ 0 & 1 & -1 \\ -4 & 2 & 3 \end{bmatrix} \quad \text{and} \quad B = \begin{bmatrix} -3 & 2 & 1 \\ 0 & -2 & 2 \\ -1 & 6 & 8 \\ 3 & 2 & 4 \end{bmatrix}$$

we enter the matrices in a graphing calculator (see Figure 3.2) and find the sum and difference of the two matrices by using the regular ⊞ and ⊟ keys (see Figure 3.3 on the following page). Details are shown in Appendix A, Section 3.1.

Figure 3.2

```
[A] + [B]
        [[-4   5    3]
         [1   -2    4]
         [-1   7    7]
         [-1   4    7]]
```

```
[A] - [B]
        [[2    1    1]
         [1    2    0]
         [1   -5   -9]
         [-7   0   -1]]
■
```

Figure 3.3

Scalar Multiplication   Consider the matrix

$$A = \begin{bmatrix} 3 & 2 \\ 1 & 1 \\ 2 & 0 \end{bmatrix}$$

Because $2A$ is $A + A$, we see that

$$2A = \begin{bmatrix} 3 & 2 \\ 1 & 1 \\ 2 & 0 \end{bmatrix} + \begin{bmatrix} 3 & 2 \\ 1 & 1 \\ 2 & 0 \end{bmatrix} = \begin{bmatrix} 6 & 4 \\ 2 & 2 \\ 4 & 0 \end{bmatrix}$$

Note that $2A$ could have been found by multiplying each entry of A by 2. In the same manner, it can be shown that $3A = A + A + A$. (Try it.)

We can define **scalar multiplication** as follows.

Scalar Multiplication

Multiplying a matrix by a real number (called a *scalar*) results in a matrix in which each entry of the original matrix is multiplied by the real number. Thus, if

$$A = \begin{bmatrix} a_{11} & a_{12} \\ a_{21} & a_{22} \end{bmatrix}, \quad \text{then} \quad cA = \begin{bmatrix} ca_{11} & ca_{12} \\ ca_{21} & ca_{22} \end{bmatrix}$$

EXAMPLE 6   Scalar Multiplication

If

$$A = \begin{bmatrix} 4 & 1 & 4 & 0 \\ 2 & -7 & 3 & 6 \\ 0 & 0 & 2 & 5 \end{bmatrix}$$

find $5A$ and $-2A$.

Solution

$$5A = \begin{bmatrix} 5 \cdot 4 & 5 \cdot 1 & 5 \cdot 4 & 5 \cdot 0 \\ 5 \cdot 2 & 5(-7) & 5 \cdot 3 & 5 \cdot 6 \\ 5 \cdot 0 & 5 \cdot 0 & 5 \cdot 2 & 5 \cdot 5 \end{bmatrix} = \begin{bmatrix} 20 & 5 & 20 & 0 \\ 10 & -35 & 15 & 30 \\ 0 & 0 & 10 & 25 \end{bmatrix}$$

$$-2A = \begin{bmatrix} -2 \cdot 4 & -2 \cdot 1 & -2 \cdot 4 & -2 \cdot 0 \\ -2 \cdot 2 & -2(-7) & -2 \cdot 3 & -2 \cdot 6 \\ -2 \cdot 0 & -2 \cdot 0 & -2 \cdot 2 & -2 \cdot 5 \end{bmatrix} = \begin{bmatrix} -8 & -2 & -8 & 0 \\ -4 & 14 & -6 & -12 \\ 0 & 0 & -4 & -10 \end{bmatrix}$$

Figure 3.4 shows the matrix $-2A$ on a graphing calculator.

```
-2[A]
[[-8    -2   -8    0 ]
 [-4    14   -6   -12]
 [0     0    -4   -10]]
■
```

Figure 3.4

4. (a) Find $3D - D$ if $D = \begin{bmatrix} 1 & 3 & 2 & 10 \\ 20 & 5 & 6 & 3 \end{bmatrix}$

(b) Does $3D - D = 2D$?

EXAMPLE 7 Supply Charges

Suppose the purchase prices and delivery costs (per unit) for wood, siding, and roofing used in construction are given in Table 3.3. Then the table of unit costs may be represented by the matrix C.

TABLE 3.3

	Wood	Siding	Roofing
Purchase	6	4	2
Delivery	1	1	0.5

$$C = \begin{bmatrix} 6 & 4 & 2 \\ 1 & 1 & 0.5 \end{bmatrix}$$

If the supplier announces a 10% increase on both purchase and delivery of these items, find the new unit cost matrix.

Solution

A 10% increase means that the new unit costs are the former costs plus 0.10 times the former cost. That is, the new costs are 1.10 times the former, so the new unit cost matrix is given by

$$1.10C = 1.10 \begin{bmatrix} 6 & 4 & 2 \\ 1 & 1 & 0.5 \end{bmatrix} = \begin{bmatrix} 6.60 & 4.40 & 2.20 \\ 1.10 & 1.10 & 0.55 \end{bmatrix}$$

EXAMPLE 8 Power to Influence

Suppose that in a government agency, paperwork is constantly flowing among offices according to the diagram.

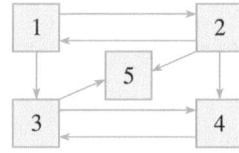

(a) Construct matrix A with elements

$$a_{ij} = \begin{cases} 1 & \text{if paperwork flows directly from } i \text{ to } j. \\ 0 & \text{if paperwork does not flow directly from } i \text{ to } j. \end{cases}$$

(b) Construct matrix B with elements

$$b_{ij} = \begin{cases} 1 & \text{if paperwork can flow from } i \text{ to } j \text{ through at most} \\ & \text{one intermediary, with } i \neq j. \\ 0 & \text{if this is not true.} \end{cases}$$

(c) The person in office i has the most power to influence others if the sum of the elements of row i in the matrix $A + B$ is the largest. What is the office number of this person?

Solution

(a) $A = \begin{bmatrix} 0 & 1 & 1 & 0 & 0 \\ 1 & 0 & 0 & 1 & 1 \\ 0 & 0 & 0 & 1 & 1 \\ 0 & 0 & 1 & 0 & 0 \\ 0 & 0 & 0 & 0 & 0 \end{bmatrix}$ (b) $B = \begin{bmatrix} 0 & 1 & 1 & 1 & 1 \\ 1 & 0 & 1 & 1 & 1 \\ 0 & 0 & 0 & 1 & 1 \\ 0 & 0 & 1 & 0 & 1 \\ 0 & 0 & 0 & 0 & 0 \end{bmatrix}$

(c) $A + B = \begin{bmatrix} 0 & 2 & 2 & 1 & 1 \\ 2 & 0 & 1 & 2 & 2 \\ 0 & 0 & 0 & 2 & 2 \\ 0 & 0 & 2 & 0 & 1 \\ 0 & 0 & 0 & 0 & 0 \end{bmatrix}$

Because the sum of the elements in row 2 is the largest (7), the person in office 2 has the most power to influence others. Because row 5 has the smallest sum (0), the person in office 5 has the least power.

Spreadsheet Note   To add two 3×3 matrices using Excel, we first enter their elements in the corresponding rows and columns of B1 to D3 and B5 to D7. Then we enter the formula = B1 + B5 in B9 and press ENTER. Next we use Fill Across from B9 to D9 and use Fill Down to B11:D11 to get the sum in B9:D11. The spreadsheet shows the sum $A + B$ where

$$A = \begin{bmatrix} 1 & 2 & 3 \\ 4 & 5 & 6 \\ 7 & 8 & 9 \end{bmatrix} \text{ and } B = \begin{bmatrix} -2 & -4 & 3 \\ 1 & 4 & -5 \\ 3 & 6 & -1 \end{bmatrix}$$

See Appendix B, Section 3.1, or the Online Excel Guide for more details.

	A	B	C	D
1	A	1	2	3
2		4	5	6
3		7	8	9
4				
5	B	−2	−4	3
6		1	4	−5
7		3	6	−1
8				
9	A + B	−1	−2	6
10		5	9	1
11		10	14	8

CHECKPOINT
ANSWERS

1. (a) Yes, A and B have the same order (size).
   (b) No; corresponding elements are not equal.
   (c) Yes.

2. $\begin{bmatrix} 3 & 8 & -1 \\ 3 & 2 & 2 \end{bmatrix}$ 3. (a) $\begin{bmatrix} -1 & 2 & -3 \\ 5 & -1 & -2 \end{bmatrix}$ (b) Yes

4. (a) $\begin{bmatrix} 2 & 6 & 4 & 20 \\ 40 & 10 & 12 & 6 \end{bmatrix}$ (b) Yes

EXERCISES 3.1

Use the following matrices for Problems 1–28.

$$A = \begin{bmatrix} 1 & 0 & -2 \\ 3 & 2 & 1 \\ 4 & 0 & 3 \end{bmatrix} \qquad B = \begin{bmatrix} 1 & 1 & 3 & 0 \\ 4 & 2 & 1 & 1 \\ 3 & 2 & 0 & 1 \end{bmatrix}$$

$$C = \begin{bmatrix} 5 & 3 \\ 1 & 2 \end{bmatrix} \qquad D = \begin{bmatrix} 4 & 2 \\ 3 & 5 \end{bmatrix} \qquad E = \begin{bmatrix} 1 & 0 & 4 \\ 5 & 1 & 0 \end{bmatrix}$$

$$F = \begin{bmatrix} 1 & 2 & 3 \\ -1 & 0 & 1 \\ 2 & -3 & -4 \end{bmatrix} \qquad G = \begin{bmatrix} 2 & 1 & 1 \\ 1 & 0 & 4 \\ 5 & 1 & 0 \end{bmatrix}$$

$$Z = \begin{bmatrix} 0 & 0 & 0 \\ 0 & 0 & 0 \\ 0 & 0 & 0 \end{bmatrix}$$

1. How many rows does matrix B have?
2. What is the order of matrix E?
3. Which matrices have the same order as G?
4. Write the negative of D.
5. Write the negative of matrix F.
6. Write a zero matrix that is the same order as D.
7. Which of these matrices are square?
8. Write the matrix that is the negative of matrix B.
9. What is the element a_{23}?
10. What is element b_{24}?
11. Write the transpose of matrix A.
12. Write the transpose of matrix F.
13. What is the sum of matrix A and its negative?
14. If matrix A has element $a_{3j} = 0$, what is j?

In Problems 15–28, perform the operations if possible.

15. $C + D$
16. $A + F$
17. $A - F$
18. $Z + G^T$
19. $A + A^T$
20. $A + F^T$
21. $D - G$
22. $B + F$
23. $3B$
24. $4D$
25. $4C + 2D$
26. $8C - 3D$
27. $2A - 3B$
28. $4F + 3G$

In Problems 29–32, find x, y, z, and w.

29. $\begin{bmatrix} x & 1 & 0 \\ 0 & y & z \\ w & 2 & 1 \end{bmatrix} = \begin{bmatrix} 3 & 1 & 0 \\ 0 & 2 & 3 \\ 4 & 2 & 1 \end{bmatrix}$

30. $\begin{bmatrix} 0 & x & 1 \\ 3 & y & y \\ z & 0 & 2 \end{bmatrix} = \begin{bmatrix} 0 & 4 & 1 \\ 3 & 1 & y \\ 1 & 0 & w \end{bmatrix}$

31. $\begin{bmatrix} x & 3 & (2x - 1) \\ y & 4 & 4y \end{bmatrix} = \begin{bmatrix} (2x - 4) & z & 7 \\ 1 & (w + 1) & (3y + 1) \end{bmatrix}$

32. $\begin{bmatrix} x & y & (x + 3) \\ z & 4 & 4y \end{bmatrix} = \begin{bmatrix} (2x - 1) & -1 & w \\ x & (5 + y) & -4 \end{bmatrix}$

33. Solve for x, y, and z if

$$3\begin{bmatrix} x & y \\ y & z \end{bmatrix} + 2\begin{bmatrix} 2x & -y \\ 3y & -4z \end{bmatrix} = \begin{bmatrix} 14 & (4 - y) \\ 18 & 15 \end{bmatrix}$$

34. Find x, y, z, and w if

$$3\begin{bmatrix} x & 4 \\ 4y & w \end{bmatrix} - 2\begin{bmatrix} 4x & 2z \\ -3 & -2w \end{bmatrix} = \begin{bmatrix} 20 & 20 \\ 6 & 14 \end{bmatrix}$$

APPLICATIONS

35. *Endangered species* The tables below give the numbers of some species of threatened and endangered wildlife in the United States and in foreign countries in 2015.

United States

	Mammals	Birds	Reptiles	Amphibians	Fishes
Endangered	74	79	14	20	93
Threatened	27	21	23	15	70

Foreign

	Mammals	Birds	Reptiles	Amphibians	Fishes
Endangered	253	214	69	8	19
Threatened	20	17	20	1	3

Source: U.S. Fish and Wildlife Service

(a) Write a matrix A that contains the number of each of these species in the United States in 2015 and a matrix B that contains the number of each of these species outside the United States in 2015.
(b) Find a matrix with the total number of these species. Assume that U.S. and foreign species are different.
(c) Find the matrix $B - A$. What do the negative entries in matrix $B - A$ mean?

36. *Asian demographics* The following tables show important demographics for China, Bangladesh, and the Philippines for 2012 and projected for 2062.
(a) Create matrix B for the 2012 table and matrix A for the 2062 table.
(b) Find a matrix C that shows the changes of demographics from 2012 to 2062 for these countries.
(c) Which negative entries in matrix C definitely indicate a positive change for the countries?

2012	China	Bangladesh	Philippines
Population (millions)	1341.3	148.7	93.3
Life expectancy	73.8	69.4	69.2
Fertility rate*	1.56	2.16	3.05
Infant mortality rate**	19.6	41.8	20.9

2062	China	Bangladesh	Philippines
Population (millions)	1211.5	192.4	165.5
Life expectancy	80.8	79.0	78.4
Fertility rate*	1.88	1.68	1.95
Infant mortality rate**	8.3	12.5	10.2

Source: Discover Almanac
*The fertility rate is the number of children an average woman will produce in her lifetime.
**Infant mortality is the number of deaths per thousand births.

37. *Pollution abatement* The following tables give the capital expenditures and gross operating costs of manufacturing establishments for pollution abatement, in millions of dollars.
   (a) Use a calculator or spreadsheet to find the sum of the matrices containing these data. This will yield the total costs of manufacturing establishments for air, water, and solid contained waste pollution abatement for the years 2016–2019.
   (b) Which type of pollution abatement was most expensive in 2019?

Pollution Abatement Capital Expenditures

	Air	Water	Solid Contained Waste
2016	6030.8	2562.0	817.5
2017	3706.3	2814.6	869.1
2018	4403.1	2509.8	953.9
2019	4122.0	2294.9	760.9

Pollution Abatement Gross Operating Costs

	Air	Water	Solid Contained Waste
2016	5010.9	6416.4	5643.5
2017	5033.5	6345.0	6008.2
2018	5395.0	6576.9	5494.5
2019	5574.6	6631.8	5348.6

38. *Population* The following tables give U.S. Census Bureau data and projections of the population (in thousands) by selected age groups and sex in the United States.
   (a) If matrix M gives the male data and Matrix F gives the female data, find $M-F$ and discuss what it means.
   (b) For which years and ages is the female population projected to be greater than the male population?

Males

	Under age 5	5–13	14–17	18–64	Over age 64
2015	10,763	18,784	8541	99,232	21,041
2020	11,150	19,309	8478	100,904	24,970
2025	11,307	20,210	8472	102,004	29,204
2030	11,377	20,649	9078	103,510	32,709

Females

	Under age 5	5–13	14–17	18–64	Over age 64
2015	10,288	17,988	8153	99,918	26,654
2020	10,658	18,640	8104	100,863	30,999
2025	10,807	19,301	8093	101,162	35,848
2030	10,875	19,717	8653	101,839	40,066

39. *Sales* Let matrix A represent the sales (in thousands of dollars) for the Walbash Company in 2018 in various cities, and let matrix B represent the sales (in thousands of dollars) for the same company in 2019 in the same cities.

$$A = \begin{bmatrix} \overset{\text{Chicago}}{450} & \overset{\text{Atlanta}}{280} & \overset{\text{Memphis}}{850} \\ 400 & 350 & 150 \end{bmatrix} \begin{matrix} \text{Wholesale} \\ \text{Retail} \end{matrix}$$

$$B = \begin{bmatrix} \overset{\text{Chicago}}{375} & \overset{\text{Atlanta}}{300} & \overset{\text{Memphis}}{710} \\ 410 & 300 & 200 \end{bmatrix} \begin{matrix} \text{Wholesale} \\ \text{Retail} \end{matrix}$$

   (a) Write the matrix that represents the total sales by type and city for both years.
   (b) Write the matrix that represents the change in sales by type and city from 2018 to 2019.

40. *Opinion polls* A poll of 3320 people revealed that of the respondents that were registered Republicans, 843 approved of their representative's job performance, 426 did not, and 751 had no opinion. Of the registered Democrats, 257 approved of their representative's job performance, 451 did not, and 92 had no opinion. Of those registered as independents, 135 approved, 127 did not approve, and 38 had no opinion. Of the remaining respondents, who were not registered, 92 approved, 64 did not approve, and 44 had no opinion. Represent these data in a 3×4 matrix.

41. *Life expectancy* The following table gives the years of life expectancy at birth for Blacks and Whites born in the United States for selected years projected to 2060.

	Blacks		Whites	
	Males	Females	Males	Females
2020	74.0	79.8	78.6	82.9
2030	76.1	81.3	80.2	84.1
2040	78.0	82.8	81.7	85.2
2050	79.8	84.1	83.2	86.4
2060	81.4	85.3	84.5	87.4

Source: U.S. Bureau of the Census

(a) Make a matrix A containing the information for Whites and a matrix B containing the information for Blacks.

(b) Use these to find how many more years Whites in each category are expected to live than Blacks.

(c) For which of these birth years is the difference in life expectancy greatest?

42. *National health expenditures*   The following table shows the 2024 projected U.S. health expenditures of various types (both total and per capita).

Expenditure Type	Hospital care	Physician & clinical services	Personal health care	Prescriptions
Total ($billions)	1755.1	1034.8	4550.1	564.3
Per capita (dollars)	5053	2979	13,099	1624

Source: Centers for Medicare and Medicaid Services

(a) Use the data to make a 2×4 matrix E with each column representing a type of health expenditure.

(b) These costs are predicted to change by about 6.1% for the next year. Assuming a 6.1% change in all these expenditures, use a matrix operation to find the predicted 2025 amounts, correct to the nearest tenth of a billion dollars for total amounts and the nearest dollar for per capita.

43. *Energy trade and consumption*   The following tables give U.S. energy imports, exports, and consumption data and projections (in quadrillion BTUs) for various energy types (with liquid fuels and petroleum abbreviated as LF&P) in selected years.

Imports	2015	2020	2025
LF&P	5.63	5.55	5.47
Natural gas	3.38	2.58	2.36
Other	16.29	15.18	15.74

Exports	2015	2020	2025
LF&P	6.04	5.37	5.14
Natural gas	1.89	2.67	3.92
Other	3.00	3.13	3.18

Consumption	2015	2020	2025
LF&P	37.04	37.54	36.87
Natural gas	25.86	26.77	27.28
Other	34.82	36.73	38.19

Source: U.S. Energy Information Administration

Let M be the 3×3 matrix of import data, E be the matrix of export data, and C be the matrix of consumption data. Find each of the following and indicate what information each provides.

(a) $E - M$ (b) $\dfrac{1}{12} C$ (c) $C + E - M$

44. *Debt payment*   Ace, Baker, and Champ are being purchased by ALCO, Inc., and their outstanding debts must be paid by the purchaser. The following matrix gives the amounts of debt in dollars and the terms for the companies being purchased.

$$
\begin{array}{c}
\text{Ace} \\
\text{Baker} \\
\text{Champ}
\end{array}
\begin{bmatrix}
120{,}000 & 180{,}000 \\
75{,}000 & 45{,}000 \\
105{,}000 & 174{,}000
\end{bmatrix}
$$

with column headers *Due in 30 days* and *Due in 60 days*.

(a) If ALCO pays 35% of the amount owed on each debt, write the matrix giving the remaining debts.

(b) Suppose ALCO decides to pay 80% of all debts due in 30 days and to increase the debts due in 60 days by 20%. Write a matrix that gives the debts after these transactions are made.

45. *Expense accounts*   A sales associate's expense account for the first week of a certain month has the daily expenses (in dollars) shown in matrix A.

$$
A = \begin{array}{c}
\\ \\ \\ \\ \\
\end{array}
\begin{bmatrix}
88 & 160 & 400 & 20 \\
80 & 160 & 80 & 0 \\
112 & 280 & 180 & 0 \\
60 & 280 & 80 & 40 \\
80 & 0 & 400 & 20
\end{bmatrix}
\begin{array}{l}
\text{Monday} \\
\text{Tuesday} \\
\text{Wednesday} \\
\text{Thursday} \\
\text{Friday}
\end{array}
$$

with column headers *Meals*, *Lodging*, *Travel*, *Other*.

(a) The associate finds that expenses for the second week are 5% more (in each category) than for the first week. Find the expenses matrix for the second week (note that this is $1.05A$).

(b) Find the associate's expenses matrix for the third week if expenses for that week are 10% more (in each category) than they were in the first week.

46. *Debt payment*   When a firm buys another company, the company frequently has some outstanding debt that the purchaser must pay. Consider three companies, A, B, and C, that are purchased by Maxx Industries. The following table gives the amount of each company's debt, classified by the number of days remaining until the debt must be paid.

Company	30 Days	60 Days	More Than 60 Days
A	$50,000	$52,000	$24,000
B	30,000	104,000	10,000
C	16,000	40,000	240,000

(a) Suppose Maxx Industries pays 20% of the amount owed on each loan. Write the matrix that would give the remaining debt in each category.

(b) What payment plan did Maxx Industries use if the outstanding debt is given by the following matrix?

$$\begin{bmatrix} 50,000 & 52,000 & 24,000 \\ 30,000 & 104,000 & 10,000 \\ 16,000 & 40,000 & 240,000 \end{bmatrix}$$

$$-0.50 \begin{bmatrix} 0 & 52,000 & 0 \\ 0 & 104,000 & 0 \\ 0 & 40,000 & 0 \end{bmatrix} - \begin{bmatrix} 50,000 & 0 & 0 \\ 30,000 & 0 & 0 \\ 16,000 & 0 & 0 \end{bmatrix}$$

47. *Management* Management is attempting to identify the most active person in labor's efforts to unionize. The following diagram shows how influence flows from one employee to another among the four most active employees.

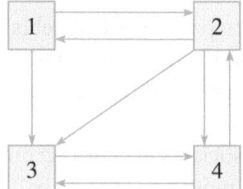

(a) Construct matrix A with elements

$$a_{ij} = \begin{cases} 1 & \text{if } i \text{ influences } j \text{ directly.} \\ 0 & \text{otherwise.} \end{cases}$$

(b) Construct matrix B with elements

$$b_{ij} = \begin{cases} 1 & \text{if } i \text{ influences } j \text{ through at most} \\ & \text{one person, with } i \neq j. \\ 0 & \text{otherwise.} \end{cases}$$

(c) The person i is most active in influencing others if the sum of the elements in row i of the matrix $A + B$ is the largest. Who is the most active person?

48. *Ranking* To rank the five members of a school's chess team for play against another school, the coach draws the following diagram. An arrow from 1 to 2 means that player 1 has defeated player 2.

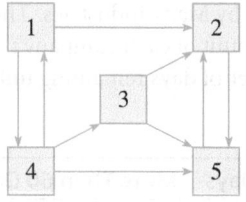

(a) Construct matrix A with elements

$$a_{ij} = \begin{cases} 1 & \text{if } i \text{ defeated } j. \\ 0 & \text{otherwise.} \end{cases}$$

(b) Construct matrix B with elements

$$b_{ij} = \begin{cases} 1 & \text{if } i \text{ defeated someone who} \\ & \text{defeated } j \text{ and } i \neq j. \\ 0 & \text{otherwise.} \end{cases}$$

(c) The player i is the top-ranked player if the sum of row i in the matrix $A + B$ is the largest. What is the number of this player?

49. *Production and inventories* Operating from two plants, the Book Equipment Company (BEC) produces bookcases and filing cabinets. Matrix A summarizes its production for a week, with row 1 representing the number of bookcases and row 2 representing the number of filing cabinets. Matrix B gives the production for the second week, and matrix C gives that of the third and fourth weeks combined.

$$A = \begin{bmatrix} 50 & 30 \\ 36 & 44 \end{bmatrix} \quad B = \begin{bmatrix} 30 & 45 \\ 22 & 62 \end{bmatrix} \quad C = \begin{bmatrix} 96 & 52 \\ 81 & 37 \end{bmatrix}$$

If column 1 in each matrix represents production from plant 1 and column 2 represents production from plant 2, answer the following.

(a) Write a matrix that describes production for the first 2 weeks.

(b) Find a matrix that describes production for the first 4 weeks.

(c) If matrix

$$D = \begin{bmatrix} 40 & 26 \\ 29 & 42 \end{bmatrix}$$

describes the shipments made during the first week, write the matrix that describes the units added to the plants' inventories in the first week.

(d) If D also describes the shipments during the second week, describe the change in inventory at the end of two weeks. What happened at plant 1?

50. *Management* The following figure depicts the mean (average) flow time for a job when the critical-ratio rule is used to dispatch workers at several machines required to complete the job. In the figure, WHN 1, WHN 2, and WHN 3 represent three different rules for determining when a worker should be transferred to another machine, and Where represents six rules for determining the machine to which the worker is transferred. Construct a 3 × 6 matrix A to represent these data, with entries rounded to the nearest integer.

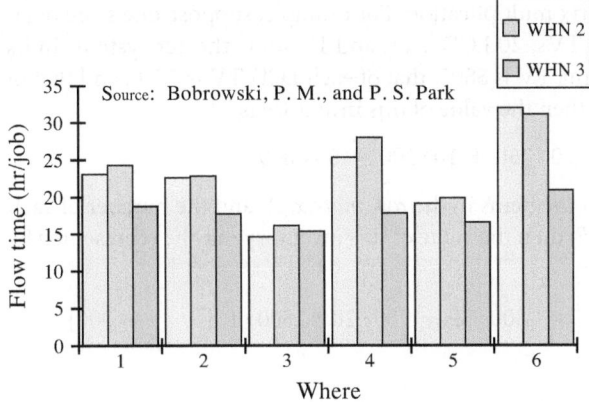

Work Centers

$$
\begin{bmatrix}
1.00 & 0.95 & 0.95 & 0.95 & 0.95 & 0.85 & 0.85 & 0.85 & 0.85 \\
0.85 & 1.00 & 0.95 & 0.95 & 0.95 & 0.95 & 0.85 & 0.85 & 0.85 \\
0.85 & 0.85 & 1.00 & 0.95 & 0.95 & 0.95 & 0.95 & 0.85 & 0.85 \\
0.85 & 0.85 & 0.85 & 1.00 & 0.95 & 0.95 & 0.95 & 0.95 & 0.85 \\
0.85 & 0.85 & 0.85 & 0.85 & 1.00 & 0.95 & 0.95 & 0.95 & 0.95 \\
0.95 & 0.85 & 0.85 & 0.85 & 0.85 & 1.00 & 0.95 & 0.95 & 0.95 \\
0.95 & 0.95 & 0.85 & 0.85 & 0.85 & 0.85 & 1.00 & 0.95 & 0.95 \\
0.95 & 0.95 & 0.95 & 0.85 & 0.85 & 0.85 & 0.85 & 1.00 & 0.95 \\
0.95 & 0.95 & 0.95 & 0.95 & 0.85 & 0.85 & 0.85 & 0.85 & 1.00 \\
\end{bmatrix}
\begin{matrix}
\text{W} \\ \text{o} \\ \text{r} \\ \text{k} \\ \text{e} \\ \text{r} \\ \text{s}
\end{matrix}
$$

51. *Management* In an evaluation of labor assignment rules when workers are not perfectly interchangeable, Paul M. Bobrowski and Paul Sungchil Park created a dynamic job shop with 9 work centers and 9 workers, both numbered 1–9. The efficiency of each worker is specified in the following labor efficiency matrix, which represents the degree of worker cross-training (*Source:* Bobrowski, P. M., and P. S. Park, "An evaluation of labor assignment rules," *Journal of Operations Management,* Vol. 11, September 1993).
    (a) For what work center(s) is worker 7 least efficient?
    (b) For what work center is worker 1 most efficient?

52. Suppose that for the workers and the work centers described in the matrix in Problem 51, changes in rules cause efficiency to decrease by 0.01 at work centers 2 and 5 and to decrease by 0.02 at work center 7. Write the matrix that describes the new efficiencies.

53. For the data in Problem 51, use an Excel spreadsheet to find the average efficiency for each worker over the first four work centers. Which worker is the least efficient? Where does this worker perform best?

54. For the data in Problem 51, use an Excel spreadsheet to find the average efficiency for each work center over the first five workers. Which work center is the most efficient? Which work center should be studied for improvement?

SECTION 3.2

Multiplication of Matrices

OBJECTIVE

• To multiply two matrices

APPLICATION PREVIEW

Pentico Industries is a manufacturing company that has two divisions located at Clarion and Brooks, each needing different amounts (units) of production materials as described by the following table.

	Steel	Wood	Plastic
Clarion	20	30	8
Brooks	22	25	15

These raw materials are supplied by Western Supply and Coastal Supply, with prices given in dollars per unit in the following table.

	Western	Coastal
Steel	300	290
Wood	100	90
Plastic	145	180

If one supplier must be chosen to provide all materials for either or both divisions of Pentico, company officials can decide which supplier to choose by constructing matrices from these tables and using matrix multiplication. (See Example 2.)

In this section, we will discuss finding the product of two matrices.

Many computations that occur in business and manufacturing operations can be expressed and analyzed using matrix multiplication. For example, suppose one store of an electronics retailer has 30 plasma TVs, 20 LCD TVs, and 10 home theater systems in its inventory. If the value of each plasma TV is $800, that of each LCD TV is $750, and that of each home theater system is $500, then the value of this inventory is

$$30 \cdot 800 + 20 \cdot 750 + 10 \cdot 500 = \$44{,}000$$

If we write the value of each of the items in the *row matrix, A,* and the number of each of the items in the *column matrix, B,* then the value of this inventory may be represented by

$$AB = [800 \quad 750 \quad 500] \begin{bmatrix} 30 \\ 20 \\ 10 \end{bmatrix} = [800 \cdot 30 + 750 \cdot 20 + 500 \cdot 10] = [\$44{,}000]$$

This useful way of operating with a row matrix and a column matrix is called the product *AB.*

In general, we can multiply a row matrix *A* times a column matrix *B* if *A* and *B* have the same number of elements. The product *AB* is then

$$AB = [a_1 \quad a_2 \quad a_3 \cdots a_n] \begin{bmatrix} b_1 \\ b_2 \\ b_3 \\ \vdots \\ b_n \end{bmatrix} = [a_1b_1 + a_2b_2 + a_3b_3 + \cdots + a_nb_n]$$

Suppose the retailer has a second store with 40 plasma TVs, 25 LCD TVs, and 5 home theater systems. We can use matrix *C* to represent the inventories of the two stores.

$$\begin{array}{cc} & \text{Store I} \quad \text{Store II} \\ C = & \begin{bmatrix} 30 & 40 \\ 20 & 25 \\ 10 & 5 \end{bmatrix} \begin{array}{l} \text{Plasma TVs} \\ \text{LCD TVs} \\ \text{Home theater systems} \end{array} \end{array}$$

If the values of the items are $800, $750, and $500, respectively, we have already seen that the value of the inventory of store I is $44,000. The value of the inventory of store II is

$$800 \cdot 40 + 750 \cdot 25 + 500 \cdot 5 = \$53{,}250$$

Because the value of the inventory of store I can be found by multiplying the row matrix *A* times the first column of matrix *C* and the value of the inventory of store II can be found by multiplying matrix *A* times the second column of matrix *C,* we can write this result as

$$AC = [800 \quad 750 \quad 500] \begin{bmatrix} 30 & 40 \\ 20 & 25 \\ 10 & 5 \end{bmatrix} = [44{,}000 \quad 53{,}250]$$

The matrix we have represented as *AC* is called the **product** of the row matrix *A* and the 3 × 2 matrix *C.* We should note that matrix *A* is a 1 × 3 matrix, matrix *C* is a 3 × 2 matrix, and their product is a 1 × 2 matrix. In general, we can multiply an *m* × *n* matrix times an *n* × *p* matrix and the product will be an *m* × *p* matrix, as follows.

Product of Two Matrices

Given an *m* × *n* matrix *A* and an *n* × *p* matrix *B,* the **matrix product** *AB* is an *m* × *p* matrix *C,* with the *ij* entry of *C* given by the formula

$$c_{ij} = a_{i1}b_{1j} + a_{i2}b_{2j} + \cdots + a_{in}b_{nj}$$

which is illustrated in Figure 3.5.

$$
\begin{bmatrix} a_{11} & a_{12} & \cdots & a_{1n} \\ a_{21} & a_{22} & \cdots & a_{2n} \\ & \vdots & & \\ a_{i1} & a_{i2} & \cdots & a_{in} \\ & \vdots & & \\ a_{m1} & a_{m2} & \cdots & a_{mn} \end{bmatrix}
\begin{bmatrix} b_{11} & b_{12} & \cdots & b_{1j} & \cdots & b_{1p} \\ b_{21} & b_{22} & \cdots & b_{2j} & \cdots & b_{2p} \\ & \vdots & & & & \\ b_{n1} & b_{n2} & \cdots & b_{nj} & \cdots & b_{np} \end{bmatrix}
=
\begin{bmatrix} c_{11} & c_{12} & \cdots & c_{1j} & \cdots & c_{1p} \\ c_{21} & c_{22} & \cdots & c_{2j} & \cdots & c_{2p} \\ & \vdots & & & & \\ c_{i1} & c_{i2} & \cdots & c_{ij} & \cdots & c_{ip} \\ & \vdots & & & & \\ c_{m1} & c_{m2} & \cdots & c_{mj} & \cdots & c_{mp} \end{bmatrix}
$$

Figure 3.5

EXAMPLE 1 Matrix Product

(a) Find AB if

$$
A = \begin{bmatrix} 3 & 4 \\ 2 & 5 \\ 6 & 10 \end{bmatrix} \quad \text{and} \quad B = \begin{bmatrix} a & b & c & d \\ e & f & g & h \end{bmatrix}
$$

(b) Find AB and BA if

$$
A = \begin{bmatrix} 3 & 2 \\ 1 & 0 \end{bmatrix} \quad \text{and} \quad B = \begin{bmatrix} 1 & 2 \\ 3 & 1 \end{bmatrix}
$$

Solution

(a) A is a 3×2 matrix and B is a 2×4 matrix, so the number of columns of A equals the number of rows of B. Thus we can find the product AB, which is a 3×4 matrix, as follows:

$$
AB = \begin{bmatrix} 3 & 4 \\ 2 & 5 \\ 6 & 10 \end{bmatrix} \begin{bmatrix} a & b & c & d \\ e & f & g & h \end{bmatrix}
$$

$$
= \begin{bmatrix} 3a + 4e & 3b + 4f & 3c + 4g & 3d + 4h \\ 2a + 5e & 2b + 5f & 2c + 5g & 2d + 5h \\ 6a + 10e & 6b + 10f & 6c + 10g & 6d + 10h \end{bmatrix}
$$

This example shows that if $AB = C$, element c_{32} is found by multiplying each entry of A's *third* row by the corresponding entry of B's *second* column and then adding these products.

(b) Both A and B are 2×2 matrices, so both AB and BA are defined.

$$
AB = \begin{bmatrix} 3 & 2 \\ 1 & 0 \end{bmatrix} \begin{bmatrix} 1 & 2 \\ 3 & 1 \end{bmatrix} = \begin{bmatrix} 3 \cdot 1 + 2 \cdot 3 & 3 \cdot 2 + 2 \cdot 1 \\ 1 \cdot 1 + 0 \cdot 3 & 1 \cdot 2 + 0 \cdot 1 \end{bmatrix} = \begin{bmatrix} 9 & 8 \\ 1 & 2 \end{bmatrix}
$$

$$
BA = \begin{bmatrix} 1 & 2 \\ 3 & 1 \end{bmatrix} \begin{bmatrix} 3 & 2 \\ 1 & 0 \end{bmatrix} = \begin{bmatrix} 1 \cdot 3 + 2 \cdot 1 & 1 \cdot 2 + 2 \cdot 0 \\ 3 \cdot 3 + 1 \cdot 1 & 3 \cdot 2 + 1 \cdot 0 \end{bmatrix} = \begin{bmatrix} 5 & 2 \\ 10 & 6 \end{bmatrix}
$$

Note that for these matrices, the two products AB and BA are matrices of the same size, but they are not equal. That is, $BA \neq AB$. Thus we say that *matrix multiplication is not commutative.*

CHECKPOINT

1. What is element c_{23} if $C = AB$ with

$$
A = \begin{bmatrix} 1 & 2 & 0 \\ 2 & 1 & 3 \end{bmatrix} \quad \text{and} \quad B = \begin{bmatrix} 1 & 0 & 2 \\ 3 & 1 & 1 \\ -2 & 1 & 0 \end{bmatrix} ?
$$

2. Find the product AB.

EXAMPLE 2 | Material Supply | APPLICATION PREVIEW |

Pentico Industries must choose a supplier for the raw materials it uses in its two manufacturing divisions at Clarion and Brooks. Each division uses different unit amounts of steel, wood, and plastic as shown in the table below.

	Steel	Wood	Plastic
Clarion	20	30	8
Brooks	22	25	15

The two supply companies being considered, Western and Coastal, can each supply all of these materials but at different prices per unit, as described in the following table.

	Western	Coastal
Steel	300	290
Wood	100	90
Plastic	145	180

Use matrix multiplication to decide which supplier should be chosen to supply (a) the Clarion division and (b) the Brooks division.

Solution

The different amounts of products needed are placed in matrix A, and the prices charged by the suppliers are placed in matrix B.

$$A = \begin{bmatrix} 20 & 30 & 8 \\ 22 & 25 & 15 \end{bmatrix} \begin{matrix} \text{Clarion} \\ \text{Brooks} \end{matrix} \qquad B = \begin{bmatrix} 300 & 290 \\ 100 & 90 \\ 145 & 180 \end{bmatrix} \begin{matrix} \text{Steel} \\ \text{Wood} \\ \text{Plastic} \end{matrix}$$

The price from each supplier for each division is found from the product AB.

$$AB = \begin{bmatrix} 20 & 30 & 8 \\ 22 & 25 & 15 \end{bmatrix} \begin{bmatrix} 300 & 290 \\ 100 & 90 \\ 145 & 180 \end{bmatrix}$$

$$= \begin{bmatrix} 20 \cdot 300 + 30 \cdot 100 + 8 \cdot 145 & 20 \cdot 290 + 30 \cdot 90 + 8 \cdot 180 \\ 22 \cdot 300 + 25 \cdot 100 + 15 \cdot 145 & 22 \cdot 290 + 25 \cdot 90 + 15 \cdot 180 \end{bmatrix}$$

$$= \begin{bmatrix} 10{,}160 & 9940 \\ 11{,}275 & 11{,}330 \end{bmatrix} \begin{matrix} \text{Clarion} \\ \text{Brooks} \end{matrix}$$

(a) The price for the Clarion division for supplies from Western is in the first row, first column and is $10,160; the price for Clarion for supplies from Coastal is in the first row, second column and is $9940. Thus the best price for Clarion is from Coastal.

(b) The price for the Brooks division for supplies from Western is in the second row, first column and is $11,275; the price for Brooks for supplies from Coastal is in the second row, second column and is $11,330. Thus the best price for Brooks is from Western.

An $n \times n$ (square) matrix (where n is any natural number) that has 1s down its diagonal and 0s everywhere else is called an **identity matrix.** The matrix

$$I = \begin{bmatrix} 1 & 0 & 0 \\ 0 & 1 & 0 \\ 0 & 0 & 1 \end{bmatrix}$$

is a 3×3 identity matrix. The matrix I is called an identity matrix because for any 3×3 matrix A, $AI = IA = A$. That is, if I is multiplied by a 3×3 matrix A, the product matrix is A. Note that when one of two square matrices being multiplied is an identity matrix, the product is *commutative*.

EXAMPLE 3 Identity Matrix

(a) Write the 2×2 identity matrix.

(b) Given $A = \begin{bmatrix} 4 & -7 \\ 13 & 2 \end{bmatrix}$, show that $AI = IA = A$.

Solution

(a) We denote the 2×2 identity matrix by

$$I = \begin{bmatrix} 1 & 0 \\ 0 & 1 \end{bmatrix}$$

(b) $AI = \begin{bmatrix} 4 & -7 \\ 13 & 2 \end{bmatrix} \begin{bmatrix} 1 & 0 \\ 0 & 1 \end{bmatrix} = \begin{bmatrix} 4+0 & 0-7 \\ 13+0 & 0+2 \end{bmatrix} = \begin{bmatrix} 4 & -7 \\ 13 & 2 \end{bmatrix}$

$IA = \begin{bmatrix} 1 & 0 \\ 0 & 1 \end{bmatrix} \begin{bmatrix} 4 & -7 \\ 13 & 2 \end{bmatrix} = \begin{bmatrix} 4 & -7 \\ 13 & 2 \end{bmatrix}$

Therefore, $AI = IA = A$.

EXAMPLE 4 Encoding Messages

Encoding and decoding messages has always been important during wartime and now is an essential part of cybersecurity. Messages can be encoded through the use of a code and an encoding matrix. For example, given the simple code

a	b	c	d	e	f	g	h	i	j	k	l
1	2	3	4	5	6	7	8	9	10	11	12

m	n	o	p	q	r	s	t	u	v	w	x
13	14	15	16	17	18	19	20	21	22	23	24

y	z	blank
25	26	27

and the encoding matrix

$$A = \begin{bmatrix} 3 & 5 \\ 4 & 6 \end{bmatrix}$$

we can encode a message by separating it into number pairs (because A is a 2×2 matrix) and then multiplying each pair by A. Use this code and matrix to encode the message "good job."

Solution

The phrase "good job" is written

g	o	o	d	blank	j	o	b
7	15	15	4	27	10	15	2

and is encoded by writing each pair of numbers as a column matrix and multiplying each matrix by matrix A. Performing this multiplication gives the encoded message.

$$\begin{bmatrix} 3 & 5 \\ 4 & 6 \end{bmatrix} \begin{bmatrix} 7 \\ 15 \end{bmatrix} = \begin{bmatrix} 96 \\ 118 \end{bmatrix}$$

$$\begin{bmatrix} 3 & 5 \\ 4 & 6 \end{bmatrix} \begin{bmatrix} 15 \\ 4 \end{bmatrix} = \begin{bmatrix} 65 \\ 84 \end{bmatrix}$$

$$\begin{bmatrix} 3 & 5 \\ 4 & 6 \end{bmatrix} \begin{bmatrix} 27 \\ 10 \end{bmatrix} = \begin{bmatrix} 131 \\ 168 \end{bmatrix}$$

$$\begin{bmatrix} 3 & 5 \\ 4 & 6 \end{bmatrix} \begin{bmatrix} 15 \\ 2 \end{bmatrix} = \begin{bmatrix} 55 \\ 72 \end{bmatrix}$$

Thus the code sent is 96, 118, 65, 84, 131, 168, 55, 72. Notice that the letter "o" occurred three times in the original message but was encoded differently each time. We can get the same code to send by putting the pairs of numbers as columns in one 2 × 4 matrix and multiplying by A.

$$\begin{bmatrix} 3 & 5 \\ 4 & 6 \end{bmatrix} \begin{bmatrix} 7 & 15 & 27 & 15 \\ 15 & 4 & 10 & 2 \end{bmatrix} = \begin{bmatrix} 96 & 65 & 131 & 55 \\ 118 & 84 & 168 & 72 \end{bmatrix}$$

In this case, the code is sent column by column.

Note in Example 4 that if we used a different encoding matrix, then the same message would be sent with a different sequence of code. We will discuss the methods of decoding messages in Section 3.4, "Inverse of a Square Matrix; Matrix Equations."

CHECKPOINT

3. (a) Compute AB if $A = \begin{bmatrix} 2 & 4 \\ 3 & 6 \end{bmatrix}$ and $B = \begin{bmatrix} 2 & -6 \\ -1 & 3 \end{bmatrix}$.

(b) Can the product of two matrices be a zero matrix even if neither matrix is a zero matrix?

(c) Does BA result in a zero matrix?

Calculator Note Graphing calculators can be used to perform matrix multiplications. Entering $[A] \times [B]$ or $[A] [B]$ and pressing ENTER gives the product of $[A]$ and $[B]$ (if it exists). For example, if

$$A = \begin{bmatrix} 2 & 3 & 4 & 5 \\ 3 & 1 & 3 & 5 \\ 3 & -4 & 3 & 1 \end{bmatrix} \quad B = \begin{bmatrix} 2 & 2 & 5 \\ 3 & 5 & 7 \\ 1 & 1 & 2 \\ 5 & 4 & 3 \end{bmatrix} \quad C = \begin{bmatrix} 0.5 & 3.5 & 2.4 \\ 2 & 7 & 0.8 \\ 5.5 & 3.5 & 7 \\ 2.5 & 4 & 3 \end{bmatrix}$$

then Figure 3.6 shows the matrix products AB and BA and Figure 3.7 shows that the product BC is not defined. Details of finding matrix products with graphing calculators are shown in Appendix A, Section 3.2.

```
[A][B]
      [[42    43    54]
       [37    34    43]
       [2     -7    -4]]
```

```
[B][A]
      [[25    -12    29    25]
       [42    -14    48    47]
       [11    -4     13    12]
       [31    7      41    48]]
```

(a)   (b)

Figure 3.6

Figure 3.7

Spreadsheet Note   Like graphing calculators and software, Excel can be used to multiply two matrices. The next example discusses using Excel to multiply matrices; additional details can be found in Appendix B, Section 3.2, and the Online Excel Guide.

EXAMPLE 5 Investment Banking

Suppose that a bank has three main sources of income—business loans, auto loans, and home mortgages—and that it draws funds from these sources to provide funds for expansion of existing businesses and community investment. Suppose the income from these sources for each of 3 years is given in Table 3.4, and the bank uses 45% of its income from business loans, 20% of its income from auto loans, and 30% of its income from home mortgages to get its investment funds. Write a matrix product that gives the investment funds for these years and find the available investment funds in each of the 3 years.

TABLE 3.4

INCOME FROM LOANS

Year	Business	Auto	Home
2018	633,000	200,240	518,200
2019	483,050	158,170	637,220
2020	551,100	186,210	641,050

Solution

The matrix that describes the sources of income for the 3 years is

$$\begin{bmatrix} 633,000 & 200,240 & 518,200 \\ 483,050 & 158,170 & 637,220 \\ 551,100 & 186,210 & 641,050 \end{bmatrix}$$

and the matrix that describes the percent of each that is used for investment funds is

$$\begin{bmatrix} 0.45 \\ 0.20 \\ 0.30 \end{bmatrix}$$

We can find the product of these matrices with Excel by using the MMULT command.* We enter the matrix entries as corresponding cells in B3:D5 and B7:B9 in the following spreadsheet, and select a range of cells that is correct to get the product (B11:B13). Then we type the formula =MMULT(and select the cells B3:D5, type a comma, select the cells B7:B9, and close the parentheses. Holding down the CTRL and SHIFT keys while pressing ENTER gives the product in B11:B13, as shown in the following spreadsheet.

*Uppercase or lowercase will work for any Excel formula.

= MMULT(B3:D5,B7:B9)			
	A	**B**	**C**	**D**
1		Income from Loans		
2		Business	Auto	Home
3	Matrix A	633,000	200,240	518,200
4		483,050	158,170	637,220
5		551,100	186,210	641,050
6				
7	Matrix B	0.45		
8		0.20		
9		0.30		
10				
11	Product A × B	480,358		
12		440,172.50		
13		477,552		

Thus the available investment funds for each of the 3 years are as follows.

$$
\begin{aligned}
2018: & \quad \$480,358 \\
2019: & \quad \$440,172.50 \\
2020: & \quad \$477,552
\end{aligned}
$$

CHECKPOINT
ANSWERS

1. $c_{23} = 5$

2. $\begin{bmatrix} 7 & 2 & 4 \\ -1 & 4 & 5 \end{bmatrix}$

3. (a) $AB = \begin{bmatrix} 0 & 0 \\ 0 & 0 \end{bmatrix}$ (b) Yes. (c) No. $BA = \begin{bmatrix} -14 & -28 \\ 7 & 14 \end{bmatrix}$

EXERCISES 3.2

In Problems 1–4, multiply the matrices.

1. $[1 \quad 2 \quad 3] \begin{bmatrix} 4 \\ 5 \\ 6 \end{bmatrix}$

2. $[2 \quad 0 \quad 3] \begin{bmatrix} 0 \\ 1 \\ -3 \end{bmatrix}$

3. $[1 \quad 2] \begin{bmatrix} 3 & 5 \\ 4 & 6 \end{bmatrix}$

4. $[3 \quad 0] \begin{bmatrix} 1 & 2 \\ 4 & 5 \end{bmatrix}$

In Problems 5–24, use matrices A through F. In Problems 5–20, perform the indicated operations when possible.

$$
A = \begin{bmatrix} 1 & 0 & 2 \\ 3 & 2 & 1 \\ 4 & 0 & 3 \end{bmatrix} \quad B = \begin{bmatrix} 1 & 1 & 3 & 0 \\ 4 & 2 & 1 & 1 \\ 3 & 2 & 0 & 1 \end{bmatrix}
$$

$$
C = \begin{bmatrix} 5 & 3 \\ 1 & 2 \end{bmatrix} \quad D = \begin{bmatrix} 4 & 2 \\ 3 & 5 \end{bmatrix}
$$

$$
E = \begin{bmatrix} 1 & 0 & 4 \\ 5 & 1 & 0 \end{bmatrix} \quad F = \begin{bmatrix} 1 & 0 & -1 & 3 \\ 2 & -1 & 3 & -4 \end{bmatrix}
$$

5. CD
6. DC
7. DE
8. CF
9. AB
10. EC
11. BA
12. FB^T
13. EB

14. BE 　　　　15. EA^T 　　　　16. AE^T
17. A^2 　　　　18. A^3 　　　　19. C^3
20. F^2
21. Does $(AA^T)^T = A^TA$?
22. Are $(CD)E$ and $C(DE)$ equal?
23. Does $CD = DC$? (See Problems 5 and 6.)

24. Are $\left(\dfrac{1}{4}A\right)B$ and $\dfrac{1}{4}(AB)$ equal?

In Problems 25–34, use the matrices below. Perform the indicated operations.

$$A = \begin{bmatrix} 2 & 5 & 4 \\ 1 & 4 & 3 \\ 1 & -3 & -2 \end{bmatrix} \quad B = \begin{bmatrix} -1 & 2 & 1 \\ -5 & 8 & 2 \\ -7 & 11 & -3 \end{bmatrix}$$

$$I = \begin{bmatrix} 1 & 0 & 0 \\ 0 & 1 & 0 \\ 0 & 0 & 1 \end{bmatrix} \quad C = \begin{bmatrix} 3 & 0 & 4 \\ 1 & 7 & -1 \\ 3 & 0 & 4 \end{bmatrix}$$

$$D = \begin{bmatrix} 4 & 4 & -8 \\ -1 & -1 & 2 \\ -3 & -3 & 6 \end{bmatrix} \quad F = \begin{bmatrix} 0 & 1 & 2 \\ 0 & 0 & -4 \\ 0 & 0 & 0 \end{bmatrix}$$

$$Z = \begin{bmatrix} 0 & 0 & 0 \\ 0 & 0 & 0 \\ 0 & 0 & 0 \end{bmatrix}$$

25. AB 　　26. BA 　　27. CD 　　28. DC
29. F^3 　　30. AZ 　　31. AI 　　32. IA
33. ZCI 　　34. IFZ
35. Is it true for matrices (as it is for real numbers) that AB equals a zero matrix if and only if either A or B equals a zero matrix? (Refer to Problems 25–34.)
36. Is it true for matrices (as it is for real numbers) that multiplication by a zero matrix gives a result of a zero matrix?
37. (a) Find AB and BA if

$$A = \begin{bmatrix} a & b \\ c & d \end{bmatrix} \quad \text{and} \quad B = \frac{1}{ad - bc}\begin{bmatrix} d & -b \\ -c & a \end{bmatrix}$$

(b) For B to exist, what restriction must $ad - bc$ satisfy?

38. For $F = \begin{bmatrix} 1 & 0 & -1 & 3 \\ 2 & -1 & 3 & -4 \end{bmatrix}$:

(a) Are FF^T and F^TF defined?
(b) What size is each product?
(c) Can $FF^T = F^TF$? Explain.

In each of Problems 39–42, substitute the given values of x, y, and z into the matrix equation and use matrix multiplication to see whether the values are the solution of the equation.

39. $\begin{bmatrix} 1 & 2 & 1 \\ 3 & 4 & -2 \\ 2 & 0 & -1 \end{bmatrix}\begin{bmatrix} x \\ y \\ z \end{bmatrix} = \begin{bmatrix} 2 \\ -2 \\ 2 \end{bmatrix}$ $\quad x = 2, y = -1, z = 2$

40. $\begin{bmatrix} 3 & 1 & 0 \\ 2 & -2 & 1 \\ 1 & 1 & 2 \end{bmatrix}\begin{bmatrix} x \\ y \\ z \end{bmatrix} = \begin{bmatrix} 4 \\ 9 \\ 2 \end{bmatrix}$ $\quad x = 2, y = -2, z = 1$

41. $\begin{bmatrix} 1 & 1 & 2 \\ 4 & 0 & 1 \\ 2 & 1 & 1 \end{bmatrix}\begin{bmatrix} x \\ y \\ z \end{bmatrix} = \begin{bmatrix} 5 \\ 5 \\ 5 \end{bmatrix}$ $\quad x = 1, y = 2, z = 1$

42. $\begin{bmatrix} 1 & 0 & 2 \\ 3 & 1 & 0 \\ 1 & 2 & 1 \end{bmatrix}\begin{bmatrix} x \\ y \\ z \end{bmatrix} = \begin{bmatrix} 0 \\ 7 \\ 3 \end{bmatrix}$ $\quad x = 2, y = 1, z = 1$

In Problems 43 and 44, use technology to find the product AB of the following matrices.

43. $A = \begin{bmatrix} 0.1 & 0.0 & 0.1 & 0.1 & 0.2 \\ 0.1 & 0.2 & -0.1 & 0.1 & -0.1 \\ 0.1 & -0.1 & 0.1 & -0.2 & 0.1 \\ 0.1 & 0.2 & 0.1 & 0.1 & 0.1 \\ 0.1 & 0.0 & 0.0 & 0.0 & 0.0 \end{bmatrix}$

$$B = \begin{bmatrix} 0 & 0 & 0 & 0 & 10 \\ 0 & 5 & \frac{10}{3} & \frac{5}{3} & -10 \\ -10 & -15 & -\frac{20}{3} & \frac{35}{3} & 20 \\ 0 & -5 & -\frac{20}{3} & \frac{5}{3} & 10 \\ 10 & 10 & \frac{20}{3} & -\frac{20}{3} & -20 \end{bmatrix}$$

44. $A = \dfrac{1}{12}\begin{bmatrix} 3 & 15 & -9 & -15 & 6 \\ 3 & -9 & 3 & 9 & -6 \\ -1 & -17 & 3 & 23 & -4 \\ 0 & 12 & 0 & -12 & 0 \\ -1 & -5 & 3 & 5 & 2 \end{bmatrix}$

$$B = \begin{bmatrix} 2 & 3 & 0 & 1 & 3 \\ 1 & 0 & 2 & 3 & 1 \\ 0 & 1 & 0 & 2 & 3 \\ 1 & 0 & 2 & 2 & 1 \\ 1 & 0 & 0 & 0 & 3 \end{bmatrix}$$

APPLICATIONS

45. *Car pricing* A car dealer can buy midsize cars for 12% under the list price, and he can buy luxury cars for 15% under the list price. The following table gives the list prices for two midsize and two luxury cars.

Midsize	36,000	42,000
Luxury	50,000	56,000

Write these data in a matrix and multiply it on the left by the matrix

$$\begin{bmatrix} 0.88 & 0 \\ 0 & 0.85 \end{bmatrix}$$

What does each entry in this product matrix represent?

46. *Revenue* A clothing manufacturer has factories in Atlanta, Chicago, and New York. Sales (in thousands) during the first quarter are summarized in the matrix below.

	Atl.	Chi.	N.Y.
Coats	40	63	18
Shirts	85	56	42
Pants	6	18	8
Ties	7	10	8

During this period, the selling price of a coat was $200, a shirt $40, a pair of pants $50, and a tie $30. Use matrix multiplication to find the total revenue received by each factory.

47. *Household energy usage* Delivered energy is provided by a vendor such as an electric company. For households with solar panels, windmills, wood-burning furnaces, or other on-site energy sources, only a portion of the total energy used would be delivered. The following table gives data and projections for selected years for the number of various types of U.S. households (in millions) and the delivered energy consumption per household (in millions of BTUs).

Households	2015	2020	2025
Single-family	86.86	91.25	95.37
Multifamily	27.57	29.82	32.05
Mobile home	6.36	6.45	6.60
Delivered energy consumption	91.1	86.0	82.5

Source: U.S. Energy Information Administration

Let A be the 3×3 matrix representing the households data (with single-family data in row 1). Let B be the 3×3 matrix with diagonal entries as the delivered energy data (with 2015 data as the 1-1 entry, 2020 data as the 2-2 entry, etc.) and 0s elsewhere.
(a) Write A and B.
(b) Calculate AB.
(c) Interpret the 1-1 entry and the 2-3 entry of AB.
(d) Use AB as stored in your calculator to find $\begin{bmatrix} 1 & 1 & 1 \end{bmatrix} AB$ and interpret each entry.

48. *Area and population* Matrix A below gives the fraction of the earth's area and the projected fraction of its population for five continents in 2050. Matrix B gives the earth's area (in square miles) and its projected 2050 population. Find the area and population of each given continent by finding AB.

$$A = \begin{bmatrix} 0.162 & 0.047 \\ 0.119 & 0.086 \\ 0.066 & 0.065 \\ 0.298 & 0.582 \\ 0.202 & 0.215 \end{bmatrix} \begin{matrix} \text{North America} \\ \text{South America} \\ \text{Europe} \\ \text{Asia} \\ \text{Africa} \end{matrix}$$

$$B = \begin{bmatrix} 57{,}850{,}000 & 0 \\ 0 & 9{,}322{,}000{,}000 \end{bmatrix} \begin{matrix} \text{Area} \\ \text{Population} \end{matrix}$$

Source: U.S. Census Bureau

49. *Population dynamics* Suppose that for a certain metropolitan area and the surrounding counties, during each 5-year period, an average of 20% of the metropolitan population M moves to the surrounding counties and the rest remains. Similarly, suppose that in the same period, an average of 30% of the surrounding counties' population S moves to the metropolitan area and the rest remains. This population dynamic can be represented as the matrix

$$D = \begin{bmatrix} 80\% & 20\% \\ 30\% & 70\% \end{bmatrix} \begin{matrix} M \\ S \end{matrix} = \begin{bmatrix} 0.8 & 0.2 \\ 0.3 & 0.7 \end{bmatrix}$$

where row 1 shows how the metropolitan population M changed (80% remained in M and 20% moved to S) and row 2 shows how the population of the surrounding counties changed. Currently, the population is evenly divided between the two areas, which can be represented by the row matrix

$$P = \begin{bmatrix} \% \text{ in } M & \% \text{ in } S \end{bmatrix} = \begin{bmatrix} 50\% & 50\% \end{bmatrix} = \begin{bmatrix} 0.5 & 0.5 \end{bmatrix}$$

(a) Form the product PD and interpret its entries.
(b) Predictions of this population distribution after 10 years and after 15 years could be found from what matrix products?
(c) Suppose that at some future time, the populations reach the point where 60% live in the metropolitan area and 40% live in the surrounding counties. Find the predicted distribution 5 years later.

50. *Nutrition* Suppose the weights (in grams) and lengths (in centimeters) of three groups of laboratory animals are given by matrix A, where column 1 gives the lengths and each row corresponds to one group.

$$A = \begin{bmatrix} 12.5 & 250 \\ 11.8 & 215 \\ 9.8 & 190 \end{bmatrix}$$

If the increase in both weight and length over the next 2 weeks is 20% for group I, 7% for group II, and 0% for group III, then the increases in the measures during the 2 weeks can be found by computing GA, where

$$G = \begin{bmatrix} 0.20 & 0 & 0 \\ 0 & 0.07 & 0 \\ 0 & 0 & 0 \end{bmatrix}$$

(a) What are the increases in respective weights and measures at the end of these 2 weeks?

(b) Find the matrix that gives the new weights and measures at the end of this period by computing

$$(I + G)A$$

where I is the 3×3 identity matrix.

Encoding messages **Multiplication by a matrix can be used to encode messages. (We'll discuss decoding in the next section.) Given the code**

a	b	c	d	e	f	g	h	i	j
1	2	3	4	5	6	7	8	9	10

k	l	m	n	o	p	q	r	s	t
11	12	13	14	15	16	17	18	19	20

u	v	w	x	y	z	blank
21	22	23	24	25	26	27

and the code matrix

$$A = \begin{bmatrix} 5 & 9 \\ 6 & 11 \end{bmatrix}$$

complete Problems 51 and 52.

51. Use matrix A to encode the message "Waste not want not."

52. Use matrix A to encode the message "To be or not to be."

53. *Oil refineries* When gasoline is refined from crude oil, each gallon of regular, midgrade, and premium uses a different blend of two different grades of crude oil according to the following matrix.

		Gasoline Blends		
		Reg.	Mid.	Prem.
Crude Grade	Black	$\frac{3}{4}$	$\frac{2}{5}$	$\frac{1}{4}$
	Gold	$\frac{1}{4}$	$\frac{3}{5}$	$\frac{3}{4}$

In addition, the daily demand (in thousands of gallons) from a Houston refinery is 22 regular, 12 midgrade, and 8 premium, and the demand from a Gulfport refinery is 30 regular, 20 midgrade, and 11 premium.

(a) Make a 2×3 matrix B that contains the blending information and a 3×2 matrix D for the demands at each refinery. Then use a matrix product to find each refinery's need for each type of crude oil.

(b) If the cost of black crude is $1.16 per gallon and the cost of gold crude is $1.58 per gallon, then the matrix

$$P = [1.16 \quad 1.58]$$

represents these crude prices. Write a matrix product involving B, D, and P that could be used to find the total cost for crude oil at each refinery. Then find those total costs.

54. *Production* A manufacturer of small kitchen appliances has the following unit costs for labor and materials for three of its products: a blender, a mixer, and a food processor.

	Blender	Mixer	Food Proc.
Labor	$8.50	$5.50	$12.00
Materials	$6.00	$4.00	$15.00

Furthermore, the quarterly demand for each appliance is summarized as follows.

	1st Qtr	2nd Qtr	3rd Qtr	4th Qtr
Blender	1200	1500	1500	2000
Mixer	1200	1000	1000	1500
Food Proc.	500	500	400	1000

(a) Identify matrices and use their product to find the quarterly costs for labor and materials for these appliances. What are the first quarter's labor costs?

(b) From part (a), let C be the 2×3 cost matrix and let D be the 3×4 demand matrix. Let T be a 4×1 matrix in which each entry is a 1. Find the product CDT and explain what it represents.

55. *Accounting* The annual budget of the Magnum Company has the following expenses, in thousands of dollars, for selected departments.

	Mfg.	Office	Sales	Shp.	Act.	Mgt.
Supplies	0.7	8.5	10.2	1.1	5.6	3.6
Phone	0.5	0.2	6.1	1.3	0.2	1.0
Transp.	2.2	0.4	8.8	1.2	1.2	4.8
Salaries	251.8	63.4	81.6	35.2	54.3	144.2
Utilities	30.0	1.0	1.0	1.0	1.0	1.0
Materials	788.9	0	0	0	0	0

Mfg. = Manufacturing; Shp. = Shipping;
Act. = Accounting; Mgt. = Management

(a) Write a matrix B for these budget amounts.

(b) Write a matrix A so that BA would contain new budget figures that reflect an 11% increase in manufacturing, sales, and shipping, and a 5% decrease in the other departments.

56. *Accounting* Consider the original budget matrix in Problem 55. Assume that there is a 20% increase in manufacturing, a 3% increase in office, a 5% increase in sales, a 20% increase in shipping, a 5% increase in accounting, and a 3% decrease in management. Find the new budget matrix by developing a matrix A to represent these departmental increases and then multiplying it from the left by the matrix B in Problem 55.

Gauss-Jordan Elimination: Solving Systems of Equations

OBJECTIVES

- To use matrices to solve systems of linear equations with unique solutions
- To use matrices to solve systems of linear equations with nonunique solutions, including nonsquare systems.

APPLICATION PREVIEW

The Walters Manufacturing Company makes three types of metal storage sheds. The company has three departments: stamping, painting, and packaging. The following table gives the number of hours each department requires for each shed.

Department	Shed		
	Type I	Type II	Type III
Stamping	2	3	4
Painting	1	2	1
Packaging	1	1	2

Using the information in the table and solving a system of equations, we can determine how many of each type of shed can be produced if the stamping department has 3200 hours available, the painting department has 1700 hours, and the packaging department has 1300 hours. The set of equations used to solve this problem (in Example 2) is

$$\begin{cases} 2x_1 + 3x_2 + 4x_3 = 3200 \\ x_1 + 2x_2 + x_3 = 1700 \\ x_1 + x_2 + 2x_3 = 1300 \end{cases}$$

In this section, we will solve such systems using matrices and the Gauss-Jordan elimination method.

Systems with Unique Solutions

In solving systems with the left-to-right elimination method used in Example 7 in Section 1.5, "Solutions of Systems of Linear Equations," we operated on the coefficients of the variables x, y, and z and on the constants. If we keep the coefficients of the variables x, y, and z in distinctive columns, we do not need to write the equations. In solving a system of linear equations with matrices, we first write the coefficients and constants from the system in an **augmented matrix**—for example, the augmented matrix associated with

$$\begin{cases} x + 2y + 3z = 6 \\ x - z = 0 \\ x - y - z = -4 \end{cases} \text{ is } \begin{bmatrix} 1 & 2 & 3 & 6 \\ 1 & 0 & -1 & 0 \\ 1 & -1 & -1 & -4 \end{bmatrix}$$

In the augmented matrix, the numbers on the left side of the solid line form the **coefficient matrix,** with each column containing the coefficients of a variable (0 represents any missing variable). The column on the right side of the line (called the *augment*) contains the constants. Each row of the matrix gives the corresponding coefficients and constant of an equation.

CHECKPOINT

1. (a) Write the augmented matrix for the following system of linear equations.

$$\begin{cases} 3x + 2y - z = 3 \\ x - y + 2z = 4 \\ 2x + 3y - z = 3 \end{cases}$$

(b) Write the coefficient matrix for the system.

We can use matrices to solve systems of linear equations by performing the same operations on the rows of a matrix to reduce it as we do on equations in a linear system. The three different operations we can use to reduce the matrix are called **elementary row operations**, which are similar to the operations with equations that result in equivalent systems. These operations are

1. Interchange two rows.
2. Add a multiple of one row to another row.
3. Multiply a row by a nonzero constant.

When a new matrix results from one or more of these elementary row operations being performed on a matrix, the new matrix is said to be **equivalent** to the original because both matrices represent equivalent systems of equations. Thus, if it can be shown that the augmented matrix

$$\left[\begin{array}{ccc|c} 1 & 2 & 3 & 6 \\ 1 & 0 & -1 & 0 \\ 1 & -1 & -1 & -4 \end{array}\right] \text{ is equivalent to } \left[\begin{array}{ccc|c} 1 & 0 & 0 & -0.5 \\ 0 & 1 & 0 & 4 \\ 0 & 0 & 1 & -0.5 \end{array}\right]$$

then the systems corresponding to these matrices have the same solution. That is,

$$\begin{cases} x + 2y + 3z = 6 \\ x \quad\quad - z = 0 \\ x - y - z = -4 \end{cases} \text{ has the same solution as } \begin{cases} x = -0.5 \\ y = 4 \\ z = -0.5 \end{cases}$$

Thus if a system of linear equations has a unique solution, we can solve the system by reducing the associated matrix to one whose coefficient matrix is the identity matrix and then "reading" the values of the variables that give the solution.

The process we use to solve a system of equations with matrices (called the **elimination method** or **Gauss-Jordan elimination method**) is a systematic procedure that uses row operations to attempt to reduce the coefficient matrix to an identity matrix.

For example, the system

$$\begin{cases} 2x + 5y + 4z = 4 \\ x + 4y + 3z = 1 \\ x - 3y - 2z = 5 \end{cases}$$

can be represented by the augmented matrix

$$\left[\begin{array}{ccc|c} 2 & 5 & 4 & 4 \\ 1 & 4 & 3 & 1 \\ 1 & -3 & -2 & 5 \end{array}\right]$$

The following procedure (using the augmented matrix above) is used to reduce the augmented matrix for a system of equations to an equivalent matrix from which the solutions to the system may be found.

GAUSS-JORDAN ELIMINATION METHOD

Goal (for Each Step)	Row Operation	Equivalent Matrix
1. Get a 1 in row 1, column 1.	Interchange row 1 and row 2.	$\left[\begin{array}{ccc|c} 1 & 4 & 3 & 1 \\ 2 & 5 & 4 & 4 \\ 1 & -3 & -2 & 5 \end{array}\right]$
2. Add multiples of row 1 *only* to the other rows to get zeros as the other entries of column 1.	Add -2 times row 1 to row 2; put the result in row 2. Add -1 times row 1 to row 3; put the result in row 3.	$\left[\begin{array}{ccc|c} 1 & 4 & 3 & 1 \\ 0 & -3 & -2 & 2 \\ 0 & -7 & -5 & 4 \end{array}\right]$

(continued)

Goal (for Each Step)	Row Operation	Equivalent Matrix
3. Use rows below row 1 to get a 1 in row 2, column 2.	Multiply row 2 by $-\frac{1}{3}$; put the result in row 2.	$\begin{bmatrix} 1 & 4 & 3 & \vert & 1 \\ 0 & 1 & \frac{2}{3} & \vert & -\frac{2}{3} \\ 0 & -7 & -5 & \vert & 4 \end{bmatrix}$
4. Add multiples of row 2 *only* to the other rows to get zeros as the other entries in column 2.	Add -4 times row 2 to row 1; put the result in row 1. Add 7 times row 2 to row 3; put the result in row 3.	$\begin{bmatrix} 1 & 0 & \frac{1}{3} & \vert & \frac{11}{3} \\ 0 & 1 & \frac{2}{3} & \vert & -\frac{2}{3} \\ 0 & 0 & -\frac{1}{3} & \vert & -\frac{2}{3} \end{bmatrix}$
5. Use rows below row 2 to get a 1 in row 3, column 3.	Multiply row 3 by -3; put the result in row 3.	$\begin{bmatrix} 1 & 0 & \frac{1}{3} & \vert & \frac{11}{3} \\ 0 & 1 & \frac{2}{3} & \vert & -\frac{2}{3} \\ 0 & 0 & 1 & \vert & 2 \end{bmatrix}$
6. Add multiples of row 3 *only* to the other rows to get zeros as the other entries in column 3.	Add $-\frac{1}{3}$ times row 3 to row 1; put the result in row 1. Add $-\frac{2}{3}$ times row 3 to row 2; put the result in row 2.	$\begin{bmatrix} 1 & 0 & 0 & \vert & 3 \\ 0 & 1 & 0 & \vert & -2 \\ 0 & 0 & 1 & \vert & 2 \end{bmatrix}$
7. Repeat the process until it cannot be continued.	All rows have been used. The matrix is in reduced form.	

The previous display shows a series of step-by-step goals for reducing a matrix and a series of row operations that reduce this 3×3 matrix. The reduction procedure and row operations apply regardless of the size of the system.

In the Gauss-Jordan method box, the systems of equations corresponding to the initial and the final augmented matrices are

$$\text{Initial} \qquad\qquad\qquad \text{Final}$$
$$\begin{aligned} 2x + 5y + 4z &= 4 \\ x + 4y + 3z &= 1 \\ x - 3y - 2z &= 5 \end{aligned} \quad \text{and} \quad \begin{aligned} x + 0y + 0z &= 3 \\ 0x + y + 0z &= -2 \\ 0x + 0y + z &= 2 \end{aligned}$$

Because the augmented matrices for these systems are equivalent, both systems have the same solution, $x = 3$, $y = -2$, and $z = 2$.

When a system of linear equations has a unique solution, the coefficient part of the reduced augmented matrix will be an identity matrix. Note that for this to occur, the coefficient matrix must be square; that is, the number of equations must equal the number of variables.

EXAMPLE 1   Using the Gauss-Jordan Method

Solve the system

$$\begin{aligned} x_1 + x_2 + x_3 + 2x_4 &= 6 \\ x_1 + 2x_2 \quad\;\; + x_4 &= -2 \\ x_1 + x_2 + 3x_3 - 2x_4 &= 12 \\ x_1 + x_2 - 4x_3 + 5x_4 &= -16 \end{aligned}$$

Solution
First note that a variable is missing in the second equation. When we form the augmented matrix, we must insert a zero in this place so that each column represents the coefficients of one variable.

To solve this system, we must reduce the augmented matrix.

$$\begin{bmatrix} 1 & 1 & 1 & 2 & \vert & 6 \\ 1 & 2 & 0 & 1 & \vert & -2 \\ 1 & 1 & 3 & -2 & \vert & 12 \\ 1 & 1 & -4 & 5 & \vert & -16 \end{bmatrix}$$

The reduction process follows. The entry in row 1, column 1 is 1. To get zeros in the first column, add -1 times row 1 to row 2 and put the result in row 2, add -1 times row 1 to row 3 and put the result in row 3, and add -1 times row 1 to row 4 and put the result in row 4. These steps follow with row operation descriptions noted in red.

$$\begin{bmatrix} 1 & 1 & 1 & 2 & | & 6 \\ 1 & 2 & 0 & 1 & | & -2 \\ 1 & 1 & 3 & -2 & | & 12 \\ 1 & 1 & -4 & 5 & | & -16 \end{bmatrix} \xrightarrow[\substack{(-1)R_1 + R_2 \to R_2 \\ (-1)R_1 + R_3 \to R_3 \\ (-1)R_1 + R_4 \to R_4}]{} \begin{bmatrix} 1 & 1 & 1 & 2 & | & 6 \\ 0 & 1 & -1 & -1 & | & -8 \\ 0 & 0 & 2 & -4 & | & 6 \\ 0 & 0 & -5 & 3 & | & -22 \end{bmatrix}$$

The entry in row 2, column 2 is 1. To get zeros in the second column, add -1 times row 2 to row 1 and put the result in row 1.

$$\xrightarrow[(-1)R_2 + R_1 \to R_1]{} \begin{bmatrix} 1 & 0 & 2 & 3 & | & 14 \\ 0 & 1 & -1 & -1 & | & -8 \\ 0 & 0 & 2 & -4 & | & 6 \\ 0 & 0 & -5 & 3 & | & -22 \end{bmatrix}$$

The entry in row 3, column 3 is 2. To get a 1 in this position, multiply row 3 by $\frac{1}{2}$.

$$\xrightarrow[\frac{1}{2}R_3 \to R_3]{} \begin{bmatrix} 1 & 0 & 2 & 3 & | & 14 \\ 0 & 1 & -1 & -1 & | & -8 \\ 0 & 0 & 1 & -2 & | & 3 \\ 0 & 0 & -5 & 3 & | & -22 \end{bmatrix}$$

Using row 3, add -2 times row 3 to row 1 and put the result in row 1, add row 3 to row 2 and put the result in row 2, and add 5 times row 3 to row 4 and put the result in row 4.

$$\xrightarrow[\substack{(-2)R_3 + R_1 \to R_1 \\ R_3 + R_2 \to R_2 \\ 5R_3 + R_4 \to R_4}]{} \begin{bmatrix} 1 & 0 & 0 & 7 & | & 8 \\ 0 & 1 & 0 & -3 & | & -5 \\ 0 & 0 & 1 & -2 & | & 3 \\ 0 & 0 & 0 & -7 & | & -7 \end{bmatrix}$$

Multiplying $-\frac{1}{7}$ times row 4 and putting the result in row 4 gives a 1 in row 4, column 4.

$$\xrightarrow[-\frac{1}{7}R_4 \to R_4]{} \begin{bmatrix} 1 & 0 & 0 & 7 & | & 8 \\ 0 & 1 & 0 & -3 & | & -5 \\ 0 & 0 & 1 & -2 & | & 3 \\ 0 & 0 & 0 & 1 & | & 1 \end{bmatrix}$$

Adding appropriate multiples of row 4 to the other rows gives

$$\xrightarrow[\substack{(-7)R_4 + R_1 \to R_1 \\ 3R_4 + R_2 \to R_2 \\ 2R_4 + R_3 \to R_3}]{} \begin{bmatrix} 1 & 0 & 0 & 0 & | & 1 \\ 0 & 1 & 0 & 0 & | & -2 \\ 0 & 0 & 1 & 0 & | & 5 \\ 0 & 0 & 0 & 1 & | & 1 \end{bmatrix}$$

This corresponds to the system

$$\begin{aligned} x_1 & & & & = 1 \\ & x_2 & & & = -2 \\ & & x_3 & & = 5 \\ & & & x_4 & = 1 \end{aligned}$$

Thus the solution is $x_1 = 1$, $x_2 = -2$, $x_3 = 5$, and $x_4 = 1$.

Calculator Note   Graphing calculators are especially useful in solving systems of equations because they can be used to perform the row reductions necessary to obtain a reduced matrix. On some calculators, a direct command will give a reduced form for the augmented matrix. Figure 3.8(a) shows the augmented matrix A for the system of equations in Example 1.

Selecting MATRIX, moving to MATH, choosing B:rref(, and pressing ENTER give rref(on the display. Then selecting MATRIX [A] gives rref([A]) on the display. Finally, pressing ENTER gives the reduced form of A shown in Figure 3.8(b). This is the same as the reduced matrix in Example 1, from which the solutions can be read. The steps used to solve a system of linear equations by finding the reduced matrix are shown in Appendix A, Section 3.3.

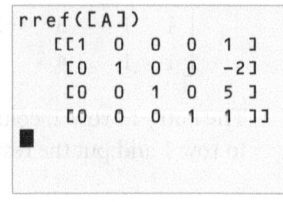

Figure 3.8   (a)   (b)

CHECKPOINT

2. Solve the system.

$$\begin{cases} 3x + 2y - z = 3 \\ x - y + 2z = 4 \\ 2x + 3y - z = 3 \end{cases}$$

EXAMPLE 2 Manufacturing | APPLICATION PREVIEW |

The Walters Manufacturing Company needs to know how best to use the time available within its three manufacturing departments in the construction and packaging of the three types of metal storage sheds. Each one must be stamped, painted, and packaged. Table 3.5 shows the number of hours required for the processing of each type of shed. Using the information in the table, determine how many of each type of shed can be produced if the stamping department has 3200 hours available, the painting department has 1700 hours, and the packaging department has 1300 hours.

TABLE 3.5

Department	Shed		
	Type I	Type II	Type III
Stamping	2	3	4
Painting	1	2	1
Packaging	1	1	2

Solution

If we let x_1 be the number of type I sheds, x_2 be the number of type II sheds, and x_3 be the number of type III sheds, we can develop the following equations.

Stamping hours: $2x_1 + 3x_2 + 4x_3 = 3200$

Painting hours: $1x_1 + 2x_2 + 1x_3 = 1700$

Packaging hours: $1x_1 + 1x_2 + 2x_3 = 1300$

The augmented matrix for this system of equations is

$$\begin{bmatrix} 2 & 3 & 4 & | & 3200 \\ 1 & 2 & 1 & | & 1700 \\ 1 & 1 & 2 & | & 1300 \end{bmatrix}$$

Reducing this augmented matrix proceeds as follows:

$$\begin{bmatrix} 2 & 3 & 4 & | & 3200 \\ 1 & 2 & 1 & | & 1700 \\ 1 & 1 & 2 & | & 1300 \end{bmatrix} \xrightarrow{\text{Switch } R_1 \text{ and } R_3} \begin{bmatrix} 1 & 1 & 2 & | & 1300 \\ 1 & 2 & 1 & | & 1700 \\ 2 & 3 & 4 & | & 3200 \end{bmatrix}$$

$$\xrightarrow[(-2)R_1 + R_3 \to R_3]{(-1)R_1 + R_2 \to R_2} \begin{bmatrix} 1 & 1 & 2 & | & 1300 \\ 0 & 1 & -1 & | & 400 \\ 0 & 1 & 0 & | & 600 \end{bmatrix}$$

$$\xrightarrow[(-1)R_2 + R_3 \to R_3]{(-1)R_2 + R_1 \to R_1} \begin{bmatrix} 1 & 0 & 3 & | & 900 \\ 0 & 1 & -1 & | & 400 \\ 0 & 0 & 1 & | & 200 \end{bmatrix} \xrightarrow[R_3 + R_2 \to R_2]{(-3)R_3 + R_1 \to R_1} \begin{bmatrix} 1 & 0 & 0 & | & 300 \\ 0 & 1 & 0 & | & 600 \\ 0 & 0 & 1 & | & 200 \end{bmatrix}$$

Thus the solution to the system is

$$x_1 = 300 \qquad x_2 = 600 \qquad x_3 = 200$$

The company should make 300 type I, 600 type II, and 200 type III sheds.   ◼

Systems with Nonunique Solutions

All the systems considered so far have unique solutions, but it is possible for a system of linear equations to have an infinite number of solutions or no solution at all. Although coefficient matrices for systems with an infinite number of solutions or no solution will not reduce to identity matrices, row operations can be used to obtain a reduced form from which the solutions, if they exist, can be determined.

A matrix is said to be in **reduced form** when it is in the following form:

1. The first nonzero element in each row is 1.
2. Every column containing a first nonzero element for some row has zeros everywhere else.
3. The first nonzero element of each row is to the right of the first nonzero element of every row above it.
4. All rows containing zeros are grouped together below the rows containing nonzero entries.

The following matrices are in reduced form because they satisfy these conditions.

$$\begin{bmatrix} 1 & 0 & | & 4 \\ 0 & 1 & | & 2 \\ 0 & 0 & | & 0 \end{bmatrix} \qquad \begin{bmatrix} 1 & 0 & 0 & | & 0 \\ 0 & 1 & 0 & | & 3 \\ 0 & 0 & 1 & | & 1 \\ 0 & 0 & 0 & | & 0 \end{bmatrix} \qquad \begin{bmatrix} 1 & 4 & 0 & | & 1 \\ 0 & 0 & 1 & | & 2 \\ 0 & 0 & 0 & | & 0 \end{bmatrix}$$

The following matrices are *not* in reduced form.

$$\begin{bmatrix} 1 & ① & | & 0 \\ 0 & 1 & | & 3 \\ 0 & 0 & | & 0 \end{bmatrix} \qquad \begin{bmatrix} 1 & 0 & | & 1 \\ 0 & ② & | & 1 \\ 0 & 0 & | & 0 \end{bmatrix} \qquad \begin{bmatrix} 0 & 1 & | & 0 \\ 1 & 0 & | & 0 \\ 0 & 0 & | & 1 \end{bmatrix}$$

In the first two matrices, the circled element must be changed to obtain a reduced form. Can you see what row operations would transform each of these matrices into reduced form? The third matrix does not satisfy condition 3.

We can solve a system of linear equations by using row operations on the augmented matrix until the coefficient matrix is transformed to an equivalent matrix in reduced form. We begin by following the goals outlined in the Gauss-Jordan elimination method and in the Example 1 discussion.

EXAMPLE 3   Matrix Solution of a System

Solve the system

$$\begin{cases} x_1 + x_2 - x_3 + x_4 = 3 \\ x_2 + x_3 + x_4 = 1 \\ x_1 \qquad - 2x_3 + x_4 = 6 \\ 2x_1 - x_2 - 5x_3 - 3x_4 = -5 \end{cases}$$

Solution

We attempt to reduce the coefficient matrix of the associated augmented matrix to an identity matrix as follows.

$$\begin{bmatrix} 1 & 1 & -1 & 1 & 3 \\ 0 & 1 & 1 & 1 & 1 \\ 1 & 0 & -2 & 1 & 6 \\ 2 & -1 & -5 & -3 & -5 \end{bmatrix} \xrightarrow[\substack{(-1)R_1 + R_3 \to R_3 \\ (-2)R_1 + R_4 \to R_4}]{} \begin{bmatrix} 1 & 1 & -1 & 1 & 3 \\ 0 & 1 & 1 & 1 & 1 \\ 0 & -1 & -1 & 0 & 3 \\ 0 & -3 & -3 & -5 & -11 \end{bmatrix}$$

$$\xrightarrow[\substack{(-1)R_2 + R_1 \to R_1 \\ R_2 + R_3 \to R_3 \\ 3R_2 + R_4 \to R_4}]{} \begin{bmatrix} 1 & 0 & -2 & 0 & 2 \\ 0 & 1 & 1 & 1 & 1 \\ 0 & 0 & 0 & 1 & 4 \\ 0 & 0 & 0 & -2 & -8 \end{bmatrix}$$

The entry in row 3, column 3 cannot be made 1 using rows *below* row 2. Moving to column 4, the entry in row 3, column 4 is a 1. Using row 3 gives

$$\xrightarrow[\substack{(-1)R_3 + R_2 \to R_2 \\ 2R_3 + R_4 \to R_4}]{} \begin{bmatrix} 1 & 0 & -2 & 0 & 2 \\ 0 & 1 & 1 & 0 & -3 \\ 0 & 0 & 0 & 1 & 4 \\ 0 & 0 & 0 & 0 & 0 \end{bmatrix}$$

The augmented matrix is now reduced; this matrix corresponds to the system

$$\begin{cases} x_1 - 2x_3 = 2 \\ x_2 + x_3 = -3 \\ x_4 = 4 \\ 0 = 0 \end{cases}$$

If we solve each of the equations for the lead variable (the variable corresponding to the first 1 in each row of the reduced form of a matrix) and let any non-lead variables equal any real number (x_3 in this case), we obtain the **general solution** of the system.

$$x_1 = 2 + 2x_3$$
$$x_2 = -3 - x_3$$
$$x_4 = 4$$
$$x_3 = \text{any real number}$$

The general solution gives the values of x_1 and x_2 dependent on the value of x_3, so we can get many different solutions of the system by specifying different values of x_3. For example, if $x_3 = 1$, then $x_1 = 4$, $x_2 = -4$, $x_3 = 1$, and $x_4 = 4$ is a solution of the system; if we let $x_3 = -2$, then $x_1 = -2$, $x_2 = -1$, $x_3 = -2$, and $x_4 = 4$ is another solution.

We have seen two different possibilities for solutions of systems of linear equations. In Examples 1 and 2, there was only one solution, whereas in Example 3, we saw that there were infinitely many solutions, one for each possible value of x_3. A third possibility exists: that the system has no solution. Recall that these possibilities also existed for two equations in two unknowns, as discussed in Chapter 1, "Linear Equations and Functions."

EXAMPLE 4   A System with No Solution

Solve the system

$$\begin{cases} x + 2y - z = 3 \\ 3x + y = 4 \\ 2x - y + z = 2 \end{cases}$$

Solution

The augmented matrix for this system is reduced as follows:

$$\begin{bmatrix} 1 & 2 & -1 & 3 \\ 3 & 1 & 0 & 4 \\ 2 & -1 & 1 & 2 \end{bmatrix} \xrightarrow[\substack{(-2)R_1 + R_3 \to R_3}]{(-3)R_1 + R_2 \to R_2} \begin{bmatrix} 1 & 2 & -1 & 3 \\ 0 & -5 & 3 & -5 \\ 0 & -5 & 3 & -4 \end{bmatrix}$$

$$\xrightarrow{-\frac{1}{5}R_2 \to R_2} \begin{bmatrix} 1 & 2 & -1 & 3 \\ 0 & 1 & -\frac{3}{5} & 1 \\ 0 & -5 & 3 & -4 \end{bmatrix}$$

$$\xrightarrow[\substack{(5)R_2 + R_3 \to R_3}]{(-2)R_2 + R_1 \to R_1} \begin{bmatrix} 1 & 0 & \frac{1}{5} & 1 \\ 0 & 1 & -\frac{3}{5} & 1 \\ 0 & 0 & 0 & 1 \end{bmatrix}$$

The system of equations corresponding to the reduced matrix has $0 = 1$ as the third equation. This is clearly an impossibility, so there is no solution.

Now that we have seen examples of each of the different solution possibilities for n equations in n variables, let us consider what we have learned. In all cases, we began the solution procedure by setting up and then reducing the augmented matrix. Once the matrix is reduced, we can write the corresponding reduced system of equations. The solutions, if they exist, are easily found from this reduced system. We summarize the possibilities in Table 3.6.

TABLE 3.6

UNIQUE AND NONUNIQUE SOLUTIONS

Reduced Form of Augmented Matrix for n Equations in n Variables	Solution to System
1. Coefficient array is an identity matrix.	Unique solution (see Examples 1 and 2).
2. Coefficient array is *not* an identity matrix with either:	
(a) A row of 0s in the coefficient array with a nonzero entry in the augment.	(a) No solution (see Example 4).
(b) Or otherwise.	(b) Infinitely many solutions. Solve for lead variables in terms of non-lead variables; non-lead variables can equal any real number (see Example 3).

Calculator Note   Whether or not a unique solution exists, we can use a graphing calculator to reduce an augmented matrix and then find any solution that exists (or that no solution exists). For example, following is a system of equations along with the calculator screens for its augmented matrix and the reduced form of its augmented matrix.

$$\begin{cases} x + 2y - 2z = 4 \\ 2x + 5y \quad\quad = 3 \\ x + \ y - 6z = 9 \end{cases}$$

```
[A]
        [[1 2 -2 4]
         [2 5 0  3]
         [1 1 -6 9]]
```

```
rref([A])
        [[1 0 -10 14]
         [0 1  4  -5]
         [0 0  0   0 ]]
```

From the reduced matrix, we obtain the following equations and general solution.

$$x - 10z = 14 \qquad\qquad x = 10z + 14$$
$$y + 4z = -5 \qquad\qquad y = -4z - 5$$
$$\qquad\qquad\qquad\qquad z = \text{ any real number}$$

As with systems that have a unique solution, the command rref([A]) gives the reduced form of a matrix A for any system. See Appendix A, Section 3.3, for details. ◼

CHECKPOINT

For each system of equations, the reduced form of the augmented matrix is given. Give the solution to the system, if it exists.

3. $\begin{cases} 2x + 3y + 2z = 180 \\ -x + 2y + 4z = 180 \\ 2x + 6y + 5z = 270 \end{cases}$ $\begin{bmatrix} 1 & 0 & 0 & | & 100 \\ 0 & 1 & 0 & | & -80 \\ 0 & 0 & 1 & | & 110 \end{bmatrix}$

4. $\begin{cases} x - 2y + 9z = 12 \\ 2x - y + 3z = 18 \\ x + y - 6z = 6 \end{cases}$ $\begin{bmatrix} 1 & 0 & -1 & | & 8 \\ 0 & 1 & -5 & | & -2 \\ 0 & 0 & 0 & | & 0 \end{bmatrix}$

5. $\begin{cases} x - 4y + 3z = 4 \\ 2x - 2y + z = 6 \\ x + 2y - 2z = 4 \end{cases}$ $\begin{bmatrix} 1 & 0 & -\frac{1}{3} & | & 0 \\ 0 & 1 & -\frac{5}{6} & | & 0 \\ 0 & 0 & 0 & | & 1 \end{bmatrix}$

Nonsquare Systems

Finally, we consider systems with fewer equations than variables*. Because the coefficient matrix for such a system is not square, it cannot reduce to an identity matrix. Hence these systems of equations cannot have a unique solution but may have no solution or infinitely many solutions. Nevertheless, they are solved in the same manner as those considered so far but with the following two possible results.

1. If the reduced augmented matrix contains a row of 0s in the coefficient matrix with a nonzero number in the augment, the system has no solution.
2. Otherwise, the system has infinitely many solutions.

EXAMPLE 5 **Investment**

A trust account manager has $500,000 from a new client that is to be invested in three different accounts. The accounts pay annual interest rates of 8%, 10%, and 14%, and the goal is to earn $49,000 a year. To accomplish this, assume that x dollars is invested at 8%, y dollars at 10%, and z dollars at 14%. Find how much should be invested in each account to satisfy the conditions.

Solution
The sum of the three investments is $500,000, so we have the equation

$$x + y + z = 500,000$$

The interest earned from the 8% investment is $0.08x$, the amount earned from the 10% investment is $0.10y$, and the amount earned from the 14% investment is $0.14z$, so the total amount earned from the investments is given by the equation

$$0.08x + 0.10y + 0.14z = 49,000$$

These two equations represent all the given information, so the system is

$$\begin{cases} x + y + z = 500,000 \\ 0.08x + 0.10y + 0.14z = 49,000 \end{cases}$$

*We do not discuss systems with more equations than variables.

We solve this system using matrices as follows:

$$\begin{bmatrix} 1 & 1 & 1 & | & 500{,}000 \\ 0.08 & 0.10 & 0.14 & | & 49{,}000 \end{bmatrix} \xrightarrow{-0.08R_1 + R_2 \to R_2} \begin{bmatrix} 1 & 1 & 1 & | & 500{,}000 \\ 0 & 0.02 & 0.06 & | & 9{,}000 \end{bmatrix}$$

$$\xrightarrow{50R_2 \to R_2} \begin{bmatrix} 1 & 1 & 1 & | & 500{,}000 \\ 0 & 1 & 3 & | & 450{,}000 \end{bmatrix} \xrightarrow{-R_2 + R_1 \to R_1} \begin{bmatrix} 1 & 0 & -2 & | & 50{,}000 \\ 0 & 1 & 3 & | & 450{,}000 \end{bmatrix}$$

This matrix represents the equivalent system

$$\begin{cases} x - 2z = 50{,}000 \\ y + 3z = 450{,}000 \end{cases} \quad \text{so} \quad \begin{aligned} x &= 50{,}000 + 2z \\ y &= 450{,}000 - 3z \\ z &= \text{any real number} \end{aligned}$$

Because a negative amount cannot be invested, x, y, and z must all be nonnegative. Note that $x \geq 0$ when $z \geq 0$ and that $y \geq 0$ when $450{,}000 - 3z \geq 0$, or when $z \leq 150{,}000$. Thus the amounts invested are

$$\begin{aligned} \$z \text{ at } 14\%, &\quad \text{where} &\quad 0 \leq z \leq 150{,}000 \\ \$x \text{ at } 8\%, &\quad \text{where} &\quad x = 50{,}000 + 2z \\ \$y \text{ at } 10\%, &\quad \text{where} &\quad y = 450{,}000 - 3z \end{aligned}$$

There are many possible investment plans. One example is with $z = \$100{,}000$, $x = \$250{,}000$, and $y = \$150{,}000$. Observe that the values for x and y depend on z, and once z is chosen, x will be between \$50,000 and \$350,000, and y will be between \$0 and \$450,000. ■

CHECKPOINT
ANSWERS

1. (a) $\begin{bmatrix} 3 & 2 & -1 & | & 3 \\ 1 & -1 & 2 & | & 4 \\ 2 & 3 & -1 & | & 3 \end{bmatrix}$ (b) $\begin{bmatrix} 3 & 2 & -1 \\ 1 & -1 & 2 \\ 2 & 3 & -1 \end{bmatrix}$

2. $x = 1, y = 1, z = 2$
3. $x = 100, y = -80, z = 110$
4. $x = z + 8, y = 5z - 2, z = $ any real number
5. No solution

EXERCISES 3.3

In Problems 1 and 2, use the indicated row operation to change matrix A, where

$$A = \begin{bmatrix} 1 & -2 & -1 & | & -7 \\ 3 & 1 & 2 & | & 0 \\ 4 & 2 & 2 & | & 1 \end{bmatrix}$$

1. Add -3 times row 1 to row 2 of matrix A and place the result in row 2 to get 0 in row 2, column 1.
2. Add -4 times row 1 to row 3 of matrix A and place the result in row 3 to get 0 in row 3, column 1.

In Problems 3 and 4, write the augmented matrix associated with each system of linear equations.

3. $\begin{cases} x - 3y + 4z = 2 \\ 2x \quad\quad + 2z = 1 \\ x + 2y + \quad z = 1 \end{cases}$

4. $\begin{cases} x + 2y + 2z = 3 \\ x - 2y \quad\quad = 4 \\ \quad\quad y - \quad z = 1 \end{cases}$

In Problems 5–10, an augmented matrix for a system of linear equations in x, y, and z is given. Find the solution of each system.

5. $\begin{bmatrix} 1 & 0 & 0 & | & 2 \\ 0 & 1 & 0 & | & \frac{1}{2} \\ 0 & 0 & 1 & | & -5 \end{bmatrix}$

6. $\begin{bmatrix} 1 & 0 & 0 & | & -8 \\ 0 & 1 & 0 & | & 1 \\ 0 & 0 & 1 & | & \frac{1}{3} \end{bmatrix}$

7. $\begin{bmatrix} 1 & 1 & 2 & | & -1 \\ 0 & 3 & 1 & | & 7 \\ 0 & -2 & 4 & | & 0 \end{bmatrix}$

8. $\begin{bmatrix} 1 & 5 & 2 & | & 6 \\ 0 & -2 & 3 & | & 9 \\ 0 & 1 & 3 & | & 0 \end{bmatrix}$

9. $\begin{bmatrix} 1 & 2 & 5 & | & -4 \\ 2 & -2 & 4 & | & -2 \\ 0 & 1 & -3 & | & 7 \end{bmatrix}$

10. $\begin{bmatrix} 1 & 1 & 1 & | & 3 \\ 3 & -2 & 4 & | & 5 \\ 1 & 2 & 1 & | & 4 \end{bmatrix}$

In Problems 11–16, use row operations on augmented matrices to solve the given systems of linear equations.

11. $\begin{cases} x + y - z = 0 \\ x + 2y + 3z = -5 \\ 2x - y - 13z = 17 \end{cases}$ 12. $\begin{cases} x + 2y - z = 3 \\ 2x + 5y - 2z = 7 \\ -x + y + 5z = -12 \end{cases}$

13. $\begin{cases} 2x - 6y - 12z = 6 \\ 3x - 10y - 20z = 5 \\ 2x - 17z = -4 \end{cases}$

14. $\begin{cases} -3x + 6y - 9z = 3 \\ x - y - 2z = 0 \\ 5x + 5y - 7z = 63 \end{cases}$

15. $\begin{cases} x - 2y + 3z + w = -2 \\ x - 3y + z - w = -7 \\ x - y = -2 \\ x + z + w = 2 \end{cases}$

16. $\begin{cases} x + 4y - 6z - 3w = 3 \\ x - y + 2w = -5 \\ x + z + w = 1 \\ y + z + w = 0 \end{cases}$

In Problems 17–20, a system of linear equations and a reduced matrix for the system are given. (a) Use the reduced matrix to find the general solution of the system, if one exists. (b) If multiple solutions exist, find two specific solutions.

17. $\begin{cases} x + 2y + 3z = 1 \\ 2x - y = 3 \\ x + 2y + 3z = 2 \end{cases}$ $\begin{bmatrix} 1 & 0 & \frac{3}{5} & | & 0 \\ 0 & 1 & \frac{6}{5} & | & 0 \\ 0 & 0 & 0 & | & 1 \end{bmatrix}$

18. $\begin{cases} 2x + 3y + 4z = 2 \\ x + 2y + 2z = 1 \\ x + y + 2z = 2 \end{cases}$ $\begin{bmatrix} 1 & 0 & 2 & | & 0 \\ 0 & 1 & 0 & | & 0 \\ 0 & 0 & 0 & | & 1 \end{bmatrix}$

19. $\begin{cases} 2x + y - z = 7 \\ x - y - z = 4 \\ 3x + 3y - z = 10 \end{cases}$ $\begin{bmatrix} 1 & 0 & -\frac{2}{3} & | & \frac{11}{3} \\ 0 & 1 & \frac{1}{3} & | & -\frac{1}{3} \\ 0 & 0 & 0 & | & 0 \end{bmatrix}$

20. $\begin{cases} x - y + z = 3 \\ 3x + 2z = 7 \\ x - 4y + 2z = 5 \end{cases}$ $\begin{bmatrix} 1 & 0 & \frac{2}{3} & | & \frac{7}{3} \\ 0 & 1 & -\frac{1}{3} & | & -\frac{2}{3} \\ 0 & 0 & 0 & | & 0 \end{bmatrix}$

21. How can you tell that a system of linear equations has no solution by looking at its reduced matrix?

22. Describe the procedure for finding the general solution of a system of linear equations if its reduced matrix indicates that it has an infinite number of solutions.

The systems of equations in Problems 23–36 may have unique solutions, an infinite number of solutions, or no solution. Use matrices to find the general solution of each system, if a solution exists.

23. $\begin{cases} x + y + z = 0 \\ 2x - y - z = 0 \\ -x + 2y + 2z = 0 \end{cases}$ 24. $\begin{cases} 2x - y + 3z = 0 \\ x + 2y + 2z = 0 \\ x - 3y + z = 0 \end{cases}$

25. $\begin{cases} 3x + 2y + z = 0 \\ x + y + 2z = 2 \\ 2x + y - z = -1 \end{cases}$ 26. $\begin{cases} x + 3y + 2z = 2 \\ 2x - y - 2z = 1 \\ 3x + 2y = 1 \end{cases}$

27. $\begin{cases} x - 3y + 3z = 7 \\ x + 2y - z = -2 \\ 3x + 2y + 4z = 5 \end{cases}$ 28. $\begin{cases} 2x + y - z = 2 \\ x - y + 2z = 3 \\ x + y - z = 1 \end{cases}$

29. $\begin{cases} 2x - 5y + z = -9 \\ x + 4y - 6z = 2 \\ 3x - 4y - 2z = -10 \end{cases}$ 30. $\begin{cases} 2x - y + z = 2 \\ 3x + y - 6z = -7 \\ x - y + 2z = 3 \end{cases}$

31. $\begin{cases} x + y + z = 3 \\ x - y + z = 4 \end{cases}$ 32. $\begin{cases} 3x + 2y + z = 3 \\ x - y - z = 2 \end{cases}$

33. $\begin{cases} 3x - 2y + 5z = 14 \\ 2x - 3y + 4z = 8 \end{cases}$ 34. $\begin{cases} x - 4y + z = -4 \\ 2x - 5y - 5z = -9 \end{cases}$

35. $\begin{cases} -0.6x_1 + 0.1x_2 + 0.4x_3 = 10 \\ 0.4x_1 - 0.7x_2 + 0.2x_3 = -26 \\ 0.2x_1 + 0.6x_2 - 0.5x_3 = 20 \end{cases}$

36. $\begin{cases} 0.1x_1 - 0.1x_2 - 0.3x_3 = 17 \\ 0.2x_1 + 0.3x_2 + 0.1x_3 = -9 \\ 0.3x_1 + 0.2x_2 - 0.5x_3 = 5 \end{cases}$

In Problems 37–42, use technology to solve each system of equations, if a solution exists.

37. $\begin{cases} x_1 + 3x_2 + 2x_3 + 2x_4 = 3 \\ x_1 + x_2 + 3x_3 = 4 \\ 2x_1 + 2x_3 - 3x_4 = 4 \\ x_1 - 3x_2 = 1 \end{cases}$

38. $\begin{cases} x_1 + x_2 + x_3 + 2x_4 = 1 \\ x_1 - 3x_3 = 2 \\ x_1 - 3x_2 + x_4 = -2 \\ x_2 - 4x_3 + x_4 = 0 \end{cases}$

39. $\begin{cases} x_1 + 2x_2 - x_3 + x_4 = 3 \\ x_1 + 3x_2 + 4x_3 + x_4 = -2 \\ 2x_1 + 5x_2 + 2x_3 + 2x_4 = 1 \\ 2x_1 + 3x_2 - 6x_3 + 2x_4 = 3 \end{cases}$

40. $\begin{cases} x_1 + 2x_2 + 3x_3 + 4x_4 = 2 \\ x_1 + 2x_2 + 4x_3 + 3x_4 = 2 \\ 2x_1 + 4x_2 + 6x_3 + 8x_4 = 4 \\ x_1 + 4x_2 + 3x_3 = 4 \end{cases}$

41. $\begin{cases} x_1 + 3x_2 + 4x_3 - x_4 + 2x_5 = 1 \\ x_1 - x_2 - 2x_3 + x_4 = 3 \\ x_1 + 2x_2 + 3x_3 + x_4 + 4x_5 = 0 \\ 2x_1 + 2x_2 + 2x_3 + 2x_5 = 4 \end{cases}$

42. $\begin{cases} 2x_1 - x_2 + x_3 + 3x_4 + 3x_5 = 7 \\ x_1 + x_2 + x_3 + 2x_4 + 2x_5 = 0 \\ 2x_1 + x_2 - x_3 + x_4 + x_5 = -3 \\ 4x_1 - x_2 - 3x_3 + x_4 + x_5 = 1 \end{cases}$

43. Solve $\begin{cases} a_1x + b_1y = c_1 \\ a_2x + b_2y = c_2 \end{cases}$ for x. This gives a formula for solving two equations in two variables for x.

44. Solve $\begin{cases} a_1x + b_1y = c_1 \\ a_2x + b_2y = c_2 \end{cases}$ for y. This gives a formula for solving two equations in two variables for y.

APPLICATIONS

45. *Nutrition* A preschool has Campbell's Chunky Beef soup, which contains 2.5 g of fat and 15 mg of cholesterol per serving (cup), and Campbell's Chunky Sirloin Burger soup, which contains 7 g of fat and 15 mg of cholesterol per serving. By combining the soups, it is possible to get 10 servings of soup that will have 61 g of fat and 150 mg of cholesterol. How many cups of each soup should be used?

46. *Ticket sales* A 3500-seat theater sells tickets for $75 and $110. Each night the theater's expenses total $245,000. When all 3500 seats sell, the owners want ticket revenues to cover expenses and give a profit of 25% of expenses. How many tickets of each price should be sold to achieve this?

47. *Investment* A man has $235,000 invested in three properties. One earns 12%, one earns 10%, and one earns 8%. His annual income from the properties is $22,500, and the amount invested at 8% is twice that invested at 12%.
(a) How much is invested in each property?
(b) What is the annual income from each property?

48. *Loans* A bank lent $1.2 million for the development of three new products, with one loan each at 6%, 7%, and 8%. The amount lent at 8% was equal to the sum of the amounts lent at the other two rates, and the bank's annual income from the loans was $88,000. How much was lent at each rate?

49. *Car rental patterns* A car rental agency in a major city has a total of 2200 cars that it rents from three locations: Metropolis Airport, downtown, and the smaller City Airport. Some weekly rental and return patterns are shown in the table. (Note that Airport means Metropolis Airport.)

	Rented from		
Returned to	AP	DT	CA
Airport (AP)	90%	10%	10%
Downtown (DT)	5%	80%	5%

At the beginning of a week, how many cars should be at each location so that same number of cars will be there at the end of the week (and hence at the start of the next week)?

50. *Nutrition* A psychologist studying the effects of nutrition on the behavior of laboratory rats is feeding one group a combination of three foods: I, II, and III. Each of these foods contains three additives (A, B, and C) that are being used in the study. Each additive is a certain percentage of each of the foods as follows:

	Foods		
	I	II	III
Additive A	10%	30%	60%
Additive B	0%	4%	5%
Additive C	2%	2%	12%

If the diet requires 53 g per day of A, 4.5 g per day of B, and 8.6 g per day of C, find the number of grams per day of each food that must be used.

51. *Nutrition* The following table gives the calories, fat, and carbohydrates per ounce for three brands of cereal. How many ounces of each brand should be combined to get 443 calories, 5.7 g of fat, and 113.4 g of carbohydrates?

Cereal	Calories	Fat (g)	Carbohydrates (g)
All Fiber	50	0	22.0
Frosted Puffs	108	0.1	25.7
Natural Grain	127	5.5	18.0

52. *Investment* A brokerage house offers three stock portfolios. Portfolio I consists of 2 blocks of common stock and 1 municipal bond. Portfolio II consists of 4 blocks of common stock, 2 municipal bonds, and 3 blocks of preferred stock. Portfolio III consists of 7 blocks of common stock, 3 municipal bonds, and

3 blocks of preferred stock. A customer wants 21 blocks of common stock, 10 municipal bonds, and 9 blocks of preferred stock. How many units of each portfolio should be offered?

53. *Investment* Suppose that portfolios I and II in Problem 52 are unchanged and portfolio III consists of 2 blocks of common stock, 2 municipal bonds, and 3 blocks of preferred stock. A customer wants 12 blocks of common stock, 6 municipal bonds, and 6 blocks of preferred stock. How many units of each portfolio should be offered?

54. *Nutrition* Each ounce of substance A supplies 5% of the required nutrition a patient needs. Substance B supplies 15% of the required nutrition per ounce, and substance C supplies 12% of the required nutrition per ounce. If dietary restrictions require that substances A and C be given in equal amounts and that the amount of substance B be one-fifth of these other amounts, find the number of ounces of each substance that should be in the meal to provide 100% nutrition.

55. *Nutrition* A glass of skim milk supplies 0.1 mg of iron, 8.5 g of protein, and 1 g of carbohydrates. A quarter pound of lean red meat provides 3.4 mg of iron, 22 g of protein, and 20 g of carbohydrates. Two slices of whole-grain bread supply 2.2 mg of iron, 10 g of protein, and 12 g of carbohydrates. If a person on a special diet must have 12.1 mg of iron, 97 g of protein, and 70 g of carbohydrates, how many glasses of skim milk, how many quarter-pound servings of meat, and how many two-slice servings of whole-grain bread will supply this?

56. *Transportation* The King Trucking Company has an order for three products for delivery. The following table gives the particulars for the products.

	Type I	Type II	Type III
Unit volume (cubic feet)	10	8	20
Unit weight (pounds)	10	20	40
Unit value (dollars)	100	20	200

If the carrier can carry 6000 cu ft, can carry 11,000 lb, and is insured for $36,900, how many units of each type can be carried?

57. *Nutrition* A botanist can purchase plant food of four different types, I, II, III, and IV. Each food comes in the same size bag, and the following table summarizes the number of grams of each of three nutrients that each bag contains.

	Foods (grams)			
	I	II	III	IV
Nutrient A	5	5	10	5
Nutrient B	10	5	30	10
Nutrient C	5	15	10	25

The botanist wants to use a food that has these nutrients in a different proportion and determines that he will need a total of 10,000 g of A, 20,000 g of B, and 20,000 g of C. Find the number of bags of each type of food that should be ordered.

58. *Traffic flow* In the analysis of traffic flow, a certain city estimates the following situation for the square of its downtown district. In the following figure, the arrows indicate the flow of traffic. If x_1 represents the number of cars traveling between intersections A and B, x_2 represents the number of cars traveling between B and C, x_3 the number between C and D, and x_4 the number between D and A, we can formulate equations based on the principle that the number of vehicles entering an intersection equals the number leaving it. That is, for intersection A, we obtain

$$200 + x_4 = 100 + x_1$$

(a) Formulate equations for the traffic at B, C, and D.
(b) Solve the system of these four equations.
(c) Can the entire traffic flow problem be studied and solved by counting only the x_4 cars that travel between A and D? Explain.

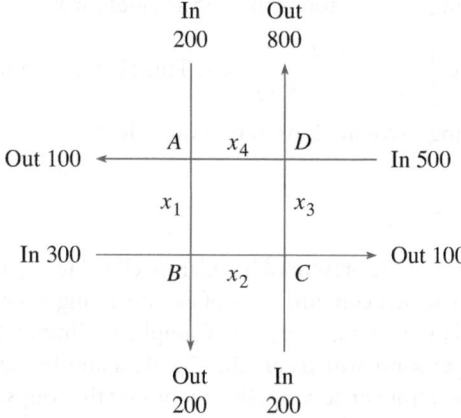

59. *Nutrition* Three different bacteria are cultured in one environment and feed on three nutrients. Each individual of species I consumes 1 unit of each of the first and second nutrients and 2 units of the third nutrient. Each individual of species II consumes 2 units of the first nutrient and 2 units of the third nutrient. Each individual of species III consumes 2 units of the first nutrient, 3 units of the second nutrient, and 5 units of the third nutrient. If the culture is given 5100 units of the first nutrient, 6900 units of the second nutrient, and 12,000 units of the third nutrient, how many of each species can be supported such that all of the nutrients are consumed?

60. *Irrigation* An irrigation system allows water to flow in the pattern shown in the figure below. Water flows into the system at A and exits at B, C, D, and E with the amounts shown. Using the fact that at each point the

water entering equals the water leaving, formulate an equation for water flow at each of the five points and solve the system.

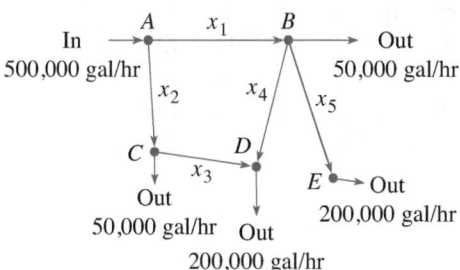

61. *Investment* An investment club has set a goal to earn 15% on the money it invests in stocks. The members are considering purchasing three possible stocks, with their cost per share (in dollars) and their projected growth per share (in dollars) summarized in the following table.

	Stocks		
	Computer (C)	Utility (U)	Retail (R)
Cost/share	30	44	26
Growth/share	6.00	6.00	2.40

(a) If they have $392,000 to invest, how many shares of each stock should they buy to meet their goal?

(b) If they buy 1000 shares of retail stock, how many shares of the other stocks should they buy? What if they buy 2000 shares of retail stock?

(c) What is the minimum number of shares of computer stock they should buy, and what is the number of shares of the other stocks in this case?

(d) What is the maximum number of shares of computer stock they should purchase, and what is the number of shares of the other stocks in this case?

62. *Investment* A trust account client has $220,000 to be invested. The investment choices have current yields of 8%, 7%, and 10%. Suppose that the investment goal is to earn interest of $16,600 and that risk factors make it prudent to invest some money in all three investments.

(a) Find a general description for the amounts invested at the three rates.

(b) If $10,000 is invested at 10%, how much should be invested at each of the other rates? What if $30,000 is invested at 10%?

(c) What is the minimum amount that should be invested at 7%, and in this case, how much should be invested at the other rates?

(d) What is the maximum amount that should be invested at 7%, and in this case, how much should be invested at the other rates?

63. *Investment* A brokerage house offers three stock portfolios. Portfolio I consists of 2 blocks of common stock and 1 municipal bond. Portfolio II consists of 4 blocks of common stock, 2 municipal bonds, and 3 blocks of preferred stock. Portfolio III consists of 2 blocks of common stock, 1 municipal bond, and 3 blocks of preferred stock. A customer wants 16 blocks of common stock, 8 municipal bonds, and 6 blocks of preferred stock. If the numbers of the three portfolios offered must be integers, find all possible offerings.

SECTION 3.4

OBJECTIVES

• To find the inverse of a square matrix

• To use inverse matrices to solve systems of linear equations

• To find determinants of certain matrices

Inverse of a Square Matrix; Matrix Equations

| APPLICATION PREVIEW |

Enigma Machine

mark higgins/Shutterstock.com

During World War II, military commanders sent instructions that used simple substitution codes. These codes were easily broken, so they were further coded using a coding matrix and matrix multiplication. The resulting coded messages, when received, could be unscrambled with a decoding matrix that was the

(Continued)

inverse matrix of the coding matrix. In Section 3.2, "Multiplication of Matrices," we encoded messages using the following code:

a	b	c	d	e	f	g	h	i	j	k	l
1	2	3	4	5	6	7	8	9	10	11	12

m	n	o	p	q	r	s	t	u	v	w	x
13	14	15	16	17	18	19	20	21	22	23	24

y	z	blank
25	26	27

and the encoding matrix

$$A = \begin{bmatrix} 3 & 5 \\ 4 & 6 \end{bmatrix}$$

which converts the numbers to the coded message (in pairs of numbers). To decode a message encoded by this matrix A, we find the inverse of matrix A, which is denoted A^{-1}, and multiply A^{-1} by the coded message. (See Example 4.) In this section, we will discuss how to find and apply the inverse of a given square matrix.

Inverse Matrices   If the product of square matrices A and B is the identity matrix, I, we say that B is the inverse of A (and A is the inverse of B). The matrix B is called the **inverse matrix** of A, denoted A^{-1}.

Inverse Matrices

> Two square matrices, A and B, are called **inverses** of each other if
>
> $$AB = I \quad \text{and} \quad BA = I$$
>
> In this case, $B = A^{-1}$ and $A = B^{-1}$.

EXAMPLE 1   Inverse Matrices

Is B the inverse of A if $A = \begin{bmatrix} 1 & 2 \\ 1 & 1 \end{bmatrix}$ and $B = \begin{bmatrix} -1 & 2 \\ 1 & -1 \end{bmatrix}$?

Solution

$$AB = \begin{bmatrix} 1 & 2 \\ 1 & 1 \end{bmatrix} \cdot \begin{bmatrix} -1 & 2 \\ 1 & -1 \end{bmatrix} = \begin{bmatrix} 1 & 0 \\ 0 & 1 \end{bmatrix} = I$$

$$BA = \begin{bmatrix} -1 & 2 \\ 1 & -1 \end{bmatrix} \cdot \begin{bmatrix} 1 & 2 \\ 1 & 1 \end{bmatrix} = \begin{bmatrix} 1 & 0 \\ 0 & 1 \end{bmatrix} = I$$

Thus B is the inverse of A, or $B = A^{-1}$. We also say that A is the inverse of B, or $A = B^{-1}$. Thus $(A^{-1})^{-1} = A$.

CHECKPOINT

1. Are the matrices A and B inverses if

$$A = \begin{bmatrix} 1 & 1 & -1 \\ 1 & -1 & 3 \\ 4 & 2 & 1 \end{bmatrix} \quad \text{and} \quad B = \begin{bmatrix} 3.5 & 1.5 & -1 \\ -5.5 & -2.5 & 2 \\ -3 & -1 & 1 \end{bmatrix}?$$

We have seen how to use elementary row operations on augmented matrices to solve systems of linear equations. We can also find the inverse of a matrix using elementary row operations.

If the inverse exists for a square matrix A, we find A^{-1} as follows.

FINDING THE INVERSE OF A SQUARE MATRIX

Procedure	Example

To find the inverse of the square matrix A:

Find the inverse of matrix $A = \begin{bmatrix} 1 & 2 \\ 1 & 1 \end{bmatrix}$.

1. Form the augmented matrix $[A|I]$, where A is the $n \times n$ matrix and I is the $n \times n$ identity matrix.

1. $\begin{bmatrix} 1 & 2 & | & 1 & 0 \\ 1 & 1 & | & 0 & 1 \end{bmatrix}$

2. Perform elementary row operations on $[A|I]$ until we have an augmented matrix of the form $[I|B]$—that is, until the matrix A on the left is transformed into the identity matrix.
    If A has no inverse, the reduction process on $[A|I]$ will yield a row of zeros in the left half of the augmented matrix.

2. $\begin{bmatrix} 1 & 2 & | & 1 & 0 \\ 1 & 1 & | & 0 & 1 \end{bmatrix}$

$\xrightarrow{-R_1 + R_2 \to R_2} \begin{bmatrix} 1 & 2 & | & 1 & 0 \\ 0 & -1 & | & -1 & 1 \end{bmatrix}$

$\xrightarrow[{-R_2 \to R_2}]{2R_2 + R_1 \to R_1} \begin{bmatrix} 1 & 0 & | & -1 & 2 \\ 0 & 1 & | & 1 & -1 \end{bmatrix}$

3. The matrix B (on the right) is the inverse of matrix A.

3. The inverse of A is $B = \begin{bmatrix} -1 & 2 \\ 1 & -1 \end{bmatrix}$.

We verified this in Example 1.

EXAMPLE 2   Finding an Inverse Matrix

Find the inverse of matrix A.

$$A = \begin{bmatrix} 2 & 5 & 4 \\ 1 & 4 & 3 \\ 1 & -3 & -2 \end{bmatrix}$$

Solution

To find the inverse of matrix A, we reduce A in $[A|I]$ (the matrix A augmented with the identity matrix I). When the left side becomes an identity matrix, the inverse is in the augment.

$\begin{bmatrix} 2 & 5 & 4 & | & 1 & 0 & 0 \\ 1 & 4 & 3 & | & 0 & 1 & 0 \\ 1 & -3 & -2 & | & 0 & 0 & 1 \end{bmatrix} \xrightarrow{\text{Switch } R_1 \text{ and } R_2} \begin{bmatrix} 1 & 4 & 3 & | & 0 & 1 & 0 \\ 2 & 5 & 4 & | & 1 & 0 & 0 \\ 1 & -3 & -2 & | & 0 & 0 & 1 \end{bmatrix}$

$\xrightarrow[{-R_1 + R_3 \to R_3}]{-2R_1 + R_2 \to R_2} \begin{bmatrix} 1 & 4 & 3 & | & 0 & 1 & 0 \\ 0 & -3 & -2 & | & 1 & -2 & 0 \\ 0 & -7 & -5 & | & 0 & -1 & 1 \end{bmatrix}$

$\xrightarrow{-\frac{1}{3}R_2 \to R_2} \begin{bmatrix} 1 & 4 & 3 & | & 0 & 1 & 0 \\ 0 & 1 & \frac{2}{3} & | & -\frac{1}{3} & \frac{2}{3} & 0 \\ 0 & -7 & -5 & | & 0 & -1 & 1 \end{bmatrix}$

$\xrightarrow[{7R_2 + R_3 \to R_3}]{-4R_2 + R_1 \to R_1} \begin{bmatrix} 1 & 0 & \frac{1}{3} & | & \frac{4}{3} & -\frac{5}{3} & 0 \\ 0 & 1 & \frac{2}{3} & | & -\frac{1}{3} & \frac{2}{3} & 0 \\ 0 & 0 & -\frac{1}{3} & | & -\frac{7}{3} & \frac{11}{3} & 1 \end{bmatrix}$

$\xrightarrow[{-3R_3 \to R_3}]{\substack{R_3 + R_1 \to R_1 \\ 2R_3 + R_2 \to R_2}} \begin{bmatrix} 1 & 0 & 0 & | & -1 & 2 & 1 \\ 0 & 1 & 0 & | & -5 & 8 & 2 \\ 0 & 0 & 1 & | & 7 & -11 & -3 \end{bmatrix}$

Thus the inverse of A is

$$A^{-1} = \begin{bmatrix} -1 & 2 & 1 \\ -5 & 8 & 2 \\ 7 & -11 & -3 \end{bmatrix}$$

Calculator Note

If the inverse of a matrix A exists, we can find it with a graphing calculator by entering $[A]$ and getting $[A]^{-1}$ by using the x^{-1} key. For example, the inverse of the matrix

$$A = \begin{bmatrix} -1 & 0 & 1 \\ 1 & 4 & -3 \\ 1 & -2 & 1 \end{bmatrix}$$

is found by entering this matrix and using the inverse key, as the following figure shows. See Appendix A, Section 3.4 for more details.

```
[A]⁻¹
  [.5  .5   1]
  [ 1  .5  .5]
  [1.5 .5   1]
■
```

$$\text{so } A^{-1} = \begin{bmatrix} \frac{1}{2} & \frac{1}{2} & 1 \\ 1 & \frac{1}{2} & \frac{1}{2} \\ \frac{3}{2} & \frac{1}{2} & 1 \end{bmatrix}$$

Spreadsheet Note

We can use Excel to find the inverse of a matrix, if it exists. To find the inverse of matrix A in the Calculator Note, we enter A's entries in cells B1:D3, select the cells B5:D7 to contain the inverse, and type =minverse(B1:D3). Holding down the CTRL and SHIFT keys while pressing ENTER gives the inverse matrix in B5:D7. Note that the inverse matrix, shown in the following spreadsheet, agrees with the one found with a graphing calculator. More details can be found in Appendix B, Section 3.4, and in the Online Excel Guide.

=minverse(B1:D3)			
	A	**B**	**C**	**D**
1	Matrix A	−1	0	1
2		1	4	−3
3		1	−2	1
4				
5	Inverse A	0.5	0.5	1
6		1	0.5	0.5
7		1.5	0.5	1

Warning: Roundoff error can occur when technology is used to find the inverse of a matrix.

CHECKPOINT

2. Find the inverse of the matrix

$$A = \begin{bmatrix} 1 & 2 & 1 \\ 0 & 1 & 1 \\ 1 & 2 & 2 \end{bmatrix}$$

The technique of reducing $[A|I]$ can be used to find A^{-1} or to find that A^{-1} doesn't exist for any square matrix A. However, a special formula can be used to find the inverse of a 2×2 matrix, if the inverse exists.

Inverse of a 2 × 2 Matrix

If $A = \begin{bmatrix} a & b \\ c & d \end{bmatrix}$, then $A^{-1} = \dfrac{1}{ad - bc} \begin{bmatrix} d & -b \\ -c & a \end{bmatrix}$, provided $ad - bc \neq 0$.

If $ad - bc = 0$, then A^{-1} does not exist.

This result can be verified by direct calculation or by reducing $[A|I]$.

| EXAMPLE | 3 | **Inverse of a 2 × 2 Matrix** |

Find the inverse, if it exists, for each of the following.

(a) $A = \begin{bmatrix} 3 & 7 \\ 2 & 5 \end{bmatrix}$ (b) $B = \begin{bmatrix} 2 & -1 \\ -4 & 2 \end{bmatrix}$

Solution

(a) For A, $ad - bc = (3)(5) - (2)(7) = 1 \neq 0$, so A^{-1} exists.

$$A^{-1} = \frac{1}{1} \begin{bmatrix} 5 & -7 \\ -2 & 3 \end{bmatrix} = \begin{bmatrix} 5 & -7 \\ -2 & 3 \end{bmatrix}$$

(b) For B, $ad - bc = (2)(2) - (-4)(-1) = 4 - 4 = 0$, so B^{-1} does not exist.

| EXAMPLE | 4 | **Decoding Messages** | APPLICATION PREVIEW |

In the Application Preview, we recalled how to encode messages with

a	b	c	d	e	f	g	h	i	j	k	l
1	2	3	4	5	6	7	8	9	10	11	12

m	n	o	p	q	r	s	t	u	v	w	x
13	14	15	16	17	18	19	20	21	22	23	24

y	z	blank
25	26	27

and with the encoding matrix

$$A = \begin{bmatrix} 3 & 5 \\ 4 & 6 \end{bmatrix}$$

which converts the numbers to the coded message (in pairs of numbers).

To decode any message encoded by A, we must find the inverse of A and multiply A^{-1} by the coded message. Use the inverse of A to decode the coded message 96, 118, 65, 84, 131, 168, 55, 72.

Solution

We first find the inverse of matrix A.

$$A^{-1} = \frac{1}{18 - 20} \begin{bmatrix} 6 & -5 \\ -4 & 3 \end{bmatrix} = -\frac{1}{2} \begin{bmatrix} 6 & -5 \\ -4 & 3 \end{bmatrix} = \begin{bmatrix} -3 & 2.5 \\ 2 & -1.5 \end{bmatrix}$$

We can write the coded message numbers (in pairs) as columns of a matrix B and then find the product $A^{-1}B$.

$$A^{-1}B = \begin{bmatrix} -3 & 2.5 \\ 2 & -1.5 \end{bmatrix} \begin{bmatrix} 96 & 65 & 131 & 55 \\ 118 & 84 & 168 & 72 \end{bmatrix} = \begin{bmatrix} 7 & 15 & 27 & 15 \\ 15 & 4 & 10 & 2 \end{bmatrix}$$

Reading the numbers (down the respective columns) gives the result 7, 15, 15, 4, 27, 10, 15, 2, which is the message "good job."

Matrix Equations   The system $\begin{cases} 2x + 5y + 4z = 4 \\ x + 4y + 3z = 1 \\ x - 3y - 2z = 5 \end{cases}$ can be written as either of the following matrix equations.

$$\begin{bmatrix} 2x + 5y + 4z \\ x + 4y + 3z \\ x - 3y - 2z \end{bmatrix} = \begin{bmatrix} 4 \\ 1 \\ 5 \end{bmatrix} \quad \text{or} \quad \begin{bmatrix} 2 & 5 & 4 \\ 1 & 4 & 3 \\ 1 & -3 & -2 \end{bmatrix} \begin{bmatrix} x \\ y \\ z \end{bmatrix} = \begin{bmatrix} 4 \\ 1 \\ 5 \end{bmatrix}$$

We can see that this second form of a matrix equation is equivalent to the first if we carry out the multiplication. With the system written in this second form, we can solve the system by multiplying both sides of the equation by the inverse of the coefficient matrix.

EXAMPLE 5   Solution with Inverse Matrices

Use an inverse matrix to solve the system.

$$\begin{cases} 2x + 5y + 4z = 4 \\ x + 4y + 3z = 1 \\ x - 3y - 2z = 5 \end{cases}$$

Solution

To solve the system, we multiply both sides of the associated matrix equation (written on the previous page) by the inverse of the coefficient matrix, which we found in Example 2.

$$\begin{bmatrix} -1 & 2 & 1 \\ -5 & 8 & 2 \\ 7 & -11 & -3 \end{bmatrix} \begin{bmatrix} 2 & 5 & 4 \\ 1 & 4 & 3 \\ 1 & -3 & -2 \end{bmatrix} \begin{bmatrix} x \\ y \\ z \end{bmatrix} = \begin{bmatrix} -1 & 2 & 1 \\ -5 & 8 & 2 \\ 7 & -11 & -3 \end{bmatrix} \begin{bmatrix} 4 \\ 1 \\ 5 \end{bmatrix}$$

Note that we must be careful to multiply both sides *from the left* because matrix multiplication is not commutative. If we carry out the multiplications, we obtain

$$\begin{bmatrix} 1 & 0 & 0 \\ 0 & 1 & 0 \\ 0 & 0 & 1 \end{bmatrix} \begin{bmatrix} x \\ y \\ z \end{bmatrix} = \begin{bmatrix} 3 \\ -2 \\ 2 \end{bmatrix}, \text{ or } \begin{bmatrix} x \\ y \\ z \end{bmatrix} = \begin{bmatrix} 3 \\ -2 \\ 2 \end{bmatrix}$$

which yields $x = 3, y = -2, z = 2$, the same solution as that found in the previous section.

Just as we wrote the system of three equations as a matrix equation of the form $AX = B$, this can be done in general. If A is an $n \times n$ matrix and if B and X are $n \times 1$ matrices, then

$$AX = B$$

is a **matrix equation.**

If the inverse of a matrix A exists, then we can use A^{-1} to solve the matrix equation $AX = B$ for X by multiplying both sides of the equation (from the left) by A^{-1}. Thus

$$AX = B \Rightarrow A^{-1}(AX) = A^{-1}B$$

Because $A^{-1}A = I$, this can be simplified to obtain the following.

If $AX = B$ and A^{-1} exists, then $X = A^{-1}B$.

Thus inverse matrices can be used to solve systems of equations. Unfortunately, this method will work only if the solution to the system is unique. In fact, a system $AX = B$ has a unique solution if and only if A^{-1} exists. If the inverse of the coefficient matrix exists, the solution method above can be used to solve the system.

CHECKPOINT   3. Use inverse matrices to solve the system.

$$\begin{cases} 7x - 5y = 12 \\ 2x - 3y = 6 \end{cases}$$

Calculator Note   Because we often can find the inverse of a matrix with a graphing calculator, it is easy to use a graphing calculator to solve a system of linear equations using the inverse of the coefficient matrix. This will be demonstrated in the following example.

EXAMPLE 6   Freight Logistics with Technology

On-Time Freight carries three classes of cargo (I, II, and III) and sets its delivery rates according to the class. The following table gives the details of each class and On-Time's capacity limits.

	Class I	Class II	Class III	Limits
Volume (cubic feet)	25	20	50	15,000
Weight (pounds)	25	50	100	27,500
Insured value (dollars)	2500	500	5000	922,500

(a) Create a system of linear equations that could be used to find the number of units of each cargo class that should be hauled. Then use the inverse of the coefficient matrix to solve the system.

(b) Use the inverse from part (a) to find how to change the hauling decision if an additional 300 cubic feet of volume becomes available.

(c) What is the connection between column 1 of the inverse matrix used in parts (a) and (b) and the answer found in part (b)?

Solution

(a) Let x = the number of units of class I cargo
y = the number of units of class II cargo
z = the number of units of class III cargo
Then we can formulate the following system of equations:

$$25x + 20y + 50z = 15,000$$
$$25x + 50y + 100z = 27,500$$
$$2500x + 500y + 5000z = 922,500$$

The matrix equation for this system is $AX = B$, as follows:

$$AX = \begin{bmatrix} 25 & 20 & 50 \\ 25 & 50 & 100 \\ 2500 & 500 & 5000 \end{bmatrix} \begin{bmatrix} x \\ y \\ z \end{bmatrix} = \begin{bmatrix} 15,000 \\ 27,500 \\ 922,500 \end{bmatrix} = B$$

We use technology to find the inverse of the coefficient matrix, A. If we multiply both sides (from the left) by A^{-1}, we get $X = A^{-1}B$. (See Figure 3.9.)

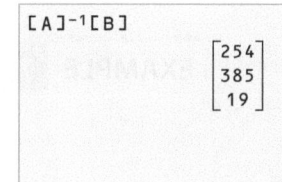

Figure 3.9

Thus the solution is $x = 254$ units of class I cargo, $y = 385$ units of class II cargo, and $z = 19$ units of class III cargo.

(b) The additional 300 cubic feet of cargo space changes only the first entry of B. The new B and the new solution, $A^{-1}B$, are shown in Figures 3.10(a) and (b).

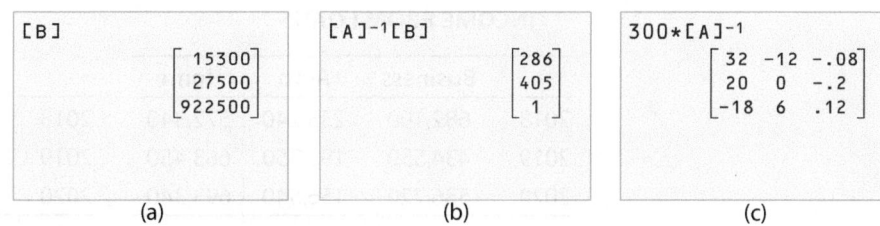

Figure 3.10   (a)   (b)   (c)

(c) Figure 3.10(c) shows the matrix $300[A^{-1}]$, whose column 1 gives the amount that the original solution is changed to get the new solution.

$$[\text{original } X] + 300[\text{column 1 of } A^{-1}] = \begin{bmatrix} 254 \\ 385 \\ 19 \end{bmatrix} + \begin{bmatrix} 32 \\ 20 \\ -18 \end{bmatrix} = \begin{bmatrix} 286 \\ 405 \\ 1 \end{bmatrix}$$

The relationship observed here is true in general about A^{-1}. Namely, if a resource quantity is increased by k in a row of the augment, the new solution has entries that equal the old solution increased by the amounts in the corresponding column of kA^{-1}.

Spreadsheet Note We can use Excel to solve a system of linear equations if a unique solution exists. We can solve such a system by finding the inverse of the coefficient matrix and multiplying this inverse times the matrix containing the constants. The spreadsheet that follows shows the solution of Example 5. See Appendix B, Section 3.4, or the Online Excel Guide.

	A	B	C	D
1	Matrix A	2	5	4
2		1	4	3
3		1	−3	−2
4				
5	Inverse A	−1	2	1
6		−5	8	2
7		7	−11	−3
8				
9	Matrix B	4		
10		1		
11		5		
12				
13	Solution X	3		
14		−2		
15		2		

EXAMPLE   7   Investment Banking

Suppose a bank draws its investment funds from three main sources of income—business loans, auto loans, and home mortgages. The income from these sources for each of 3 years is given in Table 3.7, and the investment funds for these years are given in Table 3.8. If the bank uses a fixed percent of its income from each of the business loans (x), auto loans (y), and home mortgages (z) to get its investment funds, find the percent of income used for each of these sources of income.

TABLE 3.7

INCOME FROM LOANS

	Business	Auto	Home
2018	682,100	233,240	572,340
2019	434,550	193,350	663,450
2020	586,720	156,540	693,340

TABLE 3.8

	Investment Funds
2018	534,487.40
2019	434,475.00
2020	505,897.80

Solution

The matrix equation describing this problem is $AX = F$, or

$$
\begin{bmatrix}
682{,}100 & 233{,}240 & 572{,}340 \\
434{,}550 & 193{,}350 & 663{,}450 \\
586{,}720 & 156{,}540 & 693{,}340
\end{bmatrix}
\begin{bmatrix} x \\ y \\ z \end{bmatrix}
=
\begin{bmatrix}
534{,}487.40 \\
434{,}475.00 \\
505{,}897.80
\end{bmatrix}
$$

Finding the inverse of matrix A and multiplying both sides of the matrix equation (from the left) by A^{-1} give the solution $X = A^{-1}F$:

$$
\begin{bmatrix} x \\ y \\ z \end{bmatrix}
=
\begin{bmatrix} 0.47 \\ 0.23 \\ 0.28 \end{bmatrix}
$$

Thus 47%, 23%, and 28% come from business, auto, and home loans, respectively. ■

Determinants Recall that the inverse of $A = \begin{bmatrix} a & b \\ c & d \end{bmatrix}$ can be found using the formula

$$
A^{-1} = \frac{1}{ad - bc} \begin{bmatrix} d & -b \\ -c & a \end{bmatrix}
$$

if $ad - bc \neq 0$.

The value $ad - bc$ used in finding the inverse of this 2×2 matrix is used so frequently that it is given a special name: the **determinant** of A (denoted $det\ A$ or $|A|$).

**Determinant of a
2 × 2 Matrix**

$$
det \begin{bmatrix} a & b \\ c & d \end{bmatrix} = \begin{vmatrix} a & b \\ c & d \end{vmatrix} = ad - bc
$$

EXAMPLE 8 **Determinant of a 2 × 2 Matrix**

Find $det\ A$ if $A = \begin{bmatrix} 2 & 4 \\ 3 & -4 \end{bmatrix}$.

Solution

$$
det\ A = (2)(-4) - (3)(4) = -8 - 12 = -20
$$

We have already seen that the inverse of a 2×2 matrix A does not exist if $det\ A = 0$. In general, the inverse of an $n \times n$ matrix B does not exist if $det\ B = 0$. This also means that if the coefficient matrix of a system of linear equations has a determinant equal to 0, the system does not have a unique solution.

Calculator Note   There are different formulas for finding the determinants of square matrices of orders larger than 2×2. But for the matrices used in this text, graphing calculators make it easy to find determinants. (See Example 9.) ■

EXAMPLE 9 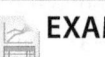 **Solution with Technology**

Consider the following matrix equation $AX = B$.

$$
\begin{bmatrix}
2 & 3 & 0 & 1 & 3 \\
1 & 0 & 2 & 3 & 1 \\
0 & 1 & 0 & 2 & 3 \\
1 & 0 & 2 & 2 & 1 \\
1 & 0 & 0 & 0 & 3
\end{bmatrix}
\begin{bmatrix} x_1 \\ x_2 \\ x_3 \\ x_4 \\ x_5 \end{bmatrix}
=
\begin{bmatrix} 16 \\ 2 \\ 9 \\ 3 \\ 10 \end{bmatrix}
$$

(a) Use a calculator to find the determinant of A.

(b) Use the result from part (a) to determine whether $AX = B$ has a unique solution.

Solution

(a) To find the determinant of a square matrix A with a graphing calculator, select MATRIX, move to MATH, and select 1:det. This gives det(. Selecting MATRIX [A] gives det ([A]); pressing ENTER gives the determinant of matrix A. Thus,

$$\det(A) = 24.$$

See Appendix A, Section 3.4, for details.

(b) Note that A is the coefficient matrix for the system and det $A = 24$. Because det $A \neq 0$, A^{-1} exists and the system has a unique solution. Using the inverse matrix gives the solution $x_1 = 1$, $x_2 = 2$, $x_3 = 0.5$, $x_4 = -1$, $x_5 = 3$.

CHECKPOINT
ANSWERS

1. Yes, because both AB and BA give the 3×3 identity matrix.

2. $A^{-1} = \begin{bmatrix} 0 & -2 & 1 \\ 1 & 1 & -1 \\ -1 & 0 & 1 \end{bmatrix}$

3. For $\begin{bmatrix} 7 & -5 \\ 2 & -3 \end{bmatrix} \begin{bmatrix} x \\ y \end{bmatrix} = \begin{bmatrix} 12 \\ 6 \end{bmatrix}$, $A^{-1} = \begin{bmatrix} \frac{3}{11} & -\frac{5}{11} \\ \frac{2}{11} & -\frac{7}{11} \end{bmatrix}$

The solution is $x = \frac{6}{11}$, $y = -\frac{18}{11}$.

EXERCISES 3.4

1. If A is a 3×3 matrix and B is its inverse, what does the product AB equal?

2. If $C = \begin{bmatrix} 2 & -4 & 12 \\ 0 & 6 & -12 \\ 1 & -2 & 3 \end{bmatrix}$ and

$D = \dfrac{1}{6}\begin{bmatrix} 1 & 2 & 4 \\ 2 & 1 & -4 \\ 1 & 0 & -2 \end{bmatrix}$, are C and D inverse matrices?

3. If $A = \begin{bmatrix} 1 & 2 & 1 \\ 0 & 0 & 3 \\ 1 & 0 & 1 \end{bmatrix}$ and $B = \begin{bmatrix} 0 & -\frac{1}{3} & 1 \\ \frac{1}{2} & 0 & -\frac{1}{2} \\ 0 & \frac{1}{3} & 0 \end{bmatrix}$,

does $B = A^{-1}$?

4. If $D = \begin{bmatrix} 3 & -2 & 3 \\ 3 & 2 & -3 \\ 0 & 2 & 0 \end{bmatrix}$ and $C = \dfrac{1}{3}\begin{bmatrix} 1 & 1 & 0 \\ 0 & 0 & 3 \\ 1 & -1 & 2 \end{bmatrix}$,

does $C = D^{-1}$?

In Problems 5–10, find the inverse matrix for each matrix that has an inverse.

5. $\begin{bmatrix} 4 & 7 \\ 1 & 2 \end{bmatrix}$
6. $\begin{bmatrix} 4 & 5 \\ 7 & 9 \end{bmatrix}$
7. $\begin{bmatrix} 2 & -1 \\ -4 & 2 \end{bmatrix}$

8. $\begin{bmatrix} 3 & 12 \\ 1 & 4 \end{bmatrix}$
9. $\begin{bmatrix} 4 & 7 \\ 2 & 1 \end{bmatrix}$
10. $\begin{bmatrix} 6 & -4 \\ -1 & 1 \end{bmatrix}$

In Problems 11–14, find the inverse of matrix A and check it by calculating AA^{-1}.

11. $A = \begin{bmatrix} 3 & 0 & 0 \\ 0 & 3 & 2 \\ 0 & 0 & 1 \end{bmatrix}$
12. $A = \begin{bmatrix} 4 & 0 & 8 \\ 0 & 3 & 0 \\ 0 & 0 & 1 \end{bmatrix}$

13. $A = \begin{bmatrix} 0 & 1 & 0 \\ 1 & 1 & 0 \\ 0 & 1 & 1 \end{bmatrix}$
14. $A = \begin{bmatrix} 0 & 2 & 1 \\ 3 & 0 & 1 \\ 1 & 1 & 1 \end{bmatrix}$

In Problems 15–20, find the inverse matrix for each matrix that has an inverse.

15. $\begin{bmatrix} 3 & 1 & 2 \\ 1 & 2 & 3 \\ 1 & 1 & 1 \end{bmatrix}$
16. $\begin{bmatrix} 1 & 2 & 3 \\ -1 & 5 & 6 \\ -1 & 3 & 3 \end{bmatrix}$

17. $\begin{bmatrix} 1 & 3 & 5 \\ -1 & -1 & 2 \\ 1 & 5 & 12 \end{bmatrix}$
18. $\begin{bmatrix} 1 & -1 & 4 \\ -1 & 0 & -2 \\ -1 & -3 & 4 \end{bmatrix}$

19. $\begin{bmatrix} 1 & 2 & 4 \\ 1 & -1 & -3 \\ 2 & 1 & 1 \end{bmatrix}$
20. $\begin{bmatrix} 3 & 4 & -1 \\ 4 & 2 & 2 \\ 2 & 6 & -4 \end{bmatrix}$

21. Find the inverse of

$$C = \begin{bmatrix} 1 & 1 & 0 & -1 & 0 \\ 1 & 2 & -1 & -2 & 0 \\ 1 & 3.5 & -2 & -2.5 & -0.5 \\ 2 & 2.5 & -2 & 1.5 & -1.5 \\ 1 & 3 & -1 & -3 & 0 \end{bmatrix}$$

 22. Find the inverse of $B = \begin{bmatrix} 2 & 3 & 0 & 1 & 3 \\ 3 & 3 & 2 & 4 & 4 \\ 0 & 1 & 0 & 2 & 3 \\ 2 & 2 & 1 & 3 & 5 \\ 1 & 1 & 0.5 & 1 & 1.5 \end{bmatrix}$.

In Problems 23–26, the inverse of matrix A is given. Use the inverse to solve for X.

23. $A^{-1} = \begin{bmatrix} 3 & 2 \\ 1 & 1 \end{bmatrix}$ Solve $AX = \begin{bmatrix} 3 \\ 2 \end{bmatrix}$.

24. $A^{-1} = \begin{bmatrix} 1 & -2 \\ 1 & 3 \end{bmatrix}$ Solve $AX = \begin{bmatrix} 5 \\ -1 \end{bmatrix}$.

25. $A^{-1} = \begin{bmatrix} 3 & 2 & 1 \\ 1 & 1 & 2 \\ 1 & 2 & 1 \end{bmatrix}$ Solve $AX = \begin{bmatrix} 3 \\ -1 \\ 2 \end{bmatrix}$.

26. $A^{-1} = \begin{bmatrix} 3 & 0 & -3 \\ 1 & 1 & 2 \\ 1 & 2 & 1 \end{bmatrix}$ Solve $AX = \begin{bmatrix} -1 \\ 2 \\ 3 \end{bmatrix}$.

27. Use the inverse found in Problem 13 to solve

$$\begin{bmatrix} 0 & 1 & 0 \\ 1 & 1 & 0 \\ 0 & 1 & 1 \end{bmatrix} \begin{bmatrix} x \\ y \\ z \end{bmatrix} = \begin{bmatrix} 1 \\ 2 \\ 3 \end{bmatrix}$$

28. Use the inverse found in Problem 14 to solve

$$\begin{bmatrix} 0 & 2 & 1 \\ 3 & 0 & 1 \\ 1 & 1 & 1 \end{bmatrix} \begin{bmatrix} x \\ y \\ z \end{bmatrix} = \begin{bmatrix} 1 \\ 0 \\ 4 \end{bmatrix}$$

In Problems 29–32, use inverse matrices to solve each system of linear equations.

29. $\begin{cases} x + 2y = 4 \\ 3x + 4y = 10 \end{cases}$

30. $\begin{cases} 3x - 4y = 11 \\ 2x + 3y = -4 \end{cases}$

31. $\begin{cases} 2x + y = 4 \\ 3x + y = 5 \end{cases}$

32. $\begin{cases} 5x - 2y = 6 \\ 3x + 3y = 12 \end{cases}$

 In Problems 33–38, use inverse matrices to find the solution of the systems of equations.

33. $\begin{cases} x + y + z = 3 \\ 2x + y + z = 4 \\ 2x + 2y + z = 5 \end{cases}$

34. $\begin{cases} 2x - y - 2z = 2 \\ 3x - y + z = -3 \\ x + y - z = 7 \end{cases}$

35. $\begin{cases} x + y + 2z = 8 \\ 2x + y + z = 7 \\ 2x + 2y + z = 10 \end{cases}$

36. $\begin{cases} x - 2y + z = 0 \\ 2x + y - 2z = 2 \\ 3x + 2y - 3z = 2 \end{cases}$

37. $\begin{cases} -x_2 + x_4 = 0.7 \\ x_1 + x_2 - x_3 - 1.5x_4 - 0.5x_5 = -1.6 \\ 0.5x_1 + 1.75x_2 - x_3 - 1.25x_4 - 0.25x_5 = 1.275 \\ -0.5x_1 - x_2 + x_3 + x_4 = 1.15 \\ 0.5x_2 - 0.5x_4 + 0.5x_5 = -0.15 \end{cases}$

38. $\begin{cases} 2x_1 + 3x_2 + x_4 + 3x_5 = 0 \\ x_1 + 2x_3 + 3x_4 + x_5 = 27 \\ x_2 + 2x_4 + 3x_5 = -15 \\ x_1 + 2x_3 + 2x_4 + x_5 = 24 \\ x_1 + 3x_5 = -24 \end{cases}$

In Problems 39–46, (a) evaluate each determinant and (b) use the determinant to decide whether each matrix has an inverse. Use technology in Problems 43–46.

39. $\begin{vmatrix} 1 & 2 \\ 3 & 4 \end{vmatrix}$

40. $\begin{vmatrix} 4 & 5 \\ -1 & -2 \end{vmatrix}$

41. $\begin{vmatrix} 3 & -1 \\ 12 & -4 \end{vmatrix}$

42. $\begin{vmatrix} -1 & 2 \\ 4 & -8 \end{vmatrix}$

43. $\begin{vmatrix} 3 & 2 & 1 \\ -1 & 0 & 2 \\ 0 & 1 & 1 \end{vmatrix}$

44. $\begin{vmatrix} 1 & 2 & 2 \\ 3 & 0 & 1 \\ -1 & 0 & -2 \end{vmatrix}$

45. $\begin{vmatrix} 0 & 1 & 2 \\ 3 & 1 & 1 \\ 4 & -1 & 3 \end{vmatrix}$

46. $\begin{vmatrix} 3 & 1 & 4 & 2 \\ -1 & 2 & 0 & 5 \\ 4 & 3 & 0 & -1 \\ 0 & 4 & 2 & 1 \end{vmatrix}$

APPLICATIONS

Decoding **In Problems 47–50, use the code from the Application Preview and the given encoding matrix A to decode the given message.**

47. If the code matrix is

$$A = \begin{bmatrix} 5 & 9 \\ 6 & 11 \end{bmatrix}$$

decode the message

$$49, 59, 133, 161, 270, 327, 313, 381$$

48. If the code matrix is

$$A = \begin{bmatrix} 3 & 5 \\ 1 & 2 \end{bmatrix}$$

decode the message

$$157, 59, 73, 29, 147, 58, 63, 24, 119, 44$$

49. If the code matrix is

$$A = \begin{bmatrix} 0 & 2 & 1 \\ 3 & 0 & 1 \\ 1 & 1 & 1 \end{bmatrix}$$

decode the message

47, 22, 34, 28, 87, 46, 63, 66, 55, 56, 44, 43, 17, 14, 15

(Because A and A^{-1} are 3×3 matrices, use triples of numbers.)

50. If the code matrix is

$$A = \begin{bmatrix} 1 & 2 & 1 \\ 5 & 8 & 2 \\ 7 & 11 & 3 \end{bmatrix}$$

decode the message

49, 165, 231, 49, 154, 220, 39, 162, 226

51. *Competition* A product is made by only two competing companies. Suppose Company X retains two-thirds of its customers and loses one-third to Company Y each year, and Company Y retains three-quarters of its customers and loses one-quarter to Company X each year. We can represent the number of customers each company had last year by

$$\begin{bmatrix} x_0 \\ y_0 \end{bmatrix}$$

where x_0 is the number Company X had and y_0 is the number Company Y had. Then the number that each will have this year can be represented by

$$\begin{bmatrix} x \\ y \end{bmatrix} = \begin{bmatrix} \frac{2}{3} & \frac{1}{4} \\ \frac{1}{3} & \frac{3}{4} \end{bmatrix} \begin{bmatrix} x_0 \\ y_0 \end{bmatrix}$$

If Company X has 1900 customers and Company Y has 1700 customers this year, how many customers did each have last year?

52. *Demographics* Suppose that a government study showed that 90% of urban families remained in an urban area in the next generation (and 10% moved to a rural area), whereas 70% of rural families remained in a rural area in the next generation (and 30% moved to an urban area). This means that if $\begin{bmatrix} u_0 \\ r_0 \end{bmatrix}$ represents the current percents of urban families, u_0, and of rural families, r_0, then

$$\begin{bmatrix} u \\ r \end{bmatrix} = \begin{bmatrix} 0.90 & 0.30 \\ 0.10 & 0.70 \end{bmatrix} \begin{bmatrix} u_0 \\ r_0 \end{bmatrix}$$

represents the percents of urban families, u, and rural families, r, one generation from now. Currently the population is 60% urban and 40% rural. Find the percents in each group one generation before this one.

In Problems 53–63, set up each system of equations and then solve it using inverse matrices.

53. *Medication* Medication A is given every 4 hours, and medication B is given twice per day; the ratio of the dosage of A to the dosage of B is always 5 to 8.
    (a) For patient I, the total intake of the two medications is 50.6 mg per day. Find the dosage of each administration of each medication for patient I.
    (b) For patient II, the total intake of the two medications is 92 mg per day. Find the dosage of each administration of each medication for patient II.

54. *Transportation* Ace Freight Company has an order for two products to be delivered to two stores of a company. The table gives information regarding the two products.

	Product I	Product II
Unit volume (cu ft)	20	30
Unit weight (lb)	100	400

    (a) If truck A can carry 2350 cu ft and 23,000 lb, how many of each product can it carry?
    (b) If truck B can carry 2500 cu ft and 24,500 lb, how many of each product can it carry?

55. *Investment* One safe investment pays 10% per year, and a more risky investment pays 18% per year. A woman has $145,600 to invest and would like to have an income of $20,000 per year from her investments. How much should she invest at each rate?

56. *Nutrition* A biologist has a 40% solution and a 10% solution of the same plant nutrient. How many cubic centimeters of each solution should be mixed to obtain 25 cc of a 28% solution?

57. *Manufacturing* A manufacturer of table saws has three models (Deluxe, Premium, and Ultimate) that must be painted, assembled, and packaged for shipping. The table gives the number of hours required for each of these operations for each type of table saw.
    (a) If the manufacturer has 96 hours available per day for painting, 156 hours for assembly, and 37 hours for packaging, how many of each type of saw can be produced each day?

(b) If 8 more hours of painting time become available, find the new production strategy and explain how it is related to the inverse matrix used in part (a).

	Deluxe	Premium	Ultimate
Painting	1.6	2	2.4
Assembly	2	3	4
Packaging	0.5	0.5	1

58. *Transportation* Ace Trucking Company has an order for three products (A, B, and C) for delivery. The table gives the volume in cubic feet, the weight in pounds, and the value for insurance in dollars for a unit of each of the products.
    (a) If each truck can carry 8000 cu ft and 12,400 lb and is insured for $526,000, how many units of each product can be carried?
    (b) If the insured value increases by $64,000, find the new delivery scheme and explain how it is related to the inverse matrix used in (a).

	Product A	Product B	Product C
Unit volume (cu ft)	24	20	40
Weight (lb)	40	30	60
Value ($)	1500	1800	2000

59. *Investment* A trust account manager has $1,000,000 to be invested in three different accounts. The accounts pay 6%, 8%, and 10%, and the goal is to earn $86,000 per year with the amount invested at 10% equal to the sum of the other two investments. To accomplish this, assume that x dollars are invested at 8%, y dollars at 10%, and z dollars at 6%. Find how much should be invested in each account to satisfy the conditions.

60. *Investment* A company offers three mutual fund plans for its employees. Plan I consists of 4 blocks of common stock and 2 municipal bonds. Plan II consists of 8 blocks of common stock, 4 municipal bonds, and 6 blocks of preferred stock. Plan III consists of 14 blocks of common stock, 6 municipal bonds, and 6 blocks of preferred stock. An employee wants to combine these plans so that she has 84 blocks of common stock, 40 municipal bonds, and 36 blocks of preferred stock. How many units of each plan does she need?

61. *Attendance* Suppose that during the first 2 weeks of a controversial art exhibit, the daily number of visitors to the gallery is the sum of the numbers of visitors on the previous 3 days. We represent the numbers of visitors on 3 successive days by

$$N = \begin{bmatrix} n_t \\ n_{t+1} \\ n_{t+2} \end{bmatrix}$$

(a) Find the matrix M such that

$$MN = \begin{bmatrix} n_{t+1} \\ n_{t+2} \\ n_t + n_{t+1} + n_{t+2} \end{bmatrix}$$

(b) If the numbers of visitors on 3 successive days are given by

$$\begin{bmatrix} 191 \\ 346 \\ 645 \end{bmatrix}$$

use M^{-1} to find the number of visitors 1 day earlier (before the 191-visitor day).

62. *Bee ancestry* Because a female bee comes from a fertilized egg and a male bee comes from an unfertilized egg, the number (n_{t+2}) of ancestors of a male bee $t + 2$ generations before the present generation is the sum of the number of ancestors t and $t + 1$ generations (n_t and n_{t+1}) before the present. If the numbers of ancestors of a male bee in a given generation t and in the previous generation are given by

$$N = \begin{bmatrix} n_t \\ n_{t+1} \end{bmatrix}$$

then there is a matrix M such that the numbers of ancestors in the two generations preceding generation t are given by

$$MN = \begin{bmatrix} 0 & 1 \\ 1 & 1 \end{bmatrix} \begin{bmatrix} n_t \\ n_{t+1} \end{bmatrix} = \begin{bmatrix} n_{t+1} \\ n_t + n_{t+1} \end{bmatrix}$$

For a given male bee, the numbers of ancestors 5 and 6 generations back are given by

$$\begin{bmatrix} 8 \\ 13 \end{bmatrix}$$

Find the numbers of ancestors 4 and 5 generations back by multiplying both sides of

$$MN = \begin{bmatrix} 8 \\ 13 \end{bmatrix}$$

by the inverse of M.

SECTION 3.5

Applications of Matrices: Leontief Input-Output Models

OBJECTIVES

- To interpret Leontief technology matrices
- To use Leontief models to solve input-output problems

APPLICATION PREVIEW

Suppose a simple economy is based on three industries (agricultural products, manufactured goods, and fuels), and in this economy each industry uses outputs from the other industries as inputs for its own production. Table 3.9 summarizes this interdependency for each industry in terms of the various inputs required for 1 unit of production (output).

The first column represents the units of agricultural products, manufactured goods, and fuels that are needed to produce 1 unit of agricultural products. Column 2 represents the units required to produce 1 unit of manufactured goods, and column 3 represents the units required to produce 1 unit of fuels.

TABLE 3.9

| | Outputs | | |
Inputs	Agricultural Products	Manufactured Goods	Fuels
Agricultural products	0.5	0.1	0.1
Manufactured goods	0.2	0.5	0.3
Fuels	0.1	0.3	0.4

From Table 3.9, we can form matrix A, which is called a **technology matrix** or a Leontief matrix.

$$A = \begin{bmatrix} 0.5 & 0.1 & 0.1 \\ 0.2 & 0.5 & 0.3 \\ 0.1 & 0.3 & 0.4 \end{bmatrix}$$

We can use matrix A to determine the production levels necessary in each industry in this economy to provide a specified level of surpluses for sale or export. (See Example 2.)

Leontief input-output models are named for Wassily Leontief. In this section, we will interpret Leontief technology matrices for simple economies and solve input-output problems for these economies using Leontief models.

Leontief's original work with input-output models divided the economy into 500 sectors which, in a subsequent article in *Scientific American* (October 1951), were reduced to a more manageable 42 departments of production. The model Leontief developed was useful in predicting the effects on the economy of price changes or shifts in government spending.*

In Table 3.9, we note that the sum of the units of agricultural products, manufactured goods, and fuels required to produce 1 unit of fuels (column 3) does not add up to 1 unit. This is because not all commodities or industries are represented in the model. In particular, it is customary to omit labor from models of this type.

---

*Leontief's work dealt with a massive analysis of the American economy. He was awarded a Nobel Prize in economics in 1973 for his study.

EXAMPLE **1**   **Leontief Model**

Use Table 3.9 on the previous page to answer the following questions.
(a) How many units of agricultural products and of fuels are required to produce 100 units of manufactured goods?
(b) Production of which commodity is least dependent on the other two?
(c) If fuel costs rise, which two industries will be most affected?

Solution
(a) Referring to column 2, manufactured goods, we see that 1 unit requires 0.1 unit of agricultural products and 0.3 unit of fuels. Thus 100 units of manufactured goods require 10 units of agricultural products and 30 units of fuels.
(b) Looking down the columns, we see that 1 unit of agricultural products requires 0.3 unit of the other two commodities, 1 unit of manufactured goods requires 0.4 unit of the other two, and 1 unit of fuels requires 0.4 unit of the other two. Thus production of agricultural products is least dependent on the others.
(c) A rise in the cost of fuels would most affect those industries that use the larger amounts of fuels. One unit of agricultural products requires 0.1 unit of fuels, whereas a unit of manufactured goods requires 0.3 unit, and a unit of fuels requires 0.4 of its own units. Thus manufacturing and the fuel industry would be most affected by a cost increase in fuels.

CHECKPOINT

The following technology matrix for a simple economy describes the relationship of certain industries to each other in the production of 1 unit of product.

	Ag	Mfg	Fuels	Util
Agriculture	0.32	0.06	0.09	0.06
Manufacturing	0.11	0.41	0.19	0.31
Fuels	0.31	0.14	0.18	0.20
Utilities	0.18	0.26	0.21	0.25

1. Which industry is most dependent on its own goods for its operation?
2. How many units of fuels are required to produce 100 units of utilities?

Open Leontief Model

For a simplified model of the economy, such as that described in Table 3.9, not all information is contained within the technology matrix. In particular, each industry has a gross production. The **gross production matrix** for the economy can be represented by the column matrix

$$X = \begin{bmatrix} x_1 \\ x_2 \\ x_3 \end{bmatrix}$$

where x_1 is the gross production of agricultural products, x_2 is the gross production of manufactured goods, and x_3 is the gross production of fuels.

The amounts of the gross productions (outputs) used within the economy by the various industries are given by AX. Those units of gross production not used by these industries are called **final demands** or **surpluses** and are considered as being available for consumers, the government, or export. If we place these surpluses in a column matrix D, then they can be represented by the equation

$$X - AX = D, \text{ or } (I - A)X = D$$

where I is an identity matrix of appropriate size. This matrix equation is called the **technological equation** for an **open Leontief model.** This is called an open model because some of the goods from the economy are "open," or available to those outside the economy.

Open Leontief Model

The technological equation for an open Leontief model is

$$(I - A)X = D$$

where A is the technology matrix, X is the gross production matrix, and D is the final demands matrix.

EXAMPLE 2   Gross Outputs | APPLICATION PREVIEW |

Technology matrix A represents a simple economy with an agricultural industry, a manufacturing industry, and a fuels industry (as introduced in Table 3.9). If we want to have surpluses of 85 units of agricultural products, 65 units of manufactured goods, and 0 units of fuels, what should the gross outputs be?

$$A = \begin{bmatrix} 0.5 & 0.1 & 0.1 \\ 0.2 & 0.5 & 0.3 \\ 0.1 & 0.3 & 0.4 \end{bmatrix}$$

Solution

Let X be the matrix of gross outputs for the industries and let D be the column matrix of each industry's surpluses. Then the technological equation is $(I - A)X = D$. We begin by finding the matrix $I - A$.

$$I - A = \begin{bmatrix} 1 & 0 & 0 \\ 0 & 1 & 0 \\ 0 & 0 & 1 \end{bmatrix} - \begin{bmatrix} 0.5 & 0.1 & 0.1 \\ 0.2 & 0.5 & 0.3 \\ 0.1 & 0.3 & 0.4 \end{bmatrix} = \begin{bmatrix} 0.5 & -0.1 & -0.1 \\ -0.2 & 0.5 & -0.3 \\ -0.1 & -0.3 & 0.6 \end{bmatrix}$$

To find the desired surpluses, we must solve the matrix equation

$$\begin{bmatrix} 0.5 & -0.1 & -0.1 \\ -0.2 & 0.5 & -0.3 \\ -0.1 & -0.3 & 0.6 \end{bmatrix} \begin{bmatrix} x_1 \\ x_2 \\ x_3 \end{bmatrix} = \begin{bmatrix} 85 \\ 65 \\ 0 \end{bmatrix}$$

The augmented matrix is

$$\left[\begin{array}{ccc|c} 0.5 & -0.1 & -0.1 & 85 \\ -0.2 & 0.5 & -0.3 & 65 \\ -0.1 & -0.3 & 0.6 & 0 \end{array} \right]$$

If we reduce by the methods of Section 3.3, "Gauss-Jordan Elimination: Solving Systems of Equations," we obtain

$$\left[\begin{array}{ccc|c} 1 & 0 & 0 & 300 \\ 0 & 1 & 0 & 400 \\ 0 & 0 & 1 & 250 \end{array} \right]$$

So the gross outputs for the industries are

Agriculture: $x_1 = 300$
Manufacturing: $x_2 = 400$
Fuels: $x_3 = 250$

In general, the technological equation for the open Leontief model can be solved using the inverse of $I - A$. That is,

$$(I - A)X = D \quad \text{has the solution} \quad X = (I - A)^{-1}D$$

Calculator Note   If we have the technology matrix A and the surplus matrix D, we can solve the technological equation for an open Leontief model with a graphing calculator by defining matrices I, A, and D and evaluating $X = (I - A)^{-1}D$. Figure 3.11 shows the solution of Example 2 using a graphing calculator; it agrees with the solution found there.

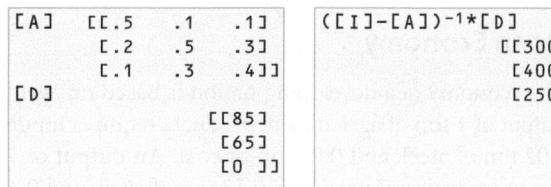

Figure 3.11

EXAMPLE 3 Production

A primitive economy with a lumber industry and a power industry has the following technology matrix.

$$A = \begin{bmatrix} \overset{\text{Lumber}}{0.1} & \overset{\text{Power}}{0.2} \\ 0.2 & 0.4 \end{bmatrix} \begin{matrix} \text{Lumber} \\ \text{Power} \end{matrix}$$

(a) If surpluses of 30 units of lumber and 70 units of power are desired, find the gross production of each industry.

(b) If an additional 5 units of surplus power were required, how much additional output would be required from each industry?

Solution

(a) Let x be the gross production of lumber and let y be the gross production of power. Then

$$I - A = \begin{bmatrix} 0.9 & -0.2 \\ -0.2 & 0.6 \end{bmatrix}, \ X = \begin{bmatrix} x \\ y \end{bmatrix}, \text{ and } D = \begin{bmatrix} 30 \\ 70 \end{bmatrix}$$

We must solve the matrix equation $(I - A)X = D$ for X, and we can do this by using

$$X = (I - A)^{-1}D$$

We can find $(I - A)^{-1}$ with the formula from Section 3.4, "Inverse of a Square Matrix; Matrix Equations," or with a graphing calculator.

$$(I - A)^{-1} = \frac{1}{0.54 - 0.04} \begin{bmatrix} 0.6 & 0.2 \\ 0.2 & 0.9 \end{bmatrix} = 2 \begin{bmatrix} 0.6 & 0.2 \\ 0.2 & 0.9 \end{bmatrix} = \begin{bmatrix} 1.2 & 0.4 \\ 0.4 & 1.8 \end{bmatrix}$$

Then we can find the gross production of each industry:

$$X = (I - A)^{-1}D = \begin{bmatrix} 1.2 & 0.4 \\ 0.4 & 1.8 \end{bmatrix} \begin{bmatrix} 30 \\ 70 \end{bmatrix} = \begin{bmatrix} 64 \\ 138 \end{bmatrix}$$

Hence the gross productions are

$$\text{Lumber: } x = 64$$
$$\text{Power: } y = 138$$

(b) If 5 more units of surplus power were required, then the new gross productions would be

$$(I - A)^{-1} \begin{bmatrix} 30 \\ 70 + 5 \end{bmatrix} = \begin{bmatrix} 1.2 & 0.4 \\ 0.4 & 1.8 \end{bmatrix} \begin{bmatrix} 30 \\ 75 \end{bmatrix} = \begin{bmatrix} 66 \\ 147 \end{bmatrix}$$

Thus, for 5 additional units of power, the increased production required from each industry would be

$$\begin{bmatrix} \text{Lumber} \\ \text{Power} \end{bmatrix} = \begin{bmatrix} 66 \\ 147 \end{bmatrix} - \begin{bmatrix} 64 \\ 138 \end{bmatrix} = \begin{bmatrix} 2 \\ 9 \end{bmatrix} \text{ which is } 5 \left(\begin{matrix} \text{Col 2 of} \\ (I - A)^{-1} \end{matrix} \right) = 5 \begin{bmatrix} 0.4 \\ 1.8 \end{bmatrix} = \begin{bmatrix} 2 \\ 9 \end{bmatrix} \ \blacksquare$$

The relationship observed in part (b) of Example 3 is true in general about $(I - A)^{-1}$. Namely, the entries in column j of $(I - A)^{-1}$ are the increased amounts needed from each industry to satisfy an increase of 1 unit of surplus from industry j.

EXAMPLE 4 Open Economy

The economy of a developing nation is based on agricultural products, steel, and coal. An output of 1 ton of agricultural products requires inputs of 0.1 ton of agricultural products, 0.02 ton of steel, and 0.05 ton of coal. An output of 1 ton of steel requires inputs of 0.01 ton of agricultural products, 0.13 ton of steel, and 0.18 ton of coal. An output of 1 ton of coal requires inputs of 0.01 ton of agricultural products, 0.20 ton of steel, and 0.05 ton of coal. Write the technology matrix for this economy. Find the necessary gross productions to provide surpluses of 2350 tons of agricultural products, 4552 tons of steel, and 911 tons of coal.

Solution

The technology matrix for the economy is

$$
\begin{array}{ccc}
\text{Ag} & \text{Steel} & \text{Coal}
\end{array}
$$
$$
\begin{bmatrix}
0.1 & 0.01 & 0.01 \\
0.02 & 0.13 & 0.20 \\
0.05 & 0.18 & 0.05
\end{bmatrix}
\begin{array}{l}
\text{Ag} \\
\text{Steel} \\
\text{Coal}
\end{array}
$$

The technological equation for this economy is $(I - A)X = D$, or

$$
\left(
\begin{bmatrix}
1 & 0 & 0 \\
0 & 1 & 0 \\
0 & 0 & 1
\end{bmatrix}
-
\begin{bmatrix}
0.1 & 0.01 & 0.01 \\
0.02 & 0.13 & 0.20 \\
0.05 & 0.18 & 0.05
\end{bmatrix}
\right) X =
\begin{bmatrix}
2350 \\
4552 \\
911
\end{bmatrix}
$$

Thus the solution is

```
[A] [[.1   .01  .01]        ([I]-[A])⁻¹*[D]
     [.02  .13  .2 ]                  [[2700]
     [.05  .18  .05]]                  [5800]
[D]                                    [2200]]
         [[2350]        ■
          [4552]
          [911 ]]
```

Thus the necessary gross productions of the industries are

$$
X =
\begin{bmatrix}
2700 \\
5800 \\
2200
\end{bmatrix}
\begin{array}{l}
\text{Ag} \\
\text{Steel} \\
\text{Coal}
\end{array}
$$

CHECKPOINT

3. Suppose a primitive economy has a wood products industry and a minerals industry, with technology matrix A (open Leontief model).

$$
\begin{array}{cc}
 \text{W} & \text{M}
\end{array}
$$
$$
A =
\begin{bmatrix}
0.12 & 0.11 \\
0.09 & 0.15
\end{bmatrix}
\begin{array}{l}
\text{Wood products} \\
\text{Minerals}
\end{array}
$$

If surpluses of 1738 units of wood products and 1332 units of minerals are desired, find the gross production of each industry.

Closed Leontief Model The model we have considered is referred to as an open Leontief model because not all inputs and outputs were incorporated within the technology matrix. If a model is developed in which all inputs and outputs are used within the system, then such a model is called a **closed Leontief model.** In such a model, labor (and perhaps other factors) must be included. Labor is included by considering a new industry, households, which produces labor. When such a closed model is developed, all outputs are used within the system and the sum of the entries in each column equals 1. In this case, there is no surplus, so $D = 0$, and we have the following:

Closed Leontief Model

The technological equation for a closed Leontief model is

$$(I - A)X = 0$$

where A is the technology matrix, X is the gross production matrix, and 0 is a zero column matrix.

For closed models, the technological equation does *not* have a unique solution, so the matrix $(I - A)^{-1}$ does *not* exist and hence cannot be used to find the solution.

EXAMPLE 5   Closed Economy

The following closed Leontief model with technology matrix A might describe the economy of the entire country, with x_1 equal to the government budget, x_2 equal to the value of industrial output (profit-making organizations), x_3 equal to the budget of nonprofit organizations, and x_4 equal to the households budget.

$$A = \begin{array}{c} \\ \\ \\ \\ \\ \end{array} \begin{array}{cccc} \text{G} & \text{I} & \text{N} & \text{H} \\ \begin{bmatrix} 0.4 & 0.2 & 0.1 & 0.3 \\ 0.2 & 0.2 & 0.2 & 0.1 \\ 0.2 & 0 & 0.2 & 0.1 \\ 0.2 & 0.6 & 0.5 & 0.5 \end{bmatrix} & \begin{array}{l} \text{Government} \\ \text{Industry} \\ \text{Nonprofit} \\ \text{Households} \end{array} \end{array}$$

Find the total budgets (or outputs) x_1, x_2, x_3, and x_4.

Solution

This is a closed Leontief model; therefore, we solve the technological equation $(I - A)X = 0$.

$$\left(\begin{bmatrix} 1 & 0 & 0 & 0 \\ 0 & 1 & 0 & 0 \\ 0 & 0 & 1 & 0 \\ 0 & 0 & 0 & 1 \end{bmatrix} - \begin{bmatrix} 0.4 & 0.2 & 0.1 & 0.3 \\ 0.2 & 0.2 & 0.2 & 0.1 \\ 0.2 & 0 & 0.2 & 0.1 \\ 0.2 & 0.6 & 0.5 & 0.5 \end{bmatrix} \right) X = \begin{bmatrix} 0 \\ 0 \\ 0 \\ 0 \end{bmatrix}$$

or

$$\begin{bmatrix} 0.6 & -0.2 & -0.1 & -0.3 \\ -0.2 & 0.8 & -0.2 & -0.1 \\ -0.2 & 0 & 0.8 & -0.1 \\ -0.2 & -0.6 & -0.5 & 0.5 \end{bmatrix} \begin{bmatrix} x_1 \\ x_2 \\ x_3 \\ x_4 \end{bmatrix} = \begin{bmatrix} 0 \\ 0 \\ 0 \\ 0 \end{bmatrix}$$

The augmented matrix for this system is

$$\left[\begin{array}{cccc|c} 0.6 & -0.2 & -0.1 & -0.3 & 0 \\ -0.2 & 0.8 & -0.2 & -0.1 & 0 \\ -0.2 & 0 & 0.8 & -0.1 & 0 \\ -0.2 & -0.6 & -0.5 & 0.5 & 0 \end{array} \right]$$

Reducing this matrix with row operations, we obtain

$$\left[\begin{array}{cccc|c} 1 & 0 & 0 & -\frac{55}{82} & 0 \\ 0 & 1 & 0 & -\frac{15}{41} & 0 \\ 0 & 0 & 1 & -\frac{12}{41} & 0 \\ 0 & 0 & 0 & 0 & 0 \end{array} \right]$$

This reduction can also be found with a graphing calculator. See Figure 3.12.

```
rref([[I]-[A]]▶Fr
ac
[[1    0    0    -55/82]
 [0    1    0    -15/41]
 [0    0    1    -12/41]
 [0    0    0        0]]
```

Figure 3.12

The system of equations that corresponds to this augmented matrix is

$$x_1 - \tfrac{55}{82}x_4 = 0 \qquad x_1 = \tfrac{55}{82}x_4$$
$$x_2 - \tfrac{15}{41}x_4 = 0 \quad \text{or} \quad x_2 = \tfrac{15}{41}x_4$$
$$x_3 - \tfrac{12}{41}x_4 = 0 \qquad x_3 = \tfrac{12}{41}x_4$$

$$x_4 = \text{households budget}$$

Note that the economy satisfies the given equation if the government budget is $\tfrac{55}{82}$ times the households budget, if the value of industrial output is $\tfrac{15}{41}$ times the households budget, and if the budget of nonprofit organizations is $\tfrac{12}{41}$ times the households budget. The dependency here is expected because industrial output is limited by labor supply.

CHECKPOINT

4. For a closed Leontief model:
   (a) What is the sum of the column entries of the technology matrix?
   (b) State the technological equation.

We have examined two types of input-output models as they pertain to the economy as a whole. Since Leontief's original work with the economy, various other applications of input-output models have been developed. The next example shows how an open Leontief model can be used to determine parts availability for manufacturing.

EXAMPLE 6   Manufacturing

A storage shed consists of 4 walls and a roof. The walls and roof are made from stamped aluminum panels and are reinforced with 4 braces, each of which is held with 6 bolts. The final assembly joins the walls to each other and to the roof, using a total of 20 more bolts. The parts listing for these sheds can be described by the following matrix.

$$
Q = \begin{matrix}
 & \begin{matrix} S & W & R & P & \text{Br} & \text{Bo} \end{matrix} & \\
\begin{bmatrix}
0 & 0 & 0 & 0 & 0 & 0 \\
4 & 0 & 0 & 0 & 0 & 0 \\
1 & 0 & 0 & 0 & 0 & 0 \\
0 & 1 & 1 & 0 & 0 & 0 \\
0 & 4 & 4 & 0 & 0 & 0 \\
20 & 24 & 24 & 0 & 0 & 0
\end{bmatrix}
&
\begin{matrix}
\text{Sheds} \\
\text{Walls} \\
\text{Roofs} \\
\text{Panels} \\
\text{Braces} \\
\text{Bolts}
\end{matrix}
\end{matrix}
$$

This matrix is a type of input-output matrix, with the rows representing inputs that are used directly to produce the items that head the columns. We note that the entries here are quantities used rather than proportions used. Also, the columns containing all zeros indicate primary assembly items because they are not made from other parts.

Thus to produce a shed requires 4 walls, 1 roof, and 20 bolts, and to produce a roof requires 1 aluminum panel, 4 braces, and 24 bolts.

Suppose that an order is received for 4 completed sheds and spare parts including 2 walls, 1 roof, 8 braces, and 24 bolts. How many of each of the assembly items are required to fill the order?

Solution

If matrix D represents the order and matrix X represents the gross production, we have

$$D = \begin{bmatrix} 4 \\ 2 \\ 1 \\ 0 \\ 8 \\ 24 \end{bmatrix} \begin{matrix} \text{Sheds} \\ \text{Walls} \\ \text{Roofs} \\ \text{Panels} \\ \text{Braces} \\ \text{Bolts} \end{matrix} \qquad X = \begin{bmatrix} x_1 \\ x_2 \\ x_3 \\ x_4 \\ x_5 \\ x_6 \end{bmatrix} = \begin{bmatrix} \text{total sheds required} \\ \text{total walls required} \\ \text{total roofs required} \\ \text{total panels required} \\ \text{total braces required} \\ \text{total bolts required} \end{bmatrix}$$

Then X must satisfy $X - QX = D$, which is the technological equation for an open Leontief model.

We can find X by solving the system $(I - Q)X = D$, which is represented by the augmented matrix

$$\left[\begin{array}{cccccc|c} 1 & 0 & 0 & 0 & 0 & 0 & 4 \\ -4 & 1 & 0 & 0 & 0 & 0 & 2 \\ -1 & 0 & 1 & 0 & 0 & 0 & 1 \\ 0 & -1 & -1 & 1 & 0 & 0 & 0 \\ 0 & -4 & -4 & 0 & 1 & 0 & 8 \\ -20 & -24 & -24 & 0 & 0 & 1 & 24 \end{array} \right]$$

Although this matrix is quite large, it is easily reduced and yields

$$\left[\begin{array}{cccccc|c} 1 & 0 & 0 & 0 & 0 & 0 & 4 \\ 0 & 1 & 0 & 0 & 0 & 0 & 18 \\ 0 & 0 & 1 & 0 & 0 & 0 & 5 \\ 0 & 0 & 0 & 1 & 0 & 0 & 23 \\ 0 & 0 & 0 & 0 & 1 & 0 & 100 \\ 0 & 0 & 0 & 0 & 0 & 1 & 656 \end{array} \right]$$

This matrix tells us that the order will have 4 complete sheds. The 18 walls from the matrix include the 16 from the complete sheds, and the 5 roofs include the 4 from the complete sheds. The 23 panels, 100 braces, and 656 bolts are the total number of *primary assembly items* (bolts, braces, and panels) required to fill the order.

The inverse of $I - Q$ exists, so it could be used directly or with technology to find the solution to the parts-listing problem of Example 6.

CHECKPOINT ANSWERS

1. Manufacturing
2. 20 units of fuels
3. 2200 units of wood products
   1800 units of minerals
4. (a) The sum of the column entries is 1.
   (b) $(I - A)X = 0$

EXERCISES 3.5

1. The following technology matrix for a simple economy describes the relationship of certain industries to each other in the production of 1 unit of product.

	A	M	F	U	
	0.36	0.03	0.10	0.04	Agriculture
	0.06	0.42	0.25	0.33	Manufacturing
	0.18	0.15	0.10	0.41	Fuels
	0.10	0.20	0.31	0.15	Utilities

   (a) For each 100 units of manufactured products produced, how many units of fuels are required?
   (b) How many units of utilities are required to produce 40 units of agricultural products?

2. For the economy in Problem 1, what industry is most dependent on utilities?

The following technology matrix describes the relationship of certain industries within the economy to each other. (A&F, agriculture and food; RM, raw materials; M, manufacturing; F, fuels industry; U, utilities; SI, service industries)

	A&F	RM	M	F	U	SI	
	0.410	0.008	0	0.002	0	0.006	A&F
	0.025	0.493	0.190	0.024	0.030	0.150	RM
	0.015	0.006	0.082	0.009	0.001	0.116	M
	0.097	0.096	0.040	0.053	0.008	0.093	F
	0.028	0.129	0.039	0.058	0.138	0.409	U
	0.043	0.008	0.010	0.012	0.002	0.095	SI

Use this matrix in Problems 3–10.

3. For each 1000 units of raw materials produced, how many units of agricultural and food products were required?

4. For each 1000 units of raw materials produced, how many units of service were required?

5. How many units of fuels were required to produce 1000 units of manufactured goods?

6. How many units of fuels were required to produce 1000 units of power (utilities' goods)?

7. Which industry is most dependent on its own goods for its operations? Which industry is least dependent on its own goods?

8. Which industry is most dependent on the fuels industry?

9. Which three industries would be most affected by a rise in the cost of raw materials?

10. Which industry would be most affected by a rise in the cost of manufactured goods?

11. Suppose a primitive economy consists of two industries, farm products and farm machinery. Also suppose that its technology matrix is

$$A = \begin{bmatrix} 0.5 & 0.1 \\ 0.1 & 0.3 \end{bmatrix} \begin{matrix} \text{Products} \\ \text{Machinery} \end{matrix}$$

   (with columns labeled P and M)

   If surpluses of 96 units of farm products and 8 units of farm machinery are desired, find the gross production of each industry.

12. Suppose an economy has two industries, agriculture and minerals. Suppose further that the technology matrix for this economy is A.

$$A = \begin{bmatrix} 0.3 & 0.1 \\ 0.1 & 0.2 \end{bmatrix} \begin{matrix} \text{Agriculture} \\ \text{Minerals} \end{matrix}$$

   (with columns labeled A and M)

   If surpluses of 60 agricultural units and 70 mineral units are desired, find the gross production for each industry.

13. An economy is based on two industries, utilities and manufacturing. The technology matrix for these industries is A.

$$A = \begin{bmatrix} 0.3 & 0.15 \\ 0.3 & 0.4 \end{bmatrix} \begin{matrix} \text{Utilities} \\ \text{Manufacturing} \end{matrix}$$

   (with columns labeled U and M)

   If surpluses of 80 units of utilities output and 180 units of manufacturing are desired, find the gross production of each industry.

14. A primitive economy has a mining industry and a fishing industry, with technology matrix A.

$$A = \begin{bmatrix} 0.25 & 0.05 \\ 0.05 & 0.40 \end{bmatrix} \begin{matrix} \text{Mining} \\ \text{Fishing} \end{matrix}$$

   (with columns labeled M and F)

   If surpluses of 147 units of mining output and 26 units of fishing output are desired, find the gross production of each industry.

15. Suppose the economy of an underdeveloped country has an agricultural industry and an oil industry, with technology matrix A.

$$A = \begin{bmatrix} 0.4 & 0.2 \\ 0.2 & 0.1 \end{bmatrix} \begin{matrix} \text{Agricultural products} \\ \text{Oil products} \end{matrix}$$

   (with columns labeled A and O)

   (a) If surpluses of 0 units of agricultural products and 610 units of oil products are desired, find the gross production of each industry.
   (b) Find the additional production needed from each industry for 1 more unit of oil products surplus.

16. Suppose a simple economy with only an agricultural industry and a steel industry has the following technology matrix.

$$A = \begin{bmatrix} 0.3 & 0.2 \\ 0.1 & 0.4 \end{bmatrix} \begin{matrix} \text{Agriculture} \\ \text{Steel} \end{matrix}$$

with column labels A and S.

   (a) If surpluses of 15 units of agricultural products and 35 units of steel are desired, find the gross production of each industry.
   (b) Find the additional production needed from each industry for 1 more unit of agricultural surplus.

17. One sector of an economy consists of a mining industry and a manufacturing industry, with technology matrix A.

$$A = \begin{bmatrix} 0.2 & 0.1 \\ 0.6 & 0.3 \end{bmatrix} \begin{matrix} \text{Mining} \\ \text{Manufacturing} \end{matrix}$$

with column labels M and Mfg.

   (a) Surpluses of 36 units of mining output and 278 units of manufacturing output are desired. Find the gross production of each industry.
   (b) Find the additional production needed from each industry for 1 more unit of mining surplus.

18. An underdeveloped country has an agricultural industry and a manufacturing industry, with technology matrix A.

$$A = \begin{bmatrix} 0.20 & 0.20 \\ 0.20 & 0.45 \end{bmatrix} \begin{matrix} \text{Agriculture} \\ \text{Manufacturing} \end{matrix}$$

with column labels A and M.

   (a) Surpluses of 8 units of agricultural products and 620 units of manufactured products are desired. Find the gross production of each industry.
   (b) Find the additional production needed from each industry for 1 more unit of manufacturing surplus.

19. A simple economy has an electronic components industry and a computer industry. Each unit of electronic components output requires inputs of 0.3 unit of electronic components and 0.2 unit of computers. Each unit of computer industry output requires inputs of 0.6 unit of electronic components and 0.2 unit of computers.
   (a) Write the technology matrix for this simple economy.
   (b) If surpluses of 648 units of electronic components and 16 units of computers are desired, find the gross production of each industry.

20. An economy has an agricultural industry and a textile industry. Each unit of agricultural output requires 0.4 unit of agricultural input and 0.1 unit of textiles input. Each unit of textiles output requires 0.1 unit of agricultural input and 0.2 unit of textiles input.
   (a) Write the technology matrix for this economy.
   (b) If surpluses of 5 units of agricultural products and 195 units of textiles are desired, find the gross production of each industry.

21. A primitive economy consists of a fishing industry and an oil industry. A unit of fishing industry output requires 0.30 unit of fishing industry input and 0.35 unit of oil industry input. A unit of oil industry output requires inputs of 0.04 unit of fishing products and 0.10 unit of oil products.
   (a) Write the technology matrix for this primitive economy.
   (b) If surpluses of 20 units of fishing products and 1090 units of oil products are desired, find the gross production of each industry.

22. An economy has a manufacturing industry and a banking industry. Each unit of manufacturing output requires inputs of 0.5 unit of manufacturing and 0.2 unit of banking. Each unit of banking output requires inputs of 0.3 unit each of manufacturing and banking.
   (a) Write the technology matrix for this economy.
   (b) If surpluses of 141 units of manufacturing and 106 units of banking are desired, find the gross production of each industry.

Interdepartmental costs **Within a company is a (micro) economy that is monitored by the accounting procedures. In terms of the accounts, the various departments "produce" costs, some of which are internal and some of which are direct costs. Problems 23–26 show how an open Leontief model can be used to determine departmental costs.**

23. Suppose the development department of a firm charges 10% of its total monthly costs to the promotional department and the promotional department charges 5% of its total monthly costs to the development department. The direct costs of the development department are $20,400, and the direct costs of the promotional department are $9,900. The solution to the matrix equation

$$\begin{bmatrix} 20,400 \\ 9,900 \end{bmatrix} + \begin{bmatrix} 0 & 0.05 \\ 0.1 & 0 \end{bmatrix} \begin{bmatrix} x \\ y \end{bmatrix} = \begin{bmatrix} x \\ y \end{bmatrix}$$

for the column matrix $\begin{bmatrix} x \\ y \end{bmatrix}$ gives the total costs for each department. Note that this equation can be written in the form

$$D + AX = X, \quad \text{or} \quad X - AX = D$$

which is the form for an open economy. Find the total costs for each department in this (micro)economy.

24. Suppose the shipping department of a firm charges 20% of its total monthly costs to the printing department and that the printing department charges 10% of its total monthly costs to the shipping department. If the direct costs of the shipping department are $16,500 and the direct costs of the printing department are $11,400, find the total costs for each department.

25. Suppose the engineering department of a firm charges 20% of its total monthly costs to the computer department and the computer department charges 25% of its total monthly costs to the engineering department. If during a given month the direct costs are $11,750 for the engineering department and $10,000 for the computer department, what are the total costs of each department?

26. The sales department of an auto dealership charges 10% of its total monthly costs to the service department, and the service department charges 20% of its total monthly costs to the sales department. During a given month, the direct costs are $88,200 for sales and $49,000 for service. Find the total costs of each department.

27. Suppose that an economy has three industries (fishing, agriculture, and mining), and that matrix A is the technology matrix for this economy.

$$
A = \begin{bmatrix} 0.5 & 0.1 & 0.1 \\ 0.3 & 0.5 & 0.2 \\ 0.1 & 0.3 & 0.4 \end{bmatrix} \begin{matrix} \text{Fishing} \\ \text{Agriculture} \\ \text{Mining} \end{matrix}
$$

with column headers F, A, M.

If surpluses of 110 units of fishing output and 50 units each of agricultural and mining goods are desired, find the gross production of each industry.

28. Suppose that an economy has the same technology matrix as the economy in Problem 27. If surpluses of 180 units of fishing output, 90 units of agricultural goods, and 40 units of mining goods are desired, find the gross production of each industry.

29. Suppose that the economy of a small nation has an electronics industry, a steel industry, and an auto industry, with the following technology matrix.

$$
A = \begin{bmatrix} 0.6 & 0.2 & 0.2 \\ 0.1 & 0.4 & 0.5 \\ 0.1 & 0.2 & 0.2 \end{bmatrix} \begin{matrix} \text{Electronics} \\ \text{Steel} \\ \text{Autos} \end{matrix}
$$

with column headers E, S, A.

If the nation wants to have surpluses of 100 units of electronics production, 272 units of steel production, and 200 automobiles, find the gross production of each industry.

30. Suppose an economy has the same technology matrix as that in Problem 29. If surpluses of 540 units of electronics, 30 units of steel, and 140 autos are desired, find the gross production for each industry.

31. Suppose that a simple economy has three industries, (service, manufacturing, and agriculture), and that matrix A is the technology matrix for this economy.

$$
A = \begin{bmatrix} 0.4 & 0.1 & 0.1 \\ 0.2 & 0.5 & 0.2 \\ 0.2 & 0.1 & 0.3 \end{bmatrix} \begin{matrix} \text{Service} \\ \text{Manufacturing} \\ \text{Agriculture} \end{matrix}
$$

with column headers S, M, A.

If surpluses of 24 units of service output, 62 units of manufactured goods, and 32 units of agricultural goods are desired, find the gross production of each industry.

32. Suppose that an economy has the same technology matrix as the economy in Problem 31. If surpluses of 14 units of manufactured goods and 104 units of agricultural goods are desired, find the gross production of each industry.

Problems 33–38 refer to closed Leontief models.

33. Suppose the technology matrix for a closed model of a simple economy is given by

$$
A = \begin{bmatrix} 0.5 & 0.1 & 0.2 \\ 0.1 & 0.3 & 0 \\ 0.4 & 0.6 & 0.8 \end{bmatrix} \begin{matrix} \text{Products} \\ \text{Machinery} \\ \text{Households} \end{matrix}
$$

with column headers P, M, H.

Find the gross productions for the industries.

34. Suppose the technology matrix for a closed model of a simple economy is given by matrix A. Find the gross productions for the industries.

$$
A = \begin{bmatrix} 0.4 & 0.1 & 0.3 \\ 0.4 & 0.3 & 0.2 \\ 0.2 & 0.6 & 0.5 \end{bmatrix} \begin{matrix} \text{Government} \\ \text{Industry} \\ \text{Households} \end{matrix}
$$

with column headers G, I, H.

35. Suppose the technology matrix for a closed model of a simple economy is given by matrix A. Find the gross productions for the industries.

$$
A = \begin{bmatrix} 0.4 & 0.2 & 0.2 \\ 0.2 & 0.3 & 0.3 \\ 0.4 & 0.5 & 0.5 \end{bmatrix} \begin{matrix} \text{Government} \\ \text{Industry} \\ \text{Households} \end{matrix}
$$

with column headers G, I, H.

36. Suppose the technology matrix for a closed model of an economy is given by matrix A. Find the gross productions for the industries.

$$
A = \begin{bmatrix} 0.2 & 0.1 & 0.1 \\ 0.6 & 0.5 & 0.1 \\ 0.2 & 0.4 & 0.8 \end{bmatrix} \begin{matrix} \text{Shipping} \\ \text{Manufacturing} \\ \text{Households} \end{matrix}
$$

with column headers S, M, H.

37. A closed model for an economy has a manufacturing industry, utilities industry, and households industry. Each unit of manufacturing output uses 0.5 unit of manufacturing input, 0.4 unit of utilities input, and 0.1 unit of households input. Each unit of utilities output requires 0.4 unit of manufacturing input, 0.5 unit of utilities input, and 0.1 unit of households input. Each unit of household output requires 0.3 unit each of manufacturing and utilities input and 0.4 unit of households input.
    (a) Write the technology matrix for this closed model of the economy.
    (b) Find the gross production for each industry.

38. A closed model for an economy identifies government, the profit sector, the nonprofit sector, and households as its industries. Each unit of government output requires 0.3 unit of government input, 0.2 unit of profit sector input, 0.2 unit of nonprofit sector input, and 0.3 unit of households input. Each unit of profit sector output requires 0.2 unit of government input, 0.3 unit of profit sector input, 0.1 unit of nonprofit sector input, and 0.4 unit of households input. Each unit of nonprofit sector output requires 0.1 unit of government input, 0.1 unit of profit sector input, 0.2 unit of nonprofit sector input, and 0.6 unit of households input. Each unit of households output requires 0.05 unit of government input, 0.1 unit of profit sector input, 0.1 unit of nonprofit sector input, and 0.75 unit of households input.
    (a) Write the technology matrix for this closed model of the economy.
    (b) Find the gross production for each industry.
39. For the storage shed in Example 6, find the number of each primary assembly item required to fill an order for 24 sheds, 12 braces, and 96 bolts.
40. Card tables are made by joining 4 legs and a top using 4 bolts. Each leg is made from a steel rod. The top has a frame made from 4 steel rods. A cover and 4 special clamps that brace the top and hold the legs are joined to the frame using a total of 8 bolts. The parts-listing matrix for the card table assembly is given by

$$A = \begin{bmatrix} \text{CT} & \text{L} & \text{T} & \text{R} & \text{Co} & \text{Cl} & \text{B} & \\ 0 & 0 & 0 & 0 & 0 & 0 & 0 & \text{Card table} \\ 4 & 0 & 0 & 0 & 0 & 0 & 0 & \text{Legs} \\ 1 & 0 & 0 & 0 & 0 & 0 & 0 & \text{Top} \\ 0 & 1 & 4 & 0 & 0 & 0 & 0 & \text{Rods} \\ 0 & 0 & 1 & 0 & 0 & 0 & 0 & \text{Cover} \\ 0 & 0 & 4 & 0 & 0 & 0 & 0 & \text{Clamps} \\ 4 & 0 & 8 & 0 & 0 & 0 & 0 & \text{Bolts} \end{bmatrix}$$

If an order is received for 10 card tables, 4 legs, 1 top, 1 cover, 6 clamps, and 12 bolts, how many of each primary assembly item are required to fill the order?

41. A sawhorse is made from 2 pairs of legs and a top joined with 4 nails. The top is a 2×4-in. board 3 ft long. Each pair of legs is made from two 2×4-in. boards 3 ft long, a brace, and a special clamp, with the brace and the clamp joined using 8 nails. The parts-listing matrix for the sawhorse is given by

$$A = \begin{bmatrix} \text{SH} & \text{T} & \text{LP} & 2\times4 & \text{B} & \text{C} & \text{N} & \\ 0 & 0 & 0 & 0 & 0 & 0 & 0 & \text{Sawhorse} \\ 1 & 0 & 0 & 0 & 0 & 0 & 0 & \text{Top} \\ 2 & 0 & 0 & 0 & 0 & 0 & 0 & \text{Leg pair} \\ 0 & 1 & 2 & 0 & 0 & 0 & 0 & 2\times4s \\ 0 & 0 & 1 & 0 & 0 & 0 & 0 & \text{Brace} \\ 0 & 0 & 1 & 0 & 0 & 0 & 0 & \text{Clamp} \\ 4 & 0 & 8 & 0 & 0 & 0 & 0 & \text{Nails} \end{bmatrix}$$

How many of each primary assembly item are required to fill an order for 10 sawhorses, 6 extra 2×4s, 6 extra clamps, and 100 nails?

42. A log carrier has a body made from a 4-ft length of reinforced cloth having a patch on each side and a dowel slid through each end to act as handles. The parts-listing matrix for the log carrier is given by

$$A = \begin{bmatrix} \text{LC} & \text{B} & \text{H} & \text{C} & \text{P} & \\ 0 & 0 & 0 & 0 & 0 & \text{Log carrier} \\ 1 & 0 & 0 & 0 & 0 & \text{Body} \\ 2 & 0 & 0 & 0 & 0 & \text{Handles} \\ 0 & 1 & 0 & 0 & 0 & \text{Cloth} \\ 0 & 2 & 0 & 0 & 0 & \text{Patch} \end{bmatrix}$$

How many of each primary assembly item are required to fill an order for 500 log carriers and 20 handles?

③ CHAPTER SUMMARY & REVIEW

KEY TERMS AND FORMULAS

Section 3.1

Matrices (p. 181)
  Order
  Entries
  Square, row, column, and zero matrices
Equal matrices (p. 183)

Transpose of A (p. 183)
  A^T
Sum of two matrices (p. 184)
Negative of a matrix (p. 184)
Scalar multiplication (p. 186)

Section 3.2

Matrix product (p. 194)

Identity matrix (p. 196)

$$2 \times 2 \text{ is } \begin{bmatrix} 1 & 0 \\ 0 & 1 \end{bmatrix}$$

Section 3.3

Section 3.4

$$\det\begin{bmatrix} a & b \\ c & d \end{bmatrix} = \begin{vmatrix} a & b \\ c & d \end{vmatrix} = ad - bc$$

Section 3.5

REVIEW EXERCISES

Use the matrices below as needed to complete Problems 1–25.

$$A = \begin{bmatrix} 4 & 4 & 2 & -5 \\ 6 & 3 & -1 & 0 \\ 0 & 0 & -3 & 5 \end{bmatrix} \quad B = \begin{bmatrix} 2 & -5 & -11 & 8 \\ 4 & 0 & 0 & 4 \\ -2 & -2 & 1 & 9 \end{bmatrix}$$

$$C = \begin{bmatrix} 4 & -2 \\ 5 & 0 \\ 6 & 0 \\ 1 & 3 \end{bmatrix} \quad D = \begin{bmatrix} 3 & 5 \\ 1 & 2 \end{bmatrix} \quad E = \begin{bmatrix} 1 & 1 \\ 1 & 1 \\ 4 & 6 \\ 0 & 5 \end{bmatrix}$$

$$F = \begin{bmatrix} -1 & 6 \\ 4 & 11 \end{bmatrix} \quad G = \begin{bmatrix} 2 & -5 \\ -1 & 3 \end{bmatrix} \quad I = \begin{bmatrix} 1 & 0 \\ 0 & 1 \end{bmatrix}$$

Section 3.1

1. Find a_{12} in matrix A.
2. Find b_{23} in matrix B.
3. Which of the matrices, if any, are 3×4?
4. Which of the matrices, if any, are 2×4?
5. Which matrices are square?
6. Write the negative of matrix B.
7. If a matrix is added to its negative, what kind of matrix results?
8. Two matrices can be added if they have the same _____.

Perform the indicated operations in Problems 9–25.

9. $A + B$
10. $C - E$
11. $D^T - I$
12. $3C$
13. $4I$
14. $-2F$
15. $4D - 3I$
16. $F + 2D$
17. $3A - 5B$

Section 3.2

18. AC
19. CD
20. DF
21. FD
22. FI
23. IF
24. DG^T
25. $(DG)F$

Section 3.3

In Problems 26–28, the reduced matrix for a system of equations is given. (a) Identify the type of solution for the system (unique solution, no solution, or infinitely many solutions). Explain your reasoning. (b) For each system that has a solution, find it. If the system has infinitely many solutions, find the general solution.

26. $\begin{bmatrix} 1 & 0 & -2 & | & 6 \\ 0 & 1 & 3 & | & 7 \\ 0 & 0 & 0 & | & 0 \end{bmatrix}$
27. $\begin{bmatrix} 1 & 0 & -4 & | & 0 \\ 0 & 1 & 3 & | & 0 \\ 0 & 0 & 0 & | & 1 \end{bmatrix}$

28. $\begin{bmatrix} 1 & 0 & 0 & | & 0 \\ 0 & 1 & 0 & | & -10 \\ 0 & 0 & 1 & | & 14 \end{bmatrix}$

29. Given the following augmented matrix representing a system of linear equations, find the solution.

$$\begin{bmatrix} 1 & 1 & 2 & | & 5 \\ 4 & 0 & 1 & | & 5 \\ 2 & 1 & 1 & | & 5 \end{bmatrix}$$

In Problems 30–36, solve each system using matrices.

30. $\begin{cases} x - 2y = 4 \\ -3x + 10y = 24 \end{cases}$

31. $\begin{cases} x + y + z = 4 \\ 3x + 4y - z = -1 \\ 2x - y + 3z = 3 \end{cases}$

32. $\begin{cases} -x + y + z = 3 \\ 3x \qquad - z = 1 \\ 2x - 3y - 4z = -2 \end{cases}$ 33. $\begin{cases} x + y - 2z = 5 \\ 3x + 2y + 5z = 10 \\ -2x - 3y + 15z = 2 \end{cases}$

34. $\begin{cases} x - y \qquad = 3 \\ x + y + 4z = 1 \\ 2x - 3y - 2z = 7 \end{cases}$ 35. $\begin{cases} x - 3y + z = 4 \\ 2x - 5y - z = 6 \end{cases}$

36. $\begin{cases} x_1 + x_2 + x_3 + x_4 = 3 \\ x_1 - 2x_2 + x_3 - 4x_4 = -5 \\ x_1 \qquad - x_3 + x_4 = 0 \\ x_2 + x_3 + x_4 = 2 \end{cases}$

Section 3.4

37. Are D and G inverse matrices if

$$D = \begin{bmatrix} 3 & 5 \\ 1 & 2 \end{bmatrix} \text{ and } G = \begin{bmatrix} 2 & -5 \\ -1 & 3 \end{bmatrix}?$$

In Problems 38–40, find the inverse of each matrix.

38. $\begin{bmatrix} 7 & -1 \\ -10 & 2 \end{bmatrix}$ 39. $\begin{bmatrix} 1 & 0 & 2 \\ 3 & 4 & -1 \\ 1 & 1 & 0 \end{bmatrix}$

40. $\begin{bmatrix} 3 & 3 & 2 \\ -1 & 4 & 2 \\ 2 & 5 & 3 \end{bmatrix}$

In Problems 41–43, solve each system of equations using inverse matrices.

41. $\begin{cases} x \qquad + 2z = 5 \\ 3x + 4y - z = 2 \\ x + y \qquad = -3 \end{cases}$ (See Problem 39.)

42. $\begin{cases} 3x + 3y + 2z = 1 \\ -x + 4y + 2z = -10 \\ 2x + 5y + 3z = -6 \end{cases}$ (See Problem 40.)

43. $\begin{cases} x + 3y + z = 0 \\ x + 4y + 3z = 2 \\ 2x - y - 11z = -12 \end{cases}$

44. Does the following matrix have an inverse?

$$\begin{bmatrix} 1 & 2 & 4 \\ 2 & 0 & -4 \\ 1 & 0 & -2 \end{bmatrix}$$

In Problems 45 and 46:
   (a) **Find the determinant of the matrix.**
   (b) **Use it to decide whether the matrix has an inverse.**

45. $\begin{bmatrix} 4 & 4 \\ -2 & 2 \end{bmatrix}$ 46. $\begin{bmatrix} 1 & 2 & 3 \\ 4 & -1 & 8 \\ 6 & 3 & 14 \end{bmatrix}$

APPLICATIONS

The Burr Cabinet Company manufactures bookcases and filing cabinets at two plants, A and B. Matrix M gives the production for the two plants during June, and matrix N gives the production for July. Use them in Problems 47–49.

$$M = \begin{matrix} & A & B \\ \begin{bmatrix} 150 & 80 \\ 280 & 300 \end{bmatrix} & \begin{matrix} \text{Bookcases} \\ \text{Files} \end{matrix} \end{matrix} \qquad N = \begin{matrix} & A & B \\ \begin{bmatrix} 100 & 60 \\ 200 & 400 \end{bmatrix} \end{matrix}$$

Section 3.1

47. *Production* Write the matrix that represents total production at the two plants for the 2 months.
48. *Production* If matrix P represents the inventories at the plants at the beginning of June and matrix S represents shipments from the plants during June, write the matrix that represents the inventories at the end of June.

$$S = \begin{bmatrix} 120 & 80 \\ 180 & 300 \end{bmatrix} \qquad P = \begin{bmatrix} 1000 & 800 \\ 600 & 1200 \end{bmatrix}$$

Section 3.2

49. *Production* If the company sells its bookcases to wholesalers for \$100 and its filing cabinets for \$120, for which month was the value of production higher: (a) at plant A? (b) at plant B?

A small church choir is made up of men and women who wear choir robes in the sizes shown in matrix A.

$$A = \begin{matrix} & \text{Men} & \text{Women} \\ \begin{bmatrix} 1 & 14 \\ 12 & 10 \\ 8 & 3 \end{bmatrix} & \begin{matrix} \text{Small} \\ \text{Medium} \\ \text{Large} \end{matrix} \end{matrix}$$

$$B = \begin{matrix} & S & M & L \\ \begin{bmatrix} 25 & 40 & 45 \\ 10 & 10 & 10 \end{bmatrix} & \begin{matrix} \text{Robes} \\ \text{Hoods} \end{matrix} \end{matrix}$$

Matrix B contains the prices (in dollars) of new robes and hoods according to size. Use these matrices in Problems 50 and 51.

50. *Cost* Find the product BA and label the rows and columns to show what each entry represents.
51. *Cost* To find a matrix that gives the cost of new robes and the cost of new hoods, find

$$BA \begin{bmatrix} 1 \\ 1 \end{bmatrix}$$

52. *Manufacturing* Two departments of a firm, A and B, need different amounts of the same products. The following table gives the amounts of the products needed by the two departments.

	Steel	Plastic	Wood
Department A	30	20	10
Department B	20	10	20

These three products are supplied by two suppliers, Ace and Kink, with the unit prices given in the following table.

	Ace	Kink
Steel	300	280
Plastic	150	100
Wood	150	200

(a) Use matrix multiplication to find how much these two orders will cost at the two suppliers. The result should be a 2 × 2 matrix.

(b) From which supplier should each department make its purchase?

53. *Investment* Over the period of time 2009–2018, the return (per dollar invested) on Maura stock was 0.013469 per month, the return on Ward was 0.013543 per month, and the return on Goldsmith was 0.006504 per month. Under certain assumptions, including that whatever underlying process generated the past set of observations will continue to hold in the present and near future, we can estimate the expected return for a stock portfolio containing these assets in some combination.

Suppose we have a portfolio that has 20% of our total wealth in Maura, 30% in Ward, and 50% in Goldsmith stock. Use the following steps to estimate the portfolio's historical return, which can be used to estimate the future return.

(a) Write a 1 × 3 matrix that defines the decimal part of our total wealth in Maura, in Ward, and in Goldsmith.

(b) Write a 3 × 1 matrix that gives the monthly returns from each of these companies.

(c) Find the historical return of the portfolio by computing the product of these two matrices.

(d) What is the expected monthly return of the stock portfolio, as a percent?

Sections 3.3 and 3.4

54. *Investment* A woman has $50,000 to invest. She has decided to invest all of it by purchasing some shares of stock in each of three companies: a fast-food chain that sells for $50 per share and has an expected growth of 11.5% per year, a software company that sells for $20 per share and has an expected growth of 15% per year, and a pharmaceutical company that sells for $80 per share and has an expected growth of 10% per year. She plans to buy twice as many shares of stock in the fast-food chain as in the pharmaceutical company. If her goal is 12% growth per year, how many shares of each stock should she buy?

55. *Nutrition* A biologist is growing three different types of slugs (types A, B, and C) in the same laboratory environment. Each day, the slugs are given a nutrient mixture that contains three different ingredients (I, II, and III). Each type A slug requires 1 unit of I, 3 units of II, and 1 unit of III per day. Each type B slug requires 1 unit of I, 4 units of II, and 2 units of III per day. Each type C slug requires 2 units of I, 10 units of II, and 6 units of III per day.

(a) If the daily mixture contains 2000 units of I, 8000 units of II, and 4000 units of III, find the number of slugs of each type that can be supported.

(b) Is it possible to support 500 type A slugs? If so, how many of the other types are there?

(c) What is the maximum number of type A slugs possible? How many of the other types are there in this case?

56. *Transportation* An airline company has three types of aircraft that carry three types of cargo. The payload of each type is summarized in the table below.

Units Carried	Passenger	Transport	Jumbo
First-class mail	100	100	100
Passengers	150	20	350
Air freight	20	65	35

Plane Type spans the Passenger, Transport, and Jumbo columns.

(a) Suppose that on a given day the airline must move 1100 units of first-class mail, 460 units of air freight, and 1930 passengers. How many aircraft of each type should be scheduled? Use inverse matrices.

(b) How should the schedule from part (a) be adjusted to accommodate 730 more passengers?

(c) What column of the inverse matrix used in part (a) can be used to answer part (b)?

Section 3.5

57. *Economy models* An economy has a shipping industry and an agricultural industry with technology matrix A.

$$A = \begin{bmatrix} 0.1 & 0.2 \\ 0.2 & 0.4 \end{bmatrix} \begin{matrix} \text{Shipping} \\ \text{Agriculture} \end{matrix}$$

with column headers S and A.

(a) Surpluses of 4720 tons of shipping output and 40 tons of agricultural output are desired. Find the gross production of each industry.

(b) Find the additional production needed from each industry for 1 more unit of agricultural surplus.

58. *Economy models* A simple economy has a shoe industry and a cattle industry. Each unit of shoe output requires inputs of 0.1 unit of shoes and 0.2 unit of cattle

products. Each unit of cattle products output requires inputs of 0.1 unit of shoes and 0.05 unit of cattle products.
(a) Write the technology matrix for this simple economy.
(b) If surpluses of 850 units of shoes and 275 units of cattle products are desired, find the gross production of each industry.

59. *Economy models* A look at the industrial sector of an economy can be simplified to include three industries: the mining industry, the manufacturing industry, and the fuels industry. The technology matrix for this sector of the economy is given by

$$
A = \begin{array}{c} \\ \\ \\ \\ \end{array}
\begin{array}{ccc} M & Mf & F \\ \left[\begin{array}{ccc} 0.4 & 0.2 & 0.2 \\ 0.2 & 0.4 & 0.2 \\ 0.1 & 0.2 & 0.2 \end{array}\right] & \begin{array}{l} \text{Mining} \\ \text{Manufacturing} \\ \text{Fuels} \end{array} \end{array}
$$

Find the gross production of each industry if surpluses of 72 units of mined goods, 40 units of manufactured goods, and 220 units of fuels are desired.

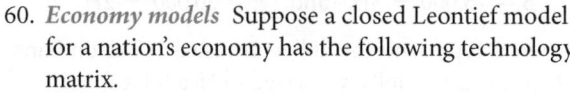

60. *Economy models* Suppose a closed Leontief model for a nation's economy has the following technology matrix.

$$
A = \begin{array}{cccc} G & A & M & H \\ \left[\begin{array}{cccc} 0.4 & 0.2 & 0.2 & 0.2 \\ 0.2 & 0.4 & 0.1 & 0.2 \\ 0.2 & 0.1 & 0.3 & 0.1 \\ 0.2 & 0.3 & 0.4 & 0.5 \end{array}\right] & \begin{array}{l} \text{Government} \\ \text{Agriculture} \\ \text{Manufacturing} \\ \text{Households} \end{array} \end{array}
$$

Find the gross production of each industry.

3 CHAPTER TEST

In Problems 1–6, perform the indicated matrix operations with the following matrices.

$$
A = \begin{bmatrix} 1 & -2 \\ 3 & 2 \\ 4 & 1 \end{bmatrix} \quad B = \begin{bmatrix} 2 & -2 & 1 \\ 3 & 1 & 5 \end{bmatrix}
$$

$$
C = \begin{bmatrix} 3 & -4 & -1 \\ 2 & 2 & -1 \end{bmatrix} \quad D = \begin{bmatrix} 1 & 2 & 4 \\ 3 & 5 & 41 \\ 3 & 2 & 3 \end{bmatrix}
$$

1. $A^T + B$ 2. $B - C$ 3. CD

4. DA 5. BA 6. ABD

7. Find the inverse of the matrix $\begin{bmatrix} 1 & 3 \\ 2 & 4 \end{bmatrix}$.

8. Find the inverse of the matrix
$$
\begin{bmatrix} 1 & 2 & 4 \\ 1 & 2 & 2 \\ 1 & 1 & 4 \end{bmatrix}
$$

9. If $AX = B$ and
$$
A^{-1} = \begin{bmatrix} 1 & 2 & 0 \\ 3 & 1 & 2 \\ 4 & 1 & 1 \end{bmatrix} \text{ and } B = \begin{bmatrix} 3 \\ 1 \\ 2 \end{bmatrix}
$$
find the matrix X.

10. Solve
$$
\begin{cases} x - y + 2z = 4 \\ x + 4y + z = 4 \\ 2x + 2y + 4z = 10 \end{cases}
$$

11. Solve
$$
\begin{cases} x - y + 2z = 4 \\ x + 4y + z = 4 \\ 2x + 3y + 3z = 8 \end{cases}
$$

12. Solve
$$
\begin{cases} x - y + 3z = 4 \\ x + 5y + 2z = 3 \\ 2x + 4y + 5z = 8 \end{cases}
$$

13. Use an inverse matrix to solve
$$
\begin{cases} x + y + 2z = 4 \\ x + 2y + z + w = 4 \\ 2x + 5y + 4z + 2w = 10 \\ 2y + z + 2w = 0 \end{cases}
$$

14. Solve
$$
\begin{cases} x - y + 2z - w = 4 \\ x + 4y + z + w = 4 \\ 2x + 2y + 4z + 2w = 10 \\ - y + z + 2w = 2 \end{cases}
$$

15. Suppose that the solution of an investment problem involving a system of linear equations is given by

$$B = 75{,}000 - 3H \quad \text{and} \quad E = 20{,}000 + 2H$$

where B represents the dollars invested in Barton Bank stocks, H is the dollars invested in Heath Healthcare stocks, and E is the dollars invested in Electronics Depot stocks.

(a) If $10,000 is invested in the Heath Healthcare stocks, how much is invested in the other two stocks?

(b) What is the dollar range that could be invested in the Heath Healthcare stocks?

(c) What is the minimum amount that could be invested in the Electronics Depot stocks? How much is invested in the other two stocks in this case?

16. In an ecological model, matrix A gives the fractions of several types of plants consumed by the herbivores in the ecosystem. Similarly, matrix B gives the fraction of each type of herbivore that is consumed by the carnivores in the system. Each row of matrix A refers to a type of plant, and each column refers to a kind of herbivore. Similarly, each row of matrix B is a kind of herbivore and each column is a kind of carnivore.

$$A = \begin{array}{c} \text{Herbivores} \\ \begin{bmatrix} 0.2 & 0.1 & 0.4 \\ 0.3 & 0.3 & 0.1 \\ 0.2 & 0.1 & 0.1 \\ 0.1 & 0.2 & 0.5 \\ 0.4 & 0.4 & 0 \end{bmatrix} \end{array} \text{Plants}$$

$$B = \begin{array}{c} \text{Carnivores} \\ \begin{bmatrix} 0.1 & 0.1 & 0.2 \\ 0.2 & 0 & 0.4 \\ 0.1 & 0.5 & 0.1 \end{bmatrix} \end{array} \text{Herbivores}$$

The matrix AB gives the fraction of each plant that is effectively consumed by each carnivore.

(a) Find AB.

(b) What fraction of plant type 1 (row 1 of matrix A) is effectively consumed by each carnivore?

(c) Identify the plant type that each carnivore effectively consumes the most.

17. A furniture manufacturer produces four styles of chairs and has orders for 1000 of style A, 4000 of style B, 2000 of style C, and 1000 of style D. The following table lists the numbers of units of raw materials the manufacturer needs for each style. Suppose wood costs $5 per unit, nylon costs $3 per unit, velvet costs $4 per unit, and springs cost $4 per unit.

	Wood	Nylon	Velvet	Springs
Style A	10	5	0	0
Style B	5	0	20	10
Style C	5	20	0	10
Style D	5	10	10	10

(a) Form a 1×4 matrix containing the number of units of each style ordered.

(b) Use matrix multiplication to determine the total number of units of each raw material needed.

(c) Write a 4×1 matrix representing the costs of the raw materials.

(d) Use matrix multiplication to find the 1×1 matrix that represents the total investment to fill the orders.

(e) Use matrix multiplication to determine the cost of materials for each style of chair.

18. Complete parts (a) and (b) using the code discussed in Sections 3.2 and 3.4 (where a is 1, …, z is 26, and blank is 27), and the coding matrix is

$$A = \begin{bmatrix} 8 & 5 \\ 3 & 2 \end{bmatrix}$$

(a) Encode the message "Less is more," the motto of architect Mies van der Rohe.

(b) Decode the message 200, 76, 175, 69, 77, 30, 175, 69, 167, 65, 231, 87, 103, 41, 295, 114.

19. A young couple with a $120,000 inheritance wants to invest all this money. They plan to diversify their investments, choosing some of each of the following types of stock.

Type	Cost/Share	Expected Total Growth/Share
Growth	$ 30	$ 4.60
Blue-chip	100	11.00
Utility	50	5.00

Their strategy is to have the total investment in growth stocks equal to the sum of the other investments, and their goal is a 13% growth for their investment. How many shares of each type of stock should they purchase?

20. Suppose an economy has two industries, agriculture and minerals, and the economy has the technology matrix

$$A = \begin{array}{cc} & \begin{array}{cc} \text{Ag} & \text{M} \end{array} \\ \begin{bmatrix} 0.4 & 0.2 \\ 0.1 & 0.3 \end{bmatrix} & \begin{array}{c} \text{Ag} \\ \text{M} \end{array} \end{array}$$

(a) If surpluses of 100 agriculture units and 140 minerals units are desired, find the gross production of each industry.

(b) How many additional units must each industry produce to have 4 more units of agricultural surplus?

(c) How many additional units must each industry produce for 1 more unit of minerals surplus?

21. Suppose the technology matrix for a closed model of a simple economy is given by matrix A. Find the gross productions of the industries.

$$A = \begin{array}{c} \\ \\ \\ \end{array} \begin{array}{ccc} P & NP & H \\ \left[\begin{array}{ccc} 0.4 & 0.3 & 0.4 \\ 0.2 & 0.4 & 0.2 \\ 0.4 & 0.3 & 0.4 \end{array} \right] & \begin{array}{l} \text{Profit} \\ \text{Nonprofit} \\ \text{Households} \end{array} \end{array}$$

Use the following information in Problems 22 and 23. The national economy of Swiziland has four products: agricultural products, machinery, fuel, and steel. Producing 1 unit of agricultural products requires 0.2 unit of agricultural products, 0.3 unit of machinery, 0.2 unit of fuel, and 0.1 unit of steel. Producing 1 unit of machinery requires 0.1 unit of agricultural products, 0.2 unit of machinery, 0.2 unit of fuel, and 0.4 unit of steel.

Producing 1 unit of fuel requires 0.1 unit of agricultural products, 0.2 unit of machinery, 0.3 unit of fuel, and 0.2 unit of steel. Producing 1 unit of steel requires 0.1 unit of agricultural products, 0.2 unit of machinery, 0.3 unit of fuel, and 0.2 unit of steel.

22. Create the technology matrix for this economy.

23. Determine how many units of each product will give surpluses of 1700 units of agriculture products, 1900 units of machinery, 900 units of fuel, and 300 units of steel.

24. A simple closed economy has the technology matrix A. Find the total outputs of the four sectors of the economy.

$$A = \begin{array}{c} \\ \\ \\ \\ \end{array} \begin{array}{cccc} Ag & S & F & H \\ \left[\begin{array}{cccc} 0.25 & 0.25 & 0.3 & 0.1 \\ 0.3 & 0.25 & 0.2 & 0.4 \\ 0.15 & 0.2 & 0.1 & 0.3 \\ 0.3 & 0.3 & 0.4 & 0.2 \end{array} \right] & \begin{array}{l} \text{Agriculture} \\ \text{Steel} \\ \text{Fuel} \\ \text{Households} \end{array} \end{array}$$

3   EXTENDED APPLICATIONS & GROUP PROJECTS

I. Taxation

Federal income tax allows a deduction for any state income tax paid during the year. In addition, the state of Alabama allows a deduction from its state income tax for any federal income tax paid during the year. The federal corporate income tax rate is equivalent to a flat rate of 34% if the taxable federal income is between $335,000 and $10,000,000, and the Alabama rate is 5% of the taxable state income.*

Both the Alabama and federal taxable income for a corporation are $1,000,000 *before* either tax is paid. Because each tax is deductible on the other return, the taxable income will differ for the state and federal taxes. One procedure often used by tax accountants to find the tax due in this and similar situations is called *iteration* and is described by the first five steps below.[†]

1. Make an estimate of the federal taxes due by assuming no state tax is due, deduct this estimated federal tax due from the state taxable income, and calculate an estimate of the state taxes due on the basis of this assumption.

2. Deduct the estimated state tax due as computed in (1) from the federal taxable income, and calculate a new estimate of the federal tax due under this assumption.

3. Deduct the new estimated federal income tax due as computed in (2) from the state taxable income, and calculate a new estimate of the state taxes due on the basis of these calculations.

4. Repeat the process in (2) and (3) to get a better estimate of the taxes due to both governments.

5. Continue this process until the federal tax changes from one repetition to another by less than $1. What federal tax is due? What state tax is due?

To find the tax due each government directly, we can solve a matrix equation.

6. Create two linear equations that describe this taxation situation, convert the system to a matrix equation, and solve the system to find the tax due to each government.

7. What is the effective rate that this corporation pays to each government?

II. Company Profits after Bonuses and Taxes

A company earns $800,000 profit before paying bonuses and taxes. Suppose that a bonus package of 2% is paid to the employees after all taxes are paid, that state taxes of 6% are paid on the profit after the bonuses are paid, and that federal taxes are 34% of the profit that remains after bonuses and state taxes are paid.

1. How much profit remains after all taxes and bonuses are paid? Give your answer to the nearest dollar.

2. If the employee bonus package is increased to 3%, employees would receive 50% more bonus money. How

much more profit would this cost the company than the 2% bonuses?

3. Use a calculator or spreadsheet to determine the loss of profit associated with bonus packages of 4%, 5%, etc., up to 10%, and make a management decision about what bonuses to give to balance employee morale with loss of profit.

4. Use technology and the data points found above to create an equation that models the company's profit after expenses as a function of the employee bonus percent.

*Source: Federal Income Tax Tables and Alabama Income Tax Instructions.
[†]Performing these steps with an electronic spreadsheet is described by Kenneth H. Johnson in "A Simplified Calculation of Mutually Dependent Federal and State Tax Liabilities," in *The Journal of Taxation*, December 1994.

Inequalities and Linear Programming

Most companies seek to maximize profits subject to the limitations imposed by product demand and available resources (such as raw materials and labor) or to minimize production costs subject to the need to fill customer orders. If the relationships among the various resources, production requirements, costs, and profits are all linear, then these activities may be planned (or programmed) in the best possible (optimal) way using **linear programming.** Because linear programming provides the best possible solution to problems involving allocation of limited resources among various activities, its impact has been tremendous.

In this chapter, we introduce and discuss this important method. Chapter topics and some representative applications include the following.

Prerequisite Problem Type	For Section	Answer	Section for Review
(a) Solve $3x - 2y \geq 4$ for y. (b) Solve $2x + 4y = 60$ for y.	**4.1**	(a) $y \leq \frac{3}{2}x - 2$ (b) $y = 15 - \frac{1}{2}x$	1.1 Linear equations and inequalities
Graph the equation $y = \frac{3}{2}x - 2$.	**4.1–4.2**		1.3 Graphing linear equations
Solve the systems: (a) $\begin{cases} x + 2y = 10 \\ 2x + y = 14 \end{cases}$ (b) $\begin{cases} x + 0.5y = 16 \\ x + y = 24 \end{cases}$	**4.1–4.2**	(a) $x = 6, y = 2$ (b) $x = 8, y = 16$	1.5 Systems of linear equations
Write the system in an augmented matrix: $\begin{cases} x + 2y + s_1 = 10 \\ 2x + y + s_2 = 14 \\ -2x - 3y + f = 0 \end{cases}$	**4.3–4.5**	$\begin{bmatrix} 1 & 2 & 1 & 0 & 0 & \vline & 10 \\ 2 & 1 & 0 & 1 & 0 & \vline & 14 \\ -2 & -3 & 0 & 0 & 1 & \vline & 0 \end{bmatrix}$	3.3 Gauss-Jordan elimination
Write a matrix equivalent to matrix A with the entry in row 1, column 2 equal to 1 and with all other entries in column 2 equal to 0. First multiply row 1 by $\frac{1}{2}$. $A = \begin{bmatrix} 1 & 2 & 1 & 0 & 0 & \vline & 10 \\ 2 & 1 & 0 & 1 & 0 & \vline & 14 \\ -2 & -3 & 0 & 0 & 1 & \vline & 0 \end{bmatrix}$	**4.3–4.5**	$\begin{bmatrix} \frac{1}{2} & 1 & \frac{1}{2} & 0 & 0 & \vline & 5 \\ \frac{3}{2} & 0 & -\frac{1}{2} & 1 & 0 & \vline & 9 \\ -\frac{1}{2} & 0 & \frac{3}{2} & 0 & 1 & \vline & 15 \end{bmatrix}$	3.3 Gauss-Jordan elimination

SECTION 4.1

Linear Inequalities in Two Variables

OBJECTIVES

- To graph linear inequalities in two variables
- To solve systems of linear inequalities in two variables

APPLICATION PREVIEW

CDF Appliances has assembly plants in Atlanta and Fort Worth, where the company produces a variety of kitchen appliances, including a 12-cup coffee maker and a cappuccino machine. The following table shows each factory's assembly capabilities for the two products and the numbers needed to fill orders.

	Atlanta	Fort Worth	Needed
Coffee maker	160/hr	800/hr	At least 64,000
Cappuccino machine	200/hr	200/hr	At least 40,000

At each plant, the number of assembly hours available for these two appliances is limited (constrained) by each plant's capacity and the need to fill the orders. Finding the assembly hours for each plant that satisfy all these constraints at the same time is called solving the system of inequalities. (See Example 4.)

One Linear Inequality in Two Variables

Before we look at systems of inequalities, we will discuss solutions of one inequality in two variables, such as $y < x$. The solutions of this inequality are the ordered pairs (x, y) that satisfy the inequality. Thus $(1, 0)$, $(3, 2)$, $(0, -1)$, and $(-2, -5)$ are solutions of $y < x$, but $(3, 7)$, $(-4, -3)$, and $(2, 2)$ are not.

The graph of $y < x$ consists of all points in which the y-coordinate is less than the x-coordinate. The graph of the region $y < x$ can be found by graphing the line $y = x$ (as a dashed line because the given inequality does not include $y = x$). This line separates the xy-plane into two **half-planes,** $y < x$ and $y > x$. We can determine which half-plane is the solution region by selecting as a **test point** any point *not on the line*; let's choose $(2, 0)$. Because the coordinates of this test point satisfy the inequality $y < x$, the half-plane containing this point is the solution region for $y < x$. (See Figure 4.1.) If the coordinates of the test point do not satisfy the inequality, then the other half-plane is the solution region. For example, say that we had chosen $(0, 4)$ as our test point. Its coordinates do not satisfy $y < x$, so the half-plane that does *not* contain $(0, 4)$ is the solution region. (Note that we get the same region.)

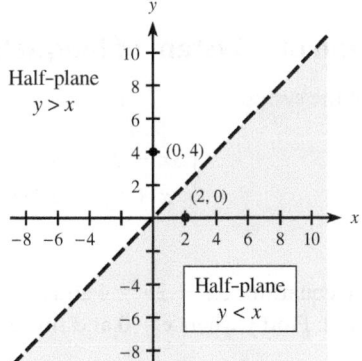

Figure 4.1

EXAMPLE 1 **Graphing an Inequality**

Graph the inequality $4x - 2y \leq 6$.

Solution

First we graph the line $4x - 2y = 6$, or (equivalently) $y = 2x - 3$, as a solid line because points lying on the line satisfy the given inequality. Next, we pick a test point that is not on the line. If we use $(0, 0)$, we see that its coordinates satisfy $4x - 2y \leq 6$—that is, $y \geq 2x - 3$. Hence the **solution region** is the line $y = 2x - 3$ and the half-plane that contains the test point $(0, 0)$. See Figure 4.2.

Figure 4.2

Figure 4.3

Calculator Note To shade the region that is the solution for $y \geq 2x - 3$, shown in Figure 4.2, enter the equation $y = 2x - 3$ in Y_1, move the cursor to the left of Y_1, and press ENTER until a triangle in the right upper corner appears in place of the "\" that was there originally. Then press GRAPH. Details are shown in Appendix A, Section 4.1. Figure 4.3 shows the solution region a graphing calculator screen with the standard window.

Systems of Linear Inequalities

If we have two or more inequalities in two variables, we can find the solutions that satisfy all the inequalities. We call the inequalities a **system of inequalities,** and the solution of the system can be found by finding the intersection of the solution sets of all the inequalities.

The solution set of the system of inequalities can be found by graphing the inequalities on the same set of axes and noting their points of intersection.

EXAMPLE 2 **Graphical Solution of a System of Inequalities**

Graph the solution of the system

$$\begin{cases} 3x - 2y \geq 4 \\ x + y - 3 > 0 \end{cases}$$

Solution

Begin by graphing the equations $3x - 2y = 4$ and $x + y = 3$ (from $x + y - 3 = 0$) by the intercept method: Find y when $x = 0$ and find x when $y = 0$.

$3x - 2y = 4$		$x + y = 3$	
x	y	x	y
0	-2	0	3
$4/3$	0	3	0

We graph $3x - 2y = 4$ as a solid line and $x + y = 3$ as a dashed line [see Figure 4.4(a)]. We use any point not on either line as a test point; let's use $(0, 0)$. Note that the coordinates of $(0, 0)$ do not satisfy either $3x - 2y \geq 4$ or $x + y - 3 > 0$. Thus the solution region for each individual inequality is the half-plane that does not contain the point $(0, 0)$. Figure 4.4(b) indicates the half-plane solution for each inequality with arrows pointing from the line into the desired half-plane (away from the test point). The points that satisfy both of these inequalities lie in the intersection of the two individual solution regions, shown in Figure 4.4(c). This solution region is the graph of the solution of this system of inequalities.

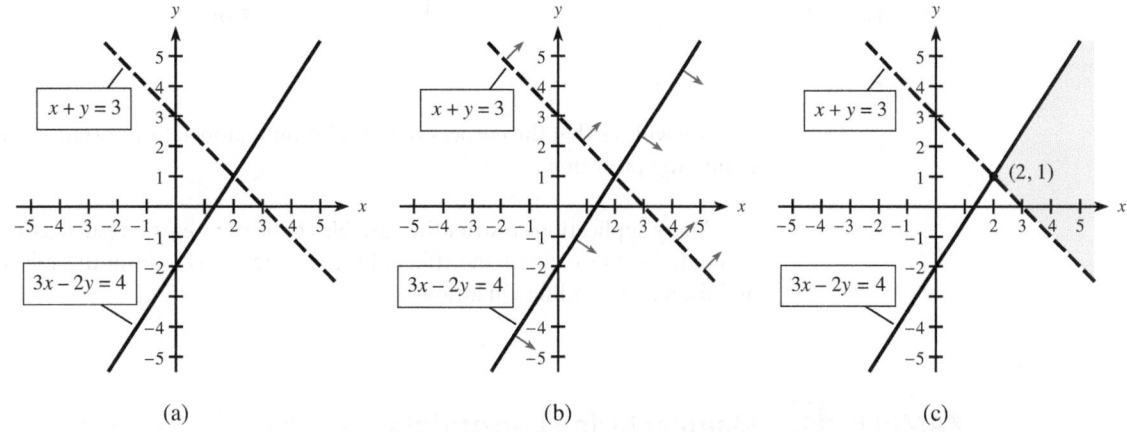

Figure 4.4   (a)   (b)   (c)

The point $(2, 1)$ in Figure 4.4(c), where the two regions form a "corner," can be found by solving the *equations* $3x - 2y = 4$ and $x + y = 3$ simultaneously.

EXAMPLE 3   Graphical Solution of a System of Inequalities

Graph the solution of the system

$$\begin{cases} x + 2y \leq 10 \\ 2x + y \leq 14 \\ x \geq 0, y \geq 0 \end{cases}$$

Solution

The two inequalities $x \geq 0$ and $y \geq 0$ restrict the solution to Quadrant I (and the axes bounding Quadrant I).

We seek points in the first quadrant (on or above $y = 0$ and on or to the right of $x = 0$) that satisfy $x + 2y \leq 10$ *and* $2x + y \leq 14$. Note that the test point $(0, 0)$ satisfies both of these inequalities. Thus the solution region lies in Quadrant I and toward the origin from the lines $x + 2y = 10$ and $2x + y = 14$. (See Figure 4.5.) We can observe from the graph that the points $(0, 0)$, $(7, 0)$, and $(0, 5)$ are corners of the solution region. The corner $(6, 2)$ is found by solving the *equations* $y = 5 - \frac{1}{2}x$ and $y = 14 - 2x$ simultaneously as follows:

$$5 - \frac{1}{2}x = 14 - 2x$$
$$\frac{3}{2}x = 9$$
$$x = 6$$
$$y = 2$$

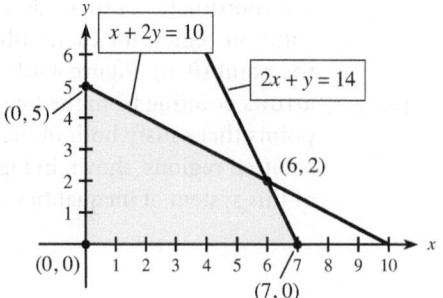

Figure 4.5

We will see that the corners of the solution region are important in solving linear programming problems.

Many applications restrict the variables to be nonnegative (such as $x \geq 0$ and $y \geq 0$ in Example 3). As we noted, the effect of this restriction is to limit the solution to Quadrant I and the axes bounding Quadrant I.

EXAMPLE 4 Manufacturing Constraints | APPLICATION PREVIEW |

CDF Appliances has assembly plants in Atlanta and Fort Worth, where the company produces a variety of kitchen appliances, including a 12-cup coffee maker and a cappuccino machine. The following table shows each factory's assembly capabilities for the two products and the numbers needed to fill orders.

	Atlanta	Fort Worth	Needed
Coffee maker	160/hr	800/hr	At least 64,000
Cappuccino machine	200/hr	200/hr	At least 40,000

Write the system of inequalities that describes the number of assembly hours needed at each plant to fill the orders and graph the solution region for the system.

Solution

Let x be the number of assembly hours at the Atlanta plant and let y be the number of assembly hours at the Fort Worth plant. The information in the table and the fact that both x and y must be nonnegative give the following constraints.

$$160x + 800y \geq 64{,}000$$
$$200x + 200y \geq 40{,}000$$
$$x \geq 0, y \geq 0$$

The solution is restricted to Quadrant I and the axes that bound Quadrant I. The equation $160x + 800y = 64{,}000$ can be graphed with x- and y-intercepts:

$$x\text{-intercept: } y = 0 \quad \text{gives} \quad 160x = 64{,}000 \quad \text{or} \quad x = 400$$
$$y\text{-intercept: } x = 0 \quad \text{gives} \quad 800y = 64{,}000 \quad \text{or} \quad y = 80$$

The test point $(0, 0)$ does not satisfy $160x + 800y \geq 64{,}000$, so the region lies above the line [see Figure 4.6(a)]. In like manner, the region satisfying $200x + 200y \geq 40{,}000$ lies above the line $200x + 200y = 40{,}000$ with intercepts $(200, 0)$ and $(0, 200)$, and the solution region for this system is shown in Figure 4.6(b).

The corner $(150, 50)$ is found by solving simultaneously as follows.

$$\begin{cases} 160x + 800y = 64{,}000 \\ 200x + 200y = 40{,}000 \end{cases} \quad \text{is equivalent to} \quad \begin{cases} x + 5y = 400 & (1) \\ x + y = 200 & (2) \end{cases}$$

Finding equation (1) minus equation (2) gives one equation in one variable and allows us to complete the solution.

$$4y = 200, \quad \text{so} \quad y = 200/4 = 50 \quad \text{and} \quad x = 200 - y = 150$$

Any point in the shaded region of Figure 4.6(b) represents a possible number of assembly hours at each plant that would fill the orders.

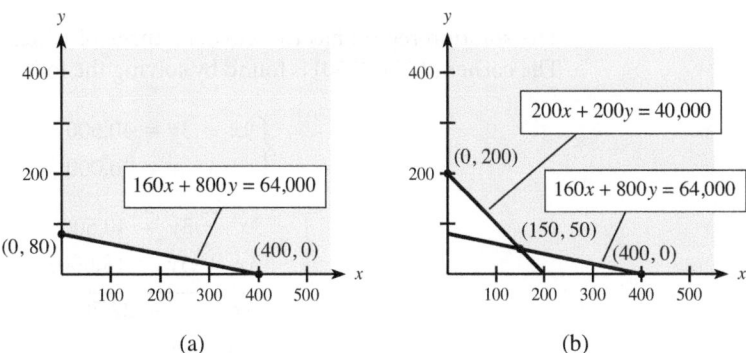

Figure 4.6   (a)   (b)

EXAMPLE 5   Land Management

A farm co-op has 6000 acres available to plant with corn and soybeans. Each acre of corn requires 9 gallons of fertilizer/herbicide and 3/4 hour of labor to harvest. Each acre of soybeans requires 3 gallons of fertilizer/herbicide and 1 hour of labor to harvest. The co-op has available at most 40,500 gallons of fertilizer/herbicide and at most 5250 hours of labor for harvesting. The number of acres of each crop is limited (constrained) by the available resources: land, fertilizer/herbicide, and labor for harvesting. Write the system of inequalities that describes the constraints and graph the solution region for the system.

Solution

If x represents the number of acres of corn and y represents the number of acres of soybeans, then both x and y must be nonnegative and we have the following constraints.

Land acres:	$x + y \leq 6{,}000$	(1)
Fertilizer/herbicide gallons:	$9x + 3y \leq 40{,}500$	(2)
Labor hours:	$\dfrac{3}{4}x + y \leq 5{,}250$	(3)
	$x \geq 0, y \geq 0$	

The solution region for this system of constraints is in Quadrant I. In addition, the test point $(0, 0)$ satisfies all the constraints, so the origin must be part of the solution region.

The intercepts of the lines associated with the inequalities are

$$(6000, 0) \text{ and } (0, 6000) \text{ for the line } x + y = 6000 \qquad \text{[from inequality (1)]}$$

$$(4500, 0) \text{ and } (0, 13{,}500) \text{ for the line } 9x + 3y = 40{,}500 \quad \text{[from inequality (2)]}$$

$$(7000, 0) \text{ and } (0, 5250) \text{ for the line } \frac{3}{4}x + y = 5250 \qquad \text{[from inequality (3)]}$$

The solution region has five corners, three of which are (0, 0), (4500, 0), and (0, 5250). The corner (3750, 2250) is found by solving the following system.

$$\begin{cases} 9x + 3y = 40{,}500 & (4) \\ x + y = 6{,}000 & (5) \end{cases}$$

$$\begin{cases} 9x + 3y = 40{,}500 & (4) \\ -(3x + 3y = 18{,}000) & [3 \times \text{ eq. (5)}] \end{cases}$$

$$6x \qquad = 22{,}500$$

$$x = \frac{22{,}500}{6} = 3750 \qquad \text{so} \qquad y = 6000 - x = 2250$$

The corner (3000, 3000) is found similarly by solving $x + y = 6000$ and $\frac{3}{4}x + y = 5250$ simultaneously. (See the solution region in Figure 4.7.)

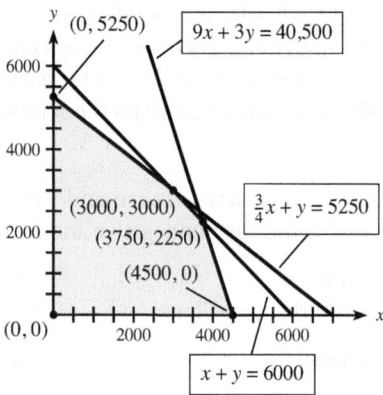

Figure 4.7

These five corners and the line segments joining them determine the borders of the solution region, shaded in Figure 4.7. Any point in this region represents a possible number of acres of corn and of soybeans that the co-op could plant, treat with fertilizer/herbicide, and harvest.

CHECKPOINT

1. Graph the region determined by the inequalities

$$2x + 3y \le 12$$
$$4x + 2y \le 16$$
$$x \ge 0, y \ge 0$$

2. Determine the corners of the region.

Calculator Note   Graphing calculators can be used in the graphical solution of a system of inequalities. See Appendix A, Section 4.1, and Example 6 for details.

EXAMPLE 6   **Finding a Solution Region with a Graphing Calculator**

Use a graphing calculator to find the following:
(a) The region determined by the inequalities below.

$$5x + 2y \leq 54$$
$$2x + 4y \leq 60$$
$$x \geq 0, y \geq 0$$

(b) The corners of this region.

Solution

(a) We first write the inequalities solved for y.

$$5x + 2y \leq 54 \Rightarrow y \leq 27 - \frac{5}{2}x \quad \text{and} \quad 2x + 4y \leq 60 \Rightarrow y \leq 15 - \frac{1}{2}x$$

Enter these inequalities using the lower triangle to the left of Y_1 and Y_2 in the Y= menu. [See Figure 4.8(a).] The cross-hatched region in Figure 4.8(b) shows the solution.

Figure 4.8   (a)   (b)

(b) Finding the x- and y-intercepts and using INTERSECT (Calc, 5: intersect) with pairs of lines that form the borders of this region will give the points where the boundaries intersect. These points—$(0, 0)$, $(0, 15)$, $(6, 12)$, and $(10.8, 0)$—also can be found algebraically. These points are the corners of the solution region. These corners will be important in the graphical solutions of linear programming problems in the next section.

**CHECKPOINT
ANSWERS**

1.

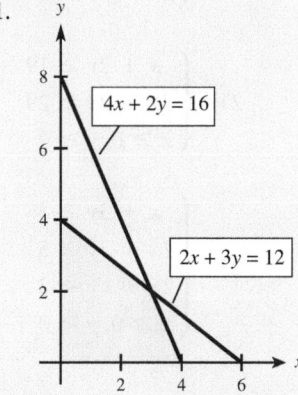

2. Corners at $(0, 0)$, $(0, 4)$, $(4, 0)$, and $(3, 2)$.

EXERCISES 4.1

In Problems 1–6, graph each inequality.

1. $y \le 2x - 1$

2. $y \ge 4x - 5$

3. $\dfrac{x}{2} + \dfrac{y}{4} < 1$

4. $x - \dfrac{y}{3} < \dfrac{-2}{3}$

5. $0.4x \ge 0.8$

6. $\dfrac{-y}{8} > \dfrac{1}{4}$

In Problems 7–12, the graph of the boundary equations for each system of inequalities is shown with that system. Locate the solution region and find the corners.

7. $\begin{cases} x + 4y \le 60 \\ 4x + 2y \le 100 \\ x \ge 0, y \ge 0 \end{cases}$

8. $\begin{cases} 4x + 3y \le 240 \\ 5x - y \le 110 \\ x \ge 0, y \ge 0 \end{cases}$

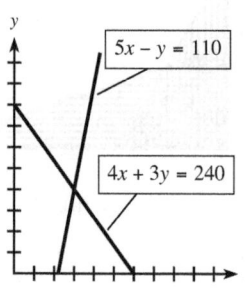

9. $\begin{cases} -3x + 4y \le 18 \\ 2x + y \ge 10 \\ x + y \le 15 \\ x \ge 0, y \ge 0 \end{cases}$

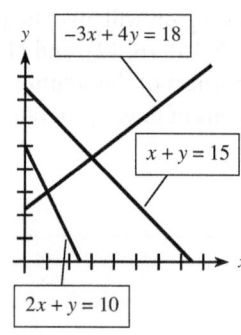

10. $\begin{cases} x + y \le 25 \\ 4x + y \le 40 \\ 3x + 8y \ge 88 \\ x \ge 0, y \ge 0 \end{cases}$

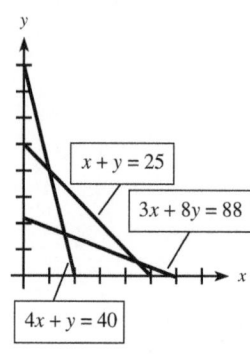

11. $\begin{cases} x + 3y \ge 6 \\ 2x + 4y \ge 10 \\ 3x + y \ge 5 \\ x \ge 0, y \ge 0 \end{cases}$

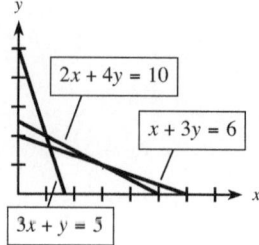

12. $\begin{cases} x + 4y \ge 10 \\ 4x + 2y \ge 10 \\ x + y \ge 4 \\ x \ge 0, y \ge 0 \end{cases}$

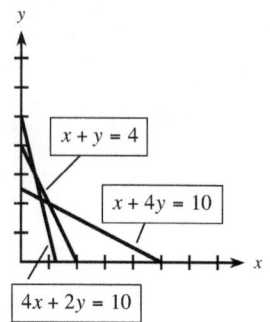

In Problems 13–26, graph the solution of each system of inequalities.

13. $\begin{cases} y < 2x \\ y > x - 1 \end{cases}$

14. $\begin{cases} y > 3x - 4 \\ y < 2x + 3 \end{cases}$

15. $\begin{cases} 2x + y < 3 \\ x - 2y \ge -1 \end{cases}$

16. $\begin{cases} 3x + y > 4 \\ x - 2y < -1 \end{cases}$

17. $\begin{cases} x + 5y \le 200 \\ 2x + 3y \le 134 \\ x \ge 0, y \ge 0 \end{cases}$

18. $\begin{cases} -x + y \le 2 \\ x + 2y \le 10 \\ 3x + y \le 15 \\ x \ge 0, y \ge 0 \end{cases}$

19. $\begin{cases} x + 2y \le 48 \\ x + y \le 30 \\ 2x + y \le 50 \\ x \ge 0, y \ge 0 \end{cases}$

20. $\begin{cases} 3x + y \le 9 \\ 3x + 2y \le 12 \\ x + 2y \le 8 \\ x \ge 0, y \ge 0 \end{cases}$

21. $\begin{cases} x + 2y \ge 19 \\ 3x + 2y \ge 29 \\ x \ge 0, y \ge 0 \end{cases}$

22. $\begin{cases} 4x + y \ge 12 \\ x + y \ge 9 \\ x + 3y \ge 15 \\ x \ge 0, y \ge 0 \end{cases}$

23. $\begin{cases} x + 3y \ge 3 \\ 2x + 3y \ge 5 \\ 2x + y \ge 3 \\ x \ge 0, y \ge 0 \end{cases}$

24. $\begin{cases} x + 2y \ge 10 \\ 2x + y \ge 11 \\ x + y \ge 9 \\ x \ge 0, y \ge 0 \end{cases}$

25. $\begin{cases} x + 2y \geq 20 \\ -3x + 2y \leq 4 \\ x \geq 12 \\ x \geq 0, y \geq 0 \end{cases}$ 26. $\begin{cases} 3x + 2y \geq 75 \\ -3x + 5y \geq 30 \\ y \leq 40 \\ x \geq 0, y \geq 0 \end{cases}$

APPLICATIONS

27. *Management* The Wellbuilt Company produces two types of wood chippers, economy and deluxe. The deluxe model requires 3 hours to assemble and 1/2 hour to paint, and the economy model requires 2 hours to assemble and 1 hour to paint. The maximum number of assembly hours available is 24 per day, and the maximum number of painting hours available is 8 per day.
    (a) Write the system of inequalities that describes the constraints on the number of each type of wood chipper produced. Begin by identifying what x and y represent.
    (b) Graph the solution of the system of inequalities and find the corners of the solution region.

28. *Learning environments* An experiment that involves learning in animals requires placing white mice and rabbits into separate, controlled environments: environment I and environment II. The maximum amount of time available in environment I is 420 minutes, and the maximum amount of time available in environment II is 600 minutes. The white mice must spend 10 minutes in environment I and 25 minutes in environment II, and the rabbits must spend 12 minutes in environment I and 15 minutes in environment II.
    (a) Write a system of inequalities that describes the constraints on the number of each type of animal used in the experiment. Begin by identifying what x and y represent.
    (b) Graph the solution of the system of inequalities and find the corners of the solution region.

29. *Manufacturing* A company manufactures two types of electric hedge trimmers, one of which is cordless. The cord-type trimmer requires 2 hours to make, and the cordless model requires 4 hours. The company has only 800 work hours to use in manufacturing each day, and the packaging department can package only 300 trimmers per day.
    (a) Write the inequalities that describe the constraints on the number of each type of hedge trimmer produced. Begin by identifying what x and y represent.
    (b) Graph the region determined by these constraint inequalities.

30. *Manufacturing* Sierra Wood Products manufactures two products, rockers and bookshelf units. Its profit is $30 per rocker and $42 per bookshelf unit. Next week's production will be constrained by two limited resources, labor and wood. The labor available next week is expected to be at most 930 hours, and the amount of wood available is expected to be at most 2400 board feet. Each rocker requires 4 labor hours and 8 board feet of wood. Each bookshelf unit requires 3 labor hours and 12 board feet of wood.
    (a) Write the inequalities that describe the constraints on the number of each product produced next week. Begin by identifying what x and y represent.
    (b) Graph the region determined by these constraint inequalities.

31. *Advertising* Apex Motors manufactures luxury cars and sport-utility vehicles. The most likely customers are high-income men and women, and company managers want to initiate an advertising campaign targeting these groups. They plan to run 1-minute spots on business/investment programs, where they can reach 7 million women and 4 million men from their target groups. They also plan 1-minute spots during sporting events, where they can reach 2 million women and 12 million men from their target groups. Apex believes that the ads must reach at least 30 million women and at least 28 million men who are prospective customers.
    (a) Write the inequalities that describe the constraints on the number of each type of 1-minute spots needed to reach these target groups.
    (b) Graph the region determined by these constraint inequalities.

32. *Manufacturing* The Digital Star Company makes two different models of computer tablets, which are assembled on two different assembly lines. Line 1 can assemble 30 units of the Star model and 40 units of the Prostar model per hour, and Line 2 can assemble 150 units of the Star model and 40 units of the Prostar model per hour. The company needs to produce at least 270 units of the Star model and 200 units of the Prostar model to fill an order.
    (a) Write the inequalities that describe the production constraints on the number of each type of tablet needed to fill the order.
    (b) Graph the region determined by these constraint inequalities.

33. *Politics* A candidate wants to use a combination of radio and television advertisements in her campaign. Research has shown that each 1-minute spot on television reaches 0.09 million people and each 1-minute spot on radio reaches 0.006 million. The candidate believes she must reach at least 2.16 million people,

and she must buy a total of at least 80 minutes of advertisements.

(a) Write the inequalities that relate the number of each type of advertising to her needs.

(b) Graph the region determined by these constraint inequalities.

34. *Nutrition* In a hospital ward, the patients can be grouped into two general categories depending on their condition and the amount of solid foods they require in their diet. A combination of two diets is used for solid foods because they supply essential nutrients for recovery. The following table summarizes the patient groups and their minimum daily requirements.

	Diet A	Diet B	Daily Requirement
Group 1	4 oz per serving	1 oz per serving	26 oz
Group 2	2 oz per serving	1 oz per serving	18 oz

(a) Write the inequalities that describe how many servings of each diet are needed to provide the nutritional requirements.

(b) Graph the region determined by these constraint inequalities.

35. *Manufacturing* A sausage company makes two different kinds of hot dogs, regular and all beef. Each type of hot dog uses some ingredients that are always available, but supplies of beef, pork, and spices are limited. Each pound of all-beef hot dogs requires 0.75 lb of beef and 0.2 lb of spices, and each pound of regular hot dogs requires 0.18 lb of beef, 0.3 lb of pork, and 0.2 lb of spices. Suppliers can deliver at most 1020 lb of beef, at most 600 lb of pork, and at least 500 lb of spices.

(a) Write the inequalities that describe how many pounds of each type of hot dog can be produced.

(b) Graph the region determined by these constraint inequalities.

36. *Manufacturing* A cereal manufacturer makes two different kinds of cereal, Senior Citizen's Feast and Kids Go. Each pound of Senior Citizen's Feast requires 0.6 lb of wheat and 0.2 lb of vitamin-enriched syrup, and each pound of Kids Go requires 0.4 lb of wheat, 0.2 lb of sugar, and 0.2 lb of vitamin-enriched syrup. Suppliers can deliver at most 2800 lb of wheat, at most 800 lb of sugar, and at least 1000 lb of the vitamin-enriched syrup.

(a) Write the inequalities that describe how many pounds of each type of cereal can be made.

(b) Graph the region determined by these constraint inequalities.

SECTION 4.2   Linear Programming: Graphical Methods

OBJECTIVES

- To use graphical methods to find the optimal value of a linear function subject to constraints

APPLICATION PREVIEW

Many practical problems in business and economics seek to optimize some function (such as cost or profit) subject to complex relationships among capital, raw materials, labor, etc. Consider the following example.

A farm co-op has 6000 acres available on which to plant corn and soybeans. The following table summarizes each crop's requirements for fertilizer/herbicide, harvesting labor hours, and the available amounts of these resources.

	Corn	Soybeans	Available
Fertilizer/herbicide	9 gal/acre	3 gal/acre	40,500 gal
Harvesting labor	3/4 hr/acre	1 hr/acre	5250 hr

Thus the co-op's resources of land, fertilizer/herbicide, and harvest time are limited (constrained). If profits per acre are $240 for corn and $160 for soybeans, how many acres of each crop should the co-op plant to maximize profit? What is the maximum profit?

The farm co-op's maximum profit can be found by using a mathematical technique called **linear programming**. (See Example 2.)

Linear Programming

Linear programming is a technique that can be used to solve problems such as the one posed in the Application Preview. If the limitations on the variables (called **constraints**) can be expressed as linear inequalities and the function that is to be maximized or minimized (called the **objective function**) is a linear function, then the problem is called a **linear programming problem** (LP-problem). Linear programming is widely used by businesses for problems that involve many variables (sometimes more than 100).

In this section, we begin our study of this important topic by considering problems involving two variables, which can be solved with graphical methods. The constraints form a system of linear inequalities in two variables whose solution determines a region, any point of which may yield the *optimal* (maximum or minimum) value for the objective function.* Hence any point in the region determined by the constraints is called a **feasible solution,** and the region itself is called the **feasible region**. In a linear programming problem, we seek the feasible solution that maximizes (or minimizes) the objective function.

EXAMPLE   1

Maximize the objective function $F = 3x + y$ subject to the following constraints (whose solution region is shown in Figure 4.9).

$$\begin{cases} x + 5y \le 50 \\ 2x + \ y \le 28 \\ x \ge 0, y \ge 0 \end{cases}$$

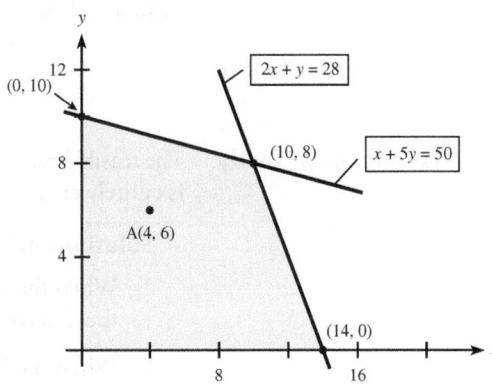

Figure 4.9

Solution

The shaded region of Figure 4.9 is the feasible region for this problem, and *any* point in this region is a possible solution. Notice that at point A (4, 6), the value of F is $F = 3(4) + 6 = 18$, and when $F = 18$, the objective function becomes

$$3x + y = 18 \quad \text{or} \quad y = -3x + 18$$

The line with this equation has slope $m = -3$ and y-intercept 18. Many points in the feasible region lie on this line [see Figure 4.10(a) on the next page], and their coordinates all give $F = 18$.

In general, when we write

$$3x + y = F \quad \text{as} \quad y = -3x + F$$

we see that for any value of F, the graph will be a line parallel to the one corresponding to $F = 18$. Figure 4.10(b) shows the feasible region and lines representing the objective function values $F = 18$, $F = 42$, and $F = 60$. If any part of one of these lines intersects the region, we have feasible solutions for that F-value. Note that the line representing $F = 42$ intersects the feasible region *only* at the corner point (14, 0). In addition, values of F greater than 42 give lines that miss the feasible region and hence cannot be solutions to the problem. This means that $F = 42$ is the largest value for which there is a feasible solution.

---

*The region determined by the constraints must be *convex* for the optimal value to exist. A convex region is one such that for any two points in the region, the segment joining those points lies entirely within the region. We restrict our discussion to convex regions.

Thus, subject to the given constraints, the maximum value of the objective function is $F = 42$ when $x = 14$ and $y = 0$.

Notice in Example 1 that the objective function was maximized at one of the "corners" (vertices) of the feasible region. This is not a coincidence; it turns out that a corner will always lie on the objective function line corresponding to the optimal value.

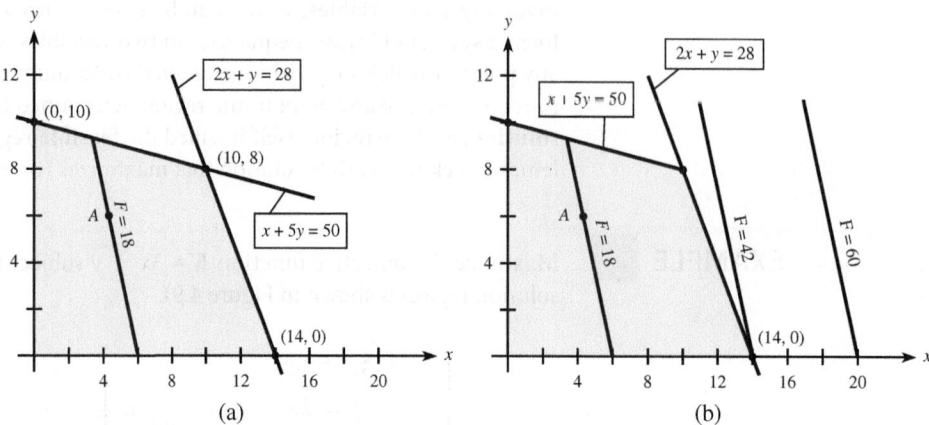

Figure 4.10   (a)   (b)

Solving Graphically   The feasible region in Figure 4.10 is an example of a **closed and bounded region** because it is entirely enclosed by, and includes, the lines associated with the constraints.

Solutions of Linear Programming Problems

1. When the feasible region for a linear programming problem is closed and bounded, the objective function has a maximum value and a minimum value.

2. When the feasible region is not closed and bounded, the objective function may have a maximum only, a minimum only, or no solution.

3. If a linear programming problem has a solution, then the optimal (maximum or minimum) value of an objective function occurs at a corner of the feasible region determined by the constraints.

4. If the objective function has its optimal value at two corners, then it also has that optimal value at any point on the boundary line connecting those two corners.

Thus, for a closed and bounded region, we can find the maximum or minimum value of the objective function by evaluating the function at each of the corners of the feasible region formed by the solution of the constraint inequalities. If the feasible region is not closed and bounded, we must check to make sure the objective function has an optimal value.

The steps involved in solving a linear programming problem are as follows.

LINEAR PROGRAMMING (GRAPHICAL METHOD)

Procedure	Example
To find the optimal value of a function subject to constraints:	Find the maximum and minimum values of $C = 2x + 3y$ subject to the constraints $$\begin{cases} x + 2y \le 10 \\ 2x + y \le 14 \\ x \ge 0, y \ge 0 \end{cases}$$

1. Write the objective function and constraint inequalities from the problem.

1. Objective function: $C = 2x + 3y$
   Constraints: $x + 2y \leq 10$
                    $2x + y \leq 14$
                    $x \geq 0, y \geq 0$

2. Graph the solution of the constraint system.
   (a) If the feasible region is closed and bounded, proceed to Step 3.
   (b) If the region is not closed and bounded, check whether an optimal value exists. If not, state this. If so, proceed to Step 3.

2. The constraint region is closed and bounded. See Figure 4.11.

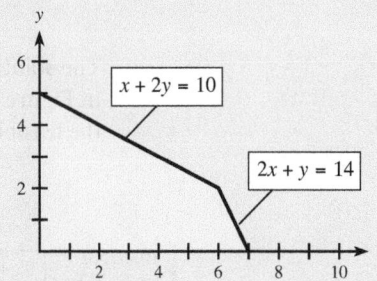

Figure 4.11

3. Find the corners of the resulting feasible region. This may require simultaneous solution of two or more pairs of boundary equations.

3. Corners $(0, 0)$, $(0, 5)$, $(6, 2)$, $(7, 0)$ were found in Example 3 of Section 4.1.

4. Evaluate the objective function at each corner of the feasible region determined by the constraints.

4. At $(0, 0)$, $C = 2x + 3y = 2(0) + 3(0) = 0$
   At $(0, 5)$, $C = 2x + 3y = 2(0) + 3(5) = 15$
   At $(6, 2)$, $C = 2x + 3y = 2(6) + 3(2) = 18$
   At $(7, 0)$, $C = 2x + 3y = 2(7) + 3(0) = 14$

5. If two corners give the optimal value of the objective function, then all points on the boundary line joining these two corners also optimize the function.

5. The function is maximized at $x = 6, y = 2$.
   The maximum value is $C = 18$.
   The function is minimized at $x = 0, y = 0$.
   The minimum value is $C = 0$.

EXAMPLE 2 **Maximizing Profit** | APPLICATION PREVIEW |

A farm co-op has 6000 acres available on which to plant corn and soybeans. The following table summarizes each crop's requirements for fertilizer/herbicide, harvesting labor hours, and the available amounts of these resources.

	Corn	Soybeans	Available
Fertilizer/herbicide	9 gal/acre	3 gal/acre	40,500 gal
Harvesting labor	3/4 hr/acre	1 hr/acre	5250 hr

(a) If the co-op's profits per acre are $240 for corn and $160 for soybeans, how many acres of each crop should the co-op plant to maximize profit? What is the maximum profit?

(b) If market conditions change so that the co-op's profits per acre change to $300 for corn and $100 for soybeans, how should the co-op adjust its planting to maximize profit? What is the maximum profit?

Solution

(a) If we let x equal the number of acres of corn and y equal the number of acres of soybeans, then the function that describes the co-op's profit is given by

$$\text{Profit} = P = 240x + 160y \text{ (in dollars)}$$

The constraints for this farm co-op application were developed in Example 5 of Section 4.1. Combining the constraints with the profit equation gives the linear programming problem:

$$\text{Maximize profit} \quad P = 240x + 160y$$
$$\text{subject to} \qquad x + y \le 6000 \qquad \text{Land constraint}$$
$$9x + 3y \le 40{,}500 \qquad \text{Fertilizer/herbicide constraint}$$
$$(3/4)x + y \le 5250 \qquad \text{Harvesting time constraint}$$
$$x \ge 0, y \ge 0$$

The solution of the system of constraint inequalities forms the feasible region shaded in Figure 4.12 (which was found in Example 5 of Section 4.1). We use the corners of the feasible region to complete the solution.

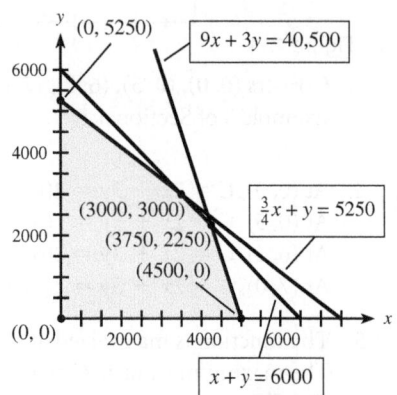

Corner	$P = 240x + 160y$
$(0, 0)$	$P = 240(0) + 160(0) = 0$
$(4500, 0)$	$P = 240(4500) + 160(0) = 1{,}080{,}000$
$(3750, 2250)$	$P = 240(3750) + 160(2250) = 1{,}260{,}000$
$(3000, 3000)$	$P = 240(3000) + 160(3000) = 1{,}200{,}000$
$(0, 5250)$	$P = 240(0) + 160(5250) = 840{,}000$

Figure 4.12

Thus the farm co-op's maximum profit, subject to the constraints (in other words, the solution of the co-op's linear programming problem), is $P = \$1{,}260{,}000$ when $x = 3750$ and $y = 2250$. That is, when the co-op plants 3750 acres of corn and 2250 acres of soybeans, it achieves maximum profit of $\$1{,}260{,}000$.

(b) In this case, the co-op's profit function is given by
$$\text{Profit}^* = P^* = 300x + 100y$$
where the asterisk is used to distinguish this function from the one in part (a). The feasible region is the same, so we use the corners to complete the solution. (See Figure 4.12.)

Corner	$P^* = 300x + 100y$
$(0, 0)$	$P^* = 300(0) + 100(0) = 0$
$(4500, 0)$	$P^* = 300(4500) + 100(0) = 1{,}350{,}000$
$(3750, 2250)$	$P^* = 300(3750) + 100(2250) = 1{,}350{,}000$
$(3000, 3000)$	$P^* = 300(3000) + 100(3000) = 1{,}200{,}000$
$(0, 5250)$	$P^* = 300(0) + 100(5250) = 525{,}000$

Hence the maximum profit of $\$1{,}350{,}000$ occurs at either the point $(4500, 0)$ or the point $(3750, 2250)$. This means that the profit function P^* will be maximized not only at these two corner points but also at any point on the segment joining them. Thus the co-op has maximum profit of $\$1{,}350{,}000$ at any pair of values along the segment joining $(4500, 0)$ and $(3750, 2250)$. For example, the point $(4000, 1500)$ is on this segment and the profit at this point is also $\$1{,}350{,}000$:

$$P^* = 300(4000) + 100(1500) = 1{,}350{,}000$$

CHECKPOINT

1. Find the maximum and minimum values of the objective function $f = 4x + 3y$ on the shaded region in the figure, determined by the following constraints.

$$\begin{cases} 2x + 3y \leq 12 \\ 4x - 2y \leq 8 \\ x \geq 0, y \geq 0 \end{cases}$$

The examples so far have involved closed and bounded regions. Similar procedures apply for an unbounded region, but optimal solutions are no longer guaranteed.

EXAMPLE 3   Minimization

Find the maximum and minimum values (if they exist) of $C = x + y$ subject to the constraints

$$3x + 2y \geq 12$$
$$x + 3y \geq 11$$
$$x \geq 0, y \geq 0$$

Solution

The graph of the constraint system is shown in Figure 4.13(a). The corners $(0, 6)$ and $(11, 0)$ can be identified from the graph. The third corner, $(2, 3)$, can be found by solving the equations $3x + 2y = 12$ and $x + 3y = 11$ simultaneously.

$$\begin{array}{r} 3x + 2y = 12 \\ -3x - 9y = -33 \\ \hline -7y = -21 \quad \Rightarrow y = 3 \quad \text{and} \quad x = 2 \end{array}$$

Note that the feasible region is not closed and bounded, so we must check whether optimal values exist. This check is done by graphing $C = x + y$ for selected values of C and noting the trend. Figure 4.13(b) shows the solution region with graphs of $C = x + y$ for $C = 3, C = 5$, and $C = 8$. Note that the objective function has a minimum but no maximum.

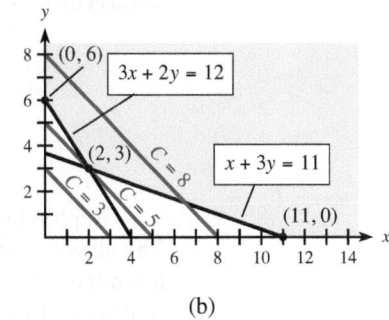

Figure 4.13   (a)   (b)

Examining the value of C at each corner point, we have

$$\text{At } (0, 6), \quad C = x + y = 0 + 6 = 6$$
$$\text{At } (11, 0), \quad C = x + y = 11 + 0 = 11$$
$$\text{At } (2, 3), \quad C = x + y = 2 + 3 = 5$$

Thus we conclude the following:

$$\text{Minimum value of } C = x + y \text{ is 5 at } (2, 3).$$
$$\text{Maximum value of } C = x + y \text{ does not exist.}$$

Note that C can be made arbitrarily large in the feasible region.

CHECKPOINT

2. Find the maximum and minimum values (if they exist) of the objective function
    $g = 3x + 4y$ subject to the following constraints.

$$x + 2y > 12, \quad x > 0$$
$$3x + 4y \geq 30, \quad y \geq 2$$

EXAMPLE 4   Minimizing Production Costs

Two chemical plants, one at Macon and one at Jonesboro, produce three types of fertilizer: low phosphorus (LP), medium phosphorus (MP), and high phosphorus (HP). At each plant, the fertilizer is produced in a single production run, so the three types are produced in fixed proportions. The Macon plant produces 1 ton of LP, 2 tons of MP, and 3 tons of HP in a single operation and charges $600 for what is produced in one operation. On the other hand, one operation of the Jonesboro plant produces 1 ton of LP, 5 tons of MP, and 1 ton of HP, and it charges $1000 for what it produces in one operation. If a customer needs 100 tons of LP, 260 tons of MP, and 180 tons of HP, how many production runs should be ordered from each plant to minimize costs?

Solution

If x represents the number of operations requested from the Macon plant and y represents the number of operations requested from the Jonesboro plant, then we seek to minimize cost

$$C = 600x + 1000y$$

The following table summarizes production capabilities and requirements.

	Macon Plant	Jonesboro Plant	Requirements
Units of LP	1	1	100
Units of MP	2	5	260
Units of HP	3	1	180

Using the number of operations requested and the fact that requirements must be met or exceeded, we can formulate the following constraints.

$$\begin{cases} x + \ y \geq 100 \\ 2x + 5y \geq 260 \\ 3x + \ y \geq 180 \\ x \geq 0, y \geq 0 \end{cases}$$

Graphing this system gives the feasible set shown in Figure 4.14 on the next page. The objective function has a minimum even though the feasible set is not closed and bounded. The corners are $(0, 180)$, $(40, 60)$, $(80, 20)$, and $(130, 0)$, where $(40, 60)$ is obtained by solving $x + y = 100$ and $3x + y = 180$ simultaneously and where $(80, 20)$ is obtained by solving $x + y = 100$ and $2x + 5y = 260$ simultaneously.

Evaluating $C = 600x + 1000y$ at each corner, we obtain

$$\text{At } (0, 180), \quad C = 600(0) + 1000(180) = 180,000$$
$$\text{At } (40, 60), \quad C = 600(40) + 1000(60) = 84,000$$
$$\text{At } (80, 20), \quad C = 600(80) + 1000(20) = 68,000$$
$$\text{At } (130, 0), \quad C = 600(130) + 1000(0) = 78,000$$

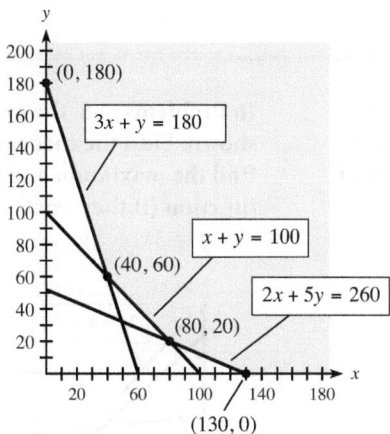

Figure 4.14

Thus by placing orders requiring 80 production runs from the Macon plant and 20 production runs from the Jonesboro plant, the customer's needs will be satisfied at a minimum cost of $68,000.

Calculator Note   Graphing calculators can be used to perform the steps in the solution of linear programming problems. The constraint inequalities can be graphed as equations solved for y. Test points can be used to find the feasible region. INTERSECT can be used to find the corners of the region, where the borders intersect. Finally, the objective function can be evaluated at each of the corners using TABLE. See Example 5 and Appendix A, Section 4.2, for details.

EXAMPLE 5   Maximization Subject to Constraints with Graphing Calculators

Use a graphing calculator to maximize $f = 5x + 11y$ subject to the constraints

$$5x + 2y \le 54$$
$$2x + 4y \le 60$$
$$x \ge 0, y \ge 0$$

Solution
The feasible region (with dark shading) is shown in Figure 4.15. The boundaries intersect at $(0, 0)$, $(0, 15)$, $(6, 12)$ and $(10.8, 0)$. These corners can be found with INTERSECT. Testing the objective function at each corner gives the values of f shown below.

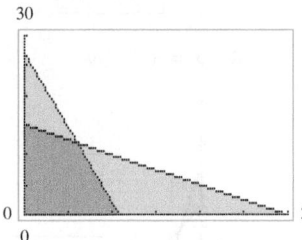

Figure 4.15

At $(0, 0)$, $f = 5(0) + 11(0) = 0$
At $(0, 15)$, $f = 5(0) + 11(15) = 165$
At $(6, 12)$, $f = 5(6) + 11(12) = 162$
At $(10.8, 0)$, $f = 5(10.8) + 11(0) = 54$

The maximum value is $f = 165$ at $x = 0, y = 15$.

1. The maximum value is $f = 18$ at $(3, 2)$; the minimum value is $f = 0$ at $(0, 0)$.
2. The minimum value of g is 30 at both $(0, 7.5)$ and $(6, 3)$. Thus any point on the border joining $(0, 7.5)$ and $(6, 3)$ will give the minimum value 30. The maximum value of g does not exist.

EXERCISES 4.2

In Problems 1–4, use the given feasible region determined by the constraint inequalities to find the maximum and minimum of the given objective function (if they exist).

1. $C = 9x + 10y$

2. $C = 2x + 7y$

3. $f = 5x + 2y$

4. $f = 4x + 5y$

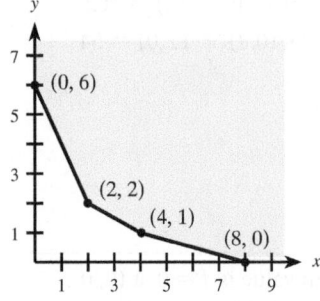

In Problems 5–8, the graph of the feasible region is shown. Find the corners of each feasible region and then find the maximum and minimum of the given objective function (if they exist).

5. $f = 3x + 2y$

6. $f = 5x + 8y$

7. $g = 2x + 3y$

8. $g = x + 3y$

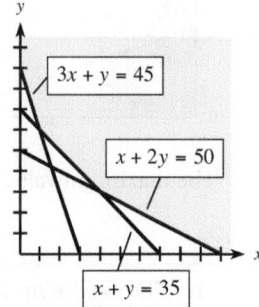

In Problems 9–12, find the indicated maximum or minimum value of the objective function in the linear programming problem. Note that the feasible regions for these problems are found in the answers to Problems 19, 20, 23, and 24 in the Section 4.1 Exercises.

9. Maximize $f = 30x + 50y$ subject to
$$x + 2y \le 48$$
$$x + y \le 30$$
$$2x + y \le 50$$
$$x \ge 0, y \ge 0$$

10. Maximize $f = 7x + 10y$ subject to
$$3x + y \le 9$$
$$3x + 2y \le 12$$
$$x + 2y \le 8$$
$$x \ge 0, y \ge 0$$

11. Minimize $g = 100x + 22y$ subject to
$$x + 3y \ge 3$$
$$2x + 3y \ge 5$$
$$2x + y \ge 3$$
$$x \ge 0, y \ge 0$$

12. Minimize $g = 12x + 8y$ subject to
$$x + 2y \ge 10$$
$$2x + y \ge 11$$
$$x + y \ge 9$$
$$x \ge 0, y \ge 0$$

In Problems 13–24, solve the following linear programming problems. Restrict $x \ge 0$ and $y \ge 0$.

13. Maximize $f = 3x + 4y$ subject to
$$x + y \le 6$$
$$2x + y \le 10$$
$$y \le 4$$

14. Maximize $f = x + 3y$ subject to
$$x + 4y \le 12$$
$$y \le 2$$
$$x + y \le 9$$

15. Maximize $f = 2x + 6y$ subject to
$$x + y \le 7$$
$$2x + y \le 12$$
$$x + 3y \le 15$$

16. Maximize $f = 4x + 2y$ subject to
$$x + 2y \le 20$$
$$x + y \le 12$$
$$4x + y \le 36$$

17. Minimize $g = 7x + 6y$ subject to
$$5x + 2y \ge 16$$
$$3x + 7y \ge 27$$

18. Minimize $g = 22x + 17y$ subject to
$$8x + 5y \ge 100$$
$$12x + 25y \ge 360$$

19. Minimize $g = 3x + y$ subject to
$$4x + y \ge 11$$
$$3x + 2y \ge 12$$

20. Minimize $g = 50x + 70y$ subject to
$$11x + 15y \ge 225$$
$$x + 3y \ge 27$$

21. Maximize $f = x + 2y$ subject to
$$x + y \ge 4$$
$$2x + y \le 8$$
$$y \le 4$$

22. Maximize $f = 3x + 5y$ subject to
$$2x + 4y \ge 8$$
$$3x + y \le 7$$
$$y \le 4$$

23. Minimize $g = 40x + 25y$ subject to
$$x + y \ge 100$$
$$-x + y \le 20$$
$$-2x + 3y \ge 30$$

24. Minimize $g = 3x + 8y$ subject to
$$4x - 5y \ge 50$$
$$-x + 2y \ge 4$$
$$x + y \le 80$$

APPLICATIONS

25. *Manufacturing* The Wellbuilt Company produces two types of wood chippers, economy and deluxe. The deluxe model requires 3 hours to assemble and 1/2 hour to paint, and the economy model requires 2 hours to assemble and 1 hour to paint. The maximum number of assembly hours available is 24 per day, and the maximum number of painting hours available is 8 per day. If the profit on the deluxe model is $90 per unit and the profit on the economy model is $72 per unit, how many units of each model will maximize profit? (See Problem 27 in the Section 4.1 Exercises.)

26. *Learning environments* An experiment involving learning in animals requires placing white mice and rabbits into separate, controlled environments: environment I and environment II. The maximum amount of time available in environment I is 420 minutes, and the maximum amount of time available in environment II is 600 minutes. The white mice must spend 10 minutes in environment I and 25 minutes in environment II, and the rabbits must spend 15 minutes in environment I and 12 minutes in environment II. Find the maximum possible number of animals that can be used in the experiment and find the number of white mice and the number of rabbits that can be used. (See Problem 28 in the Section 4.1 Exercises.)

27. *Manufacturing* A company manufactures two types of electric hedge trimmers, one of which is cordless. The cord-type trimmer requires 2 hours to make, and the cordless model requires 4 hours. The company has only 800 work hours to use in manufacturing each day, and the packaging department can package only 300 trimmers per day. If the company profits are $22.50 for the cord-type model and $45.00 for the cordless model, how many of each type should the company produce per day to maximize profits?

28. *Manufacturing* Sierra Wood Products manufactures two products, rockers and bookshelf units. Its profit is $30 per rocker and $42 per bookshelf unit. Next week's production will be constrained by two limited resources, labor and wood. The labor available next week is expected to be at most 930 hours, and the amount of wood available is expected to be at most 2400 board feet. Each rocker requires 4 labor hours and 8 board feet of wood. Each bookshelf unit requires 3 labor hours and 12 board feet of wood. Find how many rockers and bookshelf units should be produced next week to maximize Sierra's profit. Find the maximum profit.

29. *Politics* A candidate wants to use a combination of radio and television advertisements in her campaign. Research has shown that each 1-minute spot on television reaches 0.09 million people and that each 1-minute spot on radio reaches 0.006 million. The candidate believes she must reach at least 2.16 million people, and she must buy a total of at least 80 minutes of advertisements. How many minutes of each medium should be used to minimize costs if television costs $500/minute and radio costs $100/minute?

30. *Nutrition* In a hospital ward, the patients can be grouped into two general categories depending on their condition and the amount of solid foods they require in their diet. A combination of two diets is used for solid foods because they supply essential nutrients for recovery, but each diet has an amount of a substance deemed detrimental. The following table summarizes the patient group, minimum diet requirements, and the amount of the detrimental substance. How many servings from each diet should be given each day to minimize the intake of this detrimental substance?

	Diet A	Diet B	Daily Requirement
Group 1	4 oz per serving	1 oz per serving	26 oz
Group 2	2 oz per serving	1 oz per serving	18 oz
Detrimental substance	0.18 oz per serving	0.09 oz per serving	

31. *Production scheduling* Newjet, Inc. manufactures inkjet printers and laser printers. The company has the capacity to make 70 printers per day, and it has 120 hours of labor per day available. It takes 1 hour to make an inkjet printer and 3 hours to make a laser printer. The profits are $40 per inkjet printer and $60 per laser printer. Find the number of each type of printer that should be made to give maximum profit and find the maximum profit.

32. *Production scheduling* At one of its factories, a jeans manufacturer makes two styles: #891 and #917. Each pair of style 891 takes 10 minutes to cut out and 20 minutes to assemble and finish. Each pair of style 917 takes 10 minutes to cut out and 30 minutes to assemble and finish. The plant has enough workers to provide at most 7500 minutes per day for cutting and at most 19,500 minutes per day for assembly and finishing. The profit on each pair of style 891 is $18.00, and the profit on each pair of style 917 is $22.50. How many pairs of each style should be produced per day to obtain maximum profit? Find the maximum daily profit.

33. *Nutrition* A privately owned lake contains two types of game fish, bass and trout. The owner provides two types of food, A and B, for these fish. Bass require 2 units of food A and 4 units of food B, and trout require 5 units of food A and 2 units of food B. If the owner has 800 units of each food, find the maximum number of fish the lake can support.

34. *Nutrition* In a zoo, there is a natural habitat containing several feeding areas. One of these areas serves as a feeding area for two species, I and II, and is supplied each day with 120 pounds of food A, 110 pounds of food B, and 57 pounds of food C. Each individual of species I requires 5 lb of A, 5 lb of B, and 2 lb of C, and each individual of species II requires 6 lb of A, 4 lb of B, and 3 lb of C. Find the maximum number of the two species that can be supported.

Shadow prices—land management **For Problems 35 and 36, refer to the farm co-op application in Example 2(a). Rework that linear programming problem with the indicated changes in one constraint and answer the questions.**

35. (a) If one more acre of land became available (for a total of 6001 acres), how would this change the co-op's planting strategy and its maximum profit?
   (b) Repeat part (a) if 8 more acres of land were available.
   (c) Based on parts (a) and (b), what is the profit value of each additional acre of land? This value is called the **shadow price** of an acre of land.

36. (a) If one more gallon of fertilizer/herbicide became available (for a total of 40,501 gallons), how would this change the co-op's planting strategy and its maximum profit?
   (b) Repeat part (a) if 8 more gallons of fertilizer/herbicide were available.
   (c) Based on parts (a) and (b), what is the profit value of each additional gallon of fertilizer/herbicide (that is, the shadow price of a gallon of fertilizer/herbicide)?

37. *Manufacturing* Two factories produce three different types of kitchen appliances. The following table summarizes the production capacity, the number of each type of appliance ordered, and the daily operating costs for the factories. How many days should each factory operate to fill the orders at minimum cost? Find the minimum cost.

	Factory 1	Factory 2	Number Ordered
Appliance 1	80/day	20/day	1600
Appliance 2	10/day	10/day	500
Appliance 3	20/day	70/day	2000
Daily cost	$10,000	$20,000	

38. *Nutrition* In a laboratory experiment, two separate foods are given to experimental animals. Each food contains essential ingredients, A and B, for which the animals have a minimum requirement; each food also has an ingredient C, which can be harmful to the animals. The following table summarizes this information.

	Food 1	Food 2	Required
Ingredient A	10 units/g	3 units/g	49 units
Ingredient B	6 units/g	12 units/g	60 units
Ingredient C	3 units/g	1 unit/g	

How many grams of foods 1 and 2 should be given to the animals to satisfy the requirements for A and B while minimizing the amount of ingredient C ingested?

39. *Manufacturing* The Janie Gioffre Drapery Company makes three types of draperies at two different locations. At location I, it can make 10 pairs of deluxe drapes, 20 pairs of better drapes, and 13 pairs of standard drapes per day. At location II, it can make 20 pairs of deluxe, 50 pairs of better, and 6 pairs of standard per day. The company has orders for 2000 pairs of deluxe drapes, 4200 pairs of better drapes, and 1200 pairs of standard drapes. If the daily costs are $500 per day at location I and $800 per day at location II, how many days should Janie schedule at each location to fill the orders at minimum cost? Find the minimum cost.

40. *Nutrition* Two foods contain proteins, carbohydrates, and fats. Food A costs $1 per pound and contains 30% protein, 10% fat, and 50% carbohydrates. Food B costs $1.50 per pound and contains 20% protein, 4% fat, and 75% carbohydrates. What combination of these two foods provides at least 1 pound of protein, $2\frac{1}{2}$ pounds of carbohydrates, and $\frac{1}{5}$ pound of fat at the lowest cost?

41. *Manufacturing* A sausage company makes two different kinds of hot dogs, regular and all beef. Each pound of all-beef hot dogs requires 0.75 lb of beef and 0.2 lb of spices, and each pound of regular hot dogs requires 0.18 lb of beef, 0.3 lb of pork, and 0.2 lb of spices. Suppliers can deliver at most 1020 lb of beef, at most 600 lb of pork, and at least 500 lb of spices. If the profit is $1.50 on each pound of all-beef hot dogs and $1.00 on each pound of regular hot dogs, how many pounds of each should be produced to obtain maximum profit? What is the maximum profit?

42. *Manufacturing* A cereal manufacturer makes two different kinds of cereal, Senior Citizen's Feast and Kids Go. Each pound of Senior Citizen's Feast requires 0.6 lb of wheat and 0.2 lb of vitamin-enriched syrup, and each pound of Kids Go requires 0.4 lb of wheat, 0.2 lb of sugar, and 0.2 lb of vitamin-enriched syrup. Suppliers can deliver at most 2800 lb of wheat, at most 800 lb of sugar, and at least 1000 lb of the vitamin-enriched syrup. If the profit is $0.90 on each pound of Senior Citizen's Feast and $1.00 on each pound of Kids Go, find the number of pounds of each cereal that should be produced to obtain maximum profit. Find the maximum profit.

43. *Shipping costs* TV Circuit has 30 large-screen televisions in a warehouse in Erie and 60 large-screen televisions in a warehouse in Pittsburgh. Thirty-five are needed in a store in Blairsville, and 40 are needed in a store in Youngstown. It costs $18 to ship from Pittsburgh to Blairsville and $22 to ship from Pittsburgh to Youngstown, whereas it costs $20 to ship from Erie to Blairsville and $25 to ship from Erie to Youngstown. How many televisions should be shipped from each warehouse to each store to minimize the shipping cost? *Hint:* If the number shipped from Pittsburgh to Blairsville is represented by x, then the number shipped from Erie to Blairsville is represented by $35 - x$.

44. *Construction* A contractor builds two types of homes. The Carolina requires one lot, $160,000 capital, and 160 worker-days of labor, whereas the Savannah requires one lot, $240,000 capital, and 160 worker-days of labor. The contractor owns 300 lots and has $48,000,000 available capital and 43,200 worker-days of labor. The profit on the Carolina is $40,000 and the profit on the Savannah is $50,000. Find how many of each type of home should be built to maximize profit. Find the maximum profit.

45. *Management* A bank has two types of branches. A satellite branch employs 3 people, requires $400,000 to construct and open, and generates an average daily revenue of $10,000. A full-service branch employs 6 people, requires $560,000 to construct and open, and generates an average daily revenue of $18,000. The bank has up to $11.92 million available to open new branches and has decided to limit the new branches to a maximum of 25 and to hire at most 120 new employees.

(a) How many branches of each type should the bank open to maximize the average daily revenue? Find the maximum average daily revenue.

(b) At the optimal solution from part (a), analyze the bank's constraints (number of new branches, number of new employees, and budget) to determine the "Amount Available," "Amount Used," and "Amount Not Used (Slack)."

(c) Obtaining additional quantities of which constraint items would have the potential to increase the bank's average daily revenue? Explain.

(d) Obtaining more of which constraint item would not increase average daily revenue? Explain.

46. *Manufacturing* A company manufactures two different sizes of boat lifts. Each size requires some time in the welding and assembly department and some time in the parts and packaging department. The smaller lift requires $\frac{3}{4}$ hour in welding and assembly and $1\frac{2}{3}$ hours in parts and packaging. The larger lift requires $1\frac{1}{2}$ hours in welding and assembly and 1 hour in parts and packaging. The factory has 156 hours/day available in welding and assembly and 174 hours/day available in parts and packaging. Furthermore, daily demand for the lifts is at most 90 large and at most 100 small, and profits are $200 for each large lift and $120 for each small lift.

(a) How many of each type of boat lift should be manufactured each day to maximize the profit? Find the maximum profit.

(b) At the optimal solution in part (a), analyze the company's constraints (welding and assembly hours, parts and packaging hours, and demand) to determine the "Amount Available," "Amount Used," and "Amount Not Used (Slack)."

(c) Obtaining additional quantities of which constraint items would have the potential to increase the company's profit? Explain.

(d) Obtaining more of which constraint item would not increase profit? Explain.

SECTION 4.3

The Simplex Method: Maximization

OBJECTIVE

- To use the simplex method to maximize functions subject to constraints

APPLICATION PREVIEW

The Solar Technology Company manufactures three different types of hand calculators and classifies them as scientific, business, and graphing according to their calculating capabilities. The three types have production requirements given by the following table.

	Scientific	Business	Graphing
Electronic circuit components	5	7	10
Assembly time (hours)	1	3	4
Cases	1	1	1

The firm has a monthly limit of 90,000 circuit components, 30,000 hours of labor, and 9000 cases. If the profit is $12 for each scientific, $26 for each business, and $40 for each graphing calculator, the number of each that should be produced to yield maximum profit and the amount of that maximum possible profit can be found by using the simplex method of linear programming. (See Example 3.)

The Simplex Method: Unique Solutions

The graphical method for solving linear programming problems is practical only when there are two variables. The method discussed in this section, the **simplex method,** is especially useful if there are more than two variables in a problem. This method gives a systematic way of moving from one feasible corner of the convex region to another in such a way that the value of the objective function increases until an optimal value is reached or it is discovered that no solution exists.

The simplex method was developed by George Dantzig in 1947. One of the earliest applications of the method was to the scheduling problem that arose in connection with the Berlin airlift in 1948 at the beginning of the Cold War. Since then, linear programming and the simplex method have been used to solve optimization problems in a wide variety of businesses. In fact, in a recent survey of Fortune 500 firms, 85% of the respondents indicated that they use linear programming.

In 1984, N. Karmarkar, a researcher at Bell Labs, developed a new method (that uses interior points rather than corner points) for solving linear programming problems. When the number of variables is very large, Karmarkar's method is more efficient than the simplex method. However, the simplex method is just as effective for many applications and is still widely used.

In discussing the simplex method, we initially restrict ourselves to **standard maximization problems,** which satisfy the following conditions.

1. The objective function is to be maximized.
2. All variables are nonnegative.
3. The constraints are of the form

$$a_1x_1 + a_2x_2 + \cdots + a_nx_n \leq b$$

where $b > 0$.

These conditions may seem to restrict the types of problems unduly, but in applied situations where the objective function is to be maximized, the constraints often satisfy conditions 2 and 3.

Before outlining a procedure for the simplex method, let us develop the procedure and investigate its rationale by seeing how the simplex method compares with the graphical method. Because this method requires non-negative variables, we no longer state these conditions.

EXAMPLE 1   Maximizing Profit

Reconsider the farm co-op application solved graphically in Example 2(a) of Section 4.2, where x is the number of acres of corn and y is the number of acres of soybeans.

Maximize profit	$P = 240x + 160y$	
subject to	$x + y \leq 6000$	Land constraint, acres
	$9x + 3y \leq 40{,}500$	Fertilizer/herbicide constraint, gallons
	$\frac{3}{4}x + y \leq 5250$	Labor constraint, hours

Solution

Notice in each constraint inequality that the right side represents the available amount of the resource and the left side represents the amount used (which cannot exceed the amount available).

The simplex method uses matrix methods on systems of equations, so we convert each constraint inequality to an equation by using a new variable, called a **slack variable.** We introduce a different slack variable for each inequality and can think of it as representing the amount of the constraint resource left unused. Let s_1 equal the unused (unplanted) acres of land ($s_1 \geq 0$). Let s_2 equal the unused gallons of fertilizer/herbicide ($s_2 \geq 0$). Let s_3 equal the unused hours of labor ($s_3 \geq 0$). With these slack variables, we can rewrite each constraint inequality as a constraint equation, as follows.

$x + y \leq 6{,}000$	becomes	$x + y + s_1 = 6000$
$9x + 3y \leq 40{,}500$	becomes	$9x + 3y + s_2 = 40{,}500$
$\frac{3}{4}x + y \leq 5{,}250$	becomes	$\frac{3}{4}x + y + s_3 = 5250$

In addition, if we rewrite the objective function

$$P = 240x + 160y \quad \text{as} \quad -240x - 160y + P = 0$$

then the following system of equations describes this problem.

$$\begin{cases} x + y + s_1 & = 6000 \\ 9x + 3y + s_2 & = 40{,}500 \\ \frac{3}{4}x + y + s_3 & = 5250 \\ -240x - 160y + P & = 0 \end{cases}$$

We seek to maximize P in the last equation subject to the constraints in the first three equations.

We can place this system of equations in a matrix called a **simplex matrix** or a **simplex tableau.** Note that the objective function is in the last (bottom) row of this matrix with all variables on the left side, the rows above the function row correspond to the constraints, and the last column before the augment represents the profit function.

$$A = \begin{bmatrix} & x & y & s_1 & s_2 & s_3 & P & \\ & 1 & 1 & 1 & 0 & 0 & 0 & 6000 \\ & 9 & 3 & 0 & 1 & 0 & 0 & 40{,}500 \\ & \frac{3}{4} & 1 & 0 & 0 & 1 & 0 & 5250 \\ \hline & -240 & -160 & 0 & 0 & 0 & 1 & 0 \end{bmatrix} \begin{matrix} \\ \text{Land constraint} \\ \text{Fertilizer/herbicide constraint} \\ \text{Labor hours constraint} \\ \text{Objective function (maximum profit)} \end{matrix}$$

From the graph in Figure 4.16, we know that (0, 0) is a feasible solution giving a value of 0 for P. Because the origin is always a feasible solution of the type of linear programming problems we are considering, the simplex method begins there and systematically moves to new corners while increasing the value of P.

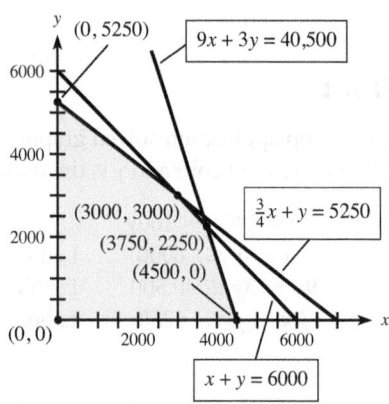

Corners	P = 240x + 160y
(0, 0)	P = 0
(4500, 0)	P = 1,080,000
(3750, 2250)	P = 1,260,000
(3000, 3000)	P = 1,200,000
(0, 5250)	P = 840,000

Figure 4.16

Recall that the last row of A corresponds to the objective function $P = 240x + 160y$. If we seek to increase the value of $P = 240x + 160y$ by changing the value of only one of the variables, then because the coefficient of x is larger, the rate of increase is greatest by increasing x.

In general, we can find the variable that will increase the objective function most rapidly by looking for the *most negative* value in the last row (the objective function row) of the simplex matrix. The column that contains this value is called the **pivot column.**

The simplex matrix A is shown again below with the x-column indicated as the pivot column.

$$A = \begin{bmatrix} & x & y & s_1 & s_2 & s_3 & P & \\ & 1 & 1 & 1 & 0 & 0 & 0 & 6{,}000 \\ & ⑨ & 3 & 0 & 1 & 0 & 0 & 40{,}500 \\ & \frac{3}{4} & 1 & 0 & 0 & 1 & 0 & 5{,}250 \\ \hline & -240 & -160 & 0 & 0 & 0 & 1 & 0 \end{bmatrix} \begin{matrix} 6000 \div 1 = 6000 \\ 40{,}500 \div 9 = 4500 \text{ smallest} \\ 5250 \div \left(\frac{3}{4}\right) = 5250\left(\frac{4}{3}\right) = 7000 \\ \\ \end{matrix}$$

$\uparrow$ Most negative entry; pivot column

The amount by which x can be increased is limited by the constraining equations (rows 1, 2, and 3 of the simplex matrix). As the graph in Figure 4.16 shows, the constraints limit x to no larger than $x = 4500$. In A, when the positive coefficients in the pivot column (the x-column) are divided into the constants in the augment, the *smallest* quotient is $40{,}500 \div 9 = 4500$. This smallest quotient identifies the **pivot row.** The **pivot entry** (or **pivot**) is the entry in both the pivot column and the pivot row. The 9 (circled) in matrix A is the pivot entry. Notice that the smallest quotient, 4500, represents the maximum amount that x can be increased (while $y = 0$) and the point (4500, 0) corresponds to a corner adjoining (0, 0) on the constraint region. (See Figure 4.16.)

To continue, we use row operations with the pivot row of A to simulate moving to another corner of the constraint region. First, we multiply the second row by $\frac{1}{9}$ to convert the pivot entry to 1 (circled in the following matrix on the left). Next, we add multiples of the pivot row (row 2) to each of the other rows to make all elements of the pivot column, except the pivot entry, equal to 0. This is the new simplex matrix B.

$$
\begin{array}{ccccccc}
 & x & y & s_1 & s_2 & s_3 & P \\
\end{array}
\left[\begin{array}{cccccc|c}
1 & 1 & 1 & 0 & 0 & 0 & 6{,}000 \\
①& \frac{1}{3} & 0 & \frac{1}{9} & 0 & 0 & 4{,}500 \\
\frac{3}{4} & 1 & 0 & 0 & 1 & 0 & 5{,}250 \\
-240 & -160 & 0 & 0 & 0 & 1 & 0
\end{array}\right]
\begin{array}{c}
-R_2 + R_1 \to R_1 \\
-\frac{3}{4}R_2 + R_3 \to R_3 \\
\hline
240R_2 + R_4 \to R_4
\end{array}
$$

$$
\begin{array}{ccccccc}
 & x & y & s_1 & s_2 & s_3 & P \\
\end{array}
\left[\begin{array}{cccccc|c}
0 & \frac{2}{3} & 1 & -\frac{1}{9} & 0 & 0 & 1{,}500 \\
1 & \frac{1}{3} & 0 & \frac{1}{9} & 0 & 0 & 4{,}500 \\
0 & \frac{3}{4} & 0 & -\frac{1}{12} & 1 & 0 & 1{,}875 \\
0 & -80 & 0 & \frac{80}{3} & 0 & 1 & 1{,}080{,}000
\end{array}\right] = B
$$

Notice that the columns of B that correspond to the variables x, s_1, and s_3 and to the objective function P are all different, but each contains a single entry of 1 and the other entries are 0. Variables with columns of this type (but *not* the objective function) are called **basic variables.** Similarly, the columns for variables y and s_2 do not have this special form and these columns correspond to **nonbasic variables.** Notice also that the bottom row of B represents

$$-80y + \frac{80}{3}s_2 + P = 1{,}080{,}000, \quad \text{so} \quad P = 1{,}080{,}000 + 80y - \frac{80}{3}s_2$$

depends on y and s_2 (the nonbasic variables). If these nonbasic variables equal 0 (that is, $y = 0$ and $s_2 = 0$), then rows 1, 2, 3, and 4 of matrix B allow us to read the values of s_1, x, s_3, and P, respectively.

$$s_1 = 1500, \qquad x = 4500, \qquad s_3 = 1875, \qquad P = 1{,}080{,}000$$

These solution values correspond to the feasible solution at the corner $(4500, 0)$ in Figure 4.16 and are called a **basic feasible solution.**

We also see that the value of $P = 1{,}080{,}000 + 80y - \frac{80}{3}s_2$ can be increased by increasing the value of y while holding the value of s_2 at 0. In matrix B, we can see this fact by observing that the most negative number in the last row (objective function row) occurs in the y-column. This means that the y-column is the new pivot column.

The amount of increase in y is limited by the constraints. In matrix B, we can discover the limitations on y by dividing the coefficient of y (if positive) into the constant term in the augment of each row and choosing the smallest nonnegative quotient. This identifies the pivot row, and hence the pivot entry, circled in matrix B.

$$
B =
\begin{array}{ccccccc}
 & x & y & s_1 & s_2 & s_3 & P \\
\end{array}
\left[\begin{array}{cccccc|c}
0 & ②\!\!/\!3 & 1 & -\frac{1}{9} & 0 & 0 & 1{,}500 \\
1 & \frac{1}{3} & 0 & \frac{1}{9} & 0 & 0 & 4{,}500 \\
0 & \frac{3}{4} & 0 & -\frac{1}{12} & 1 & 0 & 1{,}875 \\
0 & -80 & 0 & \frac{80}{3} & 0 & 1 & 1{,}080{,}000
\end{array}\right]
\begin{array}{l}
1500 \div \left(\frac{2}{3}\right) = 1500\left(\frac{3}{2}\right) = 2250 \quad \text{smallest} \\
4500 \div \left(\frac{1}{3}\right) = 4500\left(\frac{3}{1}\right) = 13{,}500 \\
1875 \div \left(\frac{3}{4}\right) = 1875\left(\frac{4}{3}\right) = 2500
\end{array}
$$

$\underset{\text{Largest negative; pivot column}}{\uparrow}$

We now transform the simplex matrix B by multiplying row 1 by $\frac{3}{2}$ to convert the pivot entry to 1 (circled in the following matrix on the left). Then we add multiples of the pivot row (row 1) to the other rows to make all other entries in the y-column (pivot column) equal to 0. The new simplex matrix is C.

$$
\begin{array}{ccccccc}
 & x & y & s_1 & s_2 & s_3 & P \\
\end{array}
\left[\begin{array}{cccccc|c}
0 & ① & \frac{3}{2} & -\frac{1}{6} & 0 & 0 & 2{,}250 \\
1 & \frac{1}{3} & 0 & \frac{1}{9} & 0 & 0 & 4{,}500 \\
0 & \frac{3}{4} & 0 & -\frac{1}{12} & 1 & 0 & 1{,}875 \\
0 & -80 & 0 & \frac{80}{3} & 0 & 1 & 1{,}080{,}000
\end{array}\right]
\begin{array}{c}
-\frac{1}{3}R_1 + R_2 \to R_2 \\
-\frac{3}{4}R_1 + R_3 \to R_3 \\
\hline
80R_1 + R_4 \to R_4
\end{array}
$$

$$
\begin{array}{ccccccc}
 & x & y & s_1 & s_2 & s_3 & P \\
\end{array}
\left[\begin{array}{cccccc|c}
0 & 1 & \frac{3}{2} & -\frac{1}{6} & 0 & 0 & 2{,}250 \\
1 & 0 & -\frac{1}{2} & \frac{1}{6} & 0 & 0 & 3{,}750 \\
0 & 0 & -\frac{9}{8} & \frac{1}{24} & 1 & 0 & 187.5 \\
0 & 0 & 120 & \frac{40}{3} & 0 & 1 & 1{,}260{,}000
\end{array}\right] = C
$$

In matrix C, the basic variables (corresponding to the columns with a single entry of 1) are x, y, and s_3, the nonbasic variables are s_1 and s_2, and the objective function (last) row corresponds to

$$120s_1 + \frac{40}{3}s_2 + P = 1{,}260{,}000 \qquad \text{or} \qquad P = 1{,}260{,}000 - 120s_1 - \frac{40}{3}s_2$$

From the objective function, we see that any increase in s_1 or s_2 will cause a *decrease* in P. Observing this or noting that all entries in the last row are nonnegative tells us that we have found the optimal value of the objective function and it occurs when $s_1 = 0$ and $s_2 = 0$. Using this, rows 1, 2, 3, and 4 of matrix C give the values for y, x, s_3, and P, respectively.

$$y = 2250, \quad x = 3750, \quad s_3 = 187.5, \quad P = 1{,}260{,}000, \quad \text{with} \quad s_1 = 0 \quad \text{and} \quad s_2 = 0$$

This corresponds to the corner (3750, 2250) on the graph and to the maximum value of $P = 1{,}260{,}000$ at this corner. (See Figure 4.16.)

These values mean that the co-op should plant $x = 3750$ acres of corn and $y = 2250$ acres of soybeans for a maximum profit of \$1,260,000. And this planting scheme results in $s_1 = 0$ unused acres of land, $s_2 = 0$ unused gallons of fertilizer/herbicide, and $s_3 = 187.5$ unused hours of labor.

Figure 4.17 illustrates how, in Example 1, the simplex method moved us from corner to corner until the optimal solution was obtained.

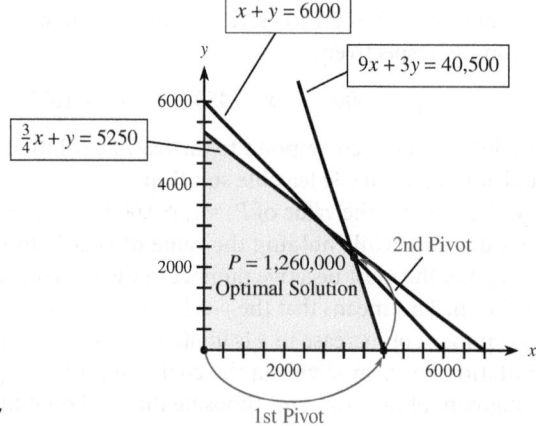

Pivoting Summary

1st Pivot:
from: (0, 0) where $P = 0$
to: (4500, 0) where $P = 1{,}080{,}000$

2nd Pivot:
from: (4500, 0) where $P = 1{,}080{,}000$
to: (3750, 2250) where $P = 1{,}260{,}000$
The Optimal Solution

Figure 4.17

The Simplex Method: Tasks and Procedure

The simplex method involves a series of decisions and operations using matrices. It involves three major tasks.

Simplex Method Tasks	
Task A:	Set up the matrix for the simplex method.
Task B:	Determine the pivot elements and the necessary row operations with the pivot rows to reach a solution.
Task C:	Read the solution from the simplex matrix.

From Example 1, it should be clear that the pivot selection and row operations of Task B are designed to move the system to the corner that achieves the most rapid increase in the function and at the same time is sensitive to the nonnegative limitations on the variables. The procedure that combines these three tasks to maximize a function is given next.

LINEAR PROGRAMMING (SIMPLEX METHOD)

Procedure	Example
To use the simplex method to solve linear programming problems:	Maximize $f = 2x + 3y$ subject to $x + 2y \leq 10$ $2x + y \leq 14$

1. Use a different slack variable to write each constraint inequality as an equation, with positive constants on the right side.

1. $x + 2y \leq 10$ becomes $x + 2y + s_1 = 10$.
   $2x + y \leq 14$ becomes $2x + y + s_2 = 14$.
   Maximize f in $-2x - 3y + f = 0$.

2. Set up the simplex matrix. It contains the system of constraint equations with the objective function in the last row with all variables on the left and coefficient 1 for f.

2.

	x	y	s_1	s_2	f	
	1	2	1	0	0	10
	2	1	0	1	0	14
	-2	-3	0	0	1	0

3. Find the pivot entry:
   (a) The pivot column has the most negative number in the last row. (If a tie occurs, use either column.)

3. (a)

$$\begin{bmatrix} 1 & \boxed{2} & 1 & 0 & 0 & | & 10 \\ 2 & 1 & 0 & 1 & 0 & | & 14 \\ -2 & \boxed{-3} & 0 & 0 & 1 & | & 0 \end{bmatrix}$$

↑ Most negative entry; pivot column

   (b) The positive coefficient in the pivot column that gives the smallest nonnegative quotient when divided into the constant in the constraint rows of the augment is the pivot entry. If there is a tie, either coefficient may be chosen. If there are no positive coefficients in the pivot column, no solution exists. Stop.

   (b) Row 1 quotient: $10 \div 2 = 5$ (smallest)
   Row 2 quotient: $14 \div 1 = 14$
   Therefore, pivot row is row 1.

$$\begin{bmatrix} 1 & ② & 1 & 0 & 0 & | & 10 \\ 2 & 1 & 0 & 1 & 0 & | & 14 \\ -2 & -3 & 0 & 0 & 1 & | & 0 \end{bmatrix}$$

Pivot entry is 2, circled.

4. Use row operations with only the row containing the pivot entry to make the pivot entry a 1 and all other entries in the pivot column zeros. This process is called **pivoting**. This makes the variable corresponding to the pivot column a basic variable.

4. Row operations:
   Multiply row 1 by $\frac{1}{2}$.
   Add -1 times new row 1 to row 2.
   Add 3 times new row 1 to row 3.

Result: $\begin{bmatrix} \frac{1}{2} & 1 & \frac{1}{2} & 0 & 0 & | & 5 \\ \frac{3}{2} & 0 & -\frac{1}{2} & 1 & 0 & | & 9 \\ -\frac{1}{2} & 0 & \frac{3}{2} & 0 & 1 & | & 15 \end{bmatrix}$

Indicators

5. The numerical entries in the last row are the indicators of what to do next.
   (a) If there is a negative indicator, return to Step 3.
   (b) If all indicators are positive or zero, an optimum value has been obtained for the objective function.
   (c) In a complete solution, the variables that have positive entries in the last row are nonbasic variables.

5. $-\frac{1}{2}$ is negative, so we identify a new pivot column and reduce again.

$$\begin{bmatrix} \frac{1}{2} & 1 & \frac{1}{2} & 0 & 0 & | & 5 \\ ③\frac{3}{2} & 0 & -\frac{1}{2} & 1 & 0 & | & 9 \\ -\frac{1}{2} & 0 & \frac{3}{2} & 0 & 1 & | & 15 \end{bmatrix}$$ $\begin{aligned} 5 \div \frac{1}{2} &= 10 \\ 9 \div \frac{3}{2} &= 6^\star \end{aligned}$

Pivot column   *6 is smaller quotient.

The new pivot entry is $\frac{3}{2}$ (circled). Now reduce, using the new pivot row, to obtain:

$$\begin{bmatrix} 0 & 1 & \frac{2}{3} & -\frac{1}{3} & 0 & | & 2 \\ 1 & 0 & -\frac{1}{3} & \frac{2}{3} & 0 & | & 6 \\ 0 & 0 & \frac{4}{3} & \frac{1}{3} & 1 & | & 18 \end{bmatrix}$$

Indicators all 0 or positive, so the solution is complete.
Nonbasic variables: s_1 and s_2. Basic variables: x and y.

6. After setting the nonbasic variables equal to 0, read the values of the basic variables and the objective function from the rows of the matrix.

6. f is maximized at 18 when $y = 2$, $x = 6$, $s_1 = 0$, and $s_2 = 0$. (This same example was solved graphically in the Procedure/Example in Section 4.2.)

As we review our work, we can observe the following:

1. Steps 1 and 2 complete Task A (setting up the simplex matrix).
2. Steps 3–5 complete Task B (pivoting to obtain the final matrix).
3. Step 6 completes Task C (reading the optimal solution).

In addition, at each step in the simplex method, the *basic variables* correspond to the columns that contain a *single entry* of 1 and the other entries are 0. The remaining columns identify the *nonbasic variables*. To obtain a feasible solution, we set the nonbasic variables equal to zero and read the values of the basic variables and the objective function from the rows of the simplex matrix.

EXAMPLE 2   Simplex Method Tasks

Complete Tasks A, B, and C to find the maximum value of $f = 4x + 3y$ subject to

$$x + 2y \le 8$$
$$2x + y \le 10$$

Solution

Task A: Introducing the slack variables and rewriting the objective function give the system of equations

$$\begin{cases} x + 2y + s_1   = 8 \\ 2x + y + s_2 = 10 \\ -4x - 3y   + f = 0 \end{cases}$$

Writing this in a matrix with the objective function in the last row gives

$$A = \begin{array}{c} \\ \\ \\ \end{array}\begin{array}{ccccc} x & y & s_1 & s_2 & f \\ \end{array}$$

$$A = \left[\begin{array}{ccccc|c} 1 & 2 & 1 & 0 & 0 & 8 \\ ② & 1 & 0 & 1 & 0 & 10 \\ \hline -4 & -3 & 0 & 0 & 1 & 0 \end{array}\right] \begin{array}{l} 8/1 = 8 \\ 10/2 = 5^* \\ \end{array}$$

↑
Most negative   *Smallest quotient

Note that in this initial simplex matrix A, variables x and y are nonbasic (so set to 0) and this corresponds to the basic feasible solution $x = 0$, $y = 0$ and $s_1 = 8$, $s_2 = 10$, $f = 0$.

Task B: The most negative entry in the last row of A is -4 (indicated by the arrow), so the pivot column is column 1. The smallest quotient formed by dividing the positive coefficients from column 1 into the constants in the augment is 5 (indicated by the asterisk), so row 2 is the pivot row. Thus the pivot entry is in row 2, column 1 (circled in matrix A).

Next, multiply row 2 of A by $\frac{1}{2}$ to get a 1 as the new pivot entry, circled in the following matrix on the left. Then use row operations with row 2 only to make all other entries in column 1 equal to zero and to obtain the simplex matrix B below.

$$\begin{array}{ccccc} x & y & s_1 & s_2 & f \end{array}$$
$$\left[\begin{array}{ccccc|c} 1 & 2 & 1 & 0 & 0 & 8 \\ ① & \frac{1}{2} & 0 & \frac{1}{2} & 0 & 5 \\ -4 & -3 & 0 & 0 & 1 & 0 \end{array}\right] \begin{array}{l} (-1)R_2 + R_1 \rightarrow R_1 \\ (4)\,R_2 + R_3 \rightarrow R_3 \\ \xrightarrow{} \end{array} \quad B = \begin{array}{ccccc} x & y & s_1 & s_2 & f \end{array} \left[\begin{array}{ccccc|c} 0 & \frac{3}{2} & 1 & -\frac{1}{2} & 0 & 3 \\ 1 & \frac{1}{2} & 0 & \frac{1}{2} & 0 & 5 \\ 0 & -1 & 0 & 2 & 1 & 20 \end{array}\right]$$

This gives the simplex matrix B, which has nonbasic variables $y = 0$ and $s_2 = 0$ and corresponds to the basic feasible solution $x = 5$, $s_1 = 3$, and $f = 20$.

The last row contains a negative entry, so the solution is not optimal and we locate another pivot column to continue. The pivot column is indicated with an arrow, and the smallest quotient is indicated with an asterisk. The new pivot entry is circled.

$$B = \begin{bmatrix} x & y & s_1 & s_2 & f & \\ 0 & \boxed{\frac{3}{2}} & 1 & -\frac{1}{2} & 0 & 3 \\ 1 & \frac{1}{2} & 0 & \frac{1}{2} & 0 & 5 \\ \hline 0 & -1 & 0 & 2 & 1 & 20 \end{bmatrix} \begin{matrix} 3 \div \frac{3}{2} = 2^* \\ 5 \div \frac{1}{2} = 10 \\ \\ \end{matrix}$$

Most negative   *Smallest quotient

After multiplying row 1 of B by $2/3$ to get a 1 as the new pivot (circled in the following matrix on the left), we use row operations with row 1 only, as follows, to obtain C.

$$\begin{bmatrix} x & y & s_1 & s_2 & f & \\ 0 & \boxed{1} & \frac{2}{3} & -\frac{1}{3} & 0 & 2 \\ 1 & \frac{1}{2} & 0 & \frac{1}{2} & 0 & 5 \\ \hline 0 & -1 & 0 & 2 & 1 & 20 \end{bmatrix} \begin{matrix} (-\frac{1}{2})R_1 + R_2 \to R_2 \\ R_1 + R_3 \to R_3 \end{matrix} \quad C = \begin{bmatrix} x & y & s_1 & s_2 & f & \\ 0 & 1 & \frac{2}{3} & -\frac{1}{3} & 0 & 2 \\ 1 & 0 & -\frac{1}{3} & \frac{2}{3} & 0 & 4 \\ \hline 0 & 0 & \frac{2}{3} & \frac{5}{3} & 1 & 22 \end{bmatrix}$$

Because there are no negative indicators in the last row, the solution is complete.

Task C: s_1 and s_2 are nonbasic variables, so they equal zero. Thus f is maximized at 22 when $y = 2$, $x = 4$, $s_1 = 0$, and $s_2 = 0$.

EXAMPLE 3 Manufacturing | APPLICATION PREVIEW |

The Solar Technology Company manufactures three different types of hand calculators and classifies them as scientific, business, and graphing according to their calculating capabilities. The three types have production requirements given by the following table.

	Scientific	Business	Graphing
Electronic circuit components	5	7	10
Assembly time (hours)	1	3	4
Cases	1	1	1

The firm has a monthly limit of 90,000 circuit components, 30,000 hours of labor, and 9000 cases. If the profit is $12 for each scientific, $26 for each business, and $40 for each graphing calculator, how many of each should be produced to yield the maximum profit? What is the maximum profit?

Solution

Let x_1 be the number of scientific calculators produced, x_2 the number of business calculators produced, and x_3 the number of graphing calculators produced. Then the problem is to maximize the profit $f = 12x_1 + 26x_2 + 40x_3$ subject to

Inequalities	Equations with Slack Variables
$5x_1 + 7x_2 + 10x_3 \le 90{,}000$	$5x_1 + 7x_2 + 10x_3 + s_1 = 90{,}000$
$x_1 + 3x_2 + 4x_3 \le 30{,}000$	$x_1 + 3x_2 + 4x_3 + s_2 = 30{,}000$
$x_1 + x_2 + x_3 \le 9000$	$x_1 + x_2 + x_3 + s_3 = 9000$

The slack variables can be interpreted as follows: s_1 is the number of unused circuit components, s_2 is the number of unused hours of labor, and s_3 is the number of unused calculator cases. The simplex matrix, with the first pivot entry circled, is shown below.

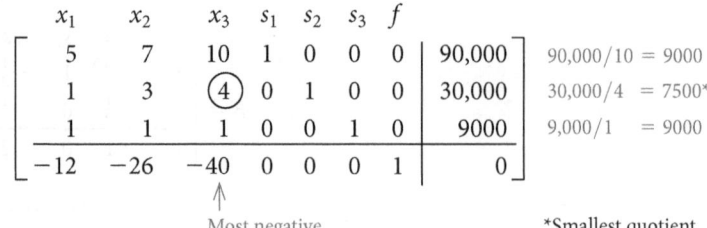

$$\begin{array}{ccccccc|c}
x_1 & x_2 & x_3 & s_1 & s_2 & s_3 & f & \\
5 & 7 & 10 & 1 & 0 & 0 & 0 & 90,000 \\
1 & 3 & \boxed{4} & 0 & 1 & 0 & 0 & 30,000 \\
1 & 1 & 1 & 0 & 0 & 1 & 0 & 9000 \\
\hline
-12 & -26 & -40 & 0 & 0 & 0 & 1 & 0
\end{array}$$

$90{,}000/10 = 9000$
$30{,}000/4\ = 7500*$
$9{,}000/1\ = 9000$

↑
Most negative   *Smallest quotient

We now use row operations to change the pivot entry to 1 and create zeros elsewhere in the pivot column. The row operations are

1. Multiply row 2 by $\frac{1}{4}$ to convert the pivot entry to 1.
2. Using the new row 2,
    (a) Add -10 times new row 2 to row 1.
    (b) Add -1 times new row 2 to row 3.
    (c) Add 40 times new row 2 to row 4.

The result is the second simplex matrix.

$$\begin{array}{ccccccc|c}
x_1 & x_2 & x_3 & s_1 & s_2 & s_3 & f & \\
\frac{5}{2} & -\frac{1}{2} & 0 & 1 & -\frac{5}{2} & 0 & 0 & 15,000 \\
\frac{1}{4} & \frac{3}{4} & 1 & 0 & \frac{1}{4} & 0 & 0 & 7500 \\
\boxed{\frac{3}{4}} & \frac{1}{4} & 0 & 0 & -\frac{1}{4} & 1 & 0 & 1500 \\
\hline
-2 & 4 & 0 & 0 & 10 & 0 & 1 & 300,000
\end{array}$$

$15{,}000 \div \frac{5}{2} =\ 6000$
$7{,}500 \div \frac{1}{4} = 30{,}000$
$1{,}500 \div \frac{3}{4} =\ 2000*$

↑
Most negative   *Smallest quotient

We check the last row indicators. Because there is an entry that is negative, we repeat the simplex process. Again the pivot entry is circled, and we apply row operations similar to those above. The resulting matrix is

$$\begin{array}{ccccccc|c}
x_1 & x_2 & x_3 & s_1 & s_2 & s_3 & f & \\
0 & -\frac{4}{3} & 0 & 1 & -\frac{5}{3} & -\frac{10}{3} & 0 & 10,000 \\
0 & \frac{2}{3} & 1 & 0 & \frac{1}{3} & -\frac{1}{3} & 0 & 7000 \\
1 & \frac{1}{3} & 0 & 0 & -\frac{1}{3} & \frac{4}{3} & 0 & 2000 \\
\hline
0 & \frac{14}{3} & 0 & 0 & \frac{28}{3} & \frac{8}{3} & 1 & 304,000
\end{array}$$

Checking the last row, we see that all the entries in this row are 0 or positive, so the solution is complete. From the final simplex matrix, we see that the nonbasic variables are $x_2, s_2,$ and s_3, and with these equal to zero, we determine all the solution values:

$$x_2 = 0, s_2 = 0, s_3 = 0 \quad \text{and} \quad x_1 = 2000, x_3 = 7000, s_1 = 10,000, f = 304,000$$

Thus the numbers of calculators that should be produced are

$$x_1 = 2000 \text{ scientific calculators}$$
$$x_2 = 0 \text{ business calculators}$$
$$x_3 = 7000 \text{ graphing calculators}$$

and these give a maximum profit of $304,000 for the month. Note also that the slack variables tell us that with this optimal solution, there were $s_1 = 10,000$ unused circuit components, $s_2 = 0$ unused labor hours, and $s_3 = 0$ unused calculator cases.

CHECKPOINT

1. Write the following constraints as equations by using slack variables.

$$3x_1 + x_2 + x_3 \leq 9$$
$$2x_1 + x_2 + 3x_3 \leq 8$$
$$2x_1 + x_2 \quad\quad \leq 5$$

2. Set up the simplex matrix to maximize $f = 2x_1 + 5x_2 + x_3$ subject to the constraints discussed in Problem 1.

Using the simplex matrix from Problem 2, perform the following.

3. Find the first pivot entry.
4. Use row operations to make the variable of the first pivot entry basic.
5. Find the second pivot entry and make a second variable basic.
6. Find the solution.

Spreadsheet Note

As our discussion indicates, the simplex method is quite complicated, even when the number of variables is relatively small (2 or 3). For this reason, computer software is often used to solve linear programming problems.

The following Excel screen shows entries for beginning to solve the linear programming problem that we solved "by hand" with the simplex method in Example 3.

Note that cells B3–B5 contain 0s that are the initial values of the variables, cell B9 contains the objective function that is to be maximized, and cells B13–B15 and cells C13–C15 contain the constrains for the problem.

	A	B	C
1	Variables		
2			
3	# scientific calculators (x)	0	
4	# business calculators (y)	0	
5	# graphing calculators (z)	0	
6			
7	Objective		
8			
9	Maximize profit	= 12*B3 + 26*B4 + 40*B5	
10			
11	Constraints		
12		Amount used	Maximum
13	Circuit components	= 5*B3 + 7*B4 + 10*B5	90000
14	Labor hours	= B3 + 3*B4 + 4*B5	30000
15	Cases	= B3 + B4 + B5	9000

The Excel steps used to obtain the solution to this and other linear programming problems are quite detailed and involve choosing *Data>Solver* and selecting the correct options in the dialog box. They are shown in Appendix B, Sections 4.3–4.5, and in the Online Excel Guide.

The following spreadsheet gives the solution. This indicates that profit is maximized at $304,000 when 2000 scientific and 7000 graphing calculators are produced. Note that under "Constraints," the difference between the columns labeled "Maximum" and "Amount used" gives the amount of each resource that was unused—that is, the value of each slack variable: $s_1 = 10,000$, $s_2 = 0$, and $s_3 = 0$. This is the same solution found in Example 3. ▪

	A	B	C
1	Variables		
2			
3	# scientific calculators (x)	2000	
4	# business calculators (y)	0	
5	# graphing calculators (z)	7000	
6			
7	Objective		
8			
9	Maximize profit	304000	
10			
11	Constraints		
12		Amount used	Maximum
13	Circuit components	80000	90000
14	Labor hours	30000	30000
15	Cases	9000	9000

Nonunique Solutions: Multiple Solutions and No Solution

As we've seen with graphical methods, a linear programming problem can have multiple solutions when the optimal value for the objective function occurs at two adjacent corners of the feasible region. Consider the following problem.

Maximize $f = 2x + y$ subject to

$$x + \frac{1}{2}y \leq 16$$

$$x + y \leq 24$$

$$x \geq 0, y \geq 0$$

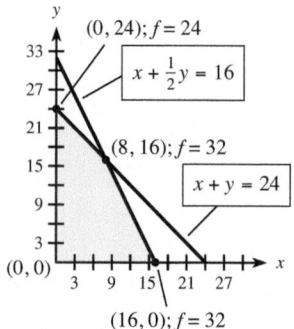

Figure 4.18

From Figure 4.18, we can see that the maximum value is $f = 32$ at the two corners (8, 16) and (16, 0). This means that $f = 32$ at any point on the segment joining those corners. Thus this problem has infinitely many solutions. Let's examine how we can discover these multiple solutions with the simplex method.

The simplex matrix for this problem (with the slack variables introduced) is

$$\begin{array}{ccccc} x & y & s_1 & s_2 & f \\ \end{array}$$
$$\left[\begin{array}{ccccc|c} ① & \frac{1}{2} & 1 & 0 & 0 & 16 \\ 1 & 1 & 0 & 1 & 0 & 24 \\ \hline -2 & -1 & 0 & 0 & 1 & 0 \end{array}\right]$$

The most negative value in the last row is -2, so the x-column is the pivot column. The smallest quotient occurs in row 1; the pivot entry (circled) is 1. Making x a basic variable gives the following transformed simplex matrix.

$$\begin{array}{ccccc} x & y & s_1 & s_2 & f \\ \end{array}$$
$$\left[\begin{array}{ccccc|c} 1 & \frac{1}{2} & 1 & 0 & 0 & 16 \\ 0 & \frac{1}{2} & -1 & 1 & 0 & 8 \\ \hline 0 & 0 & 2 & 0 & 1 & 32 \end{array}\right]$$

This simplex matrix has no negative indicators, so the optimal value of f has been found ($f = 32$ when $x = 16, y = 0$). Note that one of the nonbasic variables (y) has a zero indicator. When this occurs, we can use the column with the 0 indicator as our pivot column and often obtain a new solution that has the same value for the objective function. In this final tableau, if we used the y-column as the pivot column, then we could find the second solution (at $x = 8, y = 16$) that gives the same optimal value of f.

Multiple Solutions

When the simplex matrix for the optimal value of f has a nonbasic variable with a zero indicator in its column, there may be multiple solutions giving the same optimal value for f. We can discover whether another solution exists by using the column of that nonbasic variable as the pivot column.

Spreadsheet Note

Note that with Excel, multiple solutions may be found by using different initial values for the variables when the problem is entered into Excel.

It is possible for a linear programming problem to have an unbounded solution (and thus no maximum value for f).

EXAMPLE 4

Simplex Method When No Maximum Exists

Maximize $f = 2x_1 + x_2 + 3x_3$ subject to

$$x_1 - 3x_2 + x_3 \leq 3$$
$$x_1 - 6x_2 + 2x_3 \leq 6$$

if a maximum exists.

Solution

The simplex matrix for this problem (after introduction of slack variables) is

$$
\begin{array}{ccccccc}
x_1 & x_2 & x_3 & s_1 & s_2 & f & \\
\left[\begin{array}{cccccc|c}
1 & -3 & \boxed{1} & 1 & 0 & 0 & 3 \\
1 & -6 & 2 & 0 & 1 & 0 & 6 \\
\hline
-2 & -1 & -3 & 0 & 0 & 1 & 0
\end{array}\right]
\end{array}
$$

We see that the x_3 column has the most negative number, so we use that column as the pivot column.

We see that the smallest quotient is 3. Both coefficients give this quotient, so we can use either coefficient as the pivot entry. Using the element in row 1, we can make x_3 basic. The new simplex matrix is

$$
\begin{array}{cccccc}
x_1 & x_2 & x_3 & s_1 & s_2 & f \\
\left[\begin{array}{cccccc|c}
1 & -3 & 1 & 1 & 0 & 0 & 3 \\
-1 & 0 & 0 & -2 & 1 & 0 & 0 \\
\hline
1 & -10 & 0 & 3 & 0 & 1 & 9
\end{array}\right]
\end{array}
$$

The most negative value in the last row of this matrix is -10, so the pivot column is the x_2-column. But there are no positive coefficients in the x_2-column; what does this mean? Even if we could pivot using the x_2-column, the variables x_1 and s_1 would remain equal to 0. And the relationships among the remaining variables x_2, x_3, and s_2 would be the same.

$$-3x_2 + x_3 = 3 \quad \text{or} \quad x_3 = 3 + 3x_2$$
$$s_2 = 0$$

As x_2 is increased, x_3 also increases because all variables are nonnegative. This means that no matter how much we increase x_2, all other variables remain nonnegative. Furthermore, as we increase x_2 (and hence x_3), the value of f also increases. That is, there is no maximum value for f.

This example indicates that when a linear programming problem has an unbounded solution (and thus no maximum value for f), this is identified by the following condition in the simplex method.

No Solution

If, after a pivot column has been found, there are no positive coefficients in that column, no maximum solution exists.

Some difficulties can arise in using the simplex method to solve linear programming problems. These "difficulties" are discussed in more advanced courses, and we shall not encounter them in this text.

Shadow Prices   Finally, we note that one of the most powerful aspects of the simplex method is that in addition to giving the solution to a given problem, it tells how to adapt the solution if the situation changes. In particular, from the final simplex matrix (final tableau), not only can the solution to the problem be read, but also there is information about the amount of change in the objective function if 1 additional unit of a resource becomes available (this change is called the **shadow price** of the resource) and how this additional resource changes the optimal solution values.

For example, if one more acre of land became available in the Example 1 application (for a total of 6001 acres), it can be shown that if the co-op planted 3749.5 acres of corn and 2251.5 acres of soybeans, the profit would increase by $120. That is, the shadow price of land is $120/acre (or the marginal profit value of the land is $120/acre). The following simplex matrix C is the final one from Example 1 (where x = acres of corn, y = acres of soybeans, and s_1 = the slack variable for the land constraint). The bottom entry in the s_1-column of C is the shadow price for land. Furthermore, if the s_1-column is added to the last column in C, then matrix D results. The solution obtained from D gives the new planting scheme and the new maximum profit if one more acre of land is planted (x = 3749.5 acres of corn and y = 2251.5 acres of soybeans for a new maximum profit of P = $1,260,120).

$$
C = \begin{array}{c} \begin{array}{ccccccc} x & y & s_1 & s_2 & s_3 & P & \end{array} \\ \left[\begin{array}{cccccc|c} 0 & 1 & \frac{3}{2} & -\frac{1}{6} & 0 & 0 & 2{,}250 \\ 1 & 0 & -\frac{1}{2} & \frac{1}{6} & 0 & 0 & 3{,}750 \\ 0 & 0 & -\frac{9}{8} & \frac{1}{24} & 1 & 0 & 187.5 \\ 0 & 0 & 120 & \frac{40}{3} & 0 & 1 & 1{,}260{,}000 \end{array} \right] \end{array}
$$

$$
D = \begin{array}{c} \begin{array}{ccccccc} x & y & s_1 & s_2 & s_3 & P & \end{array} \\ \left[\begin{array}{cccccc|c} 0 & 1 & \frac{3}{2} & -\frac{1}{6} & 0 & 0 & 2{,}251.5 \\ 1 & 0 & -\frac{1}{2} & \frac{1}{6} & 0 & 0 & 3{,}749.5 \\ 0 & 0 & -\frac{9}{8} & \frac{1}{24} & 1 & 0 & 186\frac{3}{8} \\ 0 & 0 & 120 & \frac{40}{3} & 0 & 1 & 1{,}260{,}120 \end{array} \right] \end{array}
$$

Additional material on shadow prices appears in the second Extended Application/Group Project at the end of this chapter.

CHECKPOINT ANSWERS

1. $3x_1 + x_2 + x_3 + s_1 \qquad\qquad = 9$
   $2x_1 + x_2 + 3x_3 \qquad + s_2 \qquad = 8$
   $2x_1 + x_2 \qquad\qquad\qquad + s_3 = 5$

2. $$\left[\begin{array}{ccccccc|c} 3 & 1 & 1 & 1 & 0 & 0 & 0 & 9 \\ 2 & 1 & 3 & 0 & 1 & 0 & 0 & 8 \\ 2 & 1 & 0 & 0 & 0 & 1 & 0 & 5 \\ -2 & -5 & -1 & 0 & 0 & 0 & 1 & 0 \end{array} \right]$$

3. The first pivot entry is the 1 in row 3, column 2.

4. $$\left[\begin{array}{ccccccc|c} 1 & 0 & 1 & 1 & 0 & -1 & 0 & 4 \\ 0 & 0 & 3 & 0 & 1 & -1 & 0 & 3 \\ 2 & 1 & 0 & 0 & 0 & 1 & 0 & 5 \\ 8 & 0 & -1 & 0 & 0 & 5 & 1 & 25 \end{array} \right]$$

5. The second pivot entry is the 3 in row 2, column 3.
   $$\left[\begin{array}{ccccccc|c} 1 & 0 & 0 & 1 & -\frac{1}{3} & -\frac{2}{3} & 0 & 3 \\ 0 & 0 & 1 & 0 & \frac{1}{3} & -\frac{1}{3} & 0 & 1 \\ 2 & 1 & 0 & 0 & 0 & 1 & 0 & 5 \\ 8 & 0 & 0 & 0 & \frac{1}{3} & \frac{14}{3} & 1 & 26 \end{array} \right]$$

6. f is maximized at 26 when $x_1 = 0$, $x_2 = 5$, and $x_3 = 1$. Note also that $s_1 = 3$, $s_2 = 0$, and $s_3 = 0$.

EXERCISES 4.3

1. Convert the constraint inequalities $3x + 5y \leq 15$ and $3x + 6y \leq 20$ to equations containing slack variables.
2. Convert the constraint inequalities $2x + y \leq 4$ and $3x + 2y \leq 8$ to equations containing slack variables.

In Problems 3–6, set up the simplex matrix used to solve each linear programming problem. Assume that all variables are nonnegative.

3. Maximize $f = 3x + 7y$ subject to

$$2x + 5y \leq 400$$
$$x + 2y \leq 175$$

4. Maximize $f = x + 3y$ subject to

$$5x + y \leq 50$$
$$x + 2y \leq 50$$

5. Maximize $f = 2x + 5y + 2z$ subject to

$$2x + 7y + 9z \leq 100$$
$$6x + 5y + z \leq 145$$
$$x + 2y + 7z \leq 90$$

6. Maximize $f = 3x + 5y + 11z$ subject to

$$2x + 3y + 4z \leq 60$$
$$x + 4y + z \leq 48$$
$$5x + y + z \leq 48$$

In Problems 7–10, a simplex matrix is given in which the solution is complete. Identify the maximum value of f and a set of values of the variables that gives this maximum value.

7.
$$\begin{bmatrix} 1 & 0 & \frac{3}{4} & -\frac{3}{4} & 0 & 11 \\ 0 & 1 & \frac{5}{12} & \frac{11}{12} & 0 & 9 \\ 0 & 0 & 2 & 4 & 1 & 20 \end{bmatrix}$$

8.
$$\begin{bmatrix} 0 & 4 & 1 & -\frac{1}{5} & 0 & 2 \\ 1 & 2 & 0 & 1 & 0 & 4 \\ 0 & 2 & 0 & 2 & 1 & 12 \end{bmatrix}$$

9.
$$\begin{bmatrix} 4 & 1 & 0 & 0 & \frac{3}{4} & 4 & 0 & 14 \\ -2 & 0 & 0 & 1 & -\frac{8}{5} & -2 & 0 & 6 \\ 3 & 0 & 1 & 0 & 2 & 6 & 0 & 11 \\ 4 & 0 & 0 & 0 & 2 & \frac{1}{2} & 1 & 525 \end{bmatrix}$$

10.
$$\begin{bmatrix} 0 & 1 & 0 & -3 & -1 & -4 & 0 & 12 \\ 1 & 0 & 0 & -2 & -1 & -5 & 0 & 16 \\ 0 & 0 & 1 & -1 & 2 & 1 & 0 & 22 \\ 0 & 0 & 0 & 4 & 1 & 2 & 1 & 150 \end{bmatrix}$$

In Problems 11–18, a simplex matrix for a standard maximization problem is given.

(a) **Write the values of *all* the variables (use $x_1, x_2, x_3, \ldots$ and $s_1, s_2, s_3, \ldots$) and of the objective function f.**

(b) **Indicate whether the solution from part (a) is complete (optimal).**

(c) **If the solution is not complete, find the next pivot and state *all* row operations with that pivot (that is, row operations that make that pivot equal to 1, and then make other entries in the pivot column equal to 0). Do not perform the row operations.**

11.
$$\begin{bmatrix} 2 & 0 & 1 & -\frac{3}{4} & 0 & 14 \\ 3 & 1 & 0 & \frac{1}{3} & 0 & 45 \\ -6 & 0 & 0 & 3 & 1 & 75 \end{bmatrix}$$

12.
$$\begin{bmatrix} 0 & 4 & 1 & -\frac{1}{5} & 0 & 2 \\ 1 & 2 & 0 & 1 & 0 & 4 \\ 0 & 2 & 0 & 2 & 1 & 12 \end{bmatrix}$$

13.
$$\begin{bmatrix} 10 & 27 & 1 & 0 & 0 & 0 & 200 \\ 4 & 51 & 0 & 1 & 0 & 0 & 400 \\ 15 & 27 & 0 & 0 & 1 & 0 & 350 \\ -8 & -7 & 0 & 0 & 0 & 1 & 0 \end{bmatrix}$$

14.
$$\begin{bmatrix} 5 & 5 & 7 & 1 & 0 & 0 & 0 & 12 \\ 4 & 0 & 6 & 0 & 1 & 0 & 0 & 48 \\ 0 & 1 & 1 & 0 & 0 & 1 & 0 & 8 \\ -1 & -3 & -1 & 0 & 0 & 0 & 1 & 0 \end{bmatrix}$$

15.
$$\begin{bmatrix} 1 & 4 & 0 & 0 & \frac{3}{4} & 4 & 0 & 24 \\ 0 & -2 & 0 & 1 & -\frac{5}{8} & -2 & 0 & 16 \\ 0 & 3 & 1 & 0 & 2 & 6 & 0 & 21 \\ 0 & 4 & 0 & 0 & 2 & \frac{1}{2} & 1 & 780 \end{bmatrix}$$

16.
$$\begin{bmatrix} 2 & 1 & 1 & 1 & 0 & 0 & 0 & 12 \\ -2 & 0 & -1 & -2 & 0 & 1 & 0 & 5 \\ 4 & 0 & 2 & -1 & 1 & 0 & 0 & 6 \\ -2 & 0 & 5 & 7 & 0 & 0 & 1 & 30 \end{bmatrix}$$

17.
$$\begin{bmatrix} 4 & 4 & 1 & 0 & 0 & 2 & 0 & 12 \\ 2 & 4 & 0 & 1 & 0 & -1 & 0 & 4 \\ -3 & -11 & 0 & 0 & 1 & -1 & 0 & 6 \\ -3 & -3 & 0 & 0 & 0 & 4 & 1 & 150 \end{bmatrix}$$

18.
$$\begin{bmatrix} 1 & 0 & -3 & 4 & -4 & 0 & 0 & 12 \\ 0 & 1 & -4 & 2 & 5 & 0 & 0 & 100 \\ 0 & 0 & -1 & -6 & -3 & 1 & 0 & 40 \\ 0 & 0 & 6 & -1 & -3 & 0 & 1 & 380 \end{bmatrix}$$

In Problems 19–26, use the simplex method to maximize the given functions. Assume that all variables are nonnegative.

19. Maximize $f = 3x + 10y$ subject to

$$14x + 7y \le 35$$
$$5x + 5y \le 50$$

20. Maximize $f = 7x + 10y$ subject to

$$14x + 14y \le 98$$
$$8x + 10y \le 100$$

21. Maximize $f = 2x + 3y$ subject to

$$x + 2y \le 10$$
$$x + y \le 7$$

22. Maximize $f = 5x + 30y$ subject to

$$2x + 10y \le 96$$
$$x + 10y \le 90$$

23. Maximize $f = 2x + y$ subject to

$$-x + y \le 2$$
$$x + 2y \le 10$$
$$3x + y \le 15$$

24. Maximize $f = 2x + 6y$ subject to

$$2x + 5y \le 30$$
$$x + 5y \le 25$$
$$x + y \le 11$$

25. Maximize $f = 7x + 10y + 4z$ subject to

$$3x + 5y + 4z \le 30$$
$$3x + 2y \le 4$$
$$x + 2y \le 8$$

26. Maximize $f = 20x + 12y + 12z$ subject to

$$x + z \le 40$$
$$x + y \le 30$$
$$y + z \le 40$$

In Problems 27–30, use Excel to solve each linear programming problem.

27. Maximize $f = x + 3y + z$ subject to

$$x + 4y \le 12$$
$$3x + 6y + 4z \le 48$$
$$y + z \le 8$$

28. Maximize $f = 64x + 36y + 38z$ subject to

$$4x + 2y + 2z \le 40$$
$$8x + 10y + 5z \le 90$$
$$4x + 4y + 3z \le 30$$

29. Maximize $f = 24x_1 + 30x_2 + 18x_3 + 18x_4$ subject to

$$12x_1 + 16x_2 + 20x_3 + 8x_4 \le 880$$
$$5x_1 + 10x_2 + 10x_3 + 5x_4 \le 460$$
$$10x_1 - 5x_2 + 8x_3 + 5x_4 \le 280$$

30. Maximize $f = 8x_1 + 17x_2 + 24x_3 + 31x_4 + 36x_5$ subject to

$$x_1 + x_2 + 5x_3 + 3x_4 + 2x_5 \le 5000$$
$$2x_1 + x_2 + 4x_3 + 4x_4 + 2x_5 \le 6000$$
$$3x_1 + x_2 + 5x_3 + 2x_4 + 3x_5 \le 7000$$

Problems 31–38 involve linear programming problems that have nonunique solutions.

In Problems 31–34, a simplex matrix is given for which the associated maximization problem either has no solution or has multiple solutions. If there is no solution, explain how you know this. If there are multiple solutions, give one solution and explain how you would find another.

31.
$$\begin{bmatrix} 4 & -1 & 0 & 1 & -5 & 0 & 0 & | & 5 \\ 1 & 0 & 1 & 0 & 1 & 0 & 0 & | & 12 \\ 3 & -3 & 0 & 0 & -2 & 1 & 0 & | & 6 \\ \hline -2 & -5 & 0 & 0 & 10 & 0 & 1 & | & 120 \end{bmatrix}$$

32.
$$\begin{bmatrix} 0 & 20 & -6 & 1 & 0 & -3 & 0 & | & 4 \\ 0 & 5 & -6 & 0 & 1 & -2 & 0 & | & 2 \\ 1 & -1 & 0 & 0 & 0 & 4 & 0 & | & 6 \\ \hline 0 & -9 & -12 & 0 & 0 & 10 & 1 & | & 20 \end{bmatrix}$$

33.
$$\begin{bmatrix} 1 & 0 & 3 & 0 & 6 & 0 & | & 50 \\ 0 & 0 & 4 & 1 & -4 & 0 & | & 6 \\ 0 & 1 & -2 & 0 & 2 & 0 & | & 10 \\ \hline 0 & 0 & 9 & 0 & 0 & 1 & | & 100 \end{bmatrix}$$

34.
$$\begin{bmatrix} 0 & 1 & 2 & 1 & 0 & 0 & | & 20 \\ 1 & 0 & 6 & 1 & 0 & 0 & | & 50 \\ 0 & 0 & -1 & -2 & 1 & 0 & | & 10 \\ \hline 0 & 0 & 4 & 0 & 0 & 1 & | & 88 \end{bmatrix}$$

In Problems 35–38, use the simplex method to maximize each function (whenever possible) subject to the given constraints. If there is no solution, indicate this; if multiple solutions exist, find two of them.

35. Maximize $f = 3x + 2y$ subject to

$$x - 10y \le 10$$
$$-x + y \le 40$$

36. Maximize $f = 10x + 15y$ subject to

$$-5x + y \le 24$$
$$2x - 3y \le 9$$

37. Maximize $f = 3x + 12y$ subject to

$$2x + y \le 120$$
$$x + 4y \le 200$$

38. Maximize $f = 8x + 6y$ subject to

$$4x + 3y \le 24$$
$$10x + 9y \le 198$$

APPLICATIONS

39. *Manufacturing* Q-RAM Inc. manufactures solid-state drives (SSDs) of two sizes, 500 GB and 1.5 TB. The company can make a total of 60 drives per day, and it has available 120 labor-hours per day. It takes 1 labor-hour to make a 500 GB drive and 3 hours to make a 1.5 TB drive. The profits are $40 per 500 GB drive and $60 per 1.5 TB drive.
    (a) Write the simplex matrix to maximize the daily profit.
    (b) Find the maximum profit and the number of each type of drive that will give the maximum profit.

40. *Construction* A contractor builds two types of homes. The Carolina requires one lot, $160,000 capital, and 160 worker-days of labor, and the Savannah requires one lot, $240,000 capital, and 160 worker-days of labor. The contractor owns 300 lots and has $48,000,000 available capital and 43,200 worker-days of labor. The profit on the Carolina is $40,000, and the profit on the Savannah is $50,000.
    (a) Write the simplex matrix to maximize the profit.
    (b) Use the simplex method to find how many of each type of home should be built to maximize profit, and find the maximum possible profit.

41. *Production scheduling* At one of its factories, a manufacturer of college logo sweatshirts makes two styles: crewneck pullover and hooded. Each pullover sweatshirt takes 5 minutes to cut out and 20 minutes to assemble and finish. Each hooded sweatshirt takes 5 minutes to cut out and 30 minutes to assemble and finish. The plant has enough workers to provide at most 3750 minutes per day for cutting and at most 19,500 minutes per day for assembly and finishing. The profit on each pullover sweatshirt is $8 and on each hooded sweatshirt is $10. How many of each sweatshirt type should be produced each day to obtain maximum profit? Find the maximum daily profit.

42. *Budget utilization* A car rental agency has a budget of $1.8 million to purchase at most 100 new cars. The agency will purchase either subcompact cars at $15,000 each or midsized cars at $30,000 each. From past rental patterns, the agency decides to purchase at most 50 midsized cars and expects an annual profit of $7500 per subcompact car and $11,000 per midsized car. How many of each type of car should be purchased to obtain the maximum profit while satisfying budgetary and other planning constraints? Find the maximum profit.

43. *Production scheduling* Happy Valley Ice Cream Company is planning its production for next week. Demand for Happy Valley's premium and light ice creams continues to outpace the company's production capacities. Two resources used in ice cream production are in short supply for next week. The mixing machines will be available for only 140 hours, and only 28,000 gallons of high-grade milk will be available. One hundred gallons of premium ice cream requires 0.3 hour of mixing and 90 gallons of milk. One hundred gallons of light ice cream requires 0.5 hour of mixing and 70 gallons of milk. If Happy Valley earns a profit of $100 per hundred gallons on both of its ice creams, how many hundreds of gallons of premium and of light ice cream should Happy Valley produce next week to maximize profit? How much profit will result?

44. *Experimentation* An experiment involves placing the males and females of a laboratory animal species in two separate controlled environments. There is a limited time available in these environments, and the experimenter wants to maximize the number of animals subject to the constraints described.

	Males	Females	Time Available
Environment A	20 min	25 min	800 min
Environment B	20 min	15 min	600 min

How many males and how many females will maximize the total number of animals?

Problems 45–48 involve three variables. Solve them with the simplex method, Excel, or some other technology.

45. *Construction* A contractor builds three types of houses: the Aries, the Belfair, and the Wexford. Each house requires one lot, and the following table gives the number of labor-hours and the amount of capital needed for each type of house, as well as the profit on the sale of each house. There are 12 lots, 47,500 labor-hours, and $3,413,000 available for the contractor's use.
    (a) Building how many of each type of house will maximize his profit?
    (b) What is the maximum possible profit?

	Aries	Belfair	Wexford
Labor-hours	3,000	3,700	5,000
Capital	$205,000	$279,600	$350,000
Profit	$20,000	$25,000	$30,000

46. *Medicine* A medical clinic performs three types of medical tests that use the same machines. Tests A, B, and C take 15 minutes, 30 minutes, and 1 hour, respectively, with respective profits of $150, $250, and $500. The clinic has four machines available. One person is qualified to do test A, two to do test B, and one to do test C. If the clinic has a rush of customers for these tests, how many of each type should it schedule in a 12-hour day to maximize its profit?

47. *Revenue* A woman has a building with 26 one-bedroom apartments, 40 two-bedroom apartments, and 60 three-bedroom apartments available to rent to students. She has set the rent at $500 per month for the one-bedroom units, $800 per month for the two-bedroom units, and $1150 per month for the three-bedroom units. She must rent to one student per bedroom, and zoning laws limit her to at most 250 students in

this building. There are enough students available to rent all the apartments.

(a) How many of each type of apartment should she rent to maximize her revenue?

(b) What is the maximum possible revenue?

48. *Manufacturing* Patio Iron makes wrought iron outdoor dining tables, chairs, and stools. Each table uses 8 feet of a standard width wrought iron, 4 hours of labor for cutting and assembly, and 2 hours of labor for detail and finishing work. Each chair uses 6 feet of the wrought iron, 2 hours of cutting and assembly labor, and 1.5 hours of detail and finishing labor. Each stool uses 1 foot of the wrought iron, 1.5 hours for cutting and assembly, and 0.5 hour for detail and finishing work, and the daily demand for stools is at most 16. Each day Patio Iron has available at most 108 feet of wrought iron, 50 hours for cutting and assembly, and 40 hours for detail and finishing. If the profits are $60 for each dining table, $48 for each chair, and $36 for each stool, how many of each item should be made each day to maximize profit? Find the maximum profit.

In Problems 49–54, use Excel to solve each linear programming problem.

49. *Advertising* Tire Corral has $6000 available per month for advertising. Newspaper ads cost $100 each and can occur a maximum of 21 times per month. Radio ads cost $300 each and can occur a maximum of 28 times per month at this price. Each newspaper ad reaches 6000 men over 20 years of age, and each radio ad reaches 8000 of these men. The company wants to maximize the number of ad exposures to this group. How many of each ad should it purchase? What is the maximum possible number of exposures?

50. *Manufacturing* A bicycle manufacturer makes mountain bikes and road bikes. Each mountain bike requires 2 units of steel and 6 units of aluminum in its frame and 12 special components for the hub, sprocket, and gear assembly. Each road bike requires 5 units each of steel and aluminum for its frame and 5 of the special components. Shipments are such that steel is limited to 100 units per day, aluminum is limited to 120 units per day, and the special components are limited to 180 units per day. If the profits are $300 on each mountain bike and $200 on each road bike, how many of each should be produced to yield the maximum profit? What is the maximum profit?

51. *Manufacturing* A firm has decided to discontinue production of an unprofitable product. This will create excess capacity, and the firm is considering one or more of three possible new products: A, B, and C. The available daily hours in the plant will be 477 hours in tool and die, 350 hours on drill presses, and 150 hours on lathes. The hours of production required in each of these areas are as follows for each of the products.

	Tool and Die	Drill Press	Lathe
A	9	5	3
B	3	4	0
C	0.5	0	2

Furthermore, the sales department foresees no limitations on the sale of products A and C but anticipates sales of only 20 or fewer per day for product B. If the unit profits expected are $30 for A, $9 for B, and $15 for C, how many of each should be produced to maximize overall profit? What is the maximum profit?

52. *Advertising* The Laposata Pasta Company has $12,000 available for advertising. The following table gives the costs per ad and the numbers of people exposed to its ads for three different media (with numbers in thousands).

Ad Packages	Newspaper	Radio	TV
Cost	2	2	4
Total audience	30	21	54
Working mothers	6	12	8

If the total available audience is 420,000 and the company wants to maximize the number of exposures to working mothers, how many ads of each type should it purchase?

53. *Manufacturing* At one of its factories, a manufacturer of televisions makes one or more of four models of HD units (without cases): a 20-in. LCD, a 42-in. LCD, a 42-in. plasma, and a 50-in. plasma. The assembly and testing time requirements for each model are shown in the following table, together with the maximum amounts of time available per week for assembly and testing. In addition to these constraints, the supplier of cases indicated that it would supply no more than 200 cases per week and that of these, no more than 40 could be for the 20-in. LCD model.

	20-in. LCD	42-in. LCD	42-in. Plasma	50-in. Plasma	Total Available
Assembly time (hours)	7	10	12	15	2000
Test time (hours)	2	2	4	5	500
Profit (dollars)	46	60	75	100	

Use the profit for each television shown in the table to find the number of completed models of each type that should be produced to obtain the maximum profit for the week. Find the maximum profit.

54. *Investment analysis* Conglomo Corporation is considering investing in other smaller companies, and it can purchase any fraction of each company. Each investment by Conglomo requires a partial payment now

and a final payment 1 year from now. For each investment, the following table summarizes the amount of each payment (in millions of dollars) and the projected 5-year profit (also in millions of dollars).

	Company 1	Company 2	Company 3	Company 4	Company 5
Paid now	13.2	63.6	6.0	6.0	34.8
Paid in 1 year	3.6	7.2	6.0	1.2	40.8
Projected profit	15.6	19.2	19.2	16.8	46.8

This table may be interpreted as follows: If Conglomo purchases one-fifth of Company 4, then it pays $\frac{1}{5}(6.0) = \$1.2$ million now and $\frac{1}{5}(1.2) = \$0.24$ million $= \$240{,}000$ after 1 year, and the one-fifth share has a projected 5-year profit of $\frac{1}{5}(16.8) = \$3.36$ million. Conglomo has $48 million available for investment now and $24 million available for investment 1 year from now. What fraction of each smaller company should Conglomo purchase to maximize the projected 5-year profit? What is the maximum profit? *Hint:* If x_1 represents the fraction of Company 1 that is purchased, then $x_1 \le 1$ is a constraint.

SECTION **4.4**

The Simplex Method: Duality and Minimization

OBJECTIVES

- To formulate the dual for minimization problems
- To solve minimization problems using the simplex method on the dual

APPLICATION PREVIEW

A beef producer is considering two different types of feed. Each feed contains some or all of the necessary ingredients for fattening beef. Brand 1 feed costs 20 cents per pound, and brand 2 costs 30 cents per pound. Table 4.1 contains all the relevant data about nutrition and cost of each brand and the minimum requirements per unit of beef. The producer would like to determine how much of each brand to buy to satisfy the nutritional requirements for Ingredients A and B at minimum cost. (See Example 3.)

TABLE 4.1

	Brand 1	Brand 2	Minimum Requirement
Ingredient A	3 units/lb	5 units/lb	40 units
Ingredient B	4 units/lb	3 units/lb	46 units
Cost per pound	20¢	30¢	

In this section, we will use the simplex method to solve minimization problems such as this one.

Dual Problems   We have solved both maximization and minimization problems using graphical methods, but the simplex method, as discussed in the previous section, applies only to maximization problems. Now we turn our attention to extending the use of the simplex method to solve minimization problems. Such problems might arise when a company seeks to minimize its production costs yet fill customers' orders or purchase items necessary for production.

As with maximization problems, we shall consider only **standard minimization problems,** in which the constraints satisfy the following conditions.

1. All variables are nonnegative.
2. The constraints are of the form

$$a_1 y_1 + a_2 y_2 + \cdots + a_n y_n \ge b \text{ where } b \text{ is positive.}$$

Because the simplex method specifically seeks to increase the objective function, it does not apply to minimization problems. However, associated with each minimization problem is a related maximization problem called the **dual problem** or **dual.**

EXAMPLE **1**   **A Minimization Problem and Its Dual**

Given the standard minimization problem

$$\text{Minimize } g = 11y_1 + 7y_2$$
$$\text{subject to} \quad y_1 + 2y_2 \geq 10$$
$$3y_1 + \quad y_2 \geq 15$$

find the dual maximization problem.

Solution
First, we write a matrix A that has a form similar to the simplex matrix, but without slack variables and with positive coefficients for the variables in the last row and with g (the function name) in the augment.

The matrix for the dual problem is formed by interchanging the rows and columns of matrix A. Matrix B is the result of this procedure, and recall that B is the **transpose** of A.

$$\text{Minimization} \qquad\qquad \text{Dual}$$

$$A = \begin{bmatrix} 1 & 2 & 10 \\ 3 & 1 & 15 \\ \hline 11 & 7 & g \end{bmatrix} \qquad B = \begin{bmatrix} 1 & 3 & 11 \\ 2 & 1 & 7 \\ \hline 10 & 15 & g \end{bmatrix}$$

Note that row 1 of A becomes column 1 of B, row 2 of A becomes column 2 of B, and row 3 of A becomes column 3 of B.

In the same way we formed matrix A, we can now "convert back" from matrix B to the maximization problem that is the dual of the original minimization problem. We state this dual problem using different letters to emphasize that this is a different problem from the original.

$$\text{Maximize } f = 10x_1 + 15x_2$$
$$\text{subject to} \quad x_1 + 3x_2 \leq 11$$
$$2x_1 + \quad x_2 \leq 7$$

Next, let's see how the solutions of these problems are related. The following box shows the solution of the Example 1 minimization problem and its dual maximization problem.

COMPARISON OF A MINIMIZATION PROBLEM AND ITS DUAL

Maximization Problem—Simplex Method

1.
$$\begin{array}{ccccc|c} x_1 & x_2 & s_1 & s_2 & f & \\ 1 & ③ & 1 & 0 & 0 & 11 \\ 2 & 1 & 0 & 1 & 0 & 7 \\ \hline -10 & -15 & 0 & 0 & 1 & 0 \end{array}$$

2.
$$\begin{array}{ccccc|c} \frac{1}{3} & 1 & \frac{1}{3} & 0 & 0 & \frac{11}{3} \\ ⑤⁄₃ & 0 & -\frac{1}{3} & 1 & 0 & \frac{10}{3} \\ \hline -5 & 0 & 5 & 0 & 1 & 55 \end{array}$$

Minimization Problem—Graphical Method

$3y_1 + y_2 = 15$

$y_1 + 2y_2 = 10$

Corners:

$A = (0, 15)$
$B = (4, 3)$ $\left. \begin{array}{l} \text{obtained by solving} \\ \text{simultaneously} \end{array} \right.$
$C = (10, 0)$

3. $\begin{bmatrix} 0 & 1 & \frac{2}{5} & -\frac{1}{5} & 0 & 3 \\ 1 & 0 & -\frac{1}{5} & \frac{3}{5} & 0 & 2 \\ 0 & 0 & 4 & 3 & 1 & 65 \end{bmatrix}$

Maximum $f = 65$ occurs at $x_1 = 2$, $x_2 = 3$.

$g = 11y_1 + 7y_2$

At A, $g = 11(0) + 7(15) = 105$

At B, $g = 11(4) + 7(3) = 65$

At C, $g = 11(10) + 7(0) = 110$

Minimum $g = 65$ occurs at $y_1 = 4$, $y_2 = 3$.

In comparing the solutions of the minimization problem and its dual, the first thing to note is that the maximum value of f in the maximization problem and the minimum value of g in the minimization problem are the same. Furthermore, looking at the final simplex matrix, we can find the values of y_1 and y_2 that give the minimum value of g by looking at the last (bottom) entries in the slack variable columns of the matrix.

$$\begin{array}{ccccc} x_1 & x_2 & s_1 & s_2 & f \end{array}$$
$$\begin{bmatrix} 0 & 1 & \frac{2}{5} & -\frac{1}{5} & 0 & 3 \\ 1 & 0 & -\frac{1}{5} & \frac{3}{5} & 0 & 2 \\ 0 & 0 & 4 & 3 & 1 & 65 \end{bmatrix}$$

These values give the values of y_1 and y_2 in the minimization problem.

Duality and Solving From Example 1 and the previous discussion, we see that the given minimization problem and its dual maximization problem are very closely related. In fact, each problem is the dual of the other. Furthermore, when a pair of problems are duals of each other, the simplex method can be used to solve them both. This fact was proved by John von Neumann, and it is summarized by the Principle of Duality.

Principle of Duality

1. When a standard minimization problem and its dual have a solution, the maximum value of the function to be maximized is the same value as the minimum value of the function to be minimized.
2. When the simplex method is used to solve the maximization problem, the values of the variables that solve the dual minimization problem are *the last entries in the columns corresponding to the slack variables.*

EXAMPLE 2   Minimization with the Simplex Method

Given the problem

$$\begin{aligned} \text{Minimize } 18y_1 + 12y_2 &= g \\ \text{subject to } \quad 2y_1 + \quad y_2 &\geq 8 \\ 6y_1 + 6y_2 &\geq 36 \end{aligned}$$

(a) State the dual of this minimization problem.
(b) Solve this minimization problem using the simplex method to solve the dual maximization problem.

Solution

(a) The dual of this minimization problem will be a maximization problem. To form the dual, first write the matrix A (without slack variables and with positive coefficients for the variables in the last row) for the given problem.

$$A = \begin{bmatrix} 2 & 1 & 8 \\ 6 & 6 & 36 \\ 18 & 12 & g \end{bmatrix}$$

Next, transpose matrix A to yield matrix B.

$$B = \left[\begin{array}{cc|c} 2 & 6 & 18 \\ 1 & 6 & 12 \\ \hline 8 & 36 & g \end{array}\right]$$

Then write the dual maximization problem, renaming the variables and the function.

Dual problem

Maximize $f = 8x_1 + 36x_2$

subject to $2x_1 + 6x_2 \le 18$

$x_1 + 6x_2 \le 12$

(b) To solve the given minimization problem, we use the simplex method on its dual maximization problem. The complete simplex matrix for each step is given, and each pivot
entry is circled.

1.
$$\left[\begin{array}{ccccc|c} 2 & 6 & 1 & 0 & 0 & 18 \\ 1 & ⑥ & 0 & 1 & 0 & 12 \\ \hline -8 & -36 & 0 & 0 & 1 & 0 \end{array}\right]$$
2.
$$\left[\begin{array}{ccccc|c} ① & 0 & 1 & -1 & 0 & 6 \\ \frac{1}{6} & 1 & 0 & \frac{1}{6} & 0 & 2 \\ \hline -2 & 0 & 0 & 6 & 1 & 72 \end{array}\right]$$

3. $x_1 \ x_2 \quad s_1 \quad s_2 \quad f$
$$\left[\begin{array}{ccccc|c} 1 & 0 & 1 & -1 & 0 & 6 \\ 0 & 1 & -\frac{1}{6} & \frac{2}{6} & 0 & 1 \\ \hline 0 & 0 & 2 & 4 & 1 & 84 \end{array}\right]$$

The solution of the maximization problem is $f = 84$ (at $x_1 = 6$, $x_2 = 1$). By the Principle of Duality, $g = 84$ is the minimum value of the objective function $g = 18y_1 + 12y_2$,
and the values that give this minimum are the last entries in the slack variable columns,
$y_1 = 2$ and $y_2 = 4$. ∎

CHECKPOINT

Perform the following steps to begin the process of finding the minimum value of
$g = y_1 + 4y_2$ subject to the following constraints.

$$2y_1 + 4y_2 \ge 18$$
$$y_1 + 5y_2 \ge 15$$

1. Form the matrix associated with the minimization problem.
2. Find the transpose of this matrix.
3. State the dual problem using the matrix from number 2.
4. Write the simplex matrix for the dual problem in number (3).
5. The dual of this minimization problem has the following solution matrix. What is the
solution of the minimization problem?

$$\left[\begin{array}{ccccc|c} 1 & 0 & \frac{5}{6} & -\frac{1}{6} & 0 & \frac{1}{6} \\ 0 & 1 & -\frac{2}{3} & \frac{1}{3} & 0 & \frac{2}{3} \\ \hline 0 & 0 & 5 & 2 & 1 & 13 \end{array}\right]$$

EXAMPLE 3   **Purchasing** | APPLICATION PREVIEW |

A beef producer is considering two different types of feed. Each feed contains some or
all of the necessary ingredients for fattening beef. Brand 1 feed costs 20 cents per pound,
and brand 2 costs 30 cents per pound. How much of each brand should the producer buy

to satisfy the nutritional requirements for ingredients A and B at minimum cost? Table 4.2 contains all the relevant data about nutrition, cost of each brand, and the minimum requirements per unit of beef.

TABLE 4.2

	Brand 1	Brand 2	Minimum Requirement
Ingredient A	3 oz/lb	5 oz/lb	40 oz
Ingredient B	4 oz/lb	3 oz/lb	46 oz
Cost per pound	20¢	30¢	

Solution

Let y_1 be the number of pounds of brand 1 and let y_2 be the number of pounds of brand 2. Then we can formulate the problem as follows:

$$\text{Minimize cost } C = 20y_1 + 30y_2$$
$$\text{subject to } 3y_1 + 5y_2 \geq 40$$
$$4y_1 + 3y_2 \geq 46$$

The original linear programming problem is usually called the **primal problem.** If we write this in an augmented matrix, without the slack variables, then we can use the transpose to find the dual problem.

$$
\begin{array}{c}
\text{Primal} \\
\left[
\begin{array}{cc|c}
3 & 5 & 40 \\
4 & 3 & 46 \\
\hline
20 & 30 & C
\end{array}
\right]
\end{array}
\qquad
\begin{array}{c}
\text{Dual} \\
\text{(with function renamed)} \\
\left[
\begin{array}{cc|c}
3 & 4 & 20 \\
5 & 3 & 30 \\
\hline
40 & 46 & f
\end{array}
\right]
\end{array}
$$

Thus the dual maximization problem is

$$\text{Maximize } f = 40x_1 + 46x_2$$
$$\text{subject to } 3x_1 + 4x_2 \leq 20$$
$$5x_1 + 3x_2 \leq 30$$

The simplex matrix for this maximization problem, with slack variables included, is

$$
1. \left[
\begin{array}{ccccc|c}
3 & ④ & 1 & 0 & 0 & 20 \\
5 & 3 & 0 & 1 & 0 & 30 \\
\hline
-40 & -46 & 0 & 0 & 1 & 0
\end{array}
\right]
$$

Solving the problem gives

$$
2. \left[
\begin{array}{ccccc|c}
\frac{3}{4} & 1 & \frac{1}{4} & 0 & 0 & 5 \\
\frac{11}{4} & 0 & -\frac{3}{4} & 1 & 0 & 15 \\
\hline
-\frac{11}{2} & 0 & \frac{23}{2} & 0 & 1 & 230
\end{array}
\right]
\qquad
3. \left[
\begin{array}{ccccc|c}
0 & 1 & \frac{5}{11} & -\frac{3}{11} & 0 & \frac{10}{11} \\
1 & 0 & -\frac{3}{11} & \frac{4}{11} & 0 & \frac{60}{11} \\
\hline
0 & 0 & 10 & 2 & 1 & 260
\end{array}
\right]
$$

The solution to this problem is

$$y_1 = 10 \text{ lb of brand 1}$$
$$y_2 = 2 \text{ lb of brand 2}$$
$$\text{Minimum cost} = 260 \text{ cents or \$2.60 per unit of beef}$$

In a more extensive study of linear programming, the duality relationship we used in this section as a means of solving minimization problems can be shown to have more properties than we mentioned.

Spreadsheet Note When we use Excel, minimization problems are solved in a manner similar to maximization problems. Because of the constraints, the Solver for this problem has different directions on the inequality symbols; Solver is also set to find the minimum (min) rather than the maximum (max) value of the objective function. (For details on using the Excel Solver, see Appendix B, Section 4.3, or the Online Excel Guide.)

The solution to the minimization problem in Example 3, found with Solver and shown below, is that cost is minimized at 260 cents per unit of beef when 10 lb of brand 1 and 2 lb of brand 2 are used. This is the same solution we found with the simplex method. ▓

		A	B	C
1		Variables		
2				
3		Pounds Brand 1	10	
4		Pounds Brand 2	2	
5				
6		Objective		
7				
8		Minimize cost	260	
9				
10		Constraints		
11			Amount in feeds	Required
12		Ingredient A	40	40
13		Ingredient B	46	46

CHECKPOINT ANSWERS

1. $\begin{bmatrix} 2 & 4 & 18 \\ 1 & 5 & 15 \\ 1 & 4 & g \end{bmatrix}$
2. $\begin{bmatrix} 2 & 1 & 1 \\ 4 & 5 & 4 \\ 18 & 15 & g \end{bmatrix}$

3. Maximize $f = 18x_1 + 15x_2$ subject to
$$2x_1 + x_2 \leq 1$$
$$4x_1 + 5x_2 \leq 4$$

4. $\begin{bmatrix} 2 & 1 & 1 & 0 & 0 & 1 \\ 4 & 5 & 0 & 1 & 0 & 4 \\ -18 & -15 & 0 & 0 & 1 & 0 \end{bmatrix}$

5. The minimum value is $g = 13$ when $y_1 = 5$ and $y_2 = 2$.

EXERCISES 4.4

In Problems 1–4, complete the following.
(a) Form the matrix associated with each given minimization problem and find its transpose.
(b) Write the dual maximization problem. Be sure to rename the variables.

1. Minimize $g = 4y_1 + 5y_2$ subject to
$$5y_1 + 2y_2 \geq 16$$
$$y_1 + 2y_2 \geq 8$$

2. Minimize $g = 3y_1 + 2y_2$ subject to
$$3y_1 + y_2 \geq 6$$
$$3y_1 + 4y_2 \geq 12$$

3. Minimize $g = 7y_1 + 3y_2$ subject to
$$y_1 + 2y_2 \geq 30$$
$$y_1 + 4y_2 \geq 50$$

4. Minimize $g = 9y_1 + 10y_2$ subject to
$$y_1 + 2y_2 \geq 21$$
$$3y_1 + 2y_2 \geq 27$$

In Problems 5 and 6, suppose a primal minimization problem and its dual maximization problem were solved using the simplex method on the dual problem and the final simplex matrix is given.

(a) Find the solution of the minimization problem. Use y_1, y_2, y_3 as the variables and g as the function.

(b) Find the solution of the maximization problem. Use x_1, x_2, x_3 as the variables and f as the function.

5.
$$\left[\begin{array}{ccccccc|c} 1 & -\frac{2}{5} & 0 & 3 & -\frac{3}{5} & 0 & 0 & 15 \\ 0 & -\frac{3}{5} & 0 & -2 & -\frac{11}{5} & 1 & 0 & 13 \\ 0 & -\frac{4}{5} & 1 & -1 & -\frac{2}{5} & 0 & 0 & 29 \\ \hline 0 & 2 & 0 & 7 & 4 & 0 & 1 & 452 \end{array}\right]$$

6.
$$\left[\begin{array}{ccccccc|c} 0 & 0 & 1 & \frac{2}{5} & \frac{5}{3} & \frac{4}{15} & 0 & 16 \\ 1 & 0 & 0 & -\frac{1}{5} & \frac{11}{3} & \frac{1}{5} & 0 & 19 \\ 0 & 1 & 0 & \frac{3}{5} & -\frac{2}{3} & \frac{2}{3} & 0 & 22 \\ \hline 0 & 0 & 0 & 12 & 15 & 20 & 1 & 554 \end{array}\right]$$

In Problems 7–10, write the dual maximization problem and then solve both the primal and dual problems with the simplex method.

7. Minimize $g = 2y_1 + 10y_2$ subject to
$$2y_1 + y_2 \ge 11$$
$$y_1 + 3y_2 \ge 11$$
$$y_1 + 4y_2 \ge 16$$

8. Minimize $g = 8y_1 + 4y_2$ subject to
$$3y_1 - 2y_2 \ge 6$$
$$2y_1 + y_2 \ge 11$$

9. Minimize $g = 3y_1 + y_2$ subject to
$$4y_1 + y_2 \ge 11$$
$$3y_1 + 2y_2 \ge 12$$
$$3y_1 + y_2 \ge 6$$

10. Minimize $g = 2y_1 + 5y_2$ subject to
$$4y_1 + y_2 \ge 12$$
$$y_1 + y_2 \ge 9$$
$$y_1 + 3y_2 \ge 15$$

Use the simplex method in Problems 11–14.

11. Minimize $g = 8x + 7y + 12z$ subject to
$$x + y + z \ge 3$$
$$y + 2z \ge 2$$
$$x \ge 2$$

12. Minimize $g = 12y_1 + 8y_2 + 10y_3$ subject to
$$y_1 + 2y_3 \ge 10$$
$$y_1 + y_2 \ge 12$$
$$2y_1 + 2y_2 + y_3 \ge 8$$

13. Minimize $g = 12y_1 + 48y_2 + 8y_3$ subject to
$$y_1 + 3y_2 \ge 1$$
$$4y_1 + 6y_2 + y_3 \ge 3$$
$$4y_2 + y_3 \ge 1$$

14. Minimize $g = 20x + 30y + 36z$ subject to
$$x + 2y + 3z \ge 48$$
$$2x + 2y + 3z \ge 70$$
$$2x + 3y + 4z \ge 96$$

In Problems 15 and 16, a primal maximization problem is given.

(a) Form the dual minimization problem.

(b) Solve both the primal and dual problems with the simplex method.

15. Maximize $f = 40x_1 + 20x_2$ subject to
$$3x_1 + 2x_2 \le 120$$
$$x_1 + x_2 \le 50$$

16. Maximize $f = 28x_1 + 12x_2$ subject to
$$7x_1 + 12x_2 \le 50$$
$$2x_1 + 6x_2 \le 100$$

In Problems 17–20, use Excel or some other technology.

17. Minimize $g = 40y_1 + 90y_2 + 30y_3$ subject to
$$y_1 + 2y_2 + y_3 \ge 16$$
$$y_1 + 5y_2 + 2y_3 \ge 18$$
$$2y_1 + 5y_2 + 3y_3 \ge 38$$

18. Minimize $w = 48y_1 + 20y_2 + 8y_3$ subject to
$$4y_1 + 2y_2 + y_3 \ge 30$$
$$12y_1 + 4y_2 + 3y_3 \ge 60$$
$$2y_1 + 3y_2 + y_3 \ge 40$$

19. Minimize $g = 50y_1 + 20y_2 + 30y_3 + 80y_4$ subject to
$$40y_1 + 20y_2 + 15y_3 + 50y_4 \ge 50$$
$$3y_1 + 2y_2 + 5y_4 \ge 6$$
$$2y_1 + 2y_2 + 4y_3 + 4y_4 \ge 10$$
$$2y_1 + 4y_2 + y_3 + 5y_4 \ge 8$$

20. Minimize $g = 200y_1 + 100y_2 + 200y_3 + 40y_4$ subject to
$$3y_1 + 2y_2 + y_3 + y_4 \ge 88$$
$$2y_1 + 2y_2 + y_3 \ge 86$$
$$2y_1 + 4y_2 + y_3 \ge 100$$
$$5y_1 + 5y_2 + y_3 \ge 100$$

APPLICATIONS

21. *Production scheduling* CDF Appliances has assembly plants in Atlanta and Fort Worth where it produces a variety of kitchen appliances, including a 12-cup coffee-maker and a cappuccino machine. In each hour at the Atlanta plant, 160 of the coffeemakers and 200 of the cappuccino machines can be assembled, and the hourly cost is $700. In each hour at the Fort Worth plant, 800 of the coffeemakers and 200 of the cappuccino machines can be assembled, and the hourly cost is $2100. CDF Appliances expects orders each week for at least 64,000 of the coffeemakers and at least 40,000 of the cappuccino machines. How many hours per week should each plant be operated to provide inventory for the orders at minimum cost? Find the minimum cost.

22. *Manufacturing* Nekita Corporation assembles tablets and smart phones at two different factories in the same city. During each hour at the first factory, 150 tablets and 300 smart phones can be assembled at a cost of $1000/hour. During each hour at the second factory,

100 tablets and 600 smart phones can be assembled at a cost of $1500/hour. If Nekita expects weekly orders for at least 30,000 tablets and at least 90,000 smart phones, how many hours per week should it schedule at each location to be able to fill the orders at minimum cost? What is the minimum cost?

23. *Manufacturing* The Digital Star Company makes two different models of computer tablets, which are assembled on two different assembly lines. Line 1 can assemble 30 units of the Star model and 40 units of the Prostar model per hour, and line 2 can assemble 150 units of the Star model and 40 units of the Prostar model per hour. The company needs to produce at least 270 units of the Star model and 200 units of the Prostar model to fill an order. If it costs $200 per hour to run line 1 and $400 per hour to run line 2, how many hours should each line be run to fill the order at the minimum cost? What is the minimum cost?

24. *Nutrition* A pork producer is considering two types of feed that contain the necessary ingredients for the nutritional requirements for fattening hogs. Red Star Brand contains 9 units of ingredient A and 12 units of ingredient B, and Blue Chip Brand contains 15 units of ingredient A and 9 units of ingredient B. The nutritional requirements for the hogs are at least 120 units of ingredient A and at least 138 units of ingredient B.
   (a) If Red Star Brand costs 50 cents per pound and Blue Chip Brand costs 75 cents, how many pounds of each brand should be bought to satisfy the nutritional requirements at the minimum cost?
   (b) What is the minimum cost?

25. *Production* A small company produces two products, I and II, at three facilities, A, B, and C. It has orders for 2000 of product I and 1200 of product II. The production capacities and costs per week to operate the three facilities are summarized in the following table.

	A	B	C
I	200	200	400
II	100	200	100
Cost/week	$1000	$3000	$4000

How many weeks should each facility operate to fill the company's orders at a minimum cost, and what is the minimum cost?

26. *Nutrition* In a hospital ward, the patients can be grouped into two general categories depending on their conditions and the amounts of solid foods they require in their diet. A combination of two diets is used for solid foods because they supply essential nutrients for recovery, but each diet has an amount of a substance deemed detrimental. For each patient group, the following table summarizes the diet requirements and the amounts of the detrimental substance. How many servings from each diet should be given each day to minimize the intake of this detrimental substance?

	Diet A	Diet B	Required Daily
Group 1	4 oz per serving	1 oz per serving	26 oz
Group 2	2 oz per serving	1 oz per serving	18 oz
Detrimental substance	0.18 oz per serving	0.07 oz per serving	

27. *Production* Two factories produce three different types of kitchen appliances. The following table summarizes the production capacities, the numbers of each type of appliance ordered, and the daily operating costs for the factories. How many days should each factory operate to fill the orders at minimum cost?

	Factory 1	Factory 2	Number Ordered
Appliance 1	80/day	20/day	1600
Appliance 2	10/day	10/day	500
Appliance 3	50/day	20/day	1900
Daily cost	$10,000	$20,000	

28. *Nutrition* In a laboratory experiment, two separate foods are given to experimental animals. Each food contains essential ingredients, A and B, for which the animals have minimum requirements, and each food also has an ingredient C, which can be harmful to the animals. The following table summarizes this information.

	Food 1	Food 2	Required
Ingredient A	10 units/g	3 units/g	49 units
Ingredient B	6 units/g	12 units/g	60 units
Ingredient C	3 units/g	1 unit/g	

How many grams of foods 1 and 2 will satisfy the requirements for A and B and minimize the amount of ingredient C that is ingested?

29. *Politics* A political candidate wants to use a combination of radio and TV advertisements in her campaign. Research has shown that each 1-minute spot on TV reaches 0.9 million people and that each 1-minute spot on radio reaches 0.6 million. The candidate believes she must reach 63 million people, and she must buy at least 90 minutes of advertisements. How many minutes of each medium should be used if TV costs $500 per minute, radio costs $100 per minute, and the candidate wants to minimize costs?

30. *Production* The James MacGregor Mining Company owns three mines: I, II, and III. Three grades of ore (A, B, and C) are mined at these mines. For each grade of ore, the number of tons per week available from each mine and the number of tons per week required to fill orders are given in the following table.

	I	II	III	Required Tons/Week
A	10	10	10	90
Ore Grades B	0	10	10	50
C	10	0	10	60
Cost/day	$6000	$8000	$12,000	

Find the number of days the company should operate each mine so that orders are filled at minimum cost. Find the minimum cost.

In Problems 31–36, use the simplex method, Excel, or some other technology.

31. *Supply costs* DeTurris Office Supplies carries reams of printer paper in three different grades: recycled, satin white, and glossy white. Three wholesalers offer special purchase packages consisting of different numbers of reams of these three grades, as shown in the following table. DeTurris Office Supplies needs at least 230 reams of the recycled paper, 240 reams of the satin white paper, and 210 reams of the glossy white paper.
    (a) How many of each package should DeTurris buy to minimize its cost?
    (b) What is the minimum possible cost?

	Recycled	Satin White	Glossy White	Package Cost
Georgia package	10	5	6	$120
Union package	5	8	6	140
Pacific package	6	6	6	126

32. *Dieting* A dieting company offers three foods (A, B, and C) and groups its customers into two groups according to their nutritional needs. The following table gives the percent of the daily nutritional requirements that a serving of each food provides and the number of ounces of detrimental substances in each food. Determine the combination of food types that will provide at least 100% of the daily requirements *and* will minimize the detrimental substances. What is the minimum amount of the detrimental substance?

	Food A	Food B	Food C	Daily Requirement
Group I	30% per serving	10% per serving	20% per serving	100%
Group II	10% per serving	20% per serving	40% per serving	100%
Detrimental substances	0.1 oz per serving	0.2 oz per serving	0.25 oz per serving	

33. *Nutrition* A hospital wants to provide at least 24 units of nutrient A and 16 units of nutrient B in a meal while minimizing the cost of the meal. Three types of food are available, with the nutritional values and costs (in dollars per ounce) given in the following table.
    (a) What is the minimum possible cost?
    (b) How many ounces of each food should be served to minimize cost? Find two solutions that give the minimum cost.

	Units of Nutrient A	Units of Nutrient B	Cost ($)
Food I	2	1	0.25
Food II	2	5	1.25
Food III	2	1	0.50

34. *Pollution* Three factories each dump waste water containing three different types of pollutants into a river. State regulations require the factories to treat their waste to reduce pollution levels. The following table shows the possible percent reduction of each pollutant at each site and the cost per ton to process the waste.

	Factory 1	Factory 2	Factory 3
Pollutant 1	75%	45%	20%
Pollutant 2	65%	30%	15%
Pollutant 3	10%	15%	5%
Cost/ton	$50	$20	$8

If the state requires a reduction of at least 65 tons per day of pollutant 1, at least 40 tons per day of pollutant 2, and at least 20 tons per day of pollutant 3, find the number of tons of waste that must be treated each day at each site so that the state's requirements are satisfied and the treatment costs are minimized. Find the minimum cost.

35. *Scheduling* Package Express delivers packages and overnight mailers. At each of several decentralized delivery depots in one district, Package Express hires a number of full- and part-time unskilled employees (so one-half of an employee is an individual who works half a day for 5 days). Each employee works the same shift (or part of a shift) for 5 consecutive days. Thus if x_1 is the number of employees who begin work on Monday, then those same x_1 employees work Monday through Friday. The following table shows the minimum number of unskilled workers needed at a depot on each day of the week.

Mon.	Tues.	Wed.	Thurs.	Fri.	Sat.	Sun.
20	16	16	20	22	12	17

How many unskilled employees should begin their shifts on each day of the week to staff a depot properly but minimize the total number of these workers that Package Express needs? *Hint:* The total number of workers on Monday is the sum of those who begin their shifts on any of the days Thursday through Monday. Total numbers of workers on other days are found similarly.

36. *Scheduling* Each nurse works 8 consecutive hours at the Beaver Medical Center. The center has the following staffing requirements for each 4-hour work period.

Work Period	Nurses Needed
1 (7–11)	40
2 (11–3)	20
3 (3–7)	30
4 (7–11)	40
5 (11–3)	20
6 (3–7)	10

(a) If y_1 represents the number of nurses starting in period 1, y_2 the number starting in period 2, etc., write the linear programming problem that will minimize the total number of nurses needed. (Note that the nurses who begin work in period 6 work periods 6 and 1 for their 8-hour shift.)

(b) Solve the problem in (a).

SECTION 4.5   The Simplex Method with Mixed Constraints

OBJECTIVES

• To solve maximization problems with mixed constraints

• To solve minimization problems with mixed constraints

APPLICATION PREVIEW

The Laser Company manufactures two models of home theater systems, the Star and the Allstar, at two plants located in Ashville and Cleveland. The maximum daily output at the Ashville plant is 900, and the profits there are $200 per unit of the Allstar and $100 per unit of the Star. The maximum daily output at the Cleveland plant is 800, and the profits there are $210 per unit of the Allstar and $80 per unit of the Star. In addition, restrictions at the Ashville plant mean that the number of units of the Star model cannot exceed 100 more than the number of units of the Allstar model produced. If the company gets a rush order for 800 units of the Allstar model and 600 units of the Star model, finding the number of units of each model that should be produced at each location to fill the order and obtain the maximum profit is a mixed constraint linear programming problem. (See Example 3.)

Mixed Constraints and Maximization

In the previous two sections, we used the simplex method to solve two different types of standard linear programming problems. These types are summarized as follows.

	Maximization Problems	Minimization Problems
Function	Maximized	Minimized
Variables	Nonnegative	Nonnegative
Constraints	$a_1x_1 + a_2x_2 + \cdots$ $+ a_nx_n \le b \, (b \ge 0)$	$c_1y_1 + c_2y_2 + \cdots + c_ny_n \ge d \, (d \ge 0)$
Simplex method	Applied directly	Applied to dual

In this section, we will show how to apply the simplex method to mixed constraint linear programming problems that do not fit either of these types. The term *mixed constraint* is used because some inequalities describing the constraints contain "≤" and some contain "≥" signs.

We begin by considering maximization problems with constraints that have a form different from those noted in the preceding table. This can happen in one of the following ways.

1. If a constraint has the form $a_1x_1 + a_2x_2 + \cdots + a_nx_n \le b$, where $b < 0$, such as with $x - 2y \le -8$

2. If a constraint has the form $a_1x_1 + a_2x_2 + \cdots + a_nx_n \geq b$, where $b \geq 0$, such as with $2x - 3y \geq 6$

Note that in the latter case, multiplying both sides of the inequality by (-1) changes it as follows:

$$a_1x_1 + a_2x_2 + \cdots + a_nx_n \geq b \text{ becomes } -a_1x_1 - a_2x_2 - \cdots - a_nx_n \leq -b$$

That is,

$$2x - 3y \geq 6 \text{ becomes } -2x + 3y \leq -6$$

Thus we see that the two possibilities for mixed constraints are actually one: constraints that have the form $a_1x_1 + a_2x_2 + \cdots + a_nx_n \leq b$, where b is any constant. We call these **less than or equal to constraints** and denote them as **≤ constraints.**

EXAMPLE 1 **Maximization with Mixed Constraints**

Maximize $f = x + 2y$ subject to

$$\begin{aligned} x + y &\leq 13 \\ 2x - 3y &\geq 6 \\ x \geq 0, y &\geq 0 \end{aligned}$$

Solution

We begin by expressing all constraints as ≤ constraints. In this case, we multiply $2x - 3y \geq 6$ by (-1) to obtain $-2x + 3y \leq -6$. Now we can use slack variables to write the inequalities as equations and form the simplex matrix.

$$\begin{aligned} x + y + s_1 &= 13 \\ -2x + 3y + s_2 &= -6 \\ -x - 2y + f &= 0 \end{aligned} \quad \text{gives} \quad \begin{array}{c} \begin{array}{ccccc} x_1 & y_2 & s_1 & s_2 & f \end{array} \\ \left[\begin{array}{ccccc|c} 1 & 1 & 1 & 0 & 0 & 13 \\ -2 & 3 & 0 & 1 & 0 & -6 \\ -1 & -2 & 0 & 0 & 1 & 0 \end{array} \right] \end{array}$$

The -6 in the upper portion of the last column is a problem. If we compute values for the variables x, y, s_1, and s_2 that are associated with this matrix, we get $s_2 = -6$. This violates the condition of the simplex method that all variables be nonnegative. To use the simplex method, we must change the sign of any negative entry that appears in the upper portion of the last column (above the line separating the objective function from the constraints). If the problem has a solution, there will always be another negative entry in the same row as this negative entry, but in a different column. We choose this column as the pivot column because pivoting with it will give a positive entry in the last column.

$$\begin{array}{c} \begin{array}{ccccc} x & y & s_1 & s_2 & f \end{array} \\ \left[\begin{array}{ccccc|c} 1 & 1 & 1 & 0 & 0 & 13 \\ -2 & 3 & 0 & 1 & 0 & -6 \\ -1 & -2 & 0 & 0 & 1 & 0 \end{array} \right] \begin{array}{l} \\ \leftarrow \text{ Negative in} \\ \quad \text{last column} \end{array} \end{array}$$

$\uparrow$
Pivot column (negative entry in the same row as
the negative entry in the last column)

Once we have identified the pivot column, we choose the pivot entry by forming *all* quotients and choosing the entry that gives the *smallest positive quotient*. Often, this will mean pivoting by a negative number, which is the case in this problem.

$$\begin{array}{c} \begin{array}{ccccc} x & y & s_1 & s_2 & f \end{array} \\ \left[\begin{array}{ccccc|c} 1 & 1 & 1 & 0 & 0 & 13 \\ \boxed{-2} & 3 & 0 & 1 & 0 & -6 \\ -1 & -2 & 0 & 0 & 1 & 0 \end{array} \right] \begin{array}{l} 13/1 = 13 \\ (-6)/(-2) = 3* \\ \\ \end{array} \end{array}$$

$\uparrow$
Pivot entry circled   *Smallest positive quotient

Pivoting with this entry gives the following matrix.

$$
\begin{array}{ccccc}
x & y & s_1 & s_2 & f \\
\end{array}
$$

$$
\left[
\begin{array}{ccccc|c}
0 & \frac{5}{2} & 1 & \frac{1}{2} & 0 & 10 \\
1 & -\frac{3}{2} & 0 & -\frac{1}{2} & 0 & 3 \\
0 & -\frac{7}{2} & 0 & -\frac{1}{2} & 1 & 3 \\
\end{array}
\right] \quad \}\text{No negatives}
$$

Most negative

This new matrix has no negatives in the upper portion of the last column, so we proceed with the simplex method as we used it previously. The new pivot column is found from the most negative entry in the last row (indicated), and the pivot is found from the smallest positive quotient (circled). Using this pivot completes the solution.

$$
\begin{array}{ccccc}
x & y & s_1 & s_2 & f \\
\end{array}
$$

$$
\left[
\begin{array}{ccccc|c}
0 & 1 & \frac{2}{5} & \frac{1}{5} & 0 & 4 \\
1 & 0 & \frac{3}{5} & -\frac{1}{5} & 0 & 9 \\
0 & 0 & \frac{7}{5} & \frac{1}{5} & 1 & 17 \\
\end{array}
\right]
$$

We see that when $x = 9$ and $y = 4$, then the maximum value of $f = x + 2y$ is 17. ∎

CHECKPOINT

1. Write the simplex matrix to maximize $f = 4x + y$ subject to the constraints

$$3x + 2y \leq 12$$
$$3x - 4y \geq 6$$
$$x \geq 0, y \geq 0$$

2. Using the matrix from Problem 1, find the maximum value of $f = 4x + y$ subject to the constraints.

Mixed Constraints and Minimization

If mixed constraints occur in a minimization problem, the simplex method does not apply to the dual problem. However, the same techniques used in Example 1 can be slightly modified and applied to minimization problems with mixed constraints. If our objective is to minimize f, then we alter the problem to maximize $-f$ subject to "$\leq$ constraints" and then proceed as in Example 1.

EXAMPLE 2   Minimization with Mixed Constraints

Minimize the function $f = 3x + 4y$ subject to the constraints

$$x + y \geq 20$$
$$x + 2y \geq 25$$
$$-5x + y \leq 4$$
$$x \geq 0, y \geq 0$$

Solution

Because of the mixed constraints, we seek to maximize $-f = -3x - 4y$ subject to

$$-x - y \leq -20$$
$$-x - 2y \leq -25$$
$$-5x + y \leq 4$$

The simplex matrix for this problem is

$$
\begin{array}{cccccc}
x & y & s_1 & s_2 & s_3 & -f \\
\end{array}
$$

$$
\left[
\begin{array}{cccccc|c}
-1 & -1 & 1 & 0 & 0 & 0 & -20 \\
-1 & -2 & 0 & 1 & 0 & 0 & -25 \\
-5 & 1 & 0 & 0 & 1 & 0 & 4 \\
3 & 4 & 0 & 0 & 0 & 1 & 0 \\
\end{array}
\right] \quad \text{Negative}
$$

In this case, there are two negative entries in the upper portion of the last column. When this happens, we can start with either one; we choose -20 (row 1). In row 1 (to the left of -20), we find negative entries in columns 1 and 2. We can choose our pivot column as either of these columns; we choose column 1. Once this choice is made, the pivot is determined from the quotients.

$$
\begin{array}{ccccccc}
x & y & s_1 & s_2 & s_3 & -f & \\
\end{array}
$$

$$
\left[
\begin{array}{cccccc|c}
\boxed{-1} & -1 & 1 & 0 & 0 & 0 & -20 \\
-1 & -2 & 0 & 1 & 0 & 0 & -25 \\
-5 & 1 & 0 & 0 & 1 & 0 & 4 \\
\hline
3 & 4 & 0 & 0 & 0 & 1 & 0
\end{array}
\right]
\begin{array}{l}
-20/(-1) = 20^* \\
-25/(-1) = 25 \\
4/(-5) = -4/5 \\
\\
\end{array}
$$

↑
Pivot column (pivot entry circled)   *Smallest positive quotient

Pivoting with this entry gives the following matrix.

$$
\begin{array}{ccccccc}
x & y & s_1 & s_2 & s_3 & -f & \\
\end{array}
$$

$$
\left[
\begin{array}{cccccc|c}
1 & 1 & -1 & 0 & 0 & 0 & 20 \\
0 & \boxed{-1} & -1 & 1 & 0 & 0 & -5 \\
0 & 6 & -5 & 0 & 1 & 0 & 104 \\
\hline
0 & 1 & 3 & 0 & 0 & 1 & -60
\end{array}
\right]
\begin{array}{l}
\\
\leftarrow \text{Negative} \\
\\
\\
\end{array}
$$

↑
Pivot column

Now there is only one negative in the upper portion of the last column. Looking for negatives in this same row, we see that we can choose either column 2 or column 3 for our pivot column. We choose column 2 and check the quotients; the pivot is circled. Pivoting gives the following.

$$
\begin{array}{ccccccc}
x & y & s_1 & s_2 & s_3 & -f & \\
\end{array}
$$

$$
\left[
\begin{array}{cccccc|c}
1 & 0 & -2 & 1 & 0 & 0 & 15 \\
0 & 1 & 1 & -1 & 0 & 0 & 5 \\
0 & 0 & -11 & 6 & 1 & 0 & 74 \\
\hline
0 & 0 & 2 & 1 & 0 & 1 & -65
\end{array}
\right]
$$

At this point, we have all positives in the upper portion of the last column, so the simplex method can be applied. (The negative value in the lower portion is acceptable because $-f$ is our function.) Looking at the indicators, we see that the solution is complete.

From the matrix, we have $x = 15$, $y = 5$, and $-f = -65$. Thus the solution is $x = 15$ and $y = 5$, which gives the minimum value for the function $f = 3x + 4y = 65$.   ▨

A careful review of these examples allows us to summarize the key procedural steps for solving linear programming problems with mixed constraints.

Summary: Simplex Method for Mixed Constraints

1. If the problem is to minimize f, then maximize $-f$.
2. a. Make all constraints $\leq$ constraints by multiplying both sides of any $\geq$ constraints by (-1).
   b. Use slack variables and form the simplex matrix.
3. In the simplex matrix, scan the *upper portion* of the last column for any negative entries.
   a. If there are no negative entries, apply the simplex method.
   b. If there are negative entries, go to Step 4.
4. When there is a negative value in the upper portion of the last column, proceed as follows:
   a. Select any negative entry in the same row and use its column as the pivot column.
   b. In the pivot column, compute all quotients for the entries above the line and determine the pivot from the *smallest positive quotient*.
   c. After completing the pivot operations, return to Step 3.

| EXAMPLE | 3 | **Production Scheduling for Maximum Profit** | APPLICATION PREVIEW |

The Laser Company manufactures two models of home theater systems, the Star and the Allstar, at two plants located in Ashville and Cleveland. The maximum daily output at the Ashville plant is 900, and the profits there are $200 per unit of the Allstar and $100 per unit of the Star. The maximum daily output at the Cleveland plant is 800, and the profits there are $210 per unit of the Allstar and $80 per unit of the Star. In addition, restrictions at the Ashville plant mean that the number of units of the Star model cannot exceed 100 more than the number of units of the Allstar model produced. If the company gets a rush order for 800 units of the Allstar model and 600 units of the Star model, how many units of each model should be produced at each location to fill the order and obtain the maximum profit?

Solution

The following table identifies the variables x and y and relates other important facts in the problem. In particular, we see that only variables x and y are required.

	Ashville Plant	Total Needed	Cleveland Plant
Allstar	x produced (profit = $200 each)	800	800−x produced (profit = $210 each)
Star	y produced (profit = $100 each)	600	600−y produced (profit = $80 each)
Capacity	900	–	800

We want to maximize profit, and from the table, we see that total profit is given by

$$P = 200x + 100y + 210(800 - x) + 80(600 - y)$$

or

$$P = 216{,}000 - 10x + 20y$$

We can read capacity constraints from the table.

$$x + y \leq 900 \text{ (Ashville)}$$
$$(800 - x) + (600 - y) \leq 800 \text{ or } x + y \geq 600 \text{ (Cleveland)}$$

An additional Ashville plant constraint from the statement of the problem is

$$y \leq x + 100 \quad \text{or} \quad -x + y \leq 100$$

Thus our problem is

$$\text{Maximize } P = 216{,}000 - 10x + 20y$$
$$\text{subject to} \quad x + y \leq 900$$
$$x + y \geq 600$$
$$-x + y \leq 100$$
$$x \geq 0, y \geq 0$$

We must express $x + y \geq 600$ as a $\leq$ constraint; multiplying both sides by (-1) gives $-x - y \leq -600$. The simplex matrix is

$$
\begin{array}{cccccc|c}
x & y & s_1 & s_2 & s_3 & P & \\
1 & 1 & 1 & 0 & 0 & 0 & 900 \\
\boxed{-1} & -1 & 0 & 1 & 0 & 0 & -600 \\
-1 & 1 & 0 & 0 & 1 & 0 & 100 \\
\hline
10 & -20 & 0 & 0 & 0 & 1 & 216{,}000
\end{array}
$$

$\leftarrow$ Negative

$\uparrow$
Pivot column

The negative in the upper portion of the last column is indicated. In row 2 we find negatives in both column 1 and column 2, so either of these may be our pivot column. Our choice is indicated. Checking quotients determines the pivot, circled. The matrix that results from the pivot operations follows.

$$
\begin{array}{ccccccc}
x & y & s_1 & s_2 & s_3 & P & \\
\left[\begin{array}{cccccc|c}
0 & 0 & 1 & 1 & 0 & 0 & 300 \\
1 & 1 & 0 & -1 & 0 & 0 & 600 \\
0 & ② & 0 & -1 & 1 & 0 & 700 \\
0 & -30 & 0 & 10 & 0 & 1 & 210{,}000
\end{array}\right]
\end{array}
$$
$$\uparrow$$
Pivot column

No entry in the upper portion of the last column is negative, so we can proceed with the simplex method. From the indicators, we see that column 2 is the pivot column (indicated above) and the pivot entry is circled. The simplex matrix that results from pivoting follows.

$$
\begin{array}{ccccccc}
x & y & s_1 & s_2 & s_3 & P & \\
\left[\begin{array}{cccccc|c}
0 & 0 & 1 & ① & 0 & 0 & 300 \\
1 & 0 & 0 & -\frac{1}{2} & -\frac{1}{2} & 0 & 250 \\
0 & 1 & 0 & -\frac{1}{2} & \frac{1}{2} & 0 & 350 \\
0 & 0 & 0 & -5 & 15 & 1 & 220{,}500
\end{array}\right]
\end{array}
$$
$$\uparrow$$
Pivot column

The new pivot column is indicated, and the pivot entry is circled. The pivot operation yields the following matrix.

$$
\begin{array}{ccccccc}
x & y & s_1 & s_2 & s_3 & P & \\
\left[\begin{array}{cccccc|c}
0 & 0 & 1 & 1 & 0 & 0 & 300 \\
1 & 0 & \frac{1}{2} & 0 & -\frac{1}{2} & 0 & 400 \\
0 & 1 & \frac{1}{2} & 0 & \frac{1}{2} & 0 & 500 \\
0 & 0 & 5 & 0 & 15 & 1 & 222{,}000
\end{array}\right]
\end{array}
$$

This matrix shows that the solution is complete. We see that $x = 400$ (so $800 - x = 400$), $y = 500$ (so $600 - y = 100$), and $P = \$222{,}000$.

Thus the company should operate the Ashville plant at capacity and produce 400 units of the Allstar model and 500 units of the Star model. The remainder of the order, 400 units of the Allstar model and 100 units of the Star model, should be produced at the Cleveland plant. This production schedule gives maximum profit $P = \$222{,}000$. ■

Spreadsheet Note When using Excel to solve a linear programming problem with mixed constraints, it is not necessary to convert the form of the inequalities. They can be entered in their "mixed" form, and the objective function can be maximized or minimized with Solver. See Appendix B, Section 4.5, or the Online Excel Guide for details. ■

CHECKPOINT
ANSWERS

1.
$$
\left[\begin{array}{ccccc|c}
1 & 2 & 1 & 0 & 0 & 12 \\
-3 & 4 & 0 & 1 & 0 & -6 \\
-4 & -1 & 0 & 0 & 1 & 0
\end{array}\right]
$$

2. The maximum value is $f = 48$ at $x = 12$, $y = 0$, $s_1 = 0$, and $s_2 = 30$.

EXERCISES 4.5

In Problems 1–4, express each inequality as a ≤ constraint.

1. $3x - y \geq 5$
2. $4x - 3y \geq 6$
3. $y \geq 40 - 6x$
4. $x \geq 60 - 8y$

In Problems 5–8, complete both of the following.
(a) State the given problem in a form from which the simplex matrix can be formed (that is, as a maximization problem with ≤ constraints).
(b) Form the simplex matrix and circle the first pivot entry.

5. Maximize $f = 2x + 3y$ subject to

$$7x + 4y \leq 28$$
$$-3x + y \geq 2$$
$$x \geq 0, y \geq 0$$

6. Maximize $f = 5x + 11y$ subject to

$$x - 3y \geq 3$$
$$-x + y \leq 1$$
$$x \leq 10$$
$$x \geq 0, y \geq 0$$

7. Minimize $g = 3x + 8y$ subject to

$$4x - 5y \leq 50$$
$$x + y \leq 80$$
$$-x + 2y \geq 4$$
$$x \geq 0, y \geq 0$$

8. Minimize $g = 40x + 25y$ subject to

$$x + y \leq 100$$
$$-x + y \leq 20$$
$$-2x + 3y \geq 6$$
$$x \geq 0, y \geq 0$$

In Problems 9 and 10, a final simplex matrix for a minimization problem is given. In each case, find the solution.

9.
$$
\begin{bmatrix}
x & y & z & s_1 & s_2 & s_3 & -f & \\
0 & 1 & 0 & \frac{7}{3} & \frac{1}{3} & -\frac{2}{3} & 0 & 8 \\
0 & 0 & 1 & \frac{2}{3} & -\frac{1}{3} & \frac{8}{3} & 0 & 12 \\
1 & 0 & 0 & -\frac{4}{3} & \frac{2}{3} & \frac{4}{3} & 0 & 6 \\
0 & 0 & 0 & 4 & \frac{4}{3} & 2 & 1 & -120
\end{bmatrix}
$$

10.
$$
\begin{bmatrix}
x & y & z & s_1 & s_2 & s_3 & -f & \\
1 & 0 & 0 & \frac{2}{5} & -\frac{2}{5} & 0 & 0 & 50 \\
0 & 0 & 1 & \frac{1}{5} & \frac{1}{5} & \frac{11}{5} & 0 & 12 \\
0 & 1 & 0 & 1 & -\frac{8}{5} & \frac{14}{5} & 0 & 30 \\
0 & 0 & 0 & 3 & 1 & 4 & 1 & -1200
\end{bmatrix}
$$

In Problems 11–18, use the simplex method to find the optimal solution. Assume that all variables are nonnegative.

11. Maximize $f = 4x + y$ subject to

$$5x + 2y \leq 84$$
$$-3x + 2y \geq 4$$

12. Maximize $f = x + 2y$ subject to

$$-x + 2y \leq 60$$
$$-7x + 4y \geq 20$$

13. Minimize $f = 2x + 3y$ subject to

$$x \geq 5$$
$$y \leq 13$$
$$-x + y \geq 2$$

14. Minimize $f = 3x + 9y$ subject to

$$x \leq 20$$
$$y \leq 20$$
$$x + y \geq 21$$

15. Minimize $f = 3x + 2y$ subject to

$$-x + y \leq 10$$
$$x + y \geq 20$$
$$x + y \leq 35$$

16. Minimize $f = 4x + y$ subject to

$$-x + y \leq 4$$
$$3x + y \geq 12$$
$$x + y \leq 20$$

17. Maximize $f = 2x + 5y$ subject to

$$-x + y \leq 10$$
$$x + y \leq 30$$
$$-2x + y \geq -24$$

18. Maximize $f = 3x + 2y$ subject to

$$-x + 2y \leq 20$$
$$-3x + 2y \leq -36$$
$$x + y \leq 22$$

In Problems 19–26, use the simplex method or Excel. Assume that all variables are nonnegative.

19. Minimize $f = x + 2y + 3z$ subject to

$$x + z \leq 20$$
$$x + y \geq 30$$
$$y + z \leq 20$$

20. Maximize $f = -x + 2y + 4z$ subject to

$$x + y + z \leq 40$$
$$-x + y + z \geq 20$$
$$x + y - z \geq 10$$

21. Maximize $f = 2x - y + 4z$ subject to

$$x + y + z \le 8$$
$$x - y + z \ge 4$$
$$x + y - z \ge 2$$

22. Maximize $f = 5x + 2y + z$ subject to

$$2x + 3y + z \le 30$$
$$x - 2y + z \ge 20$$
$$2x + 5y + 2z \ge 25$$

23. Minimize $f = 10x + 30y + 35z$ subject to

$$x + y + z \le 250$$
$$x + y + 2z \ge 150$$
$$2x + y + z \le 180$$

24. Minimize $f = x + 2y + z$ subject to

$$x + 3y + 2z \ge 40$$
$$x + y + z \ge 30$$
$$x + y + z \le 100$$

25. Maximize $f = 25x_1 + 25x_2 + 25x_3 + 20x_4 + 20x_5 + 20x_6$ subject to

$$x_1 + x_4 \le 100$$
$$x_2 + x_5 \le 20$$
$$x_3 + x_6 \le 30$$
$$0.8x_2 \ge 0.2x_1 + 0.2x_3$$
$$0.9x_5 \ge 0.1x_4 + 0.1x_6$$
$$0.9x_6 \ge 0.1x_4 + 0.1x_5$$

26. Minimize $g = 480x_1 + 460x_2 + 440x_3 + 420x_4 + 530y_1 + 510y_2 + 490y_3 + 470y_4 - 9500$ subject to

$$x_1 + y_1 \ge 30$$
$$x_1 + x_2 + y_1 + y_2 \ge 90$$
$$x_1 + x_2 + x_3 + y_1 + y_2 + y_3 \ge 165$$
$$x_1 + x_2 + x_3 + x_4 + y_1 + y_2 + y_3 + y_4 \ge 190$$
$$x_1 \le 40, x_2 \le 40, x_3 \le 40, x_4 \le 40$$

APPLICATIONS

Problems 27–30 involve maximization with mixed constraints.

27. *Production* A sausage company makes two different kinds of hot dogs, regular and all beef. Each pound of all-beef hot dogs requires 0.75 lb of beef and 0.2 lb of spices, and each pound of regular hot dogs requires 0.18 lb of beef, 0.3 lb of pork, and 0.2 lb of spices. Suppliers can deliver at most 1020 lb of beef, at most 600 lb of pork, and at least 500 lb of spices. If the profit is $1.50 on each pound of all-beef hot dogs and $1.00 on each pound of regular hot dogs, how many pounds of each should be produced to obtain maximum profit? What is the maximum profit?

28. *Manufacturing* A cereal manufacturer makes two different kinds of cereal, Senior Citizen's Feast and Kids

Go. Each pound of Senior Citizen's Feast requires 0.6 lb of wheat and 0.2 lb of vitamin-enriched syrup, and each pound of Kids Go requires 0.4 lb of wheat, 0.2 lb of sugar, and 0.2 lb of vitamin-enriched syrup. Suppliers can deliver at most 2800 lb of wheat, at most 800 lb of sugar, and at least 1000 lb of the vitamin-enriched syrup. If the profit is $0.90 on each pound of Senior Citizen's Feast and $1.00 on each pound of Kids Go, find the number of pounds of each cereal that should be produced to obtain maximum profit. Find the maximum profit.

29. *Manufacturing* A company manufactures commercial heating system components and domestic furnaces at its factories in Monaca, Pennsylvania, and Hamburg, New York. At the Monaca plant, no more than 1000 units per day can be produced, and the number of commercial components cannot exceed 100 more than half the number of domestic furnaces. At the Hamburg plant, no more than 850 units per day can be produced. The profit on each commercial component is $400 at the Monaca plant and $390 at the Hamburg plant. The profit on each domestic furnace is $200 at the Monaca plant and $215 at the Hamburg plant. If there is a rush order for 500 commercial components and 750 domestic furnaces, how many of each should be produced at each plant to maximize profits? Find the maximum profit.

30. *Production scheduling* A manufacturer makes Portable Satellite Radios and Auto Satellite Radios at plants in Lakeland and Rockledge. At the Lakeland plant, at most 1800 radios can be produced, and the production of the Auto Satellite Radios can be at most 200 fewer than the production of the Portable Satellite Radios. At the Rockledge plant, at most 1200 radios can be produced. The profits on the Portable Satellite Radios are $100 at Lakeland and $90 at Rockledge, and the profits on the Auto Satellite Radios are $70 at Lakeland and $75 at Rockledge. If the manufacturer gets a rush order for 1500 Portable Satellite Radios and 1300 Auto Satellite Radios, how many of each should be produced at each location to maximize profits? Find the maximum profit.

Problems 31–36 involve minimization with mixed constraints.

31. *Water purification* Nolan Industries manufactures water filters/purifiers that attach to a kitchen faucet. Each purifier consists of a housing unit that attaches to the faucet and a 60-day filter (sold separately) that is inserted into the housing. Past records indicate that on average, the number of filters produced per week should be at least 400. It takes 20 minutes to make and assemble each filter and 40 minutes for each housing. The manufacturing facility has at least 20,000 minutes per week for making and assembling these units, but due to certain parts supply constraints, the number of

housing units per week can be at most 400. If manufacturing costs (for material and labor) are $6.60 for each filter and $8.35 for each housing unit, how many of each should be produced to minimize weekly costs? Find the minimum cost.

32. *Manufacturing* Johnson City Cooperage manufactures 30-gallon and 55-gallon fiber drums. Each 30-gallon drum takes 30 minutes to make, each 55-gallon drum takes 40 minutes to make, and the company has at most 10,000 minutes available each week. Also, workplace limitations and product demand indicate that the number of 55-gallon drums produced plus half the number of 30-gallon drums produced should be at least 160, and the number of 30-gallon drums should be at least twice the number of 55-gallon drums. If Johnson City Cooperage's manufacturing costs are $10 for each 30-gallon drum and $15 for each 55-gallon drum, how many of each drum should be made each week to satisfy the constraints at minimum cost? Find the minimum cost.

33. *Manufacturing* Refer to Problem 29. Suppose that the cost of each commercial component is $380 at the Monaca plant and $400 at the Hamburg plant. The cost of each domestic furnace is $200 at the Monaca plant and $185 at the Hamburg plant. If the same rush order for 500 commercial components and 750 domestic furnaces is received, how many of each should be produced at each location to minimize cost? Find the minimum cost.

34. *Manufacturing* Refer to Problem 30. Suppose the costs associated with Portable Satellite Radios are $50 at Lakeland and $60 at Rockledge, and the costs associated with Auto Satellite Radios are $40 at Lakeland and $25 at Rockledge. If the manufacturer gets the same rush order for 1500 units of Portable Satellite Radios and 1300 units of Auto Satellite Radios, how many units of each should be produced at each location to minimize costs? Find the minimum cost.

35. *Water purification* Three water purification facilities can handle at most 10 million gallons in a certain time period. Plant I leaves 20% of certain impurities and costs $20,000 per million gallons. Plant II leaves 15% of these impurities and costs $30,000 per million gallons. Plant III leaves 10% impurities and costs $40,000 per million gallons. The desired level of impurities in the water from all three plants is at most 15%. If plant I and plant III combined must handle at least 6 million gallons, find the number of gallons each plant should handle to achieve the desired level of purity at minimum cost. Find the minimum cost.

36. *Chemical mixture* A chemical storage tank has a capacity of 200 tons. Currently, the tank contains 50 tons of a mixture that has 10% of a certain active

chemical and 1.8% of other inert ingredients. The owners of the tank want to replenish the supply in the tank and will purchase some combination of two available mixes. Mix 1 contains 70% of the active chemical and 3% of the inert ingredients; its cost is $100 per ton. Mix 2 contains 30% of the active chemical and 1% of the inert ingredients; its cost is $40 per ton. The desired final mixture should have at least 40% of the active chemical and at most 2% of the inert ingredients. How many tons of each mix should be purchased to obtain the desired final mixture at minimum cost? Find the minimum cost. Note that at least 40% of the active chemical means

$$70\% \,(\text{mix 1}) + 30\% \,(\text{mix 2}) + 10\% \,(\text{mix on hand})$$
$$\geq 40\% \,(\text{mix 1} + \text{mix 2} + \text{mix on hand})$$

In Problems 37 and 38, use Excel or some other technology.

37. *Manufacturing* A ball manufacturer produces soccer balls, footballs, and volleyballs. The manager believes that restricting the types of balls produced could increase revenue. The following table gives the price of each ball, the raw materials cost, and the profit on each ball. The monthly profit must be at least $10,000, and the raw materials costs must be no more than $20,000. How many of each type of ball should be produced to maximize the revenue, and what is the maximum revenue?

	Raw Materials Cost	Price per Ball	Profit per Ball
Footballs	$10	$30	$10
Soccer balls	12	25	8
Volleyballs	8	20	8

38. *Land management* A farm co-op has two farms, one at Spring Run and one at Willow Bend, where it grows corn and soybeans. Differences between the farms affect the associated costs and yield of each crop, as shown in the following table.

	Corn		Soybeans	
	Yield (bu/acre)	Cost/ Acre	Yield (bu/acre)	Cost/ Acre
Spring Run	450	$330	360	$297
Willow Bend	585	$396	315	$264

Each farm has 100 acres available to plant, and the total desired yields are at least 46,800 bushels of corn and at least 42,300 bushels of soybeans. (a) Write a linear programming problem that describes this land management problem. (b) Find how many acres of each crop should be planted at each farm to achieve the desired crop yields at minimum cost. What is the minimum cost?

4 CHAPTER SUMMARY & REVIEW

Section 4.1

Linear inequalities in two variables (p. 251)
  Graphs

Systems of linear inequalities (p. 252)
Solution region (p. 252)

Section 4.2

Linear programming (p. 260)
  Objective function
  Constraints

Optimal values
  Feasible region
Graphical solution method (p. 262)

Section 4.3

Standard maximization problems (p. 272)
Slack variables (p. 273)
Simplex matrix (p. 273)
Pivot entry (p. 274)
Basic and non-basic variables (p. 275)

Basic feasible solution (p. 275)
Simplex method procedure (p. 276)
  Pivoting
Non-unique solutions (p. 282)
Shadow prices (p. 284)

Section 4.4

Standard minimization problem (p. 289)
Dual (p. 289)
  Transpose
  Primal problem

Principle of duality (p. 291)
Minimization with the simplex method (p. 291)

Section 4.5

Mixed constraints and maximization (p. 298)
  Creating $\leq$ constraints

Mixed constraints and minimization (p. 300)
Mixed constraints summary (p. 301)

REVIEW EXERCISES

Section 4.1

In Problems 1–4, graph the solution set of each inequality or system of inequalities.

1. $2x + 3y \leq 12$
2. $4x + 5y > 100$

3. $\begin{cases} x + 2y \leq 20 \\ 3x + 10y \leq 80 \\ x \geq 0, \ y \geq 0 \end{cases}$

4. $\begin{cases} 3x + y \geq 4 \\ x + y \geq 2 \\ -x + y \leq 4 \\ x \quad\quad \leq 5 \end{cases}$

Section 4.2

In Problems 5–8, a function and the graph of a feasible region are given. In each case, find both the maximum

and minimum values of the function, if they exist, and the point at which each occurs.

5. $f = -x + 3y$

6. $f = 6x + 4y$

7. $f = 7x - 6y$

8. $f = 9x + 10y$

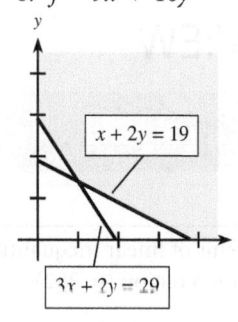

In Problems 9–15, solve the linear programming problems using graphical methods. Restrict $x \geq 0$ and $y \geq 0$.

9. Maximize $f = 5x + 6y$ subject to

$$x + 3y \leq 24$$
$$4x + 3y \leq 42$$
$$2x + y \leq 20$$

10. Maximize $f = x + 4y$ subject to

$$7x + 3y \leq 105$$
$$2x + 5y \leq 59$$
$$x + 7y \leq 70$$

11. Maximize $f = 2x + 5y$ subject to

$$4x + 5y \leq 400$$
$$x \leq 70$$
$$6x + 15y \leq 900$$

12. Minimize $g = 5x + 3y$ subject to

$$3x + y \geq 12$$
$$x + y \geq 6$$
$$x + 6y \geq 11$$

13. Minimize $g = x + 5y$ subject to

$$8x + y \geq 85$$
$$x + y \geq 50$$
$$x + 4y \geq 80$$
$$x + 10y \geq 104$$

14. Maximize $f = 5x + 2y$ subject to

$$y \leq 20$$
$$2x + y \leq 32$$
$$-x + 2y \geq 4$$

15. Minimize $f = x + 4y$ subject to

$$y \leq 30$$
$$3x + 2y \geq 75$$
$$-3x + 5y \geq 30$$

Section 4.3

In Problems 16–19, use the simplex method to solve the linear programming problems. Assume that all variables are nonnegative.

16. Maximize $f = 7x + 12y$ subject to the conditions in Problem 10.

17. Maximize $f = 3x + 4y$ subject to

$$x + 4y \leq 160$$
$$x + 2y \leq 100$$
$$4x + 3y \leq 300$$

18. Maximize $f = 3x + 8y$ subject to the conditions in Problem 17.

19. Maximize $f = 3x + 2y$ subject to

$$x + 2y \leq 48$$
$$x + y \leq 30$$
$$2x + y \leq 50$$
$$x + 10y \leq 200$$

Problems 20 and 21 have nonunique solutions. If there is no solution, indicate this; if there are multiple solutions, find two different solutions. Use the simplex method, with $x \geq 0$, $y \geq 0$.

20. Maximize $f = 4x + 4y$ subject to

$$x + 5y \leq 500$$
$$x + 2y \leq 230$$
$$x + y \leq 160$$

21. Maximize $f = 2x + 5y$ subject to

$$-4x + y \leq 40$$
$$x - 7y \leq 70$$

Section 4.4

In Problems 22–25, form the dual and use the simplex method to solve the minimization problem. Assume that all variables are nonnegative.

22. Minimize $g = 7y_1 + 6y_2$ subject to

$$5y_1 + 2y_2 \geq 16$$
$$3y_1 + 7y_2 \geq 27$$

23. Minimize $g = 3y_1 + 4y_2$ subject to

$$3y_1 + y_2 \geq 8$$
$$y_1 + y_2 \geq 6$$
$$2y_1 + 5y_2 \geq 18$$

24. Minimize $g = 2y_1 + y_2$ subject to the conditions in Problem 23.

25. Minimize $g = 12y_1 + 11y_2$ subject to

$$y_1 + y_2 \geq 100$$
$$2y_1 + y_2 \geq 140$$
$$6y_1 + 5y_2 \geq 580$$

Section 4.5

Problems 26 and 27 involve mixed constraints. Solve each with the simplex method. Assume that all variables are nonnegative.

26. Maximize $f = 3x + 5y$ subject to

$$x + y \geq 19$$
$$-x + y \geq 1$$
$$-x + 10y \leq 190$$

27. Maximize $f = 4x + 6y$ subject to

$$2x + 5y \leq 37$$
$$5x - y \leq 34$$
$$-x + 2y \geq 4$$

Section 4.3–4.5

In Problems 28–35, use the simplex method. Assume that all variables are nonnegative.

28. Maximize $f = 39x + 5y + 30z$ subject to

$$x + z \leq 7$$
$$3x + 5y \leq 30$$
$$3x + y \leq 18$$

29. Minimize $g = 12y_1 + 5y_2 + 2y_3$ subject to

$$y_1 + 2y_2 + y_3 \geq 60$$
$$12y_1 + 4y_2 + 3y_3 \geq 120$$
$$2y_1 + 3y_2 + y_3 \geq 80$$

30. Minimize $g = 25y_1 + 10y_2 + 4y_3$ subject to

$$7.5y_1 + 4.5y_2 + 2y_3 \geq 650$$
$$6.5y_1 + 3y_2 + 1.5y_3 \geq 400$$
$$y_1 + 1.5y_2 + 0.5y_3 \geq 200$$

31. Minimize $f = 10x + 3y$ subject to

$$-x + 10y \geq 5$$
$$4x + y \geq 62$$
$$x + y \leq 50$$

32. Minimize $f = 4x + 3y$ subject to

$$-x + y \geq 1$$
$$x + y \leq 45$$
$$10x + y \geq 45$$

33. Maximize $f = 88x_1 + 86x_2 + 100x_3 + 100x_4$ subject to

$$3x_1 + 2x_2 + 2x_3 + 5x_4 \leq 200$$
$$2x_1 + 2x_2 + 4x_3 + 5x_4 \leq 100$$
$$x_1 + x_2 + x_3 + x_4 \leq 200$$
$$x_1 \leq 40$$

34. Maximize $f = 8x_1 + 8x_2 + 12x_3 + 14x_4$ subject to

$$6x_1 + 3x_2 + 2x_3 + x_4 \geq 350$$
$$3x_1 + 2x_2 + 5x_3 + 6x_4 \leq 300$$
$$8x_1 + 3x_2 + 2x_3 + x_4 \leq 400$$
$$x_1 + x_2 + x_3 + x_4 \leq 100$$

35. Minimize $g = 10x_1 + 9x_2 + 12x_3 + 8x_4$ subject to

$$45x_1 + 58.5x_3 \geq 4680$$
$$36x_2 + 31.5x_4 \geq 4230$$
$$x_1 + x_2 \leq 100$$
$$x_3 + x_4 \leq 100$$

APPLICATIONS

Section 4.2

36. *Manufacturing* A company manufactures backyard swing sets of two different sizes. The larger set requires 5 hours of labor to complete, the smaller set requires 2

hours, and there are 700 hours of labor available each week. The packaging department can package at most 185 swing sets per week. If the profit is $200 on each larger set and $100 on each smaller set, how many of each should be produced to yield the maximum profit? What is the maximum profit? Use graphical methods.

37. *Production* A company produces two different grades of steel, A and B, at two different factories, 1 and 2. The following table summarizes the production capabilities of the factories, the cost per day, and the number of units of each grade of steel that is required to fill orders.

	Factory 1	Factory 2	Required
Grade A steel	1 unit	2 units	80 units
Grade B steel	3 units	2 units	140 units
Cost per day	$5000	$6000	

How many days should each factory operate to fill the orders at minimum cost? What is the minimum cost? Use graphical methods.

38. *Manufacturing* Chairco manufactures two types of chairs, standard and plush. Standard chairs require 2 hours to construct and finish, and plush chairs require 3 hours to construct and finish. Upholstering takes 1 hour for standard chairs and 3 hours for plush chairs. There are 240 hours per day available for construction and finishing, and 150 hours per day are available for upholstering. If the profit for standard chairs is $89 and for plush chairs is $133.50, how many of each type should be produced each day to maximize profit?

STANDARD

PLUSH

© Marko Bradic/Shutterstock.com

Section 4.3

39. *Production* A small industry produces two items, I and II. It operates at capacity and makes a profit of $18 on each item I and $12 on each item II. The following table gives the hours required to produce each item and the hours available per day.

	I	II	Hours Available
Assembly	2 hours	1 hour	100
Packaging & inspection	1 hour	1 hour	60

Find the number of items that should be produced each day to maximize profits and find the maximum daily profit.

40. *Production* Pinocchio Crafts makes two types of wooden crafts: Jacob's ladders and locomotive engines. The manufacture of these crafts requires both carpentry and finishing. Each Jacob's ladder requires 1 hour of finishing and $\frac{1}{2}$ hour of carpentry. Each locomotive engine requires 1 hour of finishing and 1 hour of carpentry. Pinocchio Crafts can obtain all the necessary raw materials, but only 120 finishing hours and 75 carpentry hours per week are available. Also, demand for Jacob's ladders is limited to at most 100 per week. If Pinocchio Crafts makes a profit of $9 on each Jacob's ladder and $15 on each locomotive engine, how many of each should it produce each week to maximize profits? What is the maximum profit?

41. *Profit* At its Jacksonville factory, Nolmaur Electronics manufactures 4 models of TV sets: LCD models in 32-, 42-, and 50-in. sizes and a 65-in. plasma model. The manufacturing and testing hours required for each model and available at the factory each week, as well as each model's profit, are shown in the following table.

	32-in. LCD	42-in. LCD	50-in. LCD	65-in. Plasma	Available Hours
Manufacturing (hr)	8	10	12	15	1870
Testing (hr)	2	4	4	4	530
Profit	$80	$120	$160	$200	

In addition, the supplier of the amplifier units can provide at most 200 units per week with at most 100 for the 50- and 65-in. models. The weekly demand for the 42-in. sets is at most 120. Nolmaur wants to determine the number of each type of set that should be produced each week to obtain maximum profit.

(a) Identify the variables for Nolmaur's linear programming problem.

(b) State Nolmaur's linear programming problem.

(c) Solve this linear programming problem to determine Nolmaur's manufacturing plan and maximum profit.

Section 4.4

42. *Nutrition* A nutritionist wants to find the least expensive combination of two foods that meet minimum daily vitamin requirements, which are 5 units of A and 30 units of B. Each ounce of food I provides 2 units of A and 1 unit of B, and each ounce of food II provides 10 units of A and 10 units of B. If food I costs 30 cents per ounce and food II costs 20 cents per ounce, find the number of ounces of each food that will provide the required vitamins and minimize the cost.

43. *Nutrition* A laboratory technician wants to purchase two different feeds, A and B, for its animals. The following table summarizes the nutritional contents of the feeds, the required amounts of each ingredient, and the cost of each type of feed.

	Feed A	Feed B	Required
Carbohydrates	1 unit/lb	4 units/lb	40 units
Protein	2 units/lb	1 unit/lb	80 units
Cost	14¢/lb	16¢/lb	

How many pounds of each type of feed should the laboratory technician buy to satisfy its needs at minimum cost?

44. *Production* A company makes three products (I, II, and III) at three different factories. At factory A, it can make 10 units of each product per day. At factory B, it can make 20 units of II and 20 units of III per day. At factory C, it can make 20 units of I, 20 units of II, and 10 units of III per day. The company has orders for 200 units of I, 500 units of II, and 300 units of III. If the daily costs are $2000 at A, $3000 at B, and $5000 at C, find the number of days each factory should operate to fill the company's orders at minimum cost. Find the minimum cost.

Section 4.5

45. *Profit* A company makes pancake mix and cake mix. Each pound of pancake mix uses 0.6 lb of flour and 0.1 lb of shortening. Each pound of cake mix uses 0.4 lb of flour, 0.1 lb of shortening, and 0.4 lb of sugar. Suppliers can deliver at most 6000 lb of flour, at least 500 lb of shortening, and at most 1200 lb of sugar. If the profit per pound is $0.35 for pancake mix and $0.25 for cake mix, how many pounds of each mix should be made to earn maximum profit? What is the maximum profit?

46. *Manufacturing* A company manufactures desks and computer tables at plants in Texas and Louisiana. At the Texas plant, production costs are $36 for each desk and $60 for each computer table, and the plant can produce at most 120 units per day. At the Louisiana plant, costs are $42 for each desk and $57 per computer table, and the plant can produce at most 150 units per day. The company gets a rush order for 130 desks and 130 computer tables at a time when the Texas plant is further limited by the fact that the number of computer tables it produces must be at least 10 more than the number of desks. How should production be scheduled at each location to fill the order at minimum cost? What is the minimum cost?

47. *Cost* Armstrong Industries makes two different grades of steel at its plants in Midland and Donora. Weekly demand is at least 500 tons for grade 1 steel and at least 450 tons for grade 2. Due to differences in the equipment and the labor force, production times and costs per ton for each grade of steel differ slightly at each location, as shown in the following table.

	Grade 1		Grade 2		
	Min/ Ton	Cost/ Ton	Min/ Ton	Cost/ Ton	Furnace Time/Week (in Minutes)
Midland	40	$300	42	$360	19,460
Donora	44	$330	45	$270	21,380

Find the number of tons of each grade of steel that should be made each week at each plant so that Armstrong meets demand at minimum cost. Find the minimum cost.

4 CHAPTER TEST

1. Maximize $f = 3x + 5y$ subject to the constraints determined by the shaded region shown in the figure.

2. Following are three simplex matrices in various stages of the simplex method solution of a maximization problem.
   (a) Identify the matrix for which multiple solutions exist. Circle the pivot and specify all row operations with that pivot that are needed to find a second solution.
   (b) Identify the matrix for which no solution exists. Explain how you can tell there is no solution.
   (c) For the remaining matrix, find the basic feasible solution. Use the variables $x_1, x_2, \ldots$, the slack variables $s_1, s_2, \ldots$, and the objective function f and tell whether these values give the optimal solution. If they do not, identify the next pivot.

$$A = \begin{bmatrix} 2 & 0 & -4 & 1 & -2 & 0 & 0 & | & 6 \\ -1 & 1 & 0 & 0 & 1 & 0 & 0 & | & 3 \\ 4 & 0 & -6 & 0 & -1 & 1 & 0 & | & 10 \\ -3 & 0 & -8 & 0 & 4 & 0 & 1 & | & 50 \end{bmatrix}$$

$$B = \begin{bmatrix} 0 & 1 & -2 & \frac{1}{4} & 0 & \frac{1}{5} & 0 & | & 12 \\ 0 & 0 & 4 & -\frac{3}{4} & 1 & -\frac{2}{5} & 0 & | & 20 \\ 1 & 0 & 3 & -\frac{5}{4} & 0 & \frac{4}{5} & 0 & | & 40 \\ 0 & 0 & 4 & 6 & 0 & -\frac{1}{5} & 1 & | & 170 \end{bmatrix}$$

$$C = \begin{bmatrix} 1 & 2 & 0 & 1 & 0 & -\frac{3}{2} & 0 & | & 40 \\ 0 & 1 & 0 & -2 & 1 & \frac{1}{2} & 0 & | & 15 \\ 0 & 3 & 1 & -1 & 0 & \frac{1}{4} & 0 & | & 60 \\ 0 & 0 & 0 & 4 & 0 & 6 & 1 & | & 220 \end{bmatrix}$$

3. Graph the solution region for each of the following.

   (a) $3x - 5y \le 30$ (b) $x > 2$ (c) $\begin{cases} 5y \ge 2x \\ x + y > 7 \\ 2y \le 5x \end{cases}$

4. Formulate the dual maximization problem associated with the following.
   Minimize $g = 2y_1 + 3y_2 + 5y_3$ subject to

   $$3y_1 + 5y_2 + y_3 \ge 100$$
   $$4y_1 + 6y_2 + 3y_3 \ge 120$$
   $$y_1 \ge 0, y_2 \ge 0, y_3 \ge 0$$

5. Find the maximum and minimum values of $f = 5x + 2y$ (if they exist) subject to the constraints determined by the shaded region in the figure.

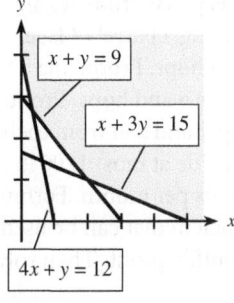

6. Use graphical methods to minimize $g = 3x + y$ subject to $5x - 4y \le 40$, $x + y \ge 80$, $2x - y \ge 4$, $x \ge 0$, and $y \ge 0$.

7. Express the following linear programming problem as a maximization problem with $\le$ constraints. Assume that $x \ge 0, y \ge 0$.
   Minimize $g = 7x + 3y$ subject to

   $$-x + 4y \ge 4$$
   $$x - y \le 5$$
   $$2x + 3y \le 30$$

8. The final simplex matrix for a problem is as follows. Give the solutions to *both* the minimization problem and the dual maximization problem. Carefully label each solution.

$$\begin{bmatrix} 0 & 1 & -0.5 & 3 & -0.7 & 0 & 0 & | & 15 \\ 1 & 0 & -0.8 & -2 & -0.5 & 0 & 0 & | & 17 \\ 0 & 0 & -0.6 & -1 & -2.4 & 1 & 0 & | & 11 \\ 0 & 0 & 12 & 4 & 18 & 0 & 1 & | & 658 \end{bmatrix}$$

9. Use the simplex method to maximize $f = 70x + 5y$ subject to $x + 1.5y \le 150$, $x + 0.5y \le 90$, $x \ge 0$, and $y \ge 0$.

10. Use graphical methods to maximize $f = 12x + 20y$ subject to

$$3x + 5y \le 1500$$
$$9x + 5y \le 3600$$
$$x + 5y \le 1000$$
$$x \ge 0, \ y \ge 0$$

11. Maximize $f = 60x + 48y + 35z$ subject to

$$8x + 6y + z \le 108$$
$$4x + 2y + 1.5z \le 50$$
$$2x + 1.5y + 0.5z \le 40$$
$$z \le 16$$
$$x \ge 0, \ y \ge 0, \ z \ge 0$$

12. River Brewery is a microbrewery that produces an amber lager and an ale. Producing a barrel of lager requires 3 lb of corn and 2 lb of hops. Producing a barrel of ale requires 2 lb each of corn and hops. Profits are $35 from each barrel of lager and $30 from each barrel of ale. Suppliers can provide at most 1200 lb of corn and at most 1000 lb of hops per month. Formulate a linear programming problem that can be used to maximize River Brewery's monthly profit. Then solve it using the simplex method.

13. A marketing research group conducting a telephone survey must contact at least 150 wives and 120 husbands. It costs $3 to make a daytime call and (because of higher labor costs) $4 to make an evening call. On average, daytime calls reach wives 30% of the time, husbands 10% of the time, and neither of them 60% of the time, whereas evening calls reach wives 30% of the time, husbands 30% of the time, and neither of them 40% of the time. Staffing considerations mean that daytime calls must be less than or equal to half of the total calls made. Formulate a linear programming problem that can be used to minimize the cost of completing the survey. Then solve it using any method from this chapter.

14. Lawn Rich, Inc., makes four different lawn care products that have fixed percents of phosphate, nitrogen, potash, and other minerals. The following table shows the percent of each of the four ingredients in each of Lawn Rich's products and the profit per ton for each product.

	Product 1	Product 2	Product 3	Product 4
% Phosphate	60	30	20	10
% Nitrogen	20	20	20	20
% Potash	9	6	15	18
% Other minerals	8	3	2	1
Profit/ton	$120	$150	$180	$210

A lawn care company buys in bulk from Lawn Rich and then blends the products for its own purposes. For the blend it desires, the lawn care company wants its Lawn Rich order to contain at least 35 tons of phosphate, at most 20 tons of nitrogen, at most 9 tons of potash, and at most 4 tons of other minerals. How many tons of each product should Lawn Rich produce to fulfill the customer's needs and maximize its own profit? What is the maximum profit?

4   EXTENDED APPLICATIONS & GROUP PROJECTS

I. Transportation

The Kimble Firefighting Equipment Company has two assembly plants: plant A in Atlanta and plant B in Buffalo. It has two distribution centers: center I in Savannah and center II in Pittsburgh. The company can produce at most 800 alarm valves per week at plant A and at most 1000 per week at plant B. Center I must have at least 900 alarm valves per week, and center II must have at least 600 alarm valves per week. The costs per unit for transportation from the plants to the centers follow.

$$
\begin{array}{lc}
\text{Plant A to center I} & \$8 \\
\text{Plant A to center II} & 12 \\
\text{Plant B to center I} & 16 \\
\text{Plant B to center II} & 4
\end{array}
$$

What weekly shipping plan will meet the market demands and minimize the total cost of shipping the valves from the assembly plants to the distribution centers? What is the minimum transportation cost? Should the company eliminate the route with the most expensive unit shipment cost?

1. To assist the company in making these decisions, use linear programming with the following variables.

y_1 = the number of units shipped from plant A to center I
y_2 = the number of units shipped from plant A to center II
y_3 = the number of units shipped from plant B to center I
y_4 = the number of units shipped from plant B to center II

2. Form the constraint inequalities that give the limits for the plants and distribution centers and form the total cost function that is to be minimized.

3. Solve the mixed constraint problem for the minimum transportation cost.

4. Determine whether any shipment route is unnecessary.

II. Slack Variables and Shadow Prices

Part A: With linear programming problems, one set of interesting questions deals with how the optimal solution changes if the constraint quantities change. Surprisingly, answers to these questions can be found in the final simplex tableau. In this investigation, we restrict ourselves to standard maximization problems and begin by reexamining the farm co-op application discussed in Example 1 in Section 4.3.

Farm Co-op Problem Statement
Maximize profit $P = 240x + 160y$ subject to

$$
\begin{array}{ll}
x + y \leq 6000 & \text{(Land constraint, in acres)} \\
9x + 3y \leq 40{,}500 & \text{(Fertilizer/herbicide constraint,} \\
& \text{in gallons)} \\
\frac{3}{4}x + y \leq 5250 & \text{(Labor constraint, in hours)}
\end{array}
$$

Initial Tableau

$$
A = \left[\begin{array}{cccccc|c}
x & y & s_1 & s_2 & s_3 & P & \\
1 & 1 & 1 & 0 & 0 & 0 & 6000 \\
9 & 3 & 0 & 1 & 0 & 0 & 40{,}500 \\
\frac{3}{4} & 1 & 0 & 0 & 1 & 0 & 5250 \\
-240 & -160 & 0 & 0 & 0 & 1 & 0
\end{array}\right]
$$

Final Tableau

$$
C = \left[\begin{array}{cccccc|c}
x & y & s_1 & s_2 & s_3 & P & \\
0 & 1 & \frac{3}{2} & -\frac{1}{6} & 0 & 0 & 2250 \\
1 & 0 & -\frac{1}{2} & \frac{1}{6} & 0 & 0 & 3750 \\
0 & 0 & -\frac{9}{8} & \frac{1}{24} & 1 & 0 & 187.5 \\
0 & 0 & 120 & \frac{40}{3} & 0 & 1 & 1{,}260{,}000
\end{array}\right]
$$

Notice in the initial tableau that the columns for the slack variables and the objective function form an identity matrix (here a 4×4 matrix) and the row operations of the simplex method transform this identity matrix into another matrix in the same columns of the final tableau. Call this matrix S.

1. (a) Identify S and calculate SA, where A is the initial tableau. What do you notice when you compare the result of SA with the final tableau, C?

   (b) Look at the Solar Technology manufacturing application in Example 3 in Section 4.3 and identify the corresponding matrix S there. Then find S times the initial tableau and compare your result with the final tableau. What do you notice?

2. (a) In the farm co-op application, if the number of gallons of fertilizer/herbicide were increased by h to $40{,}500 + h$, then the row 2 entry in the last column of A would become $40{,}500 + h$. Call this new initial tableau A_h. Find the effect this change in fertilizer/herbicide would have on the optimal solution by calculating SA_h. Describe the differences between C (the final tableau of the original co-op problem) and SA_h.

   (b) Repeat part (a) if the number of acres of land is changed by k.

   (c) Use the results of parts (a) and (b) to complete the following general statement.
   Statement A: If constraint i has slack variable s_i and the quantity of constraint i is changed by h, then the new optimal solution can be found by using

$h \cdot$ (the __ column) plus the __ column as the new __ column

(continued on next page)

II. Slack Variables and Shadow Prices *(continued)*

(d) Based on your results so far (and similar calculations with other examples if needed), decide whether the following statement is true or false.

"The process described in statement A for determining the new optimal solution applies for any increment of change in any constraint or combination of constraints as long as the last column of the new final tableau has *all* nonnegative entries."

(e) Apply these results to find the new optimal solution to the farm co-op application if the co-op obtained 16 additional acres of land and 48 more gallons of fertilizer/herbicide.

3. (a) In part 2(a), how much is the objective function changed in the new optimal solution?

(b) If $h = 1$ in part 2(a), how much would the objective function change and where in the final tableau is the value that gives this amount of change?

(c) Recall that the shadow price for a constraint measures the change in the objective function if one additional unit of the resource for that constraint becomes available. What is the shadow price for fertilizer/herbicide, and what does it tell us?

(d) Find the shadow prices for acres of land and labor hours and tell what each means.

(e) Complete the following general statement.
Statement B: The shadow price for constraint i is found in the final tableau as the _____ entry in the column for _____.

(f) From this example (and others if you check), notice that if a slack variable is nonzero, then the shadow price of the associated constraint will equal zero. Why do you think this is true?

Part B: Each week the Plush Seating Co. makes stuffed chairs (x) and love seats (y) by using hours of carpentry time (s_1), hours of assembly time (s_2), and hours of upholstery time (s_3) to maximize profit P, in dollars. Plush

Seating's final tableau is shown below; use it and the results from part A to answer the questions that follow.

$$
\begin{array}{cccccc}
x & y & s_1 & s_2 & s_3 & P \\
\end{array}
$$

$$
\left[
\begin{array}{cccccc|c}
1 & 0 & \frac{1}{3} & -1 & 0 & 0 & 28 \\
0 & 1 & -\frac{1}{3} & 2 & 0 & 0 & 8 \\
0 & 0 & \frac{4}{3} & -10 & 1 & 0 & 10 \\
\hline
0 & 0 & \frac{8}{3} & 64 & 0 & 1 & 2816
\end{array}
\right]
$$

1. Producing how many chairs and love seats will yield a maximum profit? Find the maximum profit.
2. How many hours of assembly time are left unused?
3. How many hours of upholstery time are left unused?
4. How much will profit increase if an extra hour of carpentry time becomes available? What is this amount of increase called?
5. How much will profit increase if an extra hour of upholstery time becomes available?
6. If 1 more hour of labor were available, where should Plush Seating use it? Why?
7. If each chair takes 2 hours of upholstery time and each love seat takes 6 hours, how many hours of upholstery time are available each week?
8. If Plush Seating could hire a part-timer to do 6 hours of carpentry and 1 hour of assembly, determine the new optimal solution.
9. Suppose that each worker can do any of the three jobs, and, rather than hiring a part-timer, managers want to reassign the extra upholstery hours. If they use 9 of those hours in carpentry and the other 1 in assembly, find the new optimal solution.
10. Find a way to reassign any number of the extra upholstery hours in a way different from that in Question 9 so that profit is improved even more than in Question 9.

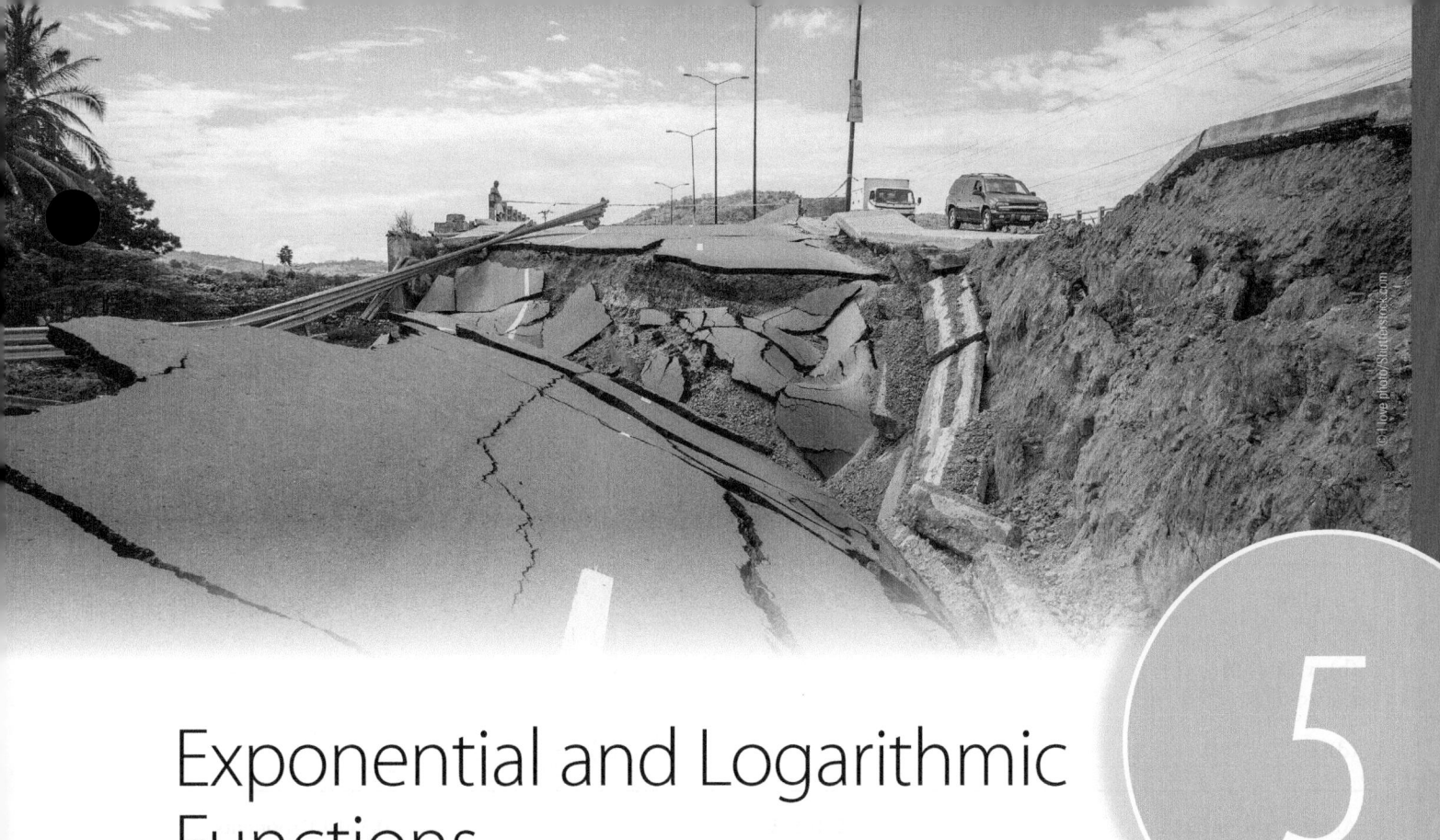

Exponential and Logarithmic Functions

5

In this chapter, we study exponential and logarithmic functions, which provide models for many applications that at first seem remote and unrelated. In our study of these functions, we will examine their descriptions, their properties, their graphs, and the special inverse relationship between these two functions. We will see how exponential and logarithmic functions are applied to some of the concerns of social scientists, business managers, and life scientists.

The chapter topics and some representative applications include the following.

APPLICATIONS

Investments, medications, purchasing power

Doubling time, market share, life expectancy, Richter scale

Sales decay, demand, organizational growth, computer tablet sales, aortic pressure, wildlife populations

Prerequisite Problem Type	For Section	Answer	Section for Review
Write the following with positive exponents: (a) x^{-3} (b) $\dfrac{1}{x^{-2}}$ (c) $\sqrt{x}$	**5.1–5.3**	(a) $\dfrac{1}{x^3}$ (b) x^2 (c) $x^{1/2}$	0.3, 0.4 Exponents and radicals
Simplify: (a) 2^0 (b) $x^0\,(x \neq 0)$ (c) $49^{1/2}$ (d) 10^{-2}	**5.1–5.3**	(a) 1 (b) 1 (c) 7 (d) $\dfrac{1}{100}$	0.3, 0.4 Exponents
Answer true or false: (a) $\left(\dfrac{1}{2}\right)^x = 2^{-x}$ (b) $\sqrt{50} = 50^{1/2}$ (c) If $8 = 2^y$, then $y = 4$. (d) If $x^3 = 8$, then $x = 2$.	**5.1–5.2**	(a) True (b) True (c) False; $y = 3$ (d) True	0.3, 0.4 Exponents and radicals
(a) If $f(x) = 2^{-2x}$, what is $f(-2)$? (b) If $f(x) = 2^{-2x}$, what is $f(1)$? (c) If $f(t) = (1 + 0.02)^t$, what is $f(0)$? (d) If $f(t) = 100(0.03)^{0.02^t}$, what is $f(0)$?	**5.1–5.3**	(a) 16 (b) $\dfrac{1}{4}$ (c) 1 (d) 3	1.2 Function notation

SECTION 5.1

Exponential Functions

OBJECTIVES

- To graph exponential functions
- To evaluate exponential functions
- To introduce, evaluate, and graph base e exponential functions
- To model with exponential functions

APPLICATION PREVIEW

If $10,000 is invested at 6%, compounded monthly, then the future value S of the investment after x years is given by the function

$$S = 10,000(1.005)^{12x}$$

This function is an example of an exponential function, which has the variable in an exponent. We will find the future value of the investment after 5 years in Example 2.

In this section, we will evaluate and graph exponential functions and we will model data with exponential functions.

Exponential Functions and Graphs

TABLE 5.1

Minutes Passed	Number of Organisms
0	1
1	2
2	4
3	8
4	16

Suppose a culture of bacteria has the characteristic that each minute, every microorganism splits into two new organisms. We can describe the number of bacteria in the culture as a function of time. That is, if we begin the culture with one microorganism, we know that after 1 minute, we will have 2 organisms; after 2 minutes, 4 organisms; etc. Table 5.1 gives a few of the values that describe this growth. If x represents the number of minutes that have passed and y represents the number of organisms, the points (x, y) lie on the graph of the function with equation

$$y = 2^x$$

The equation $y = 2^x$ is an example of a special group of functions called **exponential functions**, defined as follows.

Exponential Functions

If a is a real number with $a > 0$ and $a \neq 1$, then the function

$$f(x) = a^x$$

is an **exponential function** with base a.

A table of some values satisfying $y = 2^x$ and the graph of this function are given in Figure 5.1. This function is said to model the growth of the number of organisms in the previous discussion, even though some points on the graph do not correspond to a time and a number of organisms. For example, time x could not be negative and the number of organisms y could not be fractional.

x	$y = 2^x$
-3	$2^{-3} = \frac{1}{8}$
-2	$2^{-2} = \frac{1}{4}$
-1	$2^{-1} = \frac{1}{2}$
0	$2^0 = 1$
1	$2^1 = 2$
2	$2^2 = 4$
3	$2^3 = 8$

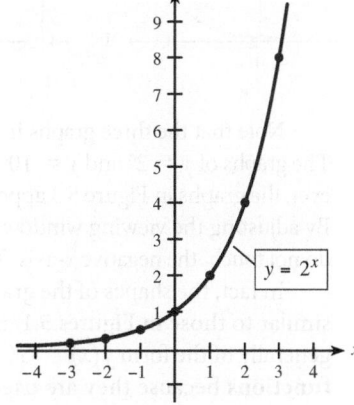

Figure 5.1

We defined rational powers of x in terms of radicals in Chapter 0, so 2^x makes sense for any rational power x. It can be shown that the laws of exponents apply for real numbers. We will assume that if we graphed $y = 2^x$ for real values of x, those points would lie on the curve in Figure 5.1. Thus in general, we can graph an exponential function by plotting easily calculated points, such as those in the table in Figure 5.1, and drawing a smooth curve through the points.

EXAMPLE 1 Graphing an Exponential Function

Graph $y = 10^x$.

Solution

A table of values and the graph are given in Figure 5.2.

x	y
-3	$10^{-3} = 1/1000$
-2	$10^{-2} = 1/100$
-1	$10^{-1} = 1/10$
0	$10^0 = 1$
1	$10^1 = 10$
2	$10^2 = 100$
3	$10^3 = 1000$

$y = 10^x$

Figure 5.2

Calculator Note We can also use a graphing calculator to graph $y = 2^x$ and $y = 10^x$. Figure 5.3 shows graphs of $f(x) = 1.5^x$, $f(x) = 4^x$, and $f(x) = 20^x$ that were obtained using a graphing calculator. Note the viewing window for each graph in the figure. See Appendix A, Section 5.1, for details.

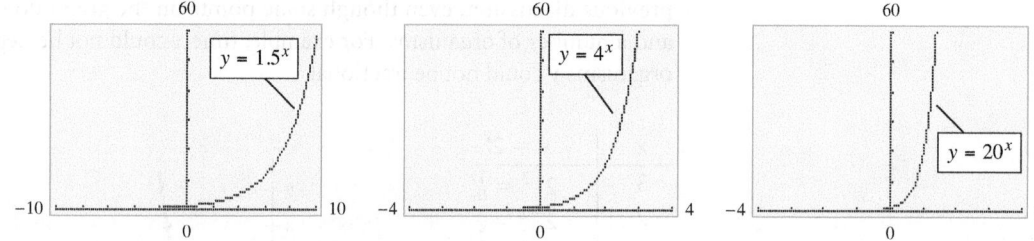

Figure 5.3

Note that the three graphs in Figure 5.3 and the graphs of $y = 2^x$ and $y = 10^x$ are similar. The graphs of $y = 2^x$ and $y = 10^x$ clearly approach, but do not touch, the negative x-axis. However, the graphs in Figure 5.3 appear as if they might eventually merge with the negative x-axis. By adjusting the viewing window, however, we would see that these graphs also approach, but do not touch, the negative x-axis. That is, the negative x-axis is an asymptote for these functions.

In fact, the shapes of the graphs of functions of the form $y = f(x) = a^x$, with $a > 1$, are similar to those in Figures 5.1, 5.2, and 5.3. Exponential functions of this type, and more generally of the form $f(x) = C(a^x)$, where $C > 0$ and $a > 1$, are called **exponential growth functions** because they are used to model growth in diverse applications. Their graphs have the basic shape shown in the following box.

Graphs of Exponential Growth Functions

Function: $y = f(x) = C(a^x)$ $(C > 0, a > 1)$
y-intercept: $(0, C)$
Graph shape:

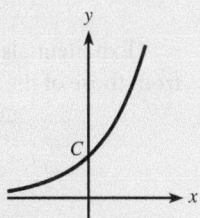

Domain: All real numbers; Range: $y > 0$.
Asymptote: The x-axis (negative half)

One exponential growth model concerns money invested at compound interest. Often we seek to evaluate rather than graph these functions.

EXAMPLE 2 **Future Value of an Investment** **| APPLICATION PREVIEW |**

If $10,000 is invested at 6%, compounded monthly, then the future value of the investment S after x years is given by

$$S = 10,000(1.005)^{12x}$$

Find the future value of the investment after (a) 5 years and (b) 30 years.

Solution
These future values can be found with a calculator.

(a) $S = 10,000(1.005)^{12(5)} = 10,000(1.005)^{60} = \$13,488.50$ (nearest cent)
(b) $S = 10,000(1.005)^{12(30)} = 10,000(1.005)^{360} = \$60,225.75$ (nearest cent)

Note that the amount after 30 years is significantly more than the amount after 5 years, a result consistent with exponential growth models.

iStockphoto.com/s-a-m

1. Can any value of x give a negative value for y if $y = a^x$ and $a > 1$?
2. If $a > 1$, what asymptote does the graph of $y = a^x$ approach?
3. Given $y = f(x) = 2.5^x$. Find $f(x)$ for $x = -2, -1, 0, 1,$ and 2. Then graph $y = f(x)$.

Exponentials whose bases are between 0 and 1, such as $y = \left(\frac{1}{2}\right)^x$, have graphs different from those of the exponentials just discussed. Using the properties of exponents, we have

$$y = \left(\frac{1}{2}\right)^x = (2^{-1})^x = 2^{-x}$$

With this technique, all exponentials of the form $y = b^x$, where $0 < b < 1$, can be rewritten in the form $y = a^{-x}$, where $a = \frac{1}{b} > 1$. Thus graphs of equations of the form $y = a^{-x}$, where $a > 1$, and of the form $y = b^x$, where $0 < b < 1$, will have the same shape.

EXAMPLE 3 Graphing an Exponential Function

Graph $y = 2^{-x}$.

Solution

A table of values and the graph are given in Figure 5.4.

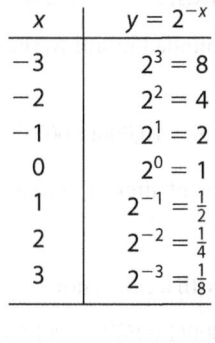

x	$y = 2^{-x}$
-3	$2^3 = 8$
-2	$2^2 = 4$
-1	$2^1 = 2$
0	$2^0 = 1$
1	$2^{-1} = \frac{1}{2}$
2	$2^{-2} = \frac{1}{4}$
3	$2^{-3} = \frac{1}{8}$

Figure 5.4

We can use a graphing utility to graph exponential functions such as the one in Example 3. Additional examples of functions with equations of this form yield graphs with the same shape. **Exponential decay functions** have the form $y = a^{-x}$, where $a > 1$, or, more generally, the form $y = C(a^{-x})$, where $C > 0$ and $a > 1$. They model decay for various phenomena, and their graphs have the characteristics and shape shown in the following box.

Graphs of Exponential Decay Functions

Function: $y = f(x) = C(a^{-x})$ $(C > 0, a > 1)$ or
$\quad\quad\quad\quad y = f(x) = C(b^x)$ $(C > 0, 0 < b < 1)$
y-intercept: $(0, C)$
Graph shape:

Domain: All real numbers; Range: $y > 0$.
Asymptote: The x-axis (positive half)

Exponential decay functions can be used to describe various physical phenomena, such as the measurement of radioactive half-life, the lingering effect of an advertising campaign on new sales after the campaign ends, the effect of inflation on purchasing power, and the changing level of medication in the body between doses.

EXAMPLE 4 Medications

Each medication has an elimination constant that corresponds to the percent of the medication the body eliminates between doses. Suppose that for a certain medication taken every 6 hours, the milligrams M present in the bloodstream t hours after a 500 mg dose is given by

$$M = 500\,(1.089)^{-t}$$

Find the amount of medication in the bloodstream after
(a) half an hour and (b) 6 hours.

Solution

We can use a calculator to answer both parts.

(a) $M = 500\,(1.089)^{-0.5} \approx 479$ mg

(b) $M = 500\,(1.089)^{-6} \approx 300$ mg

Note that after 6 hours (the time between doses), about 300 mg of medication remains, so about 200 mg (or 40% of the dosage) has been eliminated. This means that this medication's elimination constant is 0.40.

CHECKPOINT

4. True or false: The graph of $y = \left(\dfrac{1}{a}\right)^{x}$, with $a > 1$, is the same as the graph of $y = a^{-x}$.

5. True or false: The graph of $y = a^{-x}$, with $a > 1$, approaches the positive x-axis as an asymptote.

6. True or false: The graph of $y = 2^{-x}$ is the graph of $y = 2^{x}$ reflected about the y-axis.

Base e Exponentials   A special function that occurs frequently in finance, economics, and biology is $y = e^{x}$, and more generally $y = Ce^{bx}$, where e is a fixed irrational number (approximately 2.71828). As we will see in Section 6.2, the growth of money that is compounded continuously is given by $S = Pe^{rt}$, where P is the original principal, r is the annual interest rate, and t is the time in years. We will see how e arises when we discuss interest that is compounded continuously, and we will formally define e in Section 9.2, "Continuous Functions; Limits at Infinity."

EXAMPLE 5 Graphing Exponential Functions with Base e

Graph the following: (a) $y = e^{x}$ (b) $y = e^{-2x}$

Solution

We choose x-values and use a calculator to find their y-coordinates (to two decimal places) for the points to plot.

(a) Because $e > 1$, the graph of $y = e^{x}$ will have the same basic shape as other growth exponentials. A table of some values and the graph are shown in Figure.5.5.

x	$y = e^x$
-2	0.14
-1	0.37
0	1.00
1	2.72
2	7.39

Figure 5.5

(b) A table of points for $y = e^{-2x}$ and the graph are shown in Figure 5.6.

x	$y = e^{-2x}$
-3	$e^6 = 403.43$
-2	$e^4 = 54.60$
-1	$e^2 = 7.39$
0	$e^0 = 1.00$
1	$e^{-2} = 0.14$
2	$e^{-4} = 0.02$

Figure 5.6

Exponential functions with base e also arise in other natural ways. Certain populations (of insects, for example) grow exponentially, and the number of individuals can be closely approximated by the equation $y = P_0 e^{ht}$, where P_0 is the original population size, h is a constant that depends on the type of population, and y is the population size at any instant t. Also, the amount y of a radioactive substance is modeled by the exponential decay equation $y = y_0 e^{-kt}$, where y_0 is the original amount and k is a constant that depends on the radioactive substance.

Calculator Note   As with other functions, exponential functions can be graphed with graphing calculators. Because the outputs of exponential functions grow very rapidly, it is sometimes hard to find an appropriate window in which to show the graph. One way to find appropriate values of y-min and y-max when x-min and x-max are given is to use TABLE to find values of y for selected values of x. See Appendix A, Section 5.1, for details.

Figure 5.7(a) shows a table of values of $y = 1000e^{0.12x}$ that correspond to certain values of x, and Figure 5.7(b) shows the graph of this function in a window that uses the table values to set y-max $= 3500$, and y-min $= 0$.

X	Y₁
0	1000
1	1127.5
2	1271.2
4	1616.1
6	2054.4
8	2611.7
10	3320.1

$Y_1 = 1000e^{(.12X)}$

Figure 5.7   (a)   (b)

Graphing calculators also allow us to investigate variations of growth and decay exponential functions. For example, we can examine the similarities and differences between the graphs of $y = f(x) = a^x$ and those of $y = mf(x)$, $y = f(kx)$, $y = f(x + h)$, and $y = f(x) + C$ for constants m, k, h, and C. Figure 5.8 shows graphs of $y = f(x) = e^x$ and $y = mf(x) = me^x$ for $m = -6$ and 2.

From the graphs, we see that when $m > 0$, the shape of the graph is still that of a growth exponential. When $m < 0$, the shape is that of a growth exponential turned upside down, or reflected through the x-axis (making the range $y < 0$). In all cases, the asymptote is unchanged and is the negative x-axis. In each case, the y-intercept is $(0, m)$.

 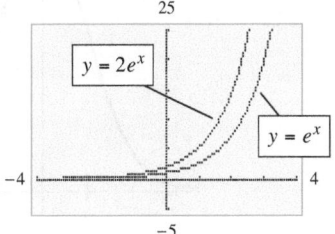

Figure 5.8

Similarly, for $a > 1$, the graphs of $y = a^{-x}$ and $y = ma^{-x}$ give graphs of exponential decay functions if $m > 0$ and give graphs of exponential decay functions turned upside down if $m < 0$. Figure 5.9(a) shows the graph of $y = 2^{-x}$, and Figure 5.9(b) shows the graph of $y = -3(2^{-x})$.

 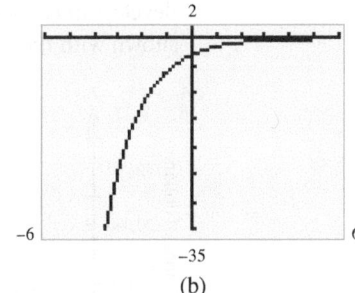

Figure 5.9   (a)   (b)

Spreadsheet Note

Exponential functions can also be graphed with Excel. Figure 5.10 shows the outputs of $y = 4(1.06^x)$ for some values of x, using the formula $= 4*(1.06)\wedge$(cell number) and the graph of the function. To graph $y = e^x$ with Excel, use the formula $= \exp$(cell number). See Appendix B, Section 5.1, or the Online Excel Guide for details.

x	$y = f(x)$
-4	3.168375
-2	3.559986
0	4
2	4.4944
4	5.049908
6	5.674076
8	6.375392
10	7.163391
12	8.048786
14	9.043616
16	10.16141
18	11.41736
20	12.82854
22	14.41415
24	16.19574

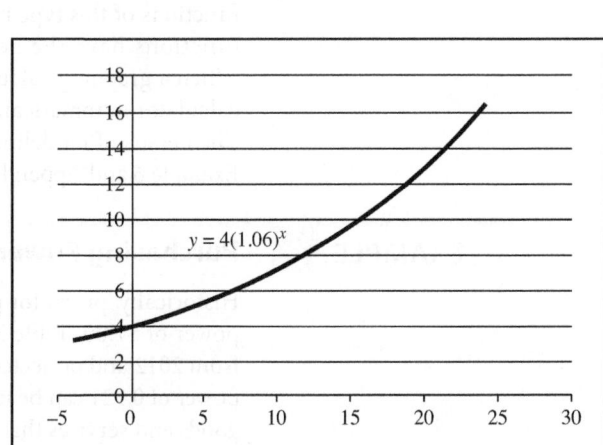

Figure 5.10

There are other important exponential functions that use base e but whose graphs are different from those we have discussed. For example, the standard normal probability curve (often referred to as a bell-shaped curve) is the graph of an exponential function with base e. (See Figure 5.11.) Later in this chapter, we will study other exponential functions that model growth but whose graphs are different from those discussed previously.

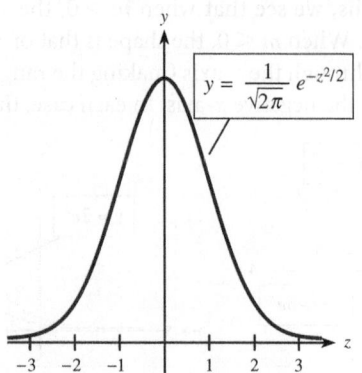

$$y = \frac{1}{\sqrt{2\pi}}\, e^{-z^2/2}$$

Figure 5.11   Standard normal probability curve

Modeling with Exponential Functions

Many types of data can be modeled using an exponential growth function. Figure 5.12(a) shows a graph of data from the Social Security Administration for U.S. total taxable payroll (in billions of dollars) for selected years from 2012 and projected to 2050. With curve-fitting tools available with some computer software or on graphing calculators, we can develop an equation that models, or approximates, these data. The model and its graph are shown with the data in Figure 5.12(b).

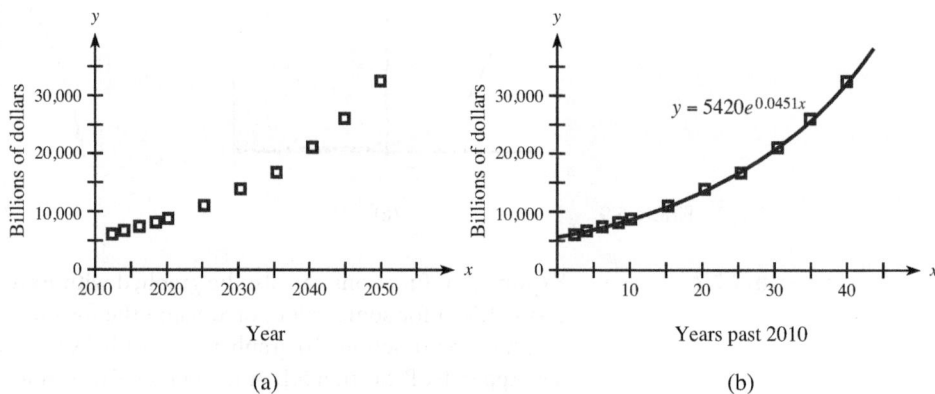

Figure 5.12   (a)   (b)

Calculator Note

The model in Figure 5.12(b) is an exponential growth function. As we have noted, functions of this type have the general form $y = C(a^x)$ with $a > 1$ and exponential decay functions have the general form $y = C(a^{-x})$ with $a > 1$ [or $y = C(b^x)$ with $0 < b < 1$]. When a graphing calculator is used to model exponentials (either growth or decay), the calculator automatically gives a growth model if $b > 1$ and a decay model if $0 < b < 1$. The details of modeling exponential functions using a graphing calculator are shown in Example 6 and Appendix A, Section 5.1.

 EXAMPLE 6   **Purchasing Power**

Historically, prices for goods and services rise, resulting in the erosion of the purchasing power of $1.00. Table 5.2 gives the purchasing power of a 2012 dollar for selected years from 2012 and projected to 2050. With the 2012 dollar as a reference, the 2016 purchasing power of 0.921 can be interpreted as meaning that in 2016, a dollar purchased 92.1% of the goods and services that could be purchased for $1.00 in 2012.

(a) Use these data, with x as the number of years after 2010, to find an exponential function that models the decay of the purchasing power of a 2012 dollar.
(b) What does the model predict as the purchasing power of $1.00 in 2028?
(c) When will the purchasing power fall below $0.25?

TABLE 5.2

Year	Purchasing Power of $1.00	Year	Purchasing Power of $1.00
2012	1.00	2030	0.629
2014	0.962	2035	0.548
2016	0.921	2040	0.477
2018	0.877	2045	0.416
2020	0.829	2050	0.362
2025	0.722		

Source: Social Security Administration

Solution
(a) From a scatter plot of the points, it appears that an exponential decay model is appropriate [see Figure 5.13(a)]. Using STAT, CALC, 0:ExpReg the data can be modeled by the equation $y = 1.078(0.9732^x)$. Figure 5.13(b) shows how the graph of this equation fits the data.

   To write this equation with a base greater than 1, we can write 0.9732 as $(1/0.9732)^{-1} \approx 1.028^{-1}$. Thus the model also can be written as

$$y = 1.078(1.028^{-x})$$

Figure 5.13   (a)   (b)

(b) Recall that we use an unrounded model in our calculations and graphs unless otherwise instructed. We use $x = 18$ for the year 2028 and evaluate the function. This gives a 2028 purchasing power of about $0.66.
(c) Evaluation using TRACE or TABLE shows that the purchasing power falls below $0.25 when $x \approx 53.8$, or in the year 2064, if the model remains valid.   ▨

Spreadsheet Note   A spreadsheet also can be used to create a scatter plot of the data in Table 5.2 and to develop an exponential model. Figure 5.14(a) on the next page shows an Excel scatter plot of the Table 5.2 data, and Figure 5.14(b) shows the scatter plot with Excel's base e exponential model, which is

$$y = 1.078e^{-0.02714x}$$

Procedural details for using Excel are provided in Appendix B, Section 5.1, and in the Online Excel Guide.

   Note that the model $y = 1.078(1.028^{-x})$ found with a graphing calculator in Example 6 is equivalent to $y = 1.078e^{-0.02714x}$ because $e^{-0.02714x} = (e^{0.02714})^{-x} \approx (1.028)^{-x}$.   ▨

Figure 5.14   (a)   (b)

CHECKPOINT
ANSWERS

1. No, all values of y are positive.
2. The left side of the x-axis ($y = 0$)
3. The table shows the values of $f(x)$ and the points to plot. The figure shows the graph of $y = 2.5^x$.

x	$y = f(x)$
-2	0.16
-1	0.4
0	1
1	2.5
2	6.25

4. True   5. True.   6. True

EXERCISES 5.1

In Problems 1–8, use a calculator to evaluate each expression.

1. $10^{0.5}$ 2. $10^{3.6}$
3. $5^{-2.7}$ 4. $8^{-2.6}$
5. $3^{1/3}$ 6. $2^{11/6}$
7. e^2 8. e^{-3}

In Problems 9–20, graph each function.

9. $y = 4^x$ 10. $y = 8^x$
11. $y = 2(3^x)$ 12. $y = 3(2^x)$

13. $y = \left(\dfrac{4}{5}\right)^x$ 14. $y = \left(\dfrac{2}{3}\right)^x$

15. $y = 5^{-x}$ 16. $y = 3^{x-1}$
17. $y = 2e^x$ 18. $y = 3^{-x}$
19. $y = 3^{-2x}$ 20. $y = 5e^{-x}$

21. (a) Find $a > 1$ to express $y = 3\left(\frac{2}{5}\right)^x$ in the form $y = 3(a^{-x})$.
    (b) Are these functions growth exponentials or decay exponentials? Explain.
    (c) Check your result by graphing both functions.

22. (a) Find $a > 1$ to express $y = 8\left(\frac{5}{7}\right)^x$ in the form $y = 8(a^{-x})$.

(b) Are these functions growth exponentials or decay exponentials? Explain.
(c) Check your result by graphing both functions.

23. (a) Graph $y = 2(1.5)^{-x}$.
    (b) Graph $2\left(\frac{2}{3}\right)^x$.
    (c) Algebraically show why these graphs are identical.

24. (a) Graph $y = 2.5(3.25)^{-x}$.
    (b) Graph $y = 2.5\left(\frac{4}{13}\right)^x$.
    (c) Algebraically show why these graphs are identical.

25. Given that $y = \left(\dfrac{4}{5}\right)^x$, write an equivalent equation in the form $y = a^{-x}$, with $a > 1$.

26. Given that $y = 2.5^{-x}$, write an equivalent equation in the form $y = b^x$, with $0 < b < 1$.

In Problems 27–30, use a graphing utility to graph the functions.

27. Given $f(x) = e^{-x}$. Graph $y = f(x)$ and $y = f(kx) = e^{-kx}$ for each k, where $k = 0.1, 0.5, 2$, and 5. Explain the effect that different values of k have on the graphs.

28. Given $f(x) = 2^{-x}$. Graph $y = f(x)$ and $y = mf(x) = m(2^{-x})$ for each m, where $m = -7, -2, 3$, and 8. Explain the effect that different values of m have on the graphs.

29. Given $f(x) = 4^x$. Graph $y = f(x)$ and $y = f(x) + C = 4^x + C$ for each C, where $C = -5, -2, 3,$ and 6. Explain the effect that C has on the graphs.

30. Given $f(x) = 3^x$. Graph $y = f(x)$ and $y = f(x - h) = 3^{x-h}$ for each h, where $h = 4, 1, -2,$ and -5. Explain the effect that h has on the graphs.

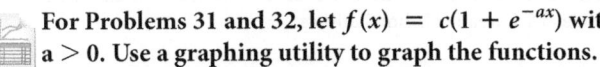

For Problems 31 and 32, let $f(x) = c(1 + e^{-ax})$ with $a > 0$. Use a graphing utility to graph the functions.

31. (a) Fix $a = 1$ and graph $y = f(x) = c(1 + e^{-x})$ for $c = 10, 50,$ and 100.
    (b) What effect does c have on the graphs?

32. (a) Fix $c = 50$ and graph $y = f(x) = 50(1 + e^{-ax})$ for $a = 0.1, 1,$ and 10.
    (b) What effect does a have on the graphs?

APPLICATIONS

33. *Compound interest* If $1000 is invested for x years at 8%, compounded quarterly, the future value is given by

$$S = 1000(1.02)^{4x}$$

What amount will result in 8 years?

34. *Purchasing power and inflation* The purchasing power P of a fixed income of $30,000 per year (such as a pension) after t years of 4% inflation can be modeled by

$$P = 30{,}000(1.04)^{-t}$$

Find the purchasing power (to the nearest dollar) after (a) 5 years and (b) 20 years.

35. *Compound interest* We will show in the next chapter that if $P is invested for n years at 10% compounded continuously, the future value of the investment is given by

$$S = Pe^{0.1n}$$

Use $P = 1000$ and graph this function for $0 \le n \le 20$.

36. *Compound interest* If $1000 is invested for x years at 10%, compounded continuously, the future value that results is

$$S = 1000e^{0.10x}$$

What amount will result in 5 years?

37. *Drug in the bloodstream* The percent concentration y of a certain drug in the bloodstream at any time t in minutes is given by the equation

$$y = 100(1 - e^{-0.462t})$$

Graph this equation for $0 \le t \le 10$. Write a sentence that interprets the graph.

38. *Bacterial growth* A single bacterium splits into two bacteria every half hour, so the number of bacteria in a culture quadruples every hour. Thus the equation by which a colony of 10 bacteria multiplies in t hours is given by

$$y = 10(4^t)$$

Graph this equation for $0 \le t \le 8$.

39. *Product reliability* A statistical study shows that the fraction of television sets of a certain brand that are still in service after x years is given by $f(x) = e^{-0.15x}$. Graph this equation for $0 \le x \le 10$. Write a sentence that interprets the graph.

40. *National health care expenditures* Using U.S. Department of Health and Human Services data for selected years from 1960 and projected to 2024, the national out-of-pocket expenditures for health care H can be modeled by

$$H = 16.5e^{0.0583t}$$

where t is the number of years after 1960 and H is in billions of dollars. Graph this equation with a graphing utility to show the graph through the year 2030.

Population growth Use the following information to answer Problems 41–44. World population can be considered as growing according to the equation

$$N = N_0(1 + r)^t$$

where N_0 is the number of individuals at time $t = 0$, r is the yearly rate of growth, and t is the number of years.

41. Sketch the graph for $t = 0$ to $t = 10$ when the growth rate is 2% and N_0 is 7.7 billion.

42. Sketch the graph for $t = 0$ to $t = 10$ when the growth rate is 3% and N_0 is 7.7 billion.

43. Repeat Problem 41 when the growth rate is 5%.

44. Repeat Problem 42 when the growth rate is 7%.

45. *Real consumption* One of the components of the U.S. real gross domestic product (GDP) is real national consumption. Using U.S. Energy Administration data for selected years from 2014 and projected to 2040, this real consumption (in trillions of dollars) can be modeled by the function

$$C(t) = 10.2\,e^{0.0227t}$$

where t is the number of years after 2010.
    (a) Is this model one of exponential growth or exponential decay? Explain.
    (b) Graph this equation with a graphing utility to show the graph from 2010 through the year 2050.

46. *Advertising and sales* Suppose that sales are related to advertising expenditures according to one of the following two models, where S_1 and S_n are sales and x is advertising, all in millions of dollars.

$$S_1 = 30 + 20x - 0.4x^2$$

$$S_n = 24.58 + 325.18(1 - e^{-x/14})$$

    (a) Graph both of these functions on the same set of axes. Use a graphing utility.
    (b) Do these two functions give approximately the same sales per million dollars of advertising for $0 \le x \le 20$?

(c) How do these functions differ for $x > 20$? Which more realistically represents the relationship between sales and advertising expenditures after $20 million is spent on advertising? Why?

47. Modeling *Carbon dioxide emissions* The following table gives the millions of metric tons of carbon dioxide (CO_2) emissions from biomass energy combustion in the United Sates for selected years from 2010 and projected to 2032.
    (a) Create a scatter plot of the data with x equal to the number of years past 2010 and y equal to the millions of metric tons of carbon dioxide.
    (b) Find an exponential function that models the data.
    (c) Graph the data and the model on the same axes and comment on the fit of the model to the data.

Year	CO$_2$ Emissions	Year	CO$_2$ Emissions
2010	338.5	2022	556.2
2012	364.5	2024	590.9
2014	396.1	2026	629.7
2016	425.8	2028	663.1
2018	453.1	2030	701.1
2020	498.4	2032	743.7

Source: U.S. Department of Energy

48. Modeling *Severe obesity* Severely obese persons (BMI ≥ 40) have a greatly increased risk of diabetes, heart disease, and many other ailments that are very expensive to treat. The table gives the percent of Americans who are severely obese for the years from 1990 and projected to 2030.
    (a) Find an exponential function that models the data, with x equal to the number of years after 1980 and y equal to the percent. Report the model with 4 significant digits.
    (b) Does the unrounded model overestimate or underestimate the percent of severely obese Americans in 2020?
    (c) According to the unrounded model, when are 8.5% of Americans expected to be severely obese?

Year	1990	2000	2010	2015	2020	2025	2030
% Severely Obese	0.8	2.2	4.9	6.4	7.9	9.5	11.1

Source: American Journal of Preventative Medicine, Vol 42, June 2012

49. Modeling *Personal income* The table shows the total personal income in the United States (in billions of dollars) for selected years from 1960 and projected to 2024.

Year	Income ($ billions)	Year	Income ($ billions)
1960	411.5	2008	12,100.7
1970	838.8	2014	14,728.6
1980	2307.9	2018	19,129.6
1990	4878.6	2024	22,685.1
2000	8429.7		

Source: U.S. Bureau of Labor Statistics

(a) These data can be modeled by an exponential function. Write the equation of this function, with x equal to the number of years after 1960. Report the model with 4 significant digits.
(b) Does the unrounded model overestimate or underestimate the total personal income given in the table for 2018?
(c) Graphically determine the year the model predicts total personal income will reach $34 trillion.

50. Modeling *Consumer price index* The table below gives the U.S. consumer price index (CPI) for selected years from 2012 and projected to 2050. With the reference year as 2012, a 2020 CPI $= 120.56$ means goods and services that cost $100.00 in 2012 are expected to cost $120.56 in 2020.
    (a) Find the exponential function that is the best fit for the data, with x as the number of years past 2010 and y as the CPI in dollars.
    (b) Graph the model and the data on the same axes.
    (c) Use the model to predict the CPI in 2038.
    (d) According to the model, in what year will the CPI pass $250?

Year	CPI	Year	CPI
2012	100.00	2030	158.90
2014	104.00	2035	182.43
2016	108.58	2040	209.44
2018	114.09	2045	240.45
2020	120.56	2050	276.05
2025	138.41		

Source: Social Security Administration

51. Modeling *Energy use* Energy use per dollar of GDP indexed to 1980 means that energy use for any year is viewed as a percent of the use per dollar of GDP in 1980. The following data show the energy use per dollar of GDP, as a percent, for selected years from 1985 and projected to 2035.
    (a) Create a scatter plot of these data, with x equal to the number of years past 1980 and y equal to the energy use per dollar of GDP, as a percent.
    (b) Find an exponential function that models these data, with x and y as in part (a).

(c) Graph the model and the data on the same axes.

(d) What does this model predict the energy use per dollar of GDP will be in 2040?

Energy Use per Dollar of GDP

Year	Percent	Year	Percent
1985	83	2015	51
1990	79	2020	45
1995	75	2025	41
2000	67	2030	37
2005	60	2035	34
2010	56		

Source: U.S. Department of Energy

52. **Modeling** *Present value* The amount of money that needs to be deposited into an account to reach some future goal is called the present value. The following table gives the present value (to the nearest dollar) for an account that earns 10% compounded annually so that the account value will be $50,000 after intervals ranging from 1 to 7 years.

Years	Present value
1	$45,455
2	41,322
3	37,566
4	34,151
5	31,046
6	28,224
7	26,658

(a) Using x as the years and y as the present value, develop an exponential model for these data. Report the model to 4 significant digits.

(b) Use the model to find the present value (to the nearest dollar) of this account for its value to be $50,000 after 10 years.

53. **Modeling** *Alzheimer's disease* As the baby boomer generation ages and the proportion of the U.S population over age 65 increases, the number of Americans with Alzheimer's disease and other dementia is projected to grow each year. The table below gives the millions of U.S. citizens age 65 or older with Alzheimer's for selected years from 2000 and projected to 2050.

(a) Find the exponential function that models the data, with x equal to the number of years past 2000 and y equal to the millions of Americans with Alzheimer's.

(b) Is the model in part (a) an exponential growth or exponential decay function?

(c) Graph the model and the data on the same axes.

(d) How many Americans are projected to have Alzheimer's in 2060?

Year	2000	2010	2020	2030	2040	2050
Millions	4.5	5.1	5.7	7.7	11.0	13.2

Source: Alzheimer's Association

SECTION 5.2

Logarithmic Functions and Their Properties

OBJECTIVES

- To use and apply the definition of logarithmic functions
- To graph logarithmic functions
- To model logarithmic functions
- To use properties of logarithmic functions
- To use the change-of-base formula

APPLICATION PREVIEW

As mentioned in Section 5.1, if P dollars is invested at an annual rate r, compounded continuously, then the future value of the investment after t years is given by

$$S = Pe^{rt}$$

A common question with investments such as this is "How long will it be before the investment doubles?" That is, when does $S = 2P$? (See Example 3.) The answer to this question gives an important formula, called a "doubling-time" formula. This requires the use of logarithmic functions.

In this section, we will evaluate and graph logarithmic functions, find logarithmic functions that model data, and use properties of logarithmic functions.

Logarithmic Functions and Graphs

Before the development and easy availability of calculators and computers, certain arithmetic computations, such as $(1.37)^{13}$ and $\sqrt[16]{3.09}$, were difficult to perform. The computations could be performed relatively easily using **logarithms,** which were developed in the seventeenth century by John Napier, or using a slide rule, which is based on logarithms. The use of logarithms as a computing technique has all but disappeared today, but the study of **logarithmic functions** is still very important because of the many applications of these functions.

For example, let us again consider the culture of bacteria described at the beginning of the previous section. If we know that the culture is begun with one microorganism and that each minute every microorganism present splits into two new ones, then we can find the number of minutes y it takes until there are 1024 organisms by solving

$$1024 = 2^y$$

The solution of this equation may be written in the form

$$y = \log_2 1024$$

which is read "y equals the logarithm of 1024 to the base 2."

In general, we may express the equation $x = a^y$ ($a > 0$, $a \neq 1$) in the form $y = f(x)$ by defining a **logarithmic function.**

Logarithmic Function

For $a > 0$ and $a \neq 1$, the **logarithmic function**

$$y = \log_a x \quad \text{(logarithmic form)}$$

has domain $x > 0$, base a, and is defined by

$$a^y = x \quad \text{(exponential form)}$$

TABLE 5.3	
Logarithmic Form	Exponential Form
$\log_{10} 100 = 2$	$10^2 = 100$
$\log_{10} 0.1 = -1$	$10^{-1} = 0.1$
$\log_2 x = y$	$2^y = x$
$\log_a 1 = 0 \ (a > 0)$	$a^0 = 1$
$\log_a a = 1 \ (a > 0)$	$a^1 = a$

From the definition, we know that $\log_3 81 = 4$ because $3^4 = 81$. In this case, the logarithm, 4, is the exponent to which we must raise the base 3 to obtain 81. In general, if $y = \log_a x$, then y is the exponent to which the base a must be raised to obtain x.

The a is called the **base** in both $\log_a x = y$ and $a^y = x$, and y is the *logarithm* in $\log_a x = y$ and the *exponent* in $a^y = x$. Thus **a logarithm is an exponent.**

Table 5.3 shows some logarithmic equations and their equivalent exponential forms.

EXAMPLE 1   Logarithms and Exponential Forms

(a) Write $64 = 4^3$ in logarithmic form.
(b) Write $\log_4 \left(\frac{1}{64} \right) = -3$ in exponential form.
(c) If $4 = \log_2 x$, find x.
(d) Evaluate: $\log_2 8$
(e) Evaluate: $\log_5 \left(\frac{1}{25} \right)$

Solution
(a) In $64 = 4^3$, the base is 4 and the exponent (or logarithm) is 3. Thus $64 = 4^3$ is equivalent to $3 = \log_4 64$.
(b) In $\log_4 \left(\frac{1}{64} \right) = -3$, the base is 4 and the logarithm (or exponent) is -3. Thus $\log_4 \left(\frac{1}{64} \right) = -3$ is equivalent to $4^{-3} = \frac{1}{64}$.
(c) If $4 = \log_2 x$, then $2^4 = x$ and $x = 16$.
(d) If $y = \log_2 8$, then $8 = 2^y$. Because $2^3 = 8$, $\log_2 8 = 3$.
(e) If $y = \log_5 \left(\frac{1}{25} \right)$, then $\frac{1}{25} = 5^y$. Because $5^{-2} = \frac{1}{25}$, $\log_5 \left(\frac{1}{25} \right) = -2$.

EXAMPLE 2 Graphing a Logarithmic Function

Graph $y = \log_2 x$.

Solution
We may graph $y = \log_2 x$ by graphing $x = 2^y$. The table of values (found by substituting values of y and calculating x) and the graph are shown in Figure 5.15.

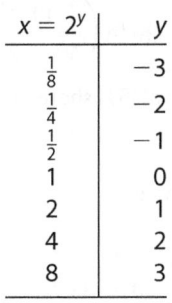

$x = 2^y$	y
$\frac{1}{8}$	-3
$\frac{1}{4}$	-2
$\frac{1}{2}$	-1
1	0
2	1
4	2
8	3

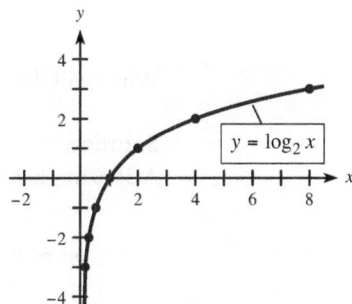

Figure 5.15

From the definition of logarithms, we see that every logarithm has a base. Most applications of logarithms involve logarithms to the base 10 (called **common logarithms**) or logarithms to the base e (called **natural logarithms**). In fact, logarithms to the base 10 and the base e are the only ones that have function keys on calculators. Thus it is important to be familiar with their names and designations.

Common and Natural Logarithms

Common logarithms: $\log x$ means $\log_{10} x$.
Natural logarithms: $\ln x$ means $\log_e x$.

Values of common and natural logarithmic functions are usually found using a calculator. For example, a calculator gives $\log 2 \approx 0.301$ and $\ln 2 \approx 0.693$.

EXAMPLE 3 Doubling Time for an Investment | APPLICATION PREVIEW |

If $\$P$ is invested for t years at interest rate r, compounded continuously, then the future value of the investment is given by $S = Pe^{rt}$. The doubling time for this investment can be found by solving for t in $S = Pe^{rt}$ when $S = 2P$. That is, we must solve $2P = Pe^{rt}$, or (equivalently) $2 = e^{rt}$. Express this equation in logarithmic form and then solve for t to find the doubling-time formula.

Solution
In logarithmic form, $2 = e^{rt}$ is equivalent to $\log_e 2 = rt$. Solving for t gives the doubling-time formula

$$t = \frac{\log_e 2}{r} = \frac{\ln 2}{r}$$

Note that if the interest rate is $r = 10\%$, compounded continuously, the time required for the investment to double is

$$t = \frac{\ln 2}{0.10} \approx \frac{0.693}{0.10} = 6.93$$

In general, we can approximate the doubling time for an investment at $r\%$, compounded continuously, with $70/r$. (In finance, this is called the **Rule of 70.**)

EXAMPLE 4   Market Share

Suppose that after a company introduces a new product, the number of months m before its market share is s percent can be modeled by

$$m = 20 \ln \left(\frac{40}{40 - s} \right)$$

When will the company's product have a 35% share of the market?

Solution

A 35% market share means $s = 35$. Hence

$$m = 20 \ln \left(\frac{40}{40 - s} \right) = 20 \ln \left(\frac{40}{40 - 35} \right) = 20 \ln \left(\frac{40}{5} \right) = 20 \ln 8 \approx 41.6$$

Thus the market share will be 35% after about 41.6 months, in the 42nd month.

EXAMPLE 5   Graphing the Natural Logarithm

Graph $y = \ln x$.

Solution

We can graph $y = \ln x$ by evaluating $y = \ln x$ for $x > 0$ (including some values $0 < x < 1$) using a calculator. The graph is shown in Figure 5.16.

x	$y = \ln x$
0.05	-2.996
0.10	-2.303
0.50	-0.693
1	0.000
2	0.693
3	1.099
5	1.609
10	2.303

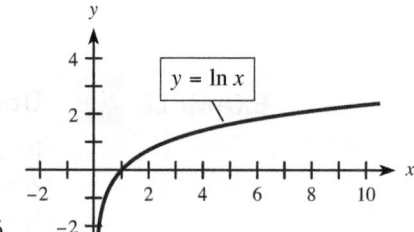

Figure 5.16

Note that because $\ln x$ is a standard function on a graphing calculator, such a calculator could easily be used to obtain the graph. Note also that the graphs of $y = \log_2 x$ (Figure 5.15) and $y = \ln x$ (Figure 5.16) are very similar. The shapes of graphs of equations of the form $y = \log_a x$ with $a > 1$ are similar to these two graphs.

Graphs of Logarithmic Functions	
Equation: $y = \log_a x$ $(a > 1)$ x-intercept: $(1, 0)$ Domain: All positive reals Range: All reals Asymptote: y-axis (negative half)	 Basic shape

Calculator Note   As with other functions, logarithmic functions can be graphed using graphic calcula-tors, using the LOG and LN buttons to graph $y = \log x$ and $y = \ln x$, respectively. See Appendix A, Section 5.2, for details.   ■

Spreadsheet Note   The graph of $y = \log x$ can also be created with Excel by entering the formula =log10(cell number). The graph of $y = \ln x$ can be created with Excel by entering the for-mula =ln(cell number). For more details see Appendix B, Section 5.2, or the Online Excel Guide.   ■

CHECKPOINT

1. What asymptote does the graph of $y = \log_a x$ approach when $a > 1$?
2. For $a > 1$, does the equation $y = \log_a x$ represent the same function as the equation $x = a^y$?
3. For what values of x is $y = \log_a x$, $a > 0$, $a \neq 1$, defined?
4. (a) Write $4 = \log_3 x$ in exponential form and find x.
    (b) Write $e^x = 31$ in logarithmic form and approximate x.

Modeling with Logarithmic Functions   The basic shape of a logarithmic function is important for two reasons. First, when we graph a logarithmic function, we know that the graph should have this shape. Second, when data points have this basic shape, they suggest a logarithmic model.

 EXAMPLE **6**   **Life Expectancy**

The expected life span of people in the United States can be modeled as a function of their year of birth. (See the table and scatter plot in Figure 5.17, with x as the number of years after 1900) In Section 2.5, "Modeling; Fitting Curves to Data with Graphing Utilities," we modeled life span with a linear function and with a quadratic function. However, the scat-ter plot suggests that a better model may be logarithmic.
(a) Use technology to find a logarithmic equation that models the data.
(b) The National Center for Health Statistics projects the expected life span for people born in 2000 to be 76.8 and for those born in 2030 to be 81.7. Use your model to project the life spans for those years.
(c) Do the expected life spans for 2010 and 2020, as given in the table, agree with the calculations found with the model found in part (a)?

Birth Year	Life Expectancy	Birth Year	Life Expectancy
1920	54.1	1990	75.4
1930	59.7	2000	76.8
1940	62.9	2010	78.7
1950	68.2	2020	80.2
1960	69.7	2030	81.7
1970	70.8	2040	83.0
1980	73.7	2050	84.4

Source: National Center for Health Statistics

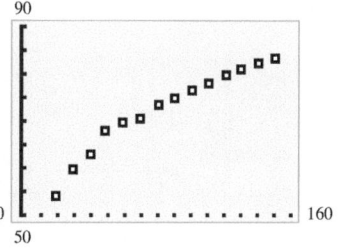

Figure 5.17

Solution
(a) Using STAT, CALC, 9:LnReg on a graphing calculator gives

$$L(x) = 8.7744 + 14.907 \ln x$$

where x is the number of years after 1900. Figure 5.18 shows the scatter plot and graph of the model.

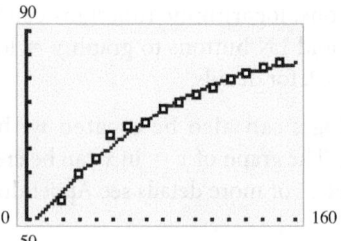

Figure 5.18

(b) For the year 2000, the value of x is 100, so the projected life span is $L(100) - 77.4$. For 2030, the model gives 81.3 as the expected life span. These calculations closely approximate the projections from the National Center for Health Statistics.

(c) The values are close; $L(110) \cong 78.8$ and $L(120) \cong 80.1$.

Properties of Logarithms   The definition of the logarithmic function and the previous examples suggest a special relationship between the logarithmic function $y = \log_a x$ and the exponential function $y = a^x$ ($a > 0, a \neq 1$). Because we can write $y = \log_a x$ in exponential form as $x = a^y$, we see that the connection between

$$y = \log_a x \quad \text{and} \quad y = a^x$$

is that x and y have been interchanged from one function to the other. This is true for the functional description and hence for the ordered pairs or coordinates that satisfy these functions. This is illustrated in Table 5.4 for the functions $y = \log x$ ($y = \log_{10} x$) and $y = 10^x$.

TABLE 5.4

$y = \log_{10} x = \log x$		$y = 10^x$	
Coordinates	Justification	Coordinates	Justification
$(1000, 3)$	$3 = \log 1000$	$(3, 1000)$	$1000 = 10^3$
$(100, 2)$	$2 = \log 100$	$(2, 100)$	$100 = 10^2$
$\left(\frac{1}{10}, -1\right)$	$-1 = \log \frac{1}{10}$	$\left(-1, \frac{1}{10}\right)$	$\frac{1}{10} = 10^{-1}$

In general, we say that $y = f(x)$ and $y = g(x)$ are **inverse functions** if, whenever the pair (a, b) satisfies $y = f(x)$, the pair (b, a) satisfies $y = g(x)$. Furthermore, because the values of the x- and y-coordinates are interchanged for inverse functions, their graphs are reflections of each other about the line $y = x$.

Thus for $a > 0$ and $a \neq 1$, the logarithmic function $y = \log_a x$ (also written $x = a^y$) and the exponential function $y = a^x$ are inverse functions.

The logarithmic function $y = \log x$ is the inverse of the exponential function $y = 10^x$. Thus the graphs of $y = \log x$ and $y = 10^x$ are reflections of each other about the line $y = x$. Some values of x and y for these functions are given in Table 5.4, and their graphs are shown in Figure 5.19.

This inverse relationship is a consequence of the definition of the logarithmic function. We can use this definition to discover several other properties of logarithms.

Because logarithms are exponents, the properties of logarithms can be derived from the properties of exponents. (The properties of exponents are discussed in Chapter 0, "Algebraic Concepts.") The following properties of logarithms are useful in simplifying expressions that contain logarithms.

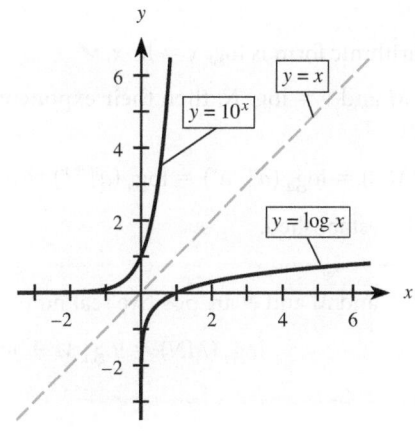

Figure 5.19

Logarithmic Property I   If $a > 0$, $a \neq 1$, then $\log_a a^x = x$, for any real number x.

To prove this result, note that the exponential form of $y = \log_a a^x$ is $a^y = a^x$, so $y = x$. That is, $\log_a a^x = x$.

EXAMPLE   7   **Logarithmic Property I**

Use Property I to simplify each of the following.
(a) $\log_4 4^3$ (b) $\ln e^x$

Solution
(a) $\log_4 4^3 = 3$
Check: The exponential form is $4^3 = 4^3$. ✔

(b) $\ln e^x = \log_e e^x = x$
Check: The exponential form is $e^x = e^x$. ✔

We note that two special cases of Property I are used frequently; these are when $x = 1$ and $x = 0$.

Special Cases of Logarithmic Property I   Because $a^1 = a$, we have $\log_a a = 1$.
Because $a^0 = 1$, we have $\log_a 1 = 0$.

The logarithmic form of $y = a^{\log_a x}$ is $\log_a y = \log_a x$, so $y = x$. This means that $a^{\log_a x} = x$ and proves Property II.

Logarithmic Property II   If $a > 0$, $a \neq 1$, then $a^{\log_a x} = x$, for any positive real number x.

EXAMPLE   8   **Logarithmic Property II**

Use Property II to simplify each of the following.
(a) $2^{\log_2 4}$ (b) $e^{\ln x}$

Solution
(a) $2^{\log_2 4} = 4$
Check: The logarithmic form is $\log_2 4 = \log_2 4$. ✔

(b) $e^{\ln x} = x$

Check: The logarithmic form is $\log_e x = \ln x.$ ✔

If $u = \log_a M$ and $v = \log_a N$, then their exponential forms are $a^u = M$ and $a^v = N$, respectively. Thus

$$\log_a (MN) = \log_a (a^u \cdot a^v) = \log_a (a^{u+v}) = u + v = \log_a M + \log_a N$$

and Property III is established.

Logarithmic Property III	If $a > 0$, $a \neq 1$, and M and N are positive real numbers, then $$\log_a (MN) = \log_a M + \log_a N$$

EXAMPLE 9 Logarithmic Property III

(a) Find $\log_2 (4 \cdot 16)$ if $\log_2 4 = 2$ and $\log_2 16 = 4$.
(b) Find $\ln 77$ if $\ln 7 = 1.9459$ and $\ln 11 = 2.3979$ (to four decimal places).

Solution

(a) $\log_2 (4 \cdot 16) = \log_2 4 + \log_2 16 = 2 + 4 = 6$
Check: $\log_2 (4 \cdot 16) = \log_2 (64) = 6$ because $2^6 = 64.$ ✔

(b) $\ln 77 = \ln (7 \cdot 11) = \ln 7 + \ln 11 = 1.9459 + 2.3979 = 4.3438$
Check: Using a calculator, we can see that $e^{4.3438} \approx 77.$ ✔

Logarithmic Property IV	If $a > 0$, $a \neq 1$, and M and N are positive real numbers, then $$\log_a (M/N) = \log_a M - \log_a N$$

The proof of this property is left to the student.

EXAMPLE 10 Logarithmic Property IV

(a) Evaluate $\log_3 \left(\frac{9}{27}\right)$.
(b) Find $\log_{10} \left(\frac{16}{5}\right)$ if $\log_{10} 16 = 1.2041$ and $\log_{10} 5 = 0.6990$ (to four decimal places).

Solution

(a) $\log_3 \left(\frac{9}{27}\right) = \log_3 9 - \log_3 27 = 2 - 3 = -1$
Check: $\log_3 \left(\frac{1}{3}\right) = -1$ because $3^{-1} = \frac{1}{3}.$ ✔

(b) $\log_{10} \left(\frac{16}{5}\right) = \log_{10} 16 - \log_{10} 5 = 1.2041 - 0.6990 = 0.5051$
Check: Using a calculator, we can see that $10^{0.5051} \approx 3.2 = \frac{16}{5}.$ ✔

Logarithmic Property V	If $a > 0$, $a \neq 1$, M is a positive real number, and N is any real number, then $$\log_a (M^N) = N \log_a M$$

The proof of this property is left to the student.

EXAMPLE 11 Logarithmic Property V

(a) Simplify $\log_3 (9^2)$.
(b) Simplify $\ln 8^{-4}$ if $\ln 8 = 2.0794$ (to four decimal places).

Solution

(a) $\log_3 (9^2) = 2\log_3 9 = 2\cdot 2 = 4$

(b) $\ln 8^{-4} = -4\ln 8 \approx -8.3178$

CHECKPOINT

5. Simplify:

   (a) $6^{\log_6 x}$ (b) $\log_7 7^3$ (c) $\ln\left(\dfrac{1}{e^2}\right)$ (d) $\log 1$

6. If $\log_7 20 = 1.5395$ and $\log_7 11 = 1.2323$, find the following.

   (a) $\log_7 220 = \log_7 (20\cdot 11)$ (b) $\log_7\left(\dfrac{11}{20}\right)$ (c) $\log_7 20^4$

Change of Base

With a calculator, we can evaluate directly only those logarithms with base 10 or base e. Also, logarithms with base 10 or base e are the only ones that are standard functions on a graphing calculator. Thus if we had a way to express a logarithmic function with any base in terms of a logarithm with base 10 or base e, we would be able to evaluate the original logarithmic function and graph it with a graphing calculator.

In general, if we use the properties of logarithms, we can write

$$y = \log_b x \quad \text{in the form} \quad b^y = x$$

If we take the base a logarithm of both sides, we have

$$\log_a b^y = \log_a x$$
$$y \log_a b = \log_a x$$
$$y = \frac{\log_a x}{\log_a b}$$

This gives us the **change-of-base formula** from base b to base a.

Change-of-Base Formulas

If $a \neq 1, b \neq 1, a > 0, b > 0$, then

$$\log_b x = \frac{\log_a x}{\log_a b}$$

For calculation purposes, we can convert logarithms to base e or base 10.

$$\text{Base } e: \quad \log_b x = \frac{\ln x}{\ln b} \qquad \text{Base 10:} \quad \log_b x = \frac{\log x}{\log b}$$

EXAMPLE   12   **Change-of-Base Formula**

Evaluate $\log_7 15$ using a change-of-base formula.

Solution

$$\log_7 15 = \frac{\ln 15}{\ln 7} = \frac{2.70805}{1.94591} = 1.39166 \text{ (approximately)}$$

As a check, a calculator shows that $7^{1.39166} \approx 15.$ ✔

Calculator Note

The change-of-base formula expands the capability of graphing calculators so that they can be used to evaluate logarithms and to graph logarithmic functions to any base. See Appendix A, Section 5.2, for details.

Figure 5.20(a) shows the graph of $y = \log_2 x = \dfrac{\ln x}{\ln 2}$. Note that it is exactly the same as the graph in Figure 5.15 in Example 2.

Figure 5.20(b) shows the graph of $y = \log_7 x = \dfrac{\ln x}{\ln 7}$.

(a)

(b)

Figure 5.20

Spreadsheet Note   We have seen how to use Excel to graph logarithmic functions with base 10 and base e. For any other base a, the graph of $y = \log_a x$ can be created by entering the formula =log(cell number, a). See Appendix B, Section 5.2, or the Online Excel Guide for details.

Natural logarithms, $y = \ln x$ (and the inverse exponentials with base e), have many practical applications, some of which are considered in the next section. Common logarithms, $y = \log x$, were widely used for computation before computers and calculators became popular. They also have several applications to scaling variables, where the purpose is to reduce the scale of variation when a natural physical variable covers a wide range.

EXAMPLE 13   Richter Scale

The Richter scale is used to measure the intensity of an earthquake. The magnitude on the Richter scale of an earthquake of intensity I is given by

$$R = \log (I/I_0)$$

where I_0 is a certain minimum intensity used for comparison.

(a) Find R if I is 15,800,000 times as great as I_0.
(b) As of 2017, the 1964 Alaskan earthquake was the most violent U.S. earthquake and one of the strongest ever; it measured 9.2 on the Richter scale. Find the intensity of the 1964 Alaskan earthquake.

Solution
(a) If $I = 15{,}800{,}000 I_0$, then $I/I_0 = 15{,}800{,}000$. Hence

$$R = \log (15{,}800{,}000)$$
$$= 7.2 \text{ (approximated to 1 decimal place)}$$

(b) For $R = 9.2$, it follows that

$$9.2 = \log (I/I_0)$$

Rewriting this in exponential form gives

$$10^{9.2} = I/I_0$$

and from a calculator we obtain

$$I/I_0 = 1{,}580{,}000{,}000 \text{ (approximately)}$$

Thus the intensity is 1,580,000,000 times I_0.

Note that a Richter scale measurement that is 2 units larger means that the intensity is $10^2 = 100$ *times* greater. Comparing parts (a) and (b) above illustrates this. ∎

CHECKPOINT
ANSWERS

1. The (negative) y-axis
2. Yes
3. $x > 0$ is the domain of $\log_a x$.
4. (a) $3^4 = x = 81$ (b) $\log_e 31 = \ln 31 = x \approx 3.434$
5. (a) x (b) 3   (c) -2 (d) 0
6. (a) 2.7718   (b) -0.3072 (c) 6.1580

EXERCISES 5.2

In Problems 1–4, use the definition of a logarithmic function to rewrite each equation in exponential form.

1. $4 = \log_2 16$
2. $4 = \log_3 81$
3. $\dfrac{1}{2} = \log_4 2$
4. $-2 = \log_3 \left(\dfrac{1}{9}\right)$

In Problems 5–14, solve for x by writing the equation in exponential form.

5. $\log_3 x = 4$
6. $\log_4 x = -2$
7. $\log_{16} x = -\dfrac{1}{2}$
8. $\log_{25} x = \dfrac{1}{2}$
9. $\log_7 (3x + 1) = 2$
10. $\log_3 (7 - x) = 3$
11. $\log (4x - 7) = 2$
12. $\log (1.34 - x) = -1$
13. $\ln (2x + 5) = 2.2$ (to three decimal places)
14. $\ln (2 - x) = -1.4$ (to three decimal places)

In Problems 15–18, write the equation in logarithmic form.

15. $2^5 = 32$
16. $5^3 = 125$
17. $4^{-1} = \dfrac{1}{4}$
18. $9^{1/2} = 3$

In Problems 19 and 20, write the equation in logarithmic form and solve for x.

19. $e^{3x+5} = 0.55$ (to three decimal places)
20. $10^{2x+1} = 0.25$ (to three decimal places)

In Problems 21–26, graph each function.

21. $y = \log_3 x$
22. $y = \log_4 x$
23. $y = \ln x$
24. $y = \log_9 x$
25. $y = \log_2 (-x)$
26. $y = \ln (-x)$

In Problems 27 and 28, use properties of logarithms or a definition to simplify each expression. Check each result with a change-of-base formula.

27. (a) $\log_3 27$ (b) $\log_5 \left(\dfrac{1}{5}\right)$

28. (a) $\log_4 16$ (b) $\log_9 3$
29. If $f(x) = \ln (x)$, find $f(e^x)$.
30. If $f(x) = \log (x)$, find $f(10^x)$.
31. If $f(x) = \log (x)$, find $f(10^{-7})$.
32. If $f(x) = \ln (x)$, find $f(\sqrt{e})$.
33. If $f(x) = e^x$, find $f(\ln 3)$.
34. If $f(x) = 10^x$, find $f(\log 2)$.

In Problems 35 and 36, evaluate each logarithm using properties of logarithms and the following facts.

$$\log_a x = 3.1 \quad \log_a y = 1.8 \quad \log_a z = 2.7$$

35. (a) $\log_a (xy)$ (b) $\log_a \left(\dfrac{x}{z}\right)$
    (c) $\log_a (x^4)$ (d) $\log_a \sqrt{y}$
36. (a) $\log_a (yz)$ (b) $\log_a \left(\dfrac{z}{y}\right)$
    (c) $\log_a (y^6)$ (d) $\log_a \sqrt[3]{z}$

Write each expression in Problems 37–40 as the sum or difference of two logarithmic functions containing no exponents.

37. $\log \left(\dfrac{x}{x+1}\right)$ 38. $\ln [(x + 1)(4x + 5)]$
39. $\log_7 (x\sqrt[3]{x+4})$ 40. $\log_5 \left(\dfrac{x^2}{\sqrt{x+4}}\right)$

Use the properties of logarithms to write each expression in Problems 41–44 as a single logarithm.

41. $\ln x - \ln y$ 42. $\log_3 (x + 1) + \log_3 (x - 1)$
43. $\log_5 (x + 1) + \dfrac{1}{2} \log_5 x$
44. $\log (2x + 1) - \dfrac{1}{3} \log (x + 1)$

In Problems 45–48, use a calculator to determine whether expression (a) is equivalent to expression (b). If they are equivalent, state what properties are being illustrated. If they are not equivalent, rewrite expression (a) so that they are equivalent.

45. (a) $\ln \sqrt{4 \cdot 6}$　　(b) $\dfrac{1}{2}(\ln 4 + \ln 6)$

46. (a) $\log \dfrac{\sqrt{56}}{23}$　　(b) $\dfrac{1}{2}\log 56 - \log 23$

47. (a) $\log \sqrt[3]{\dfrac{8}{5}}$　　(b) $\dfrac{1}{3}\log 8 - \log 5$

48. (a) $\dfrac{\log_2 34}{17}$　　(b) $\log_2 34 - \log_2 17$

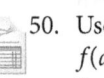

49. (a) Use a graphing utility to graph $f(x) = \ln x$ and $f(x - c) = \ln(x - c)$ for $c = -4, -2, 1$, and 5 on the same axes.
    (b) For each c-value, identify the vertical asymptote and the domain of $y = \ln(x - c)$.
    (c) For each c-value, find the x-intercept of $y = \ln(x - c)$.
    (d) Write a sentence that explains precisely how the graphs of $y = f(x)$ and $y = f(x - c)$ are related.

50. Use a graphing utility to graph $f(x) = \ln x$ and $f(ax) = \ln(ax)$ for $a = -2, -1, -0.5, 0.2$, and 3. Explain the differences between the graphs
    (a) when $a > 0$ and when $a < 0$.
    (b) when $|a| > 1$ and when $0 < |a| < 1$.

In Problems 51 and 52, use a change-of-base formula to evaluate each logarithm.

51. (a) $\log_2 17$　　(b) $\log_5(0.78)$
52. (a) $\log_3 12$　　(b) $\log_8(0.15)$

In Problems 53–56, use a change-of-base formula to rewrite each logarithm. Then use a graphing utility to graph the function.

53. $y = \log_5 x$　　54. $y = \log_6 x$
55. $y = \log_{13} x$　　56. $y = \log_{16} x$
57. Prove logarithmic Property IV.
58. Prove logarithmic Property V.

APPLICATIONS

Richter scale **Use the formula $R = \log(I/I_0)$ in Problems 59–62. (*Source:* Earthquake data from the U.S. Geological Survey.)**

59. The most devastating earthquake since 2000 was the Haiti quake in 2010 that measured 7.0 on the Richter scale and resulted in more than 222,500 deaths, 300,000 injuries, and 1.3 million displaced persons. The largest quake that year was the 8.8 quake that struck offshore Maule, Chile. How many times more intense was the quake in Chile?

60. In May 2008, an earthquake measuring 6.8 on the Richter scale struck near the east coast of Honshu, Japan. In March 2011, a quake measuring 9.0 struck that same region. How many times more intense was the 2011 quake than the one in 2008?

61. The most destructive earthquake in the United States was the 1906 San Francisco quake that measured 7.8 on the Richter scale. The quake and subsequent fires that burned for several days destroyed 80% of the city. This 1906 quake was the seventeenth most violent in the United States. Among the 40 most severe U.S. quakes, the only one that occurred east of the Mississippi River shook Charleston, South Carolina, in 1886 and measured 7.3. How many times more intense was the San Francisco quake?

62. The world's strongest earthquake struck Chile in 1960 and measured 9.5 on the Richter scale. The 2010 Chilean quake at 8.8 was the world's sixth largest. Find the ratio of their intensities.

Decibel readings **In Problems 63–66, use the fact that the loudness of sound (in decibels) perceived by the human ear depends on intensity levels according to**

$$L = 10\log(I/I_0)$$

where I_0 is the threshold of hearing for the average human ear.

63. Find the loudness when I is 10,000 times I_0. This is the intensity level of the average voice.

64. The sound level of a military jet taking off has intensity about 10^{14} times I_0. Find the decibel reading for this threshold.

65. Graph the equation for loudness of sound in decibels. Use I/I_0 as the independent variable.

66. The background noise level of a relatively quiet room is about $L_1 = 32$ decibels and of a heated argument can exceed $L_2 = 66$ decibels. Find the ratio I_2/I_1 of these associated intensities.

pH levels **In Problems 67–70, use the following information. Chemists use the pH (hydrogen potential) of a solution to measure its acidity or basicity. The pH is given by the formula**

$$\text{pH} = -\log[\text{H}^+]$$

where $[\text{H}^+]$ is the concentration of hydrogen ions in moles per liter.

67. Most common solutions have pH ranges between 1 and 14. What values of $[\text{H}^+]$ are associated with these extremes?

68. Find the approximate pH of each of the following.
    (a) blood: $[\text{H}^+] = 3.98 \times 10^{-8}$
          $= 0.0000000398$

(b) beer: $[H^+] = 6.31 \times 10^{-5} = 0.0000631$
(c) vinegar: $[H^+] = 6.3 \times 10^{-3} = 0.0063$

69. Sometimes pH is defined as the logarithm of the reciprocal of the concentration of hydrogen ions. Write an equation that represents this sentence and explain how it and the equation given in the information preceding Problem 67 can both represent pH.

70. Find the approximate hydrogen ion concentration $[H^+]$ for each of the following.
(a) apples: pH = 3.0   (b) eggs: pH = 7.79
(c) water (neutral): pH = 7.0

Doubling time **In Problems 71 and 72, use the formula**

$$2 = \left(1 + \frac{r}{100n}\right)^{nt}$$

to find the doubling time t, in years, for an investment at $r\%$ compounded n times per year. Write each exponential statement in logarithmic form. Then use a change-of-base formula to find the doubling time.

71. 8% compounded quarterly

72. 7.2% compounded monthly

73. *Women in the workforce* For selected years from 1970 and projected to 2050, the number, in millions, of women in the workforce is given by

$$w(x) = 37.6 \ln x - 81.2$$

where x is the number of years past 1950 (*Source*: U.S. Bureau of Labor Statistics).
(a) Graph this function for x representing 1960–2030.
(b) What does this model predict to be the number of women in the workforce in 2030?
(c) Use the graph drawn in part (a) to estimate the year in which the number will reach 80 million.

74. *Life span update* In Example 6 we used data from 1920 and projected to 2050 and found that the expected life span in the United States can be modeled as a function of the year of birth by

$$L(x) = 8.7744 + 14.907 \ln x$$

where x is the number of years after 1900. Using data from 1920 to 1989, the model

$$\ell(x) = 11.616 + 14.144 \ln x$$

where x is the number of years after 1900, predicts expected life span as a function of birth year. Use both models to predict the life spans for people born in 2005 and 2021. Did adding data from 1990 to 2050 give predictions that were quite different from or very similar to predictions based on the model without that data?

75. **Modeling *Diabetes*** As the following table shows, projections indicate that the percent of U.S. adults with diabetes could dramatically increase.

(a) Find a logarithmic model that fits the data in the table, with x as the number of years after 2000.
(b) Graph the function and the data on the same axes and comment on the fit.
(c) Use the model to predict the percent of U.S. adults with diabetes in 2027.

Year	Percent	Year	Percent	Year	Percent
2010	15.7	2025	24.2	2040	31.4
2015	18.9	2030	27.2	2045	32.1
2020	21.1	2035	29.0	2050	34.3

Source: Centers for Disease Control and Prevention

76. **Modeling *Female workers*** The percent of all workers 16 years or older who are female, for selected years from 1970 and projected to 2040, is given in the following table.
(a) Find the logarithmic function that models the percent as a function of the years, with x equal to the number of years past 1960.
(b) Visually determine whether this model is a good fit for the data.
(c) Use the model to predict the percent of workers who are females in 2045.

Year	Percent	Year	Percent
1970	38.1	2015	48.3
1980	42.5	2020	48.1
1990	45.2	2030	48.0
2000	46.6	2040	47.9
2010	47.9		

Source: Bureau of Labor Statistics

77. **Modeling *Internet usage*** In 2015, 88% of U.S. residents used the Internet, up from 14% in 1995. The table shows the percent who use the Internet for selected years from 2000 and projected to 2025.
(a) Find the logarithmic function that models the percent p as a function of x, the number of years after 1990. Report the model with 4 significant digit coefficients.
(b) Visually determine whether this model is a good fit for the data.
(c) Use the model to predict the percent of Internet users in the United States in 2023.

Year	Percent	Year	Percent
2000	67	2015	88
2005	79	2020	95
2010	82	2025	98

Source: Nation and Statistics, Policy Exchange Analysis

78. **Modeling** *Demographics* The table below gives the millions of White non-Hispanic individuals in the U.S. civilian non-institutional population 16 years and older for selected years from 1980 and projected to 2050.

   (a) Find a logarithmic function that models the data, with *x* equal to the number of years past 1970 and *y* equal to the White non-Hispanic population, in millions.

   (b) Graph the function and the data on the same set of axes.

   (c) What does the model predict this demographic group's population to be in 2043?

Year	Millions	Year	Millions
1980	136.8	2020	166.3
1990	146.5	2030	168.8
2000	153.1	2040	169.7
2010	162.1	2050	169.4
2015	164.6		

Source: U.S. Census Bureau

SECTION 5.3

Equations and Applications with Exponential and Logarithmic Functions

OBJECTIVES

- To solve exponential and logarithmic equations
- To solve exponential growth or decay equations
- To solve exponential equations representing demand, supply, or total cost
- To model and solve problems involving Gompertz and logistic functions

APPLICATION PREVIEW

A company's sales decline following an advertising campaign so that the number of sales is $S = 2000(2^{-0.1x})$, where *x* is the number of days after the campaign ends. When should the company begin a new campaign? In other words, how many days will elapse before sales drop below 350? (See Example 4.)

In this section, we discuss applications of exponential and logarithmic functions to the solutions of problems involving exponential growth and decay, and supply and demand. With exponential decay, we consider various applications, including decay of radioactive materials and decay of sales following an advertising campaign. With exponential growth, we focus on population growth and growth that can be modeled using Gompertz and logistic functions. Finally, we consider applications of demand functions that can be modeled using exponential functions.

Solving Exponential Equations Questions such as the one in the Application Preview can be answered by solving an equation in which the variable appears in the exponent, called an **exponential equation.** Logarithmic properties are useful in converting an exponential equation to one that can be solved easily. In this section, we limit our discussion and applications to equations involving a single exponential.

SOLVING EXPONENTIAL EQUATIONS

Procedure	Example
To solve an exponential equation using properties of logarithms:	Solve: $4(25^{2x}) = 312{,}500$
1. Isolate the exponential by rewriting the equation with a base raised to a power on one side.	1. $\dfrac{4(25^{2x})}{4} = \dfrac{312{,}500}{4}$ $25^{2x} = 78{,}125$
2. Take the logarithm (either base *e* or base 10) of both sides.	2. We choose base *e*, although base 10 would work similarly. $\ln(25^{2x}) = \ln(78{,}125)$
3. Use a property of logarithms to remove the variable from the exponent.	3. Using logarithmic Property V gives $2x \ln 25 = \ln(78{,}125)$
4. Solve for the variable.	4. Dividing both sides by $2 \ln 25$ gives $x = \dfrac{\ln(78{,}125)}{2 \ln 25} = 1.75$

In Step 2, we noted that using a logarithm base 10 would work similarly, and it gives the same result. (Try it.) Unless the exponential in the equation has base e or base 10, the choice of a logarithm in Step 2 makes no difference. However, if the exponential in the equation has base e, then choosing a base e logarithm is slightly easier (see Examples 3 and 5), and similarly for choosing a base 10 logarithm when the equation has a base 10 exponential.

EXAMPLE **1**

Solving an Exponential Equation

Solve the equation $6(4^{3x-2}) = 120$.

Solution

We first divide both sides by 6 to isolate the exponential.

$$4^{3x-2} = 20$$

Taking the logarithm, base 10, of both sides leads to the solution.

$$\log 4^{3x-2} = \log 20$$
$$(3x - 2)\log 4 = \log 20$$
$$3x - 2 = \frac{\log 20}{\log 4}$$
$$x = \frac{1}{3}\left(\frac{\log 20}{\log 4} + 2\right) \approx 1.387$$

An alternative method of solving the equation is to write $4^{3x-2} = 20$ in logarithmic form.

$$\log_4 20 = 3x - 2$$

$$x = \frac{\log_4 20 + 2}{3} \approx 1.387$$

The change-of-base formula can be used to verify that these solutions are the same.   ▪

Solving Logarithmic Equations

A logarithmic equation is one in which the variable appears in a logarithm, such as $2 = \log_5(x + 1)$. The definition of logarithms allows us to express a logarithmic statement such as $2 = \log_5(x + 1)$ in an equivalent exponential form as follows:

$$5^2 = x + 1 \quad \text{or} \quad 25 = x + 1$$

In this form, we can easily find $x = 24$.

To solve any logarithmic equation, we use logarithm properties to express the equation as a single logarithmic statement of the form $A = \log_b(X)$, where X is an expression in the variable x. We can translate the single logarithmic statement to exponential form, then solve. Because $\log_b(X)$ is defined only when $X > 0$, a quick check that our solutions do *not* result in the logarithm of a negative quantity is a good idea.

EXAMPLE **2**

Solve the following for x.

(a) $3\log_8(5x - 9) = 4$ (b) $\log(60x) - \log(x - 50) = 2$

Solution

(a) First we divide both sides by 3, and then translate to exponential form.

$$\log_8(5x - 9) = \frac{4}{3} \quad \Rightarrow \quad 5x - 9 = 8^{4/3}$$

This is equivalent to

$$5x - 9 = 16, \quad \text{so} \quad 5x = 25.$$

Thus the solution is $x = 5$.   (Note that $5x - 9$ is positive when $x = 5$.)

(b) First, we use Logarithm Property IV to write the left side as a single logarithm.

$$\log\left(\frac{60x}{x - 50}\right) = 2$$

Next, we translate to exponential form. (Note that this is a base 10 logarithm.)

$$10^2 = \frac{60x}{x - 50}$$

We multiply both sides by $(x - 50)$ and then complete the solution.

$$100(x - 50) = 60x \quad \Rightarrow \quad 100x - 5000 = 60x$$
$$40x = 5000 \quad \Rightarrow \quad x = 125$$

The solution is $x = 125$.
(Note that $60x$ and $x - 50$ are positive when $x = 125$.)

Growth and Decay Recall that **exponential decay models** can be described by a function of the following form.

Decay Models	$f(x) = C(a^{-x})$ with $a > 1$ and $C > 0$ or $f(x) = C(b^x)$ with $0 < b < 1$ and $C > 0$

Some applications that use exponential decay models are radioactive decay, demand curves, sales decay, and blood pressure in the aorta, illustrated in the following example.

EXAMPLE   **3**   **Pressure in the Aorta**

Medical research has shown that over short periods of time when the valves to the aorta of a normal adult close, the pressure in the aorta is a function of time and can be modeled by the equation

$$P = 95e^{-0.491t}$$

where t is in seconds. How long will it be before the pressure reaches 80?

Solution
Setting $P = 80$ and solving for t will give the time before the pressure reaches 80.

$$80 = 95e^{-0.491t}$$

To solve this equation for t, we first isolate the exponential containing t by dividing both sides by 95.

$$\frac{80}{95} = e^{-0.491t}$$

Because e is the base of the exponential, we take the logarithm, base e, of both sides, then use logarithmic Property I to simplify the right-hand side of the expression.

$$\ln\left(\frac{80}{95}\right) = \ln e^{-0.491t} = -0.491t$$

Evaluating the left-hand side with a calculator gives $-0.172 = -0.491t$. Thus

$$\frac{-0.172}{-0.491} = t \quad \text{so} \quad t = 0.35 \text{ second} \quad \text{(approximately)}$$

EXAMPLE   4   **Sales Decay** | APPLICATION PREVIEW |

A company finds that its daily sales begin to fall after the end of an advertising campaign, and the decline is such that the number of sales is $S = 2000(2^{-0.1x})$, where x is the number of days after the campaign ends.

(a)   How many sales will be made 10 days after the end of the campaign?
(b)   If the company does not want sales to drop below 350 per day, when should it start a new campaign?

Solution
(a)   If $x = 10$, sales are given by $S = 2000(2^{-1}) = 1000$.
(b)   Setting $S = 350$ and solving for x will give us the number of days after the end of the campaign when sales will reach 350.

$$350 = 2000(2^{-0.1x})$$

$$\frac{350}{2000} = 2^{-0.1x} \quad \text{so} \quad 0.175 = 2^{-0.1x}$$

With the base 2 exponential isolated, we take logarithms of both sides. This time we choose base 10 logarithms and complete the solution as follows.

$$\log 0.175 = \log (2^{-0.1x})$$
$$\log 0.175 = (-0.1x)(\log 2) \quad \text{Property V}$$

$$\frac{\log 0.175}{\log 2} = -0.1x$$
$$-2.515 \approx -0.1x \quad \text{so} \quad x \approx 25.15$$

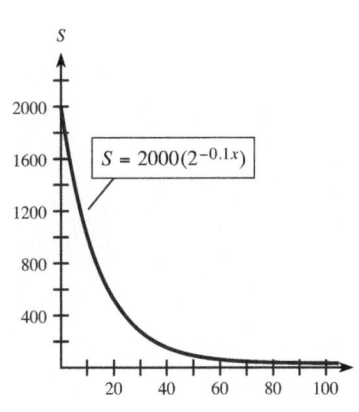

Figure 5.21

Thus sales will be 350 at day 25.15 and will fall below 350 during the 26th day after the end of the campaign. If a new campaign isn't begun on or before the 26th day, sales will drop below 350. (See Figure 5.21.)

In business, economics, biology, and the social sciences, **exponential growth models** describe the growth of money, bacteria, or population.

Growth Models   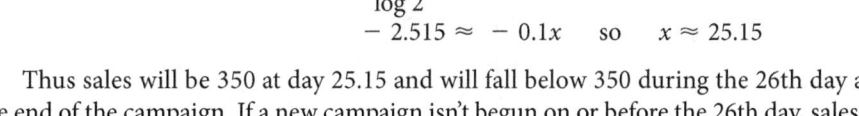 $f(x) = C(a^x) \quad$ with $a > 1$ and $C > 0$

The function $y = P_0e^{ht}$ can be used to model population growth for humans, insects, and bacteria.

EXAMPLE   5   **Population**

The population of a certain city was 30,000 in 2000 and 40,500 in 2010. If the formula $P = P_0e^{ht}$ applies to the growth of the city's population, what population is predicted for the year 2030?

Solution
In these applications, we may choose $t = 0$ to represent any convenient time, and then P_0 represents the population at $t = 0$. Letting $t = 0$ in 2000 gives $P_0 = 30{,}000$, and when $t = 10$, $P = 40{,}500$. Using these values, we find h in the formula.

$$40{,}500 = 30{,}000e^{h(10)}$$
$$1.35 = e^{10h} \qquad \text{Isolate the exponential.}$$

Taking the natural logarithms of both sides and using logarithmic Property I give

$$\ln 1.35 = \ln e^{10h} = 10h$$
$$0.3001 \approx 10h \quad \text{so} \quad h \approx 0.0300$$

Thus the formula for this population is $P = P_0 e^{0.03t}$. To predict the population for the year 2030, we reset the most recent data point (for 2010) as $t = 0$, $P_0 = 40,500$ and find P for $t = 20$. This gives

$$P = 40,500e^{0.03(20)} = 40,500e^{0.6} \approx 73,796$$

CHECKPOINT

1. Suppose the sales of a product, in dollars, are given by $S = 1000e^{-0.07x}$, where x is the number of days after the end of an advertising campaign.
    (a) What are sales 2 days after the end of the campaign?
    (b) How long will it be before sales are $300?

Sometimes cost, revenue, demand, and supply may be modeled by exponential or logarithmic equations. For example, suppose the demand for a product is given by $p = 30(3^{-q/2})$, where q is the number of thousands of units demanded at a price of p dollars per unit. Then the graph of the demand curve is as shown in Figure 5.22.

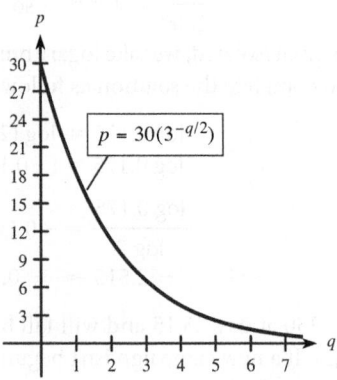

Figure 5.22

EXAMPLE 6 **Demand**

Suppose the demand function for q thousand units of a certain commodity is given by

$$p = 30(3^{-q/2})$$

(a) At what price per unit will the demand equal 4000 units?
(b) How many units, to the nearest thousand units, will be demanded if the price is $17.31?

Solution
(a) If 4000 units are demanded, then $q = 4$ and

$$p = 30(3^{-4/2}) \approx 3.33 \,\text{dollars}$$

(b) If $p = 17.31$, then $17.31 = 30(3^{-q/2})$

$$0.577 = 3^{-q/2} \qquad \text{Isolate the exponential.}$$

$$\ln 0.577 = \ln 3^{-q/2} = -\frac{q}{2}\ln 3$$

$$\frac{-2\ln 0.577}{\ln 3} = q \quad \text{so} \quad 1.00 \approx q$$

The number of units demanded will be approximately 1000 units.

CHECKPOINT

2. Suppose the monthly demand for a product is given by $p = 400e^{-0.003x}$, where p is the price in dollars and x is the number of units. How many units will be demanded when the price is $100?

Gompertz Curves and Logistic Functions

Gompertz Curves

One family of curves that has been used to describe human growth and development, the growth of organisms in a limited environment, and the growth of many types of organizations is the family of **Gompertz curves**. These curves are graphs of equations of the form

$$N = Ca^{R^t}$$

where t represents the time, R $(0 < R < 1)$ is a constant that depends on the population, a represents the proportion of initial growth, C is the maximum possible number of individuals, and N is the number of individuals at a given time t.

Suppose the equation $N = 100(0.03)^{0.2^t}$ can be used to predict the size of a deer herd introduced on a small island. Here the maximum number of deer C is 100, the proportion of the initial growth a is 0.03, and R is 0.2. For this example, t represents time, measured in decades. The graph of this equation is given in Figure 5.23.

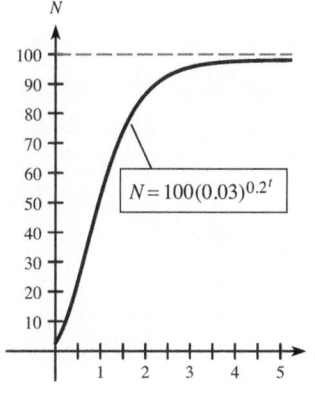

Figure 5.23

EXAMPLE 7   Organizational Growth

A hospital administrator predicts that the growth in the number of hospital employees will follow the Gompertz equation

$$N = 2000(0.6)^{0.5^t}$$

where t represents the number of years after the opening of a new facility.

(a) What is the number of employees when the facility opens?
(b) How many employees are predicted after 1 year of operation?
(c) Graph the curve.
(d) What is the maximum value of N that the curve will approach?

Solution

(a) The facility opens when $t = 0$, so $N = 2000(0.6)^{0.5^0} = 2000(0.6)^1 = 1200$.
(b) In 1 year, $t = 1$, so $N = 2000(0.6)^{0.5} = 2000 \sqrt{0.6} \approx 1549$.
(c) The graph is shown in Figure 5.24.
(d) From the graph, we can see that as larger values of t are substituted in the function, the values of N approach, but never reach, 2000. We say that the line $N = 2000$ (dashed) is an **asymptote** for this curve and that 2000 is the maximum that the number of employees will approach.

Figure 5.24

EXAMPLE 8

Wildlife Populations

The Gompertz equation

$$N = 100(0.03)^{0.2^t}$$

predicts the size of a deer herd on a small island t decades from now. During what year will the deer population reach or exceed 70?

Solution

We solve the equation with $N = 70$.

$$70 = 100(0.03)^{0.2^t}$$

$$0.7 = 0.03^{0.2^t} \qquad \text{Isolate the exponential.}$$

$$\ln 0.7 = \ln 0.03^{0.2^t} = 0.2^t \ln 0.03$$

$$\frac{\ln 0.7}{\ln 0.03} = 0.2^t \qquad \text{Again, isolate the exponential.}$$

$$\ln\left(\frac{\ln 0.7}{\ln 0.03}\right) = t \ln 0.2 \qquad \text{Take the logarithm of both sides.}$$

$$\ln(0.10172) \approx t(-1.6094)$$

$$\frac{-2.2855}{-1.6094} \approx t \quad \text{so} \quad t \approx 1.42 \text{ decades}$$

The population will exceed 70 in just over 14 years, or during the fifteenth year.

Calculator Note We can solve $f(x) = 0$ on a graphing calculator using the SOLVER feature (MATH, 0:Solver) and setting $f(x)$ equal to 0. [See figure 5.25(a)]. A solution with this feature may not be successful unless a reasonable guess at the solution (which can be seen from a graph) is chosen to start the process. Figure 5.25(a) shows the equation from Example 8 and Figure 5.25(b) shows its solution.

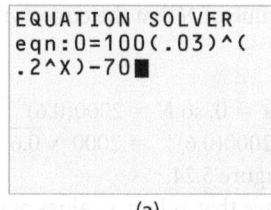

```
EQUATION SOLVER
eqn:0=100(.03)^(
.2^X)-70■
```

```
100(.03)^(.2^...=0
X=1.4201015868...
bound=(-1E99,1...
```

Figure 5.25   (a)   (b)

CHECKPOINT

3. Suppose the number of employees at a new regional hospital is predicted by the Gompertz curve

$$N = 3500(0.1)^{0.5^t}$$

where t is the number of years after the hospital opens.
(a) How many employees did the hospital have when it opened?
(b) What is the expected upper limit on the number of employees?

Logistic Functions

Gompertz curves describe situations in which growth is limited. Other equations model this phenomenon under different assumptions. Two examples are

(a) $y = c(1 - e^{-ax}), \quad a > 0$ See Figure 5.26(a).

(b) $y = \dfrac{A}{1 + ce^{-ax}}, \quad a > 0$ See Figure 5.26(b).

Figure 5.26   (a)   (b)

Very seldom will exponential growth continue indefinitely, so these equations have many applications. In general, both (a) and (b) can be used to model learning, sales of new products, and population growth, and (b) can be used to describe the spread of epidemics. The equation

$$y = \frac{A}{1 + ce^{-ax}} \qquad a > 0$$

is called a **logistic function**, and the graph in Figure 5.26(b) is called a **logistic curve**.

EXAMPLE 9   Computer Tablets

In recent years, computer tablets have been one of the most frequently purchased personal electronic devices. One company's revenues from the sales of computer tablets from 2015 to 2020 can be modeled by the logistic function

$$y = \frac{9.46}{1 + 53.08e^{-1.28x}}$$

where x is the number of years past 2014 and y is in millions of dollars.
(a) Graph this function.
(b) Use the function to estimate the sales revenue for 2020.

Solution
(a) The graph of this function is shown in Figure 5.27. Note that the graph is an S-shaped curve with a relatively slow initial rise, then a steep climb followed by a leveling off. It is reasonable that sales would eventually level off.
b)   For the 2020 estimate, use $x = 6$ in the function.

$$y = \frac{9.46}{1 + 53.08e^{-1.28(6)}} = \frac{9.46}{1 + 53.08e^{-7.68}} \approx 9.234$$

Thus the model estimates that the 2020 sales revenue from computer tablets for this company is about $9.234 million.

Figure 5.27

EXERCISES 5.3

In Problems 1–22, solve each equation. Give answers correct to three decimal places in Problems 1–12.

1. $8^{3x} = 32{,}768$

2. $7^{2x} = 823{,}543$

3. $0.13P = P(2^{-x})$

4. $0.05A = A(1.06)^{-x}$

5. $25{,}000 = 10{,}000(1.05)^{2x}$

6. $75{,}000 = 15{,}000(1.02)^{4x}$

7. $10{,}000 = 1500e^{0.10x}$

8. $2500 = 600e^{0.05x}$

9. $78 = 100 - 100e^{-0.01x}$

10. $500 = 600 - 600e^{-0.4x}$

11. $55 = \dfrac{60}{1 + 5e^{-0.6x}}$

12. $150 = \dfrac{200}{1 + 30e^{-0.3x}}$

13. $\log x = 5$

14. $\ln x = 8$

15. $\log_4(9x + 1) = 3$

16. $\log_5(x + 2) = 2$

17. $\ln x - \ln 5 = 10$

18. $\ln x + \ln 8 = 5$

19. $7 + \log(8x) = 25 - 2 \log x$

20. $3 \log x + 10 = \log(3x) + 14$

21. $\ln (x + 2) + \ln x = \ln (x + 12)$

22. $\log_4 x - \log_4(x + 3) = \log_4(x - 2)$

For Problems 23 and 24, let $f(x) = \dfrac{A}{1 + ce^{-x}}$. Use a graphing utility to make the requested graphs.

23. (a) Fix $A = 100$ and graph $y = f(x) = \dfrac{100}{1 + ce^{-x}}$ for $c = 0.25, 1, 9,$ and 49.

    (b) What effect does c have on the graphs?

24. (a) Fix $c = 1$ and graph $y = f(x) = \dfrac{A}{1 + e^{-x}}$ for $A = 50, 100,$ and 150.

    (b) What effect does A have on the graphs?

APPLICATIONS

25. *Sales decay* The sales decay for a product is given by $S = 50{,}000e^{-0.8x}$, where S is the monthly sales and x is the number of months that have passed since the end of a promotional campaign.

    (a) What will be the sales 4 months after the end of the campaign?

    (b) How many months after the end of the campaign will sales drop below 1000, if no new campaign is initiated?

26. *Sales decay* The sales of a product decline after the end of an advertising campaign, with the sales decay given by $S = 100{,}000e^{-0.5x}$, where S represents the weekly sales and x represents the number of weeks since the end of the campaign.

    (a) What will be the sales for the tenth week after the end of the campaign?

    (b) During what week after the end of the campaign will sales drop below 400?

27. *Inflation* The purchasing power P (in dollars) of an annual amount of A dollars after t years of 5% inflation decays according to

$$P = Ae^{-0.05t}$$

(a) How long will it be before a pension of \$60,000 per year has a purchasing power of \$30,000?

(b) How much pension A would be needed so that the purchasing power P is \$50,000 after 15 years?

28. *Product reliability* A statistical study shows that the fraction of television sets of a certain brand that are still in service after x years is given by $f(x) = e^{-0.15x}$.

    (a) What fraction of the sets are still in service after 5 years?

    (b) After how many years will the fraction still in service be 1/10?

29. *Radioactive half-life* An initial amount of 100 g of the radioactive isotope thorium-234 decays according to

$$Q(t) = 100e^{-0.02828t}$$

where t is in years. How long will it be before half of the initial amount has disintegrated? This time is called the half-life of this isotope.

30. *Radioactive half-life* A breeder reactor converts stable uranium-238 into the isotope plutonium-239. The decay of this isotope is given by

$$A(t) = A_0 e^{-0.00002876t}$$

where $A(t)$ is the amount of the isotope at time t, in years, and A_0 is the original amount.

    (a) If $A_0 = 500$ lb, how much will be left after a human lifetime (use $t = 80$ years)?

    (b) Find the half-life of this isotope.

31. *Population growth* If the population of a certain county was 100,000 in 1998 and 110,517 in 2008 and the formula $y = P_0 e^{ht}$ applies to the growth of the county's population, estimate the population of the county in 2023.

32. *Population growth* The population of a certain city grows according to the formula $y = P_0 e^{0.03t}$. If the population was 250,000 in 2015, estimate the year in which the population reaches 350,000.

33. *Health care* For the years from 2002 and projected to 2024, the total national health care expenditures H, in billions of dollars, can be modeled by

$$H = 1500e^{0.053t}$$

where t is the number of years past 2000 (*Source:* U.S. Department of Health and Human Services). When are national health care expenditures expected to reach \$5.0 trillion (that is, \$5000 billion)?

34. *Disposable income* Disposable income is the amount available for spending and saving after taxes have been paid and is one gauge for the state of the economy. Using U.S. Energy Administration data for selected years from 2010 and projected to 2040, the total U.S. disposable income, in billions, can be modeled by

$$D(t) = 10{,}020 \, e^{0.02292t}$$

where t is the number of years past 2010. In what year is disposable income predicted to be $15 trillion (that is, $15,000 billion)?

35. *Demand* The demand function for a certain commodity is given by $p = 100e^{-q/2}$.
    (a) At what price per unit will the quantity demanded equal 6 units?
    (b) If the price is $1.83 per unit, how many units will be demanded, to the nearest unit?

36. *Demand* The demand function for a product is given by $p = 3000e^{-q/3}$.
    (a) At what price per unit will the quantity demanded equal 6 units?
    (b) If the price is $149.40 per unit, how many units will be demanded, to the nearest unit?

37. *Supply* If the supply function for a product is given by $p = 100e^q/(q + 1)$, where q represents the number of hundreds of units, what will be the price when the producers are willing to supply 300 units?

38. *Supply* If the supply function for a product is given by $p = 200(2^q)$, where q represents the number of hundreds of units, what will be the price when the producers are willing to supply 500 units?

39. *Total cost* The total cost function for x units of a product is given by

$$C(x) = 2500 \ln (2x + 1) + 1500$$

    (a) Find the total cost of producing 80 items.
    (b) How many units can be produced before total costs reach $16,000?

40. *Total cost* The total cost function for a product is

$$C(x) = 800 \ln (x + 10) + 1700$$

    where x is the number of units produced.
    (a) Find the total cost of producing 100 units.
    (b) Producing how many units will give total costs of $7500?

41. *Demographics* The millions of White non-Hispanic individuals in the U.S. civilian non-institutional population 16 years or older for selected years from 1980 and projected to 2050 can be modeled by the function

$$y = 96.12 + 17.43 \ln x$$

    where x is equal to the number of years past 1970 (*Source:* U.S. Census Bureau). Find the year in which the number of White non-Hispanics is expected to reach 166.5 million.

42. *Diabetes* Centers for Disease Control and Prevention data from 2010 and projected to 2050 indicate that adult diabetes in the United States could dramatically increase. With x equal to the number of years after 2000, the percent of U.S. adults with diabetes can be modeled by

$$y = -13.0 + 11.9 \ln x$$

    Use the model to find the year in which the percent of U.S. adults with diabetes is predicted to reach 30%.

43. *Compound interest* If $8500 is invested at 11.5% compounded continuously, the future value S at any time t (in years) is given by

$$S = 8500e^{0.115t}$$

    (a) What is the amount after 18 months?
    (b) How long before the investment doubles?

44. *Compound interest* If $1000 is invested at 10% compounded continuously, the future value S at any time t (in years) is given by $S = 1000e^{0.1t}$.
    (a) What is the amount after 1 year?
    (b) How long before the investment doubles?

45. *Compound interest* If $5000 is invested at 9% per year compounded monthly, the future value S at any time t (in months) is given by $S = 5000(1.0075)^t$.
    (a) What is the amount after 1 year?
    (b) How long before the investment doubles?

46. *Compound interest* If $10,000 is invested at 1% per month, the future value S at any time t (in months) is given by $S = 10,000(1.01)^t$.
    (a) What is the amount after 1 year?
    (b) How long before the investment doubles?

Profits **An investment services company experienced dramatic growth in the last two decades. The following models for the company's revenue R and expenses or costs C (both in millions of dollars) are functions of the years past 1990.**

$$R(t) = 21.4e^{0.131t} \quad \text{and} \quad C(t) = 18.6e^{0.131t}$$

Use these models in Problems 47 and 48.

47. (a) Use the models to predict the company's profit in 2020.
    (b) How long before the profit found in part (a) is predicted to double?

48. Use the models to find how long before the company's profit reaches $500 million.

49. *Purchasing power* Using Social Security Administration data for selected years from 2012 and projected to 2050, based on a purchasing power of $1.00 in 2012, the function

$$P(x) = 1.078(1.028^{-x})$$

    models the purchasing power of a 2012 dollar as a function of x, the number of years past 2010.
    (a) Find and interpret $P(18)$.
    (b) Solve algebraically to find the year when the purchasing power of a 2012 dollar is expected to reach $0.48.

50. *China's shale-natural gas* The function that models the growth in the number of billions of cubic feet of shale-natural gas in China, with x as the number of years after 2010, is

$$y = 0.0117(1.75^x)$$

    Solve algebraically to find the year when the number of cubic feet is projected to be 2.5 billion (*Source:* Sanford C. Bernstein).

51. *Supply* Suppose the supply of x units of a certain product at price p dollars per unit is given by

$$p = 10 + 5 \ln (3x + 1)$$

How many units of this product would be supplied when the price is $50 each?

52. *Demand* Assume that the demand function for a product is given by $p = 100/\ln (q + 1)$.
    (a) What will be the price if 19 units are demanded?
    (b) How many units, to the nearest unit, will be demanded if the price is $29.40?

GOMPERTZ CURVES AND LOGISTIC FUNCTIONS APPLICATIONS

53. *Sales growth* The president of a company predicts that sales will increase after she assumes office and that the number of monthly sales will follow the curve given by $N = 3000(0.2)^{0.6^t}$, where t represents the months since she assumed office.
    (a) What will be the sales when she assumes office?
    (b) What will be the sales after 3 months?
    (c) What is the expected upper limit on sales?
    (d) Graph the curve.

54. *Organizational growth* Because of a new market opening, the number of employees of a firm is expected to increase according to the equation $N = 1400(0.5)^{0.3^t}$, where t represents the number of years after the new market opens.
    (a) What is the level of employment when the new market opens?
    (b) How many employees should be working at the end of 2 years?
    (c) What is the expected upper limit on the number of employees?
    (d) Graph the curve.

55. *Organizational growth* Suppose that the equation $N = 500(0.02)^{0.7^t}$ represents the number of employees working t years after a company begins operations.
    (a) How many employees are there when the company opens (at $t = 0$)?
    (b) After how many years will at least 100 employees be working?

56. *Sales growth* A firm predicts that sales will increase during a promotional campaign and that the number of daily sales will be given by $N = 200(0.01)^{0.8^t}$, where t represents the number of days after the campaign begins. How many days after the beginning of the campaign would the firm expect to sell at least 60 units per day?

57. *Drugs in the bloodstream* The concentration y of a certain drug in the bloodstream t hours after an oral dosage (with $0 \le t \le 15$) is given by the equation

$$y = 100(1 - e^{-0.462t})$$

    (a) What is y after 1 hour $(t = 1)$?
    (b) How long does it take for y to reach 50?

58. *Population growth* Suppose that the number y of otters t years after otters were reintroduced into a wild and scenic river is given by

$$y = 2500 - 2490e^{-0.1t}$$

    (a) Find the population when the otters were reintroduced (at $t = 0$).
    (b) How long will it be before the otter population numbers 1500?

59. *Spread of disease* On a college campus of 10,000 students, a single student returned to campus infected by a disease. The spread of the disease through the student body is given by

$$y = \frac{10,000}{1 + 9999e^{-0.99t}}$$

    where y is the total number infected at time t (in days).
    (a) How many are infected after 4 days?
    (b) The school will shut down if 50% of the students are ill. During what day will it close?

60. *Spread of a rumor* The number of people $N(t)$ in a community who are reached by a particular rumor at time t is given by the equation

$$N(t) = \frac{50,500}{1 + 100e^{-0.7t}}$$

    (a) Find $N(0)$.
    (b) What is the upper limit on the number of people affected?
    (c) How long before 75% of the upper limit is reached?

61. *Market share* Suppose that the market share y (as a percent) that a company expects t months after a new product is introduced is given by $y = 40 - 40e^{-0.05t}$.
    (a) What is the market share after the first month (to the nearest percent)?
    (b) How long (to the nearest month) before the market share is 25%?

62. *Advertising* An advertising agency has found that when it promotes a new product in a certain market of 350,000, the number of people x who are aware of the product t days after the ad campaign is initiated is given by

$$x = 350,000(1 - e^{-0.077t})$$

    (a) How many people (to the nearest thousand) are aware after 1 week?
    (b) How long (to the nearest day) before 300,000 are aware of the new product?

63. *Pollution* Pollution levels in a lake have been modeled by the equation

$$x = 0.05 + 0.18e^{-0.38t}$$

    where x is the volume of pollutants (in cubic kilometers) and t is the time (in years).

(a) Find the initial pollution levels; that is, find x when $t = 0$.

(b) How long before x is 30% of that initial level?

64. *Fish length* Suppose that the length x (in centimeters) of an individual of a certain species of fish is given by

$$x = 50 - 40e^{-0.05t}$$

where t is its age in months.

(a) Find the length after 1 year.

(b) How long (to the nearest month) will it be until the length is 45 cm?

65. *U.S. civilian labor force* Using U.S. Bureau of Labor Statistics data since 1950 and projected to 2040, the total civilian labor force age 16 years or older (in millions) can be modeled by

$$L = \frac{197}{1 + 3.65e^{-0.037t}}$$

where t is the number of years after 1940.

(a) Use the model to estimate the size of the civilian labor force in 2015.

(b) Use the model to estimate the year when the civilian labor force is predicted to reach 170 million.

66. *Chemical reaction* When two chemicals, A and B, react to form another chemical C (such as in the digestive process), this is a special case of the **law of mass action**, which is fundamental to studying chemical reaction rates. Suppose that chemical C is formed from A and B according to

$$x = \frac{120[1 - (0.6)^{3t}]}{4 - (0.6)^{3t}}$$

where x is the number of pounds of C formed in t minutes.

(a) How much of C is present when the reaction begins?

(b) How much of C is formed in 4 minutes?

(c) How long does it take to form 10 lb of C?

67. *Modeling Diabetes* The following table gives the total number of U.S adults with diabetes for selected years from 2010 and projected to 2050.

(a) Find the logistic function that models these data. Use x equal to the number of years past 2000.

(b) Use the model to predict the number of U.S. adults expected to have diabetes in 2028.

(c) According to the model, what is the expected upper limit on the number of U.S. adults with diabetes?

(d) In what year does the model predict that the number of U.S. adults with diabetes will reach 80.0 million?

Year	Number (millions)	Year	Number (millions)
2010	32.3	2035	76.2
2015	37.3	2040	84.1
2020	50.0	2045	91.7
2025	59.5	2050	100.0
2030	68.3		

Source: Centers for Disease Control and Prevention

68. *Modeling U.S. population, ages 20–64* The following table gives the U.S. population, ages 20–64, (in millions) for selected years from 1950 and projected to 2050.

(a) Find the logistic function that models these data. Use x as the number of years after 1950 and report your model with 3 significant digit coefficients.

(b) Use the unrounded model to predict the U.S. population ages 20–64 in 2025.

(c) When does the unrounded model predict this group's population will reach 210 million?

Year	Millions	Year	Millions
1950	92.8	2010	189.1
1960	99.8	2020	198.2
1970	113.0	2030	202.8
1980	134.0	2040	213.3
1990	152.7	2050	224.3
2000	169.8		

Source: Social Security Administration

5 — CHAPTER SUMMARY & REVIEW

KEY TERMS AND FORMULAS

Section 5.1

Exponential functions (p. 317)
Growth functions (p. 319)
$f(x) = a^x \quad (a > 1)$
$f(x) = C(a^x) \quad (C > 0, a > 1)$

Decay functions (p. 320)
$f(x) = C(a^{-x}) \quad (C > 0, a > 1)$
$f(x) = C(b^x) \quad (C > 0, 0 < b < 1)$
$e \approx 2.71828$ (p. 321)

Section 5.2

Logarithmic function (p. 330)
  $y = \log_a x$, defined by $x = a^y$
Common logarithm (p. 331)
  $\log x = \log_{10} x$
Natural logarithm (p. 331)
  $\ln x = \log_e x$
Graphs of logarithmic functions (p. 332)
Inverse functions (p. 334)
Logarithmic Properties I–V (pp. 335–337)
  I. $\log_a a^x = x$
  II. $a^{\log_a x} = x$

  III. $\log_a (MN) = \log_a M + \log_a N$
  IV. $\log_a (M/N) = \log_a M - \log_a N$
  V. $\log_a (M^N) = N(\log_a M)$
Change-of-base formula (p. 337)

$$\log_b x = \frac{\log_a x}{\log_a b}$$

Calculation formulas

  Base e: $\log_b x = \dfrac{\ln x}{\ln b}$

  Base 10: $\log_b x = \dfrac{\log x}{\log b}$

Section 5.3

Solving exponential equations (p. 342)
  Isolate the exponential; take logarithm of both sides.
Solving logarithmic equations (p. 343)
  Obtain form $A = \log_b X$; solve equivalent exponential
  equation
Exponential growth and decay (p. 344)
  Growth models
  $f(x) = Ca^x \quad (a > 1, C > 0)$

Decay models
  $f(x) = Ca^{-x} \quad (a > 1, C > 0)$
Gompertz curves (p. 347)
  $N = Ca^{R^t}$
Logistic functions (p. 349)

$$y = \frac{A}{1 + ce^{-ax}} \quad (a > 0)$$

REVIEW EXERCISES

Sections 5.1 and 5.2

1. Write each statement in logarithmic form.
   (a) $2^x = y$ (b) $3^y = 2x$
2. Write each statement in exponential form.
   (a) $\log_7 \left(\dfrac{1}{49}\right) = -2$ (b) $\log_4 x = -1$

Graph the following functions.
3. $y = e^x$
4. $y = e^{-x}$
5. $y = \log_2 x$
6. $y = 2^x$
7. $y = \frac{1}{2}(4^x)$
8. $y = \ln x$
9. $y = \log_4 x$
10. $y = 3^{-2x}$
11. $y = \log x$
12. $y = 10(2^{-x})$

In Problems 13–20, evaluate each logarithm without using a calculator. In Problems 13–17, check with the change-of-base formula.
13. $\log_5 1$
14. $\log_2 8$
15. $\log_{25} 5$
16. $\log_3 \left(\dfrac{1}{3}\right)$
17. $\log_3 3^8$
18. $\ln e$
19. $e^{\ln 5}$
20. $10^{\log 3.15}$

In Problems 21–24, if $\log_a x = 1.2$ and $\log_a y = 3.9$, find each of the following using the properties of logarithms.
21. $\log_a \left(\dfrac{x}{y}\right)$
22. $\log_a \sqrt{x}$
23. $\log_a (xy)$
24. $\log_a (y^4)$

In Problems 25 and 26, use the properties of logarithms to write each expression as the sum or difference of two logarithmic functions containing no exponents.
25. $\log (yz)$
26. $\ln \sqrt{\dfrac{x+1}{x}}$
27. Is it true that $\ln x + \ln y = \ln (x + y)$ for all positive values of x and y?
28. If $f(x) = \ln x$, find $f(e^{-2})$.
29. If $f(x) = 2^x + \log (7x - 4)$, find $f(2)$.
30. If $f(x) = e^x + \ln (x + 1)$, find $f(0)$.
31. If $f(x) = \ln (3e^x - 5)$, find $f(\ln 2)$.

In Problems 32 and 33, use a change-of-base formula to evaluate each logarithm.
32. $\log_9 2158$
33. $\log_{12} (0.0195)$

In Problems 34 and 35, rewrite each logarithm using a change-of-base formula; then graph the function with a graphing calculator.
34. $y = \log_{\sqrt{3}} x$
35. $f(x) = \log_{11} (2x - 5)$

Section 5.3

In Problems 36–42, solve each equation.
36. $6^{4x} = 46{,}656$
37. $8000 = 250(1.07)^x$
38. $11{,}000 = 45{,}000e^{-0.05x}$
39. $312 = 300 + 300e^{-0.08x}$
40. $\log_3(4x - 5) = 3$
41. $\ln (2x - 1) - \ln 3 = \ln 9$
42. $3 + 2\log_2 x = \log_2(x + 3) + 5$

APPLICATIONS

Section 5.1

43. *Medicare spending* The graph in the following figure shows the projected federal spending for Medicare as a percent of the gross domestic product. If these expenditures were modeled as a function of time, which of a growth exponential, a decay exponential, or a logarithm would be the best model? Justify your answer.

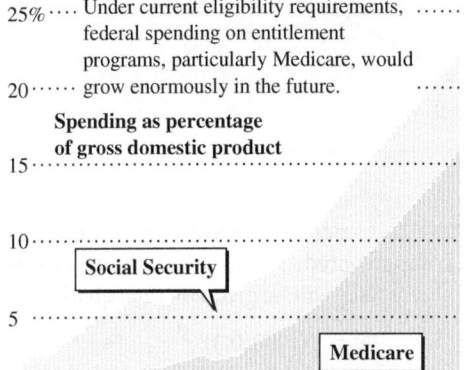

A Consuming Problem

25% ···· Under current eligibility requirements, ······ federal spending on entitlement programs, particularly Medicare, would

20 ······ grow enormously in the future.   ······

Spending as percentage of gross domestic product

15 ···

10 ···

Social Security

5 ···

Medicare

0

'60 '70 '80 '90 '00 '10 '20 '30 '40 '50

Source: Congressional Budget Office

44. *Consumer price index* Using Social Security Administration data for selected years from 2012 and projected to 2050, the U.S. consumer price index (CPI) can be modeled by the function

$$C(t) = 92.7e^{0.0271t}$$

where t is the number of years past 2010 and $C(t)$ is in 2012 dollars. With the data's reference year as 2012, a 2018 CPI of 115.14 means that goods and services costing $100.00 in 2012 are expected to cost $115.14 in 2018.
(a) Find $C(15)$ and explain its meaning.
(b) Graph the model.

45. *Inflation* The purchasing power P of a $60,000 pension after t years of 3% annual inflation is modeled by

$$P(t) = 60{,}000(0.97)^t$$

(a) What is the purchasing power after 20 years?
(b) Graph this function for $t = 0$ to $t = 25$ using a graphing utility.

46. Modeling *Average annual wage* The following table shows the U.S. average annual wage in thousands of dollars for selected years from 2012 and projected to 2050.
(a) Find an exponential function that models these data. Use x equal to the number of years past 2010.
(b) Graph the model and the data on the same axes.
(c) What does the model predict that the average annual wage will be in 2054?

Year	Average annual wage (thousands of dollars)	Year	Average annual wage (thousands of dollars)
2012	44.6	2030	93.2
2014	48.6	2035	113.2
2016	53.3	2040	137.6
2018	58.7	2045	167.1
2020	63.7	2050	202.5
2025	76.8		

Source: Social Security Administration

Section 5.2

47. *Germany's natural gas* The revenue (in millions of U.S. dollars) from natural gas extraction in Germany from 2012 and projected through 2020 can be modeled by

$$y = 3895.7 + 4783.3 \ln x$$

where x is the number of years after 2010 (*Source:* statista.com).
(a) What does the model predict the revenue to be in 2025, assuming the model remains valid?
(b) Graph the function for values of x representing 2012 through 2025 and $y \geq 4000$.

48. Modeling *U.S. population* The following table gives the total U.S. population, in millions, for selected years from 1990 and projected to 2050.
(a) Find a logarithmic function model for the data. Use x as the number of years past 1950 and report the model with 4 significant digit coefficients.
(b) Use the model to find the U.S. population in 2018.
(c) Use the reported model to find the x-value when the total U.S. population is predicted to reach 400 million.

Year	U.S. Population (in millions)	Year	U.S. Population (in millions)
1990	259.6	2020	342.9
2000	287.9	2030	369.5
2010	315.2	2040	390.8
2015	328.4	2050	409.1

Source: Social Security Administration

49. *Stellar magnitude* The stellar magnitude M of a star is related to its brightness B as seen from Earth according to

$$M = -\frac{5}{2} \log (B/B_0)$$

where B_0 is a standard level of brightness (the brightness of the star Vega).
(a) Find the magnitude of Venus if its brightness is 36.3 times B_0.
(b) Find the brightness (as a multiple of B_0) of the North Star if its magnitude is 2.1.

(c) If the faintest stars have magnitude 6, find their brightness (as a multiple of B_0).

(d) Is a star with magnitude -1.0 brighter than a star with magnitude $+1.0$?

Section 5.3

50. *Sales decay* The sales decay for a product is given by $S = 50,000e^{-0.1x}$, where S is the weekly sales (in dollars) and x is the number of weeks that have passed since the end of an advertising campaign.

(a) What will sales be 6 weeks after the end of the campaign?

(b) How many weeks will pass before sales drop below $15,000?

51. *Total cost* The total cost for x units of a product is given by

$$C(x) = 1200\ln(2x + 5) + 3400 \text{ dollars}$$

(a) Find the total cost of 40 items (to the nearest dollar).

(b) Find the number of units for which total cost is $10,000.

52. *Female workers* From 1950 and projected to 2050, the percent of workers who are females can be modeled by

$$w(x) = 9.42 + 8.70\ln x$$

where x is the number of years after 1940 (*Source*: U.S. Bureau of Labor Statistics).

(a) Find the expected percent of female workers in 2020.

(b) Find the year in which the percent of workers that are females is expected to be 49.0%.

53. *Sales decay* The sales decay for a product is given by $S = 50,000e^{-0.6x}$, where S is the monthly sales (in dollars) and x is the number of months that have passed since the end of an advertising campaign. What will sales be 6 months after the end of the campaign?

54. *Compound interest* If $1000 is invested at 12%, compounded monthly, the future value S at any time t (in years) is given by

$$S = 1000(1.01)^{12t}$$

How long will it take for the amount to double?

55. *Compound interest* If $5000 is invested at 13.5%, compounded continuously, then the future value S at any time t (in years) is given by $S = 5000e^{0.135t}$.

(a) What is the amount after 9 months?

(b) How long will it be before the investment doubles?

56. *World population* With data from the International Data Base of the U.S. Bureau of the Census, the accompanying figure shows a scatter plot of actual or projected world population (in billions) in 5-year increments from 1950 to 2050 ($x = 0$ in 1945). Which of the following functions would be the best model: exponential growth, exponential decay, logarithmic, or logistic? Explain.

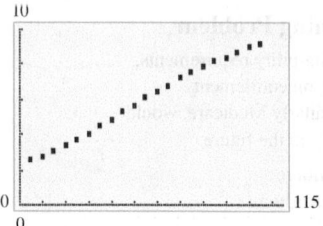

57. *Advertising and sales* After hiring a new VP for advertising, a company predicts that sales will increase and that the yearly sales will be given by the equation

$$N = 10,000(0.3)^{0.5^t}$$

where t represents the number of years after the hiring of the new VP.

(a) What are the sales when the new VP begins?

(b) What are the predicted sales for the third year?

(c) What are the maximum predicted sales?

58. *Spread of a disease* The spread of a highly contagious virus in a high school can be described by the logistic function

$$y = \frac{5000}{1 + 1000e^{-0.8x}}$$

where x is the number of days after the virus is identified in the school and y is the total number of people who are infected by the virus in the first x days.

(a) Graph the function for $0 \le x \le 15$.

(b) How many students had the virus when it was first discovered?

(c) What is the total number infected by the virus during the first 15 days?

(d) In how many days will the total number infected reach 3744?

5 CHAPTER TEST

In Problems 1–4, graph the functions.

1. $y = 5^x$

2. $y = 3^{-x}$

3. $y = \log_5 x$

4. $y = \ln x$

 In Problems 5–8, use technology to graph the functions.

5. $y = 3^{0.5x}$

6. $y = \ln(0.5x)$

7. $y = e^{2x}$

8. $y = \log_7 x$

In Problems 9–12, use a calculator to give a decimal approximation of the numbers to three decimal places.

9. e^4

10. $3^{-2.1}$

11. $\ln 4$

12. $\log 21$

13. Use the definition of a logarithmic function to write $\log_7 x = 3.1$ in exponential form. Then find x to three decimal places.

14. Write $3^{2x} = 27$ in logarithmic form.

In Problems 15 and 16, solve each equation for x to three decimal places.

15. $3 + 6e^{-2x} = 7$

16. $8 - \log_3(5x - 13) = 5$

In Problems 17–20, simplify the expressions using properties or definitions of logarithms.

17. $\log_2 8$

18. $e^{\ln x^4}$

19. $\log_7 7^3$

20. $\ln e^{x^2}$

21. Write $\ln (M \cdot N)$ as a sum involving M and N.

22. Write $\ln \left(\dfrac{x^3 - 1}{x + 2} \right)$ as a difference involving two binomials.

23. Write $\log_4 (x^3 + 1)$ as a base e logarithm using a change-of-base formula.

24. Solve for x: $47{,}500 = 1500(1.015)^{6x}$

25. The graph in the following figure shows the number of active workers who will be (or have been) supporting each Social Security beneficiary. What type of function might be an appropriate model for this situation?

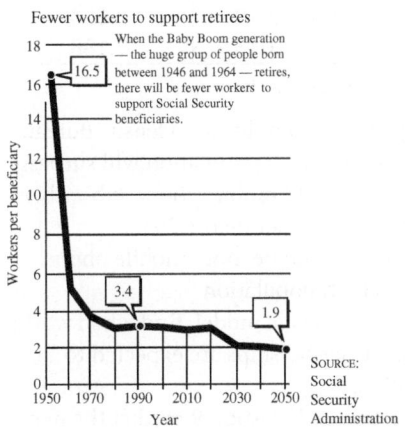

Fewer workers to support retirees

When the Baby Boom generation — the huge group of people born between 1946 and 1964 — retires, there will be fewer workers to support Social Security beneficiaries.

16.5
3.4
1.9

Workers per beneficiary

1950 1970 1990 2010 2030 2050

Year

SOURCE: Social Security Administration

26. With data from the U.S. Energy Information Administration, the following figure shows a scatter plot of tons of carbon dioxide (CO_2) emissions per person for selected years from 2010 and projected to 2040, with x as the number of years past 2010.
    (a) Which of the following functions would be an appropriate model: growth exponential, decay exponential, logarithmic, or logistic?
    (b) The point (20, 14.8) is one of the data points plotted; interpret this point in terms of the application.

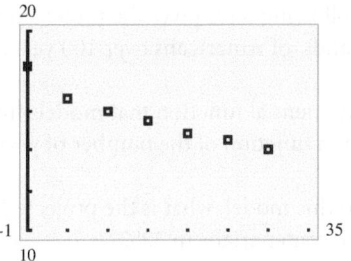

27. The total national health expenditures per capita (in dollars) for 2006 and projected to 2021 can be modeled with the equation

$$H(t) = 6791e^{0.04343t}$$

where t is the number of years past 2005 (*Source*: U.S. Centers for Medicare & Medicaid Services).
    (a) Find the predicted per capita health expenditures for 2018.
    (b) According to the model, how long will it take the 2018 expenditures to double?

28. A company plans to phase out one model of its product and replace it with a new model. An advertising campaign for the product being replaced just ended, and typically after such a campaign, monthly sales volume S (in dollars) decays according to

$$S = 22{,}000e^{-0.35t}$$

where t is in months. When the monthly sales volume for this product reaches \$2500, the company plans to discontinue production and launch the new model. How long will it be until this happens?

29. The supply function for x units of a certain product is given by

$$p = 10 + 6\ln(3x + 10)$$

    (a) Find the price per unit when 30 units are supplied.
    (b) If the price per unit is \$43, find the number of units supplied.

30. The total U.S. personal income I (in billions of dollars) from 1960 and projected to 2024 can be modeled by

$$I = \frac{42{,}990}{1 + 61.55e^{-0.066t}}$$

where t is the number of years after 1960 (*Source*: U.S. Bureau of Labor Statistics).
    (a) What does the model predict the total U.S. personal income will be in 2020?
    (b) Graphically determine the year in which the model predicts that the total U.S. personal income reaches \$22.5 trillion (that is, \$22,500 billion).

31. **Modeling** The following table gives the projected population, in thousands, of Americans over 100 years of age.
    (a) Create an exponential function that models this population as a function of the number of years past 2010.
    (b) According to this model, what is the projected population of centenarians in 2052?
    (c) When will this population reach 1,030,000 according to this model?

Year	Population (1000s)	Year	Population (1000s)
2015	78	2040	230
2020	106	2045	310
2025	143	2050	442
2030	168	2055	564
2035	188	2060	690

Source: U.S. Census Bureau

5 EXTENDED APPLICATIONS & GROUP PROJECTS

I. *Worldwide Mobile Phone Subscriberships* (Modeling)

As Table I shows, the number of worldwide mobile phone subscriberships has increased dramatically. In 1980, there were fewer than 25 thousand, but by 2013, there were more than 6.8 billion, the world population at that time. To predict how the number of subscriberships will grow in the future, complete the following.

1. Find an exponential model that fits the data shown in the table, with x equal to the number of years from 1990 and y equal to the number of billions of subscriberships. Then graph the model and the data points on the same axes.
2. Should we expect the number of subscriberships to continue to grow exponentially in the 2020s?
3. If an exponential model is not appropriate, what type of function could be used to model the growth from 1980 to 2025? Why?
4. Find a model of the type you selected in Question 3 that fits the data shown in the table. Let x equal the number of years from 1990 and y equal the number of billions of subscriberships.
5. Graph this model and the data points on the same axes.
6. Which model is the better fit for the data?
7. What does this model predict the number of mobile phone subscriberships to be in 2025? Does this seem reasonable?
8. The data points in Table II are Key Global Telecom Indicators projections from 2014 through 2020. Add the points representing these data to your data set representing 1990 through 2013; then use a scatter plot to determine if an exponential function or a logistic function is a better model for the combined data set.
9. Find the logistic function that is the best model for the combined data set from Question 8.
10. Graph the logistic model from Question 9 on the same axes with the data points.

TABLE I

WORLDWIDE MOBILE PHONE SUBSCRIBERSHIPS

Year	Billions	Year	Billions
1990	0.011	2002	1.157
1991	0.016	2003	1.417
1992	0.023	2004	1.763
1993	0.034	2005	2.219
1994	0.056	2006	2.757
1995	0.091	2007	3.305
1996	0.145	2008	4.100
1997	0.215	2009	4.720
1998	0.318	2010	5.400
1999	0.490	2011	6.053
2000	0.738	2012	6.654
2001	0.961	2013	7.188

Source: International Telecommunications Union

11. According to projections from the U.S. Census Bureau International Data Base, world population will surpass 9.0 billion in 2042, but world mobile phone subscriberships should reach that number before 2042.
    (a) Explain how there could be more mobile phone subscriberships than population.
    (b) According to your logistic model, find when world mobile phone subscriberships are expected to reach 9.23 billion.
12. What does the function in Question 9 predict the maximum number of worldwide subscriberships will be? Does this seem reasonable?

TABLE II

SUBSCRIBERSHIPS

Year	Billions	Year	Billions
2014	7.65	2018	8.79
2015	8.03	2019	8.95
2016	8.35	2020	9.07
2017	8.60		

II. Agricultural Business Management

A commercial vegetable and fruit grower carefully observes the relationship between the per-acre amount of fertilizer used on a certain variety of pumpkin and the extra revenue made from the sales of the resulting pumpkin crop. These observations are recorded in the following table.

Amount of fertilizer (pounds/acre)	Extra revenue earned (dollars/acre)
0	0
250	288
500	435
750	516
1000	555
1250	576
1500	588
1750	594
2000	597

The fertilizer costs 42¢ per pound. What advice would you give the grower as to the most profitable amount of fertilizer to use?

Check your advice by answering the following questions.

1. Is each pound of fertilizer equally effective? Explain.
2. Estimate the maximum amount of extra revenue that can be earned per acre by observing the data.

3. Graph the data points that give the extra revenue made from improved pumpkin sales as a function of the amount of fertilizer used. What does the graph tell you about the growth of the extra revenue as a function of the amount of fertilizer used?
4. Which of the following equations best models the graph you obtained in Question 3?

   (a) $N = Ca^{R^x}$ (b) $y = \dfrac{A}{1 + ce^{-ax}}$

   (c) $y = c(1 - e^{-ax})$

   Determine a specific equation that fits the observed data. That is, find the value of the constants in the model you have chosen. Graph your equation with the data.
5. Determine a function that models the total cost of the fertilizer as a function of the amount of fertilizer used. Graph your fertilizer cost function on the graph you created for Question 4. For what amount of fertilizer is the extra revenue earned from pumpkin sales offset by the cost of the fertilizer?
6. Use the graphs or the equations you created to estimate the maximum extra profit per acre that can be made and the amount of fertilizer per acre that would yield that maximum extra profit.

6

Mathematics of Finance

Regardless of whether your career is in business, understanding how interest is computed on investments and loans is important to you as a consumer. The proliferation of personal finance and money management software attests to this importance. The goal of this chapter is to provide some understanding of the methods used to determine the interest and future value (principal plus interest) resulting from savings plans and the methods used in repayment of debts.

The topics and some representative applications discussed in this chapter include the following.

SECTIONS	APPLICATIONS
CHAPTER WARM-UP	
6.1 Simple Interest; Sequences Arithmetic sequences	Loans, simple interest and return on investment, duration of an investment
6.2 Compound Interest; Geometric Sequences	529 plans, future value, present value, comparing investments, doubling time
6.3 Future Values of Annuities Ordinary annuities Annuities due	Comparing investment plans, time to reach a goal, sinking funds, required payment
6.4 Present Values of Annuities Ordinary annuities Annuities due Deferred annuities	Retirement planning, lottery prizes, court settlements, bond pricing
6.5 Loans and Amortization Unpaid balance of a loan	Business modernization, home mortgages, unpaid balance, loan refinancing

Prerequisite Problem Type	For Section	Answer	Section for Review
What is $\dfrac{(-1)^n}{2n}$ if (a) $n = 1$? (b) $n = 2$? (c) $n = 3$?	**6.1**	(a) $-\frac{1}{2}$ (b) $\frac{1}{4}$ (c) $-\frac{1}{6}$	0.2 Signed numbers
(a) What is $(-2)^6$? (b) What is $\dfrac{\frac{1}{4}\left[1 - \left(\frac{1}{2}\right)^6\right]}{1 - \frac{1}{2}}$?	**6.2**	(a) 64 (b) $\frac{63}{128}$	0.2 Signed numbers
If $f(x) = \dfrac{1}{2x}$, what is (a) $f(2)$? (b) $f(4)$?	**6.1**	(a) $\frac{1}{4}$ (b) $\frac{1}{8}$	1.2 Function notation
Evaluate: $e^{(0.08)(20)}$	**6.2**	4.95303	5.1 Exponential functions
Evaluate: (a) $\dfrac{1 - (1.05)^{-16}}{0.05}$ (b) $5000 + 5000\left[\dfrac{1-(1.059)^{-9}}{0.059}\right]$	**6.3** **6.4**	(a) 10.83777 (b) 39,156.96575	0.3 Integral exponents
Solve: (a) $1100 = 1000 + 1000(0.058)t$ (b) $12,000 = P(1.03)^6$ (c) $850 = A_n\left[\dfrac{0.0065}{1 - (1.0065)^{-360}}\right]$	**6.1–6.5**	(a) $t \approx 1.72$ (b) $P \approx 10,049.81$ (c) $A_n \approx 118,076.79$	1.1 Linear equations
Solve: (a) $2 = (1.08)^n$ (b) $20,000 = 10,000e^{0.08t}$	**6.2–6.5**	(a) $n \approx 9.01$ (b) $t \approx 8.66$	5.3 Solutions of exponential equations

SECTION 6.1

Simple Interest; Sequences

OBJECTIVES

- To find the future value of and the amount of interest from a simple interest investment
- To find the interest due on a simple interest loan
- To find the time required for a simple interest investment to reach a goal
- To write a specified number of terms of a sequence
- To find specified terms and sums of specified numbers of terms of arithmetic sequences

APPLICATION PREVIEW

Mary Spaulding purchased some Wind-Gen Electric stock for $6125.00. After 6 months, the stock had risen in value by $138.00 and had paid dividends totaling $144.14. One way to evaluate this investment is to use return on investment (ROI), which measures the amount of return on an investment relative to the investment's cost. To calculate ROI, the benefit (or return) of an investment is divided by the cost of the investment, and the result is expressed as a percent. The return on investment formula is

$$\text{ROI} = \frac{\text{Gains on investment}}{\text{Cost of investment}}$$

written as a percent. For Mary Spaulding the gains are the rise in the stock's price plus the dividends she received.

Note that return on investment does not consider time and that an ROI of 10% over 6 months is better than an ROI of 10% over a year. To include time in our evaluation of an investment, we can compare it with a bank savings plan by calculating the simple interest rate that this gain represents. (See Example 3.)

In this section, we begin our study of the mathematics of finance by considering simple interest. Simple interest forms the basis for all calculations involving interest that is paid on an investment or that is due on a loan. Also, we can evaluate short-term investments (such as in stocks or real estate) by calculating their simple interest rates.

Simple Interest If a sum of money P (called the **principal**) is invested for a time period t (frequently in years) at an interest rate r per period, the **simple interest** is given by the following formula.

Simple Interest The **simple interest** I is given by

$$I = Prt$$

where
$I =$ interest (in dollars)
$P =$ principal (in dollars)
$r =$ annual interest rate (written as a decimal)
$t =$ time (in years)*

Note that the time measurements for r and t must agree.

Simple interest is paid on investments involving time certificates issued by banks and on certain types of bonds, such as some U.S. government bonds and municipal bonds. The interest for a given period is paid to the investor, and the principal remains the same.

If you borrow money from a friend or a relative, interest on your loan might be calculated with the simple interest formula. We'll consider some simple interest loans in this section, but interest on loans from banks and other lending institutions is calculated using methods discussed later.

EXAMPLE 1 Simple Interest

(a) If $8000 is invested for 2 years at an annual interest rate of 9%, how much interest will be received at the end of the 2-year period?

(b) If $4000 is borrowed for 39 weeks at an annual interest rate of 15%, how much interest is due at the end of the 39 weeks?

*Periods of time other than years can be used, as can other monetary systems.

Solution

(a) The interest is $I = Prt = \$8000(0.09)(2) = \$1440$.

(b) Use $I = Prt$ with $t = 39/52 = 0.75$ year. Thus

$$I = \$4000(0.15)(0.75) = \$450$$

Future Value

The **future amount of an investment,** or its **future value,** at the end of an interest period is the sum of the principal and the interest. Thus in Example 1(a), the future value is

$$S = \$8000 + \$1440 = \$9440$$

Future Value	If we use the letter S to denote the **future value** of an investment, then we have Future value of investment: $S = P + I$ where P is the principal (in dollars) and I is the interest (in dollars).

The principal P of an investment is also called the **present value** of the investment. The present value of a loan is the original loan amount, which is also called the **face value** of the loan.

EXAMPLE 2 Loans and Investments

(a) If \$2000 is borrowed for one-half year at a simple interest rate of 12% per year, what amount must be repaid at the end of the half-year?

(b) An investor wants to have \$20,000 in 9 months. If the best available simple interest rate is 6.05% per year, how much must be invested now to yield the desired amount?

Solution

(a) The interest for the half-year period is $I = \$2000(0.12)(0.5) = \$120$. Thus the amount that must be repaid for the period is

$$S = P + I = \$2000 + \$120 = \$2120$$

(b) We know that $S = P + I = P + Prt$. In this case, we must solve for P, the present value. Also, the time 9 months is $(9/12)$ of a year.

$$\$20,000 = P + P(0.0605)(9/12) = P + 0.045375P$$
$$\$20,000 = 1.045375P$$
$$\frac{\$20,000}{1.045375} = P \quad \text{so} \quad P \approx \$19,131.89$$

EXAMPLE 3 Evaluating an Investment | APPLICATION PREVIEW |

Mary Spaulding bought Wind-Gen Electric stock for \$6125.00. After 6 months, the value of her shares had risen by \$138.00 and dividends totaling \$144.14 had been paid.

(a) Find the return on investment on this investment.

(b) Find the simple interest rate she earned on this investment if she sold the stock at the end of the 6 months.

Solution

(a) Mary's gains are equal to the rise in the stock's price when it is sold plus the dividends she received on the stock. The ROI on her investment is

$$\text{ROI} = \frac{138.00 + 144.14}{6125.00} \approx 0.046 = 4.6\%$$

(b) To find the simple interest rate that Mary earned on this investment, we find the rate that would yield an amount of simple interest equal to all of Mary's gains. Thus the principal is $6125.00, the time is 1/2 year, and the interest earned is the total of all gains (i.e., interest $I = \$138.00 + \$144.14 = \$282.14$). Using these values in $I = Prt$ gives

$$\$282.14 = (\$6125)r(0.5) = \$3062.5r$$

$$r = \frac{\$282.14}{\$3062.5} \approx 0.092 = 9.2\%$$

Thus Mary's return was equivalent to an annual simple interest rate of about 9.2%.

EXAMPLE 4   Duration of an Investment

If $1000 is invested at 5.8% simple interest, how long will it take to grow to $1100?

Solution

We use $P = \$1000$, $S = \$1100$, and $r = 0.058$ in $S = P + Prt$ and solve for t.

$$\$1100 = \$1000 + \$1000(0.058)t$$

$$\$100 = \$58t \quad \text{so} \quad \frac{\$100}{\$58} = t \quad \text{and} \quad t \approx 1.72 \text{ years}$$

CHECKPOINT

1. What is the simple interest formula?
2. If $8000 is invested at 6% simple interest for 9 months, find the future value of the investment.
3. If a $2500 investment grows to $2875 in 15 months, what simple interest rate was earned?

Sequences Let's look at the monthly future values of a $2000 investment that earns 1% simple interest for each of 5 months.

Month	Interest ($I = Prt$)	Future Value of the Investment
1	($2000)(0.01)(1) = $20	$2000 + $20 = $2020
2	($2000)(0.01)(1) = $20	$2020 + $20 = $2040
3	($2000)(0.01)(1) = $20	$2040 + $20 = $2060
4	($2000)(0.01)(1) = $20	$2060 + $20 = $2080
5	($2000)(0.01)(1) = $20	$2080 + $20 = $2100

These future values are outputs that result when the inputs are positive integers that correspond to the number of months of the investment. Outputs (such as these future values) that arise uniquely from positive integer inputs define a special type of function.

Sequence

A function whose domain is the set of positive integers is called a **sequence function.** The set of function outputs of a sequence function

$$f(1) = a_1, f(2) = a_2, \dots, f(n) = a_n, \dots$$

forms an ordered list called a **sequence**. The outputs $a_1, a_2, a_3, \dots$ are called **terms** of the sequence, with a_1 as the first term, a_2 as the second term, etc.

Because calculations involving interest often result from using positive integer inputs, sequences are the basis for most of the financial formulas derived in this chapter.

EXAMPLE 5 **Terms of a Sequence**

Write the first four terms of the sequence whose nth term is $a_n = (-1)^n/(2n)$.

Solution

The first four terms of the sequence are as follows:

$$a_1 = \frac{(-1)^1}{2(1)} = -\frac{1}{2} \qquad a_2 = \frac{(-1)^2}{2(2)} = \frac{1}{4}$$

$$a_3 = \frac{(-1)^3}{2(3)} = -\frac{1}{6} \qquad a_4 = \frac{(-1)^4}{2(4)} = \frac{1}{8}$$

We usually write these terms in the form $-\frac{1}{2}, \frac{1}{4}, -\frac{1}{6}, \frac{1}{8}$.

Arithmetic Sequences The sequence 2020, 2040, 2060, 2080, 2100, . . . can also be described in the following way:

$$a_1 = 2020, \quad a_n = a_{n-1} + 20 \quad \text{for } n > 1$$

This sequence is an example of a special kind of sequence called an **arithmetic sequence.** In such a sequence, each term after the first can be found by adding a constant to the preceding term. Thus we have the following definition.

Arithmetic Sequences

> A sequence is called an **arithmetic sequence** (progression) if there exists a number d, called the **common difference,** such that
>
> $$a_n = a_{n-1} + d \quad \text{for } n > 1$$

EXAMPLE 6 **Arithmetic Sequences**

Write the next three terms of each of the following arithmetic sequences.
(a) 1, 3, 5, ...
(b) 9, 6, 3, ...
(c) $\frac{1}{2}, \frac{5}{6}, \frac{7}{6}, \ldots$

Solution
(a) The common difference is 2, so the next three terms are 7, 9, 11.
(b) The common difference is -3, so the next three terms are 0, -3, -6.
(c) The common difference is $\frac{1}{3}$, so the next three terms are $\frac{3}{2}, \frac{11}{6}, \frac{13}{6}$.

Because each term after the first term in an arithmetic sequence is obtained by adding d to the preceding term, the second term is $a_1 + d$, the third is $(a_1 + d) + d = a_1 + 2d, \ldots$, and the nth term is $a_1 + (n - 1)d$. Thus we have the following formula.

nth Term of an Arithmetic Sequence

> The **nth term of an arithmetic sequence** (progression) is given by
>
> $$a_n = a_1 + (n - 1)d$$
>
> where a_1 is the first term and d is the common difference between successive terms.

EXAMPLE 7 **nth Terms of Arithmetic Sequences**

(a) Find the 11th term of the arithmetic sequence with first term 3 and common difference -2.
(b) If the first term of an arithmetic sequence is 4 and the 9th term is 20, find the 75th term.

Solution

(a) The 11th term is $a_{11} = 3 + (11 - 1)(-2) = -17$.

(b) Substituting the values $a_1 = 4$, $a_n = 20$, and $n = 9$ in $a_n = a_1 + (n - 1)d$ gives
$$20 = 4 + (9 - 1)d$$
$$\Rightarrow 16 = 8d \Rightarrow d = 2$$
Therefore, the 75th term is $a_{75} = 4 + (75 - 1)(2) = 152$.

Sum of an Arithmetic Sequence

Consider the arithmetic sequence with first term a_1, common difference d, and nth term a_n. The first n terms of an arithmetic sequence can be written in two ways, as follows.

$$\text{From } a_1 \text{ to } a_n: \quad a_1, a_1 + d, a_1 + 2d, a_1 + 3d, \ldots, a_1 + (n - 1)d$$
$$\text{From } a_n \text{ to } a_1: \quad a_n, a_n - d, a_n - 2d, a_n - 3d, \ldots, a_n - (n - 1)d$$

If we let s_n represent the sum of the first n terms of the sequence just described, then we have the following equivalent forms for the sum.

$$s_n = a_1 + (a_1 + d) + (a_1 + 2d) + \cdots + [a_1 + (n - 1)d] \qquad (1)$$
$$s_n = a_n + (a_n - d) + (a_n - 2d) + \cdots + [a_n - (n - 1)d] \qquad (2)$$

If we add equations (1) and (2) term by term, we obtain

$$2s_n = (a_1 + a_n) + (a_1 + a_n) + (a_1 + a_n) + \cdots + (a_1 + a_n)$$

in which $(a_1 + a_n)$ appears as a term n times. Thus,

$$2s_n = n(a_1 + a_n) \qquad \text{so} \qquad s_n = \frac{n}{2}(a_1 + a_n)$$

Sum of an Arithmetic Sequence

The **sum of the first n terms of an arithmetic sequence** is given by the formula

$$s_n = \frac{n}{2}(a_1 + a_n)$$

where a_1 is the first term of the sequence and a_n is the nth term.

EXAMPLE   8   **Sums of Arithmetic Sequences**

Find the sum of

(a) the first 10 terms of the arithmetic sequence with first term 2 and common difference 4

(b) the first 91 terms of the arithmetic sequence $\frac{1}{4}, \frac{7}{12}, \frac{11}{12}, \ldots$.

Solution

(a) We are given the values $n = 10$, $a_1 = 2$, and $d = 4$. Thus the 10th term is $a_{10} = 2 + (10 - 1)4 = 38$ and the sum of the first 10 terms is

$$s_{10} = \frac{10}{2}(2 + 38) = 200$$

(b) The first term is $\frac{1}{4}$, and the common difference is $\frac{1}{3}$. Therefore, the 91st term is $a_{91} = \frac{1}{4} + (91 - 1)(\frac{1}{3}) = 30\frac{1}{4} = \frac{121}{4}$. The sum of the first 91 terms is

$$s_{91} = \frac{91}{2}\left(\frac{1}{4} + \frac{121}{4}\right) = \frac{91}{2}\left(\frac{122}{4}\right) = \frac{91(61)}{4} = \left(\frac{5551}{4}\right) = 1387\frac{3}{4}$$

CHECKPOINT

4. Of the following sequences, identify each arithmetic sequence and state its common difference.
    (a) 1, 4, 9, 16, …
    (b) 1, 4, 7, 10, …
    (c) 1, 2, 4, 8, …
5. Given the arithmetic sequence $-10, -6, -2, \dots$, find
    (a) the 51st term
    (b) the sum of the first 51 terms.

Technology Note   Finally, we should note that graphing calculators and spreadsheets have the capability of defining sequence functions and then operating on them by finding additional terms, graphing the terms, or summing a fixed number of terms.

CHECKPOINT
ANSWERS

1. $I = Prt$
2. $S = \$8360$
3. $r = 0.12$,   or   12%
4. Only (b) is an arithmetic sequence; the common difference is 3.
5. (a) $a_{51} = 190$
    (b) $s_{51} = 4590$

EXERCISES 6.1

SIMPLE INTEREST

In Problems 1 and 2, find the requested value and tell what the other numbers represent.

1. (a) Find r: $250 = 1000(r)(4)$
    (b) Find P: $9600 = P + P(0.05)(4)$
2. (a) Find t: $1500 = 5000(0.05)(t)$
    (b) Find P: $11{,}800 = P + P(0.03)(6)$
3. $10,000 is invested for 6 years at an annual simple interest rate of 1.6%.
    (a) How much interest will be earned?
    (b) What is the future value of the investment at the end of the 6 years?
4. $800 is invested for 5 years at an annual simple interest rate of 14%.
    (a) How much interest will be earned?
    (b) What is the future value of the investment at the end of the 5 years?
5. $20,000 is invested for 6 months at an annual simple interest rate of 2%.
    (a) How much interest will be earned?
    (b) What is the future value of the investment after 6 months?
6. $1800 is invested for 9 months at an annual simple interest rate of 15%.
    (a) How much interest will be earned?
    (b) What is the future value of the investment after 9 months?

7. If you borrow $800 for 6 months at 6% annual simple interest, how much must you repay at the end of the 6 months?
8. If you borrow $1600 for 2 years at 14% annual simple interest, how much must you repay at the end of the 2 years?
9. If you lend $3500 to a friend for 15 months at 8% annual simple interest, find the future value of the loan.
10. Mrs. Gonzalez lent $2500 to her son Luis for 7 months at 9% annual simple interest. What is the future value of this loan?
11. A couple bought some stock for $30 per share that pays an annual dividend of $0.90 per share. After 2 years, the price of the stock was $33.
    (a) What is the return on investment?
    (b) Find the simple interest rate on the growth of their investment.
12. Jenny Reed bought SSX stock for $25 per share. The annual dividend was $1.50 per share, and after 4 years, SSX was selling for $34 per share.
    (a) What is the return on investment?
    (b) Find the simple interest rate of growth of her money.
13. (a) To buy a Treasury bill (T-bill) that matures to $10,000 in 6 months, you must pay $9750. What annual simple interest rate does this earn?
    (b) If the bank charges a fee of $40 to buy a T-bill, what is the actual interest rate you earn?

14. Janie Christopher lent $6000 to a friend for 90 days at 12%. After 30 days, she sold the note to a third party for $6000. What annual simple interest rate did the third party receive? Use 360 days in a year.

15. A firm buys 12 file cabinets at $140 each, with payment in full due in 90 days. How much must the firm deposit now to have enough to pay the bill if money is worth 3% simple interest per year? Use 360 days in a year.

16. A student has a savings account earning 9% simple interest. She must pay $1500 for first-semester tuition by September 1 and $1500 for second-semester tuition by January 1. How much must she earn in the summer (by September 1) to pay the first-semester bill on time and still have the remainder of her summer earnings grow to $1500 between September 1 and January 1?

17. If you want to earn 2% annual simple interest on an investment, how much should you pay for a note that will be worth $13,500 in 10 months?

18. What is the present value of an investment at 6% annual simple interest if it is worth $832 in 8 months?

19. If $5000 is invested at 8% annual simple interest, how long does it take to be worth $9000?

20. How long does it take for $8500 invested at 11% annual simple interest to be worth $13,000?

21. A retailer owes a wholesaler $500,000 due in 45 days. If the payment is 15 days late, there is a 1% penalty charge. The retailer can get a 45-day certificate of deposit (CD) earning 6% per year simple interest or a 60-day certificate earning 7% per year simple interest. Is it better to take the 45-day certificate and pay on time or to take the 60-day certificate and pay late with the penalty?

22. An investor owns several apartment buildings. The taxes on these buildings total $30,000 per year and are due before April 1. The late fee is 1/2% per month up to 6 months, at which time the buildings are seized by the authorities and sold for back taxes. If the investor has $30,000 available on March 31, will he save money by paying the taxes at that time or by investing the money at 8% per year simple interest for the 6 months and paying the taxes and the penalty on September 30?

23. Bill Casler bought a $2000, 9-month certificate of deposit (CD) that would earn 8% annual simple interest. Three months before the CD was due to mature, Bill needed his CD money, so a friend agreed to lend him money and receive the value of the CD when it matured.
    (a) What is the value of the CD when it matures?
    (b) If their agreement allowed the friend to earn a 10% annual simple interest return on his loan to Bill, how much did Bill receive from his friend?

24. Suppose you lent $5000 to friend 1 for 18 months at an annual simple interest rate of 9%. After 1 year, you need money for an emergency and decide to sell the note to friend 2.
    (a) How much does friend 1 owe when the loan is due?

(b) If your agreement with friend 2 means that she earns simple interest at an annual rate of 12%, how much did friend 2 pay you for the note?

SEQUENCES

25. Write the first ten terms of the sequence defined by $a_n = 3n$.

26. Write the first seven terms of the sequence defined by $a_n = 2/n$.

27. Write the first six terms of the sequence whose nth term is $(-1)^n/(2n + 1)$.

28. Write the first five terms of the sequence whose nth term is $a_n = (-1)^n/(n^2)$.

29. Write the first four terms and the 10th term of the sequence whose nth term is

$$a_n = \frac{n - 4}{n(n + 2)}$$

30. Write the sixth term of the sequence whose nth term is

$$a_n = \frac{n(n - 1)}{n + 3}$$

ARITHMETIC SEQUENCES

In Problems 31–34, (a) identify d and a_1 and (b) write the next three terms.

31. $2, 5, 8, \ldots$ 32. $3, 9, 15, \ldots$

33. $3, \frac{9}{2}, 6, \ldots$ 34. $2, 2.75, 3.5, \ldots$

35. Find the 83rd term of the arithmetic sequence with first term 6 and common difference $-\frac{1}{2}$.

36. Find the 66th term of the arithmetic sequence with first term $\frac{1}{2}$ and common difference $-\frac{1}{3}$.

37. Find the 100th term of the arithmetic sequence with first term 5 and eighth term 19.

38. Find the 73rd term of the arithmetic sequence with first term 20 and 10th term 47.

39. Find the sum of the first 38 terms of the arithmetic sequence with first term 2 and 38th term 113.

40. Find the sum of the first 56 terms of the arithmetic sequence with first term 6 and 56th term 226.

41. Find the sum of the first 70 terms of the arithmetic sequence with first term 10 and common difference $\frac{1}{2}$.

42. Find the sum of the first 80 terms of the arithmetic sequence with first term 12 and common difference -3.

43. Find the sum of the first 150 terms of the arithmetic sequence $6, \frac{9}{2}, 3, \ldots$.

44. Find the sum of the first 200 terms of the arithmetic sequence $12, 9, 6, \ldots$.

APPLICATIONS

45. *Bee reproduction* A female bee hatches from a fertilized egg, but a male bee hatches from an unfertilized egg. Thus a female bee has a male parent and a female

parent, but a male bee has only a female parent. Therefore, the number of ancestors of a male bee follows the *Fibonacci sequence*

$$1, 2, 3, 5, 8, 13, \ldots$$

Observe the pattern and write three more terms of the sequence.

46. *Salaries* Suppose you are offered a job with a relatively low starting salary but with a $3000 raise for each of the next 7 years. How much more than your starting salary would you be making in the eighth year?

47. *Profit* A new firm loses $4000 in its first month, but its profit increases by $800 in each succeeding month for the next year. What is its profit in the 12th month?

48. *Pay raises* If you make $36,000 and get $2400 raises each year, in how many years will your salary double?

49. *Salaries* Suppose you are offered two identical jobs: one paying a starting salary of $40,000 with yearly raises of $2000 and one paying a starting salary of $36,000 with yearly raises of $2400. Which job will pay you more for your 10th year on the job?

50. *Profit* A new firm loses $4000 in its first month, but its profit increases by $800 in each succeeding month for the next year. What is its profit for the year?

51. *Pay raises* If you are an employee, would you rather be given a raise of $2000 at the end of each year (plan I) or a raise of $600 at the end of each 6-month period (plan II)? Consider the table for an employee whose base salary is $40,000 per year (or $20,000 per 6-month period) and answer parts (a)–(g).

	Salary Received per 6-Month Period	
Period (months)	Plan I	Plan II
0–6	$20,000	$20,000
6–12	20,000	20,600
12–18	21,000	21,200
18–24	21,000	21,800
24–30	22,000	22,400
30–36	22,000	23,000

(a) Find the sum of the raises for plan I for the first 3 years.
(b) Find the sum of the raises for plan II for the first 3 years.
(c) Which plan is better and by how much?
(d) Find the sum of the raises in plan I for 5 years.
(e) Find the sum of the raises in plan II for 5 years.
(f) Which plan is better and by how much?
(g) Do you want plan I or plan II?

52. *Pay raises* As an employee, would you prefer being given a $2400 raise each year for 5 years or a $400 raise each quarter for 5 years?

SECTION 6.2

Compound Interest; Geometric Sequences

OBJECTIVES

- To find the future value and interest earned when interest is compounded at regular intervals or continuously
- To find the annual percentage yield (APY), or the effective annual interest rate, of money invested at compound interest
- To find the time it takes an investment to reach a specified amount
- To find specified terms, and sums of specified numbers of terms, of geometric sequences

APPLICATION PREVIEW

A common concern for young parents is how they will pay for their children's college educations. To address this, there are an increasing number of college savings plans, such as the so-called "529 plans," which are tax-deferred.

Suppose Jim and Eden established such a plan for their baby daughter Maura. If this account earns 9.8% compounded quarterly and if their goal is to have $200,000 by Maura's 18th birthday, what would be the impact of having $10,000 in the account by Maura's first birthday? (See Example 3.)

A compound interest investment (such as Jim and Eden's account) is one in which interest is paid into the account at regular intervals. In this section, we consider investments of this type and develop formulas that enable us to determine the impact of making a $10,000 investment in Maura's college tuition account by her first birthday.

Compound Interest   In the previous section, we discussed simple interest. A second method of paying interest is the **compound interest** method, where the interest for each period is added to the principal before interest is calculated for the next period. With compound interest, both the interest added and the principal earn interest for the next period. With this method, the principal grows as the interest is added to it. Think of it like building a snowman. You start with a snowball the size of your fist (your investment), and as you roll the snowball around the yard, the snowball picks up additional snow (interest). The more you roll it, the snowball itself (principal) keeps growing, and as it does, the amount of snow it picks up along the way (interest) also grows. This method is used in investments such as savings accounts and some U.S. government bonds.

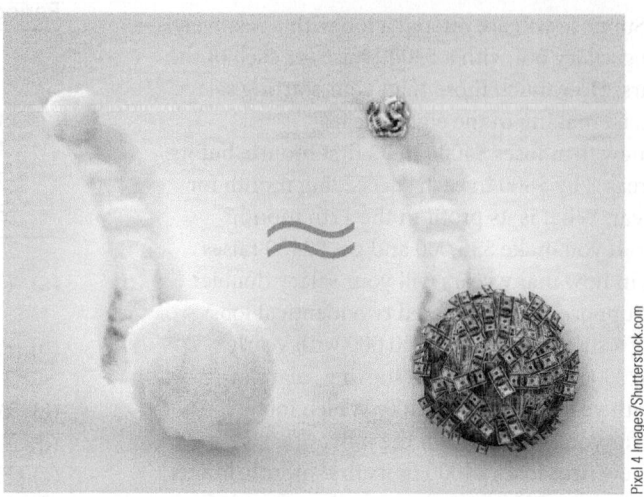

An understanding of compound interest is important not only for people planning careers with financial institutions but also for anyone planning to invest money. To see how compound interest is computed, consider the following table, which tracks the annual growth of $20,000 invested for 3 years at 10% compounded annually. (Notice that the ending principal for each year becomes the beginning principal for the next year.)

Year	Beginning Principal $= P$	10% Annual Interest $= I$	Ending Principal $= P + I$
1	$20,000	0.10($20,000) = $2000	$22,000
2	$22,000	0.10($22,000) = $2200	$24,200
3	$24,200	0.10($24,200) = $2400	$26,620

Note that the ending principal, or **future value,** for each year can be found by multiplying the beginning principal for that year by $1 + 0.10$, or 1.10. That is,

First year: $\$20{,}000(1.10) = \$22{,}000$
Second year: $[\$20{,}000(1.10)](1.10) = \$20{,}000(1.10)^2 = \$24{,}200$
Third year: $[\$20{,}000(1.10)^2](1.10) = \$20{,}000(1.10)^3 = \$26{,}620$

This suggests that if we maintained this investment for n years, the future value at the end of this time would be $\$20{,}000(1.10)^n$. Thus we have the following general formula.

Future Value (Annual Compounding)   If $\$P$ is invested at an interest rate of r per year (expressed as a decimal) compounded annually, the future value S at the end of the nth year is

$$S = P(1 + r)^n$$

EXAMPLE **1**   **Annual Compounding**

If $3000 is invested for 4 years at 9% compounded annually, how much interest is earned?

Solution

The future value is

$$S = \$3000(1 + 0.09)^4$$
$$\approx \$3000(1.4115816)$$
$$= \$4234.7448$$
$$\approx \$4234.74$$

Because $3000 of this amount was the original investment, the interest earned is
$4234.74 − $3000 = $1234.74.

Some accounts have the interest compounded semiannually, quarterly, monthly, or daily.
Unless specifically stated otherwise, a stated interest rate, called the **nominal annual rate,** is
the rate per year and is denoted by r. The interest rate *per period*, denoted by i, is the nominal
rate divided by the number of interest periods per year. The interest periods also are called
conversion periods, and the number of periods is denoted by n. Thus, if $100 is invested for 5
years at 6% compounded semiannually (twice a year), it has been invested for $n = 10$ periods
(5 years $\times$ 2 periods per year) at $i = 3\%$ per period (6% per year $\div$ 2 periods per year).
The future value of an investment of this type is found using the following formula.

Future Value (Periodic Compounding)

If P is invested for t years at a nominal interest rate r compounded m times per
year, then the total number of compounding periods is

$$n = mt$$

the interest rate per compounding period is

$$i = \frac{r}{m} \quad \text{(expressed as a decimal)}$$

and the future value is

$$S = P(1 + i)^n = P\left(1 + \frac{r}{m}\right)^{mt}$$

EXAMPLE 2   Periodic Compounding

For each of the following investments, find the interest rate per period, i, and the number
of compounding periods, n.
(a) 12% compounded monthly for 7 years
(b) 7.2% compounded quarterly for 11 quarters

Solution
(a) If the compounding is monthly and $r = 12\% = 0.12$, then $i = 0.12/12 = 0.01$. The
     number of compounding periods is $n = (7\,\text{yr})(12\,\text{periods/yr}) = 84$.
(b) $i = 0.072/4 = 0.018$, $n = 11$ (the number of quarters given)

Once we know i and n, we can calculate the future value from the formula with a
calculator.

EXAMPLE 3   Future Value | APPLICATION PREVIEW |

Jim and Eden want to have $200,000 in Maura's college fund on her 18th birthday, and
they want to know the impact on this goal of having $10,000 invested at 9.8% compounded
quarterly on her first birthday. To advise Jim and Eden regarding this, find
(a) the future value of the $10,000 investment,
(b) the amount of compound interest that the investment earns,
(c) the impact this would have on their goal.

Solution

(a) For this situation, $i = 0.098/4 = 0.0245$ and $n = 4(17) = 68$. Thus the future value of the $10,000 is given by

$$S = P(1 + i)^n = \$10,000(1 + 0.0245)^{68} \approx \$51,857.73$$

(b) The amount of interest earned is $51,857.73 - \$10,000 = \$41,857.73$.

(c) Thus $10,000 invested by Maura's first birthday grows to an amount that is slightly more than 25% of their goal. This rather large early investment has a substantial impact on their goal.

Technology Note

Graphing calculators and most spreadsheets (including Excel) have built-in finance packages that can be used to solve the compound interest problems of this section and later sections of this chapter.

We can use a graphing calculator to find the future value of a lump sum investment as follows:

1. Under the APPS menu, select Finance and then TVM Solver.
2. (a) Set N = the total number of payments
   (b) Set I% = the annual percentage rate
   (c) Set PV = lump sum invested (with a negative sign because the sum is leaving to go into the investment)
   (d) Set PMT = 0
   (e) Set both P/Y and C/Y equal to the number of compounding periods per year.
3. Highlight END; then put the cursor on FV and press ALPHA ENTER to get the future value.

Figure 6.1

Figure 6.1 shows that when $10,000 is invested at 9.8% compounded quarterly for 17 years, the future value is about $51,857.73, as we found in Example 3. See Appendix A, Section 6.2, for more details.

We can also use Excel to find the future value of the same lump sum investment by using the formula =fv(F2, B2, C2, A2, 0) where

1. Cell F2 has the periodic interest rate as a decimal.
2. Cell B2 has the number of periods.
3. Cell C2 has the value 0.
4. Cell A2 has the lump sum investment amount P.

Cell B4 of the spreadsheet shows the same future value for the Example 3 investment. See Appendix B, Section 6.2, or the Online Excel Guide for complete details.

	A	B	C	D	E	F
1	Principal	Number of Periods	Payment	Annual Rate	Periods per Year	Periodic Rate
2	–10000	68	0	0.098	4	0.0245
3						
4	Future Value	$51,857.73				

We saw previously that compound interest calculations are based on those for simple interest except that interest payments are added to the principal. In this way, interest is earned on both principal and previous interest payments. Let's examine the effect of this compounding by comparing compound interest and simple interest. If the investment in Example 3 had been at simple interest, the interest earned would have been $Prt = \$10,000(0.098)(17) = \$16,660$. This is almost $25,200 less than the amount of compound interest earned. And this difference would have been magnified over a longer period of time. Try reworking Example 3's investment over 30 years and compare the compound interest earned with the simple interest earned. This comparison begins to shed some light on why Albert Einstein characterized compound interest as "the most powerful force in the Universe."

In each of Examples 1 and 3, the beginning principal of the investment, P, also called the **present value** of the investment, and the interest rate, r, were known. Next, we consider examples where one of these quantities must be found.

EXAMPLE 4   Present Value

What amount must be invested now to have $12,000 after 3 years if money is worth 6% compounded semiannually?

Solution

We need to find the present value P, knowing that the future value is $S = \$12,000$. Use $i = 0.06/2 = 0.03$ and $n = 3(2) = 6$.

$$S = P(1 + i)^n$$
$$\$12,000 = P(1 + 0.03)^6 = P(1.03)^6 \approx P(1.1940523)$$
$$P \approx \frac{\$12,000}{1.1940523} \approx \$10,049.81$$

EXAMPLE 5   Rate Earned

As Figure 6.2 shows, 3 years after Google stock was first sold publicly, its share price had risen 500%. Google's 500% increase means that $10,000 invested in Google stock at its initial public offering (IPO) was worth $60,000 3 years later. What interest rate compounded annually does this represent? (For similar information and calculations regarding Microsoft's annual compounding performance, see Problem 31 in the exercises for this section.)

Figure 6.2

Source: Based on data from Google Finance

Solution

We use $P = \$10,000$, $S = \$60,000$, and $n = 3$ in the formula $S = P(1 + i)^n$ and solve for i.

$$\$60,000 = \$10,000(1 + i)^3$$
$$6 = (1 + i)^3$$

At this point, we take the cube root (third root) of both sides (or, equivalently, raise both sides to the 1/3 power).

$$6^{(1/3)} = [(1 + i)^3]^{(1/3)}$$
$$1.817 \approx 1 + i \quad \text{so} \quad 0.817 \approx i$$

Thus this investment earned about 81.7% compounded annually.

1. If $5000 is invested at 6% compounded quarterly for 5 years, find
   (a) the number of compounding periods per year, m,
   (b) the number of compounding periods for the investment, n,
   (c) the interest rate for each compounding period, i,
   (d) the future value of the investment.
2. Find the present value of an investment that is worth $12,000 after 5 years at 9% compounded monthly.

If we invest a sum of money, then the higher the interest rate, the greater the future value. Figure 6.3 shows a graphical comparison of the future values when $100 is invested at 5%, 8%, and 10%, all compounded annually over a period of 30 years. Note that higher interest rates yield consistently higher future values and have dramatically higher future values after 15 to 20 years. Note also that these graphs of the future values are growth exponentials.

Figure 6.3

Spreadsheet Note

We can find the future values of investments after n periods with Excel by entering formulas for specific investments. This method is useful when comparing investments with different interest rates. The spreadsheet tracks the monthly growth of two investments, both compounded monthly and both with $P = \$1000$, but one at 6% (giving $i = 0.005$) and the other at 6.9% (giving $i = 0.00575$). ▪

TWO INVESTMENTS AT DIFFERENT INTEREST RATES

	A	B	C
1	Month #	$ = 1000(1.005)^n	$ = 1000(1.00575)^n
2	22	$1115.97	$1134.44
3	23	$1121.55	$1140.96
4	24	$1127.16	$1147.52

Continuous Compounding

Because more frequent compounding means that interest is paid more often (and hence more interest on interest is earned), it would seem that the more frequently the interest is compounded, the larger the future value will become. To determine the interest that results from *continuous* compounding (compounding every instant), consider an investment of $1 for 1 year at a 100% interest rate. If the interest is compounded m times per year, the future value is given by

$$S = \left(1 + \frac{1.00}{m}\right)^m$$

Table 6.1 shows the future values that result as the number of compounding periods increases.

TABLE 6.1

Compounded	Number of Periods per Year	Future Value of $1
Annually	1	$(1 + \frac{1}{1})^1 = 2$
Monthly	12	$(1 + \frac{1}{12})^{12} = 2.61303\ldots$
Daily	365	$(1 + \frac{1}{365})^{365} = 2.71456\ldots$
Hourly	8760	$(1 + \frac{1}{8760})^{8760} = 2.71812\ldots$
Each minute	525,600	$(1 + \frac{1}{525,600})^{525,600} = 2.71827\ldots$

Table 6.1 shows that as the number of periods per year increases, the future value increases, although not very rapidly. In fact, no matter how often the interest is compounded, the future value will never exceed $2.72. We say that as the number of periods increases, the future value approaches a limit, which is the number e:

$$e = 2.7182818\ldots.$$

We discussed the number e and the function $y = e^x$ in Chapter 5, "Exponential and Logarithmic Functions." The discussion here shows one way the number we call e may be derived. We will define e more formally later.

Future Value (Continuous Compounding)

If $\$P$ is invested for t years at a nominal rate r (expressed as a decimal) compounded continuously, then the future value is given by the exponential function

$$S = Pe^{rt}$$

EXAMPLE   6   Continuous Compounding

(a) Find the future value if $1000 is invested for 20 years at 8% compounded continuously.
(b) What amount must be invested at 6.5% compounded continuously so that it will be worth $25,000 after 8 years?

Solution
(a) The future value is

$$S = \$1000e^{(0.08)(20)} = \$1000e^{1.6} \approx \$4953.03$$

(b) Solve for the present value P in $\$25,000 = Pe^{(0.065)(8)}$.

$$\$25,000 = Pe^{(0.065)(8)} = Pe^{0.52} \approx P(1.68202765)$$

$$\frac{\$25,000}{1.68202765} \approx P \quad \text{so} \quad P \approx \$14,863.01$$

EXAMPLE   7   Comparing Investments

How much more will you earn if you invest $10,000 for 15 years at 8% compounded continuously instead of at 8% compounded quarterly?

Solution

If the interest is compounded continuously, the future value at the end of the 15 years is

$$S = \$10{,}000e^{(0.08)(15)} = \$10{,}000e^{1.2} \approx \$33{,}201.17$$

If the interest is compounded quarterly, the future value at the end of the 15 years is

$$S = \$10{,}000(1.02)^{60} \approx \$32{,}810.31$$

Thus the extra interest earned by compounding continuously is

$$\$33{,}201.17 - \$32{,}810.31 = \$390.86$$

Annual Percentage Yield

As Example 7 shows, when we invest money at a given compound interest rate, the method of compounding affects the amount of interest we earn. As a result, a rate of 8% can earn more than 8% interest if compounding is more frequent than annually.

For example, suppose $1 is invested for 1 year at 8% compounded semiannually. Then $i = 0.08/2 = 0.04$, $n = 2$, the future value is $S = \$1(1.04)^2 = \$1.0816$, and the interest earned for the year is $\$1.0816 - \$1 = \$0.0816$. Note that this amount of interest represents an annual percentage yield of 8.16%, so we say that 8% compounded semiannually has an **annual percentage yield (APY)**, or **effective annual rate**, of 8.16%. Similarly, if $1 is invested at 8% compounded continuously, then the interest earned is $\$1(e^{0.08}) - \$1 = \$0.0833$, for an APY of 8.33%.

Banks acknowledge this difference between stated nominal interest rates and annual percentage yields by posting both rates for their investments. Note that the annual percentage yield is equivalent to the stated rate when compounding is annual. In general, the annual percentage yield equals I/P, or just I if $P = \$1$. Hence we can calculate the APY with the following formulas.

Annual Percentage Yield (APY)	Let r represent the annual (nominal) interest rate for an investment. Then the **annual percentage yield (APY)*** is found as follows. **Periodic Compounding.** If m is the number of compounding periods per year, then $i = r/m$ is the interest rate per period, and $$APY = \left(1 + \frac{r}{m}\right)^m - 1 = (1 + i)^m - 1$$ **Continuous Compounding** $$APY = e^r - 1$$

Thus although we cannot directly compare two nominal rates with different compounding periods, we can compare their corresponding APYs.

EXAMPLE **8** **Comparing Yields**

Suppose a young couple such as Jim and Eden from the Application Preview found three different investment companies that offered college savings plans: (a) one at 10% compounded annually, (b) another at 9.8% compounded quarterly, and (c) a third at 9.65% compounded continuously. Find the annual percentage yield (APY) for each of these plans to discover which plan is best.

---

*Note that the annual percentage yield is also called the **effective annual rate**.

Solution

(a) For annual compounding, the stated rate is the APY. Thus, $APY = 10\%$.

(b) Because the number of periods per year is $m = 4$ and the nominal rate is $r = 0.098$, the rate per period is $i = r/m = 0.098/4 = 0.0245$. Thus,

$$APY = (1 + 0.0245)^4 - 1 \approx 1.10166 - 1 = 0.10166 = 10.166\%$$

(c) For continuous compounding and a nominal rate of 9.65%, we have

$$APY = e^{0.0965} - 1 \approx 1.10131 - 1 = 0.10131 = 10.131\%$$

Hence we see that of these three choices, 9.8% compounded quarterly is best. Furthermore, even 9.65% compounded continuously has a higher APY than 10% compounded annually.

CHECKPOINT

3. For each future value formula below, decide which is used for interest that is compounded periodically and which is used for interest that is compounded continuously.
(a) $S = P(1 + i)^n$ (b) $S = Pe^{rt}$

4. If $5000 is invested at 6% compounded continuously for 5 years, find the future value of the investment.

5. Find the annual percentage yield of an investment that earns 7% compounded semi-annually.

EXAMPLE 9   **Doubling Time**

How long does it take an investment of $10,000 to double if it is invested at
(a) 8% compounded annually
(b) 8% compounded continuously?

Solution

(a) We solve for n in $\$20{,}000 = \$10{,}000(1 + 0.08)^n$.

$$2 = 1.08^n$$

Taking the logarithm, base e, of both sides of the equation gives

$$\ln 2 = \ln 1.08^n$$
$$\ln 2 = n \ln 1.08 \qquad \text{Logarithm Property V}$$

$$n = \frac{\ln 2}{\ln 1.08} \approx 9.0 \text{ (years)}$$

(b) Solve for t in $\$20{,}000 = \$10{,}000e^{0.08t}$.

$$2 = e^{0.08t} \qquad \text{Isolate the exponential.}$$
$$\ln 2 = \ln e^{0.08t} \qquad \text{Take "ln" of both sides.}$$
$$\ln 2 = 0.08t \qquad \text{Logarithm Property I}$$

$$t = \frac{\ln 2}{0.08} \approx 8.7 \text{ (years)}$$

Spreadsheet Note   To understand better the effect of compounding periods on an investment, we can use a spreadsheet to compare different compounding schemes. The following spreadsheet tracks the growth at 5-year intervals of a $100 investment for quarterly compounding and continuous compounding (both at 10%).

**COMPARISON OF TWO INVESTMENTS WITH
DIFFERENT COMPOUNDING SCHEMES**

	A	B	C
1	Year	S = 100(1.025)^(4n)	S = 100*exp(.10n)
2	5	163.86	164.87
3	10	268.51	271.83
4	15	439.98	448.17
5	20	720.96	738.91
6	25	1181.37	1218.25
7	30	1935.81	2008.55

CHECKPOINT   6.   How long does it take $5000 to double if it is invested at 9% compounded monthly?

Geometric Sequences   If $P is invested at an interest rate of i per period compounded at the end of each period, the future value at the end of each succeeding period is

$$P(1 + i), P(1 + i)^2, P(1 + i)^3, \ldots, P(1 + i)^n, \ldots$$

The future values for each of the succeeding periods form a sequence in which each term (after the first) is found by multiplying the previous term by the same number. Such a sequence is called a **geometric sequence.**

Geometric Sequence
> A sequence is called a **geometric sequence** (progression) if there exists a number r, called the **common ratio,*** such that
>
> $$a_n = ra_{n-1} \quad \text{for } n > 1$$

Geometric sequences form the foundation for other applications involving compound interest.

EXAMPLE 10   Geometric Sequences

Write the next three terms of the following geometric sequences.
(a) $1, 3, 9, \ldots$ (b) $4, 2, 1, \ldots$ (c) $3, -6, 12, \ldots$

Solution
(a) The common ratio is 3, so the next three terms are $27, 81, 243$.
(b) The common ratio is $\frac{1}{2}$, so the next three terms are $\frac{1}{2}, \frac{1}{4}, \frac{1}{8}$.
(c) The common ratio is -2, so the next three terms are $-24, 48, -96$.

Because each term after the first in a geometric sequence is obtained by multiplying the previous term by r, the second term is $a_1 r$, the third is $a_1 r^2$, etc., and the nth term is $a_1 r^{n-1}$. Thus we have the following formula.

nth Term of a Geometric Sequence
> The **nth term of a geometric sequence** (progression) is given by
>
> $$a_n = a_1 r^{n-1}$$
>
> where a_1 is the first term of the sequence and r is the common ratio.

* Note that the common ratio r used here for geometric sequences is different from the interest rate r used in the compound interest formula discussed earlier.

EXAMPLE 11 *n*th Term of a Geometric Sequence

Find the seventh term of the geometric sequence with first term 5 and common ratio -2.

Solution

The seventh term is $a_7 = 5(-2)^{7-1} = 5(64) = 320$.

EXAMPLE 12 Ball Rebounding

A ball is dropped from a height of 125 feet. If it rebounds $\frac{3}{5}$ of the height from which it falls every time it hits the ground, how high will it bounce after it strikes the ground for the fifth time?

Solution

The first rebound is $\frac{3}{5}(125) = 75$ feet; the second rebound is $\frac{3}{5}(75) = 45$ feet. The heights of the rebounds form a geometric sequence with first term 75 and common ratio $\frac{3}{5}$. Thus the fifth term is

$$a_5 = 75\left(\frac{3}{5}\right)^4 = 75\left(\frac{81}{625}\right) = \frac{243}{25} = 9\frac{18}{25} \text{ feet}$$

Sum of a Geometric Sequence

Next we develop a formula for the sum of a geometric sequence, a formula that is important in our study of annuities. The sum of the first n terms of a geometric sequence is

$$s_n = a_1 + a_1 r + a_1 r^2 + \cdots + a_1 r^{n-1} \qquad (1)$$

If we multiply equation (1) by r, we have

$$r s_n = a_1 r + a_1 r^2 + a_1 r^3 + \cdots + a_1 r^n \qquad (2)$$

Subtracting equation (2) from equation (1), we obtain

$$s_n - r s_n = a_1 + (a_1 r - a_1 r) + (a_1 r^2 - a_1 r^2) + \cdots + (a_1 r^{n-1} - a_1 r^{n-1}) - a_1 r^n$$

Thus

$$s_n(1-r) = a_1 - a_1 r^n \quad \text{so} \quad s_n = \frac{a_1 - a_1 r^n}{1-r} \quad \text{if } r \neq 1$$

This gives the following.

Sum of a Geometric Sequence

The **sum of the first n terms of the geometric sequence** with first term a_1 and common ratio r is

$$s_n = \frac{a_1(1-r^n)}{1-r} \text{ provided that } r \neq 1$$

EXAMPLE 13 Sums of Geometric Sequences

(a) Find the sum of the first five terms of the geometric progression with first term 4 and common ratio -3.

(b) Find the sum of the first six terms of the geometric sequence $\frac{1}{4}, \frac{1}{8}, \frac{1}{16}, \ldots$.

Solution

(a) We are given that $n = 5$, $a_1 = 4$, and $r = -3$. Thus

$$s_5 = \frac{4[1 - (-3)^5]}{1 - (-3)} = \frac{4[1-(-243)]}{4} = 244$$

(b) We know that $n = 6$, $a_1 = \frac{1}{4}$, and $r = \frac{1}{2}$. Thus

$$s_6 = \frac{\frac{1}{4}[1 - (\frac{1}{2})^6]}{1 - \frac{1}{2}} = \frac{\frac{1}{4}(1 - \frac{1}{64})}{\frac{1}{2}} = \frac{1 - \frac{1}{64}}{2} = \frac{64 - 1}{128} = \frac{63}{128}$$

CHECKPOINT

7. Identify any geometric sequences among the following and give each one's common ratio.
   (a) 1, 4, 9, 16, ...
   (b) 1, 4, 7, 10, ...
   (c) 1, 4, 16, 64, ...

8. (a) Find the 40th term of the geometric sequence $8, 6, \frac{9}{2}, \ldots$.
   (b) Find the sum of the first 20 terms of the geometric sequence $2, 6, 18, \ldots$.

CHECKPOINT ANSWERS

1. (a) $m = 4$ (b) $n = 20$ (c) $i = 0.015$ (d) $S \approx \$6734.28$
2. $P \approx \$7664.40$
3. (a) Periodic compounding
   (b) Continuous compounding
4. $S \approx \$6749.29$
5. APY ≈ 0.0712, or 7.12%
6. $n \approx 92.8$ months
7. Only (c) is geometric with common ratio $r = 4$.
8. (a) $a_{40} = 8(3/4)^{39} \approx 0.0001$
   (b) $s_{20} = 3{,}486{,}784{,}400$

EXERCISES 6.2

COMPOUND INTEREST

In Problems 1 and 2, find the requested value and identify each of the other values as the periodic rate, the number of periods, the principal, or the future value.

1. (a) Find S: $S = 2000(1 + 0.02)^{24}$
   (b) Find P: $25{,}000 = P(1 + 0.03)^{48}$
2. (a) Find S: $S = 15{,}000(1 + 0.005)^{360}$
   (b) Find P: $100{,}000 = P(1 + 0.06)^{25}$

For each investment situation in Problems 3–6, identify (a) the annual interest rate, (b) the length of the investment in years, (c) the periodic interest rate, and (d) the number of periods of the investment.

3. 8% compounded quarterly for 7 years
4. 12% compounded monthly for 3 years
5. 9% compounded monthly for 5 years
6. 10% compounded semiannually for 8 years
7. Find the future value if $8000 is invested for 10 years at 12% compounded annually.

8. What is the future value if $8600 is invested for 8 years at 10% compounded semiannually?
9. What are the future value and the interest earned if $3200 is invested for 5 years at 8% compounded quarterly?
10. What interest will be earned if $6300 is invested for 3 years at 12% compounded monthly?
11. What lump sum do parents need to deposit in an account earning 10% compounded monthly so that it will grow to $80,000 for their son's college fund in 18 years?
12. What lump sum should be deposited in an account that will earn 9% compounded quarterly to grow to $1.2 million for retirement in 25 years?
13. What present value amounts to $10,000 if it is invested for 10 years at 6% compounded annually?
14. What present value amounts to $300,000 if it is invested at 7% compounded semiannually for 15 years?
15. Find the future value if $5100 is invested for 4 years at 9% compounded continuously.

16. Find the interest that will result if $8000 is invested at 7% compounded continuously for 8 years.

17. What is the compound interest if $41,000 is invested for 10 years at 8% compounded continuously?

18. If $8000 is invested at 8.5% compounded continuously, find the future value after $4\frac{1}{2}$ years.

19. Grandparents want to make a gift of $100,000 for their grandchild's 20th birthday. How much would have to be invested on the day of their grandchild's birth if their investment could earn
    (a) 10.5% compounded continuously?
    (b) 11% compounded continuously?
    (c) Describe the effect this slight change in the interest rate makes over the 20 years of this investment.

20. Suppose an individual wants to have $200,000 available for her child's education. Find the amount that would have to be invested at 12% compounded continuously, if the number of years until college is
    (a) 7 years   (b) 14 years.
    (c) Does leaving the money invested twice as long mean that only half as much is needed initially? Explain.

21. Which investment will earn more money, a $1000 investment for 5 years at 8% compounded annually or a $1000 investment for 5 years compounded continuously at 7%?

22. How much more interest will be earned if $5000 is invested for 6 years at 7% compounded continuously, instead of at 7% compounded quarterly?

23. Find the annual percentage yield for an investment at
    (a) 7.3% compounded monthly
    (b) 6% compounded continuously.

24. What is the annual percentage yield (or effective annual rate) for a nominal rate of (a) 8.4% compounded quarterly and (b) 10% compounded continuously?

In Problems 25 and 26, rank each interest rate and compounding scheme in order from highest yield to lowest yield.

25. 8% compounded quarterly, 8% compounded monthly, 8% compounded annually

26. 6% compounded continuously, 6% compounded semi-annually, 6% compounded monthly

27. Two different investment companies offer college savings plans, one at 8.2% compounded continuously and the other at 8.4% compounded quarterly. Which is the better investment?

28. For life insurance policies, some of the premium pays for the cost of the insurance and the remainder goes toward the cash value of the policy and earns interest like a savings account. Suppose that on the cash value of their policies, one insurance company pays 4.8% compounded monthly and another pays 4.82% compounded semiannually. Which company offers a higher yield?

29. The figure shows a graph of the future value of $100 at 8% compounded annually, along with the graph

of $100 at 8% compounded continuously. Which is which? Explain.

30. The figure shows a graph of the future value of $350 at 6% compounded monthly, along with the graph of $350 at 6% compounded annually. Which is which? Explain.

31. Microsoft's stock price peaked at 6118% of its IPO price more than 13 years after the IPO (*Source:* Bloomberg Financial Markets). Suppose that $10,000 invested in Microsoft at its IPO price had been worth $600,000 (6000% of the IPO price) after exactly 13 years. What interest rate compounded annually does this represent?

32. If $10,000 had been invested in the Sagamore Capital Opportunity Fund on September 30, 2008, it would have been worth $46,649.55 on September 30, 2018. What interest rate compounded annually did this investment earn?

33. How long (in years) would $700 have to be invested at 11.9% compounded continuously to earn $300 interest?

34. How long (in years) would $600 have to be invested at 8% compounded continuously to amount to $970?

35. At what nominal rate compounded quarterly would $20,000 have to be invested to amount to $26,425.82 in 7 years?

36. At what nominal rate compounded annually would $10,000 have to be invested to amount to $14,071 in 7 years?

37. For her 1st birthday, Ruth's grandparents invested $1000 in an 18-year certificate for her that pays 8%

compounded annually. How much will the certificate be worth on Ruth's 19th birthday?

38. To help their son buy a car on his 16th birthday, a boy's parents invest $7500 on his 10th birthday. If the investment pays 9% compounded continuously, how much is available on his 16th birthday?

39. (a) A 40-year-old man has $432,860 in an IRA account. He decides to make no additional contributions to the account but expects it to grow at 7.5% compounded annually. How much does he expect to have in the account when he retires at age 62?

    (b) How much more money would the man have if his investments earned 8.5% compounded annually?

40. (a) The purchase of Alaska cost the United States $7 million in 1869. If this money had been placed in a savings account paying 6% compounded annually, how much money would have been available from this investment in 2015?

    (b) If the $7 million earned 7% compounded annually since 1869, how much would have been available in 2015?

    (c) Do you think either amount would have purchased Alaska in 2015? Explain in light of the value of Alaska's resources or perhaps the price per acre of land.

41. A couple needs $45,000 as a down payment for a home. If they invest the $30,000 they have at 8% compounded quarterly, how long will it take the money to grow to $45,000?

42. How long does it take an account containing $8000 to be worth $15,000 if the money is invested at 9% compounded monthly?

43. Mary Stahley invested $2500 in a 36-month certificate of deposit (CD) that earned 8.5% annual simple interest. When the CD matured, she invested the full amount in a mutual fund that had an annual growth equivalent to 18% compounded annually. How much was the mutual fund worth after 9 years?

44. Suppose Patrick Goldsmith deposited $1000 in an account that earned simple interest at an annual rate of 7% and left it there for 4 years. At the end of the 4 years, Patrick deposited the entire amount from that account into a new account that earned 7% compounded quarterly. He left the money in this account for 6 years. How much did he have after the 10 years?

In Problems 45 and 46, use a spreadsheet or financial program on a calculator or computer.

45. Track the future values of two investments of $5000, one at 6.3% compounded quarterly and another at 6.3% compounded monthly for each interest payment period for 10 years.

    (a) How long does it take each investment to be worth more than $7500?

    (b) What are the values of each investment after 3 years, 7 years, and 10 years?

46. Track the future values of two investments of $1000, one at 6.0% compounded semiannually and one at 6.6% compounded semiannually for each interest payment period for 25 years.

    (a) How long before the difference between these investments is $50?

    (b) How much sooner does the 6.6% investment reach $1500?

GEOMETRIC SEQUENCES

For each geometric sequence given in Problems 47 and 48, write the next three terms.

47. (a) 3, 6, 12, . . .

    (b) 81, 54, 36, . . .

    (c) −0.5, 2, −8, . . .

48. (a) 4, 12, 36, . . .

    (b) 32, 40, 50, . . .

    (c) −400, 40, −4, . . .

In Problems 49–58, write an expression that gives the requested term or sum.

49. The 13th term of the geometric sequence with first term 10 and common ratio 2

50. The 11th term of the geometric sequence with first term 6 and common ratio 3

51. The 16th term of the geometric sequence with first term 4 and common ratio $\frac{3}{2}$

52. The 20th term of the geometric sequence with first term 3 and common ratio −2

53. The sum of the first 17 terms of the geometric sequence with first term 6 and common ratio 3

54. The sum of the first 14 terms of the geometric sequence with first term 3 and common ratio 4

55. The sum of the first 35 terms of the geometric sequence 1, 3, 9, . . .

56. The sum of the first 14 terms of the geometric sequence 16, 64, 256, . . .

57. The sum of the first 18 terms of the geometric sequence 6, 4, $\frac{8}{3}$, . . .

58. The sum of the first 31 terms of the geometric sequence 9, −6, 4, . . .

APPLICATIONS

59. *Inflation* A house that 20 years ago was worth $160,000 has increased in value by 4% each year because of inflation. What is its worth today?

60. *Inflation* If inflation causes the cost of automobiles to increase by 3% each year, what would a car cost today if it cost $25,000 six years ago?

61. *Population growth* Suppose a country has a population of 20 million and projects a growth rate of 2% per year for the next 20 years. What will the population of this country be in 10 years?

62. *Spread of AIDS* Suppose a country is so devastated by the AIDS epidemic that its population decreases by 0.5% each year for a 4-year period. If the population was originally 10 million, what is the population at the end of the 4-year period?

63. *Population growth* If the rate of growth of a population continues at 2%, in how many years will the population double?

64. *Population* If a population of 8 million begins to increase at a rate of 0.1% each month, in how many months will it be 10 million?

65. *Ball rebounding* A ball is dropped from a height of 128 feet. If it rebounds $\frac{3}{4}$ of the height from which it falls every time it hits the ground, how high will it bounce after it strikes the ground for the fourth time?

66. *Water pumping* A pump removes $\frac{1}{3}$ of the water in a container with every stroke. What amount of water is still in a container after 5 strokes if it originally contained 81 cm^3?

67. *Depreciation* A machine is valued at $10,000. If the depreciation at the end of each year is 20% of its value at the beginning of the year, find its value at the end of 4 years.

68. *Profit* Suppose a new business makes a $1000 profit in its first month and has its profit increase by 10% each month for the next 2 years. How much profit will the business earn in its 12th month?

69. *Bacterial growth* The size of a certain bacteria culture doubles each hour. If the number of bacteria present initially is 5000, how many would be present at the end of 6 hours?

70. *Bacterial growth* If a bacteria culture increases by 20% every hour and 2000 are present initially, how many will be present at the end of 10 hours?

71. *Profit* If changing market conditions cause a company earning $8,000,000 in 2018 to project a loss of 2% of its profit in each of the next 5 years, what profit does it project in 2023?

72. *Profit* Suppose a new business makes a $1000 profit in its first month and has its profit increase by 10% each month for the next 2 years. How much profit will it earn in its first year?

73. *Chain letters* Suppose you receive a chain letter with six names on it, and to keep the chain unbroken, you are to mail a dime to the person whose name is at the top, cross out the top name, add your name to the bottom, and mail it to five friends. If your friends mail out five letters each and no one breaks the chain, you will eventually receive dimes. How many sets of mailings must occur before your name is at the top of the list to receive dimes? How many dimes would you receive? (This is a geometric sequence with first term 5.)

74. *Chain letters* Mailing chain letters that involve sending money has been declared illegal because most people would receive nothing while a comparative few would profit. Suppose the chain letter in Problem 73 were to go through 12 unbroken progressions.
    (a) How many people would receive money?
    (b) How much money would these people receive as a group?

75. *Chain letters* How many letters would be mailed if the chain letter in Problem 73 went through 12 unbroken progressions?

SECTION 6.3 — Future Values of Annuities

OBJECTIVES

- To compute the future values of ordinary annuities and annuities due
- To compute the payments required for ordinary annuities and annuities due to have specified future values
- To compute the payment required to establish a sinking fund
- To find how long it will take to reach a savings goal

APPLICATION PREVIEW

Twins graduate from college together and start their careers. Twin 1 invests $2000 at the end of each of 8 years in an account that earns 10% compounded annually. After the initial 8 years, no additional contributions are made, but the investment continues to earn 10% compounded annually. Twin 2 invests no money for 8 years but then contributes $2000 at the end of each year for a period of 36 years (to age 65) to an account that pays 10% compounded annually. How much money does each twin have at age 65? (See Examples 1 and 2.)

In this section, we consider ordinary annuities and annuities due, and we develop a formula for each type of annuity that allows us to find its future value—that is, a formula for the value of the account after regular deposits have been made over a period of time.

Each twin's contributions form an annuity. An **annuity** is a financial plan characterized by regular payments. We can view an annuity as a savings plan in which the regular payments are contributions to the account; then we can ask what the total value of the account will become (as in the Application Preview). Also, we can view an annuity as a payment plan (such as for retirement) in which regular payments are made from an account, often to an individual.

Ordinary Annuities   Most people save (or invest) money by depositing relatively small amounts at different times. If a depositor makes equal deposits at regular intervals, he or she is contributing to an annuity. The payments (deposits) may be made weekly, monthly, quarterly, yearly, or at any other interval of time. The sum of all payments plus all interest earned is called the **future amount of the annuity** or its **future value.**

In this text, we will deal with annuities in which the payments begin and end on fixed dates. First, we will deal with annuities in which the payments are made at the end of each of the equal payment intervals. This type of annuity is called an **ordinary annuity** (also an **annuity immediate**). The ordinary annuities we will consider have payment intervals that coincide with the compounding period of the interest.

Suppose you invested $100 at the end of each year for 5 years in an account that paid interest at 10% compounded annually. How much money would you have in the account at the end of the 5 years?

Because you are making payments at the end of each period (year), this annuity is an ordinary annuity.

To find the future value of your annuity at the end of the 5 years, we compute the future value of each payment separately and add the amounts. (See Figure 6.4.) The $100 invested *at the end* of the first year will draw interest for 4 years, so it will amount to $100(1.10)^4$. Figure 6.4 shows similar calculations for years 2–4. The $100 invested at the end of the fifth year will draw no interest, so it will amount to $100.

Thus the future value of the annuity is given by

$$S = 100 + 100(1.10) + 100(1.10)^2 + 100(1.10)^3 + 100(1.10)^4$$

Figure 6.4

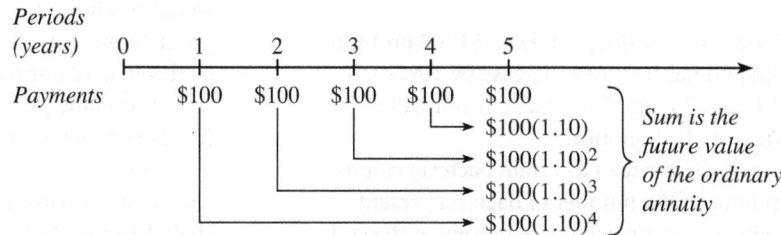

The terms of this sum are the first five values of the geometric sequence having $a_1 = 100$ and $r = 1.10$. Thus

$$S = \frac{100[1 - (1.10)^5]}{1 - 1.10} \approx \frac{100(-0.61051)}{-0.10} = 610.51$$

Thus the investment ($100 at the end of each year for 5 years at 10% compounded annually) would return $610.51.

Because every such annuity will take the same form, we can state that if a periodic payment R is made for n periods at an interest rate i per period, the **future amount of the annuity**, or its **future value**, will be given by

$$S = R \cdot \frac{1 - (1 + i)^n}{1 - (1 + i)} \qquad \text{or} \qquad S = R \left[\frac{(1 + i)^n - 1}{i} \right]$$

Future Value of an Ordinary Annuity

If $R is deposited at the end of each period for n periods in an annuity that earns interest at a rate of i per period, the **future value of the annuity** will be

$$S = R \cdot S_{\overline{n}|i} = R \cdot \left[\frac{(1 + i)^n - 1}{i} \right]$$

where $S_{\overline{n}|i}$ is read "s, n angle i" and represents the future value of an ordinary annuity of $1 per period for n periods with an interest rate of i per period.

In the Application Preview, we described savings plans for twins. In the next two examples, we answer the questions posed in the Application Preview.

EXAMPLE 1 **Future Value for Twin 2** | APPLICATION PREVIEW |

Twin 2 in the Application Preview invests $2000 at the end of each year for 36 years (until age 65) in an account that pays 10% compounded annually. How much does twin 2 have at age 65?

Solution
This savings plan is an ordinary annuity with $i = 0.10$, $n = 36$, and $R = \$2000$. The future value (to the nearest dollar) is

$$S = R\left[\frac{(1 + i)^n - 1}{i}\right] = \$2000\left[\frac{(1.10)^{36} - 1}{0.10}\right] \approx \$598,254$$

EXAMPLE 2 **Future Value for Twin 1** | APPLICATION PREVIEW |

Twin 1 invests $2000 at the end of each of 8 years in an account that earns 10% compounded annually. After the initial 8 years, no additional contributions are made, but the investment continues to earn 10% compounded annually for 36 more years (until twin 1 is age 65). How much does twin 1 have at age 65?

Solution
We seek the future values of two different investments. The first is an ordinary annuity with $R = \$2000$, $n = 8$ periods, and $i = 0.10$. The second is a compound interest investment with $n = 36$ periods and $i = 0.10$ and whose principal (that is, its present value) is the future value of this twin's ordinary annuity.

First, we find the future value of the ordinary annuity.

$$S = R\left[\frac{(1 + i)^n - 1}{i}\right] = \$2000\left[\frac{(1 + 0.10)^8 - 1}{0.10}\right] \approx \$22,871.78$$

This amount is the principal of the compound interest investment. If no deposits or withdrawals were made for the next 36 years, the future value of this investment would be

$$S = P(1 + i)^n = \$22,871.78(1 + 0.10)^{36} = \$707,028.03, \text{ to the nearest cent}$$

Thus, at age 65, twin 1's investment is worth about $707,028.

Looking back at Examples 1 and 2, we can extract the following summary and see which twin was wiser.

	Contributions	Account Value at Age 65
Twin 1	$2000/year for 8 years = $16,000	$707,028
Twin 2	$2000/year for 36 years = $72,000	$598,254

Note that twin 1 contributed $56,000 less than twin 2 but had $108,774 more at age 65. This illustrates the powerful effect that time and compounding have on investments.

Calculator Note

We can use a graphing calculator to find the future value of an ordinary annuity as follows:

1. Under the APPS menu, select Finance and then TVM Solver.
2. Set N = the total number of payments, I% = the annual percentage rate, and PV = 0.
3. Set PMT = periodic payment (with a "-" because the money is leaving) and both P/Y and C/Y equal to the number of compounding periods per year.
4. Highlight END; then put the cursor on FV and press ALPHA ENTER to get the future value.

Figure 6.5

Figure 6.5 shows that when $200 is invested at the end of each quarter for $2\frac{1}{4}$ years at 4% compounded quarterly, the future value is about $1873.71. See Appendix A, Section 6.3, for further details.

Spreadsheet Note   We can use Excel to find the future value of an ordinary annuity by using the formula =fv(F2, B2, C2, A2, 0) with the periodic interest rate as a decimal in cell F2, the number of periods in cell B2, the value 0 in cell A2, and the periodic payment in cell C2. The following spreadsheet shows the Excel display for the future value of the annuity above; cell B4 shows that the future value is $1873.71. See Appendix B, Section 6.3, or the Online Excel Guide for details.

	A	B	C	D	E	F
1	Principal	Number of Periods	Payment	Annual Rate	Periods per Year	Periodic Rate
2	0	9	−200	0.04	4	0.01
3	Ordinary Annuity					
4	Future Value	$1873.71				

Figure 6.6 shows a comparison (each graphed as a smooth curve) of the future values of two annuities that are invested at 6% compounded monthly. One annuity has monthly payments of $100, and one has payments of $125. Note the impact of a slightly larger contribution on the future value of the annuity after 5 years, 10 years, 15 years, and 20 years. Of course, a slightly higher interest rate also can have a substantial impact over time; try a graphical comparison yourself.

Figure 6.6

Spreadsheet Note   Excel also can be used to compare investments such as those compared graphically in Figure 6.6. The following spreadsheet shows the future values at the end of every two years for the first 10 years of two ordinary annuities: one of $100 per month and a second of $125 per month and both at 6% compounded monthly. The values in column B of the spreadsheet were found by entering 2 in cell A3, entering =100(1.005^(12A3)−1)/0.005 in cell B3, and filling down using the numbers in column A. The same process using 125 in place of 100 gives the entries in column C.

	A	B	C
1		Future Value for R = $100	Future Value for R = $125
2	End of Year #	at 6% compounded monthly	at 6% compounded monthly
3	2	2543.20	3178.99
4	4	5409.78	6762.23
5	6	8640.89	10,801.11
6	8	12,282.85	15,353.57
7	10	16,387.93	20,484.92

Sometimes we want to know how long it will take an annuity to reach a desired future value.

EXAMPLE 3   **Time to Reach a Goal**

A small business invests $1000 at the end of each month in an account that earns 6% compounded monthly. How long will it take until the business has $100,000 toward the purchase of its own office building?

Solution

This is an ordinary annuity with $S = \$100{,}000$, $R = \$1000$, $i = 0.06/12 = 0.005$, and $n = $ the number of months. To answer the question of how long, solve for n.

$$\text{Use } S = R\left[\frac{(1+i)^n - 1}{i}\right] \text{ and solve for } n \text{ in } 100{,}000 = 1000\left[\frac{(1+0.005)^n - 1}{0.005}\right].$$

This is an exponential equation. Hence, we isolate $(1.005)^n$, take the natural logarithm of both sides, and then solve for n as follows.

$$100{,}000 = \frac{1000}{0.005}[(1.005)^n - 1]$$
$$0.5 = (1.005)^n - 1$$
$$1.5 = (1.005)^n$$
$$\ln(1.5) = \ln[(1.005)^n] = n[\ln(1.005)]$$
$$n = \frac{\ln(1.5)}{\ln(1.005)} \approx 81.3$$

Because this investment is monthly, the company will be able to purchase its own office building after 82 months.

Sinking Funds

Consumers who are saving for an anticipated purchase using a regular savings plan to obtain some specified future amount need to know what periodic deposit will allow them to reach their goal. Similarly, some borrowers, such as municipalities, may have a debt that must be paid in a single large sum on a specified future date. If these borrowers make periodic deposits that will produce that sum on a specified date, we say that they have established a **sinking fund.** If the deposits (into the sinking fund or toward the consumer's goal) are all the same size and are made regularly, they form an ordinary annuity whose future value (on a specified date) is the desired amount. To find the size of these periodic deposits, we solve for R in the equation for the future value of an annuity.

EXAMPLE 4   **Sinking Fund**

A company establishes a sinking fund to discharge a debt of $300,000 due in 5 years by making equal semiannual deposits, the first due in 6 months. If the deposits are placed in an account that pays 6% compounded semiannually what is the size of the deposits?

Solution

For this sinking fund, we want to find the payment size, R, given that the future value is $S = \$300{,}000$, $n = 2(5) = 10$, and $i = 0.06/2 = 0.03$. Thus we have

$$S = R\left[\frac{(1+i)^n - 1}{i}\right]$$

$$\$300{,}000 = R\left[\frac{(1+0.03)^{10} - 1}{0.03}\right] \approx R(11.463879)$$

$$\frac{\$300{,}000}{11.463879} \approx R \quad \text{so} \quad R \approx \$26{,}169.15$$

Thus the semiannual deposit is $26,169.15.

Calculator Note

Example 4 can also be solved using a graphing calculator and TVM as follows: Enter N = 10, I% = 6, PV = 0, FV = 300000, and P/Y and C/Y = 2 and select END. Then put the cursor on PMT and press ALPHA ENTER to get the semiannual deposit of $26,169.15. See Figure 6.7. ∎

Figure 6.7

CHECKPOINT

1. Suppose that $500 is deposited at the end of every quarter for 6 years in an account that pays 8% compounded quarterly.
   (a) What is the total number of payments (periods)?
   (b) What is the interest rate per period?
   (c) What formula is used to find the future value of the annuity?
   (d) Find the future value of the annuity.
2. A sinking fund of $100,000 is to be established with equal payments at the end of each half-year for 15 years. Find the amount of each payment if money is worth 10% compounded semiannually.

Annuities Due

Deposits in savings accounts, rent payments, and insurance premiums are examples of **annuities due.** Unlike an ordinary annuity, an annuity due has the periodic payments made at the *beginning* of the period. The *term* of an annuity due is from the first payment to the end of one period after the last payment. Thus an annuity due draws interest for one period more than the ordinary annuity.

We can find the future value of an annuity due by treating each payment as though it were made at the *end* of the preceding period in an ordinary annuity. Then that amount, $RS_{\overline{n}|i}$, remains in the account for one additional period (see Figure 6.8), and its future value is $RS_{\overline{n}|i}(1 + i)$.

Figure 6.8   Ordinary annuity, n periods = $Rs_{\overline{n}|i}$

Thus the formula for the future value of an annuity due is as follows.

Future Value of an Annuity Due

$$S_{\text{due}} = RS_{\overline{n}|i}(1 + i) = R\left[\frac{(1 + i)^n - 1}{i}\right](1 + i)$$

EXAMPLE 5   **Future Value**

Find the future value of an investment if $150 is deposited at the beginning of each month for 9 years and the interest rate is 7.2% compounded monthly.

Solution

Because deposits are made at the *beginning* of each month, this is an annuity due with $R = \$150$, $n = 9(12) = 108$, and $i = 0.072/12 = 0.006$.

$$S_{\text{due}} = R\left[\frac{(1 + i)^n - 1}{i}\right](1 + i) = \$150\left[\frac{(1 + 0.006)^{108} - 1}{0.006}\right](1 + 0.006)$$

$$\approx \$150(151.3359308)(1.006) \approx \$22,836.59$$

3. Suppose $100 is deposited at the beginning of each month for 3 years in an account that pays 6% compounded monthly.
   (a) What is the total number of payments (or periods)?
   (b) What is the interest rate per period?
   (c) What formula is used to find the future value of the annuity?
   (d) Find the future value.

We also can use the formula for the future value of an annuity due to determine the payment size required to reach an investment goal.

EXAMPLE 6 Required Payment

Suppose a company wants to have $450,000 after $2\frac{1}{2}$ years to modernize its production equipment. How much of each previous quarter's profits should be deposited at the beginning of the current quarter to reach this goal, if the company's investment earns 6.8% compounded quarterly?

Solution

We seek the payment size, R, for an annuity due with $S_{\text{due}} = \$450{,}000$, $n = (2.5)(4) = 10$, and $i = 0.068/4 = 0.017$.

$$S_{\text{due}} = R\left[\frac{(1 + i)^n - 1}{i}\right](1 + i)$$

$$\$450{,}000 = R\left[\frac{(1 + 0.017)^{10} - 1}{0.017}\right](1 + 0.017)$$

$$\$450{,}000 \approx R(10.80073308)(1.017) \approx (10.98434554)R$$

$$R = \frac{\$450{,}000}{10.98434554} \approx \$40{,}967.39$$

Thus, the company needs to deposit about $40,967 at the beginning of each quarter for the next $2\frac{1}{2}$ years to reach its goal.

Technology Note

Solving investment problems involving annuities due with a graphing calculator uses the same operations as those for ordinary annuities *except* that the PMT is changed from END to BEGIN. See Appendix A, Section 6.3, for details.

Solving investment problems involving annuities due with Excel uses the same formulas as those for ordinary annuities *except* that the last component in fv(F2, B2, C2, A2, 1) is 1 instead of 0. See Appendix B, Section 6.3, or the Online Excel Guide for details.

1. (a) $n = 24$ periods   (b) $i = 0.02$ per period

   (c) $S = R\left[\dfrac{(1 + i)^n - 1}{i}\right]$ (d) $S \approx \$15{,}210.93$

2. $R \approx \$1505.14$
3. (a) $n = 36$ periods   (b) $i = 0.005$ per period

   (c) $S_{\text{due}} = R\left[\dfrac{(1 + i)^n - 1}{i}\right](1 + i)$ (d) $S_{\text{due}} \approx \$3953.28$

EXERCISES 6.3

ORDINARY ANNUITIES

In Problems 1 and 2, find the requested value (to the nearest dollar) and explain what each of the other values represents.

1. (a) Find S: $S = 2500\left[\dfrac{(1 + 0.02)^{60} - 1}{0.02}\right]$

    (b) Find R: $80,000 = R\left[\dfrac{(1 + 0.04)^{30} - 1}{0.04}\right]$

2. (a) Find S: $S = 1000\left[\dfrac{(1 + 0.03)^{25} - 1}{0.03}\right]$

    (b) Find R: $25,000 = R\left[\dfrac{(1 + 0.06)^{15} - 1}{0.06}\right]$

3. The figure shows a graph that compares the future values at 8% compounded annually of an annuity of $1000 per year and one of $1120 per year.
    (a) Decide which graph corresponds to which annuity.
    (b) Verify your conclusion to (a) by finding the value of each annuity and the difference between them at $t = 25$ years.

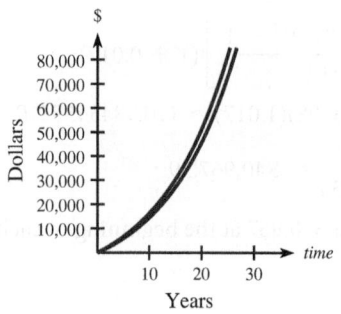

4. The figure shows a graph that compares the future values at 9% compounded monthly of an annuity of $50 per month and one of $60 per month.
    (a) Decide which graph corresponds to which annuity.
    (b) Use the graph to estimate (to the nearest 10 months) how long it will be before the larger annuity is $10,000 more than the smaller one.

5. Find the future value of an annuity of $1300 paid at the end of each year for 5 years, if interest is earned at a rate of 6% compounded annually.

6. Find the future value of an annuity of $5000 paid at the end of each year for 10 years, if it earns 9% compounded annually.

7. Find the future value of an ordinary annuity of $8000 paid quarterly for 3 years, if the interest rate is 8% compounded quarterly.

8. Find the future value of an ordinary annuity of $3000 paid quarterly for 5 years, if the interest rate is 6% compounded quarterly.

9. The Weidmans want to save $40,000 in 2 years for a down payment on a house. If they make monthly deposits in an account paying 12% compounded monthly, what is the size of the payments that are required to meet their goal?

10. A sinking fund is established to discharge a debt of $80,000 in 10 years. If deposits are made at the end of each 6-month period and interest is paid at the rate of 8% compounded semiannually, what is the amount of each deposit?

11. If $2500 is deposited at the end of each quarter in an account that earns 5% compounded quarterly, after how many quarters will the account contain $80,000?

12. If $4000 is deposited at the end of each half year in an account that earns 6.2% compounded semiannually, how long will it be before the account contains $120,000?

13. In this section's Application Preview, we considered the investment strategies of twins and found that starting early and stopping was a significantly better strategy than waiting, in terms of total contributions made as well as total value in the account at retirement. Suppose that twin 1 invests $2000 at the end of each year for 10 years only (until age 33) in an account that earns 8% compounded annually. Suppose that twin 2 waits until turning 40 to begin investing. How much must twin 2 put aside at the end of each year for the next 25 years in an account that earns 8% compounded annually to have the same amount as twin 1 at the end of these 25 years (when they turn 65)?

14. (a) Patty Stacey deposits $2000 at the end of each of 5 years in an IRA. If she leaves the money that has accumulated in the IRA account for 25 additional years, how much is in her account at the end of the 30-year period? Assume an interest rate of 9% compounded annually.

    (b) Suppose that Patty's husband delays starting an IRA for the first 10 years he works but then makes $2000 deposits at the end of each of the next 15 years. If the interest rate is 9% compounded annually and if he leaves the money in his account for 5 additional years, how much will be in his account at the end of the 30-year period?

    (c) Does Patty or her husband have more IRA money?

ANNUITIES DUE

15. Find the future value of an annuity due of $100 each quarter for $2\frac{1}{2}$ years at 12% compounded quarterly.

16. Find the future value of an annuity due of $1500 each month for 3 years if the interest rate is 12% compounded monthly.

17. Find the future value of an annuity due of $2000 paid at the beginning of each 6-month period for 8 years if the interest rate is 6% compounded semiannually.

18. A house is rented for $7200 per quarter, with each quarter's rent payable in advance. If money is worth 8% compounded quarterly and the rent is deposited in an account, what is the future value of the rent for one year?

19. How much must be deposited at the beginning of each year in an account that pays 8% compounded annually so that the account will contain $24,000 at the end of 5 years?

20. What is the size of the payments that must be deposited at the beginning of each 6-month period in an account that pays 7.8% compounded semiannually so that the account will have a future value of $120,000 at the end of 15 years?

21. A company wants to have $800,000 for office renovations. If it can deposit $40,000 at the beginning of each quarter into an account that earns 5.2% compounded quarterly, how long before the company reaches its goal?

22. Seana wants to save $20,000 toward the purchase of a new car. She can contribute $400 at the beginning of each month into an account that earns 4.8% compounded monthly. How long until she reaches her goal?

MISCELLANEOUS PROBLEMS

In Problems 23–40, (a) state whether the problem relates to an ordinary annuity or an annuity due and then (b) solve the problem.

23. Parents agree to invest $500 (at 10% compounded semiannually) for their son on the December 31 or June 30 following each semester that he makes the dean's list during his 4 years in college. If he makes the dean's list in each of the 8 semesters, how much money will his parents have to give him when he graduates?

24. Jake Werkheiser decides to invest $2000 in an IRA at the end of each year for the next 10 years. If he makes these investments and if the certificates pay 12% compounded annually, how much will he have at the end of the 10 years?

25. How much must be invested at the beginning of each year at 10% compounded annually to pay off a debt of $50,000 in 8 years?

26. If $1000 is deposited at the beginning of each quarter into an account that earns 8% compounded quarterly, how long until the account contains $31,000?

27. A family wants to have a $200,000 college fund for their children at the end of 20 years. What contribution must be made at the end of each quarter if their investment pays 7.6% compounded quarterly?

28. If $2000 is deposited at the end of each quarter into an account that earns 6% compounded quarterly, how long until the account reaches $50,000?

29. A couple has determined that they need $1.5 million to establish an annuity when they retire in 25 years. How much money should they deposit at the end of each month in an investment plan that pays 10% compounded monthly, so that they will have the $1.5 million in 25 years?

30. Sam deposits $500 at the end of every 6 months in an account that pays 8% compounded semiannually. How much will he have at the end of 8 years?

31. A company deposits $12,000 at the beginning of each quarter into an account that earns 7.2% compounded quarterly. How much will be in this account after 5 years?

32. Sofia can deposit $350 at the beginning of each month into an account that earns 4.2% compounded monthly. How long before the account contains $17,000?

33. Mr. Gordon plans to invest $300 at the end of each month in an account that pays 9% compounded monthly. After how many months will the account be worth $50,000?

34. For 3 years, $4000 is placed in a savings account at the beginning of each 6-month period. If the account pays interest at 10% compounded semiannually, how much will be in the account at the end of the 3 years?

35. Grandparents plan to open an account on their grandchild's birthday and contribute each month until she goes to college. How much must they contribute at the beginning of each month in an investment that pays 12% compounded monthly, if they want the balance to be $180,000 at the end of 18 years?

36. How much money should a couple deposit at the end of each month in an investment plan that pays 7.5% compounded monthly so that they will have $800,000 in 30 years?

37. Jane Adele deposits $1500 in an account at the beginning of each 3-month period for 9 years. If the account pays interest at the rate of 8% compounded quarterly, how much will she have in her account after 9 years?

38. A company establishes a sinking fund to discharge a debt of $750,000 due in 8 years by making equal semiannual deposits, the first due in 6 months. If the investment pays 12% compounded semiannually, what is the size of the deposits?

39. A sinking fund is established by a working couple so that they will have $60,000 to pay for part of their daughter's education when she enters college. If they make deposits at the end of each 3-month period for 10 years and if interest is paid at 12% compounded quarterly, what size deposits must they make?

40. A property owner has several rental units and wants to build more. How much of each month's rental income should be deposited at the beginning of each month in an account that earns 6.6% compounded monthly, if the goal is to have $100,000 at the end of 4 years?

COMBINED APPLICATIONS

Problems 41–44 are complex financial problems that require several skills, perhaps some from previous sections.

41. Suppose a recent college graduate's first job allows her to deposit $100 at the end of each month in a savings plan that earns 9% compounded monthly. This savings plan continues for 8 years before new obligations make it impossible to continue. If the accrued amount remains in the plan for the next 15 years without deposits or withdrawals, how much money will be in the account 23 years after the plan began?

42. Suppose a young couple deposits $1000 at the end of each quarter in an account that earns 7.6%

compounded quarterly for a period of 8 years. After the 8 years, they start a family and find that they can contribute only $200 per quarter. If they leave the money from the first 8 years in the account and continue to contribute $200 at the end of each quarter for the next $18\frac{1}{2}$ years, how much will they have in the account (to help with their child's college expenses)?

43. A small business owner contributes $3000 at the end of each quarter to a retirement account that earns 8% compounded quarterly.
  (a) How long will it be until the account is worth $150,000?
  (b) Suppose when the account reaches $150,000, the business owner increases the contributions to $5000 at the end of each quarter. What will the total value of the account be after 15 more years?

44. A young executive deposits $300 at the end of each month for 8 years and then increases the deposits. If the account earns 7.2% compounded monthly, how much (to the nearest dollar) should each new deposit be to have a total of $400,000 after 25 years?

SECTION 6.4

Present Values of Annuities

OBJECTIVES

- To compute the present values of ordinary annuities, annuities due, and deferred annuities
- To compute the payments from various annuities
- To find how long an annuity will last
- To apply present values to bond pricing

APPLICATION PREVIEW

If at retirement you wanted to receive $1000 at the end of each month for 16 years, what lump sum would you need to invest in an annuity that paid 9% compounded monthly? (See Example 1.) We call this lump sum the present value of the annuity. Note that the annuity in this case is an account from which a person receives equal periodic payments (withdrawals).

In this section, we will find present values of annuities, compute payments from annuities, and find how long annuities will last.

We have discussed how contributing to an annuity program will result in a sum of money, and we have called that sum the future value of the annuity. Just as the term *annuity* is used to describe an account in which a person makes equal periodic payments (deposits), this term is also used to describe an account from which a person receives equal periodic payments (withdrawals). That is, if you invest a lump sum of money in an account today so that at regular intervals you will receive a fixed sum of money, you have established an annuity. The single sum of money required to purchase an annuity that will provide these payments at regular intervals is the **present value** of the annuity.

Ordinary Annuities Suppose we want to invest a lump sum of money (denoted by A_n) in an annuity that earns interest at rate i per period so that we receive (withdraw) payments of size R from this account at the end of each of n periods (after which time the account balance will be $0). Recall that receiving payments at the end of each period means that this is an ordinary annuity.

To find a formula for A_n, we can find the present value of each future payment and then add these present values. (See Figure 6.9.)

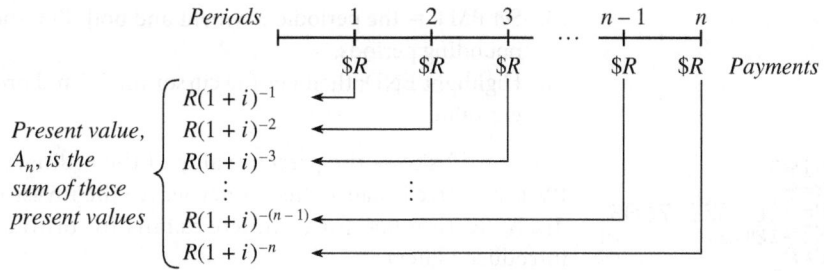

Figure 6.9

$Present\ value,$
$A_n,\ is\ the$
$sum\ of\ these$
$present\ values$

Figure 6.9 shows that we can express A_n as follows.

$$A_n = R(1 + i)^{-1} + R(1 + i)^{-2} + R(1+i)^{-3} + \cdots + R(1 + i)^{-(n-1)} + R(1 + i)^{-n} \quad (1)$$

Multiplying both sides of equation (1) by $(1 + i)$ gives

$$(1 + i)A_n = R + R(1 + i)^{-1} + R(1 + i)^{-2} + \cdots + R(1 + i)^{-(n-2)} + R(1 + i)^{-(n-1)} \quad (2)$$

If we subtract equation (1) from equation (2), we obtain $iA_n = R - R(1 + i)^{-n}$. Then solving for A_n gives the following.

Present Value of an Ordinary Annuity

If a payment of $R is to be made at the end of each period for n periods from an account that earns interest at a rate of i per period, then the account is an **ordinary annuity** and the **present value** is

$$A_n = R \cdot a_{\overline{n}|i} = R \cdot \left[\frac{1 - (1 + i)^{-n}}{i} \right]$$

where $a_{\overline{n}|i}$ represents the present value of an ordinary annuity of $1 per period for n periods with an interest rate of i per period.

For example, if money is worth 8% compounded semiannually, then an annuity that pays $1500 at the end of each 6-month period for 2 years has $R = \$1500$, $i = 0.08/2 = 0.04$, and $n = (2)(2) = 4$. Thus, the present value of this annuity is

$$A_n = \$1500 \left[\frac{1 - (1 + 0.04)^{-4}}{0.04} \right] \approx \$5444.84$$

EXAMPLE   1   **Present Value** | APPLICATION PREVIEW |

Find the lump sum that one must invest in an annuity to receive $1000 at the end of each month for the next 16 years, if the annuity pays 9% compounded monthly.

Solution
The sum we seek is the present value of an ordinary annuity, A_n, with $R = \$1000$, $i = 0.09/12 = 0.0075$, and $n = (16)(12) = 192$.

$$A_n = R \left[\frac{1 - (1 + i)^{-n}}{i} \right]$$

$$= \$1000 \left[\frac{1 - (1.0075)^{-192}}{0.0075} \right] \approx \$101,572.77$$

Thus the required lump sum, to the nearest dollar, is $101,573.

Technology Note

We can use a graphing calculator to find the present value of an ordinary annuity as follows:

1. Under the APPS menu, select Finance and then TVM Solver.
2. Set N = the total number of payments, I% = the annual percentage rate, and FV = 0.

3. Set PMT = the periodic payment and both P/Y and C/Y equal to the number of compounding periods.
4. Highlight END; then put the cursor on PV and press ALPHA ENTER to get the present value.

```
N=192
I%=9
PV=-101572.7689
PMT=1000
FV=0
P/Y=12
C/Y=12
PMT:END BEGIN
```

Figure 6.10

Figure 6.10 shows the present value of the ordinary annuity in Example 1. Note that PV is negative because this money leaves the investor to start the annuity. See Appendix A, Section 6.4, for complete details for ordinary annuities (and annuities due, introduced later).

We can also use Excel to find the present value of an ordinary annuity using the *present value* formula =pv(F2, B2, C2, A2, 0) with the periodic interest rate as a decimal in cell F2, the number of periods in cell B2, the value 0 in cell A2, and the periodic payment in cell C2. The following spreadsheet gives the present value for the annuity of Example 1. The ($101,572.77) means that the present value is negative (this money leaves the investor to start the annuity). See Appendix B, Section 6.4, or the Online Excel Guide for complete details for ordinary annuities and annuities due.

	A	B	C	D	E	F
1	Future Value	Number of Periods	Payment	Annual Rate	Periods per Year	Periodic Rate
2	0	192	1000	0.09	12	0.0075
3						
4	Present Value	($101,572.77)				

It is important to note that all annuities involve both periodic payments and a lump sum of money. It is whether this lump sum is in the present or in the future that distinguishes problems that use formulas for present values of annuities from those that use formulas for future values of annuities. In Example 1, the lump sum was needed now (in the present) to generate the $1000 payments, so we used the present value formula.

Figure 6.11 shows a graph that compares the present value of an annuity of $1000 per year at an interest rate of 6% compounded annually with the same annuity at an interest rate of 10% compounded annually. Note the impact the higher interest rate has on the present value needed to establish such an annuity for a longer period of time.

Figure 6.11

Spreadsheet Note The analysis illustrated graphically in Figure 6.11 is shown in the following a spreadsheet, for years 5, 10, 15, 20, and 25. Note that at 6% interest, a present value of more than $12,500 is needed to generate 25 years of $1000 payments, but at an interest rate of 10%, the necessary present value is less than $10,000.

PRESENT VALUE GIVING $R = \$1000$ FOR N YEARS

	A	B	C
1	Year number	at 6% compounded annually	at 10% compounded annually
2	5	4212.36	3790.79
3	10	7360.09	6144.57
4	15	9712.25	7606.08
5	20	11469.92	8513.56
6	25	12783.36	9077.04

Our graphical and spreadsheet comparisons just completed as well as those from other sections emphasize the truth of the saying "Time is money." We have seen that, given enough time, relatively small differences in contributions or in interest rates can result in substantial differences in amounts (both present and future values).

EXAMPLE 2   Payments from an Annuity

Suppose that a couple plans to set up an ordinary annuity with a $100,000 inheritance they received. What is the size of the quarterly payments they will receive for the next 6 years (while their children are in college) if the account pays 7% compounded quarterly?

Solution

The $100,000 is the amount the couple has now, so it is the present value of an ordinary annuity whose payment size, R, we seek. Using present value $A_n = \$100,000$, $n = 6(4) = 24$, and $i = 0.07/4 = 0.0175$, we solve for R.

$$A_n = R\left[\frac{1 - (1 + i)^{-n}}{i}\right]$$

$$\$100,000 = R\left[\frac{1 - (1 + 0.0175)^{-24}}{0.0175}\right]$$

$$\$100,000 \approx R(19.46068565)$$

$$R \approx \frac{\$100,000}{19.46068565} \approx \$5138.57$$

CHECKPOINT

1. Suppose an annuity pays $2000 at the end of each 3-month period for $3\frac{1}{2}$ years and money is worth 4% compounded quarterly.
   (a) What is the total number of periods?
   (b) What is the interest rate per period?
   (c) What formula is used to find the present value of the annuity?
   (d) Find the present value.
2. An inheritance of $400,000 will provide how much at the end of each year for the next 20 years, if money is worth 7% compounded annually?

EXAMPLE 3   Number of Payments from an Annuity

An inheritance of $250,000 is invested at 9% compounded monthly. If $2500 is withdrawn at the end of each month, how long will it be until the account balance is $0?

Solution

The regular withdrawals form an ordinary annuity with present value $A_n = \$250,000$, payment $R = \$2500$, $i = 0.09/12 = 0.0075$, and $n =$ the number of months.

Use $A_n = R\left[\dfrac{1 - (1 + i)^{-n}}{i}\right]$ and solve for n in $250,000 = 2500\left[\dfrac{1 - (1.0075)^{-n}}{0.0075}\right]$.

This is an exponential equation, and to solve it, we isolate $(1.0075)^{-n}$ and then take the natural logarithm of both sides.

$$\frac{250,000(0.0075)}{2500} = 1 - (1.0075)^{-n}$$

$$0.75 = 1 - (1.0075)^{-n}$$

$$(1.0075)^{-n} = 0.25$$

$$\ln\left[(1.0075)^{-n}\right] = \ln(0.25) \quad \Rightarrow \quad -n\left[\ln(1.0075)\right] = \ln(0.25)$$

$$-n = \frac{\ln(0.25)}{\ln(1.0075)} \approx -185.5, \text{ so } n \approx 185.5$$

Thus, the account balance will be \$0 in 186 months (with the last payment less than \$2500). ■

Bond Pricing

Bonds are investments with a fixed rate of return, similar to a bank certificate of deposit (CD), but unlike CDs (and like stocks), bonds can be traded. And as is also true of stocks, the trading or market price of a bond may fluctuate.

Most commonly, bonds are issued by the government, corporations, or municipalities for periods of 10 years or longer. Bonds actually constitute a loan in which the issuer of the bond is the borrower, the bondholders (or purchasers) are the lenders, and the interest payments to the bondholders are called **coupons.** In the simplest case, a bond's issue price, or **par value,** is the same as its **maturity value,** and the coupons are paid semiannually.

For example, if a corporation plans to issue \$5000 bonds at 6% semiannually, then the maturity value is \$5000, the **coupon rate** is 6%, and each semiannual coupon payment will be

$$(\$5000)(0.06/2) = (\$5000)(0.03) = \$150$$

The coupons are paid at the end of every 6 months and constitute an ordinary annuity. At maturity, the bondholder receives the final coupon payment of \$150 plus the \$5000 maturity value of the bond.

Because the amount of the coupon is fixed by the coupon rate for the entire term of the bond, the market price of the bond is strongly influenced by current interest rates. If a \$5000 bond pays a 6% coupon rate but market interest rates are higher than that, an investor will typically invest in the bond only if the bond's price makes its rate of return comparable to the market rate. The rate of return the investor requires to buy the bond is called the **yield rate.**

At any moment in time, the market price of a bond is the sum of the present value of the bond's maturity value, \$P$, and the present value of the annuity of future coupon payments, \$A_n$. (See Figure 6.12.)

Figure 6.12

EXAMPLE 4 Bond Pricing

Suppose a 15-year corporate bond has a maturity value of \$10,000 and coupons at 5% paid semiannually. If an investor wants to earn a yield of 7.2% compounded semiannually, what should she pay for this bond?

Solution

Each semiannual coupon payment is

$$(\$10,000)(0.05/2) = (\$10,000)(0.025) = \$250$$

Since the desired rate of return is 7.2% semiannually and the bond is for 15 years, we set $i = 0.072/2 = 0.036$ and $n = (15)(2) = 30$.

With these values of i and n, the market price of this bond is the sum of the following present values, (1) and (2).

(1) the principal (or present value) of a compound interest investment at $i = 0.036$ for $n = 30$ periods with future value $S = \$10,000$, the bond's maturity value

$$S = P(1 + i)^n$$
$$\$10,000 = P(1 + 0.036)^{30} = P(1.036)^{30}$$
$$P = \frac{\$10,000}{(1.036)^{30}} \approx \$3461.05$$

(2) the present value of the ordinary annuity formed by the coupon payments of $R = \$250$ at $i = 0.036$ for $n = 30$ periods

$$A_n = R\left[\frac{1 - (1 + i)^{-n}}{i}\right]$$

$$A_n = \$250\left[\frac{1 - (1.036)^{-30}}{0.036}\right] \approx \$4540.94$$

Thus, to earn the desired 7.2% yield, the market price an investor should pay for this bond is

$$\text{Price} = \$3461.05 + \$4540.94 = \$8001.99$$

Note that in Example 4, the bond's market price is less than its maturity value. In this case, the bond is said to be **selling at a discount.** This has to be the case for the yield rate to exceed the coupon rate. Similarly, if the yield rate is lower than the coupon rate, then the market price of the bond will exceed its maturity value. When this happens, the bond is said to be **selling at a premium.** In general, the market price of a bond moves in the opposite direction from current yield rates.

Annuities Due   Recall that an annuity due is one in which payments are made at the beginning of each period. This means the present value of an annuity due of n payments [denoted $A_{(n,\text{due})}$] of $\$R$ at interest rate i per period can be viewed as an initial payment of $\$R$ plus the payment program for an ordinary annuity of $n - 1$ payments of $\$R$ at interest rate i per period. (See Figure 6.13.)

Present Value of an Annuity Due

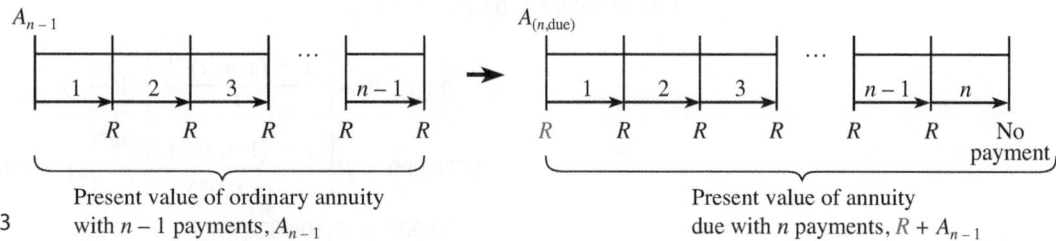

Figure 6.13 — Present value of ordinary annuity with $n - 1$ payments, A_{n-1} ; Present value of annuity due with n payments, $R + A_{n-1}$

From Figure 6.13, we have

$$A_{(n,\text{due})} = R + A_{n-1} = R + R\left[\frac{1 - (1 + i)^{-(n-1)}}{i}\right]$$

$$= R\left[1 + \frac{1 - (1 + i)^{-(n-1)}}{i}\right] = R\left[\frac{i}{i} + \frac{1 - (1 + i)^{-(n-1)}}{i}\right]$$

$$= R\left[\frac{(1 + i) - (1 + i)^{-(n-1)}}{i}\right] = R(1 + i)\left[\frac{1 - (1 + i)^{-n}}{i}\right]$$

Thus we have the following formula for the present value of an annuity due.

Present Value of an Annuity Due	If a payment of R is to be made at the beginning of each period for n periods from an account that earns interest rate i per period, then the account is an **annuity due** and its **present value** is given by

$$A_{(n,\text{due})} = R\left[\frac{1 - (1 + i)^{-n}}{i}\right](1 + i) = Ra_{\overline{n}|i}(1 + i)$$

where $a_{\overline{n}|i}$ denotes the present value of an ordinary annuity of $1 per period for n periods at interest rate i per period.

EXAMPLE 5 Lottery Prize

A lottery prize worth $1,200,000 is awarded in payments of $10,000 at the beginning of each month for 10 years. Suppose money is worth 7.8% compounded monthly. What is the *real* value of the prize?

Solution

The *real* value of this prize is its present value when it is awarded. That is, it is the present value of an annuity due with $R = 10,000$, $i = 0.078/12 = 0.0065$, and $n = 12(10) = 120$. Thus

$$A_{(120,\text{due})} = \$10,000\left[\frac{1 - (1 + 0.0065)^{-120}}{0.0065}\right](1 + 0.0065) \approx \$836,843.55.$$

This means that the lottery operator needs this amount to generate the 120 monthly payments of $10,000 each.

EXAMPLE 6 Court Settlement Payments

Suppose that a court settlement results in a $750,000 award. If this is invested at 9% compounded semiannually, how much will it provide at the beginning of each half-year for a period of 7 years?

Solution

Because payments are made at the beginning of each half-year, this is an annuity due. We seek the payment size, R, and use the present value $A_{(n,\text{due})} = \$750,000$, $n = 2(7) = 14$, and $i = 0.09/2 = 0.045$.

$$A_{(n,\text{due})} = R\left[\frac{1 - (1 + i)^{-n}}{i}\right](1 + i)$$

$$\$750,000 = R\left[\frac{1 - (1 + 0.045)^{-14}}{0.045}\right](1 + 0.045)$$

$$\$750,000 \approx R(10.682852)$$

$$R \approx \frac{\$750,000}{10.682852} \approx \$70,205.97$$

CHECKPOINT

3. What lump sum will be needed to generate payments of $5000 at the beginning of each quarter for a period of 5 years if money is worth 7% compounded quarterly?

Deferred Annuities   A **deferred annuity** is an annuity in which the first payment is made not at the beginning or end of the first period, but at some later date. An annuity that is deferred for k periods and then has payments of R per period at the end of each of the next n periods is an ordinary deferred annuity and can be illustrated by Figure 6.14.

Deferred Annuity

Figure 6.14

$A_{(n,k)}$ grows to $A_{(n,k)}(1 + i)^k$

Ordinary annuity with
present value $A_{(n,k)}(1 + i)^k$

We now consider how to find the present value of such a deferred annuity when the interest rate is i per period. If payment is deferred for k periods, then the present value deposited now, denoted by $A_{(n,k)}$, is a compound interest investment for these k periods and its future value is $A_{(n,k)}(1 + i)^k$. This amount then becomes the present value of the ordinary annuity for the next n periods. From Figure 6.14, we see that we have two equivalent expressions for the amount at the beginning of the first payment period.

$$A_{(n,k)}(1 + i)^k = R\left[\frac{1 - (1 + i)^{-n}}{i}\right]$$

Multiplying both sides by $(1 + i)^{-k}$ gives the following.

**Present Value of a
Deferred Annuity**

The **present value of a deferred annuity** of $\$R$ per period for n periods, deferred for k periods with interest rate i per period, is given by

$$A_{(n,k)} = R\left[\frac{1 - (1 + i)^{-n}}{i}\right](1 + i)^{-k}$$

EXAMPLE 7 **Present Value of a Deferred Annuity**

A deferred annuity is purchased that will pay $\$10,000$ per quarter for 15 years after being deferred for 5 years. If money is worth 6% compounded quarterly, what is the present value of this annuity?

Solution
We use $R = \$10,000$, $n = 4(15) = 60$, $k = 4(5) = 20$, and $i = 0.06/4 = 0.015$ in the formula for the present value of a deferred annuity.

$$A_{(60,20)} = R\left[\frac{1 - (1 + i)^{-60}}{i}\right](1 + i)^{-20}$$

$$= \$10,000\left[\frac{1 - (1.015)^{-60}}{0.015}\right](1.015)^{-20} \approx \$292,386.85$$

CHECKPOINT

4. Suppose an annuity at 6% compounded semiannually will pay $\$5000$ at the end of each 6-month period for 5 years with the first payment deferred for 10 years.
   (a) What is the number of payment periods and the number of deferral periods?
   (b) What is the interest rate per period?
   (c) What formula is used to find the present value of this annuity?
   (d) Find the present value of this annuity.

EXAMPLE 8   **Lottery Prize Payments**

Suppose a lottery prize of $50,000 is invested by a couple for future use as their child's college fund. The family plans to use the money as 8 semiannual payments at the end of each 6-month period after payments are deferred for 10 years. How much will each payment be if the money can be invested at 8.6% compounded semiannually?

Solution

We seek the payment R for a deferred annuity with $n = 8$ payment periods, deferred for $k = 2(10) = 20$ periods, $i = 0.086/2 = 0.043$, and $A_{(n,k)} = \$50{,}000$.

$$A_{(n,k)} = R\left[\frac{1-(1+i)^{-n}}{i}\right](1+i)^{-k}$$

$$\$50{,}000 = R\left[\frac{1-(1.043)^{-8}}{0.043}\right](1.043)^{-20}$$

$$\$50{,}000 \approx R(2.865122499)$$

$$R \approx \frac{\$50{,}000}{2.865122499} \approx \$17{,}451.26$$

In Example 8, note the effect of the deferral time. The family receives $8(\$17{,}451.26) = \$139{,}610.08$ from the original $50,000 investment.

CHECKPOINT
ANSWERS

1. (a) $n = 14$
   (b) $i = 0.01$
   (c) $A_n = R\left[\dfrac{1-(1+i)^{-n}}{i}\right]$
   (d) $A_n = \$2000\left[\dfrac{1-(1.01)^{-14}}{0.01}\right] \approx \$26{,}007.41$

2. $R \approx \$37{,}757.17$
3. $A_{(20,\text{due})} \approx \$85{,}230.28$
4. (a) $n = 10$ payment periods; $k = 20$ deferral periods
   (b) $i = 0.03$
   (c) $A_{(n,k)} = R\left[\dfrac{1-(1+i)^{-n}}{i}\right](1+i)^{-k}$
   (d) $A_{(n,k)} \approx \$23{,}614.83$

EXERCISES 6.4

ORDINARY ANNUITIES

In Problems 1 and 2, find the requested value (to the nearest dollar) and tell what each of the other values represents.

1. (a) Find A_n: $A_n = 1300\left[\dfrac{1-(1+0.04)^{-30}}{0.04}\right]$

   (b) Find R: $135{,}000 = R\left[\dfrac{1-(1+0.005)^{-360}}{0.005}\right]$

2. (a) Find A_n: $A_n = 2550\left[\dfrac{1-(1+0.01)^{-120}}{0.01}\right]$

   (b) Find R: $25{,}000 = R\left[\dfrac{1-(1+0.02)^{-20}}{0.02}\right]$

3. Find the present value of an annuity of $6000 paid at the end of each 6-month period for 8 years if the interest rate is 8% compounded semiannually.

4. Find the present value of an annuity that pays $3000 at the end of each 6-month period for 6 years if the interest rate is 6% compounded semiannually.

5. Suppose a state lottery prize of $5 million is to be paid in 20 payments of $250,000 each at the end of each of the next 20 years. If money is worth 10% compounded annually, what is the present value of the prize?

6. How much is needed in an account that earns 8.4% compounded monthly to withdraw $1000 at the end of each month for 20 years?

7. With a present value of $135,000, what is the size of the withdrawals that can be made at the end of each quarter for the next 10 years if money is worth 6.4% compounded quarterly?

8. If $88,000 is invested in an annuity that earns 5.8% compounded quarterly, what payments will it provide at the end of each quarter for the next $5\frac{1}{2}$ years?

9. A personal account earmarked as a retirement supplement contains $242,400. Suppose $200,000 is used to establish an annuity that earns 6% compounded quarterly and pays $4500 at the end of each quarter. How long will it be until the account balance is $0?

10. A professional athlete invested $2.5 million of a bonus in an account that earns 6.8% compounded semiannually. If $120,000 is to be withdrawn at the end of each six months, how long will it be until the account balance is $0?

11. Suppose that a 25-year government bond has a maturity value of $1000 and a coupon rate of 6%, with coupons paid semiannually. Find the market price of the bond if the yield rate is 5% compounded semiannually. Is this bond selling at a discount or at a premium?

12. Suppose that a 10-year corporate bond has a maturity value of $25,000 and a coupon rate of 7%, with coupons paid semiannually. Find the market price of the bond if the yield rate is 8% compounded semiannually. Is this bond selling at a discount or at a premium?

13. The figure shows a graph that compares the present values of two ordinary annuities of $1000 annually, one at 8% compounded annually and one at 10% compounded annually.
    (a) Determine which graph corresponds to the 8% rate and which corresponds to the 10% rate.
    (b) Use the graph to estimate the difference between the present values of these annuities for 25 years.
    (c) Write a sentence that explains this difference.

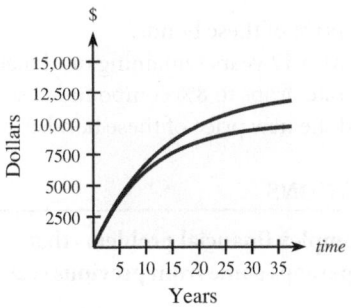

14. The figure shows a graph that compares the present values of two ordinary annuities of $800 quarterly, one at 6% compounded quarterly and one at 9% compounded quarterly.
    (a) Determine which graph corresponds to the 6% rate and which corresponds to the 9% rate.
    (b) Use the graph to estimate the difference between the present values of these annuities for 25 years (100 quarters).
    (c) Write a sentence that explains this difference.

ANNUITIES DUE

15. Explain the difference between an ordinary annuity and an annuity due.

16. Is there any difference between the present values in parts (a) and (b)? Explain.
    (a) An annuity due that pays $1000 at the beginning of each year for 10 years
    (b) Taking $1000 now and establishing an ordinary annuity that pays $1000 at the end of each year for 9 years

17. Find the present value of an annuity due that pays $3000 at the beginning of each quarter for the next 7 years. Assume that money is worth 5.8% compounded quarterly.

18. Find the present value of an annuity due that pays $25,000 every 6 months for the next $2\frac{1}{2}$ years if money is worth 6.2% compounded semiannually.

19. What amount must be set aside now to generate payments of $50,000 at the beginning of each year for the next 12 years if money is worth 5.92% compounded annually?

20. Suppose an annuity will pay $15,000 at the beginning of each year for the next 7 years. How much money is needed to start this annuity if it earns 7.3% compounded annually?

21. A year-end bonus of $25,000 will generate how much money at the beginning of each month for the next year, if it can be invested at 6.48% compounded monthly?

22. A couple inherits $89,000. How much can this generate at the beginning of each month over the next 5 years, if money is worth 6.3% compounded monthly?

MISCELLANEOUS PROBLEMS FOR ORDINARY ANNUITIES AND ANNUITIES DUE

In Problems 23–38, (a) decide whether the problem relates to an ordinary annuity or an annuity due and then (b) solve the problem.

23. An insurance settlement of $1.5 million must replace Trixie Eden's income for the next 40 years. What income will this settlement provide at the end of each month if it is invested in an annuity that earns 8.4% compounded monthly?

24. A local library receives a bequest of $100,000 from a prominent local family. How much will this provide at

the beginning of each 3-month period for the next $2\frac{1}{2}$ years if money is worth 7.4% compounded quarterly?

25. A company wants to have $40,000 at the beginning of each 6-month period for the next $4\frac{1}{2}$ years. If an annuity is set up for this purpose, how much must be invested now if the annuity earns 6.68% compounded semiannually?

26. Is it more economical to buy an automobile for $29,000 cash or to pay $8000 down and $3000 at the end of each quarter for 2 years, if money is worth 8% compounded quarterly?

27. Dr. Jane Kodiak plans to sell her practice to an HMO. The HMO will pay her $1.5 million now or will make a $500,000 partial payment now and additional payments of $140,000 at the end of each year for the next 10 years. If money is worth 6.5% compounded annually, is it better to take $1.5 million now or $500,000 now and $140,000 at the end of each year for the next 10 years? Justify your choice.

28. As a result of a court settlement, an accident victim is awarded $1.2 million. The attorney takes one-third of this amount, another third is used for immediate expenses, and the remaining third is used to set up an annuity. What amount will this annuity pay at the beginning of each quarter for the next 5 years if the annuity earns 7.6% compounded quarterly?

29. Recent sales of some real estate and record profits make it possible for a manufacturer to set aside $800,000 in a fund to be used for modernization and remodeling. How much can be withdrawn from this fund at the beginning of each half-year for the next 3 years if the fund earns 7.7% compounded semiannually?

30. A $2.4 million state lottery pays $10,000 at the beginning of each month for 20 years. How much money must the state actually have on hand to set up the payments for this prize if money is worth 6.3% compounded monthly?

31. How long will an account worth $2.2 million provide $10,000 at the end of each month, if money is worth 5.4% compounded monthly?

32. A college class's 25th reunion gift is $8.6 million. How many semiannual payments of $250,000 will this provide at the beginning of each 6-month period if money is worth 4.4% compounded semiannually?

33. A used piece of rental equipment has $2\frac{1}{2}$ years of useful life remaining. When rented, the equipment brings in $800 per month (paid at the beginning of the month). If the equipment is sold now and money is worth 4.8% compounded monthly, what must the selling price be to recoup the income the rental company loses by selling the equipment "early"?

34. As a result of a court settlement, a financial firm agreed to pay $13.4 million to Ford Motor Company, with $10 million of it going to a Ford charitable trust (*Source: The New York Times*). If the trust invested this money at 6.3% compounded annually, how much could be awarded to worthwhile organizations at the end of each year for the next 20 years?

35. As the contestant with the longest winning streak in the history of *Jeopardy*, Ken Jennings won more than $2.5 million. Suppose he invested $1.5 million in an ordinary annuity that earned 7.2% compounded monthly. How much would he receive at the end of each month for the next 20 years?

36. Suppose Becky has her choice of $10,000 at the end of each month for life or a single prize of $1.5 million. She is 35 years old, and her life expectancy is 40 more years.
    (i) Find the present value of the annuity if money is worth 7.2% compounded monthly.
    (ii) If she takes the $1.5 million, spends $700,000 of it, and invests the remainder at 7.2% compounded monthly, what amount will she receive at the end of each month for the next 40 years?

37. Juanita Domingo's parents want to establish a college trust for her. They want to make 16 quarterly withdrawals of $2000, with the first withdrawal 3 months from now. If money is worth 7.2% compounded quarterly, how much must be deposited now to provide for this trust?

38. A retiree inherits $93,000 and invests it at 6.6% compounded monthly in an annuity that provides an amount at the end of each month for the next 12 years. Find the monthly amount.

39. A 10-year Emmaco Corporate bond has a par value of $10,000 with coupons at 7.8% paid semiannually.
    (a) If this bond is bought to yield 10% compounded semiannually, find its price.
    (b) Suppose that after this bond has been held for 2 years, the desired yield is 8% compounded semiannually. Find the selling price.

40. Kodicom Inc. has 15-year bonds with a $5000 maturity value and a quoted coupon rate of 12% paid semiannually. The current yield is 10% compounded semiannually.
    (a) Compute the price of these bonds.
    (b) Suppose that with 12 years remaining until maturity, the yield rate drops to 8% compounded semiannually. Find the new price of these bonds.

COMBINED APPLICATIONS

Problems 41–44 are complex financial problems that require several skills, perhaps some from previous sections.

For each of Problems 41 and 42, answer the following questions.
(a) **How much is in the account after the last deposit is made?**
(b) **How much was deposited?**
(c) **What is the amount of each withdrawal?**
(d) **What is the total amount withdrawn?**

41. Suppose an individual makes an initial investment of $2500 in an account that earns 7.8% compounded monthly and makes additional contributions of $100 at the end of each month for a period of 12 years. After

these 12 years, this individual wants to make withdrawals at the end of each month for the next 5 years (so that the account balance will be reduced to $0).

42. Suppose that Nam Banh deposits his $12,500 bonus in an account that earns 8% compounded quarterly and makes additional deposits of $500 at the end of each quarter for the next $22\frac{1}{2}$ years until he retires. To supplement his retirement, Nam wants to make withdrawals at the end of each quarter for the next 12 years (at which time the account balance will be $0).

43. A young couple wants to have a college fund that will pay $30,000 at the end of each half-year for 8 years.
    (a) If they can invest at 8% compounded semiannually, how much do they need to invest at the end of each 6-month period for the next 18 years to begin making their college withdrawals 6 months after their last investment?
    (b) Suppose 8 years after beginning the annuity payments, they receive an inheritance of $38,000 that they contribute to the account, and they continue to make their regular payments as found in part (a). How many college withdrawals will they be able to make before the account balance is $0?

44. A recent college graduate begins a savings plan at age 27 by investing $400 at the end of each month in an account that earns 7.5% compounded monthly.
    (a) If this plan is followed for 10 years, how much should the monthly contributions be for the next 28 years to be able to withdraw $10,000 at the end of each month from the account for the next 25 years?
    (b) What is the total amount contributed?
    (c) What is the total amount withdrawn?

DEFERRED ANNUITIES

45. Find the present value of an annuity of $2000 at the end of each quarter for 5 years after being deferred for 3 years, if money is worth 8% compounded quarterly.

46. Find the present value of an annuity of $2000 per year at the end of each of 8 years after being deferred for 6 years, if money is worth 7% compounded annually.

47. The terms of a single parent's will indicate that a child will receive an ordinary annuity of $16,000 per year from age 18 to age 24 (so that the child can attend college) and that the balance of the estate goes to a niece. If the parent dies on the child's 14th birthday, how much money must be removed from the estate to purchase the annuity? (Assume an interest rate of 6% compounded annually.)

48. On his 48th birthday, a man wants to set aside enough money to provide an income of $1500 at the end of each month from his 60th birthday to his 65th birthday. If he earns 6% compounded monthly, how much will this supplemental retirement plan cost him on his 48th birthday?

49. The semiannual tuition payment at a major university is expected to be $30,000 for the 4 years beginning 18 years from now. What lump sum payment should the university accept now in lieu of tuition payments beginning 18 years, 6 months from now? Assume that money is worth 7% compounded semiannually and that tuition is paid at the end of each half-year for 4 years.

50. A community is soliciting pledges for a fitness center project to begin in 3 years. If money is worth 6% compounded quarterly, how much must a family deposit now to contribute $2500 at the end of each quarter for $2\frac{1}{2}$ years after the project begins?

51. Danny Metzger's parents invested $1600 when he was born. This money is to be used for Danny's college education and is to be withdrawn in four equal annual payments beginning when Danny is age 19. Find the amount that will be available each year, if money is worth 6% compounded annually.

52. Carol Goldsmith received a trust fund inheritance of $10,000 on her 30th birthday. She plans to use the money to supplement her income with 20 quarterly payments beginning on her 60th birthday. If money is worth 7.6% compounded quarterly, how much will each quarterly payment be?

53. The May 18, 2013, Powerball, worth $590.5 million and won by an 84-year-old resident of Zephyrillis, Florida, was the largest individual jackpot ever. (Note that in January 2016, winning ticket holders split the largest-ever Powerball prize of $1.586 billion.) Rather than take the prize in 30 annual installments totaling the $590.5 million, the winner elected a single prize payment of $370.9 million (after taxes, about $278 million). Suppose the winner set aside $150 million of the after-tax amount in a fund that earns 4.5% compounded monthly. After a deferral period of 16 years, how much would be available to the winner's heirs at the end of each month for the next 50 years?

54. A couple received a $134,000 inheritance the year they turned 48 and invested it in a fund that earns 7.7% compounded semiannually. If this amount is deferred for 14 years (until they retire), how much will it provide at the end of each half-year for the next 20 years after they retire?

In Problems 55 and 56, use a spreadsheet or financial program on a calculator or computer.

55. Suppose a couple have $100,000 at retirement that they can invest in an ordinary annuity that earns 7.8% compounded monthly. Track the balance in this annuity account until it reaches $0, if the couple receive the following monthly payments.
    (a) $1000   (b) $2500

56. Suppose you invested $250,000 in an annuity that earned interest compounded monthly. This annuity paid $3000 at the end of each month. Experiment with the following different interest rates (compounded monthly) to see how long it will be, with each rate, until this annuity has an account balance of $0.
    (a) 6.5%   (b) 9%

SECTION 6.5

Loans and Amortization

OBJECTIVES

- To find the regular payments required to amortize a debt
- To find the amount that can be borrowed for a specified payment
- To develop an amortization schedule
- To find the unpaid balance of a loan
- To analyze loan refinancing

APPLICATION PREVIEW

Chuckie and Angelica have been married for 4 years and are ready to buy their first home. They have saved $30,000 for a down payment, and their budget can accommodate a monthly mortgage payment of $1200. They want to know in what price range they can purchase a home if the rate for a 30-year loan is 7.8% compounded monthly.

When businesses, individuals, or families like Chuckie and Angelica borrow money to make a major purchase, four questions commonly arise:

1. What will the payments be?
2. How much can be borrowed and still fit a budget?
3. What is the payoff amount of the loan before the final payment is due?
4. What is the total of all payments needed to pay off the loan?

In this section, we discuss the most common way that consumers and businesses discharge debts—regular payments of fixed size made on a loan (called amortization)—and determine ways to answer Chuckie and Angelica's question (see Example 2) and the other three questions posed above.

Amortization   Just as we invest money to earn interest, banks and lending institutions lend money and collect interest for its use. Federal law now requires that the full cost of any loan and the **true annual percentage rate (APR)** be disclosed with the loan. Because of this law, loans now are usually paid off by a series of partial payments with interest charged on the unpaid balance at the end of each payment period.

This type of loan is usually repaid by making all payments (including principal and interest) of equal size. This process of repaying the loan is called **amortization.**

When a bank makes a loan of this type, it is purchasing from the borrower an ordinary annuity that pays a fixed return each payment period. The lump sum the bank gives the borrower (the principal of the loan) is the present value of the ordinary annuity, and each payment the bank receives from the borrower is a payment from the annuity. Hence, to find the size of these periodic payments, we solve for R in the formula for the present value of an ordinary annuity,

$$A_n = R \left[\frac{1 - (1 + i)^{-n}}{i} \right]$$

which yields the following algebraically equivalent formula.

Amortization Formula   If the debt of A_n, with interest at a rate of i per period, is amortized by n equal periodic payments (each payment being made at the end of a period), the size of each payment is

$$R = A_n \cdot \left[\frac{i}{1 - (1 + i)^{-n}} \right]$$

For example, suppose a debt of $1000 with interest at 16% compounded quarterly is to be amortized by 20 equal quarterly payments over the next 5 years. To find the size of each payment, we use $A_n = \$1000$, $n = 20$, and $i = 0.16/4 = 0.04$. Thus we have

$$R = A_n \left[\frac{i}{1 - (1 + i)^{-n}} \right] = \$1000 \left[\frac{0.04}{1 - (1.04)^{-20}} \right] \approx \$73.58$$

EXAMPLE 1   **Business Modernization**

A company modernizes its production by buying a new piece of equipment for $200,000. It makes a $50,000 down payment and agrees to amortize the rest of the debt with quarterly payments over the next 10 years. If the interest on the debt is 12% compounded quarterly, find (a) the size of the quarterly payments, (b) the total amount of the payments, and (c) the total amount of interest paid.

Solution

(a) We know that $A_n = \$200{,}000 - \$50{,}000 = \$150{,}000$, $n = 4(10) = 40$, and $i = 0.12/4 = 0.03$. Thus, for the quarterly payment, we have

$$R = \$150{,}000 \left[\frac{0.03}{1 - (1.03)^{-40}} \right] \approx \$6489.36$$

(b) The company made 40 payments of $6489.36, so the payments totaled

$$(40)(\$6489.36) = \$259{,}574.40$$

plus the $50,000 down payment, or $309,574.40.

(c) Of the $309,574.40 paid, $200,000 was payment for the equipment. The remaining $109,574.40 was the total amount of interest paid.

Technology Note   We can use a graphing calculator to find the payment size to amortize a debt as follows:

1. Under the APPS menu, select Finance and then TVM Solver.
2. Set N = the total number of payments, I% = the annual percentage rate, and PV = the amount borrowed.
3. Set FV = 0 and both P/Y and C/Y equal to the number of compounding periods.
4. Highlight END; then put the cursor on PMT and press ALPHA ENTER to get the payment size. (The payment is negative because it is leaving.)

Figure 6.15 shows the quarterly payment for the loan in Example 1(a). See Appendix A, Section 6.5, for more details.

We can also use Excel to find the payment size to amortize a debt by using the *payment* formula =Pmt(F2, B2, A2, C2, 0) with the periodic interest rate as a decimal in cell F2, the number of periods in cell B2, the loan amount in cell A2, and C2 = 0. Cell B4 of the following spreadsheet gives the payment size for the loan in Example 1. See Appendix B, Section 6.5, or the Online Excel Guide for more details.

```
N=40
I%=12
PV=150000
PMT=-6489.3566...
FV=0
P/Y=4
C/Y=4
PMT:END BEGIN
```

Figure 6.15

	A	B	C	D	E	F
1	Loan Amount	Number of Periods	Future Value	Annual Rate	Periods per Year	Periodic Rate
2	150,000	40	0	0.12	4	0.03
3						
4	Payment	($6,489.36)				

EXAMPLE 2   **Affordable Home** | APPLICATION PREVIEW |

Chuckie and Angelica have $30,000 for a down payment, and their budget can accommodate a monthly mortgage payment of $1200. What is the most expensive home they can buy if they borrow money for 30 years at 7.8% compounded monthly?

Solution

We seek the amount that Chuckie and Angelica can borrow, or A_n, knowing that $R = \$1200$, $n = 30(12) = 360$, and $i = 0.078/12 = 0.0065$. We can use these values in the amortization formula and solve for A_n as follows.

$$R = A_n\left[\frac{i}{1 - (1 + i)^{-n}}\right]$$

$$\$1200 = A_n\left[\frac{0.0065}{1 - (1.0065)^{-360}}\right]$$

$$A_n = \$1200\left[\frac{1 - (1.0065)^{-360}}{0.0065}\right]$$

$$A_n \approx \$166{,}696.65$$

Thus, if they borrow \$166,697 (to the nearest dollar) and put down \$30,000, the most expensive home they can buy would cost \$166,697 + \$30,000 = \$196,697. ∎

CHECKPOINT

1. A debt of \$25,000 is to be amortized with equal quarterly payments over 6 years, and money is worth 7% compounded quarterly.
    (a) Find the total number of payments.
    (b) Find the interest rate per period.
    (c) Write the formula used to find the size of each payment.
    (d) Find the amount of each payment.
2. A new college graduate determines that she can afford a car payment of \$400 per month. If the auto manufacturer is offering a special 2.1% financing rate compounded monthly for 5 years, how much can she borrow and still have a \$400 monthly payment?

Amortization Schedule

We can construct an **amortization schedule** that summarizes all the information regarding the amortization of a loan.

For example, a loan of \$10,000 with interest at 10% could be repaid in 5 equal annual payments of size

$$R = \$10{,}000\left[\frac{0.10}{1 - (1 + 0.10)^{-5}}\right] \approx \$10{,}000(0.263797) = \$2637.97$$

Each time this \$2637.97 payment is made, some is used to pay the interest on the unpaid balance and some is used to reduce the principal. For the first payment, the unpaid balance is \$10,000, so the interest payment is 10% of \$10,000, or \$1000. The remaining \$1637.97 is applied to the principal. Hence, after this first payment, the unpaid balance is \$10,000 − \$1637.97 = \$8362.03.

For the second payment of \$2637.97, the amount used for interest is 10% of \$8362.03, or \$836.20; the remainder, \$1801.77, is used to reduce the principal.

This information for these two payments and for the remaining payments is summarized in the following amortization schedule.

Period	Payment	Interest	Balance Reduction	Unpaid Balance
				10000.00
1	2637.97	1000.00	1637.97	8362.03
2	2637.97	836.20	1801.77	6560.26
3	2637.97	656.03	1981.94	4578.32
4	2637.97	457.83	2180.14	2398.18
5	2638.00	239.82	2398.18	0.00
Total	13189.88	3189.88	10000.00	

Note that the last payment was increased by 3¢ so that the balance was reduced to $0 at the end of the 5 years. Such an adjustment is normal in amortizing a loan.

Spreadsheet Note

The preceding amortization schedule involves only a few payments. For loans involving more payments, a spreadsheet program is an excellent tool for developing an amortization schedule. The spreadsheet requires the user to understand the interrelationships among the columns. The following spreadsheet output shows the amortization schedule for the first, sixth, twelfth, eighteenth, and twenty-fourth monthly payments on a $100,000 loan amortized for 30 years at 6% compounded monthly. It is interesting to observe how little the unpaid balance changes during these first 2 years—and, consequently, how much of each payment is devoted to paying interest due rather than to reducing the debt. In fact, the column labeled "Total Interest" shows a running total of how much has been paid toward interest. We see that after 12 payments of $599.55, a total of $7194.60 has been paid, and $5966.59 of this has been interest payments.

	A	B	C	D	E	F
1	Payment Number	Payment Amount	Interest	Balance Reduction	Unpaid Balance	Total Interest
2	0	0	0	0	$100,000.00	$0.00
3	1	$599.55	$500.00	$99.55	$99,900.45	$500.00
4	6	$599.55	$497.49	$102.06	$99,395.18	$2,992.48
5	12	$599.55	$494.39	$105.16	$98,771.99	$5,966.59
6	18	$599.55	$491.19	$108.36	$98,129.87	$8,921.77
7	24	$599.55	$487.90	$111.65	$97,468.25	$11,857.45

Unpaid Balance of a Loan

Many people who borrow money, such as for a car or a home, do not pay on the loan for its entire term. Rather, they pay off the loan early by making a final lump sum payment. The unpaid balance found in the amortization schedule is the "payoff amount" of the loan and represents the lump sum payment that must be made to complete payment on the loan. When the number of payments is large, we may want to find the unpaid balance of a loan without constructing an amortization schedule.

Recall that calculations for amortization of a debt are based on the present value formula for an ordinary annuity. Because of this, the **unpaid balance of a loan** (also called the **payoff amount** and the **outstanding principal of the loan**) is the present value needed to generate all remaining payments.

Unpaid Balance or Payoff Amount of a Loan

For a loan of n payments of R per period at interest rate i per period, the **unpaid balance,** or **payoff amount,** after k payments have been made is the present value of an ordinary annuity with $n - k$ payments. That is, with $n - k$ payments remaining,

$$\text{Unpaid balance} = A_{n-k} = R\left[\frac{1 - (1 + i)^{-(n-k)}}{i}\right]$$

EXAMPLE **3**   **Unpaid Balance**

A young man decides to stop using a credit card after he acquires an outstanding balance of $15,000 with an interest rate of 18% compounded monthly. He makes monthly payments of $270.28, which will pay the debt in 10 years. After 6 years, he gets a new, better-paying job and decides to pay off the unpaid balance. Find the unpaid balance after the 72nd payment.

Solution

The unpaid balance after the 72nd payment is the present value of the annuity with $120-72 = 48$ payments remaining. Thus we use $R = \$270.28$, $i = 0.18/12 = 0.015$, and $n - k = 48$ in the present value formula.

$$A_{n-k} = R\left[\frac{1 - (1 + i)^{-(n-k)}}{i}\right] = 270.28\left[\frac{1 - 1.015^{-48}}{0.015}\right] \approx \$9201$$

Thus the unpaid balance is about $9201.

Figure 6.16

The curve in Figure 6.16 shows the unpaid balance of a $100,000 loan at 6% compounded monthly for 30 years (with monthly payments of $599.55, as shown in the spreadsheet on the previous page). In the figure, the curve represents how the unpaid balance would decrease if each payment is the same amount. Note how the curve decreases slowly at first and more rapidly as the unpaid balance nears zero. The reason for this behavior is that when the unpaid balance is large, much of each payment is devoted to interest. In contrast, when the debt decreases, more of each payment goes toward the principal.

CHECKPOINT

3. A 42-month auto loan has monthly payments of $411.35. If the interest rate is 8.1% compounded monthly, find the unpaid balance immediately after the 24th payment.

A common application of determining the unpaid balance of a loan arises when a loan is refinanced. If interest rates drop during the term of a loan, refinancing often is considered because it may result in a lower periodic payment or fewer payments.

EXAMPLE 4   Loan Refinancing

Four years ago Benencorp decided to expand its production capacity and borrowed $1.3 million for 20 years at 5.2% compounded quarterly. After making 16 quarterly payments of $26,235.37, Benencorp is considering refinancing this loan for 15 years at 4.8% compounded quarterly, with refinancing charges of $5000 added to the amount of the new (refinanced) loan.

(a) Find the payoff amount of Benencorp's original loan.
(b) Find the amount of the new loan and the new quarterly payment.
(c) Should Benencorp refinance?

Solution

(a) The payoff amount of the loan is the unpaid balance after 16 payments. Thus $n - k = 80 - 16 = 64$ payments remaining, $R = \$26,235.37$, $i = 0.052/4 = 0.013$, and

$$A_{n-k} = R\left[\frac{1 - (1 + i)^{-(n-k)}}{i}\right] = 26,235.37\left[\frac{1 - (1.013)^{-64}}{0.013}\right] \approx 1,135,148.82$$

(b) The new loan needs to cover this unpaid balance and the refinancing charges of $5000; the amount of the new (refinanced) loan is

$$A_n = \$1,135,148.82 + \$5000 = \$1,140,148.82$$

This amount will be financed for 15 years at 4.8% compounded quarterly, so we use $n = (15)(4) = 60$ and $i = 0.048/4 = 0.012$. Thus, the new quarterly payment is

$$R = A_n\left[\frac{i}{1 - (1 + i)^{-n}}\right] = \$1,140,148.82\left[\frac{0.012}{1 - (1.012)^{-60}}\right] \approx \$26,766.30$$

(c) At first it seems that Benencorp should not refinance because this new payment is higher than the original. But let's compare the total amounts paid from here on:

$$\text{Original} = (\$26,235.37)(64) = \$1,679,063.68$$
$$\text{Refinance} = (\$26,766.30)(60) = \$1,605,978.00$$

Thus, Benencorp should refinance because it completes making payments 1 year sooner and saves $73,085.68.

CHECKPOINT
ANSWERS

1. (a) $n = 24$ payments
    (b) $i = 0.0175$ per period

    (c) $R = A_n \left[\dfrac{i}{1 - (1 + i)^{-n}} \right]$

    (d) $R \approx \$1284.64$
2. $A_n \approx \$22,764.08$
3. $A_{n-k} \approx \$6950.13$

EXERCISES 6.5

1. Two loans are for the same amount at the same interest rate. One is paid off in 10 years; the other, in 25 years.
    (a) Which loan results in more of each payment being directed toward principal? Explain.
    (b) Which loan results in a lower periodic payment? Explain.
2. When a debt is amortized, which interest rate is better for the borrower, 10% or 6%? Explain.
3. A debt of $8000 is to be amortized with 8 equal semiannual payments. If the interest rate is 12% compounded semiannually, what is the size of each payment?
4. A loan of $10,000 is to be amortized with 10 equal quarterly payments. If the interest rate is 6% compounded quarterly, what is the periodic payment?
5. A recent graduate's student loans total $18,000. If these loans are at 4.2% compounded quarterly for 10 years, what are the quarterly payments?
6. For equipment upgrades, a business borrowed $400,000 at 8% compounded semiannually for 5 years. What are the semiannual payments?
7. A homeowner planning a kitchen remodeling can afford a $600 monthly payment. How much can the homeowner borrow for 5 years at 6% compounded monthly and still stay within the budget?
8. AdriAnne and Anna's Auto Repair wants to add a new service bay. How much can they borrow at 5% compounded quarterly for $4\frac{1}{2}$ years, if the desired quarterly payment is $10,000?

In Problems 9–12, develop an amortization schedule for the loan described.
9. $100,000 for 3 years at 9% compounded annually
10. $30,000 for 5 years at 7% compounded annually
11. $20,000 for 1 year at 12% compounded quarterly
12. $50,000 for $2\frac{1}{2}$ years at 10% compounded semiannually

13. A $10,000 loan is to be amortized for 10 years with quarterly payments of $334.27. If the interest rate is 6% compounded quarterly, what is the unpaid balance immediately after the sixth payment?
14. A debt of $8000 is to be amortized with 8 equal semiannual payments of $1288.29. If the interest rate is 12% compounded semiannually, find the unpaid balance immediately after the fifth payment.
15. When Maria Acosta bought a car $2\frac{1}{2}$ years ago, she borrowed $28,000 for 48 months at 8.1% compounded monthly. Her monthly payments are $684.88, but she'd like to pay off the loan early. How much will she owe just after her payment at the $2\frac{1}{2}$-year mark?
16. Six-and-a-half years ago a small business borrowed $50,000 for 10 years at 9% compounded semiannually to update some equipment. Now the company would like to pay off this loan. Find the payoff amount just after the company makes the 14th semiannual payment of $3843.81.

Problems 17–20 describe a debt to be amortized. In each problem, find:
(a) **the size of each payment,**
(b) **the total amount paid for each purchase,**
(c) **the total interest paid over the life of the loan.**
17. A man buys a house for $350,000. He makes a $150,000 down payment and amortizes the rest of the purchase price with semiannual payments over the next 10 years. The interest rate on the debt is 12% compounded semiannually.
18. Sean Lee purchases $20,000 worth of supplies for his restaurant by making a $3000 down payment and amortizing the remaining cost with quarterly payments over the next 5 years. The interest rate on the debt is 16% compounded quarterly.

19. A woman buys an apartment house for $1,250,000 by making a down payment of $250,000 and amortizing the rest of the purchase price with monthly payments over the next 10 years. The interest rate on the debt is 7.2% compounded monthly.

20. John Fare purchased $10,000 worth of equipment by making a $2000 down payment and promising to pay the remainder of the cost in semiannual payments over the next 4 years. The interest rate on the debt is 10% compounded semiannually.

21. A man buys a car for $36,000. If the interest rate on the loan is 12% compounded monthly and he wants to make monthly payments of $900 for 36 months, how much must he put down?

22. A woman buys a car for $40,000. If the interest rate on the loan is 12% compounded monthly and she wants to make monthly payments of $700 for 3 years, how much must she have for a down payment?

23. A couple purchasing a home budget $1800 per month for their loan payment. If they have $20,000 available for a down payment and are considering a 25-year loan, how much can they spend on the home at each of the following rates?
    (a) 6.9% compounded monthly
    (b) 7.5% compounded monthly

24. A developer wants to buy a certain parcel of land. The developer believes she can afford payments of $44,000 each half-year for the next 7 years. How much can she borrow and hold to this budget at each of the following interest rates?
    (a) 8.9% compounded semiannually
    (b) 7.3% compounded semiannually

25. A couple who borrow $90,000 for 30 years at 7.2% compounded monthly must make monthly payments of $610.91.
    (a) Find their unpaid balance after 1 year.
    (b) During that first year, how much interest do they pay?

26. A company that purchases a piece of equipment by borrowing $250,000 for 10 years at 6% compounded monthly has monthly payments of $2775.51.
    (a) Find the unpaid balance on this loan after 1 year.
    (b) During that first year, how much interest does the company pay?

27. When Otto and Millie bought their home, they borrowed $200,000 for 30 years at 6% compounded monthly. After making 120 payments of $1199.10, they plan to refinance at 4.5% compounded monthly for 15 years, with refinancing costs of $750 added to the amount of the new loan.
    (a) Find the amount of the new loan (amount refinanced).
    (b) Find their new monthly payment.
    (c) Find the amount saved by refinancing.

28. To upgrade its equipment, Simon Reilly Chemicals (SRC) borrowed $2.8 million at 6.4% compounded quarterly for 20 years. After making 18 quarterly payments of $62,297.39, SRC plans to refinance this loan at 5.2% compounded quarterly for 10 years, with refinancing charges of $12,000 added to the amount refinanced.
    (a) Find the amount refinanced.
    (b) Find SRC's new quarterly payment.
    (c) Find the amount saved by refinancing.

29. A recent college graduate buys a new car by borrowing $18,000 at 8.4% compounded monthly for 5 years. She decides to pay $384 instead of the monthly payment required by the loan.
    (a) What is the monthly payment required by the loan, and how much extra did she pay per month?
    (b) How many $384 payments will she make to pay off the loan?
    (c) How much will she save by paying $384 per month rather than the required payment?

30. A young couple buying their first home borrow $85,000 for 30 years at 7.2% compounded monthly and make payments of $576.97. After 3 years, they are able to make a one-time payment of $2000 along with their 36th payment.
    (a) Find the unpaid balance immediately after they pay the extra $2000 and their 36th payment.
    (b) How many regular payments of $576.97 will amortize the unpaid balance from part (a)? Give the answer to one decimal point.
    (c) How much will the remaining debt be after the number of full payment periods in (b) is made? How much extra must be included with last full payment to pay off the debt?
    (d) How much will the couple pay over the life of the loan by paying the extra $2000?
    (e) How much will the couple save over the life of the loan by paying the extra $2000?

31. Jadele, Inc., borrowed $12.8 million at 7.2% compounded quarterly for 30 years for construction of a new manufacturing facility. After making 42 quarterly payments of $261,094.80, it plans to refinance the existing loan for an amount that includes an additional $1.1 million for expansion. Jadele can refinance at 6.6% compounded quarterly for 25 years, with refinancing costs of $10,000 added to the refinanced amount.
    (a) Find the total amount refinanced.
    (b) Find the new quarterly payment.
    (c) If Jadele decides to continue to pay $261,094.80 per quarter on the refinanced amount, how many payments will it take to pay off the new loan?

32. When Gustavo and Serrana bought their home, they had a 5.7% loan with monthly payments of $870.60 for 30 years. After making 78 monthly payments, they plan to refinance for an amount that includes an additional $35,000 to remodel their kitchen. They can refinance at 4.8% compounded monthly for 25 years, with refinancing costs of $625 included with the amount refinanced.
    (a) Find the amount refinanced.
    (b) Find their new monthly payment.
    (c) How long will it take to pay off this new loan if they pay $1200 each month?

A debt of $100,000 is amortized at 6% compounded monthly over 25 years with 300 monthly payments of $644.30 each. The following figure includes two graphs: One shows the total amount paid (in monthly payments) as a function of time (in months), and the other shows the amount paid toward the principal of the debt as a function of time. Use this figure to complete Problems 33 and 34.

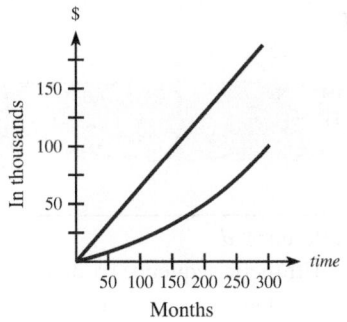

33. (a) Label each graph correctly.
    (b) Draw a vertical segment whose length represents the total amount of interest paid on the debt after 250 months.
34. Draw a vertical segment whose length represents the outstanding principal of the debt (or the payoff amount of the loan) after 150 months.
35. What difference does 0.5% make on a loan? To explore this question, find (to the nearest dollar) the monthly payment and total interest paid over the life of the loan for each of the following.
    (a) An auto loan of $15,000 at 8.0% versus 8.5%, both compounded monthly for 4 years.
    (b) A mortgage loan of $80,000 at 6.75% versus 7.25%, both compounded monthly for 30 years.
    (c) A mortgage loan of $80,000 at 8.0% versus 8.5%, both compounded monthly for 30 years.
36. Some banks now have biweekly mortgages (that is, with payments every other week). Compare a 20-year, $100,000 loan at 8.1% by finding the payment size and the total interest paid over the life of the loan under each of the following conditions.
    (a) Payments are monthly, and the rate is 8.1% compounded monthly.
    (b) Payments are biweekly, and the rate is 8.1% compounded biweekly.
37. Many banks charge points on mortgage loans. Each point is the equivalent of a 1% charge on the amount borrowed and is paid before the loan is made as part of the closing costs of buying a home. (Closing costs include points, title fees, attorney's fees, assessor's fees, etc.)
    (a) If $100,000 is borrowed for 25 years, for each of the following, find the payment size and the total paid over the life of the loan (including points).
        (i) $7\frac{1}{2}$%, compounded monthly with 0 points
        (ii) $7\frac{1}{4}$%, compounded monthly with 1 point
        (iii) 7%, compounded monthly with 2 points

(b) Which loan in part (a) has the lowest total cost over the life of the loan?
38. Time-share sales provide an opportunity for vacationers to own a resort condo for 1 week (or more) each year forever. The owners may use their week at their own condo or trade the week and vacation elsewhere. Time-share vacation sales usually require payment in full or financing through the time-share company, and interest rates are usually in the 13%–18% range. Suppose the cost to buy a 1-week time share in a 3-bedroom condo is $21,833. Also suppose a 10% down payment is required, with the balance financed for 15 years at 16.5% compounded monthly.
    (a) Find the monthly payment.
    (b) Determine the total cost over the life of the loan.
    (c) Suppose maintenance fees for this condo are $400 per year. Find the annual cost of the condo over the life of the loan. Assume that the annual maintenance fees remain constant.
    (d) Use part (c) and the 10% down payment to determine the average annual cost for having this vacation condo for 1 week over the life of the loan.

COMBINED APPLICATIONS

Problems 39 and 40 are complex financial problems that require several skills, perhaps some from previous sections.

39. During four years of college, Nolan MacGregor's student loans are $4000, $3500, $4400, and $5000 for freshman year through senior year, respectively. Each loan amount gathers interest of 1% compounded quarterly while Nolan is in school and 3% compounded quarterly during a 6-month grace period after graduation.
    (a) What is the loan balance after the grace period? Assume that the freshman year student loan costs Nolan 1% interest for 3/4 year during the first year, then for 3 full years until graduation. Make similar assumptions for the loans for the other years.
    (b) After the grace period, the loan is amortized over the next 10 years at 3% compounded quarterly. Find the quarterly payment.
    (c) If Nolan decides to pay an additional $90 per payment, how many payments will amortize the debt? What amount should be added to the last payment to pay the loan in full?
    (d) How much will Nolan save by paying the extra $90 with each payment?
40. Clark and Lana take a 30-year home mortgage of $121,000 at 7.8% compounded monthly. They make their regular monthly payments for 5 years, then decide to pay $1000 per month.
    (a) Find their regular monthly payment.
    (b) Find the unpaid balance when they begin paying the $1000.

(c) How many payments of $1000 will it take to pay off the loan? Give the answer correct to one decimal place.

(d) Use your answer to part (c) to find how much interest they save by paying the loan this way.

Use a spreadsheet or financial program on a calculator or computer to complete Problems 41 and 42.

41. Develop an amortization schedule for a 4-year car loan if $16,700 is borrowed at 8.2% compounded monthly.

42. Develop an amortization schedule for a 10-year mortgage loan of $80,000 at 7.2% compounded monthly.

6 CHAPTER SUMMARY & REVIEW

KEY TERMS AND FORMULAS

Section 6.1

Simple interest (p. 362)
$$I = Prt$$
Future value of a simple interest investment (p. 363)
$$S = P + I$$
Sequence function (p. 364)
Arithmetic sequence (p. 365)
$$a_n = a_{n-1} + d \quad (n > 1)$$

Common difference, d
nth term of an arithmetic sequence (p. 365)
$$a_n = a_1 + (n - 1)d$$
Sum of first n terms (p. 366)
$$s_n = \frac{n}{2}(a_1 + a_n)$$

Section 6.2

Future value of compound interest investment (p. 370)
Periodic compounding
$$S = P(1 + i)^n = P\left(1 + \frac{r}{m}\right)^{mt}$$
Continuous compounding
$$S = Pe^{rt}$$
Annual percentage yield (p. 376)
Periodic compounding
$$APY = \left(1 + \frac{r}{m}\right)^m - 1$$
$$= (1 + i)^m - 1$$

Continuous compounding
$$APY = e^r - 1$$
Geometric sequence (p. 378)
$$a_n = ra_{n-1} \quad (n > 1)$$
Common ratio, r
nth term of a geometric sequence (p. 378)
$$a_n = a_1 r^{n-1}$$
Sum of first n terms (p. 379)
$$s_n = \frac{a_1(1 - r^n)}{1 - r} \quad (\text{if } r \neq 1)$$

Section 6.3

Future values of annuities (p. 383)
Ordinary annuity (p. 384)
$$S = R\left[\frac{(1 + i)^n - 1}{i}\right]$$

Sinking fund (p. 387)
Annuity due (p. 388)
$$S_{\text{due}} = R\left[\frac{(1 + i)^n - 1}{i}\right](1 + i)$$

Section 6.4

Present values of annuities (p. 392)
Ordinary annuity (p. 393)
$$A_n = R\left[\frac{1 - (1 + i)^{-n}}{i}\right]$$
Bond pricing (p. 396)

Annuity due (p. 397)
$$A_{(n,\text{due})} = R\left[\frac{1 - (1 + i)^{-n}}{i}\right](1 + i)$$
Deferred annuity (p. 399)
$$A_{(n,k)} = R\left[\frac{1 - (1 + i)^{-n}}{i}\right](1 + i)^{-k}$$

Section 6.5

True annual percentage rate (APR) (p. 404)
Amortization (p. 404)
$$R = A_n\left[\frac{i}{1 - (1 + i)^{-n}}\right]$$
Amortization schedule (p. 406)

Unpaid balance ($n - k$ payments left) (p. 407)
$$A_{n-k} = R\left[\frac{1 - (1 + i)^{-(n-k)}}{i}\right]$$
Loan refinancing (p. 408)

REVIEW EXERCISES

Section 6.1

1. Find the first 4 terms of the sequence with nth term

$$a_n = \frac{1}{n^2}$$

2. Identify any arithmetic sequences and find the common differences.
   (a) $12, 7, 2, -3, \ldots$ (b) $1, 3, 6, 10, \ldots$
   (c) $\frac{1}{6}, \frac{1}{3}, \frac{1}{2}, \frac{2}{3} \ldots$

3. Find the 80th term of the arithmetic sequence with first term -2 and common difference 3.

4. Find the 36th term of the arithmetic sequence with third term 10 and eighth term 25.

5. Find the sum of the first 60 terms of the arithmetic sequence $\frac{1}{3}, \frac{1}{2}, \frac{2}{3}, \ldots$

Section 6.2

6. Identify any geometric sequences and their common ratios.
   (a) $\frac{1}{4}, 2, 16, 128, \ldots$ (b) $16, -12, 9, -\frac{27}{4}, \ldots$
   (c) $4, 16, 36, 64, \ldots$

7. Find the fourth term of the geometric sequence with first term 64 and eighth term 1/2.

8. Find the sum of the first 16 terms of the geometric sequence $\frac{1}{9}, \frac{1}{3}, 1, \ldots$

APPLICATIONS

Section 6.1

9. *Loans* If $8000 is borrowed at 12% simple interest for 3 years, what is the future value of the loan at the end of the 3 years?

10. *Loan rate* Mary Toy borrowed $2000 from her parents and repaid them $2100 after 9 months. What simple interest rate did she pay?

11. *Tuition* How much summer earnings must a college student deposit on August 31 to have $3000 for tuition and fees on December 31 of the same year if the investment earns 6% simple interest?

12. *Contest payments* Suppose the winner of a contest receives $10 on the first day of the month, $20 on the second day, $30 on the third day, etc., for a 30-day month. What is the total won?

13. *Salaries* Suppose you are offered two identical jobs: one paying a starting salary of $40,000 with yearly raises of $2000 and one paying a starting salary of $36,000 with yearly raises of $2500. Which job will pay more money over a 10-year period?

Section 6.2

14. *Investments* An investment is made at 8% compounded quarterly for 10 years.
   (a) Find the number of periods.
   (b) Find the interest rate per period.

15. *Future value* Write the formula for the future value of a compound interest investment, if interest is compounded
   (a) periodically   (b) continuously.

16. *Comparing rates* Which compounding method at 6% earns more money?
   (a) semiannually   (b) monthly

17. *Interest* If $1000 is invested for 4 years at 8% compounded quarterly, how much interest will be earned?

18. *Savings goal* How much must one invest now to have $18,000 in 4 years if the investment earns 5.4% compounded monthly?

19. *Future value* What is the future value if $1000 is invested for 6 years at 8% compounded continuously?

20. *College fund* A couple received an inheritance and plan to invest some of it for their grandchild's college education. How much must they invest if they want the fund to have $100,000 after 15 years, and their investment earns 10.31% compounded continuously?

21. *Investments* If $15,000 is invested at 6% compounded quarterly, how long will it be before it grows to $25,000?

22. *Investment rates* (a) If an initial investment of $35,000 grows to $257,000 in 15 years, what annual interest rate compounded continuously was earned? (b) What is the annual percentage yield on this investment?

23. *Comparing yields* Find the annual percentage yield equivalent to a nominal rate of 7.2% (a) compounded quarterly and (b) compounded continuously.

24. *Chess legend* Legend has it that when the king of Persia wanted to reward the inventor of chess with whatever he desired, the inventor asked for one grain of wheat on the first square of the chessboard, with the number of grains doubled on each square thereafter for the remaining 63 squares. Find the number of grains on the 64th square. (The sum of all the grains of wheat on all the squares would cover Alaska more than 3 inches deep with wheat!)

25. *Chess legend* If in Problem 24 the king granted the inventor's wish for *half* a chessboard, how many grains would the inventor receive?

Section 6.3

26. *Annuity* Find the future value of an ordinary annuity of $800 paid at the end of every 6-month period for 10 years, if it earns interest at 12% compounded semiannually.

27. *Sinking fund* How much would have to be invested at the end of each year at 6% compounded annually to pay off a debt of $80,000 in 10 years?

28. *Annuity* Find the future value of an annuity due of $800 paid at the beginning of every 6-month period for 10 years, if it earns interest at 12% compounded semiannually.

29. *Construction fund* A company wants to have $250,000 available in $4\frac{1}{2}$ years for new construction. How much must be deposited at the beginning of each quarter to reach this goal if the investment earns 10.2% compounded quarterly?

30. *Time to reach a goal* If $1200 is deposited at the end of each quarter in an account that earns 7.2% compounded quarterly, how long will it be until the account is worth $60,000?

Section 6.4

31. *Annuity* What lump sum would have to be invested at 9% compounded semiannually to provide an annuity of $10,000 at the end of each half-year for 10 years?

32. *Cruise fund* A couple want to set up an annuity that will provide 6 monthly payments of $3000 while they take an extended cruise. How much of a $15,000 inheritance must be set aside if they plan to leave in 5 years and want the first payment before they leave? Assume that money is worth 7.8% compounded monthly.

33. *Powerball lottery* Winners of lotteries receive the jackpot distributed over a period of years, usually 20 or 25 years. The winners of a Powerball lottery elected to take a one-time cash payout rather than receive the $295.7 million jackpot in 25 annual payments beginning on the date the lottery was won.
    (a) How much money would the winners have received at the beginning of each of the 25 years?
    (b) If the value of money was 5.91% compounded annually, what one-time payout did they receive in lieu of the annual payments?

34. *Payment from an annuity* A recent college graduate's gift from her grandparents is $20,000. How much will this provide at the end of each month for the next 12 months while the graduate travels? Assume that money is worth 6.6% compounded monthly.

35. *Payment from an annuity* An IRA of $250,000 is rolled into an annuity that pays a retired couple at the beginning of each quarter for the next 20 years. If the annuity earns 6.2% compounded quarterly, how much will the couple receive each quarter?

36. *Bond pricing* Suppose that a 30-year municipal bond has a maturity value of $5000 and a coupon rate of 8%, with coupons paid semiannually. Find the market price of the bond if the current yield rate is 10% compounded semiannually. Is this bond selling at a discount or at a premium?

37. *Duration of an annuity* A retirement account that earns 6.8% compounded semiannually contains $488,000. How long can $40,000 be withdrawn at the end of each half-year until the account balance is $0?

Section 6.5

38. *Amortization* A debt of $1000 with interest at 12% compounded monthly is amortized by 12 monthly payments (of equal size). What is the size of each payment?

39. *Loan payoff* A debt of $8000 is amortized with eight semiannual payments of $1288.29 each. If money is worth 12% compounded semiannually, find the unpaid balance after five payments have been made.

40. *Cash value* A woman paid $90,000 down for a house and agreed to pay 18 quarterly payments of $4500 each. If money is worth 4% compounded quarterly, how much would the house have cost if she had paid cash?

41. *Amortization schedule* Complete the amortization schedule for the next two payments of a loan for 30 years at 7.5% compounded monthly, with monthly payments of $699.22.

Payment Number	Payment Amount	Interest	Balance Reduction	Unpaid Balance
56	$699.22	$594.67	$104.55	$95,042.20

42. *Loan refinancing* A corporation borrowed $750,000 for 15 years at 5.4% compounded semiannually. After making 17 payments of $36,795.60, it refinances at 4.8% compounded semiannually for 5 years, with refinancing costs of $2200 added to the new loan.
    (a) Find the amount of the new loan.
    (b) Find the new semiannual payment.
    (c) Find the amount saved by refinancing.

Sections 6.1–6.5

MISCELLANEOUS FINANCIAL PROBLEMS

Identify which of the following formulas applies to each situation in Problems 43–48.

$$I = Prt \qquad S = P(1 + i)^n \qquad S = Pe^{rt}$$

$$S = R\left[\frac{(1 + i)^n - 1}{i}\right] \qquad A_n = R\left[\frac{1 - (1 + i)^{-n}}{i}\right]$$

43. The future value of a series of payments, with interest compounded when the payments are made

44. The simple interest earned on an investment

45. The present value of a series of payments, with interest compounded when the payments are made

46. The future value of an investment that earns interest compounded periodically

47. The regular payment size needed to amortize a debt, when interest is compounded when the payments are made

48. The future value of an investment that earns interest compounded continuously

49. If an initial investment of $2500 grows to $38,000 in 18 years, what annual interest rate compounded annually did this investment earn?

50. How much must be deposited at the end of each month in an account that earns 8.4% compounded monthly, if the goal is to have $40,000 after 10 years?

51. What is the future value if $1000 is invested for 6 years at 8% (a) simple interest and (b) compounded semiannually?

52. Quarterly payments of $500 are deposited in an account that pays 8% compounded quarterly. How much will have accrued in the account at the end of 4 years if each payment is made at the end of each quarter?

53. If $8000 is invested at 7% compounded continuously, how long will it be before it grows to $22,000?

54. An investment broker bought some stock at $87.89 per share and sold it after 3 months for $105.34 per share. What was the annual simple interest rate earned on this transaction?

55. A couple believes they can afford a monthly house payment of $2000 and would like a 30-year fixed-rate loan. Currently, the rate for such a loan is 4.8% compounded monthly. To the nearest dollar, how much can the couple afford to borrow?

56. A $5000 Mauranol, Inc., corporate bond matures in 10 years and has a coupon rate of 7.2% paid semiannually.
    (a) If the yield rate is 8% compounded semiannually, find the bond's market price.
    (b) Three years later the yield rate is 5.8%. If the bondholder wants to sell at this time, what is the bond's current market price?
    (c) If you bought a $5000 Mauranol, Inc., bond at the price in part (a), collected 3 years of coupons, and sold at the price in part (b), what amount would you have earned on your original investment?
    (d) Suppose you made a single investment with principal equal to the amount paid in part (a) and after 3 years received a single lump sum return equal to the amount from part (c). What interest rate compounded semiannually would you have earned?

57. Kevin Patrick paid off the loan he took out to buy his car, but once the loan was paid, he continued to deposit $400 on the first of each month in an account that paid 5.4% compounded monthly. After four years of making these deposits, Kevin was ready to buy a new car. How much did he have in the account?

58. A young couple receive an inheritance of $72,000 that they want to set aside for a college fund for their two children. How much will this provide at the end of each half-year for a period of 9 years if it is deferred for 11 years and can be invested at 7.3% compounded semiannually?

59. A banker is trying to decide whether to advertise some new 18-month certificates of deposit (CDs) at 6.52% compounded quarterly or at 6.48% compounded continuously. Which rate is a better investment for the consumer who buys such a CD? Which rate is better for the bank?

60. To purchase a home, a couple borrowed $280,000 at 5.1% compounded monthly for 25 years. After making 70 payments of $1653.21, they plan to refinance at 4.2% compounded monthly for 15 years, with refinancing costs of $1100 added to the new loan.
    (a) Find the amount refinanced.
    (b) Find the new monthly payment.

    (c) If this couple decides to make payments of $2000 per month on their refinanced loan, how long will it take to pay off the loan?
    (d) How much is saved in total by refinancing and making monthly payments of $2000 on the refinanced amount?

61. A divorce settlement of $40,000 is paid in $1000 payments at the end of each of 40 months. What is the present value of this settlement if money is worth 12% compounded monthly?

62. If $8000 is invested at 12% compounded continuously for 3 years, what is the total interest earned at the end of the 3 years?

63. A couple borrowed $184,000 to buy a condominium. Their loan was for 25 years, and money is worth 6% compounded monthly.
    (a) Find the size of their monthly payment.
    (b) Find the total amount they would pay over 25 years.
    (c) Find the total interest they would pay over 25 years.
    (d) Find the unpaid balance after 7 years.

COMBINED APPLICATIONS

Problems 64–67 are complex financial problems that require skills from several sections.

64. Suppose a salesperson invests his $12,500 bonus in a fund that earns 10.8% compounded monthly. Also suppose that he makes contributions of $150 at the end of each month to this fund.
    (a) Find the future value after $12\frac{1}{2}$ years.
    (b) If after the $12\frac{1}{2}$ years the fund is used to set up an annuity, how much will it pay at the end of each month for the next 10 years?

65. Three years from now, a couple plan to spend 4 months traveling in China, Japan, and Southeast Asia. When they take their trip, they would like to withdraw $10,000 at the beginning of each month to cover their expenses for that month. Starting now, how much must they deposit at the beginning of each month for the next 3 years so that the account will provide the money they want while they are traveling? Assume that such an account pays 6.6% compounded monthly.

66. At age 22, Aruam Sdlonyer receives a $4000 IRA from her parents. At age 30, she decides that at age 67, she'd like to have a retirement fund that would pay $20,000 at the end of each month for 20 years. Suppose all investments earn 8.4% compounded monthly. How much does Aruam need to deposit at the end of each month from ages 30 to 67 to realize her goal?

67. A company borrows $2.6 million for 15 years at 5.6% compounded quarterly. After 2 years of regular payments, the company's profits are such that management believes it can increase the quarterly payments to $70,000 each. How long will it take to pay off the loan, and how much interest will be saved?

CHAPTER TEST

1. If $8000 is invested at 7% compounded continuously, how long will it be before it grows to $47,000?

2. Suppose you invest $100 at the end of each month in an account that earns 6.9% compounded monthly. What is the future value of the account after $5\frac{1}{2}$ years?

3. To buy a municipal bond that matures to $10,000 in 9 months, you must pay $9510. What simple interest rate is earned?

4. A debt of $280,000 is amortized with 40 equal semiannual payments of $14,357.78. If interest is 8.2% compounded semiannually, find the unpaid balance of the debt after 25 payments have been made.

5. If an investment of $1000 grew to $13,500 in 9 years, what interest rate compounded annually did this investment earn?

6. A couple borrowed $97,000 at 7.2% compounded monthly for 25 years to purchase a condominium.
   (a) Find their monthly payment.
   (b) Over the 25 years, how much interest will they pay?

7. If you borrow $2500 for 15 months at 4% simple interest, how much money must you repay after the 15 months?

8. How much must you put aside at the beginning of each half-year if, in 6 years, you want to have $12,000 and the current interest rate is 6.2% compounded semiannually?

9. Find the annual percentage yield (the effective annual rate) for an investment that earns 8.4% compounded monthly.

10. An accountant wants to withdraw $3000 from an investment at the beginning of each quarter for the next 15 years. How much must be deposited originally if the investment earns 6% compounded quarterly? Assume that after the 15 years, the balance is zero.

11. If $10,000 is invested at 7% compounded continuously, what is the value of the investment after 20 years?

12. A $780,000 IRA is used to supplement a retired couple's income with payments at the end of each quarter for the next 15 years. If money is worth 8% compounded quarterly, what is the size of each payment?

13. What amount must you invest in an account that earns 6.8% compounded quarterly, if you want to have $9500 after 5 years?

14. If $1500 is deposited at the end of each half-year in a retirement account that earns 8.2% compounded semiannually, how long will it be before the account contains $500,000?

15. Maxine deposited $400 at the beginning of each month for 15 years in an account that earned 6% compounded monthly. Find the value of the account after the 15 years.

16. Grandparents plan to establish a college trust for their youngest grandchild. How much is needed now so that the trust, which earns 6.4% compounded quarterly, will provide $4000 at the end of each quarter for 4 years after being deferred for 10 years?

17. A couple borrows $180,000 at 5.4% compounded monthly for 30 years. After making 80 payments of $1010.76, they refinance at 4.8% compounded monthly for 25 years, with refinancing costs of $550 added to the new loan.
    (a) Find the amount refinanced.
    (b) Find the new monthly payment.
    (c) How much is saved by refinancing?

18. Suppose that a 10-year corporate bond has a maturity value of $10,000 and a coupon rate of 10%, with coupons paid semiannually. Find the market price of the bond if the current yield rate is 6% compounded semiannually. Is this bond selling at a discount or at a premium?

19. The following sequence is arithmetic: 298.8, 293.3, 287.8, 282.3, ...
    (a) If you were not told that this sequence was arithmetic, how could you tell that it was?
    (b) Find the 51st term of this sequence.
    (c) Find the sum of the first 51 terms.

20. A 400-mg dose of heart medicine is taken daily. During each 24-hour period, the body eliminates 40% of this drug (so that 60% remains in the body). Thus the amount of drug in the bloodstream just after the 31st dose is given by

$$400 + 400(0.6) + 400(0.6)^2 + 400(0.6)^3 + \cdots + 400(0.6)^{29} + 400(0.6)^{30}$$

Find the level of the drug in the bloodstream at this time.

21. If you took a home mortgage loan of $150,000 for 30 years at 8.4% compounded monthly, your monthly payments would be $1142.76. Suppose after 2 years you had an additional $2000. Would you save more over the life of the loan by paying an extra $2000 with your 24th payment or by paying $1160 per month beginning with the 25th payment? To help you answer this question, complete the following.
    (a) Find the unpaid balance after 24 payments (both including and not including the $2000 payment).
    (b) Determine how long it takes to pay off the loan with the regular $1142.76 payments and the additional $2000 payment. Then find the total interest paid.
    (c) Determine how long it takes to pay off the loan without the additional $2000 payment, but with monthly payments of $1160 from the 25th payment. Then find the total interest paid.
    (d) Which payment method costs less?

22. A couple would like to have $50,000 at the end of $4\frac{1}{2}$ years. They can invest $10,000 now and make additional contributions at the end of each quarter over the $4\frac{1}{2}$ years. If the investment earns 7.7% compounded quarterly, what size payments will enable them to reach their goal?

23. A woman makes $3000 contributions at the end of each half-year to a retirement account for a period of 8 years. For the next 20 years, she makes no additional contributions and no withdrawals.
    (a) If the account earns 7.5% compounded semi-annually, find the value of the account after the 28 years.
    (b) If this account is used to set up an annuity that pays her an amount at the beginning of each 6-month period for the next 20 years, how much will each payment be?

EXTENDED APPLICATIONS & GROUP PROJECTS

I. Mail Solicitation Home Equity Loan: Is This a Good Deal?

Discover offers a home equity line of credit that lowers the total of the monthly payments on several hypothetical loans by $366.12. (See the following table.)

The home equity loan payment is based on "10.49% APR annualized over a 10-year term." This means that the loan is amortized at 10.49% with monthly payments.

(a) Using this interest rate and monthly payments for the 10 years, how much money will still be owed at the end of the 10 years?
(b) How much is paid during the 10 years?
(c) How much would the payment have to be for the debt to be paid in the 10 years?
(d) How long would it take to pay off the debts under the original plan if interest were 15% on each loan?

Loan Type	Current Monthly Payment Example		Discover Home Equity	
	Loan Amount	Monthly Payment	Loan Amount	Monthly Payment
Bank cards	$10,000	$186.00	PAID OFF	NONE
Auto loan	$12,500	$320.03	PAID OFF	NONE
Department store cards	$2,500	$78.63	PAID OFF	NONE
Discover home equity line of credit			$25,000	$218.54
Total	$25,000	$584.66	$25,000	$218.54

Source: Discover Loan Center mailer

II. Profit Reinvestment

T. C. Hardware Store wants to construct a new building at a second location. If construction could begin immediately, the cost would be $500,000. At this time, however, the owners do not have the required 20% down payment, so they plan to invest $2000 per month of their profits until they have the necessary amount. They can invest their money in an annuity account that pays 6% compounded monthly, but they are concerned about the 3% average inflation rate in the construction industry. They would like you to give them some projections about how 3% inflation will affect the time required to accrue the down payment and the building's eventual cost. They would also like to know how their projected profits, after the new building is complete, will affect their schedule for paying off the mortgage loan.

Specifically, the owners would like you to prepare a report that answers the following questions:

1. If the 3% annual inflation rate is accurate, how long will it take to get the down payment? *Hint:* Assume that inflation is compounded monthly. Then the required down payment will be 20% of

$$500,000\left(1 + \frac{0.03}{12}\right)^n$$

where n is in months. Thus you must find n such that this amount equals the future value of the owners' annuity. The solution to the resulting equation is difficult to obtain by algebraic methods but can be found with a graphing utility.

2. If the 3% annual inflation rate is accurate (compounded monthly), what will T. C. Hardware's projected construction costs be (to the nearest hundred dollars) when it has its down payment?

3. If T. C. Hardware borrows 80% of its construction costs and amortizes that amount at 7.8% compounded monthly for 15 years, what will its monthly payment be?

4. Finally, the owners believe that 2 years after this new building is begun (that is, after 2 years of payments on the loan), their profits will increase enough so that they'll be able to make double mortgage payments each month until the loan is paid. Under these assumptions, how long will it take T. C. Hardware to pay off the loan?

III. Purchasing a Home

Buying a home is the biggest single investment or purchase that most individuals make. This project is designed to give you some insight into the home-buying process and the associated costs.

Find all the costs associated with buying a home by making a 20% down payment and borrowing 80% of the cost of the home.

1. Decide how much your home will cost (and how much you'll have to put down and how much to mortgage). Call a realtor to determine the cost of a home in your area. (This could be a typical starter home, an average home for the area, or your dream house.) Ask the realtor to identify and estimate all closing costs associated with buying your home. Closing costs include, among other items, your down payment, attorney's fees, and title fees.

2. Call at least three different banks to determine mortgage loan rates for 15 years, 25 years, and 30 years and the costs associated with obtaining your loan. These associated costs of a loan are paid at closing and include, for example, an application fee, an appraisal fee, and points.

3. For each bank and each different loan duration, develop a summary that contains
   (a) an itemization and explanation of all closing costs and the total amount due at closing
   (b) the monthly payment
   (c) the total amount paid over the life of the loan
   (d) the amortization schedule for each loan (use a spreadsheet or financial software).

4. For each duration (15 years, 25 years, and 30 years), identify which bank gives the best loan rate and explain why you think it is best. Be sure to consider what is best for someone who is likely to remain in the home for 7 years or less compared with someone who is likely to stay 20 years or more.

franz12/Shutterstock

Introduction to Probability

7

An economist cannot predict exactly how the gross national product will change, a physician cannot determine exactly the cause of lung cancer, and a psychologist cannot determine the exact effect of environment on behavior. But each of these determinations can be made with varying probabilities. Thus an understanding of the meaning and determination of the probabilities of events occurring is important to success in business, economics, the life sciences, and the social sciences. Probability was initially developed to solve gambling problems, but it is now the basis for solving problems in a wide variety of areas.

The topics and some representative applications discussed in this chapter include the following.

Prerequisite Problem Type	For Section	Answer	Section for Review
(a) The sum of x, $\frac{1}{4}$, and $\frac{2}{3}$ is 1. What is x? (b) If the sum of x, $\frac{1}{3}$, and $\frac{1}{3}$ is 1, what is x?	**7.1**	(a) $x = \frac{1}{12}$ (b) $x = \frac{1}{3}$	1.1 Linear equations
If 12 numbers are weighted so that each of the 12 numbers has an equal weight and the sum of the weights is 1, what weight should be assigned to each number?	**7.1**	$\frac{1}{12}$	1.1 Linear equations
(a) List the set of integers that satisfies $2 \leq x < 6$. (b) List the set of integers that satisfies $4 \leq s \leq 12$.	**7.1**	(a) $\{2, 3, 4, 5\}$ (b) $\{4, 5, 6, 7, 8, 9, 10, 11, 12\}$	1.1 Linear inequalities
For the sets $E = \{1, 2, 3, 4, 5\}$ and $F = \{2, 4, 6, 8\}$, find (a) $E \cup F$ (b) $E \cap F$	**7.1–7.4**	(a) $\{1, 2, 3, 4, 5, 6, 8\}$ (b) $\{2, 4\}$	0.1 Sets
Find the product: $[0.9 \quad 0.1]\begin{bmatrix} 0.8 & 0.2 \\ 0.3 & 0.7 \end{bmatrix}$	**7.7**	$[0.75 \quad 0.25]$	3.2 Matrix multiplication
Solve the system using matrices: $\begin{cases} 0.5V_1 + 0.4V_2 + 0.3V_3 = V_1 \\ 0.4V_1 + 0.5V_2 + 0.3V_3 = V_2 \\ 0.1V_1 + 0.1V_2 + 0.4V_3 = V_3 \end{cases}$	**7.7**	$V_1 = 3V_3$ $V_2 = 3V_3$ $V_3 = $ *any real number*	3.3 Gauss-Jordan elimination

SECTION 7.1

Probability; Odds

OBJECTIVES

- To compute the probability of the occurrence of an event
- To construct a sample space for a probability experiment
- To compute the empirical probability that an event will occur
- To compute the odds that an event will occur

APPLICATION PREVIEW

Before the General Standard Company can place a 3-year warranty on all of the faucets it produces, it needs to find the probability that each faucet it produces will function properly (not leak) for 3 years. (See Example 5.)

In this section, we will use sample spaces to find the probability that an event will occur by using assumptions or knowledge of the entire population of data under consideration. When knowledge of the entire population is not available, we can compute the empirical probability that an event will occur by using data collected about the probability experiment. This method can be used to compute the probability that the General Standard faucets will work properly if information about a large sample of the faucets is gathered.

Probability; Sample Spaces

When we toss a coin, it can land in one of two ways: heads or tails. If the coin is a "fair" coin, these two possible **outcomes** have an equal chance of occurring, and we say that the outcomes of this **probability experiment** are **equally likely.** If we seek the probability that an experiment has a certain result, that result is called an **event.**

Suppose that an experiment can have a total of n equally likely outcomes and that k of these outcomes would be considered successes. Then the probability of achieving a success in the experiment is k/n, the number of ways the experiment can result in a success divided by the total number of possible outcomes.

Probability of a Single Event

If an event E can happen in k ways out of a total of n equally likely possibilities, the probability of the occurrence of the event is denoted by

$$Pr(E) = \frac{\text{Number of successes}}{\text{Number of possible outcomes}} = \frac{k}{n}$$

EXAMPLE 1   Probability

If we draw a ball from a bag containing 4 white balls and 6 black balls, what is the probability of

(a) getting a white ball?   (b) getting a black ball?   (c) not getting a white ball?

Solution

(a) A white ball can be drawn in 4 ways out of 10 equally likely possibilities.

$$Pr(W) = \frac{4}{10} = \frac{2}{5}$$

(b) We can draw a black ball in 6 ways out of 10 possible outcomes.

$$Pr(B) = \frac{6}{10} = \frac{3}{5}$$

(c) The probability of not getting a white ball is $Pr(B)$, because not getting a white ball is the same as getting a black ball. Thus $Pr(\text{not } W) = Pr(B) = 3/5$.

A set that contains all the possible outcomes of an experiment is called a **sample space.** For the experiment of randomly drawing a numbered card* from a box of cards numbered 1 through 12, a sample space is

$$S = \{1, 2, 3, 4, 5, 6, 7, 8, 9, 10, 11, 12\}$$

Each element of the sample space is called a **sample point,** and an **event** is a subset of the sample space. Each sample point in the sample space is assigned a nonnegative **probability measure** or **probability weight** such that the sum of the weights in the sample space is 1. The probability of an event is the sum of the weights of the sample points in the event's **subspace** (subset of S).

For example, the experiment "drawing a number at random from the numbers 1 through 12" has the sample space S given above and each element has a probability weight of 1/12. The event "drawing an even number" in this experiment has the subspace $E = \{2, 4, 6, 8, 10, 12\}$, and the probability is

$$\text{Pr(even)} = \text{Pr}(E) = \frac{1}{12} + \frac{1}{12} + \frac{1}{12} + \frac{1}{12} + \frac{1}{12} + \frac{1}{12} = \frac{6}{12} = \frac{1}{2}$$

Some experiments have an infinite number of outcomes, but we will concern ourselves only with experiments having finite sample spaces. We can usually construct more than one sample space for an experiment. The sample space in which each sample point is equally likely is called an **equiprobable sample space.** Suppose the number of elements in a sample space is $n(S) = n$, with each element representing an equally likely outcome of a probability experiment. Then the weight (probability) assigned to each element is

$$\frac{1}{n(S)} = \frac{1}{n}$$

If an event E that is a subset of an equiprobable sample space contains $n(E) = k$ elements of S, then we can restate the probability of an event E in terms of the number of elements of E.

Probability of an Event

If an event E can occur in $n(E) = k$ ways out of $n(S) = n$ equally likely ways, then

$$\text{Pr}(E) = \frac{n(E)}{n(S)} = \frac{k}{n}$$

EXAMPLE 2 Probability of Events

If a number is to be selected at random from the integers 1 through 12, what is the probability that it is
(a) divisible by 3?   (b) even and divisible by 3?   (c) even or divisible by 3?

Solution
The set $S = \{1, 2, 3, 4, 5, 6, 7, 8, 9, 10, 11, 12\}$ is an equiprobable sample space for this experiment (as mentioned previously).
(a) The set $E = \{3, 6, 9, 12\}$ contains the numbers that are divisible by 3. Thus

$$\text{Pr(divisible by 3)} = \frac{n(E)}{n(S)} = \frac{4}{12} = \frac{1}{3}$$

(b) The set $F = \{6, 12\}$ contains the numbers that are even *and* divisible by 3. Thus

$$\text{Pr(even and divisible by 3)} = \frac{n(F)}{n(S)} = \frac{2}{12} = \frac{1}{6}$$

*Selecting a card randomly means that every card has an equal chance of being selected.

(c) The numbers that are even *or* divisible by 3 are 2, 3, 4, 6, 8, 9, 10, 12, so the set $G = \{2, 3, 4, 6, 8, 9, 10, 12\}$ describes this event. Thus

$$\text{Pr(even or divisible by 3)} = \frac{n(G)}{n(S)} = \frac{8}{12} = \frac{2}{3}$$

CHECKPOINT

1. If a coin is drawn from a box containing 4 gold, 10 silver, and 16 copper coins, all the same size, what is the probability of
   (a) getting a gold coin?
   (b) getting a copper coin?
   (c) not getting a copper coin?

Probability

If an event E is certain to occur, E contains all of the elements of the sample space, S. Hence the sum of the probability weights of E is the same as that of S, so

$$\text{Pr}(E) = 1 \qquad \text{if } E \text{ is certain to occur}$$

If event E is impossible, $E = \varnothing$, so

$$\text{Pr}(E) = 0 \qquad \text{if } E \text{ is impossible}$$

Because all probability weights of elements of a sample space are nonnegative,

$$0 \le \text{Pr}(E) \le 1 \qquad \text{for any event } E$$

EXAMPLE 3   Sample Spaces

Suppose a (fair) coin is tossed 3 times.

(a) Construct an equiprobable sample space for the experiment.
(b) Find the probability of obtaining 0 heads.
(c) Find the probability of obtaining 2 heads.

Solution

(a) Perhaps the most obvious way to record the possibilities for this experiment is to list the number of heads that could result: $\{0, 1, 2, 3\}$. But the 0 heads (3 tails) can occur only one way (see below), and 1 head can occur in 3 ways (a head on the first, second, or third toss), so the events in $\{0, 1, 2, 3\}$ are not equally likely and this sample space is not equiprobable. A sample space in which each outcome is equally likely is $\{$HHH, HHT, HTH, THH, HTT, THT, TTH, TTT$\}$, where HHT indicates that the first two tosses were heads and the third was a tail.

(b) Because there are 8 equally likely possible outcomes, $n(S) = 8$. Only one of the eight possible outcomes, $E = \{$TTT$\}$, gives 0 heads, so $n(E) = 1$. Thus

$$\text{Pr(0 heads)} = \frac{n(E)}{n(S)} = \frac{1}{8}$$

© Vladmir Wrangel/ Shutterstock.com

(c) The event "two heads" is $F = \{$HHT, HTH, THH$\}$, so

$$\text{Pr(2 heads)} = \frac{n(F)}{n(S)} = \frac{3}{8}$$

To find the probability of obtaining a given sum when a pair of dice is rolled, we need to determine the outcomes. However, the sums {2, 3, 4, 5, 6, 7, 8, 9, 10, 11, 12} are not equally likely; there is only one way to obtain a sum of 2, but there are several ways to obtain a sum of 6. If we distinguish between the two dice we are rolling and we record all the possible outcomes for each die, we see that there are 36 possibilities, each of which is equally likely. Table 7.1 shows these possibilities, with the event "sum = 9" encircled.

TABLE 7.1

First Die	Second Die					
	1	2	3	4	5	6
1	(1, 1)	(1, 2)	(1, 3)	(1, 4)	(1, 5)	(1, 6)
2	(2, 1)	(2, 2)	(2, 3)	(2, 4)	(2, 5)	(2, 6)
3	(3, 1)	(3, 2)	(3, 3)	(3, 4)	(3, 5)	(3, 6)
4	(4, 1)	(4, 2)	(4, 3)	(4, 4)	(4, 5)	(4, 6)
5	(5, 1)	(5, 2)	(5, 3)	(5, 4)	(5, 5)	(5, 6)
6	(6, 1)	(6, 2)	(6, 3)	(6, 4)	(6, 5)	(6, 6)

This list of possible outcomes for finding the sum of two dice is an equiprobable sample space for the experiment. Because the 36 elements in the sample space are equally likely, we can find the probability that a given sum results by determining the number of ways this sum can occur and dividing that number by 36.

EXAMPLE 4   Rolling Dice

Use Table 7.1 to find the following probabilities if a pair of distinguishable dice is rolled.
(a) Pr(sum is 5)   (b) Pr(sum is 2)   (c) Pr(sum is 8)

Solution
(a) If E is the event "sum is 5," then $E = \{(4, 1), (3, 2), (2, 3), (1, 4)\}$. Therefore,

$$\text{Pr(sum is 5)} = \frac{n(E)}{n(S)} = \frac{4}{36} = \frac{1}{9}.$$

(b) The sum 2 results only from {(1, 1)}. Thus Pr(sum is 2) = 1/36.
(c) The sample points that give a sum of 8 are in the subspace F, which is

$$F = \{(6, 2), (5, 3), (4, 4), (3, 5), (2, 6)\}$$

Thus $\text{Pr(sum is 8)} = \frac{n(F)}{n(S)} = \frac{5}{36}.$

CHECKPOINT

2. A ball will be drawn from a bag containing balls numbered 1, 2, 3, 4, and 5. To find the probability that a ball with an even number is drawn, we can use the sample space $S_1 = \{\text{even, odd}\}$ or $S_2 = \{1, 2, 3, 4, 5\}$.
    (a) Which of these sample spaces is an equiprobable sample space?
    (b) What is the probability of drawing a ball that is even-numbered?
3. A coin is tossed, and a die is rolled.
    (a) Write an equiprobable sample space listing the possible outcomes for this experiment.
    (b) Find the probability of getting a head on the coin and an even number on the die.
    (c) Find the probability of getting a tail on the coin and a number divisible by 3 on the die.

Empirical Probability

Up to this point, the probabilities assigned to events were determined *theoretically,* either by assumption (the probability of obtaining a head in one toss of a fair coin is 1/2) or by knowing the entire population under consideration (if 1000 people are in a room and 400 of them are males, the probability of picking a person at random and getting a male is $400/1000 = 2/5$). We also can determine probabilities **empirically,** where the assignment of the probability of an event is derived from our experiences or from data that have been gathered. Probabilities developed in this way are called **empirical probabilities.** An empirical probability is formed by conducting an experiment, or by observing a situation a number of times, and noting how many times a certain event occurs.

Empirical Probability of an Event	$$\text{Pr(Event)} = \frac{\text{Number of observed occurrences of the event}}{\text{Total number of trials or observations}}$$

In some cases, empirical probability is the only way to assign a probability to an event. For example, life insurance premiums are based on the probability that an individual will live to a certain age. These probabilities are developed empirically and organized into mortality tables.

In other cases, empirical probabilities may have a theoretical framework. For example, for tossing a coin,

$$\text{Pr(Head)} = \text{Pr(Tail)} = \frac{1}{2}$$

gives the theoretical probability. If a coin was actually tossed 1000 times, it might come up heads 517 times and tails 483 times, giving empirical probabilities for these 1000 tosses of

$$\text{Pr(Head)} = \frac{517}{1000} = 0.517 \quad \text{and} \quad \text{Pr(Tail)} = \frac{483}{1000} = 0.483$$

On the other hand, if the coin was tossed only 4 times, it might come up heads 3 times and tails once, giving empirical probabilities vastly different from the theoretical ones. In general, empirical probabilities can differ from theoretical probabilities, but they are likely to reflect the theoretical probabilities when the number of observations is large. Moreover, when this is not the case, there may be reason to suspect that the theoretical model does not fit the event (for example, that a coin may not be fair). It also should be noted that empirical probability is sometimes approximate if it is based on data from a sample.

For example, suppose that 800 of the 500,000 computer flash drives manufactured by a firm are defective. Because the 800 defective drives occurred in a very large number of those manufactured, the ratio of the number of defective drives to the total number of drives manufactured provides an *empirical* probability that should accurately represent the true probability that a drive picked at random is defective.

$$\text{Pr(defective)} = \frac{800}{500,000} = \frac{1}{625}$$

EXAMPLE 5   Quality Control | APPLICATION PREVIEW |

The General Standard Company can use information about a large sample of its faucets to compute the empirical probability that a faucet chosen at random will function properly (not leak) for 3 years. Of a sample of 12,316 faucets produced in 2014, 137 were found to fail within 3 years. Find the empirical probability that any faucet the company produces will work properly for 3 years.

Solution

If 137 of these faucets fail to work properly, then $12,316 - 137 = 12,179$ will work properly. Thus the probability that any faucet selected at random will function properly is

$$\text{Pr(not leak)} = \frac{12,179}{12,316} \approx 0.989$$

Odds and Probability
We sometimes use **odds** to describe the likelihood that an event will occur. The odds in favor of an event E occurring and the odds against E occurring are found as follows.

Odds

If the probability that event E occurs is $\Pr(E) \neq 1$, then the odds that E will occur are

$$\text{Odds in favor of } E = \frac{\Pr(E)}{1 - \Pr(E)}$$

The odds that E will not occur, if $\Pr(E) \neq 0$, are

$$\text{Odds against } E = \frac{1 - \Pr(E)}{\Pr(E)}$$

The odds $\dfrac{a}{b}$ are stated as "a to b" or "$a{:}b$."

EXAMPLE 6   Odds

If the probability of drawing a queen from a deck of playing cards is 1/13, what are the odds
(a) in favor of drawing a queen?
(b) against drawing a queen?

Solution

(a) $\dfrac{1/13}{1 - 1/13} = \dfrac{1/13}{12/13} = \dfrac{1}{12}$

The odds in favor of drawing a queen are 1 to 12, which we write as 1:12.

(b) $\dfrac{12/13}{1/13} = \dfrac{12}{1}$

The odds against drawing a queen are 12 to 1, denoted 12:1.

Odds and Probability

If the odds in favor of an event E occurring are $a{:}b$, the probability that E will occur is

$$\Pr(E) = \frac{a}{a + b}$$

If the odds against E are $b{:}a$, then

$$\Pr(E) = \frac{a}{a + b}$$

For example, according to funny2.com, the odds that an American adult does not want to live to age 120 are 3 to 2. Thus the probability that an adult American chosen at random does not want to live to age 120 is $3/(3 + 2) = 3/5$.

EXAMPLE 7   Bullying

According to nypost.com, the odds that a student age 12 to 18 will be bullied at school during a year are 10 to 21. What is the probability that such a student will not be bullied at school?

Solution
The odds of being bullied are 10:21, so the probability of *not* being bullied is

$$\Pr(\text{not bullied}) = \frac{21}{10 + 21} = \frac{21}{31} \approx 0.677$$

1. (a) $\Pr(\text{gold}) = 4/30 = 2/15$
   (b) $\Pr(\text{copper}) = 16/30 = 8/15$
   (c) $\Pr(\text{not copper}) = 14/30 = 7/15$
2. (a) $S_2 = \{1, 2, 3, 4, 5\}$ is an equiprobable sample space.
   (b) $\Pr(\text{even}) = 2/5$
3. (a) $\{H1, H2, H3, H4, H5, H6, T1, T2, T3, T4, T5, T6\}$
   (b) $\Pr(\text{head and even number}) = 3/12 = 1/4$
   (c) $\Pr(\text{tail and number divisible by 3}) = 2/12 = 1/6$

EXERCISES 7.1

1. One ball is drawn at random from a bag containing 4 red balls and 6 white balls. What is the probability that the ball is
   (a) red?   (b) green?   (c) red or white?
2. One ball is drawn at random from a bag containing 4 red balls and 6 white balls. What is the probability that the ball is
   (a) white?   (b) white or red?   (c) red and white?
3. If you draw one card at random from a deck of 12 cards numbered 1 through 12, inclusive, what is the probability that the number you draw is divisible by 4?
4. An ordinary die is tossed. What is the probability of getting a 3 or a 4?
5. A die is rolled. Find the probability of getting a number greater than 0.
6. A die is rolled. What is the probability that
   (a) a 4 will result?
   (b) a 7 will result?
   (c) an odd number will result?
7. An urn contains three red balls numbered 1, 2, 3, four white balls numbered 4, 5, 6, 7, and three black balls numbered 8, 9, 10. A ball is drawn from the urn. What is the probability that
   (a) it is red?
   (b) it is odd-numbered?
   (c) it is red and odd-numbered?
   (d) it is red or odd-numbered?
   (e) it is not black?
8. An urn contains three red balls numbered 1, 2, 3, four white balls numbered 4, 5, 6, 7, and three black balls numbered 8, 9, 10. A ball is drawn from the urn. What is the probability that the ball is
   (a) white?
   (b) white and odd?
   (c) white or even?
   (d) black or white?
   (e) black and white?
9. From a deck of 52 ordinary playing cards, one card is drawn. Find the probability that it is
   (a) a queen.
   (b) a red card.
   (c) a spade.
10. From a deck of 52 ordinary playing cards, one card is drawn. Find the probability that it is
    (a) a red king.   (b) a king or a black card.
11. Suppose a fair coin is tossed two times. Construct an equiprobable sample space for the experiment and determine each of the following probabilities.
    (a) $\Pr(0 \text{ heads})$ (b) $\Pr(1 \text{ head})$ (c) $\Pr(2 \text{ heads})$
12. Suppose a fair coin is tossed four times. Construct an equiprobable sample space for the experiment and determine each of the following probabilities.
    (a) $\Pr(2 \text{ heads})$ (b) $\Pr(3 \text{ heads})$ (c) $\Pr(4 \text{ heads})$
13. Use Table 7.1 to determine the following probabilities if a distinguishable pair of dice is rolled.
    (a) $\Pr(\text{sum is } 4)$ (b) $\Pr(\text{sum is } 10)$
    (c) $\Pr(\text{sum is } 12)$
14. (a) When a pair of distinguishable dice is rolled, what sum is most likely to occur?
    (b) When a pair of distinguishable dice is rolled, what is $\Pr(4 \leq S \leq 8)$, where S represents the sum rolled?
15. If a pair of dice, one green and one red, is rolled, what is
    (a) $\Pr(4 \leq S \leq 7)$, where S is the sum rolled?
    (b) $\Pr(8 \leq S \leq 12)$, where S is the sum rolled?
16. If a green die and a red die are rolled, find
    (a) $\Pr(2 \leq S \leq 6)$, where S is the sum rolled on the two dice.
    (b) $\Pr(4 \leq S)$, where S is the sum rolled on the two dice.
17. Suppose a die is tossed 1200 times and a 6 comes up 431 times.
    (a) Find the empirical probability for a 6 to occur.
    (b) On the basis of a comparison of the empirical probability and the theoretical probability, do you think the die is fair or biased?
18. Suppose that a coin is tossed 3000 times and 1800 heads result. What is the empirical probability that a head will occur with this coin? Is there evidence that the coin is a fair coin?
19. If the probability that an event will occur is 2/5, what are the odds
    (a) in favor of the event occurring?
    (b) against the event occurring?

20. If the probability that an event E will not occur is 8/11, what are the odds
    (a) that E will occur?
    (b) that E will not occur?
21. If the odds that a particular horse will win a race are 1:20, what is the probability
    (a) that the horse will win the race?
    (b) that the horse will lose the race?
22. If the odds that an event E will not occur are 23:57, what is the probability
    (a) that event E will occur?
    (b) that event E will not occur?

APPLICATIONS

23. *Drug use* Forty-six percent of marijuana use among youth occurs in the inner cities (*Source:* Partnership for a Drug-Free America). If an instance of such marijuana use is chosen at random, what is the probability that the use occurs in an inner city?
24. *Breast cancer* According to the American Cancer Society, 199 of 200 mammograms turn out to be normal. What is the probability that the mammogram of a woman chosen at random will turn out to be normal?
25. *Car maintenance* A car rental firm has 425 cars. Sixty-three of these cars have defective turn signals, and 32 have defective tires. What is the probability that one of these cars selected at random
    (a) has defective turn signals?
    (b) has defective tires?
26. *Testing* An unprepared student must take a 7-question multiple-choice test that has 5 possible answers per question. If the student guesses on the first question, what is the probability that she will answer that question incorrectly?
27. *Voting* The table gives the average number of voters in Springfield in each of three political parties during the last 12 years, along with the average number that voted in presidential elections during this period.
    (a) For each political party, use these data to find the probability that a person selected at random from the registered voters in the party will vote in the next election.
    (b) For which party is the probability highest?

	Political Party		
	Republican	Democratic	Independent
Registered voters	4500	6100	2200
Voted	2835	2501	1122

28. *Voting* In a survey of 350 registered voters in Belair, 123 said that they would vote for the Democratic candidate for mayor. If a registered voter is selected at random, what is the probability that this person will vote for the Democratic candidate?

29. *Sales promotion* In a sales promotion, a clothing store gives its customers a chance to draw a ticket from a box that contains a discount on their next purchase. The box contains 3000 tickets giving a 10% discount, 500 giving a 30% discount, 100 giving a 50% discount, and 1 giving a 100% discount. What is the probability that a given customer will randomly draw a ticket giving
    (a) a 100% discount?
    (b) a 50% discount?
    (c) a discount of less than 50%?
    (d) Is a given customer more likely to get a 30% discount or a discount higher than 30%?
30. *Management* A dry cleaning firm has 12 employees: 7 women and 5 men. Three of the women and five of the men are 40 years or older. The remainder are over 20 and under 40. If a person is chosen at random from this firm, what is the probability that the person is
    (a) a woman?
    (b) under 40 years of age?
    (c) 20 years old?
31. *Physical activity* The table gives the percents of U.S. residents who participated in the recommended amount of physical activity, who participated in an insufficient amount of physical activity, and who were inactive, categorized by race or origin (*Source:* Centers for Disease Control and Prevention).
    (a) What is the probability a Black person participated in the recommended amount of physical activity?
    (b) What is the probability a White person did not have the recommended amount of physical activity?
    (c) What is the sum of the probabilities in the "Hispanic" column? Does that mean that all categories of physical activity for Hispanics are included in the table?

	White	Black	Hispanic	Other
Recommended	50.9	40.2	41.1	46.1
Insufficient	37.7	38.3	36.8	37.9
Inactive	11.4	21.5	22.1	16.0

32. *Physical activity* The table gives the percent of U.S. residents who participated in no leisure-time physical activity, categorized by race or origin (*Source:* Centers for Disease Control and Prevention).
    (a) What is the probability that a Black person participated in no leisure-time physical activity?
    (b) What is the probability that a White person participated in no leisure-time physical activity?
    (c) Can we add the probabilities in the row to find the probability that a U.S. resident participated in no leisure-time physical activity? Explain?

	White	Black	Hispanic	Other
No leisure-time physical activity	21.4	32.8	38.6	25.5

33. *Blood types* Human blood is classified by blood type, which indicates the presence or absence of the antigens A, B, and Rh, as follows.

A present	Type A
B present	Type B
Both A and B present	Type AB
Neither A nor B present	Type O

    Each of these types is combined with a + or − sign to indicate whether the Rh antigen is present. Write a sample space containing all possible blood types. Do you think this is an equiprobable sample space? Explain.

34. *Genetics* Construct an equiprobable sample space that gives the possible combinations of male and female children in a family with three children.

35. *Blood types* Four percent of the population of the United States has type AB blood (*Source: aabb.org*). What is the probability that a U.S. resident chosen at random
    (a) will have type AB blood?
    (b) will not have type AB blood?

36. *Blood types* Sixteen percent of the population of the United States has a negative Rh (Rhesus) factor in their blood, and the remainder have a positive Rh factor (*Source: aabb.org*). What is the probability that a resident of the United States chosen at random
    (a) will have a negative Rh factor?
    (b) will have a positive Rh factor?

37. *Minorities* Among the residents of Los Angeles, 13% are classified as of Asian descent (*Source:* U.S. Census Bureau). If an L.A. resident is chosen at random, what is the probability that he or she is
    (a) of Asian descent?   (b) not of Asian descent?

38. *Minorities* Among the population of Houston, 41.9% are of Hispanic descent (*Source:* U.S. Census Bureau). What is the probability that a Houston resident chosen at random is
    (a) of Hispanic descent?
    (b) not of Hispanic descent?

39. *Fraud* A company selling substandard drugs to developing countries sold 2,000,000 capsules with 60,000 of them empty (*Source: 60 Minutes*). What is the probability that a person who takes a randomly chosen capsule from this company will get an empty capsule?

40. *Inventory* Forty percent of a company's total output consists of baseballs, 30% consists of softballs, and 10% consists of tennis balls. Its only remaining product is handballs. If we place balls in a box in the same ratios as the company's output and select a ball at random from the box, what is the probability that
    (a) the ball is a baseball?
    (b) the ball is a tennis ball?
    (c) the ball is not a softball?
    (d) the ball is a handball?

41. *Lactose intolerance* Lactose intolerance affects about 75% of African, Asian, and Native Americans (*Source:* Jean Carper, "Eat Smart," *USA Weekend*). If a person is selected from this group of people, what is the probability that the person will have lactose intolerance?

42. *Lactose intolerance* Lactose intolerance affects about 20% of non-Hispanic White Americans (*Source:* Jean Carper, "Eat Smart," *USA Weekend*). If a person is selected from this group of people, what is the probability that the person will be lactose-intolerant?

43. *Management* Because of a firm's growth, it is necessary to transfer one of its employees to one of its branch stores. Three of the nine employees are women, and all of the nine employees are equally qualified for the transfer. If the person to be transferred is chosen at random, what is the probability that the transferred person is a woman?

44. *Quality control* A supply of 500 plasma television displays has 6 defective displays. What is the probability that a display picked at random from the supply is not defective?

45. *Education* A professor assigns 6 homework projects and then, during the next class, rolls a die to determine which one of the 6 projects to grade. If a student has completed 2 of the assignments, what is the probability that the professor will grade a project that the student has completed?

46. *Marketing* Meow Chow offers a free coin in each bag of cat food. If each 10,000-bag shipment has one gold coin, 2 silver dollars, 5 quarters, 20 dimes, 50 nickels, and 9922 pennies, what is the probability that a bag of Meow Chow cat food selected at random will have a penny in it?

47. *Minorities* The NAACP claimed that in Volusia County, Florida, police stopped dark-skinned drivers on I-95 who were not violating the law much more frequently than they stopped White drivers and then conducted searches of the cars for drugs or large sums of money that could be related to drug sales (*Source: American Journal*, August 30, 1994). If police made routine stops of randomly selected motorists who were not violating a law and if 22% of the drivers on I-95 passing through this county were dark-skinned, what is the probability that the police stopped a driver who was not violating a law but who was dark-skinned? If 39% of the motorists stopped for routine checks were dark-skinned people, did the NAACP claim seem reasonable?

48. *Quality control* A computer store offers used computers free to local middle schools. Of the 54 machines available, four have defective memories, six others have defective keys, and the remainder have no defects. If a teacher picks one at random, what is the probability that she will select a defective computer?

49. *Genetics* A newly married couple plan to have three children. Assuming that the probability of a girl being born equals that of a boy being born, what is the probability that exactly two of the three children born will be girls? (*Hint:* Construct the sample space.)

50. *Management* A frustrated store manager is asked to make four different yes-no decisions that have no relation to each other. Because he is impatient to leave work, he flips a coin for each decision. If the correct decision in each case was yes, what is the probability that
    (a) all of his decisions were correct?
    (b) none of his decisions was correct?
    (c) half of his decisions were correct?

51. *Genetics* A couple plan to have two children and want to know the probability of having one boy and one girl.
    (a) Does {0, 1, 2} represent an equiprobable sample space for finding the probability of exactly one boy in two children?
    (b) Construct an equiprobable sample space for this problem.
    (c) What is the probability of getting one boy and one girl in two children?

52. *Genetics* What is the probability that a randomly selected couple with two children has
    (a) one child of each sex?
    (b) two children of the same sex?

53. *Testing* A quiz consists of 8 matching questions with 8 possible matches from which to choose. If a student guesses on the first question, what is the probability that he will get the correct answer?

54. *Testing* In taking a quiz with 6 multiple-choice questions, a student knows that two of the possible five answers to the first question are not correct. What is the probability of her getting the correct answer to the first question?

55. *Quality control* On average, 6 articles out of each 250 produced by a certain machine are defective. What is the probability that an article chosen at random is defective?

56. *Baseball* If a baseball player has 1150 at bats and 320 hits, what is the probability that he will get a hit his next time at bat?

57. *Traffic safety* In a certain town, citizens' groups have identified three intersections as potentially dangerous. They collected the following data.

	Intersections		
	A	B	C
Number of vehicles/day	25,500	3890	8580
Number of vehicles in accidents/year	182	51	118

For each intersection, find the probability that a vehicle entering the intersection will be involved in an accident. Which intersection is the most dangerous?

58. *Occupational fatalities* The table gives the number of fatal occupational injuries from transportation incidents. If a fatality from this group is chosen at random, what is the probability that it is
    (a) a highway fatality?   (b) an aircraft fatality?

Fatal Transportation Injuries	
Total	2480
Highway	1428
Worker struck by vehicle	390
Water vehicle	86
Aircraft	147

Source: U.S. Department of Labor

59. *Elections* Prior to an election, a poll of 1200 citizens is taken. Suppose 557 plan to vote for A, 533 plan to vote for B, and the remainder indicate that they will not vote.
    (a) If the poll is accurate, find the probability that a citizen chosen at random will vote for A.
    (b) If the poll is accurate, what is the probability that a person picked at random will not vote?

60. *Elections* Suppose a county has 800,000 registered voters, 480,000 of whom are Democrats and 290,000 of whom are Republicans. If a registered voter is chosen at random, what is the probability that
    (a) he or she is a Democrat?
    (b) he or she is neither a Democrat nor a Republican?

61. *Births* Suppose that at a certain hospital, the births on a given day consisted of 8 girls and 2 boys. Suppose that at the same hospital, the births in a given year consisted of 1220 girls and 1194 boys.
    (a) Find the empirical probabilities for the birth of each sex on the given day.
    (b) Find the empirical probabilities for the given year.
    (c) What are the theoretical probabilities, and which empirical probabilities do you think more accurately reflect reality?

62. *Traffic safety* A traffic survey showed that 5680 cars entered an intersection of the main street of a city and that 1460 of them turned onto the intersecting street at this intersection.
    (a) What is the empirical probability that a car will turn onto the intersecting street?
    (b) What is the probability that a car will not turn onto the intersecting street?

63. *Celebrity marriage* The odds that a celebrity marriage will last a lifetime are 3 to 1. What is the probability that a celebrity marriage chosen at random will last a lifetime?

64. *Ice cream* The odds of an American home having at least one container of ice cream in the freezer are 9 to 10. What is the probability that an American home chosen at random will have ice cream in its freezer?

65. *Industrial accidents* If the odds against dying in an industrial accident are 3992:3, what is the probability of dying in an industrial accident?

66. *Rain* If the probability of rain today is 30%, what are the odds against rain today?

67. *Full moon on Friday the 13th* The last time a full moon occurred on Friday the 13th was June 13, 2014, and the next time will be August 13, 2049. Use Google to find the probability of a full moon on Friday the 13th. Also give the odds against this event.

68. *Accidental deaths* The probability of being killed in a non-transportation accident is 1/70. What are the odds against being killed in a non-transportation accident?

SECTION **7.2**

Unions and Intersections of Events: One-Trial Experiments

OBJECTIVES

- To find the probability of the intersection of two events
- To find the probability of the union of two events
- To find the probability of the complement of an event
- To find the probability of mutually exclusive events

APPLICATION PREVIEW

Suppose that the directors of the Chatham County School Board consist of 8 Democrats, 3 of whom are female, and 4 Republicans, 2 of whom are female. If a director is chosen at random to discuss an issue on television, we can find the probability that the person will be a Democrat or female by finding the probability of the union of the two events "a Democrat is chosen" and "a female is chosen." (See Example 4.) In this section, we will discuss methods of finding the probabilities of the intersection and union of events by using sample spaces and formulas.

Unions, Intersections, and Complements of Events

As we stated in the previous section, events determine subsets of the sample space for a probability experiment. The **intersection, union,** and **complement** of events are defined as follows.

Intersection, Union, and Complement

If E and F are two events in a sample space S, then the **intersection of E and F** is

$$E \cap F = \{a : a \in E \text{ and } a \in F\}$$

the **union of E and F** is

$$E \cup F = \{a : a \in E \text{ or } a \in F\}$$

and the **complement of E** is

$$E' = \{a : a \in S \text{ and } a \notin E\}$$

$E \cap F$

$E \cup F$

Using these definitions, we can write the probabilities that certain events will occur as follows:

$$\Pr(E \text{ and } F \text{ both occur}) = \Pr(E \cap F)$$
$$\Pr(E \text{ or } F \text{ occurs}) = \Pr(E \cup F)$$
$$\Pr(E \text{ does not occur}) = \Pr(E')$$

In Section 7.1, "Probability; Odds," we investigated probability questions by identifying the sample space elements for each event described. We now apply the properties just stated.

EXAMPLE 1 Unions and Intersections of Events

A card is drawn from a box containing 15 cards numbered 1 to 15. What is the probability that the card is

(a) even and divisible by 3?   (b) even or divisible by 3?   (c) not even?

Solution
The sample space S contains the 15 numbers.

$$S = \{1, 2, 3, 4, 5, 6, 7, 8, 9, 10, 11, 12, 13, 14, 15\}$$

If we let E represent "even-numbered" and D represent "number divisible by 3," we have

$$E = \{2, 4, 6, 8, 10, 12, 14\} \quad \text{and} \quad D = \{3, 6, 9, 12, 15\}$$

These sets are shown in the Venn diagram in Figure 7.1.

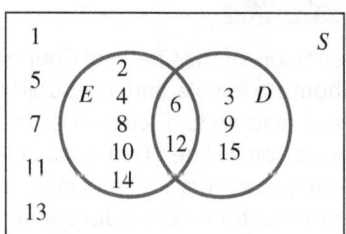

Figure 7.1

(a) The event "even and divisible by 3" is $E \cap D = \{6, 12\}$, so

$$\text{Pr(even and divisible by 3)} = \Pr(E \cap D) = \frac{n(E \cap D)}{n(S)} = \frac{2}{15}$$

(b) The event "even or divisible by 3" is $E \cup D = \{2, 3, 4, 6, 8, 9, 10, 12, 14, 15\}$, so

$$\text{Pr(even or divisible by 3)} = \Pr(E \cup D) = \frac{n(E \cup D)}{n(S)} = \frac{10}{15} = \frac{2}{3}$$

(c) The event "not even," or E', contains all elements of S not in E, so $E' = \{1, 3, 5, 7, 9, 11, 13, 15\}$, and the probability that the card is not even is

$$\text{Pr(not } E) = \Pr(E') = \frac{n(E')}{n(S)} = \frac{8}{15}$$

CHECKPOINT

1. If a ball is drawn from a bag containing 4 red balls numbered 1, 2, 3, 4 and 3 white balls numbered 5, 6, 7, what is the probability that the ball is
   (a) red and even?   (b) white and even?   (c) not red

Probability of the Complement

Because the complement of an event contains all the elements of S *except* for those elements in E (see Figure 7.2), the number of elements in E' is $n(S) - n(E)$, so

Figure 7.2

$$\Pr(E') = \frac{n(S) - n(E)}{n(S)} = 1 - \frac{n(E)}{n(S)} = 1 - \Pr(E)$$

$$\text{Pr(not } E) = \Pr(E') = 1 - \Pr(E)$$

EXAMPLE 2 **Heart Attack Risk**

Suppose that a 50-year-old man has systolic blood pressure of 110 and that 60% of his cholesterol is HDL. The risk of heart attack in the next 10 years is given in Table 7.2. If a man satisfying these conditions is selected at random and has a cholesterol level of 200, what is the probability that he will not have a heart attack by age 60?

TABLE 7.2

Total Cholesterol	Risk of Heart Attack
130	1%
150	1
175	2
200	2
250	3
300	5

Solution

If the man selected at random satisfies the given conditions and has a cholesterol level of 200, the probability that he will have a heart attack in the next 10 years (that is, by age 60) is $2\% = 0.02$. Thus the probability that he will not have a heart attack by age 60 is

$$\text{Pr(no attack)} = 1 - \text{Pr(attack)} = 1 - 0.02 = 0.98$$

Inclusion-Exclusion Principle

The number of elements in the set $E \cup F$ is the number of elements in E plus the number of elements in F *minus* the number of elements in $E \cap F$ [because this number was counted twice in $n(E) + n(F)$]. Thus,

$$n(E \cup F) = n(E) + n(F) - n(E \cap F)$$

Hence,

$$\text{Pr}(E \cup F) = \frac{n(E \cup F)}{n(S)} = \frac{n(E)}{n(S)} + \frac{n(F)}{n(S)} - \frac{n(E \cap F)}{n(S)}$$

$$= \text{Pr}(E) + \text{Pr}(F) - \text{Pr}(E \cap F)$$

This establishes what is called the **inclusion-exclusion principle.**

Inclusion-Exclusion Principle

If E and F are any two events, then the probability that one event or the other will occur, denoted $\text{Pr}(E \text{ or } F)$, is given by

$$\text{Pr}(E \text{ or } F) = \text{Pr}(E \cup F) = \text{Pr}(E) + \text{Pr}(F) - \text{Pr}(E \cap F)$$

Suppose that of 30 people interviewed for a position, 18 had a business degree, 15 had previous experience, and 8 of those with experience also had a business degree. The Venn diagram in Figure 7.3 illustrates this situation.

Because 8 of the 30 people have both a business degree and experience,

$$\text{Pr}(B \cap E) = \frac{8}{30}$$

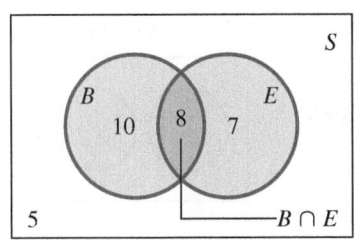

Figure 7.3

We also see that

$$\text{Pr}(B) = \frac{18}{30} \quad \text{and} \quad \text{Pr}(E) = \frac{15}{30}$$

Thus the probability of choosing a person at random who has a business degree or experience is

$$\text{Pr}(B \cup E) = \text{Pr}(B) + \text{Pr}(E) - \text{Pr}(B \cap E)$$

$$= \frac{18}{30} + \frac{15}{30} - \frac{8}{30} = \frac{25}{30} = \frac{5}{6}$$

EXAMPLE 3   Football

Suppose that in a given year, the probability that the Steelers will win their division is $1/6$, the probability that the Jets will win their division is $1/12$, and the probability that both will win their divisions is $1/24$. What is the probability that one of the teams will win their division?

Solution

Pr(one will win) = Pr(Steelers or Jets will win)

$$= \text{Pr(Steelers win)} + \text{Pr(Jets win)} - \text{Pr(Steelers and Jets win)}$$

$$= \frac{1}{6} + \frac{1}{12} - \frac{1}{24} = \frac{5}{24}$$

EXAMPLE 4   **Politics** | APPLICATION PREVIEW |

The directors of the Chatham County School Board consist of 8 Democrats, 3 of whom are female, and 4 Republicans, 2 of whom are female. If a director is chosen at random to discuss an issue on television, what is the probability that the person will be a Democrat or female?

Solution
There are 12 directors, of whom 8 are Democrats and 5 are female. But 3 of the directors are Democrats and females, and cannot be counted twice. Thus

$$\Pr(D \text{ or } F) = \Pr(D \cup F) = \Pr(D) + \Pr(F) - \Pr(D \text{ and } F)$$

$$= \frac{8}{12} + \frac{5}{12} - \frac{3}{12} = \frac{10}{12} = \frac{5}{6}$$

CHECKPOINT

2. If a ball is drawn from a bag containing 4 red balls numbered 1, 2, 3, 4 and 3 white balls numbered 5, 6, 7, what is the probability that the ball is
   (a) red or even?   (b) white or even?

Mutually Exclusive Events   We say that events E and F are **mutually exclusive** if and only if $E \cap F = \varnothing$. Thus

$$\Pr(E \cup F) = \Pr(E) + \Pr(F) - 0 = \Pr(E) + \Pr(F)$$

if and only if E and F are mutually exclusive.

Mutually Exclusive Events

If E and F are **mutually exclusive,** then $\Pr(E \cap F) = 0$, and

$$\Pr(E \text{ or } F) = \Pr(E \cup F) = \Pr(E) + \Pr(F)$$

Mutually exclusive

EXAMPLE 5   **Mutually Exclusive Events**

Find the probability of obtaining a 6 or a 4 in one roll of a die.

Solution
Rolling a 6 and rolling a 4 on one roll of a die are mutually exclusive events. Let E be the event "rolling a 6" and F be the event "rolling a 4."

$$\Pr(E) = \Pr(\text{rolling } 6) = \frac{1}{6} \quad \text{and} \quad \Pr(F) = \Pr(\text{rolling } 4) = \frac{1}{6}$$

Then

$$\Pr(E \cup F) = \Pr(E) + \Pr(F) = \frac{1}{6} + \frac{1}{6} = \frac{1}{3}$$

EXAMPLE 6   **Property Development**

A firm is considering three possible locations for a new factory. The probability that site A will be selected is 1/3, and the probability that site B will be selected is 1/5. Only one location will be chosen.
(a) What is the probability that site A or site B will be chosen?
(b) What is the probability that neither site A nor site B will be chosen?

Solution

(a) The two events are mutually exclusive, so

$$\Pr(\text{site A or site B}) = \Pr(\text{site A} \cup \text{site B})$$

$$= \Pr(\text{site A}) + \Pr(\text{site B}) = \frac{1}{3} + \frac{1}{5} = \frac{8}{15}$$

(b) The probability that neither will be chosen is $1 - 8/15 = 7/15$.

The formula for the probability of the union of mutually exclusive events can be extended beyond two events.

$$\Pr(E_1 \cup E_2 \cup \ldots \cup E_n) = \Pr(E_1) + \Pr(E_2) + \cdots + \Pr(E_n)$$

for mutually exclusive events $E_1, E_2, \ldots, E_n$.

EXAMPLE 7 **Dice**

Find the probability of rolling two distinct dice and obtaining
(a) a sum greater than 9.
(b) a 6 on the first die and a sum greater than 9.
(c) a 6 on the first die or a sum greater than 9.

Solution

The sample space for rolling two distinct dice can be found in Table 7.1 in Section 7.1. We use that table to find these probabilities.

(a) The event "sum greater than 9" consists of the mutually exclusive events "sum = 10," "sum = 11," and "sum = 12."

$$\Pr(10 \text{ or } 11 \text{ or } 12) = \Pr(10 \cup 11 \cup 12)$$

$$= \Pr(10) + \Pr(11) + \Pr(12) = \frac{3}{36} + \frac{2}{36} + \frac{1}{36} = \frac{6}{36} = \frac{1}{6}$$

(b) This event is the intersection of the events $E =$ "6 on the 1st die" and $F =$ "sum greater than 9." Thus

$$E \cap F = \{(6,4),(6,5),(6,6)\} \quad \text{and}$$

$$\Pr(E \cap F) = \frac{3}{36} = \frac{1}{12}$$

(c) We seek $\Pr(E \cup F)$. First note that from Table 7.1, $\Pr(6 \text{ on the 1st die}) = 6/36 = 1/6$. Thus

$$\Pr(E \cup F) = \Pr(E) + \Pr(F) - \Pr(E \cap F)$$

$$= \frac{1}{6} + \frac{1}{6} - \frac{1}{12} = \frac{2}{12} + \frac{2}{12} - \frac{1}{12} = \frac{1}{4}$$

CHECKPOINT ANSWERS

1. (a) $\Pr(\text{red and even}) = \Pr(\text{red} \cap \text{even}) = \frac{2}{7}$

   (b) $\Pr(\text{white and even}) = \Pr(\text{white} \cap \text{even}) = \frac{1}{7}$

   (c) $\Pr(\text{not red}) = \Pr(\text{white}) = \frac{3}{7}$

2. (a) $\Pr(\text{red or even}) = \frac{5}{7}$

   (b) $\Pr(\text{white or even}) = \frac{5}{7}$

EXERCISES 7.2

In Problems 1–4, one card is drawn from a deck of 12 cards numbered 1 through 12. In each case, find the probability that the card is

1. (a) even and divisible by 3.
   (b) even or divisible by 3.
2. (a) even and divisible by 5.
   (b) even or divisible by 5.
3. (a) odd and divisible by 4.
   (b) odd or divisible by 4.
4. (a) divisible by 3 and by 5.
   (b) divisible by 3 or by 5.
5. An ordinary die is tossed. What is the probability of getting a number divisible by 3 or an odd number?
6. A card is drawn at random from a deck of 52 playing cards. Find the probability that it is a club or a king.
7. If the probability that event E will occur is 3/5, what is the probability that E will not occur?
8. If the probability that an event will occur is 7/9, what is the probability that the event will not occur?

In Problems 9–12, one ball is drawn from a bag containing 5 red balls numbered 1–5 and 9 white balls numbered 6–14. In each case, find the probability that the ball is

9. (a) red and even-numbered.
   (b) red or even-numbered.
   (c) not divisible by 3.
10. (a) white and odd-numbered.
    (b) white or odd-numbered.
    (c) white or even-numbered.
11. (a) divisible by 3 and by 7.
    (b) divisible by 3 or by 7.
    (c) not divisible by 3.
12. (a) divisible by 3 and by 2.
    (b) divisible by 3 or by 2.
    (c) not divisible by 15.
13. Suppose a die is biased (unfair) so that each odd-numbered face has probability 1/4 of resulting and each even face has probability 1/12 of resulting. Find the probability of getting a number greater than 3.
14. A card is drawn from a deck of 52 playing cards. What is the probability that it is an ace, a king, or a jack?
15. A bag contains 4 white, 7 black, and 6 green balls. What is the probability that a ball drawn at random from the bag is white or green?
16. In a game where only one player can win, the probability that Jack will win is 1/5 and the probability that Bill will win is 1/4. Find the probability that one of them will win.
17. A cube has 2 faces painted red, 2 painted white, and 2 painted blue. What is the probability of getting a red face or a white face in one roll?
18. A cube has 3 faces painted white, 2 faces painted red, and 1 face painted blue. What is the probability that a roll will result in a red or blue face?

19. A ball is drawn from a bag containing 13 red balls numbered 1–13 and 5 white balls numbered 14–18. What is the probability that the ball is
    (a) not even-numbered?
    (b) red and even-numbered?
    (c) red or even-numbered?
    (d) neither red nor even-numbered?
20. A ball is drawn from a bag containing 13 red balls numbered 1–13 and 5 white balls numbered 14–18. What is the probability that the ball is
    (a) not red?
    (b) white and odd-numbered?
    (c) white or odd-numbered?
    (d) neither white nor odd-numbered?

APPLICATIONS

21. *Drug use* Forty-six percent of marijuana use among youth occurs in the inner cities (*Source:* Partnership for a Drug-Free America). If an instance of such marijuana use is chosen at random, what is the probability that the use does not occur in an inner city?
22. *Breast cancer* According to the American Cancer Society, 199 of 200 mammograms turn out to be normal. What is the probability that the mammogram of a woman chosen at random will show an abnormality?
23. *Car maintenance* A car rental firm has 425 cars. Sixty-three of these cars have defective turn signals, and 32 have defective tires. What is the probability that one of these cars selected at random
    (a) does not have defective turn signals?
    (b) has no defects if no car has 2 defects?
24. *Testing* An unprepared student must take a 7-question multiple-choice test that has 5 possible answers per question. If the student guesses on the first question, what is the probability that she will answer that question incorrectly?
25. *Linguistics* Of 100 students, 24 can speak French, 18 can speak German, and 8 can speak both French and German. If a student is picked at random, what is the probability that he or she can speak French or German?
26. *Management* A company employs 65 people. Eight of the 30 men and 21 of the 35 women work in the business office. What is the probability that an employee picked at random is a woman or works in the business office?
27. *Politics* Sacco and Rosen are among three candidates running for public office, and polls indicate that the probability that Sacco will win is 1/3 and the probability that Rosen will win is 1/2. Only one candidate can win.

(a) What is the probability that Sacco or Rosen will win?

(b) What is the probability that neither Sacco nor Rosen will win?

28. *Mountain biking* Rob Lee knows that he can compete successfully in a single track mountain bike race unless he gets a flat tire or his chain breaks. In such races, the probability of getting a flat is 0.3, of the chain breaking is 0.06, and of both occurring is 0.01. What is the probability that Rob completes the race successfully?

29. *Salaries* The table gives the percent of employees of the Ace Company in each of three salary brackets categorized by the sex of the employees. An employee is selected at random.

(a) What is the probability that the person selected is female and makes less than $60,000?

(b) What is the probability that the person selected makes at least $100,000?

(c) What is the probability that the person is male or makes less than $60,000?

	Earns Less Than $60,000	Earns at Least $60,000 and Less Than $100,000	Earns at Least $100,000
Male	25%	18%	5%
Female	35%	14%	3%

30. *Salaries* At the Baker Engineering Company, 40% of the employees are female and 60% of the employees earn less than $60,000. If 30% of the employees are females who earn less than $60,000, what is the probability that an employee picked at random is female or earns less than $60,000?

31. *Workers* The table gives the projected number of workers in various categories in Springfield in 2020. If one of the represented workers is chosen at random, use the table to find the probability that the person

(a) is Latino or female.

(b) is male or Black.

(c) is Asian or White.

	White	Black	Asian	Latino
Male	49,804	6084	2780	10,044
Female	36,026	6664	2078	5671
Total	85,830	12,748	4858	15,715

32. *Causes of death* In the United States in 2014, there were 614,348 deaths from heart disease, 591,699 from cancer, and 133,103 from stroke (*Source:* National Center for Health Statistics, U.S. Department of Health and Human Services). If a death is chosen at random from the 2,596,993 deaths that occurred in 2014, what is the probability that the cause of death was from cancer or stroke?

33. *HIV cases* The table gives the numbers of new HIV infections in various categories for the United States and six dependent areas in 2014. Use the table to find the probability that a person diagnosed in 2014 was:

(a) female.

(b) female and an injected drug user.

(c) male or heterosexual.

	Total	Heterosexual	Injected Drug User
Male	35,570	3285	1590
Female	9918	7242	1045

Source: HIV/AIDS Surveillance Report, 2014

34. *Accidental deaths* In 2014, the death rate from motor vehicle accidents was 10.7 per 100,000 people and the death rate from falls was 9.6 per 100,000 people (*Source:* National Safety Council). What is the probability that a death in 2014 was from a motor vehicle accident or from a fall?

35. *Cognitive complexity* The cognitive complexity of a structure was studied by Scott[*] using a technique in which a person was asked to specify a number of objects and group them into as many groupings as he or she found meaningful. A person groups 12 objects into three groups in such a way that

7 objects are in group A.
7 objects are in group B.
8 objects are in group C.
3 objects are in both group A and group B.
5 objects are in both group B and group C.
4 objects are in both group A and group C.
2 objects are in all three groups.

(a) What is the probability that an object chosen at random has been placed in group A or group B?

(b) What is the probability that an object chosen at random has been placed in group B or group C?

36. *Politics* A group of 100 people contains 60 Democrats and 35 Republicans. If there are 60 women and 40 of the Democrats are women, what is the probability that a person selected at random is a Democrat or a woman?

37. *Education* A mathematics class consists of 16 engineering majors, 12 science majors, and 4 liberal arts majors.

(a) What is the probability that a student selected at random will be a science or liberal arts major?

(b) What is the probability that a student selected at random will be an engineering or science major?

(c) Five of the engineering students, 6 of the science majors, and 2 of the liberal arts majors are female. What is the probability that a student selected at random is an engineering major or a female?

[*]W. Scott, "Cognitive Complexity and Cognitive Flexibility," *Sociometry* 25 (1962), pp. 405–414.

38. *Parts delivery* Repairing a copy machine requires that two parts be delivered from two suppliers. The probability that part A will be delivered on Thursday is 0.6, and the probability that part B will be delivered on Thursday is 0.8. If the probability that one or the other part will arrive on Thursday is 0.9, what is the probability that both will be delivered on Thursday?

Oil drilling **The table summarizes the opinions of various groups on the issue of oil drilling in national parks. Use this table to calculate probabilities in Problems 39–42.**

Opinion	Whites Reps.	Dems.	Nonwhites Reps.	Dems.	Total
Favor	300	100	25	10	435
Oppose	100	250	25	190	565
Total	400	350	50	200	1000

39. Find the probability that an individual chosen at random is a Republican or favors oil drilling in national parks.
40. Find the probability that an individual chosen at random is a Democrat or opposes oil drilling in national parks.
41. Find the probability that an individual chosen at random is White or opposes oil drilling in national parks.
42. Find the probability that an individual chosen at random is non-White or favors oil drilling in national parks.
43. *Drinking age* A survey questioned 1000 people regarding lowering the legal drinking age from 21 to 19. Of the 560 who favored lowering the age, 390 were male. Of the 440 opposition responses, 160 were male. A person is selected at random.

(a) What is the probability that the person is a male or favors lowering the age?
(b) What is the probability that the person is a female or favors lowering the age?
(c) What is the probability that the person is a female or opposes lowering the age?

44. *Job bids* Three construction companies have bid for a job. Max knows that the two companies with which he is competing have probabilities 1/3 and 1/6, respectively, of getting the job. What is the probability that Max will get the job?
45. *Management* A company employs 80 people. Twenty of the 50 men and 18 of the 30 women work in the business office. What is the probability that an employee picked at random is a man or does not work in the business office?
46. *Television* The probability that a wife watches a certain television show is 0.55, that her husband watches it is 0.45, and that both watch it is 0.30. What is the probability that the husband or the wife watches this show?
47. *Cancer testing* A long-term study has revealed that the prostate-specific antigen (PSA) test for prostate cancer in men is very effective. The study shows that 87% of the men for which the test is positive actually have prostate cancer (*Source: Journal of the American Medical Association*). If a man selected at random tests positive for prostate cancer with this test, what is the probability that he does not have prostate cancer?
48. *Cancer testing* The study described in Problem 47 also revealed that 91% of the men for whom the PSA test was negative do not have prostate cancer (*Source: Journal of the American Medical Association*). If a man selected at random tests negative for prostate cancer with this test, what is the probability that he does have prostate cancer?

Conditional Probability: The Product Rule

OBJECTIVES

- To solve conditional probability problems
- To find the probability of two or more dependent events
- To find the probability of two or more independent events

APPLICATION PREVIEW

Polk's Department Store has observed that 80% of its charge accounts have men's names on them and that 16% of the accounts with men's names on them have been delinquent at least once, whereas 5% of the accounts with women's names on them have been delinquent at least once. We can find the probability that an account selected at random is in a man's name and is delinquent by using the Product Rule. (See Example 5.) In this section, we will use the Product Rule to find the probability that two events will occur and we will solve problems involving conditional probability.

Conditional Probability

Each probability we computed has been relative to the sample space for the experiment. Sometimes information is given that reduces the sample space needed to solve a stated problem. For example, if a die is rolled, the probability that a 5 occurs, given that an odd number is rolled, is denoted by

$$\text{Pr}(5 \text{ rolled} \mid \text{odd number rolled})$$

The knowledge that an odd number occurs reduces the sample space from the numbers on a die, $S = \{1, 2, 3, 4, 5, 6\}$, to the sample space for odd numbers on a die, $S_1 = \{1, 3, 5\}$, so the event $E =$ "a 5 occurs" has probability

$$\Pr(5 \mid \text{odd number}) = \frac{n(5 \text{ and odd number rolled})}{n(\text{odd number rolled})} = \frac{n(E \cap S_1)}{n(S_1)} = \frac{1}{3}$$

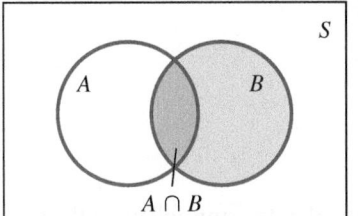

Figure 7.4

To find $\Pr(A \mid B)$, we seek the probability that A occurs, given that B occurs. Figure 7.4 shows the original sample space S with the reduced sample space B shaded. Because all elements must be contained in B, we evaluate $\Pr(A \mid B)$ by dividing the number of elements in $A \cap B$ by the number of elements in B.

Conditional Probability

The **conditional probability** that A occurs, given that B occurs, is denoted by $\Pr(A \mid B)$ and is given by

$$\Pr(A \mid B) = \frac{n(A \cap B)}{n(B)}$$

EXAMPLE 1   **Public Opinion**

Suppose the following table summarizes the opinions of various groups in a survey on the issue of increased enforcement of immigration laws. What is the probability that a person selected at random from this group of people
(a) is non-White?
(b) is non-White and favors increased enforcement of immigration laws?
(c) favors increased enforcement of immigration laws, given that the person is non-White?

	Whites		Non-Whites		
Opinion	Republicans	Democrats	Republicans	Democrats	Totals
Favor	300	100	25	10	435
Oppose	100	250	25	190	565
Total	400	350	50	200	1000

Solution
(a) Of the 1000 people in the group, $50 + 200 = 250$ are non-White, so

$$\Pr(\text{non-White}) = \frac{250}{1000} = \frac{1}{4}$$

(b) There are 1000 people in the group and $25 + 10 = 35$ who both are non-White and favor increased enforcement, so

$$\Pr(\text{non-White and favor}) = \frac{35}{1000} = \frac{7}{200}$$

(c) There are $50 + 200 = 250$ non-White and $25 + 10 = 35$ people who both are non-White and favor increased enforcement, so

$$\Pr(\text{favor} \mid \text{non-White}) = \frac{n(\text{favor and non-White})}{n(\text{non-White})} = \frac{35}{250} = \frac{7}{50}$$

Using the definition of $\Pr(A \mid B)$ and dividing the numerator and denominator by $n(S)$, the number of elements in the sample space, give

$$\Pr(A \mid B) = \frac{n(A \cap B)}{n(B)} = \frac{\dfrac{n(A \cap B)}{n(S)}}{\dfrac{n(B)}{n(S)}} = \frac{\Pr(A \cap B)}{\Pr(B)}$$

Conditional Probability Formula	Let A and B be events in the sample space S with $\Pr(B) > 0$. The **conditional probability** that event A occurs, given that event B occurs, is given by $$\Pr(A \mid B) = \frac{\Pr(A \cap B)}{\Pr(B)}$$

EXAMPLE 2   Conditional Probability

A red die and a green die are rolled. What is the probability that the sum rolled on the dice is 6, given that the sum is less than 7?

Solution
Using the conditional probability formula and the sample space in Table 7.1 in Section 7.1, we have

$$\Pr(\text{sum is } 6 \mid \text{sum} < 7) = \frac{\Pr(\text{sum is } 6 \cap \text{sum} < 7)}{\Pr(\text{sum} < 7)}$$

Because $\Pr(\text{sum is } 6 \cap \text{sum} < 7) = \Pr(\text{sum is } 6) = 5/36$, the probability is

$$\Pr(\text{sum is } 6 \mid \text{sum} < 7) = \frac{5/36}{1/36 + 2/36 + 3/36 + 4/36 + 5/36}$$

$$= \frac{5/36}{15/36} = \frac{1}{3}$$

CHECKPOINT

1. Suppose that one ball is drawn from a bag containing 4 red balls numbered 1, 2, 3, 4 and 3 white balls numbered 5, 6, 7. What is the probability that the ball is white, given that it is an even-numbered ball?

The Product Rule   We can solve the formula

$$\Pr(A \mid B) = \frac{\Pr(A \cap B)}{\Pr(B)}$$

for $\Pr(A \cap B)$ by multiplying both sides of the equation by $\Pr(B)$. This gives

$$\Pr(A \cap B) = \Pr(B) \cdot \Pr(A \mid B)$$

Similarly, we can solve

$$\Pr(B \mid A) = \frac{\Pr(B \cap A)}{\Pr(A)} = \frac{\Pr(A \cap B)}{\Pr(A)}$$

for $\Pr(A \cap B)$, getting

$$\Pr(A \cap B) = \Pr(A) \cdot \Pr(B \mid A)$$

Product Rule	If A and B are probability events, then the probability of the event "A and B" is $\Pr(A \text{ and } B)$, and it can be found by one or the other of these two formulas. $$\Pr(A \text{ and } B) = \Pr(A \cap B) = \Pr(A) \cdot \Pr(B \mid A)$$ or $$\Pr(A \text{ and } B) = \Pr(A \cap B) = \Pr(B) \cdot \Pr(A \mid B)$$

EXAMPLE 3   Cards

Suppose that from a deck of 52 cards, two cards are drawn in succession without replacement. Find the probability that both cards are kings.

Solution

We seek the probability that the first card will be a king and the probability that the second card will be a king given that the first card was a king. The probability that the first card is a king is

$$\Pr(\text{1st card is a king}) = \frac{4}{52}$$

and the probability that the second card is a king is

$$\Pr(\text{2nd king} \mid \text{1st king}) = \frac{3}{51}$$

because one king has been removed from the deck on the first draw. Thus

$$\Pr(\text{2 kings}) = \Pr(\text{1st king}) \cdot \Pr(\text{2d king} \mid \text{1st king})$$
$$= \frac{4}{52} \cdot \frac{3}{51} = \frac{1}{221}$$

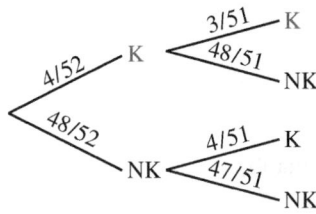

Figure 7.5

We can represent the outcomes in Example 3 with a **probability tree,** as shown in Figure 7.5. The outcome of the first draw is either a king or not a king; it is illustrated by the beginning two branches of the tree. The possible outcomes of the second trial can be treated as branches that emanate from each of the outcomes of the first trial. The tree shows that if a king occurs on the first trial, the outcome of the second trial is either a king or not a king, and the probabilities of these outcomes depend on the fact that a king occurred on the first trial. On the other hand, the probabilities of getting or not getting a king are different if the first draw does not yield a king, so the branches illustrating these possible outcomes have different probabilities.

There is only one "path" through the tree that illustrates getting kings on both draws, and the probability that both draws result in kings is the product of the probabilities on the branches of this path. Note that this gives $\frac{4}{52} \cdot \frac{3}{51} = \frac{1}{221}$, which is the same Product Rule probability found in Example 3.

In general, the connection between the Product Rule and a probability tree is as follows.

Probability Trees

- The probability attached to *each branch* of a **probability tree** is the conditional probability that the specified event will occur, given that the events on the preceding branches have occurred.
- When an event can be described by one path through a probability tree, the probability that that event will occur is the *product* of the probabilities on the branches *along the path* that represents the event.

EXAMPLE 4   **Probability Tree**

A box contains 3 black balls, 2 red balls, and 5 white balls. One ball is drawn, it is *not* replaced, and a second ball is drawn. Find the probability that the first ball is red and the second ball is black.

Solution

Let E_1 be "red ball first" and E_2 be "black ball second." The probability tree for this experiment is shown in Figure 7.6. The path representing the event whose probability we seek is the path through R (red ball) to B (black ball). The probability of this event is the product of the probabilities along this path.

$$\Pr(E_1 \cap E_2) = \Pr(E_1) \cdot \Pr(E_2 \mid E_1) = \frac{2}{10} \cdot \frac{3}{9} = \frac{1}{15}$$

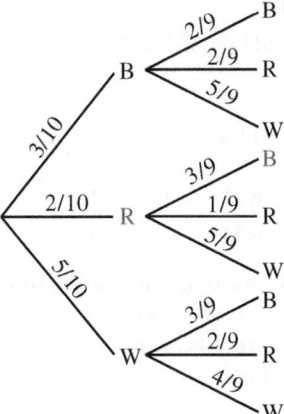

Figure 7.6

2. Two balls are drawn, without replacement, from the box described in Example 4.
   (a) Find the probability that both balls are white.
   (b) Find the probability that the first ball is white and the second ball is red.

EXAMPLE 5   **Delinquent Accounts** | APPLICATION PREVIEW |

Polk's Department Store has observed that 80% of its charge accounts have men's names on them and that 16% of the accounts with men's names on them have been delinquent at least once, while 5% of the accounts with women's names on them have been delinquent at least once. What is the probability that an account selected at random
(a) is in a man's name and is delinquent?
(b) is in a woman's name and is delinquent?

Solution

(a) Pr(man's account) = 0.80

Pr(delinquent | man's) = 0.16

Pr(man's and delinquent) = Pr(man's $\cap$ delinquent)

$$= \text{Pr(man's)} \cdot \text{Pr(delinquent | man's)}$$

$$= (0.80)(0.16) = 0.128$$

Using the probability tree in Figure 7.7 gives the same probability.

(b) Pr(woman's account) = 0.20

Pr(delinquent | woman's) = 0.05

Using the probability tree in Figure 7.7 gives the probability

$$\text{Pr(woman's and delinquent)} = (0.20)(0.05) = 0.01$$

Figure 7.7

EXAMPLE 6   **Manufacturing Inspections**

All products on an assembly line must pass two inspections. It has been determined that the probability that the first inspector will miss a defective item is 0.09. If a defective item gets past the first inspector, the probability that the second inspector will not detect it is 0.01. What is the probability that a defective item will not be rejected by either inspector? (All good items pass both inspections.)

Solution

The second inspector inspects only items passed by the first inspector. The probability that a defective item will pass both inspections is as follows.

$$\text{Pr(defective pass both)} = \text{Pr(pass first} \cap \text{pass second)}$$

$$= \text{Pr(pass first)} \cdot \text{Pr(pass second | passed first)}$$

$$= (0.09)(0.01) = 0.0009$$

Independent Events   If a coin is tossed twice, the sample space is $S = \{HH, HT, TH, TT\}$, so

$$\text{Pr(2d is H | 1st is H)} = \frac{\text{Pr(1st is H} \cap \text{2d is H)}}{\text{Pr(1st is H)}} = \frac{\text{Pr(Both H)}}{\text{Pr(1st is H)}} = \frac{1/4}{1/2} = \frac{1}{2}$$

We can see that the probability that the second toss of a coin is a head, given that the first toss was a head, was 1/2, which is the same as the probability that the second toss is a head, regardless of what happened on the first toss. This is because the results of the coin tosses are independent events. We can define **independent events** as follows.

Independent Events	The events A and B are **independent** if and only if
	$$\Pr(A \mid B) = \Pr(A) \quad \text{and} \quad \Pr(B \mid A) = \Pr(B)$$
	This means that the occurrence or nonoccurrence of one event does not affect the other.

If A and B are independent events, then this definition can be used to simplify the Product Rule:

$$\Pr(A \cap B) = \Pr(A) \cdot \Pr(B \mid A) = \Pr(A) \cdot \Pr(B)$$

Thus we have the following.

Product Rule for Independent Events	Events A and B are independent if and only if
	$$\Pr(A \text{ and } B) = \Pr(A \cap B) = \Pr(A) \cdot \Pr(B)$$

EXAMPLE 7   Independent Events

A die is rolled, and a coin is tossed. Find the probability of getting a 4 on the die and a head on the coin.

Solution
Let E_1 be "4 on the die" and E_2 be "head on the coin." The events are independent because what occurs on the die does not affect what happens to the coin.

$$\Pr(E_1) = \Pr(4 \text{ on die}) = \frac{1}{6} \quad \text{and} \quad \Pr(E_2) = \Pr(\text{head on coin}) = \frac{1}{2}$$

Then

$$\Pr(E_1 \cap E_2) = \Pr(E_1) \cdot \Pr(E_2) = \frac{1}{6} \cdot \frac{1}{2} = \frac{1}{12}$$

CHECKPOINT

3. Two balls are drawn with replacement from an urn that contains 3 red and 4 green balls.
   (a) Are these draws independent? Explain.
   (b) Find the probability of getting a green ball on both draws.

The Product Rules can be expanded to include more than two events, as the next example shows.

EXAMPLE 8   Extending the Product Rules

A bag contains 3 red marbles, 4 white marbles, and 3 black marbles. Find the probability of getting a red marble on the first draw, a black marble on the second draw, and a white marble on the third draw (a) if the marbles are drawn with replacement and (b) if the marbles are drawn without replacement.

Solution
(a) The marbles are replaced after each draw, so the contents are the same on each draw. Thus the events are independent. Let E_1 be "red on first," let E_2 be "black on second," and let E_3 be "white on third." Then

$$\Pr(E_1 \cap E_2 \cap E_3) = \Pr(E_1) \cdot \Pr(E_2) \cdot \Pr(E_3)$$

$$= \frac{3}{10} \cdot \frac{3}{10} \cdot \frac{4}{10} = \frac{36}{1000} = \frac{9}{250}$$

(b) The marbles are not replaced, so the events are dependent.

$$\Pr(E_1 \cap E_2 \cap E_3) = \Pr(E_1) \cdot \Pr(E_2 \mid E_1) \cdot \Pr(E_3 \mid E_1 \text{ and } E_2)$$

$$= \frac{3}{10} \cdot \frac{3}{9} \cdot \frac{4}{8} = \frac{1}{20}$$

EXAMPLE 9 Identity Theft

Identity theft can occur when an unscrupulous individual learns someone else's Social Security number. Suppose a person learns the first five digits of your Social Security number. Calculate the probability that the person guesses the last four digits and thus gains access to your Social Security number.

Solution

The digits in your Social Security number can repeat, so the probability that each digit is guessed correctly is 1/10. Thus the probability the person guesses the last four digits is

$$\frac{1}{10} \cdot \frac{1}{10} \cdot \frac{1}{10} \cdot \frac{1}{10} = \frac{1}{10,000}$$

The coin tossing problem in the next example belongs to a larger class of probability problems that involve repeated, independent experiments (called trials). Each trial has only two outcomes (designated as success and failure). In problems such as these, we can calculate the probability of at least one success in n trials as follows.

$$\Pr(\text{at least 1 success in } n \text{ trials}) = 1 - \Pr(0 \text{ successes})$$

EXAMPLE 10 Coin Tossing

A coin is tossed 4 times. Find the probability that
(a) no heads occur.
(b) at least one head is obtained.

Solution

(a) Each toss is independent, and on each toss, the probability that a tail occurs is 1/2. Thus the probability of 0 heads (4 tails) in 4 tosses is

$$\Pr(\text{TTTT}) = \frac{1}{2} \cdot \frac{1}{2} \cdot \frac{1}{2} \cdot \frac{1}{2} = \frac{1}{16}$$

(b) When a coin is tossed 4 times, if the event $E = \{0 \text{ heads}\}$, then

$$\text{"not } E\text{"} = \{\text{at least one head}\}$$

Thus the probability that at least one head occurs is

$$\Pr(\text{at least one head occurs}) = \Pr(\text{not 0 heads})$$

$$= 1 - \Pr(0 \text{ heads}) = 1 - \frac{1}{16} = \frac{15}{16}$$

CHECKPOINT ANSWERS

1. $\Pr(\text{white} \mid \text{even-numbered}) = \dfrac{1/7}{3/7} = \dfrac{1}{3}$

2. (a) $\Pr(\text{white on both draws}) = \dfrac{5}{10} \cdot \dfrac{4}{9} = \dfrac{2}{9}$

   (b) $\Pr(\text{white on first and red on second}) = \dfrac{5}{10} \cdot \dfrac{2}{9} = \dfrac{1}{9}$

3. (a) Yes. The result of the first draw has no effect on the probabilities for the second draw.

   (b) 16/49

EXERCISES 7.3

1. A card is drawn from a deck of 52 playing cards. Given that it is a red card, what is the probability that
   (a) it is a heart?   (b) it is a king?

2. A card is drawn from a deck of 52 playing cards. Given that it is an ace, a king, a queen, or a jack, what is the probability that it is a jack?

3. A die has been "loaded" so that the probability of rolling any even number is 2/9 and the probability of rolling any odd number is 1/9. What is the probability of
   (a) rolling a 6, given that an even number is rolled?
   (b) rolling a 3, given that a number divisible by 3 is rolled?

4. A die has been "loaded" so that the probability of rolling any even number is 2/9 and the probability of rolling any odd number is 1/9. What is the probability of
   (a) rolling a 5?
   (b) rolling a 5, given that an even number is rolled?
   (c) rolling a 5, given that an odd number is rolled?

5. A bag contains 9 red balls numbered 1, 2, 3, 4, 5, 6, 7, 8, 9 and 6 white balls numbered 10, 11, 12, 13, 14, 15. One ball is drawn from the bag. What is the probability that the ball is red, given that the ball is even-numbered?

6. If one ball is drawn from the bag in Problem 5, what is the probability that the ball is white, given that the ball is odd-numbered?

7. A bag contains 4 red balls and 6 white balls. Two balls are drawn without replacement.
   (a) What is the probability that the second ball is white, given that the first ball is red?
   (b) What is the probability that the second ball is red, given that the first ball is white?
   (c) Answer part (a) if the first ball is replaced before the second is drawn.

8. A fair die is rolled. Find the probability that the result is a 4, given that the result is even.

9. A fair coin is tossed 3 times. Find the probability of
   (a) throwing 3 heads, given that the first toss is a head.
   (b) throwing 3 heads, given that the first two tosses result in heads.

10. A fair coin is tossed 14 times. What is the probability of tossing 14 heads, given that the first 13 tosses are heads?

11. A die is thrown twice. What is the probability that a 3 will result the first time and a 6 the second time?

12. A die is rolled, and a coin is tossed. What is the probability that the die shows an even number and the coin toss results in a head?

13. (a) A coin is tossed three times. What is the probability of getting a head on all three tosses?
    (b) A coin is tossed three times. What is the probability of getting at least one tail? [*Hint:* Use the result from part (a)].

14. The probability that Sam will win in a certain game whenever he plays is 2/5. If he plays two games, what is the probability that he will win just the first game?

15. (a) A box contains 3 red balls, 2 white balls, and 5 black balls. Two balls are drawn at random from the box (with replacement of the first before the second is drawn). What is the probability of getting a red ball on the first draw and a white ball on the second?
    (b) Answer the question in part (a) if the first ball is not replaced before the second ball is drawn.
    (c) Are the events in part (a) or in part (b) independent? Explain.

16. (a) One card is drawn at random from a deck of 52 cards. The first card is replaced, and a second card is drawn. Find the probability that both are hearts.
    (b) Answer the question in part (a) if the first card is not replaced before the second card is drawn.
    (c) Are the events in part (a) or in part (b) independent? Explain.

17. Two balls are drawn from a bag containing 3 white balls and 2 red balls. If the first ball is replaced before the second is drawn, what is the probability that
    (a) both balls are red?   (b) both balls are white?
    (c) the first ball is red and the second ball is white?
    (d) one of the balls is black?

18. Answer Problem 17 if the first ball is not replaced before the second ball is drawn.

19. A bag contains 9 nickels, 4 dimes, and 5 quarters. If you draw 3 coins at random from the bag without replacement, what is the probability that you will get a nickel, a quarter, and a nickel in that order?

20. A bag contains 6 red balls and 8 green balls. If two balls are drawn together, find the probability that
    (a) both are red.   (b) both are green.

21. A red ball and 4 white balls are in a box. If two balls are drawn without replacement, what is the probability
    (a) of getting a red ball on the first draw and a white ball on the second?
    (b) of getting 2 white balls?
    (c) of getting 2 red balls?

22. From a deck of 52 playing cards, two cards are drawn, one after the other without replacement. What is the probability that
    (a) the first will be a king and the second will be a jack?
    (b) the first will be a king and the second will be a jack of the same suit?

23. One card is drawn at random from a deck of 52 cards. The first card is not replaced, and a second card is drawn. Find the probability that
    (a) both cards are spades.
    (b) the first card is a heart and the second is a club.
24. Two cards are drawn from a deck of 52 cards. What is the probability that both are aces
    (a) if the first card is replaced before the second is drawn?
    (b) if the cards are drawn without replacement?
25. Two balls are drawn without replacement from a bag containing 13 red balls numbered 1–13 and 5 white balls numbered 14–18. What is the probability that
    (a) the second ball is red, given that the first ball is white?
    (b) both balls are even-numbered?
    (c) the first ball is red and even-numbered and the second ball is even-numbered?
26. A red die and a green die are rolled. What is the probability that a 6 results on the green die and a 4 results on the red die?

APPLICATIONS

Carbon emissions **The table gives the results of a survey of 1000 people about reducing industries' carbon emissions. Use the table to answer Problems 27–30.**

	Favor	Oppose	No Opinion	Total
Democrat	310	150	60	520
Republican	125	345	10	480
Total	435	495	70	1000

27. What is the probability that a person selected at random from this group will favor reducing industries' carbon emissions, given that the person is a Democrat?
28. What is the probability that a person selected at random from this group will oppose reducing industries' carbon emissions if the person is a Republican?
29. If the group surveyed represents the people of the United States, what is the probability that a citizen selected at random will favor reducing industries' carbon emissions, given that the person is a Republican?
30. If the group surveyed represents the people of the United States, what is the probability that a citizen selected at random will oppose reducing industries' carbon emissions, given that the person is a Democrat?

Oil drilling **Suppose the table summarizes the opinions of various groups on the issue of oil drilling in national parks. Use this table to calculate the empirical probabilities in Problems 31–38.**

	Whites		Non-Whites		
Opinion	Reps.	Dems.	Reps.	Dems.	Total
Favor	300	100	25	10	435
Oppose	100	250	25	190	565
Total	400	350	50	200	1000

31. Given that a randomly selected individual is non-White, find the probability that he or she opposes oil drilling in national parks.
32. Given that a randomly selected individual is a Democrat, find the probability that he or she opposes oil drilling in national parks.
33. Given that a randomly selected individual is in favor of oil drilling in national parks, find the probability that he or she is a Republican.
34. Given that a randomly selected individual is opposed to oil drilling in national parks, find the probability that he or she is a Democrat.
35. Find the probability that a person who favors oil drilling in national parks is non-White.
36. Find the probability that an individual is White and opposes oil drilling in national parks.
37. Find the probability that an individual is a White Republican opposed to oil drilling in national parks.
38. Find the probability that an individual is a Democrat and opposes oil drilling in national parks.
39. *Golf* On July 25, 2016, two amateur golfers, ages 10 and 13, hit back-to-back holes in one at the Country Club of Hilton Head on Hilton Head Island, South Carolina (*Source: The Island Packet,* July 26, 2016). According to the National Hole-in-One Association, the probability of an amateur golfer getting a hole in one is 1/12,000. If the golfer's shots are independent of each other, what is the probability that two amateur golfers will get back-to-back holes in one?
40. *Lottery* A name is drawn at random from the 96 entrants in a golf tournament. The person whose name is selected draws a ball from a bag containing four balls, one of which is embossed with the Peggos Company logo. If the person draws the ball with the logo, he or she wins a set of Ping irons. If you are one of the entrants in the tournament, what is the probability that you will win the Ping irons?
41. *Blood types* In the pretrial hearing of the O. J. Simpson case, the prosecution stated that Mr. Simpson's blood markers included type A blood, which 33.7% of the population has; blood SD subtype 1, which 79.6% of the population has; and PGM 2+2−, which 1.6% of the population has. If these blood markers are independent, what is the probability that a person selected at random will have the same blood markers as O. J. Simpson?
42. *Education* Fifty-one percent of the U.S. population are female, and 23.6% of the female population have

college degrees (*Source:* Bureau of the Census, Current Population Survey: *Educational Attainment in the U.S.*). If a U.S. resident is chosen at random, what is the probability that the person is a female with a college degree?

43. *Quality control* Each computer component that the Peggos Company produces is independently tested twice before it is shipped. There is a 0.7 probability that a defective component will be so identified by the first test and a 0.8 probability that it will be identified as being defective by the second test. What is the probability that a defective component will not be identified as defective before it is shipped?

44. *Lactose intolerance* Lactose intolerance affects about 20% of non-Hispanic White Americans, and 75.6% of the residents of the United States are non-Hispanic Whites (*Source:* Jean Carper, "Eat Smart," *USA Weekend*). If a U.S. resident is selected at random, what is the probability that the person will be a non-Hispanic White and have lactose intolerance?

45. *Lactose intolerance* Lactose intolerance affects about 50% of Hispanic Americans, and 9% of the residents of the United States are Hispanic (*Source:* Jean Carper, "Eat Smart," *USA Weekend*). If a U.S. resident is selected at random, what is the probability that the person will be Hispanic and have lactose intolerance?

46. *Quality control* If 3% of all light bulbs a company manufactures are defective, the probability of any one bulb being defective is 0.03. What is the probability that three bulbs drawn independently from the company's stock will be defective?

47. *Quality control* To test its shotgun shells, a company fires 5 of them. What is the probability that all 5 will fire properly if 5% of the company's shells are actually defective?

48. *Quality control* One machine produces 30% of a product for a company. If 10% of the products from this machine are defective and the other machines produce no defective items, what is the probability that an article produced by this company is defective?

49. *Advertising* A company estimates that 30% of the country has seen its commercial and that if a person sees its commercial, there is a 20% probability that the person will buy its product. What is the probability that a person chosen at random in the country will have seen the commercial and bought the product?

50. *Employment* Ronald Lee has been told by a company that the probability that he will be offered a job in the quality control department is 0.6 and the probability that he will be asked to supervise the department, if he is offered the job, is 0.1. What is the probability that he will be offered the job and asked to be supervisor?

51. *Birth control* Suppose a birth control pill is 99% effective in preventing pregnancy.
    (a) What is the probability that none of 100 women using the pill will become pregnant?

    (b) What is the probability that at least 1 woman per 100 users will become pregnant?

52. *Major League Baseball* The best Major League short-stops make a fielding error on about 2.5% of their plays. If each fielding attempt is independent, find the probability of
    (a) no errors in 8 plays (a typical game).
    (b) at least one error in 35 plays.

53. *Maintenance* Twenty-three percent of the cars owned by a car rental firm have some defect. What is the probability that of 3 cars selected at random,
    (a) none has a defect?
    (b) at least one has a defect?

54. *Testing* An unprepared student must take a 7-question multiple-choice test that has 5 possible answers per question. If the student guesses on every question, what is the probability that
    (a) she will answer every question correctly?
    (b) she will answer every question incorrectly?
    (c) she will answer at least one question correctly?

55. *Testing* An unprepared student must take a 7-question multiple-choice test that has 5 possible answers per question. If the student can eliminate two of the possible answers on the first three questions, and if she guesses on every question, what is the probability that
    (a) she will answer every question correctly?
    (b) she will answer every question incorrectly?
    (c) she will answer at least one question correctly?

56. *Testing* What is the probability that a student who guesses on every question of a 10-question true-or-false test will get at least one answer correct?

57. *Racing* Suppose that the odds in favor of the horse Portia winning a race are 3:8 and the odds of the horse Trinka winning the same race are 1:10. What is the probability that Portia or Trinka will win the race? What are the odds that one or the other will win if there are no ties?

58. *Racing* Suppose that the odds that Blackjack will win a race are 1 to 3 and the odds that Snowball will win the same race are 1 to 5. If only one horse can win, what odds should be given that one of these two horses will win?

59. *Birth dates* Assuming that there are 365 different birthdays, find the probability that two people chosen at random will have
    (a) different birthdays.   (b) the same birthday.

60. *Birth dates* Assuming that there are 365 different birthdays, find the probability that of three people chosen at random,
    (a) no two will have the same birthday.
    (b) at least two will have the same birthday.

61. *Birth dates* Assuming that there are 365 different birthdays, find the probability that of 20 people chosen randomly,
    (a) no two will have the same birthday.
    (b) at least two will have the same birthday.

62. *Crime* In an actual case,* probability was used to convict a couple of mugging an elderly woman. Shortly after the mugging, a young White woman with blonde hair worn in a ponytail was seen running from the scene of the crime and entering a yellow car that was driven by a Black man with a beard. A couple matching this description was arrested for the crime. A prosecuting attorney argued that the couple arrested had to be the couple at the scene of the crime because the probability of a second couple matching the description was very small. He estimated the probabilities of six events as follows:

> Probability of Black-White couple: 1/1000
> Probability of Black man: 1/3

> Probability of bearded man: 1/10
> Probability of blonde woman: 1/4
> Probability of hair in ponytail: 1/10
> Probability of yellow car: 1/10

He multiplied these probabilities and concluded that the probability that another couple would have these characteristics is 1/12,000,000. On the basis of this circumstantial evidence, the couple was convicted and sent to prison. The conviction was overturned by the state supreme court because the prosecutor made an incorrect assumption. What error do you think he made?

*Time, January 8, 1965, p. 42, and April 26, 1968, p. 41.

SECTION 7.4   Probability Trees and Bayes' Formula

OBJECTIVES

- To use probability trees to solve problems
- To use Bayes' formula to solve probability problems

APPLICATION PREVIEW

Suppose that a test for diagnosing a certain serious illness is successful in detecting the disease in 95% of all infected persons who are tested but that it incorrectly diagnoses 4% of all healthy people as having the serious disease. Also suppose that it incorrectly diagnoses 12% of all people having another minor disease as having the serious disease. If it is known that 2% of the population have the serious disease, 90% are healthy, and 8% have the minor disease, we can use Bayes' formula to find the probability that a person has the serious disease if the test indicates that he or she does. (See Example 3.) Such a Bayes problem can be solved with the formula or with the use of probability trees.

Probability trees   Probability trees, which were introduced in Section 7.3, provide a systematic way to analyze probability experiments that have two or more trials or that use multiple paths within the tree. In this section, we will use trees to solve additional probability problems and to solve **Bayes problems.** Recall that in a probability tree, we find the probability of an event as follows.

Probability Trees

The probability attached to each branch is the conditional probability that the specified event will occur, given that the events on the preceding branches have occurred.

1. For each event that can be described by a single path through the tree, the probability that the event will occur is the product of the probabilities on the branches along the path that represents the event.
2. Because the paths represent mutually exclusive events, an event described by two or more paths through a probability tree has its probability found by adding the probabilities from the paths.

EXAMPLE   1   Probability Tree

A bag contains 5 red balls, 4 blue balls, and 3 white balls. Two balls are drawn, one after the other without replacement. Draw a tree representing the experiment and find

(a) Pr(blue on first draw and white on second draw).
(b) Pr(white on both draws).
(c) Pr(drawing a blue ball and a white ball).
(d) Pr(second ball is red).

Solution

To construct the probability tree, draw a branch for each first draw possibility (Red, Blue, and White) and write its probability along the branch. [See Figure 7.8(a).] From each first draw outcome, the tree has a branch for each possible second draw, with its probability along the branch based on the first draw result. Specifically, the branch connecting first draw Red (R_1) to second draw Red (R_2) has the probability $\Pr(R_2 \mid R_1) = 4/11$; other branches are done similarly. See Figure 7.8(b) for the completed probability tree.

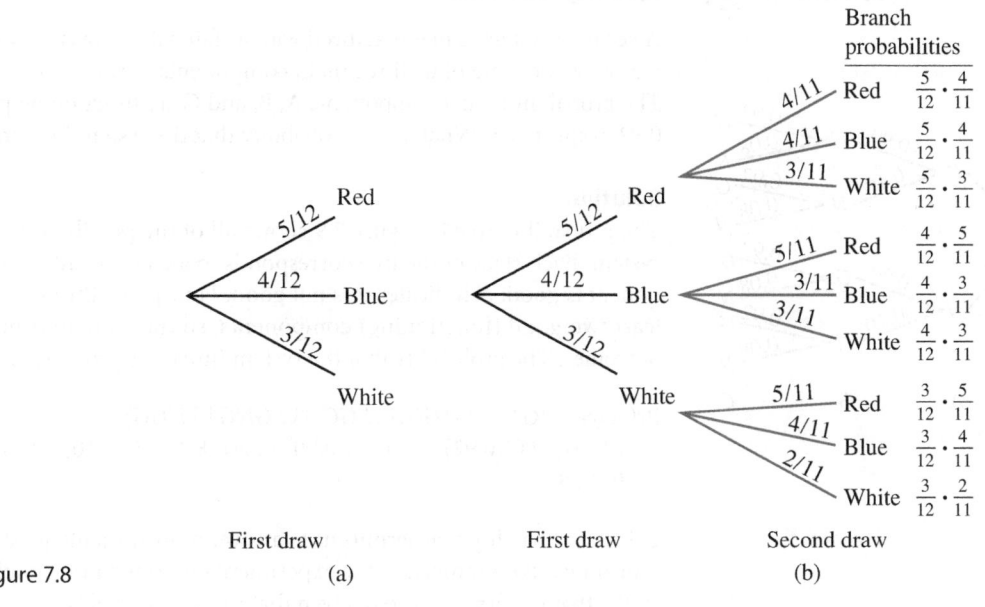

Figure 7.8   (a)   (b)

(a) By multiplying the probabilities along the path that represents blue on the first draw and white on the second draw, we obtain

$$\Pr(\text{blue on the first draw and white on second draw}) = \frac{4}{12} \cdot \frac{3}{11} = \frac{1}{11}$$

(b) Multiplying the probabilities along the path that represents white on both draws gives

$$\Pr(\text{white on both draws}) = \frac{3}{12} \cdot \frac{2}{11} = \frac{1}{22}$$

(c) The event "drawing a blue ball and a white ball" can occur as a blue ball followed by a white ball or a white ball followed by a blue ball. These two ways are mutually exclusive events and are represented by 2 paths in the tree. Representing a blue ball by B and a white ball by W, the probability we seek can be found as follows.

$$\Pr(B \text{ and } W) = \Pr(B \text{ first, then } W \text{ or } W \text{ first, then } B)$$
$$= \Pr(B \text{ first, then } W) + \Pr(W \text{ first, then } B)$$
$$= \frac{4}{12} \cdot \frac{3}{11} + \frac{3}{12} \cdot \frac{4}{11} = \frac{2}{11}$$

(d) The second ball can be red after the first is red, blue, or white.

$$\Pr(\text{2d ball is red}) = \Pr(R \text{ then } R, \text{ or } B \text{ then } R, \text{ or } W \text{ then } R)$$
$$= \Pr(R \text{ then } R) + \Pr(B \text{ then } R) + \Pr(W \text{ then } R)$$
$$= \frac{5}{12} \cdot \frac{4}{11} + \frac{4}{12} \cdot \frac{5}{11} + \frac{3}{12} \cdot \frac{5}{11} = \frac{5}{12}$$

1. Urn I contains 3 gold coins, urn II contains 1 gold coin and 2 silver coins, and urn III contains 1 gold coin and 1 silver coin. If an urn is selected at random and a coin is drawn from the urn, construct a probability tree and find the probability that a gold coin will be drawn.

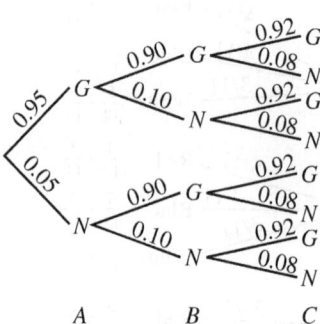

A B C

Figure 7.9

EXAMPLE 2 Quality Control

A security system is manufactured with a "fail-safe" provision so that it functions properly if any two or more of its three main components—A, B, and C—are functioning properly. The probabilities that components A, B, and C are functioning properly are 0.95, 0.90, and 0.92, respectively. What is the probability that the system functions properly?

Solution

The probability tree in Figure 7.9 shows all of the possibilities for the components of the system. Each stage of the tree corresponds to a component, and G indicates that the component is good; N indicates it is not good. Four paths through the probability tree give at least two good (functioning) components, so there are four mutually exclusive possible outcomes. The probability that the system functions properly is

$$\Pr(\text{at least } 2G) = \Pr(GGG \cup GGN \cup GNG \cup NGG)$$
$$= (0.95)(0.90)(0.92) + (0.95)(0.90)(0.08) + (0.95)(0.10)(0.92) + (0.05)(0.90)(0.92)$$
$$= 0.9838$$

Bayes' Formula

Using a probability tree permits us to answer more difficult questions regarding conditional probability. For example, in the experiment described in Example 1, we can find the probability that the first ball is red, given that the second ball is blue. To find this probability, we use the formula for conditional probability, as follows.

$$\Pr(\text{1st is red} \mid \text{2d is blue}) = \frac{\Pr(\text{1st is red and 2d is blue})}{\Pr(\text{2d is blue})}$$

Figure 7.8 on the previous page shows the probability tree with the possible outcomes for the experiment of Example 1. One path on the tree represents "1st is red and 2d is blue," and three paths (red-blue, blue-blue, white-blue) describe "2d is blue," so

$$\Pr(\text{1st is red} \mid \text{2d is blue}) = \frac{\dfrac{5}{12} \cdot \dfrac{4}{11}}{\dfrac{5}{12} \cdot \dfrac{4}{11} + \dfrac{4}{12} \cdot \dfrac{3}{11} + \dfrac{3}{12} \cdot \dfrac{4}{11}}$$

$$= \frac{5/33}{5/33 + 1/11 + 1/11} = \frac{5}{11}$$

This example illustrates a special type of problem, called a **Bayes problem.** In this type of problem, we know the result of the second stage of a two-stage experiment and want to find the probability of a specified result in the first stage.

Suppose there are n possible outcomes in the first stage of the experiment, denoted $E_1, E_2, \ldots, E_n$, and m possible outcomes in the second stage, denoted $F_1, F_2, \ldots, F_m$. (See Figure 7.10.) Then the probability that event E_1 occurs in the first stage, given that F_1 has occurred in the second stage, is

$$\Pr(E_1 \mid F_1) = \frac{\Pr(E_1 \cap F_1)}{\Pr(F_1)} \tag{1}$$

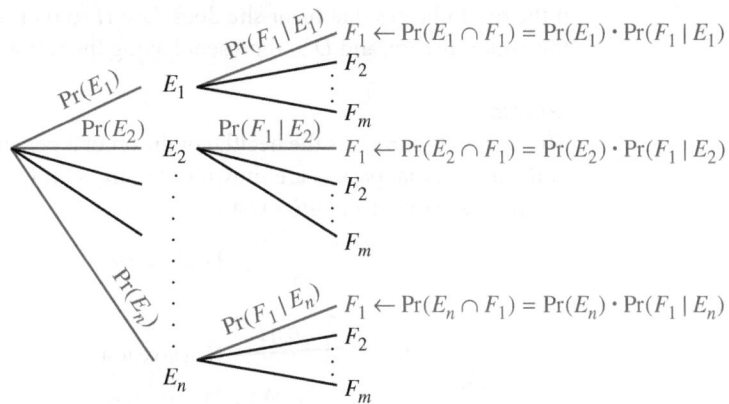

Figure 7.10

By looking at the probability tree in Figure 7.10, we see that

$$\Pr(E_1 \cap F_1) = \Pr(E_1) \cdot \Pr(F_1 \mid E_1)$$

and that

$$\Pr(F_1) = \Pr(E_1 \cap F_1) + \Pr(E_2 \cap F_1) + \cdots + \Pr(E_n \cap F_1)$$

Using these facts, equation (1) becomes

$$\Pr(E_1 \mid F_1) = \frac{\Pr(E_1) \cdot \Pr(F_1 \mid E_1)}{\Pr(E_1 \cap F_1) + \Pr(E_2 \cap F_1) + \cdots + \Pr(E_n \cap F_1)} \tag{2}$$

Using the fact that for any E_i, $\Pr(E_i \cap F_1) = \Pr(E_i) \cdot \Pr(F_1 \mid E_i)$, we can rewrite equation (2) in a form called **Bayes' formula.**

Bayes' Formula

If a probability experiment has n possible outcomes in its first stage given by E_1, $E_2, \ldots, E_n$ and if F_1 is an event in the second stage, then the probability that event E_1 occurs in the first stage, given that F_1 has occurred in the second stage, is given by **Bayes' formula:**

$$\Pr(E_1 \mid F_1) = \frac{\Pr(E_1) \cdot \Pr(F_1 \mid E_1)}{\Pr(E_1) \cdot \Pr(F_1 \mid E_1) + \Pr(E_2) \cdot \Pr(F_1 \mid E_2) + \cdots + \Pr(E_n) \cdot \Pr(F_1 \mid E_n)}$$

Note that Bayes problems can be solved either by this formula or by the use of a probability tree. Of the two methods, many students find using the tree easier because it is less abstract than the formula.

Bayes' Formula and Trees

$$\Pr(E_1 \mid F_1) = \frac{\text{Product of branch probabilities on path leading to } F_1 \text{ through } E_1}{\text{Sum of all branch products on paths leading to } F_1}$$

EXAMPLE   3   **Medical Tests** | APPLICATION PREVIEW |

Suppose a test for diagnosing a certain serious disease is successful in detecting the disease in 95% of all persons infected but that it incorrectly diagnoses 4% of all healthy people as having the serious disease. Also suppose that it incorrectly diagnoses 12% of all people having another minor disease as having the serious disease. It is known that 2% of the population have the serious disease, 90% of the population are healthy, and 8% have the minor disease. Find the probability that a person selected at random has the serious disease if the test indicates that he or she does. Use H to represent healthy, M to represent having the minor disease, and D to represent having the serious disease.

Solution

The tree that represents the health condition of a person chosen at random and the results of the test on that person are shown in Figure 7.11. (A test that indicates that a person has the disease is called a *positive* test.)

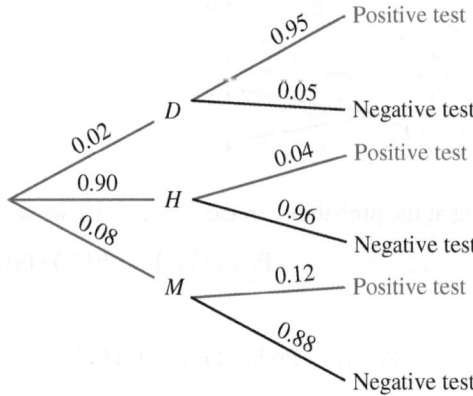

Figure 7.11

We seek $\Pr(D \mid \text{pos. test})$. Using the tree and the conditional probability formula gives

$$\Pr(D \mid \text{pos. test}) = \frac{\Pr(D \cap \text{pos. test})}{\Pr(\text{pos. test})}$$

$$= \frac{(0.02)(0.95)}{(0.90)(0.04) + (0.02)(0.95) + (0.08)(0.12)}$$

$$= \frac{0.0190}{0.0360 + 0.0190 + 0.0096}$$

$$\approx 0.2941$$

Using Bayes' formula directly gives the same result.

$\Pr(D \mid \text{pos. test})$

$$= \frac{\Pr(D) \cdot \Pr(\text{pos. test} \mid D)}{\Pr(H) \cdot \Pr(\text{pos. test} \mid H) + \Pr(D) \cdot \Pr(\text{pos. test} \mid D) + \Pr(M) \cdot \Pr(\text{pos. test} \mid M)}$$

$$= \frac{(0.02)(0.95)}{(0.90)(0.04) + (0.02)(0.95) + (0.08)(0.12)} \approx 0.2941$$

Thus when a person selected at random tests positive for a certain disease, the probability that the individual has this disease is about 0.2941.

CHECKPOINT

2. Use the information (and tree) from Example 3 to find the probability that a person chosen at random is healthy if the test is negative. (A negative result indicates that the person does not have the disease.)

Table 7.3 gives a summary of probability formulas and when they are used.

TABLE 7.3

SUMMARY OF PROBABILITY FORMULAS

		One Trial	Two Trials	More Than Two Trials
Pr(A and B)	Independent	Sample space	$\Pr(A) \cdot \Pr(B)$	Product of probabilities
	Dependent	Sample space	$\Pr(A) \cdot \Pr(B\,|\,A)$	Product of conditional probabilities
Pr(A or B)	Mutually exclusive	$\Pr(A) + \Pr(B)$	Probability tree	Probability tree
	Not mutually exclusive	$\Pr(A) + \Pr(B) - \Pr(A \text{ and } B)$	Probability tree	Probability tree

---

CHECKPOINT
ANSWERS

1. $\Pr(\text{gold}) = \Pr[(\text{I and } G) \text{ or } (\text{II and } G) \text{ or } (\text{III and } G)] = \dfrac{11}{18}$

2. $\Pr(H \mid \text{neg. test}) = \dfrac{\Pr(H \cap \text{neg. test})}{\Pr(\text{neg. test})} \approx 0.9237$

EXERCISES 7.4

In Problems 1–12, use probability trees to find the probabilities of the indicated outcomes.

1. A bag contains 5 coins, 4 of which are fair and 1 that has a head on each side. If a coin is selected from the bag and tossed twice, what is the probability of obtaining
   (a) 2 heads?   (b) 2 tails?

2. A bag contains 4 balls: 2 red, 1 white, and 1 green. Two balls are drawn without replacement. Find the probability that 2 different colors are drawn, given that
   (a) the first ball is not white.
   (b) the first ball is green.

3. An urn contains 4 red, 5 white, and 6 black balls. One ball is drawn from the urn, it is not replaced, and a second ball is drawn.
   (a) What is the probability that both balls are white?
   (b) What is the probability that one ball is white and one is red?
   (c) What is the probability that at least one ball is black?

4. An urn contains 4 red, 5 white, and 6 black balls. One ball is drawn from the urn, it is replaced, and a second ball is drawn.
   (a) What is the probability that both balls are white?
   (b) What is the probability that one ball is white and one is red?
   (c) What is the probability that at least one ball is black?

5. Three balls are drawn without replacement from a bag containing 4 red balls and 5 white balls. Find the probability that
   (a) three white balls are drawn.
   (b) two white balls and one red ball are drawn.
   (c) the third ball drawn is red.

6. An urn contains 4 red, 5 white, and 6 black balls. Three balls are drawn without replacement from the urn.
   (a) What is the probability that all three balls are red?
   (b) What is the probability that exactly two balls are red?
   (c) What is the probability that at least two balls are red?

7. A bag contains 4 white balls and 6 red balls. Three balls are drawn without replacement from the bag.
   (a) What is the probability that all three balls are white?
   (b) What is the probability that exactly one ball is white?
   (c) What is the probability that at least one ball is white?

8. A bag contains 5 coins, of which 4 are fair; the remaining coin has a head on both sides. If a coin is selected at random from the bag and tossed three times, what is the probability that
   (a) heads will occur exactly twice?
   (b) heads will occur at least twice?

9. A bag contains 4 white balls and 6 red balls. What is the probability that if 2 balls are drawn (with replacement),
   (a) the first ball is red and the second is white?
   (b) both balls are red?
   (c) one ball is red and one is white?
   (d) the first ball is red or the second is white?

10. A bag contains 13 blue balls and 7 red balls. If 2 balls are drawn at random from the bag, with the first ball being replaced before the second ball is drawn, what is the probability that
    (a) the first ball is red and the second is blue?
    (b) one ball is red and the other is blue?
    (c) the first ball is red or the second is blue?
    (d) the first ball is red given that the second is blue?

11. Two chips are drawn without replacement from a bag that contains 9 black chips numbered 1–9 and 4 white chips numbered 10–13. Find the probability that
    (a) the first chip is odd-numbered given that the second is even-numbered.
    (b) the first chip is white and the second is black.
    (c) the first chip is even-numbered or the second chip is odd-numbered.
    (d) the second chip is white given that the first chip is even-numbered.

12. Two balls are drawn without replacement from a bag containing 13 red balls numbered 1–13 and 5 white balls numbered 14–18. What is the probability that
    (a) the second ball is even-numbered, given that the first ball is even-numbered?
    (b) the first ball is red and the second ball is even-numbered?
    (c) the first ball is even-numbered and the second is white?
    (d) the first ball is even-numbered given that the second is white?

In Problems 13–16, use (a) a probability tree and (b) Bayes' formula to find the probabilities.

In Problems 13 and 14, each of urns I and II has 5 red balls, 3 white balls, and 2 green balls. Urn III has 1 red ball, 1 white ball, and 8 green balls.

13. An urn is selected at random, and a ball is drawn. If the ball is green, find the probability that urn III was selected.

14. An urn is selected at random, and a ball is drawn. If the ball is red, what is the probability that urn III was selected?

15. Three urns contain coins. Urn I contains 3 gold coins, urn II contains 1 gold coin and 1 silver coin, and urn III contains 2 silver coins. An urn is selected at random, and a coin is drawn from the urn. If the selected coin is gold, what is the probability that urn I was selected?

16. In Problem 15, what is the probability that urn III was selected if the coin selected was silver?

APPLICATIONS

17. *Lactose intolerance* Lactose intolerance affects about 20% of non-Hispanic White Americans; 50% of Hispanic Americans; and 75% of African, Asian, and Native Americans (*Source:* Jean Carper, "Eat Smart," *USA Weekend*). Seventy-six percent of U.S. residents are non-Hispanic Whites; 9% of them are Hispanic; and 15% are African, Asian, or Native American. If a person is selected from this group of people, what is the probability that the person will have lactose intolerance?

18. *Genetics* What is the probability that a couple will have at least two sons if they plan to have 3 children and if the probability of having a son equals the probability of having a daughter?

19. *Marksmanship* Suppose that a marksman hits the bull's-eye 15,000 times in 50,000 shots. If the next 4 shots are independent, find the probability that
    (a) the next 4 shots hit the bull's-eye.
    (b) two of the next 4 shots hit the bull's-eye.

20. *Majors* In a random survey of students concerning student activities, 30 engineering majors, 25 business majors, 20 science majors, and 15 liberal arts majors were selected. If two students are selected at random, what is the probability of getting
    (a) two science majors?
    (b) a science major and an engineering major?

21. *Quality control* Suppose a box contains 3 defective batteries and 12 good batteries. If 2 batteries are drawn from the box without replacement, what is the probability that
    (a) the first one is good and the second one is defective?
    (b) the first one is defective and the second one is good?
    (c) one of the batteries drawn is good and one of them is defective?

22. *Education* The probability that an individual without a college education earns more than $100,000 is 0.2, whereas the probability that a person with a B.S. or higher degree earns more than $100,000 is 0.6. The probability that a person chosen at random has a B.S. degree is 0.3. What is the probability that a person has at least a B.S. degree if it is known that he or she earns more than $100,000?

23. *Alcoholism* A small town has 8000 adult males and 6000 adult females. A sociologist conducted a survey and found that 40% of the males and 30% of the females

drink heavily. An adult is selected at random from the town.

(a) What is the probability the person is a male?

(b) What is the probability the person drinks heavily?

(c) What is the probability the person is a male or drinks heavily?

(d) What is the probability the person is a male if it is known that the person drinks heavily?

24. *TV violence* One hundred boys and 100 girls were asked if they had ever been frightened by a television program. Thirty of the boys and 60 of the girls said that they had been frightened. One of these children is selected at random.

(a) What is the probability that he or she has been frightened?

(b) What is the probability the child is a girl, given that he or she has been frightened?

25. *Public health—HIV testing* The most common HIV test is the Enzyme Immunoassay (EIA) Test. When a subject's HIV condition is known, the following probabilities about the EIA test are known.

$$\Pr(\text{Test}(+)|\text{HIV}(+)) = 0.9985$$

$$\Pr(\text{Test}(-)|\text{HIV}(-)) = 0.994$$

(a) Find $\Pr(\text{Test}(-)|\text{HIV}(+))$, the probability of a false negative.

(b) Find $\Pr(\text{Test}(+)|\text{HIV}(-))$, the probability of a false positive.

(c) Suppose that in the U.S. population, $\Pr(\text{HIV}(+)) = 0.01$. Testing the general population would be effective (both in terms of diagnosis and costs) if a positive test could pinpoint the disease. If a randomly selected person is given the EIA Test, calculate $\Pr(\text{HIV}(+)|\text{Test}(+))$ and $\Pr(\text{HIV}(-)|\text{Test}(+))$.

(d) Do the answers from part (c) suggest that testing the general population would be effective? Explain.

26. *Insurance rates* Ideally, auto insurance rates are lower for good drivers than for bad drivers, but an insurer needs to be able to tell which type of driver a client is. Assume that all drivers are considered as either "good drivers" or "bad drivers" and that the probability of a random driver being a "good driver" is 0.80. In addition, suppose that the probability of 2 accidents in a year is 0.02 for good drivers and 0.10 for bad drivers.

(a) If an insurer has no additional information about an applicant's driving history, what is the probability that the individual is a bad driver?

(b) If the insurer knows that the applicant had 2 accidents in the past year, what is the probability that he or she is a bad driver?

27. *Pregnancy test* A self-administered pregnancy test detects 85% of those who are pregnant but does not detect pregnancy in 15%. It is 90% accurate in indicating women who are not pregnant but indicates 10% of this group as being pregnant. Suppose it is known that 1% of the women in a neighborhood are pregnant. If a woman is chosen at random from those living in this neighborhood and if the test indicates she is pregnant, what is the probability that she really is?

28. *Quality control* Suppose a factory has three machines (I, II, and III) that produce identical items as follows:

    I: 500 items per day; 1% defective

    II: 200 items per day; 5% defective

    III: 300 items per day; 3% defective

Suppose one item is selected at random and tested. Find the probability that the item

(a) is defective.

(b) came from machine II given that it is defective.

29. *Survey* In a Student Activity Participation Study (SAPS) survey, 30 engineering majors, 25 business majors, 20 science majors, 15 liberal arts majors, and 10 human development majors were selected. Ten of the engineering, 12 of the science, 6 of the human development, 13 of the business, and 8 of the liberal arts majors selected for the study were female.

(a) What is the probability of selecting a female if one person from this group is selected randomly?

(b) What is the probability that a student selected randomly from this group is a science major, given that she is female?

30. *Survey* If a student is selected at random from the group in Problem 29, what is the probability that the student is

(a) an engineering major given that she is female?

(b) an engineering major given that he is male?

SECTION 7.5

Counting: Permutations and Combinations

OBJECTIVES

- To use the Fundamental Counting Principle to solve counting problems
- To calculate and apply factorials
- To use permutations and combinations to solve counting problems

APPLICATION PREVIEW

During a national television advertising campaign, Little Caesar's Pizza stated that for $9.95, you could get 2 medium-sized pizzas, each with any of 0 to 5 toppings chosen from 11 that are available. The commercial asked the question, "How many different pairs of pizzas can you get?" (See Example 7.) Answering this question uses combinations, which we discuss in this section. Other counting techniques, including permutations, also are discussed.

Fundamental Counting Principle

Suppose that you decide to dine at a restaurant that offers 3 appetizers, 8 entrees, and 6 desserts. How many different meals can you have? We can answer questions of this type using the **Fundamental Counting Principle.**

Fundamental Counting Principle

If there are $n(A)$ ways in which an event A can occur and if there are $n(B)$ ways in which a second event B can occur after the first event has occurred, then the two events can occur in $n(A) \cdot n(B)$ ways.

The Fundamental Counting Principle can be extended to any number of events as long as they are independent. Thus the total number of possible meals at the restaurant mentioned above is

$$n(\text{appetizers}) \cdot n(\text{entrees}) \cdot n(\text{desserts}) = 3 \cdot 8 \cdot 6 = 144$$

EXAMPLE 1   License Plates

Pennsylvania offers a special "Save Wild Animals" license plate, which gives Pennsylvania zoos $15 for each plate sold. These plates have the two letters P and Z followed by four numbers. When plates like these have all been purchased, additional plates will replace the final digit with a letter other than O. What is the maximum amount the zoos could receive from the sale of the plates?

Solution

The following numbers represent the number of possible digits or letters in each of the spaces on the license plates as illustrated below.

$$\underline{1} \quad \underline{1} \quad \underline{10} \quad \underline{10} \quad \underline{10} \quad \underline{35}$$

Note that the last space can be a number from 0 to 9 or a letter other than O. By the Fundamental Counting Principle, the product of these numbers gives the number of license plates that can be made satisfying the given conditions.

$$1 \cdot 1 \cdot 10 \cdot 10 \cdot 10 \cdot 35 = 35,000$$

Thus 35,000 automobiles can be licensed with these plates, so the zoos could receive ($15)(35,000) = $525,000.

CHECKPOINT

1. If a state permits either a letter or a nonzero digit to be used in each of six places on its license plates, how many different plates can it issue?

EXAMPLE 2   Head Table Seating

Suppose a person planning a banquet cannot decide how to seat 6 honored guests at the head table. In how many arrangements can they be seated in the 6 chairs on one side of a table?

Solution

If we think of the 6 chairs as spaces, we can determine how many ways each space can be filled. The planner could place any one of the 6 people in the first space (for example, the first chair on the left). One of the 5 remaining persons could then be placed in the second space, one of the 4 remaining persons in the third space, etc., as illustrated below.

$$\underline{6} \quad \underline{5} \quad \underline{4} \quad \underline{3} \quad \underline{2} \quad \underline{1}$$

The total number of arrangements that can be made is the product of these numbers. That is, the total number of possible arrangements is

$$6 \cdot 5 \cdot 4 \cdot 3 \cdot 2 \cdot 1 = 720$$

Because special products such as $6 \cdot 5 \cdot 4 \cdot 3 \cdot 2 \cdot 1$ frequently occur in counting theory, we use special notation to denote them. We write 6! (read "6 **factorial**") to denote $6 \cdot 5 \cdot 4 \cdot 3 \cdot 2 \cdot 1$. Likewise, $4! = 4 \cdot 3 \cdot 2 \cdot 1$.

Factorial

For any positive integer n, we define **n factorial,** written $n!$, as

$$n! = n(n - 1)(n - 2) \cdots 3 \cdot 2 \cdot 1$$

We define $0! = 1$.

Calculator Note

The factorial of a positive integer can be found on a graphing calculator by entering the number, then going to MATH, PRB, and scrolling to 4: !. Pressing ENTER gives the factorial. (See Figure 7.12.) See Appendix A, Section 7.5, for details.

Figure 7.12   (a)   (b)

EXAMPLE 3 **Banquet Seating**

Suppose the planner in Example 2 knows that 8 people think they should be at the head table, but only 6 spaces are available. How many arrangements can be made that place 6 of the 8 people at the head table?

Solution
There are again 6 spaces to fill, but any of 8 people can be placed in the first space, any of 7 people in the second space, etc. Thus the total number of possible arrangements is

$$8 \cdot 7 \cdot 6 \cdot 5 \cdot 4 \cdot 3 = 20{,}160$$

Permutations
The number of possible arrangements in Example 3 is called the number of **permutations** of 8 things taken 6 at a time, and it is denoted $_8P_6$. Note that $_8P_6$ gives the first 6 factors of 8!, so we can use factorial notation to write the product.

$$_8P_6 = \frac{8!}{2!} = \frac{8!}{(8 - 6)!}$$

Permutations

The number of possible ordered arrangements of r objects chosen from a set of n objects is called the number of **permutations** of n objects taken r at a time, and it equals

$$_nP_r = \frac{n!}{(n - r)!}$$

Note that $_nP_n = n!$

EXAMPLE 4 **Club Officers**

In how many ways can a president, a vice president, a secretary, and a treasurer be selected from an organization with 20 members?

Solution

We seek the number of orders (arrangements) in which 4 people can be selected from a group of 20. This number is

$$_{20}P_4 = \frac{20!}{(20-4)!} = 116{,}280$$

Calculator Note   The permutations of n things taken r at a time, for positive integers n and r, can be found on a graphing calculator by entering the value n, then going to MATH, PRB, and scrolling to 2: nPr. Pressing ENTER, entering r, and pressing ENTER again give the value. Figure 7.13 shows the number of permutations of 7 things taken 4 at a time. Details are shown in Appendix A, Section 7.5.

Figure 7.13   (a)   (b)

CHECKPOINT

2. In a 5-question matching test, how many different answer sheets are possible if no answer can be used twice and there are
   (a) 5 answers available for matching?
   (b) 7 answers available for matching?

Combinations When we talk about arrangements of people at a table or arrangements of digits on a license plate, order is important. We now consider counting problems in which order is not important.

To find the number of ways we can select 3 people from 5 without regard to order, we first find the number of ways to select them *with order*, $_5P_3$, and then divide by the number of ways the 3 people could be ordered (3!). Thus 3 people can be selected from 5 (without regard for order) in $_5P_3/3! = 10$ ways. We say that the number of **combinations** of 5 things taken 3 at a time is 10.

Combinations

> The number of ways in which r objects can be chosen from a set of n objects without regard to the order of selection is called the number of **combinations** of n objects taken r at a time, and it equals
>
> $$_nC_r = \frac{_nP_r}{r!}$$

Note that the fundamental difference between permutations and combinations is that permutations are used when order is a factor in the selection and combinations are used when it is not. Because $_nP_r = n!/(n-r)!$, we have

$$_nC_r = \frac{_nP_r}{r!} = \frac{\dfrac{n!}{(n-r)!}}{r!} = \frac{n!}{r!(n-r)!}$$

Combination Formula

The number of combinations of n objects taken r at a time is also denoted by $\binom{n}{r}$; that is,

$$\binom{n}{r} = {}_nC_r = \frac{n!}{r!(n-r)!}$$

EXAMPLE 5 **Auto Options**

An auto dealer is offering any 4 of 6 special options at one price on a specially equipped car being sold. How many different choices of specially equipped cars do you have?

Solution
The order in which we choose the options is not relevant, so we seek the number of combinations of 6 things taken 4 at a time. Thus, the number of possible choices is

$$_6C_4 = \frac{6!}{4!(6-4)!} = \frac{6!}{4!2!} = 15$$

Calculator Note

The number of combinations of n things taken r at a time, for positive integers n and r, can be found on a graphing calculator by entering the value n, then going to MATH, PRB, and scrolling to 3: nCr. Pressing ENTER, entering r, and pressing ENTER again give the value. Figure 7.14 shows the number of combinations of 7 things taken 4 at a time. Details are shown in Appendix A, Section 7.5.

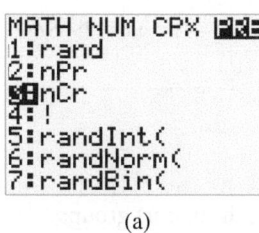

Figure 7.14　　　(a)　　　　　　　　(b)

EXAMPLE 5 **Project Teams**

Six men and eight women are qualified to serve on a project team to revise operational procedures. How many different teams can be formed containing three men and three women?

Solution
Three men can be selected from six in $\binom{6}{3}$ ways, and three women can be selected from eight in $\binom{8}{3}$ ways. Therefore, three men *and* three women can be selected in

$$\binom{6}{3}\binom{8}{3} = \frac{6!}{3!3!} \cdot \frac{8!}{5!3!} = 1120 \text{ ways}$$

CHECKPOINT

Determine whether each of the following counting problems involving the formation of tech support groups can be solved using permutations or combinations and answer each question.
3. Find how many tech support groups with 8 members can be selected from 20 available applicants.
4. The leadership structure of the support groups is determined by the order in which applicants are selected. How many different leadership structures are possible if 8 applicants are selected from the 20 that are available?
5. If 14 men and 6 women are available for the project's tech support group, how many groups are possible that have 5 men and 3 women?

EXAMPLE 7   **Little Caesar's Pizza Choices** | APPLICATION PREVIEW |

During a national television advertising campaign, Little Caesar's Pizza stated that for $9.95, you could get 2 medium-sized pizzas, each with any of 0 to 5 toppings chosen from 11 that are available. The commercial asked the question, "How many different pairs of pizzas can you get?" Answer the question if the first pizza has a thin crust and the second has a thick crust.

Solution

Because you can get 0, 1, 2, 3, 4, or 5 toppings from the 11 choices, the possible choices for the first pizza are

$$_{11}C_0 + {}_{11}C_1 + {}_{11}C_2 + {}_{11}C_3 + {}_{11}C_4 + {}_{11}C_5 = 1 + 11 + 55 + 165 + 330 + 462 = 1024$$

Because the same number of choices is available for the second pizza, the number of choices for two pizzas is

$$1024 \cdot 1024 = 1{,}048{,}576$$

EXAMPLE 8   **Quality Control**

Suppose a batch of 35 CPUs has 10 defective CPUs. In how many ways can a sample of 15 from this batch have 5 defective CPUs?

Solution

We seek the number of ways to find 5 of 10 defective and 10 of 25 good CPUs. This is

$$_{10}C_5 \cdot {}_{25}C_{10} = 823{,}727{,}520$$

CHECKPOINT ANSWERS

1. $35^6 = 1{,}838{,}265{,}625$
2. (a) $_5P_5 = 5! = 120$
   (b) $_7P_5 = 2520$
3. $_{20}C_8 = 125{,}970$ possible tech support groups
4. $_{20}P_8 = 5{,}079{,}110{,}400$ possible leadership structures
5. $_{14}C_5 \cdot {}_6C_3 = 2002 \cdot 20 = 40{,}040$ possible tech support groups

EXERCISES 7.5

PERMUTATIONS

1. Compute $_6P_4$.
2. Compute $_8P_5$.
3. Compute $_{10}P_6$.
4. Compute $_7P_4$.
5. Compute $_5P_0$.
6. Compute $_3P_3$.
7. How many four-digit numbers can be formed from the digits 1, 3, 5, 7, 8, and 9
   (a) if each digit may be used once in each number?
   (b) if each digit may be used repeatedly in each number?
8. How many four-digit numbers can be formed from the digits 1, 4, 5, 7, 8, and 9
   (a) if the numbers must be even and digits are not used repeatedly?
   (b) if the numbers are less than 3000 and digits are not repeated? (*Hint:* In both parts, begin with the digit where there is a restriction on the choices.)

9. Compute $_nP_n$.
10. Compute $_nP_1$.
11. Find $\dfrac{(n+1)!}{n!}$.
12. Find $\dfrac{(2n+2)!}{(2n)!}$.
13. If $(n+1)! = 17n!$, find n.
14. If $(n+1)! = 30(n-1)!$, find n.

COMBINATIONS

15. Compute $_{100}C_{98}$.
16. Compute $_{80}C_{76}$.
17. Compute $_4C_4$.
18. Compute $_3C_1$.
19. Compute $\begin{pmatrix} 5 \\ 0 \end{pmatrix}$.
20. Compute $\begin{pmatrix} n \\ 0 \end{pmatrix}$.
21. If $_nC_6 = {}_nC_4$, find n.
22. If $_nC_8 = {}_nC_7$, find n.

APPLICATIONS

23. *Binz, not Benz* Mercedes Benz E-Class sedans are converted to limousines by a coach company. The limousines, named Binz, come in two models, XL Six Door and XL Vis-à-Vis, and are available with a choice of 2 gasoline engines or 2 diesel engines.
    (a) If no other options are considered, how many different Binz limos are available?
    (b) If, in addition, 5 option packages and 6 colors are available, how many different Binz limos are available?

24. *Ice cream cones* Baskin-Robbins' logo includes "31" because its stores offer 31 flavors of ice cream cones in sizes small, medium, and large.
    (a) How many different selections of cones are possible if each cone has one flavor?
    (b) If 4 toppings are available to put on a cone and a cone can be bought without a topping, how many different selections of ice cream cones are available if each cone has one flavor?

25. *Volvo XC90* The new Volvo XC90 Twin-Engine Plug-in Hybrid has a self-programmable mode with four different powertrain settings, three settings for the air suspension, three for the steering, three for the instrument display, two for the brakes, and two for the climate control (*Source: Car and Driver*).
    (a) How many differently set cars are possible?
    (b) Suppose one owner finds that preference and habit result in narrowing these possibilities to only two of the settings for powertrain, suspension, and steering, just one instrument display, and both settings for brakes and climate control. How many fewer settings does this owner use than are available?

26. *Menu selections* A restaurant has an early dining *fixe prix* (fixed price) dinner special that offers one soup or salad from 5 available, one entrée from 5 chef's specials, and one dessert from 4 choices.
    (a) How many different *fixe prix* dinners are possible?
    (b) Suppose one particular diner wants a salad and a fish entrée with any of the dessert choices. If 3 different salads and 2 fish entrees are available, how many *fewer* meal choices does this diner have?

27. *License plates* A state wants each of its license plates to contain 7 digits. How many different license plates can it make if
    (a) all the digits are different?
    (b) any 7 digits may be used?

28. *Racing* Eight horses are entered in a race. In how many ways can the horses finish? Assume no ties.

29. *Management* Four candidates for manager of a department store are ranked according to the weighted average of several criteria. How many different rankings are possible if no two candidates receive the same rank?

30. *Testing* An examination consists of 12 questions. If 10 questions must be answered, find the number of different orders in which a student can answer the questions.

31. *Molecules* Biologists have identified 4 kinds of small molecules: adenine, cytosine, guanine, and thymine, which link together to form larger molecules in genes. How many 3-molecule chains can be formed if the order of linking is important and each small molecule can occur more than once in a chain?

32. *Families* A member of a family of four is asked to rank all members of the family in the order of their power in the family. How many possible rankings are there?

33. *Management* A department store manager wants to display 6 brands of a product along one shelf of an aisle. In how many ways can he arrange the brands?

34. *Call letters* The call letters for radio stations begin with K or W, followed by 3 additional letters. How many sets of call letters having 4 letters are possible?

35. *Testing* How many ways can a 10-question true-false test be answered?

36. *Testing* How many ways can a 10-question multiple-choice test be answered if each question has 4 possible answers?

37. *Poker* A flush (5 cards from the same suit) is an excellent hand in poker. If 13 cards are in each of four suits in a deck of playing cards and 5 cards are in a hand, how many flush hands are possible?

38. *Committees* In how many ways can a committee of 5 be selected from 10 people willing to serve?

39. *License plates* South Carolina previously had license plates containing two letters followed by four digits but now has plates with three letters followed by three digits. How many more plates are now available?

40. *Astronauts* If 8 people are qualified for the next flight of a new space vehicle, how many different groups of 3 people can be chosen for the flight?

41. *Sales* A traveling salesperson has 30 products to sell but has room in her sample case for only 20 of the products. If all the products are the same size, in how many ways can she select 20 different products for her case?

42. *Gambling* A poker hand consists of 5 cards dealt from a deck of 52 playing cards. How many different poker hands are possible?

43. *Psychology* A psychological study of outstanding salespeople is to be made. If 5 salespeople are needed and 12 are qualified, in how many ways can the 5 be selected?

44. *Banking* A company wants to use the services of 3 different banks in the city. If 15 banks are available, in how many ways can it choose the 3 banks?

45. *Politics* To determine voters' feelings regarding an issue, a candidate asks a sample of people to pick 4 words out of 10 that they think best describe the issue. How many different groupings of 4 words are possible?

46. *Sociology* A sociologist wants to pick 3 fifth-grade students from each of four schools. If each of the schools has 50 fifth-grade students, how many different groups of 12 students can he select? (Set up in combination symbols; do not work out.)

47. *Committees* In how many ways can a committee consisting of 6 men and 6 women be selected from a group consisting of 20 men and 22 women?

48. *Bridge* In how many ways can a hand consisting of 6 spades, 4 hearts, 2 clubs, and 1 diamond be selected from a deck of 52 cards?

49. *Evaluations* A regional medical center plans to evaluate its administrative personnel and procedures. Ten of the center's 80 nurses will be chosen to complete an in-depth evaluation.
    (a) In how many ways can the 10 nurses be chosen?
    (b) If 52 of the nurses are women, in how many ways can the 10 nurses consist of 7 women and 3 men?

50. *Auto dealerships* An auto dealer has 4 cars, 2 trucks, and 3 SUVs that it plans to display in a line across the front of the dealership.
    (a) In how many orders can these vehicles be displayed?
    (b) If the cars are grouped together at the left end of the line, in how many orders can the vehicles be displayed?

SECTION 7.6

Permutations, Combinations, and Probability

OBJECTIVES

- To use counting techniques to solve probability problems

APPLICATION PREVIEW

Suppose that of the 20 prospective jurors for a trial, 11 favor the death penalty, whereas 9 do not, and that 12 are chosen at random from these 20. To find the probability that 7 of the 12 will favor the death penalty, we can use combinations to find the number of ways to choose 12 jurors from 20 prospective jurors and to find the number of ways to choose 7 from the 11 who favor the death penalty and 5 from the 9 who oppose it. (See Example 4.) In finding the probability that an event *E* occurs, we frequently use counting principles to determine the number of ways in which the event can occur, *n(E)*, and the total number of outcomes, *n(S)*.

Recall that if an event E can happen in $n(E)$ ways out of a total of $n(S)$ equally likely possibilities, the probability of the occurrence of the event is

$$\Pr(E) = \frac{n(E)}{n(S)}$$

EXAMPLE 1   Intelligence Tests

A psychologist claims that she can teach four-year-old children to spell three-letter words very quickly. To test her, one of her students was given cards with the letters A, C, D, K, and T on them and told to spell CAT. What is the probability that the child will spell CAT by chance?

Solution

The number of different three-letter "words" that can be formed using these 5 cards is $n(S) = {}_5P_3 = 5!/(5 - 3)! = 60$. Because only one of those 60 arrangements will be CAT, $n(E) = 1$, and the probability that the child will be successful by guessing is 1/60.

EXAMPLE 2   **License Plates**

Suppose that a state issues license plates with three letters followed by three digits and that there are 12 three-letter words that are not permitted on license plates. If all possible plates are produced and a plate is selected at random, what is the probability that the plate is unacceptable and will not be issued?

Solution
The total number of license plates that could be produced with three letters followed by three digits is

$$n(S) = 26^3 \cdot 10^3 = 17{,}576{,}000$$

and the number that will be unacceptable is

$$n(E) = 12 \cdot 10^3 = 12{,}000$$

Thus the probability that a plate selected at random will be unacceptable is

$$\frac{12{,}000}{17{,}576{,}000} = \frac{12}{17{,}576} = \frac{3}{4394} \approx 0.0006827$$

CHECKPOINT

1. If three wires (red, black, and white) are randomly attached to a three-way switch (which has 3 poles to which wires can be attached), what is the probability that the wires will be attached at random in the one order that makes the switch work properly?

EXAMPLE 3   **Auto Keys**

Prior to wireless keys, General Motors keys had six parts, with three patterns for each part, plus an electronic chip containing a code from 1 to 15. What is the probability that one of these keys selected at random would start a GM car requiring a key of this type?

Solution
Each of the six parts had three patterns, and the chip had any of 15 codes, so there were

$$3 \cdot 3 \cdot 3 \cdot 3 \cdot 3 \cdot 3 \cdot 15 = 10{,}935$$

possible keys. Because only one key of this type would start the car, the probability that a key selected at random would start a given car is 1/10,935.

EXAMPLE 4   **Jury Selection** | APPLICATION PREVIEW |

Suppose that of the 20 prospective jurors for a trial, 11 favor the death penalty and 9 do not. If 12 jurors are chosen at random from these 20, what is the probability that 7 of the jurors will favor the death penalty?

Solution
The number of ways in which 7 jurors of the 12 will favor the death penalty is the number of ways in which 7 favor and 5 do not favor, or

$$n(E) = {}_{11}C_7 \cdot {}_9C_5 = \frac{11!}{7!4!} \cdot \frac{9!}{5!4!}$$

The total number of ways in which 12 jurors can be selected from 20 people is

$$n(S) = {}_{20}C_{12} = \frac{20!}{12!8!}$$

Thus the probability we seek is

$$Pr(E) = \frac{n(E)}{n(S)} = \frac{\dfrac{11!}{7!4!} \cdot \dfrac{9!}{5!4!}}{\dfrac{20!}{12!8!}} \approx 0.3301$$

CHECKPOINT
2. If 5 people are chosen from a group that contains 4 men and 6 women, what is the probability that 3 men and 2 women will be chosen?

EXAMPLE **5** **Quality Control**

A manufacturing process for computer chips is such that 5 out of 100 chips are defective. If 10 chips are chosen at random from a box containing 100 newly manufactured chips, what is the probability
(a) that none of the chips will be defective?
(b) that 8 will be good and 2 defective?

Solution
(a) The number of ways to choose any 10 chips from 100 is $n(S) = {}_{100}C_{10}$, and 10 good chips can be chosen from the 95 good ones in $n(E) = {}_{95}C_{10}$ ways. Thus

$$Pr(10 \text{ good}) = Pr(E) = \frac{n(E)}{n(S)} = \frac{{}_{95}C_{10}}{{}_{100}C_{10}}$$

As Figure 7.15(a) shows,

$$Pr(10 \text{ good}) \approx 0.58375$$

(b) Eight good chips and two defective chips can be selected in

$$n(E) = {}_{95}C_8 \cdot {}_5C_2$$

ways. Thus

$$Pr(8 \text{ good and 2 defective}) = \frac{n(E)}{n(S)} = \frac{{}_{95}C_8 \cdot {}_5C_2}{{}_{100}C_{10}}$$

As Figure 7.15(b) shows,

$$Pr(8 \text{ good and 2 defective}) \approx 0.07022$$

```
(95 nCr 10)/(100
nCr 10)
        .5837523669
```

(a)

```
(95 nCr 8)(5 nCr
2)/(100 nCr 10)
        .0702188092
```

(b)

Figure 7.15

CHECKPOINT ANSWERS

1. 1/6

2. The probability is $60/252 = 5/21$.

EXERCISES 7.6

APPLICATIONS

1. *Education* If a child is given cards with A, C, D, G, O, and T on them, what is the probability that he or she could spell DOG by guessing the correct arrangement of 3 cards from the 6?

2. *Racing* Eight horses in a race wear numbers 1, 2, 3, 4, 5, 6, 7, and 8. What is the probability that the first three horses to finish the race will be numbered 1, 2, and 3, respectively?

3. *Politics* A poll asks voters to rank Social Security, the economy, the war on terror, health care, and education in order of importance.
   (a) How many rankings are possible?
   (b) What is the probability that one reply chosen at random has the issues ranked in the order they appear on the survey?

4. *Photography* Two men and a woman are lined up to have their picture taken. If they are arranged at random, what is the probability that
   (a) the woman will be on the left in the picture?
   (b) the woman will be in the middle in the picture?

5. *License plates* Suppose that all license plates in a state have three letters then three digits. If a plate is chosen at random, what is the probability that all three letters and all three numbers on the plate will be different?

6. *Spelling*
   (a) In how many different orders can the letters R, A, N, D, O, M be written?
   (b) If the letters R, A, N, D, O, M are placed in random order, what is the probability that they will spell RANDOM?

7. *ATMs*
   (a) An automatic teller machine requires that each customer enter a four-digit personal identification number (PIN) when he or she inserts a bank card. If a person finds a bank card and guesses at a PIN to use the card fraudulently, what is the probability that the person will succeed in one attempt?
   (b) If the person knows that the PIN will not have any digit repeated, what is the probability that the person will succeed in guessing in one attempt?

8. *Keys* Keys for antique General Motors cars had six parts with three patterns for each part.
   (a) How many different key designs are possible for these cars?
   (b) If you find an antique GM key and own an antique GM car, what is the probability that it will fit your trunk?

9. *Phone numbers* If the first digit of a seven-digit phone number cannot be a 0 or a 1, what is the probability that a number chosen at random will have all seven digits the same?

10. *License plates* If a license plate has seven different digits, what is the probability that it contains a zero?

11. *Rewards* As a reward for a record year, the Ace Software Company is randomly selecting 4 people from its 500 employees for a free trip to Hawaii, but it will not pay for a traveling companion. If John and Jill are married and both are employees, what is the probability that they will both win?

12. *Mutual funds* The retirement plan for a company allows employees to invest in 10 different mutual funds. If Sam selected 4 of these funds at random and 6 of the 10 grew by at least 10% over the last year, what is the probability that 3 of Sam's 4 funds grew by at least 10% last year?

13. *Testing* In a 10-question matching test with 10 possible answers to match and no answer used more than once, what is the probability of guessing and getting every answer correct?

14. *Testing* In a 10-question matching test with 15 possible answers to match and no answer used more than once, what is the probability of guessing and getting every answer correct?

15. *Quality control* A box of 12 batteries has 3 defective ones. If 2 batteries are drawn from the box together, what is the probability that
   (a) both are defective?
   (b) neither one is defective?
   (c) one is defective?

16. *Quality control* Suppose that 6 batteries are drawn at random from a box containing 18 good batteries and 2 defective ones. What is the probability that
   (a) all 6 are good?
   (b) exactly 4 are good?
   (c) exactly 2 are good?

17. *Quality control* A retailer purchases 100 of a new brand of DVD player, of which 2 are defective. The purchase agreement says that if he tests 5 chosen at random and finds 1 or more defective, he receives all the DVD players free of charge. What is the probability that he will not have to pay for the DVD players?

18. *Quality control* A box containing 500 smart phones has 20 defective phones. If 10 phones are selected together from the box, what is the probability that
   (a) all 10 are defective?
   (b) none is defective?
   (c) half of them are defective?

19. *Banking* To see whether a bank has enough minority construction company loans, a social agency selects 30 loans to construction companies at random and finds that 2 of them are loans to minority companies. If the bank's claim that 10 of every 100 of its loans to construction companies are minority loans is true, what

is the probability that 2 loans out of 30 are minority loans? Leave your answer with combination symbols.

20. *Diversity* A high school principal must select 12 girls at random from the freshman class to serve as hostesses at the junior-senior prom. There are 200 freshman girls, including 20 from minorities, and the principal would like at least one minority girl to have this honor. If he selects the girls at random, what is the probability that
    (a) he will select exactly one minority girl?
    (b) he will select no minority girls?
    (c) he will select at least one minority girl?

21. *Diversity* Suppose that an employer plans to hire four people from a group of nine equally qualified people of whom three are minority candidates. If the employer does not know which candidates are minority candidates and if she selects her employees at random, what is the probability that
    (a) no minority candidates are hired?
    (b) all three minority candidates are hired?
    (c) one minority candidate is hired?

22. *Lottery* Four men and three women are semifinalists in a lottery. From this group, three finalists are to be selected by a drawing. What is the probability that all three finalists will be men?

23. *Management* Suppose that a children's basketball coach knows the best 6 players to use on his team, but pressure from parents to give everyone a chance to start in a game causes him to pick the starting team by choosing 5 players at random from the 10 team members. What is the probability that this will give him a team with 5 of his 6 best players?

24. *Sales* A car dealer has 12 different cars that he would like to display, but he has room to display only 5.
    (a) In how many ways can he pick 5 cars to display?
    (b) Suppose 8 of the cars are the same color, with the remaining 4 having distinct colors. If the dealer tells a salesperson to display any 5 cars, what is the probability that all 5 cars will be the same color?

25. *Diversity* Suppose that two openings on an appellate court bench are to be filled from current municipal court judges. The municipal court judges consist of 23 men and 4 women. Find the probability that
    (a) both appointees are men.
    (b) one man and one woman are appointed.
    (c) at least one woman is appointed.

26. *Politics* Suppose that four of the eight students running for class officers (president, vice president, secretary, and treasurer) have grade point averages (GPAs) above 3.0. If the officers are selected at random, what is the probability that all four officers will be students with GPAs above 3.0?

27. *Management* Suppose that an indecisive company owner has ranked the three top officers of his company

at random but claims that they earned their jobs because of ability.
    (a) What is the probability that the most able person is ranked at the top?
    (b) What is the probability that the top three officers are ranked according to their ability?

28. *Quality control* Suppose that 10 computer chips are drawn from a box containing 12 good chips and 4 defective chips. What is the probability that
    (a) exactly 4 of the chips are defective?
    (b) all 10 of the chips are good?
    (c) exactly 8 of the chips are good?

29. *Lotteries* In New York State, there is a state lottery game called Pick 10. The state chooses 20 numbers from 80 numbers, and each player chooses 10 numbers from the same 80 numbers. If all 10 of a player's numbers are among the 20 numbers the state picked, then that player is a "big winner." Find the probability of being a big winner.

30. *Diversity* A task force studying age discrimination wants to establish a subcommittee. If the subcommittee is to consist of 11 members chosen from a group of 23 men and 19 women, find the probability that the subcommittee consists of
    (a) 6 men and 5 women.   (b) all women.

31. *Insurance* An insurance company receives 25 claims in a certain month. Company policy mandates that a random selection of 5 of these claims be thoroughly investigated. If 2 of the 25 claims are fraudulent, find the probability that
    (a) both fraudulent claims are thoroughly investigated.
    (b) neither fraudulent claim is thoroughly investigated.

32. *Evaluation* Employees of a firm receive annual reviews. In a certain department, 4 employees received excellent ratings, 15 received good ratings, and 1 received a marginal rating. If 3 employees in this department are randomly selected to complete a form for an internal study of the firm, find the probability that
    (a) all 3 selected were rated excellent.
    (b) one from each category was selected.

33. *Poker* What is the probability of being dealt a poker hand of 5 cards in which
    (a) all 5 cards are spades?
    (b) 4 of the 5 cards are hearts?

34. *Bridge* A standard deck of cards contains 13 spades, 13 hearts, 13 diamonds, and 13 clubs. A bridge hand contains 13 cards selected at random from the 52-card deck. Find the probability that a hand contains
    (a) 13 hearts.   (b) exactly 8 spades.

35. *Poker* A flush (5 cards from the same suit) is an excellent hand in poker. If 13 cards are in each of four suits in a deck used in the game and 5 cards are in a hand, what is the probability that a flush occurs?

36. *Bridge* Find the probability of being dealt a hand containing 1 spade, 6 hearts, 4 diamonds, and 2 clubs. Assume that a normal deck of 52 cards is used.

37. *Lottery scandal* On April 24, 1980, the winning Pennsylvania daily number was 666. It was later discovered that on that day, the drawing had been fixed by injecting a liquid into all balls except the 4 and the 6, ensuring that only those numbers would appear as digits in the winning number. Interestingly, several weeks later the Pennsylvania lottery scandal was exposed, and within hours of the announcement of the lottery fix in Pennsylvania, the winning number in the Connecticut lottery was 666. This coincidence was highly suspicious, but investigation of the Connecticut drawing concluded that its 666 drawing was legitimate (*Source: LA Times*, September 21, 1980).

(a) Find the probability that 666 wins in a fair lottery—like the one in Connecticut.

(b) List all possible outcomes for the Pennsylvania lottery on the day it was fixed.

(c) Find the probability that 666 would win in the fixed Pennsylvania lottery of April 24, 1980.

SECTION 7.7

Markov Chains

OBJECTIVES

- To use transition matrices to find specific stages of Markov chains
- To write transition matrices for Markov chain problems
- To find steady-state vectors for certain Markov chain problems

APPLICATION PREVIEW

Suppose a department store has determined that a woman who uses a credit card in the current month will use it again next month with probability 0.8. That is,

Pr(woman will use card next month | she used it this month) = 0.8

and

Pr(woman will not use card next month | she used it this month) = 0.2

Furthermore, suppose the store has determined that the probability that a woman who does not use a credit card this month will not use it next month is 0.7. That is,

Pr(woman will not use card next month | she did not use it this month) = 0.7

and

Pr(woman will use card next month | she did not use it this month) = 0.3

To find the probability that the woman will use the credit card in some later month, we use Markov chains and put the conditional probabilities in a transition matrix. (See Example 1.) Markov chains are named for the famous Russian mathematician A. A. Markov, who developed this theory in 1906. They are useful in the analysis of price movements, consumer behavior, laboratory animal behavior, and many other processes in business, the social sciences, and the life sciences.

Markov Chains Suppose that a sequence of experiments with the same set of outcomes is performed, with the probabilities of the outcomes in one experiment depending on the outcomes of the previous experiment. The outcomes of the experiments are called **states,** and the sequence of the experiments forms a **Markov chain** if the next state depends solely on the present state and doesn't directly depend on the previous states. The changes of state are called **transitions,** the probability of moving from one state to another is called the **transition probability,** and these probabilities can often be organized into a **transition matrix.**

EXAMPLE **1** **Credit Card Use** | APPLICATION PREVIEW |

Create the transition matrix that contains the conditional probabilities from the problem described in the Application Preview.

Solution

If the card is used this month, the probabilities that the woman will or will not use the card next month can be represented by the probability tree

$$\text{Used current month} \left\langle \begin{array}{l} 0.8 \nearrow \text{Used next month} \\ 0.2 \searrow \text{Not used next month} \end{array} \right.$$

We can enter these numbers in the first row of the transition matrix

$$\begin{array}{c} & \text{Next month} \\ & \begin{array}{cc} \text{Card} & \text{Card} \\ \text{used} & \text{not used} \end{array} \\ \textit{Current month} \begin{array}{c} \text{Card used} \\ \text{Card not used} \end{array} & \left[\begin{array}{cc} 0.8 & 0.2 \\ & \end{array} \right] \end{array}$$

If the card is not used this month, the probabilities that the woman will or will not use the card next month can be represented by the probability tree

$$\text{Not used current month} \left\langle \begin{array}{l} 0.7 \nearrow \text{Not used next month} \\ 0.3 \searrow \text{Used next month} \end{array} \right.$$

Putting these conditional probabilities in the second row completes the transition matrix:

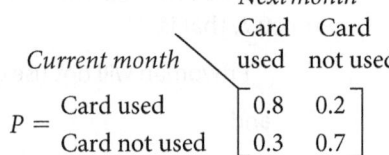

$$P = \begin{array}{c} & \text{Next month} \\ & \begin{array}{cc} \text{Card} & \text{Card} \\ \textit{Current month} & \text{used} & \text{not used} \end{array} \\ \begin{array}{c} \text{Card used} \\ \text{Card not used} \end{array} & \left[\begin{array}{cc} 0.8 & 0.2 \\ 0.3 & 0.7 \end{array} \right] \end{array}$$

In Example 1, two states for the Markov chain were described. State 1 was "used next month," and state 2 was "not used next month." The transition matrix was a 2 × 2 matrix.

Transition Matrix

A **transition matrix** for a Markov chain with n states is an $n \times n$ matrix characterized by the following properties.

1. The ij-entry in the matrix is
   $$\text{Pr(moving from state } i \text{ to state } j) = \text{Pr(state } j \mid \text{state } i)$$
2. The entries are nonnegative.
3. The sum of the entries in each row equals 1.

Now suppose the department store data show that during the first month a credit card is received, the probabilities for each state are as follows:

$$\text{Pr(a woman used a credit card)} = 0.9$$
$$\text{Pr(a woman did not use a credit card)} = 0.1$$

These probabilities can be placed in the row matrix

$$A = [0.9 \quad 0.1]$$

which is called the **initial probability vector** for the problem. This vector gives the probabilities for each state at the outset of the trials. In general, a probability vector is defined as follows.

Probability Vector	For a vector to be a **probability vector**, the sum of its entries must be 1 and each of its entries must be nonnegative.

Note that if a woman used her credit card in the initial month, the probability is 0.8 that she will use it the next month, and if she didn't use the card, the probability is 0.3 that she will use it the next month. Thus,

$$\text{Pr(will use 2nd month)} = \text{Pr(used 1st month)} \cdot \text{Pr(will use 2nd | used 1st)}$$
$$+ \text{Pr(not used 1st month)} \cdot \text{Pr(will use 2nd | not used 1st)}$$
$$= (0.9)(0.8) + (0.1)(0.3)$$
$$= 0.72 + 0.03 = 0.75$$

Note that this is one element of the product matrix AP. Similarly, the second element of the product matrix is the probability that a woman will not use the card in the second month.

$$AP = \begin{bmatrix} 0.9 & 0.1 \end{bmatrix} \begin{bmatrix} 0.8 & 0.2 \\ 0.3 & 0.7 \end{bmatrix} = \begin{bmatrix} 0.75 & 0.25 \end{bmatrix}$$

Initial   Transition   Second
month   matrix   month

Thus

$$\text{Pr(a woman will use a credit card in 2nd month)} = 0.75$$

and

$$\text{Pr(a woman will not use a credit card in 2nd month)} = 0.25$$

To find the probabilities for each state for the third month, we multiply the second-month probability vector times the transition matrix.

$$\begin{bmatrix} 0.75 & 0.25 \end{bmatrix} \begin{bmatrix} 0.8 & 0.2 \\ 0.3 & 0.7 \end{bmatrix} = \begin{bmatrix} 0.675 & 0.325 \end{bmatrix}$$

Second   Transition   Third
month   matrix   month

Continuing in this manner, we can find the probabilities for later months.

EXAMPLE 2   Politics

Suppose that in a certain city, the Democratic, Republican, and Consumer parties have members of their parties on the city council. The probability of a member of one of these parties winning in any election depends on the proportional membership of his or her party at the time of the election. The probabilities for all these parties are given by the following transition matrix P.

Proportion of party in office next term

Proportion of party in office		D	R	C
	Democrat	0.5	0.4	0.1
$P =$	Republican	0.4	0.5	0.1
	Consumer	0.3	0.3	0.4

Suppose that the current proportional distribution of parties on the council is given in the initial probability vector $A_0 = [0.4 \ 0.4 \ 0.2]$. The probable distribution of parties after the third election from now is given by the probability vector for the third election. Find this probability vector.

Solution

We multiply the initial probability vector by the transition matrix to get the probability vector for the first election.

$$A_1 = A_0P = [0.4 \quad 0.4 \quad 0.2]\begin{bmatrix} 0.5 & 0.4 & 0.1 \\ 0.4 & 0.5 & 0.1 \\ 0.3 & 0.3 & 0.4 \end{bmatrix} = [0.42 \quad 0.42 \quad 0.16]$$

We multiply the probability vector for the first election by the transition matrix to get the probability vector for the second election.

$$A_2 = A_1P = [0.42 \quad 0.42 \quad 0.16]\begin{bmatrix} 0.5 & 0.4 & 0.1 \\ 0.4 & 0.5 & 0.1 \\ 0.3 & 0.3 & 0.4 \end{bmatrix} = [0.426 \quad 0.426 \quad 0.148]$$

We multiply the probability vector for the second election by the transition matrix to get the probability vector for the third election. This probability vector gives the probable distribution after the third election.

$$A_3 = A_2P = [0.426 \quad 0.426 \quad 0.148]\begin{bmatrix} 0.5 & 0.4 & 0.1 \\ 0.4 & 0.5 & 0.1 \\ 0.3 & 0.3 & 0.4 \end{bmatrix} = [0.4278 \quad 0.4278 \quad 0.1444]$$

Thus the probable distribution of parties on the council after the third election is approximately 43% Democrat, 43% Republican, and 14% Consumer.

Steady-State Vectors

The multiplications done in Example 2 can be written in a second way, which gives us a general method to find the probability vectors for later elections.

$$A_1 = A_0P$$
$$A_2 = A_1P = A_0PP = A_0P^2$$
$$A_3 = A_2P = A_0P^2P = A_0P^3$$

Thus the probability vector for the third election can be found by multiplying the initial probability vector A_0 by the transition matrix P three times—that is, $A_3 = A_0P^3$.

If A_0 represents the $1 \times n$ initial probability vector and P is the $n \times n$ transition matrix for a Markov chain, then mth probability vector A_m is

$$A_m = A_0P^m$$

We can use this formula to compute the probability vectors for large numbers of elections. In Example 2, the probability vector for the 10th election (to five decimal places) can be found with technology:

$$A_{10} = A_0P^{10} = [0.4 \quad 0.4 \quad 0.2]P^{10} = [0.42857 \quad 0.42857 \quad 0.14286]$$

Calculator Note Figure 7.16 shows this calculation on a graphing calculator. See Appendix A, Section 7.7, for details.

```
[A]
        [[.4   .4   .2]]
[B]
        [[.5   .4   .1]
         [.4   .5   .1]
         [.3   .3   .4]]
```

```
[A][B]^10
.42857 .42857 .14286
```

Figure 7.16

Note that the probability vector for the 21st election (to five decimal places) is

$$A_{21} = A_0 P^{21} = [0.4 \quad 0.4 \quad 0.2]P^{21} = [0.42857 \quad 0.42857 \quad 0.14286]$$

Repeated multiplications will not change the probability vectors (for at least five decimal places), so this system appears to be stabilizing. The vector that is being approached has the form $[V_1 \quad V_2 \quad V_3]$ such that

$$[V_1 \quad V_2 \quad V_3] \cdot P = [V_1 \quad V_2 \quad V_3]$$

The exact probability vector for which this is true in Example 2 is $\begin{bmatrix} \dfrac{3}{7} & \dfrac{3}{7} & \dfrac{1}{7} \end{bmatrix}$ because

$$\begin{bmatrix} \dfrac{3}{7} & \dfrac{3}{7} & \dfrac{1}{7} \end{bmatrix} \begin{bmatrix} 0.5 & 0.4 & 0.1 \\ 0.4 & 0.5 & 0.1 \\ 0.3 & 0.3 & 0.4 \end{bmatrix} = \begin{bmatrix} \dfrac{3}{7} & \dfrac{3}{7} & \dfrac{1}{7} \end{bmatrix}$$

This vector is called the **fixed-probability vector** for the given transition matrix. Because this vector is where the process eventually stabilizes, it is also called the **steady-state vector.**

Rather than trying to guess this steady-state vector by repeated multiplication, we can solve the following equation for V_1, V_2, and V_3.

$$[V_1 \quad V_2 \quad V_3] \begin{bmatrix} 0.5 & 0.4 & 0.1 \\ 0.4 & 0.5 & 0.1 \\ 0.3 & 0.3 & 0.4 \end{bmatrix} = [V_1 \quad V_2 \quad V_3]$$

$$\begin{array}{lcl}
0.5V_1 + 0.4V_2 + 0.3V_3 = V_1 & & -0.5V_1 + 0.4V_2 + 0.3V_3 = 0 \\
0.4V_1 + 0.5V_2 + 0.3V_3 = V_2 & \text{or} & 0.4V_1 - 0.5V_2 + 0.3V_3 = 0 \\
0.1V_1 + 0.1V_2 + 0.4V_3 = V_3 & & 0.1V_1 + 0.1V_2 - 0.6V_3 = 0
\end{array}$$

Solving by Gauss-Jordan elimination gives

$$\begin{bmatrix} -0.5 & 0.4 & 0.3 & | & 0 \\ 0.4 & -0.5 & 0.3 & | & 0 \\ 0.1 & 0.1 & -0.6 & | & 0 \end{bmatrix} \xrightarrow[\text{Switch } R_1 \text{ \& } R_3]{10\,(\text{each row})} \begin{bmatrix} 1 & 1 & -6 & | & 0 \\ 4 & -5 & 3 & | & 0 \\ -5 & 4 & 3 & | & 0 \end{bmatrix}$$

$$\xrightarrow[5R_1 + R_3 \to R_3]{-4R_1 + R_2 \to R_2} \begin{bmatrix} 1 & 1 & -6 & | & 0 \\ 0 & -9 & 27 & | & 0 \\ 0 & 9 & -27 & | & 0 \end{bmatrix} \xrightarrow[\substack{\text{then} \\ -R_2 + R_1 \to R_1 \\ -9R_2 + R_3 \to R_3}]{-\frac{1}{9}R_2 \to R_2} \begin{bmatrix} 1 & 0 & -3 & | & 0 \\ 0 & 1 & -3 & | & 0 \\ 0 & 0 & 0 & | & 0 \end{bmatrix}$$

Thus $V_1 = 3V_3$ $V_2 = 3V_3$ $V_3 =$ any real number

Any vector that satisfies these conditions is a solution of the system. Because $[V_1 \quad V_2 \quad V_3]$ is a probability vector, we have $V_1 + V_2 + V_3 = 1$. Substituting gives $3V_3 + 3V_3 + V_3 = 1$, so $V_3 = 1/7$ and the steady-state vector is

$$\begin{bmatrix} \dfrac{3}{7} & \dfrac{3}{7} & \dfrac{1}{7} \end{bmatrix}$$

Calculator Note

When the transition matrix B contains only positive entries, the steady-state vector can be found by finding $[C] = [I] - [B]$ and then rref($[C]^T$). Figure 7.17 shows the matrices used to determine the steady-state vector found above. See Appendix A, Section 7.7, for details.

Figure 7.17   (a)   (b)   (c)

As we have seen, the Markov chain in Example 2 has a steady-state vector, but not every Markov chain has one. If the transition matrix P for a Markov chain is a special matrix called a **regular transition matrix,** there is a unique steady-state vector for the Markov chain. A transition matrix P is a regular transition matrix if some power of P contains only positive entries. Note that a regular transition matrix may contain zeros; the only requirement is that some power of P contain all positive entries. In this text, we limit ourselves to regular transition matrices. These matrices are related to **regular Markov chains** as follows.

Regular Markov Chain

- If P is a regular transition matrix, the sequence $P, P^2, P^3, \ldots$ approaches a matrix in which all of its rows are equal.
- If the transition matrix for a Markov chain is regular, the chain is called a **regular Markov chain,** and this chain has a steady-state vector.

If a steady-state vector exists for a Markov chain, then the effect of the initial probabilities diminishes as the number of steps in the process increases. This means that the probability vectors for the elections in Example 2 would approach the steady-state vector regardless of the initial probabilities. For example, even if all members of the council are Democrats at the initial stage (that is, the initial probability vector is $[1 \quad 0 \quad 0]$), the probability vector after the fourth election is $[0.4292 \quad 0.4291 \quad 0.1417]$, which approximates the steady-state vector $[3/7 \quad 3/7 \quad 1/7]$ found previously.

CHECKPOINT

1. Use the transition matrix $P = \begin{bmatrix} 0.1 & 0.3 & 0.6 \\ 0.3 & 0.5 & 0.2 \\ 0.1 & 0.1 & 0.8 \end{bmatrix}$ and the initial probability vector

   $A_0 = [0.2 \quad 0.3 \quad 0.5]$ to
   (a) find the second probability vector (two steps after the initial probability vector).
   (b) find the steady-state vector associated with the matrix.

EXAMPLE 3   Educational Attainment

Suppose that in a certain city, the probabilities that a woman with less than a high school education has a daughter with less than a high school education, with a high school degree, and with education beyond high school are 0.2, 0.6, and 0.2, respectively. The probabilities that a woman with a high school degree has a daughter with less than a high school education, with a high school degree, and with education beyond high school are 0.1, 0.5, and 0.4, respectively. The probabilities that a woman with education beyond high school has a daughter with less than a high school education, with a high school degree, and with education beyond high school are 0.1, 0.1, and 0.8, respectively. The population of women in the city is now 60% with less than a high school education, 30% with a high school degree, and 10% with education beyond high school.

(a) What is the transition matrix for this information?

(b) What is the probable distribution of women according to educational level two generations from now?

(c) What is the steady-state vector for this information?

Solution

(a) The transition matrix is

	Daughter's educational level		
Mother's educational level	Less than H.S.	H.S. degree	More than H.S.
Less than H.S.	0.2	0.6	0.2
H.S. degree	0.1	0.5	0.4
More than H.S.	0.1	0.1	0.8

(b) The probable distribution after one generation is

$$[0.6 \quad 0.3 \quad 0.1] \begin{bmatrix} 0.2 & 0.6 & 0.2 \\ 0.1 & 0.5 & 0.4 \\ 0.1 & 0.1 & 0.8 \end{bmatrix} = [0.16 \quad 0.52 \quad 0.32]$$

The probable distribution after two generations is

$$[0.16 \quad 0.52 \quad 0.32] \begin{bmatrix} 0.2 & 0.6 & 0.2 \\ 0.1 & 0.5 & 0.4 \\ 0.1 & 0.1 & 0.8 \end{bmatrix} = [0.116 \quad 0.388 \quad 0.496]$$

(c) The steady-state vector is found by solving

$$[V_1 \quad V_2 \quad V_3] \begin{bmatrix} 0.2 & 0.6 & 0.2 \\ 0.1 & 0.5 & 0.4 \\ 0.1 & 0.1 & 0.8 \end{bmatrix} = [V_1 \quad V_2 \quad V_3]$$

$$\begin{cases} 0.2V_1 + 0.1V_2 + 0.1V_3 = V_1 \\ 0.6V_1 + 0.5V_2 + 0.1V_3 = V_2 \\ 0.2V_1 + 0.4V_2 + 0.8V_3 = V_3 \end{cases} \quad \text{or} \quad \begin{cases} -0.8V_1 + 0.1V_2 + 0.1V_3 = 0 \\ 0.6V_1 - 0.5V_2 + 0.1V_3 = 0 \\ 0.2V_1 + 0.4V_2 - 0.2V_3 = 0 \end{cases}$$

Using Gauss-Jordan elimination or technology gives

$$\begin{bmatrix} -0.8 & 0.1 & 0.1 & | & 0 \\ 0.6 & -0.5 & 0.1 & | & 0 \\ 0.2 & 0.4 & -0.2 & | & 0 \end{bmatrix} \rightarrow \begin{bmatrix} 1 & 0 & -\frac{3}{17} & | & 0 \\ 0 & 1 & -\frac{7}{17} & | & 0 \\ 0 & 0 & 0 & | & 0 \end{bmatrix}$$

Thus $V_1 = \frac{3}{17}V_3$ and $V_2 = \frac{7}{17}V_3$. The probability vector that satisfies these conditions and $V_1 + V_2 + V_3 = 1$ must satisfy

$$\frac{3}{17}V_3 + \frac{7}{17}V_3 + V_3 = 1 \quad \text{or} \quad \frac{27}{17}V_3 = 1 \quad \text{so} \quad V_3 = \frac{17}{27}$$

Thus the steady-state vector is

$$\begin{bmatrix} \dfrac{3}{27} & \dfrac{7}{27} & \dfrac{17}{27} \end{bmatrix}$$

1. (a) The first-stage probability vector is

$$A_1 = [0.16 \quad 0.26 \quad 0.58]$$

and the second stage is

$$A_2 = [0.152 \quad 0.236 \quad 0.612]$$

(b) The steady-state vector is $\left[\dfrac{1}{7} \quad \dfrac{3}{14} \quad \dfrac{9}{14}\right]$.

EXERCISES 7.7

Can the vectors in Problems 1–4 be probability vectors? If not, why?

1. $\begin{bmatrix} \dfrac{1}{4} & \dfrac{3}{4} \end{bmatrix}$

2. $\begin{bmatrix} \dfrac{5}{6} & \dfrac{2}{3} \end{bmatrix}$

3. $\begin{bmatrix} \dfrac{1}{4} & \dfrac{3}{5} & \dfrac{1}{6} \end{bmatrix}$

4. $\begin{bmatrix} \dfrac{2}{3} & \dfrac{1}{12} & \dfrac{1}{4} \end{bmatrix}$

Can the matrices in Problems 5–8 be transition matrices? If not, why?

5. $\begin{bmatrix} 0.3 & 0.5 & 0.2 \\ 0.1 & 0.6 & 0.3 \end{bmatrix}$

6. $\begin{bmatrix} 0.6 & 0.2 & 0.2 \\ 0.1 & 0.5 & 0.4 \\ 0.3 & 0.5 & 0.1 \end{bmatrix}$

7. $\begin{bmatrix} 0.1 & 0.3 & 0.6 \\ 0.5 & 0.2 & 0.3 \\ 0.1 & 0.7 & 0.2 \end{bmatrix}$

8. $\begin{bmatrix} 0.6 & 0.5 & -0.1 \\ 0.2 & 0.6 & 0.2 \\ 0.3 & 0.3 & 0.4 \end{bmatrix}$

In Problems 9–12, use the given transition matrix and the initial probability vector to find the second probability vector (two steps after the initial probability vector).

$$A = \begin{bmatrix} 0.1 & 0.9 \\ 0.3 & 0.7 \end{bmatrix} \qquad B = \begin{bmatrix} 0.5 & 0.5 \\ 0.9 & 0.1 \end{bmatrix}$$

$$C = \begin{bmatrix} 0.5 & 0.3 & 0.2 \\ 0.3 & 0.5 & 0.2 \\ 0.1 & 0.1 & 0.8 \end{bmatrix} \qquad D = \begin{bmatrix} 0.8 & 0.1 & 0.1 \\ 0.2 & 0.6 & 0.2 \\ 0.3 & 0.3 & 0.4 \end{bmatrix}$$

9. Transition matrix A, initial probability vector [0.2 0.8].
10. Transition matrix B, initial probability vector [0.6 0.4].
11. Transition matrix C, initial probability vector [0.1 0.3 0.6].

12. Transition matrix D, initial probability vector [0.9 0 0.1].
13. Use the matrix and initial probability vector in Problem 9 and find the resulting 10th probability vector.
14. Use the matrix and initial probability vector in Problem 10 and find the resulting 18th probability vector.
15. Use the matrix and initial probability vector in Problem 11 and find the resulting eighth probability vector.
16. Use the matrix and initial probability vector in Problem 12 and find the resulting ninth probability vector.

In Problems 17–20, find the steady-state vector associated with the given transition matrix from Problems 9–12.

17. A 18. B 19. C 20. D

APPLICATIONS

Politics **Use the following information for Problems 21 and 22. In a certain city, the Democratic, Republican, and Consumer parties have members of their parties on the city council. The probability of a member of this party winning any election depends on the proportional membership of his or her party at the time of the election. The probabilities for all these parties winning are given by the following transition matrix P.**

	Party in office next term		
Party in office now	D	R	C
Democrat	0.5	0.4	0.1
Republican	0.4	0.5	0.1
Consumer	0.3	0.3	0.4

21. Using the given transition matrix and assuming that the initial probability vector is [1 0 0], find the probability vectors for the next four steps of the Markov chain. (This initial probability vector indicates that all members are Democrats.)

22. Using the given transition matrix and assuming that all members of the council are Republicans, find the probability vectors for the next four steps of the Markov chain.

Church attendance **Use the following information for Problems 23–26. The probability that daughters of a mother who attends church regularly will also attend church regularly is 0.8, whereas the probability that daughters of a mother who does not attend regularly will attend regularly is 0.3.**

23. What is the transition matrix for this information?
24. If a woman attends church regularly and has one daughter who in turn has one daughter, what is the probability that the granddaughter attends church regularly?
25. If a woman does not attend church, what is the probability that her granddaughter attends church regularly?
26. What is the steady-state vector for this information?

Car selection **Use the following information for Problems 27–32. A man owns an Audi, a Ford, and a VW. He drives every day and never drives the same car two days in a row. These are the probabilities that he drives each of the other cars the next day:**

Pr(Ford after Audi) = 0.7   Pr(VW after Audi) = 0.3
Pr(Audi after Ford) = 0.6   Pr(VW after Ford) = 0.4
Pr(Audi after VW) = 0.8   Pr(Ford after VW) = 0.2

27. Write the transition matrix for his selection of a car.
28. If he drove the Ford today, what are the probabilities for the cars that he will drive 2 days from today?
29. If he drove the Ford today, what are the probabilities for the cars that he will drive 4 days from today?
30. If he drove the Audi today, what are the probabilities for the cars that he will drive 4 days from now?
31. What is the steady-state vector for this problem?
32. Would the probabilities for which car he drives 100 days from now depend on whether he drove a Ford or an Audi today?
33. *Population demographics* Suppose a government study estimated that the probability of successive generations of a rural family remaining in a rural area was 0.7 and the probability of successive generations of an urban family remaining in an urban area was 0.9. Assuming that a Markov chain applies to these facts, find the steady-state vector.
34. *Psychology* A psychologist found that a laboratory mouse placed in a T-maze with food at the end of one branch will go down the same branch with probability 0.8 if food was there on the previous trial and that it will go down the same branch with probability 0.6 if no

food was there on the previous trial. Find the steady-state vector for this experiment. If the mouse takes the branches with equal probability when no reward is found, does it appear that the mouse "learns" to choose the food path?

35. *Charitable contributions* The local community service funding organization in a certain county has classified the population into those who did not give the previous year, those who gave less than their "fair share," and those who met or exceeded their "fair share." Suppose the organization developed the following transition matrix for these groups.

		This year	
Last year	N	L	F
No contribution	0.7	0.2	0.1
Less than fair share	0.1	0.6	0.3
Fair share	0	0.1	0.9

Find the steady-state vector for this county's contribution habits.

Advertising **Use the following information for Problems 36 and 37. A local business A has two competitors, B and C. No customer patronizes more than one of these businesses at the same time. Initially, the probabilities that a customer patronizes A, B, or C are 0.2, 0.6, and 0.2, respectively. Suppose A initiates an advertising campaign to improve its business and finds the following transition matrix to describe the effect.**

Last week's customers went to	This week's customers go to		
	A	B	C
A	0.7	0.2	0.1
B	0.4	0.4	0.2
C	0.4	0.4	0.2

36. If A runs the advertising campaign for 3 weeks, find the probability of a customer patronizing each business in the third week.
37. Find the steady-state vector for this market—that is, the long-range share of the market that each business can expect if the transition matrix holds.

Genetics **Use the following information for Problems 38–40. For species that reproduce sexually, characteristics are determined by a gene from each parent. Suppose that for a certain trait, there are two possible genes available from each parent: a dominant gene D and a recessive gene r. Then the different gene combinations (called *genotypes*) for the offspring are DD, Dr, rD, and rr, where**

Dr and rD produce the same trait. Suppose further that these genotypes are the states of a Markov chain with the following transition matrix.

	Offspring genotype		
Parent genotype	DD	Dr	rr
DD	0.7	0.3	0
Dr	0.35	0.5	0.15
rr	0	0.7	0.3

38. If the initial occurrence of those genotypes in the population is 0.5 for DD, 0.4 for Dr, and 0.1 for rr, find the distribution (probability) of each type after the first and second generations.
39. Find the steady-state vector for this genotype.
40. To which generation(s) does the steady-state vector correspond? This is called the **Hardy-Weinberg model.**

7   CHAPTER SUMMARY & REVIEW

KEY TERMS AND FORMULAS

Section 7.1

Equally likely events (p. 421)
$$Pr(E) = k/n$$
Sample space (p. 422)
Certain event (p. 423)
$$Pr(E) = 1$$

Impossible event (p. 425)
$$Pr(E) = 0$$
Empirical probability (p. 427)
Odds and probability (p. 428)

Section 7.2

Intersection of events (p. 431)
$$Pr(E \text{ and } F) = Pr(E \cap F)$$
Union of events (p. 431)
$$Pr(E \text{ or } F) = Pr(E \cup F)$$
$$= Pr(E) + Pr(F) - Pr(E \cap F)$$

Complement (p. 433)
$$Pr(\text{not } E) = Pr(E') = 1 - Pr(E)$$
Mutually exclusive events (p. 436)
$$Pr(E \text{ or } F) = Pr(E) + Pr(F)$$

Section 7.3

Conditional probability (p. 439)
$$Pr(E \mid F) = \frac{Pr(E \cap F)}{Pr(F)}$$
Product Rule (p. 440)
$$Pr(E \cap F) = Pr(F) \cdot Pr(E \mid F)$$

Probability trees (p. 441)
Independent events (p. 443)
$$Pr(A \mid B) = Pr(A) \text{ and}$$
$$Pr(A \cap B) = Pr(A) \cdot Pr(B)$$

Section 7.4

Probability tree (p. 448)
Bayes' formula and trees (p. 451)

$$Pr(E_1 \mid F_1) = \frac{\text{Branch product on path leading through } E_1 \text{ to } F_1}{\text{Sum of all branch products on paths leading to } F_1}$$

Probability formulas summary (p. 453)

Section 7.5

Fundamental Counting Principle (p. 456)
$$n(A) \cdot n(B)$$
n-factorial (p. 457)
$$n! = n(n - 1)\cdots(3)(2)(1) \quad \text{and} \quad 0! = 1$$

Permutations (p. 457)
$$_nP_r = \frac{n!}{(n - r)!}$$

Combinations (p. 458)
$$_nC_r = \frac{n!}{r!(n - r)!}$$

Section 7.6

Probability using permutations and
combinations (p. 462)

Section 7.7

Markov chains (p. 467)   Steady-state vectors (p. 470)
Transition matrix (p. 468)   Fixed probability vectors
Probability vectors (p. 469)   Regular Markov chain (p. 472)

REVIEW EXERCISES

Section 7.1

1. If one ball is drawn from a bag containing 9 balls numbered 1 through 9, what is the probability that the ball's number is
   (a) odd?
   (b) divisible by 3?
   (c) odd and divisible by 3?
2. Suppose a ball is drawn from a bag containing 9 red balls numbered 1 through 9 and 3 white balls numbered 10 through 12. Two possible sample spaces for this event are $S_1 = \{1, 2, 3, \ldots \ldots 12\}$ and $S_2 = \{R, W\}$.
   (a) Which of these sample spaces is equiprobable? What is the probability that
   (b) the ball is red?
   (c) the ball is odd-numbered?
   (d) the ball is white and even-numbered?
   (e) the ball is white or odd-numbered?
3. If the probability that an event E occurs is 3/7, what are the odds that
   (a) E will occur?   (b) E will not occur?
4. Suppose that a fair coin is tossed two times. Construct an equiprobable sample space for the experiment and determine each of the following probabilities.
   (a) Pr(0 heads)   (b) Pr(1 head)   (c) Pr(2 heads)
5. Suppose that a fair coin is tossed three times. Construct an equiprobable sample space for the experiment and determine each of the following probabilities.
   (a) Pr(2 heads)   (b) Pr(3 heads)   (c) Pr(1 head)

Section 7.2

6. A card is drawn at random from an ordinary deck of 52 playing cards. What is the probability that it is a queen or a jack?
7. A deck of 52 cards is shuffled. A card is drawn, it is replaced, the pack is shuffled again, and a second card is drawn. What is the probability that each card drawn is an ace, a king, a queen, or a jack?
8. If the probability of winning a game is 1/4 and there can be no ties, what is the probability of losing the game?
9. A card is drawn from a deck of 52 playing cards. What is the probability that it is an ace or a 10?

10. A card is drawn at random from a deck of playing cards. What is the probability that it is a king or a red card?
11. A bag contains 4 red balls numbered 1, 2, 3, 4 and 5 white balls numbered 5, 6, 7, 8, 9. A ball is drawn. What is the probability that the ball
    (a) is red and even-numbered?
    (b) is red or even-numbered?
    (c) is white or odd-numbered?

Section 7.3

12. A bag contains 4 red balls and 3 black balls. Two balls are drawn at random from the bag without replacement. Find the probability that
    (a) both balls are red.
    (b) one is red and one is black.
13. A box contains 2 red balls and 3 black balls. Two balls are drawn from the box without replacement. Find the probability that
    (a) the first ball is black and the second is red.
    (b) the second ball is red, given that the first ball is black.
14. A bag contains 8 white balls, 5 red balls, and 7 black balls. If 3 balls are drawn at random from the bag, with replacement, what is the probability that
    (a) the first two balls are red and the third is black?
    (b) 2 of the balls are red and 1 is black?
15. A bag contains 8 white balls, 5 red balls, and 7 black balls. If 3 balls are drawn at random from the bag, without replacement, what is the probability that
    (a) the first two balls are red and the third is black?
    (b) the third ball is black given that the first is black?

Section 7.4

16. A bag contains 3 red, 5 black, and 8 white balls. Three balls are drawn, without replacement. What is the probability that one of each color is drawn?
17. An urn contains 4 red and 6 white balls. One ball is drawn, it is not replaced, and a second ball is drawn. What is the probability that one ball is white and one is red?

18. Urn I contains 3 red and 4 white balls, and urn II contains 5 red and 2 white balls. An urn is selected, and a ball is drawn.
    (a) What is the probability that urn I is selected and a red ball is drawn?
    (b) What is the probability that a red ball is selected?
    (c) If a red ball is selected, what is the probability that urn I was selected?

19. Bag A contains 3 red, 6 black, and 5 white balls, and bag B contains 4 red, 5 black, and 7 white balls. A bag is selected at random, and a ball is drawn. If the ball is white, what is the probability that bag B was selected?

Section 7.5

20. Compute $_6P_2$.
21. Compute $_7C_3$.
22. How many 3-letter sets of initials are possible?
23. How many combinations of 8 things taken 5 at a time are possible?

Section 7.7

24. Explain why each given matrix is not a transition matrix for a Markov chain.

(a) $\begin{bmatrix} 0.2 & 0.7 & 0.1 \\ 0.3 & 0.2 & 0.5 \end{bmatrix}$ (b) $\begin{bmatrix} 0.4 & 0.7 \\ 0.6 & 0.3 \end{bmatrix}$

25. For the initial probability vector $[0.1 \quad 0.9]$ and the transition matrix A, find the next two probability vectors.

$$A = \begin{bmatrix} 0.4 & 0.6 \\ 0.8 & 0.2 \end{bmatrix}$$

26. Find the steady-state vector associated with the transition matrix.

$$\begin{bmatrix} 0.6 & 0.4 \\ 0.1 & 0.9 \end{bmatrix}$$

APPLICATIONS

Section 7.1

27. *Senior citizens* In a certain city, 30,000 citizens out of 80,000 are over 50 years of age. What is the probability that a citizen selected at random will be 50 years old or younger?

28. *Newspapers* According to funny2.com, the odds that a person aged 18–29 reads a newspaper regularly are 1 to 3. What is the probability that such a person selected at random reads a newspaper regularly?

Section 7.2

29. *United Nations* Of 100 job applicants to the United Nations, 30 speak French, 40 speak German, and 12 speak both French and German. If an applicant is

chosen at random, what is the probability that the applicant speaks French or German?

Productivity **Suppose that in a study of leadership style versus industrial productivity, the following data were obtained. Use these empirical data to answer Problems 30–32.**

	Leadership Style			
Productivity	**Demo-cratic**	**Authori-tarian**	**Laissez-faire**	**Total**
Low	40	15	40	95
Medium	25	75	10	110
High	25	30	20	75
Total	90	120	70	280

30. Find the probability that a person chosen at random has a democratic style and medium productivity.
31. Find the probability that an individual chosen at random has high productivity or an authoritarian style.

Section 7.3

32. Find the probability that an individual chosen at random has an authoritarian style given that he or she has medium productivity.
33. *Quality control* A product must pass an initial inspection, where the probability that it will be rejected is 0.2. If it passes this inspection, it must pass a second inspection where the probability that it will be rejected is 0.1. What is the probability that it will pass both inspections?
34. *Auto styles* A certain make of car comes with either an automatic or a manual transmission and in one of three styles: convertible, sedan, or SUV. The following table shows the probability for each possible style and transmission.

	Convertible	**Sedan**	**SUV**
Automatic	0.32	0.27	0.21
Manual	0.08	0.05	0.07

    (a) Find the probability that a car is an automatic.
    (b) Find the probability that a car is an automatic given that it is an SUV.
    (c) Are "automatic" and "SUV" independent? Explain.
    (d) Find the probability that a car is a convertible given that it is a manual.
    (e) Are "convertible" and "manual" independent? Explain.

Section 7.4

35. *Color blindness* Sixty men out of 1000 and 3 women out of 1000 are color blind. A person is picked at random from a group containing 10 men and 10 women.
    (a) What is the probability that the person is color blind?
    (b) What is the probability that the person is a man if the person is color blind?

36. *Purchasing* A regional survey found that 70% of all families who indicated an intention to buy a new car bought a new car within 3 months, that 10% of families who did not indicate an intention to buy a new car bought one within 3 months, and that 22% indicated an intention to buy a new car. If a family chosen at random bought a car, find the probability that the family had not previously indicated an intention to buy a car.

37. *Quality control* In a manufacturing process where 8% of all items are defective, an inspector at the end of the production line selects some items for inspection. Suppose that 64% of the defective items and 16% of the good items go through the inspection. Find the probability that an item
    (a) has an inspection.
    (b) is defective given that it has an inspection.

Section 7.5

38. *Management* A personnel director ranks 4 applicants for a job. How many rankings are possible?

39. *Management* An organization wants to select a president, vice president, secretary, and treasurer. If 8 people are willing to serve and each of them is eligible for any of the offices, in how many different ways can the offices be filled?

40. *Utilities* A utility company sends teams of 4 people each to perform repairs. If it has 12 qualified people, how many different ways can people be assigned to a team?

41. *Committees* An organization wants to select a committee of 4 members from a group of 8 eligible members. How many different committees are possible?

42. *Juries* A jury will be deadlocked if one or more persons disagree with the rest. One person can disagree in 12 ways because any one of the 12 jurors could disagree. In how many ways can a jury be deadlocked if
    (a) 2 people disagree?
    (b) 3 people disagree?

43. *License plates* The RBC Heritage Classic Foundation license plate is available to anyone with a vehicle registered in the state of South Carolina. It costs $75 every two years with $66–$71 going to the foundation for its Scholar and Birdies for Charity Programs. The plate has the Heritage Classic symbol and four spaces for nonzero digits and/or letters. How many possible plates can be produced using from 1 to 4 digits or letters if they can be repeated?

44. *Blood types* In a book describing the mass murder of 18 people in northern California, a policewoman was quoted as stating that there are blood groups O, A, B, and AB, positive and negative, blood types M, N, MN, and P, and 8 Rh blood types, so there are 288 unique groups (*Source:* Joseph Harrington and Robert Berger, *Eye of Evil*, St. Martin's Press, 1993). Comment on this conclusion.

Section 7.6

45. *Scheduling* A college registrar adds 4 new courses to the list of offerings for the spring semester. If he added the course names in random order at the end of the list, what is the probability that these 4 courses are listed in alphabetical order?

46. *Lottery* Pennsylvania's Daily Number pays 500 to 1 to people who play the winning 3-digit number exactly as it is drawn. However, players can "box" a number so that they can win $80 from a $1 bet if the 3 digits they pick come out in any order. What is the probability that a "boxed" number with 3 different digits will be a winner?

47. *Lottery* If a person "boxes" (see Problem 46) a 4-digit number with 4 different digits in Pennsylvania's Pick Four Lottery, what is the probability that the person will win?

48. *Quality control* A supplier has 200 compact discs, of which 10% are known to be defective. If a music store purchases 10 of these discs, what is the probability that
    (a) none of the discs is defective?
    (b) 2 of the discs are defective?

49. *Stocks* Mr. Way must sell stocks from 3 of the 5 companies whose stocks he owns so that he can send his children to college. If he chooses the companies at random, what is the probability that the 3 companies will be the 3 with the best future earnings?

50. *Quality control* A sample of 6 fuses is drawn from a lot containing 10 good fuses and 2 defective fuses. Find the probability that the number of defective fuses is
    (a) exactly 1.   (b) at least 1.

Section 7.7

Income levels **Use the following information for Problems 51 and 52. Suppose people in a certain community are classified as being low-income (L), middle-income (M), or high-income (H). Suppose further that the probabilities for children being in a given state depend on which state their parents were in according to the following Markov chain transition matrix.**

Income level of parents	Income level of children		
	L	M	H
L	0.15	0.6	0.25
M	0.15	0.35	0.5
H	0	0.2	0.8

51. If the initial distribution probabilities of families in a certain population are [0.7 0.2 0.1], find the distribution for the next three generations.

52. Find the expected long-term probability distribution of families by income level.

7   CHAPTER TEST

A bag contains three white balls numbered 1, 2, 3 and four black balls numbered 4, 5, 6, 7. If one ball is drawn at random, find the probability of each event described in Problems 1–3.

1. (a) The ball is odd-numbered.
   (b) The ball is white.

2. (a) The ball is black and even-numbered.
   (b) The ball is white or even-numbered.

3. (a) The ball is red.
   (b) The ball is numbered less than 8.

A bag contains three white balls numbered 1, 2, 3 and four black balls numbered 4, 5, 6, 7. Two balls are drawn without replacement. Find the probability of each event described in Problems 4–9.

4. The sum of the numbers is 7.

5. Both balls are white.

6. (a) The first ball is white, and the second ball is black.
   (b) A white ball and a black ball are drawn.

7. Both balls are odd-numbered.

8. The second ball is white. (Use a tree.)

9. The first ball is black, given that the second ball is white.

10. A cat hits the letters on a computer keyboard three times. What is the probability that the word RAT appears?

11. In a certain region of the country with a large number of cars, 45% of the cars are from Asian manufacturers, 35% are American, and 20% are European. If 3 cars are chosen at random, what is the probability that 2 American cars are chosen?

12. In a group of 20 people, 15 are right-handed, 4 are left-handed, and 1 is ambidextrous. What is the probability that a person selected at random is
    (a) left-handed?   (b) ambidextrous?

13. In a group of 20 people, 15 are right-handed, 4 are left-handed, and 1 is ambidextrous. If 2 people are selected at random, without replacement, use a tree to find the following probabilities.
    (a) Both are left-handed.
    (b) One is right-handed, and one is left-handed.
    (c) Two are right-handed.
    (d) Two are ambidextrous.

14. The state of Arizona has a "6 of 42" game in which 6 balls are drawn without replacement from 42 balls numbered 1–42. The order in which the balls are drawn does not matter.
    (a) How many different drawing results are possible?
    (b) What is the probability that a person holding one ticket will win (match all the numbers drawn)?

15. The multistate "5 of 50" game draws 5 balls without replacement from 50 balls numbered 1–50.
    (a) How many different drawing results are possible if order does not matter?
    (b) What is the probability that a person holding one ticket will win (match all the numbers drawn)?

16. Computer chips come from two suppliers, with 80% coming from supplier 1 and 20% coming from supplier 2. Six percent of the chips from supplier 1 are defective, and 8% of the chips from supplier 2 are defective. If a chip is chosen at random, what is the probability that it is defective?

17. A placement test is given by a university to predict student success in a calculus course. On average, 70% of students who take the test pass it, and 87% of those who pass the test also pass the course, whereas 8% of those who fail the test pass the course.
    (a) What is the probability that a student taking the placement test and the calculus course will pass the course?
    (b) If a student passed the course, what is the probability that he or she passed the test?

18. Lactose intolerance affects about 20% of non-Hispanic White Americans and 50% of White Hispanic Americans. Nine percent of Americans are Hispanic Whites, and 75.6% are non-Hispanic Whites (*Source:* Jean Carper, "Eat Smart," *USA Weekend*). If a White American is chosen at random and is lactose-intolerant, what is the probability that he or she is Hispanic?

19. A car rental firm has 350 cars. Seventy of the cars have only defective windshield wipers and 25 have only defective tail lights. Two hundred of the cars have no defects; the remainder have other defects. What is the probability that a car chosen at random
    (a) has defective windshield wipers?
    (b) has defective tail lights?
    (c) does not have defective tail lights?

20. NACO Body Shops has found that 14% of the cars on the road need to be painted and that 3% need major body work and painting. What is the probability that a

car selected at random needs major body work if it is known that it needs to be painted?

21. Garage door openers have 10 on-off switches on the opener in the garage and on the remote control used to open the door. The door opens when the remote control is pressed and all the switches on both the opener and the remote agree.
    (a) How many different sequences of the on-off switches are possible on the door opener?
    (b) If the switches on the remote control are set at random, what is the probability that it will open a given garage door?
    (c) Remote controls and the openers in the garage for a given brand of door opener have the controls and openers matched in one of three sequences. If an owner does not change the sequence of switches on her or his remote control and opener after purchase, what is the probability that a different new remote control purchased from this company will open that owner's door?

(d) What should the owner of a new garage door opener do to protect the contents of his or her garage (and home)?

22. A publishing company has determined that a new edition of an existing mathematics textbook will be readopted by 80% of its current users and will be adopted by 7% of the users of other texts if the text is not changed radically. To determine whether it should change the book radically to attract more sales, the company uses Markov chains. Assume that the text in question currently has 25% of its possible market.
    (a) Create the transition matrix for this chain.
    (b) Find the probability vector for the text three editions later and, from that, determine the percent of the market for that future edition.
    (c) Find the steady-state vector for this text to determine what percent of its market this text will have if this policy is continued.

7 EXTENDED APPLICATIONS & GROUP PROJECTS

I. Phone Numbers

Primarily because of the rapid growth in the use of cellular phones, the number of available phone numbers had to be increased. This was accomplished by increasing the number of available area codes in the United States. Investigate how this was done by completing the following, remembering that an area code cannot begin with a 0 or a 1.
1. Prior to 1995, all area codes had a 0 or a 1 as the middle digit. How many area codes were available then?
2. Consult nanpa.com to see the one digit that is still not used as the middle digit of an area code.
3. Assuming that all the middle-digit restrictions except the one mentioned in Question 2 were removed in 1995, how many additional area codes became available?
4. The second set of three numbers, called the exchange numbers, cannot start with a 0 or 1 and cannot have a

1 as the third digit if the second digit is a 1. How many different exchange numbers are possible?
5. Each of the last four digits of a phone number can be any digit 0 through 9. Using this information and that from Question 4, in addition to the fact that the numbers 555-0100 through 555-0199 cannot be used because they are reserved for fictional use, determine how many phone numbers can be assigned to each area code.
6. In one proposal to expand the number of area codes, existing codes would be changed to "x9xx" (for example, Savannah's 912 would become 9912) and the new second digit would be opened to the other digits for a new range of area codes. If the same restrictions applied to the first digit and no other restrictions applied, how many more area codes than the number currently in use would this permit?

II. Quality Control

Drill-True manufactures drill bits at two locations: its original Birmingham factory built in 1958 and a new facility in Longview built in 2006. These facilities, respectively, produce 40% and 60% of Drill-True's output. The overall rate of defective bits is 2%, with Birmingham's defective rate equal to twice that of Longview. To better understand the quality of each facility's output, answer the following.

1. If a customer complains about an excessive number of defective items in a large shipment, which factory's manager should be contacted? *Hint:* For each factory, find the probability it produced the defective items.

2. If the overall defective rate remains at 2%, what output ratio (old/new) would make the probability of a defective item the same for both the older facility and the newer one?

3. Suppose the newer facility continues to produce 60% of Drill-True's output. What defective rate ratio (of old/new—currently that ratio is 2/1) would make the probability of a defective item the same for both the older facility and the newer one?

4. How can the results of Questions 2 and 3 help management pinpoint manufacturing problems identified by customer complaints of an excessive number of defective items?

III. Competition in the Telecommunications Industry

Of the 100,000 persons in a particular city who have cellular telephones, 10,000 use AT&T, 85,000 use Verizon, and 5000 use T-Mobile. A research firm has surveyed cell users to determine the level of customer satisfaction and to learn what company each expects to be using in a year's time. The results are depicted below.

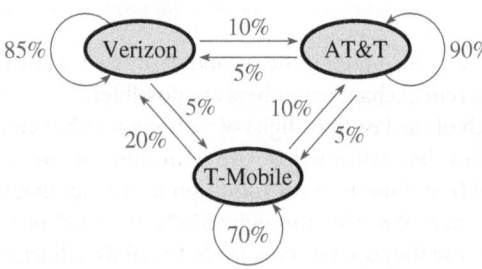

Although Verizon clearly dominates this city's cellular service now, the situation could change in the future.

1. Calculate the percent of the cell users who will be using each company in a year's time.
2. What will the long-term end result be if this pattern of change continues year after year?

3. In your answer to Question 1, you should have found that the number of T-Mobile customers increases in a year's time. Explain how this can happen when T-Mobile loses 30% of its customers and gains only 5% of AT&T's and Verizon's customers.

4. AT&T managers have been presented with two proposals for increasing its market share, and each proposal has the same cost. It is estimated that plan A would increase its customer retention rate from 90% to 95% through an enhanced customer services department. Plan B, an advertising campaign targeting Verizon's customers, is intended to increase the percent of people switching from Verizon to AT&T from 10% to 11%. If the company has sufficient funds to implement only one plan, which one would you advise it to approve and why?

5. Suppose that because of budget constraints, AT&T implements neither plan. A year later it faces the same choice. What should it do then?

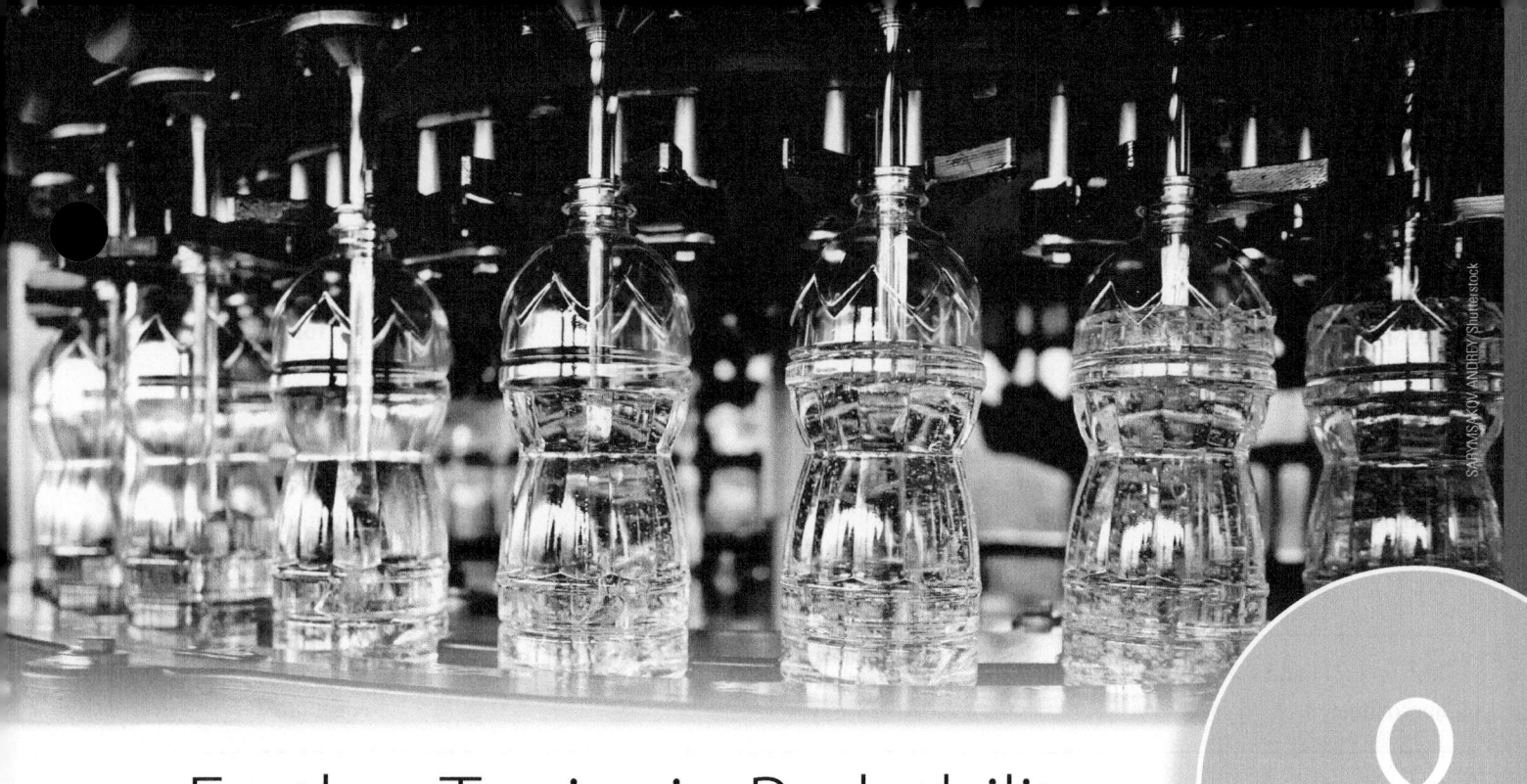

Further Topics in Probability; Data Description

8

The probability that the birth of three children will result in two boys and a girl can be found efficiently by treating it as a binomial experiment. In this chapter, we discuss how a set of data can be described with descriptive statistics, including mode, median, mean, and standard deviation. Descriptive statistics are used by businesses to summarize data about advertising effectiveness, production costs, and profit. We continue our discussion of probability by considering binomial probability distributions, discrete probability distributions, and normal probability distributions. Social and behavioral scientists collect data about carefully selected samples and use probability distributions to reach conclusions about the populations from which the samples were drawn.

The topics and some representative applications discussed in this chapter include the following.

Prerequisite Problem Type	For Section	Answer	Section for Review
If a fair coin is tossed 3 times, find $Pr(2 \text{ heads and } 1 \text{ tail})$.	8.1	$\frac{3}{8}$	7.4 Probability trees
Evaluate: (a) $\binom{4}{3}$ (b) $\binom{5}{2}$ (c) $\binom{24}{0}$	8.1 8.3	(a) 4 (b) 10 (c) 1	7.5 Counting: Permutations and Combinations
If $s^2 = 56/11$ and $s > 0$, approximate s.	8.2	2.26	2.1 Quadratic equations
Expand: (a) $(p + q)^2$ (b) $(p + q)^3$	8.3	(a) $p^2 + 2pq + q^2$ (b) $p^3 + 3p^2q + 3pq^2 + q^3$	0.5 Special products
Graph all real numbers satisfying: (a) $100 \le x \le 115$ (b) $-1 \le z \le 2$	8.4	(a) (b)	1.1 Linear inequalities
If 68% of the IQ scores of adults lie between 85 and 115, what is the probability that an adult chosen at random will have an IQ score between 85 and 115?	8.4	0.68	7.1 Probability

SECTION 8.1

Binomial Probability Experiments

OBJECTIVE

- To solve probability problems related to binomial experiments

APPLICATION PREVIEW

It has been determined with probability 0.01 that any child whose mother lives in a specific area near a chemical dump will be born with a birth defect. To find the probability that 2 of 10 children whose mothers live in the area will be born with birth defects, we could use a probability tree that lists all the possibilities and then select the paths that give 2 children with birth defects. However, it is easier to find the probability by using a formula developed in this section. (See Example 3.) This formula can be used when the probability experiment is a binomial probability experiment.

Suppose you have a coin that is biased so that when the coin is tossed, the probability of getting a head is 2/3 and the probability of getting a tail is 1/3. What is the probability of getting 2 heads in 3 tosses of this coin?

Suppose the question were "What is the probability that the first two tosses will be heads and the third will be tails?" In that case, the answer would be

$$\text{Pr(HHT)} = \frac{2}{3} \cdot \frac{2}{3} \cdot \frac{1}{3} = \frac{4}{27}$$

However, the original question did not specify the order, so we must consider other orders that will give us 2 heads and 1 tail. We can use a tree to find all the possibilities. (See Figure 8.1.) We can see that 3 paths through the tree correspond to 2 heads and 1 tail in 3 tosses. In this problem we can find the probability of 2 heads in 3 tosses by finding the probability for any one path of the tree (such as HHT) and then multiplying that probability by the number of paths that result in 2 heads. Notice that the 3 paths in the tree that result in 2 heads correspond to the different orders in which 2 heads and 1 tail can occur.

Because the probability for each successful path is $4/27$,

$$\text{Pr(2H and 1T)} = 3 \cdot \frac{4}{27} = \frac{4}{9}$$

Figure 8.1

This is the number of ways we can pick 2 positions out of 3 for the heads to occur, which is $_3C_2 = \binom{3}{2}$. Thus the probability of 2 heads resulting from 3 tosses is

$$\text{Pr(2H and 1T)} = \binom{3}{2} \frac{2}{3} \cdot \frac{2}{3} \cdot \frac{1}{3} = \frac{3!}{1!2!}\left(\frac{2}{3}\right)^2\left(\frac{1}{3}\right)^1 = \frac{4}{9}$$

The experiment just discussed (tossing a coin 3 times) is an example of a general class of experiments called **binomial probability experiments.** These experiments also are called **Bernoulli experiments,** or **Bernoulli trials,** after the 18th-century mathematician Jacob Bernoulli.

Binomial Probability Experiment

A **binomial probability experiment** satisfies the following properties:

1. There are n repeated trials of the experiment.
2. Each trial results in one of two outcomes, with one denoted success (S) and the other failure (F).
3. The trials are independent, with the probability of success, p, the same for every trial. The probability of failure is $q = 1 - p$ for every trial.
4. The probability of x successes in n trials is

$$Pr(x) = \binom{n}{x} p^x q^{n-x}$$

$Pr(x)$ is called a **binomial probability.**

EXAMPLE 1   Binomial Experiment

A die is rolled 4 times, and the number of times a 6 results is recorded.

(a) Is the experiment a binomial experiment?
(b) What is the probability that three 6s will result?

Solution

(a) Yes. There are 4 trials, resulting in success (a 6) or failure (not a 6). The result of each roll is independent of previous rolls; the probability of success on each roll is $p = 1/6$.
(b) There are $n = 4$ trials with Pr(rolling a 6) $= p = 1/6$ and Pr(not rolling a 6) $= q = 5/6$, and we seek the probability of $x = 3$ successes (because we want three 6s). Thus

$$Pr(\text{three 6s}) = \binom{4}{3}\left(\frac{1}{6}\right)^3\left(\frac{5}{6}\right)^1 = \frac{4!}{1!3!}\left(\frac{1}{216}\right)\left(\frac{5}{6}\right) = \frac{5}{324}$$

CHECKPOINT

Determine whether the following experiments satisfy the conditions for a binomial probability experiment.

1. A coin is tossed 8 times, and the number of times a tail occurs is recorded.
2. A die is rolled twice, and the sum that occurs is recorded.
3. A ball is drawn from a bag containing 4 white and 7 red balls and then replaced. This is done a total of 6 times, and the number of times a red ball is drawn is recorded.

EXAMPLE 2   Quality Control

A manufacturer of motorcycle parts guarantees that a box of 24 parts will contain at most 1 defective part. If the records show that the manufacturer's machines produce 1% defective parts, what is the probability that a box of parts will satisfy the guarantee?

Solution

The problem is a binomial experiment problem with $n = 24$ and (considering getting a defective part as a success) $p = 0.01$. Then the probability that the manufacturer will have no more than 1 defective part in a box is

$$Pr(x \leq 1) = Pr(0) + Pr(1) = \binom{24}{0}(0.01)^0(0.99)^{24} + \binom{24}{1}(0.01)^1(0.99)^{23}$$

$$\approx 0.9761$$

We interpret this to mean that there is a 97.61% likelihood that no more than 1 defective part will be in a box of 24 parts.

EXAMPLE **3** **Birth Defects** | APPLICATION PREVIEW |

It has been found that the probability is 0.01 that any child whose mother lives in an area near a chemical dump will be born with a birth defect. Suppose that 10 children with mothers living in the area are born in a given month.

(a) What is the probability that 2 of the 10 will be born with birth defects?
(b) What is the probability that at least 2 of them will have birth defects?

Solution

(a) Note that we may consider a child having a birth defect as a success for this problem even though it is not true in reality. Each of the 10 births is independent, with probability of success $p = 0.01$ and probability of failure $q = 0.99$. Therefore, the experiment is a binomial experiment, and

$$Pr(2) = \binom{10}{2}(0.01)^2(0.99)^8 = 0.00415$$

(b) The probability of at least 2 of the children having birth defects is

$$1 - [Pr(0) + Pr(1)] = 1 - \left[\binom{10}{0}(0.01)^0(0.99)^{10} + \binom{10}{1}(0.01)^1(0.99)^9\right]$$
$$= 1 - [0.90438 + 0.09135] = 0.00427$$

We interpret this to mean that there is a 0.427% likelihood that at least 2 of these children will have birth defects.

CHECKPOINT

4. A bag contains five red balls and three white balls. If 3 balls are drawn with replacement from the bag, what is the probability that
   (a) two balls will be red?   (b) at least two balls will be red?

Calculator Note

We can use a graphing calculator to find probabilities in binomial experiments as follows: Select binompdf in the DISTR menu and use binompdf(n,p,x) to find the probability of exactly x successes in n trials of a binomial experiment with the probability of success p. For example, if a binomial experiment has Pr(Success) = 0.3, then we can find Pr(10 successes in 25 trials) by using bimonpdf(25,0.3,10) and pressing ENTER to get probability 0.092 to three decimal places. [See Figure 8.2(a).]

To find the cumulative probability of at most k successes in n trials, we can use binomcdf(n,p,k). For example, Figure 8.2(b) shows that by using binomcdf(25,0.3,10), we find

Pr(at most 10 successes in 25 trials with $p = 0.3$) ≈ 0.902

See Appendix A, Section 8.1, for additional details.

Figure 8.2

(a)   (b)

Spreadsheet Note

We find binomial probabilities with Excel using the command =binomdist(k, n, p, false), where false gives the probability of obtaining exactly k successes, with n equal to the number of trials and p equal to the probability of success on each trial. Replacing false with true gives the probability of k or fewer successes.

The following spreadsheet gives the probability of exactly 3 heads in 6 tosses of a fair coin [using =binomdist(3,6,0.5,false) in cell B4] and the probability of 3 or fewer heads [using =binomdist(3,6,0.5,true) in cell B5]. See Appendix B, Section 8.1, or the Online Excel Guide for details of how Excel can be used to find binomial probabilities.

	A	B
1	Desired successes, k	3
2	Trials, n	6
3	Probability of success per trial, p	0.5
4	Pr(3 successes)	0.3125
5	Pr(3 or fewer successes)	0.65625

CHECKPOINT ANSWERS

1. A tail is a success on each trial, and all of the conditions of a binomial probability distribution are satisfied.
2. Each trial in this experiment does not result in a success or failure, so this is not a binomial probability experiment.
3. A red ball is a success on each trial, and each condition of a binomial distribution is satisfied.
4. (a) $\Pr(2 \text{ red}) = \dfrac{225}{512}$

   (b) $\Pr(\text{at least 2 red}) = \dfrac{175}{256}$

EXERCISES 8.1

1. Suppose a fair die is rolled 18 times.
   (a) What is the probability p that a 4 will occur each time the die is rolled?
   (b) What is the probability q that a 4 will not occur each time the die is rolled?
   (c) What is n for this experiment?
   (d) What is the probability that a 4 will occur 6 times in the 18 rolls?

2. Suppose a fair coin is tossed 12 times.
   (a) What is the probability p that a head will occur each time the coin is tossed?
   (b) What is the probability q that a head will not occur each time the coin is tossed?
   (c) What is n for this experiment?
   (d) What is the probability that a head will occur 6 times in the 12 tosses?

3. If the probability of success on each of 6 independent trials of an experiment is 0.3, what is the probability of
   (a) 4 successes?   (b) at least 1 success?

4. If the probability of success on each of 8 independent trials of an experiment is 0.4, what is the probability of
   (a) 5 successes?   (b) at most 7 successes?

5. Suppose a fair coin is tossed 6 times. What is the probability of
   (a) 6 heads?
   (b) 3 heads?
   (c) 2 heads?
   (d) at least 2 heads?

6. If a fair die is rolled 3 times, what is the probability that
   (a) a 5 will result 2 times out of the 3 rolls?
   (b) an odd number will result 2 times?
   (c) a number divisible by 3 will occur 3 times?
   (d) at least one 5 will occur?

7. A fair die is rolled 12 times. What is the probability that an "ace" (a 1) will occur
   (a) on any one roll?
   (b) 5 times in 12 rolls?
   (c) on none of the 12 rolls?

8. When a pair of dice is rolled, a sum of 5 occurs with probability 1/9. If these dice are rolled 13 times, find the probability that a sum of 5
   (a) occurs exactly 6 times.
   (b) does not occur.
   (c) occurs at least once.

In Problems 9 and 10, five balls are drawn with replacement from a bag containing 6 red balls and 4 black balls. Find the probability that

9. (a) 2 of the balls will be red.
    (b) all 5 balls will be black.
    (c) at least 3 of the balls will be black.
10. (a) all 5 balls will be red.
    (b) 4 of the balls will be black.
    (c) at least 2 red balls will be drawn.
11. Suppose a pair of dice is thrown 4 times. What is the probability that a sum of 9 occurs exactly 2 times?
12. If a pair of dice is thrown 4 times, find the probability that a sum of 7 occurs at least 3 times.
13. Suppose the probability that a marksman will hit a target each time he shoots is 0.85. If he fires 10 independent shots at a target, what is the probability that he will hit it 8 times?
14. The probability that a sharpshooter will hit a target each time he shoots is 0.98. What is the probability that he will hit the target 10 times in 10 independent shots?

APPLICATIONS

15. *Genetics* A family has 4 children. If the probability that each child is a girl is 0.5, what is the probability that
    (a) half of the children are girls?
    (b) all of the children are girls?
16. *Testing* A multiple-choice test has 10 questions and 5 choices for each question. If a student is totally unprepared and guesses on each question, what is the probability that
    (a) she will answer every question correctly?
    (b) she will answer half of the questions correctly?
17. *Management* The manager of a store buys marine radios in lots of 48. Suppose that on the average, 4 out of each group of 48 are defective. The manager randomly selects 4 radios out of the group to test. Assume independence.
    (a) What is the probability that he will find 2 defective radios?
    (b) What is the probability that he will find no defective radios?
18. *Quality control* A hospital buys blood pressure monitors in lots of 1000. On average, 1 out of 1000 is defective. If 10 are selected from one lot, what is the probability that none is defective?
19. *Safety devices* A fire detection device uses 4 temperature sensors that work independently so that any one of them can activate an alarm. If the temperature reaches 200°F, each sensor has probability 0.8 of activating the alarm.
    (a) Find the probability that the alarm is not activated when the temperature reaches 200°F.
    (b) Find the probability that the alarm is activated when the temperature reaches 200°F.

    (c) Find the probability that at least 2 sensors work when the temperature reaches 200°F.
20. *Genetics* The probability that a certain couple will have a blue-eyed child is 1/4, and they have 4 children. What is the probability that
    (a) 1 of their children has blue eyes?
    (b) 2 of their children have blue eyes?
    (c) at least 1 of their children has blue eyes?
21. *Health care* Suppose that 10% of the patients who have a certain disease die from it. If 5 patients have the disease, what is the probability that
    (a) exactly 2 patients will die from it?
    (b) no patients will die from it?
    (c) no more than 2 patients will die from it?
22. *Employee benefits* In a certain school district, 3% of the faculty use none of their sick days in a school year. Find the probability that 5 faculty members selected at random used no sick days in a given year.
23. *Genetics* If the ratio of boys born to girls born is 105 to 100 and if 6 children are born in a certain hospital in a day, what is the probability that 4 of them are boys?
24. *Biology* It has been determined empirically that the probability that a given cell will survive for a given period of time is 0.4. Find the probability that 3 out of 6 of these cells will survive for this period of time if the survival of the cells is independent.
25. *Insurance* If records indicate that 4 houses out of 1000 are expected to be damaged by fire in any year, what is the probability that a woman who owns 10 houses will have fire damage in 2 of them in a year?
26. *Psychology* Suppose 4 rats are placed in a T-maze in which they must turn right or left. If each rat makes a choice by chance, what is the probability that 2 of the rats will turn to the right?
27. *Sports* A baseball player has a lifetime batting average of 0.300. If each at bat is independent and he comes to bat 5 times in a given game, what is the probability that
    (a) he will get 3 hits?
    (b) he will get more than 3 hits?
28. *Quality control* If the probability of an automobile part being defective is 0.02, find the probability of getting exactly 3 defective parts in a sample of 12.
29. *Quality control* A company produces shotgun shells in batches of 300. A sample of 10 is tested from each batch, and if more than one defect is found, the entire batch is tested. If 1% of the shells are actually defective and we assume independence, what is the probability of
    (a) 0 defective shells in the sample?
    (b) 1 defective shell?
    (c) more than 1 defective shell?
30. *Quality control* A baseball pitching machine throws a bad pitch with probability 0.1. What is the probability that the machine will throw 5 or fewer bad pitches out of 20 pitches? (Set up only.)

31. *Testing* A quiz consists of 10 multiple-choice questions with 5 choices for each question. Suppose a student is sure of the first 5 answers and has each of the last 5 questions narrowed to 3 of the possible 5 choices. If the student guesses among the narrowed choices on the last 5 questions, find the probability of
    (a) passing the quiz (getting at least 60%).
    (b) getting at least a B (at least 80%).
32. *Demographics* In a certain community, 10% of the population is Jewish. A study shows that of 7 social service agencies, 4 have board presidents who are Jewish. Find the probability that this could happen by chance.
33. *Suicide rates* Suppose the probability of suicide among a certain age group is 0.003. If a randomly selected group of 100 Native Americans within this age group had no suicides, find the probability of this occurring by chance.

SECTION 8.2

OBJECTIVES

- To set up frequency tables and construct frequency histograms for sets of data
- To find the mode of a set of scores (numbers)
- To find the median of a set of scores
- To find the mean of a set of scores
- To find the range of a set of data
- To find the variance and standard deviation of a set of data

Data Description

APPLICATION PREVIEW

In modern business, a vast amount of data is collected for use in making decisions about the production, distribution, and sale of merchandise. Businesses also collect and summarize data about advertising effectiveness, production costs, sales, wages, and profits. Behavioral scientists attempt to reach conclusions about general behavioral characteristics by studying the characteristics of small samples of people. For example, election predictions are based on careful sampling of the votes; correct predictions are frequently announced on television even though only 5% of the vote has been counted. Life scientists can use statistical methods with laboratory animals to detect substances that may be dangerous to humans.

The following table gives the number of items that fail to meet quality standards for each of 16 sample production runs of 5000 units of a product. We will see in this section how to display these data and how to summarize them by finding the mean and standard deviation of the data. (See Example 8.)

Production Run	Defective Items	Production Run	Defective Items	Production Run	Defective Items
1	96	7	31	13	20
2	67	8	14	14	20
3	66	9	33	15	16
4	58	10	16	16	7
5	46	11	31		
6	48	12	30		

As mentioned in the Application Preview, we frequently collect data from a total group of interest (a **population**) or a subset of the population (a **sample**) so that we can better understand or make decisions about the group. The first steps after collecting a set of data are to organize it in a meaningful way and to make some preliminary calculations. These organizational steps are part of what is called **descriptive statistics.**

Statistical data that have been collected can be visualized with a graph that shows the relationships among various quantities. Statistical graphs include **pie charts** (see Figure 8.3), **bar graphs,** and **frequency histograms.**

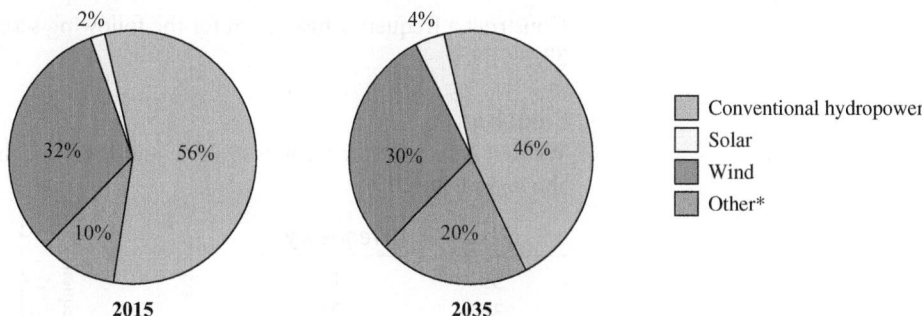

Figure 8.3

Renewable Power Generation

2015   2035

Conventional hydropower
Solar
Wind
Other*

*Other includes geothermal, municipal waste, and wood and other biomass products.
Source: U.S. Department of Energy

Bar graphs are useful in showing qualitative data as well as quantitative data. Bar graphs are often used to represent frequencies of data in different periods of time. Figure 8.4 is a bar graph that shows the U.S. unit sales of light duty trucks (one of the key indicators of energy demand) for the years from 2016 and projected to 2028 (*Source:* U.S. Energy Information Administration).

Figure 8.4

Spreadsheet Note

Bar graphs can be constructed using Excel. First enter the numbers or ranges in column A and the frequencies in column B. Then click *Insert*, the *bar graph* icon, and the 2-D bar graph icon; the graph will appear. See Appendix B, Section 8.2, or the Online Excel Guide for details.

Data can also be organized in a **frequency table,** which lists data values (individually or grouped in intervals called classes) along with their corresponding frequencies. A **frequency histogram** is a special bar graph that gives a graphical view of a frequency table. It is constructed by putting the data values or data classes along the horizontal axis and putting the frequencies with which they occur along the vertical axis.

EXAMPLE 1   **Frequency Histogram**

Construct a histogram from the frequency table.

Interval	Frequency
0–5	0
6–10	2
11–15	5
16–20	1
21–25	3

Solution

The histogram is shown in Figure 8.5.

Figure 8.5

EXAMPLE 2 **Frequency Histogram**

Construct a frequency histogram for the following scores: 38, 37, 36, 40, 35, 40, 38, 37, 36, 37, 39, 38.

Solution

We first construct the frequency table and then use the table to construct the histogram shown in Figure 8.6.

Score	Frequency
35	1
36	2
37	3
38	3
39	1
40	2

Figure 8.6

Calculator Note

To use a graphing calculator to graph the histogram of a set of data, we do the following.
1. Enter the numbers in list L1 and their frequencies in L2.
2. Press 2nd STAT PLOT, Plot1; select On; highlight the histogram icon; and then put L1 in Xlist: and L2 in Freq:.
3. Press ZOOM, 9:ZoomStat to get the histogram.
See Appendix A, Section 8.2, for details.

Measures of Central Tendency

A set of data can be described by listing all the scores or by drawing a frequency histogram. But we often want to describe a set of scores by giving the *average score* or the typical score in the set. Three types of measures are called *averages,* or measures of central tendency: **mode, median,** and **mean.**

To determine what value represents the most "typical" score in a set of scores, we use the **mode** of the scores.

Mode

The **mode** of a set of scores is the score that occurs most frequently. The mode of a set of scores may not be unique.

The mode is the most popular score—the one that is most likely to occur. The mode can be readily determined from a frequency table or frequency histogram because it is determined according to the frequencies of the scores. The score associated with the highest bar on a histogram is the mode.

EXAMPLE 3 **Mode**

(a) Find the mode of the following scores: 10, 4, 3, 6, 4, 2, 3, 4, 5, 6, 8, 10, 2, 1, 4, 3.
(b) Determine the mode of the scores shown in the histogram in Figure 8.7.
(c) Find the mode of the following scores: 4, 3, 2, 4, 6, 5, 5, 7, 6, 5, 7, 3, 1, 7, 2.

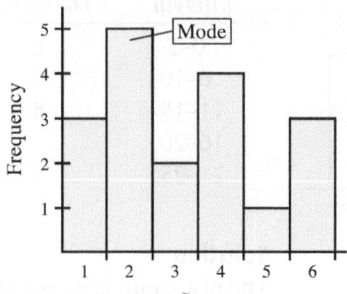

Figure 8.7

Solution

(a) Arranging the scores in order gives: 1, 2, 2, 3, 3, 3, 4, 4, 4, 4, 5, 6, 6, 8, 10, 10. The mode is 4 because it occurs more frequently than any other score.

(b) The most frequent score, as the histogram reveals, is 2.

(c) Arranging the scores in order gives 1, 2, 2, 3, 3, 4, 4, 5, 5, 5, 6, 6, 7, 7, 7. Both 5 and 7 occur three times. Thus they are both modes. This set of data is said to be *bimodal* because it has two modes.

Although the mode of a set of scores tells us the most frequent score, it does not always represent the typical performance, or central tendency, of the set of scores. For example, the scores 2, 3, 3, 3, 5, 8, 9, 10, 13 have a mode of 3. But 3 is not a good measure of central tendency for this set of scores, for it is nowhere near the middle of the distribution.

One value that gives a better measure of central tendency is the **median.**

Median

> The **median** is the score or point above and below which an equal number of the scores lie when the scores are arranged in ascending or descending order.
>
> If there is an odd number of scores, we find the median by ranking the scores from smallest to largest and picking the middle score.
>
> If the number of scores is even, there will be no middle score when the scores are ranked, so the *median* is the point that is the average *of the two middle scores.*

EXAMPLE 4   Median

Find the median of each of the following sets of scores.

(a) 2, 3, 16, 5, 15, 38, 18, 17, 12

(b) 3, 2, 6, 8, 12, 4, 3, 2, 1, 6

Solution

(a) We rank the scores from smallest to largest: 2, 3, 5, 12, 15, 16, 17, 18, 38. The median is the middle score, which is 15. Note that there are 4 scores above and 4 scores below 15.

(b) We rank the scores from smallest to largest: 1, 2, 2, 3, 3, 4, 6, 6, 8, 12. The two scores that lie in the middle of the distribution are 3 and 4. Thus the median is a point that is midway between 3 and 4; that is, it is the arithmetic average of 3 and 4. The median is

$$\frac{3 + 4}{2} = \frac{7}{2} = 3.5$$

In this case we say that the median is a point because there is no *score* that is 3.5.

The median is a measure of central tendency that is easy to find and that is not influenced by extreme scores. On a histogram, the area to the left of the median is equal to the area to the right of the median. The scores in the histogram shown in Figure 8.8 are 1, 1, 1, 2, 2, 2, 2, 2, 3, 3, 4, 4, 4, 4, 5, 6, 6, 6, and the median is 3. Note that the area of the histogram to the left of 3 equals the area to the right of 3.

Some calculators have keys or functions for finding the median of a set of data. Use of such calculators is valuable when the set of data is large.

The median is the most easily interpreted measure of central tendency, and it is the best indicator of central tendency when the set of scores contains extreme values. However, the most frequently used measure of central tendency is the **mean.**

Figure 8.8

Mean

> Suppose x is a variable representing the individual scores in a sample of n scores and Σx represents the sum of the scores. Then the symbol $\bar{x}$ is used to represent the **mean** of a set of scores in a sample and the formula for the mean is
>
> $$\bar{x} = \frac{\text{sum of scores}}{\text{number of scores}} = \frac{\Sigma x}{n}$$

The mean is used most often as a measure of central tendency because it is more useful than the median in the general applications of statistics.

EXAMPLE 5 Mean

Find the mean of the following sample of numbers: 12, 8, 7, 10, 6, 14, 7, 6, 12, 9.

Solution

$$\bar{x} = \frac{\Sigma x}{10} = \frac{12 + 8 + 7 + 10 + 6 + 14 + 7 + 6 + 12 + 9}{10} = \frac{91}{10}$$

so $\bar{x} = 9.1$.

Note that the mean need not be one of the numbers (scores) given. ■

If the data are given in a frequency table or a frequency histogram, we can use a more efficient formula for finding the mean.

Mean of Grouped Data

If a set of n scores is grouped into k classes with x representing the score in a given class and $f(x)$ representing the number of scores in that class, then $n = \Sigma f(x)$ and the mean of the data is given by

$$\bar{x} = \frac{\Sigma(x \cdot f(x))}{\Sigma f(x)}$$

with each value of x used once.

The following table gives a set of data values, x, and their frequencies.

x	1	2	3	4
f(x)	3	1	4	2

The mean of the data in this frequency table is

$$\bar{x} = \frac{\Sigma(x \cdot f(x))}{\Sigma f(x)} = \frac{1(3) + 2(1) + 3(4) + 4(2)}{3 + 1 + 4 + 2} = 2.5$$

EXAMPLE 6 Test Scores

Find the mean of the following sample of test scores for a math class.

Scores	Class Marks	Frequencies
40–49	44.5	2
50–59	54.5	0
60–69	64.5	6
70–79	74.5	12
80–89	84.5	8
90–99	94.5	2

Solution

For the purpose of finding the mean of interval data, we assume that all scores within an interval are represented by the class mark (midpoint of the interval). Thus

$$\bar{x} = \frac{(44.5)(2) + (54.5)(0) + (64.5)(6) + (74.5)(12) + (84.5)(8) + (94.5)(2)}{30} = 74.5 \ ■$$

If a set of data is represented by a histogram, the mean of the data is at the point where the histogram could be balanced. The mean of the data in Figure 8.9 is

$$\frac{1(3) + 2(6) + 3(2) + 4(4) + 5(1) + 6(2)}{3 + 6 + 2 + 4 + 1 + 2} = \frac{54}{18} = 3$$

Figure 8.9

Any of the three measures of central tendency (mode, median, mean) may be referred to as an average. The measure of central tendency that should be used with data depends on the purpose for which the data were collected. The mode is the number that is used if we want the most popular value. For example, the mode salary for a company is the salary that is received by most of the employees. The median salary for the company is the salary that falls in the middle of the distribution. The mean salary is the arithmetic average of the salaries. It is quite possible that the mode, median, and mean salaries for a company will be different. Figure 8.10 illustrates how the mode, median, and mean salaries might look for a company.

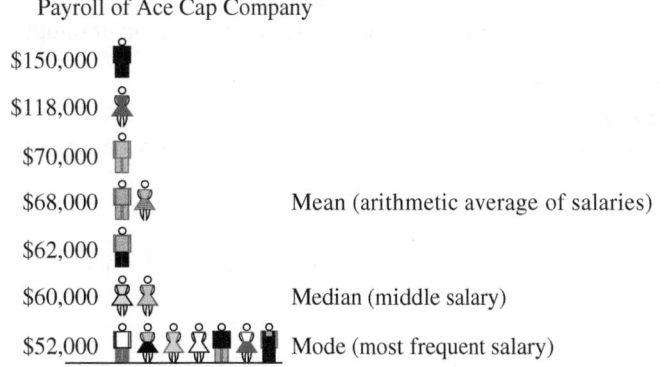

Figure 8.10

Which of the three measures represents the "average" salary? To say that the average salary is $68,000 (the mean) helps conceal two things: the bosses' (or owners') large salaries ($150,000 and $118,000) and the laborers' comparatively small salaries ($52,000). The mode tells us that the most common salary in this company is $52,000. The median gives us more information about these salaries than any other single figure. It tells us that if the salaries are ranked from lowest to highest, then the salary that lies in the middle is $60,000.

Because any of the three measures may be referred to as the average of a set of data, we must be careful to avoid being misled. The owner of the Ace Cap Company will probably state that the average salary for his company is $68,000 because it makes it appear that he pays high salaries. The local union president will likely claim that the mode ($52,000) is the "average" salary. Advertising agencies may make use of an "average" that will make their product appear in the best light. We run the risk of being misled if we do not know which average is being cited.

One reason we may be misled concerning these three measures is that they frequently fall very close to each other. Also, since the mean is the most frequently used of the three, we tend to associate it with the word *average*.

CHECKPOINT

Consider the data 10, 12, 12, 8, 30, 12, 8, 10, 5, 23.
1. Find the mode.
2. Find the mean.
3. Find the median.

Measures of Dispersion

Although the mean of a set of data is useful in locating the center of the distribution of the data, it doesn't tell us as much about the distribution as we might think at first. For example, a basketball team with five 6-foot players is quite different from a team with one 6-foot, two 5-foot, and two 7-foot players. The distributions of the heights of these teams differ not in the mean height but in how the heights *vary* from the mean.

One measure of how a distribution varies is the **range** of the distribution.

Range	The **range** of a set of numbers is the difference between the largest and smallest numbers in the set.

Consider the following set of heights of players on a basketball team, in inches: 69, 70, 75, 69, 73, 78, 74, 73, 78, 71. The range of this set of heights is $78 - 69 = 9$ inches. Note that this range is determined by only two numbers and does not give any information about how the other heights vary.

To measure how a set of data varies in relation to its mean, we might calculate the deviation of each score from the mean, $(x - \bar{x})$, and then average these deviations. However, this result is always zero. (Try it!) In an effort to find a meaningful measure of dispersion about the mean, statisticians developed the **variance,** which uses the squares of these deviations (to make them all positive). We find the variance of sample data by summing the squared deviations and dividing the sum by $n - 1$.

To get a measure comparable to these original deviations before they were squared, we introduce the **standard deviation,** which is the square root of the variance. The formulas for the variance and standard deviation of sample data follow.

Variance and Standard Deviation	$$\text{Sample Variance } s^2 = \frac{\Sigma(x - \bar{x})^2}{n - 1}$$ $$\text{Sample Standard Deviation } s = \sqrt{s^2} = \sqrt{\frac{\Sigma(x - \bar{x})^2}{n - 1}}$$

The standard deviation of a sample is a measure of the concentration of the scores about their mean. The smaller the standard deviation, the closer the scores lie to the mean. For example, the histograms in Figure 8.11 describe two sets of data with the same means and the same ranges. From looking at the histograms, we see that more of the data are concentrated about the mean $\bar{x} = 4$ in Figure 8.11(b) than in Figure 8.11(a). In the following example we will see that the standard deviation is smaller for the data in Figure 8.11(b) than in Figure 8.11(a).

EXAMPLE 7   Standard Deviation

Figure 8.11(a) is the histogram for the sample data 1, 1, 1, 3, 3, 4, 4, 5, 6, 6, 7, 7. Figure 8.11(b) is the histogram for the data 1, 2, 3, 3, 4, 4, 4, 4, 5, 5, 6, 7. Both sets of data have a range of 6 and a mean of 4. Find the standard deviations of these samples.

Figure 8.11   (a)   (b)

Solution

For the sample data in Figure 8.11(a), we have

$$\Sigma(x - \bar{x})^2 = (1 - 4)^2 + (1 - 4)^2 + (1 - 4)^2 + (3 - 4)^2 + (3 - 4)^2 + (4 - 4)^2$$
$$+ (4 - 4)^2 + (5 - 4)^2 + (6 - 4)^2 + (6 - 4)^2 + (7 - 4)^2 + (7 - 4)^2$$
$$= 56$$

$$s^2 = \frac{\Sigma(x - \bar{x})^2}{n - 1} = \frac{56}{11} \approx 5.0909 \quad \text{and} \quad s = \sqrt{s^2} = \sqrt{\frac{56}{11}} \approx 2.26$$

For the sample data in Figure 8.11(b), we have

$$\Sigma(x - \bar{x})^2 = (1 - 4)^2 + (2 - 4)^2 + (3 - 4)^2 + (3 - 4)^2 + (4 - 4)^2 + (4 - 4)^2$$
$$+ (4 - 4)^2 + (4 - 4)^2 + (5 - 4)^2 + (5 - 4)^2 + (6 - 4)^2 + (7 - 4)^2$$
$$= 30$$

$$s^2 = \frac{30}{11} \approx 2.7273 \quad \text{and} \quad s = \sqrt{\frac{30}{11}} \approx 1.65$$

Calculator Note   To find the mean, standard deviation, and other statistical measures with a graphing calculator, select STAT, then 1: Edit, and enter the data in list L1. Then select STAT, CALC, 1:1-Var Stats, and press Enter to obtain the mean, standard deviation, and other measures for those data. For example, if we enter in list L1 the heights of the basketball team mentioned earlier (69, 70, 75, 69, 73, 78, 74, 73, 78, and 71 inches) and select 1-Var Stats, we find $\bar{x} = 73$ inches and the sample standard deviation is $s = 3.333$ inches. See Appendix A, Section 8.2, for more details. ∎

Spreadsheet Note   The mean, standard deviation, and other statistical measures can be found with individual formulas in Excel. If the data are entered in row 1 and we denote as n1 the cell of the last data point, then the sample mean, standard deviation, and median can be found with Excel by using the formulas =average(A1:n1), =stdev(A1:n1), and =median(A1:n1). Appendix B, Section 8.2, and the Online Excel Guide show the details for finding these measures for raw and grouped data. ∎

 EXAMPLE 8 **Quality Control** | APPLICATION PREVIEW |

The following table gives the number of items that fail to meet quality standards for each of 16 sample production runs of 5000 units of a product.
(a) Construct a bar graph to represent the number of defective items for each production run.
(b) Find the mean number of defective items per production run for the 16 runs.
(c) What is the standard deviation of the data?

Production Run	Defective Items	Production Run	Defective Items	Production Run	Defective Items
1	96	7	31	13	20
2	67	8	14	14	20
3	66	9	33	15	16
4	58	10	16	16	7
5	46	11	31		
6	48	12	30		

Solution
(a) The bar graph displaying the number of defective items per production run is shown in Figure 8.12.

Figure 8.12

(b) The mean number of defective items per production run for these 16 runs is

$$\bar{x} = \frac{\Sigma x}{n} = \frac{599}{16} = 37.4375 \approx 37.4$$

(c) Using technology gives the standard deviation of the number of defective items per production run for these 16 runs:

$$s = 24.341922 \approx 24.3$$

This shows that the number of defective items per production run varied considerably over these production runs.

CHECKPOINT

4. Find the standard deviation of the data:

10, 12, 12, 8, 30, 12, 8, 10, 5, 23

CHECKPOINT
ANSWERS

1. 12
2. 13
3. 11
4. $s \approx 7.63$

EXERCISES 8.2

Construct frequency histograms for the data given in Problems 1–8.

1.

Score	Frequency
12	2
13	3
14	4
15	3
16	1

2.

Score	Frequency
22	1
23	4
24	3
25	2
26	3

3.

x	3	4	5	6	7	8	9	10	11	12
$f(x)$	6	0	5	3	4	3	2	1	0	4

4.

x	5	6	8	9	11	12
$f(x)$	3	4	2	7	3	2

5. 3, 2, 5, 6, 3, 2, 6, 5, 4, 2, 1, 6
6. 5, 4, 6, 5, 4, 6, 3, 6, 5, 4, 1, 7

7.

Interval	Frequency
1–4	1
5–8	0
9–12	2
13–16	3
17–20	1

8.

Interval	Frequency
10–14	2
15–19	4
20–24	3
25–29	2
30–34	3

Find the modes of the sets of scores in Problems 9–12.

9. 3, 4, 3, 2, 2, 3, 5, 7, 6, 2, 3
10. 5, 8, 10, 12, 5, 4, 6, 3, 5
11. 14, 17, 13, 16, 15, 12, 13, 12, 13
12. 5, 7, 7, 7, 9, 12, 4, 6, 6, 8

Find the medians of the sets of scores in Problems 13–16.

13. 1, 3, 6, 7, 5
14. 2, 1, 3, 4, 2, 1, 2
15. 4, 7, 9, 18, 36, 14, 3, 12
16. 1, 0, 2, 1, 1, 0, 2, 14, 37

Find the modes, medians, and means of the scores in Problems 17–22.

17. 3, 2, 1, 6, 8, 12, 14, 2
18. 5, 8, 7, 6, 1, 1, 31
19. 14, 17, 20, 31, 17, 42
20. 3.2, 3.2, 3.5, 3.7, 3.4
21. 2.8, 6.4, 5.3, 5.3, 6.8
22. 1.14, 2.28, 7.58, 6.32, 5.17
23. Use class marks to find the mean, mode, and median of the data in Problem 7.
24. Use class marks to find the mean, mode, and median of the data in Problem 8.

In Problems 25–28, find the range of the set of numbers given.

25. 3, 5, 7, 8, 2, 11, 6, 5
26. 5, 1, 3, 1.4, 6.3, 8
27. −1, 2, 4, 3, 6, 11, −3, 4, 2
28. 2, 3, 3, 3, 3, 3, 9

Find the mean, variance, and standard deviation of each of the sets of sample data in Problems 29–32.

29. 5, 7, 1, 3, 0, 8, 6, 2
30. 7, 13, 5, 11, 8, 10, 9
31. 11, 12, 13, 14, 15, 16, 17
32. 4, 3, 6, 7, 8, 9, 12

In Problems 33–36, find the mean and standard deviation of the sample data in each table.

33.

x	1	2	3	4	5
$f(x)$	3	1	4	2	1

34.

x	3	4	5	6	8
$f(x)$	1	3	4	1	3

35.

x	3	4	5	6	7	8	9	10	11	12
$f(x)$	6	0	5	3	4	3	2	1	0	4

36.

x	5	6	7	8	9	10	11	12	13	14	15
$f(x)$	3	2	1	0	2	5	3	1	2	4	6

APPLICATIONS

Assume all data are sample data.

37. *Centenarians* The following table shows the U.S. population (in thousands) of individuals age 100 years or older for selected years from 2010 and projected to 2050.

Year	Centenarians (in 1000s)	Year	Centenarians (in 1000s)
2010	79	2035	239
2015	105	2040	298
2020	135	2045	409
2025	175	2050	601
2030	208		

Source: U.S. Census Bureau

(a) Display these data with a bar graph.
(b) Find the mean and standard deviation of these data for the U.S. population of centenarians.

38. *Youth population* The population (in millions) of Americans under the age of 18 for years from 2016 and projected through 2050 is shown in the table. Construct a bar graph of the population for the given time intervals.

Year	Population (millions)	Year	Population (millions)
2016–2020	75.5	2036–2040	82.5
2021–2025	77	2041–2045	83.5
2026–2030	79	2046–2050	85
2031–2035	81		

Source: U.S. Census Bureau

39. *Cell phones* The table summarizes the number of mobile phones per 100 people in the population of each of the countries with at least 100 mobile phones per 100 people. Construct a frequency histogram of the number of mobile phones per 100 people.

Number of Mobile Phones per 100 People Population	Number of Countries
100–119	20
120–139	14
140–159	6
160–179	2
180–199	1
200–219	1

Source: www.cia.gov/library/publications/the-world-factbook

40. *Product testing* A taxi company tests a new brand of tires by putting a set of four on each of three taxis. The table indicates the numbers of miles the tires lasted. Display these data with a histogram and find the mode, median, and mean number of miles the tires lasted.

Number of Miles	Number of Tires
30,000	4
32,000	2
34,000	3
36,000	2
38,000	1

41. *Real estate* Suppose you live in a neighborhood with a few expensive homes and many modest homes. Which measure would you give as the "average" property value
(a) if you wanted to impress people with the neighborhood where you lived? Explain.
(b) if you wanted to convince the property tax committee that property values aren't very high in your neighborhood? Explain.
(c) if you wanted to give the most representative "average" property value for your neighborhood? Explain.

42. *Birth weights* The birth weights (in kilograms) of a sample of 160 children are given in the table. Find the mean and standard deviation of the weights.

Weight (kg)	Frequency	Weight (kg)	Frequency
2.0	4	3.5	26
2.3	12	3.8	20
2.6	20	4.1	16
2.9	26	4.4	10
3.2	20	4.7	6

43. *Renewable energy* The following table gives projections for 2062 of the percent of energy that will be renewable in the top five world regions.
   (a) Find the mean and standard deviation of the data.
   (b) Does the standard deviation indicate that the percent of energy that is renewable will be widely distributed in these regions?

Region	% Renewable
Latin America	87
Africa	81
Europe	55
Middle East	49
United States	45

Source: International Energy Agency, The Discover Almanac 2062

44. *Malpractice* Four states had recent ballot measures about imposing limits on damage awards or attorneys' fees in medical malpractice cases. Find the mean and the standard deviation of the numbers of voters per state in favor of this measure, using the data in the table.

State	Number in Favor
Florida	4,435,179
Nevada	465,321
Oregon	744,267
Wyoming	15,628

Source: The *New York Times*

45. *Aged dependency ratio* The aged dependency ratio, the ratio of the U.S. population ages 65 or over to that of ages 20–64, can be used to estimate the number of Medicare enrollees per worker. The following table shows Social Security Administration data for this ratio every 5 years from 1945 and projected to 2050. Construct a frequency histogram for these ratios using intervals of width 0.05.

Year	Ratio	Year	Ratio
1945	0.124	2000	0.209
1950	0.138	2005	0.206
1955	0.157	2010	0.218
1960	0.173	2015	0.247
1965	0.182	2020	0.285
1970	0.185	2025	0.328
1975	0.190	2030	0.364
1980	0.196	2035	0.384
1985	0.202	2040	0.387
1990	0.209	2045	0.383
1995	0.214	2050	0.385

46. *Beet sugar shipments* The following table gives the total value (in millions of dollars) of shipments of beet sugar manufactured in the United States from 2008 and projected to 2020. Construct a frequency histogram of the values, using intervals of $500 million and starting at $3000 million.

Year	$million	Year	$million
2008	3126	2015	5219
2009	3221	2016	5295
2010	3525	2017	5347
2011	4223	2018	5491
2012	4250	2019	5587
2013	4682	2020	5560
2014	4991		

(*Source:* statista.com)

47. *Disposable income* Disposable income is the amount left after taxes have been paid. The following table gives the U.S. per capita disposable income (in thousands of dollars) for selected years from 2016 and projected to 2030. For these data, find the (a) mean and (b) standard deviation.

Per Capita Disposable Income (thousands of dollars)

Year	Dollars (1000's)	Year	Dollars (1000's)
2016	44.2	2024	49.7
2018	45.5	2026	51.0
2020	47.0	2028	52.5
2022	48.3	2030	53.8

Source: U.S. Energy Administration

48. *Salaries* S & S Printing has 15 employees and 5 job classifications. Positions and wages for these employees are given in the table.

Job	Number	Weekly Salary
Supervisor	1	$2400
Printers	8	1200
Designers	3	1500
Secretaries	2	1100
Web Developer	1	1640

(a) What is the mean salary per job classification?

(b) What is the mean salary per person?

49. *Salaries* Suppose a company has 10 employees—1 earning $160,000, 1 earning $120,000, 2 earning $60,000, 1 earning $40,000, and 5 earning $32,000.

(a) What is the mean salary for the company?

(b) What is the median salary?

(c) What is the mode of the salaries?

50. *Sales* A new car with a $38,000 list price can be bought for different prices from different dealers. In one city, the car can be bought for $36,400 from 2 dealers, for $36,000 from 1 dealer, for $35,600 from 3 dealers, for $35,200 from 2 dealers, and for $35,000 from 2 dealers. What are the mean and standard deviation of this sample of car prices?

51. *Insurance rates* The table gives the monthly insurance rates for a $100,000 life insurance policy for smokers ages 35–49.

(a) Find the mean monthly insurance rate for these ages.

(b) Find the standard deviation of the monthly insurance rates for these ages.

Age (years)	Monthly Insurance Rate (dollars)	Age (years)	Monthly Insurance Rate (dollars)
35	17.32	43	23.71
36	17.67	44	25.11
37	18.02	45	26.60
38	18.46	46	28.00
39	19.07	47	29.40
40	19.95	48	30.80
41	21.00	49	32.55
42	22.22		

Source: American General Life Insurance Company

52. *Youth population* The population (in millions) of Americans under the age of 18 for selected years from 2015 and projected through 2060 is shown in the following table.

(a) Find the mean of this population over this period.

(b) Find the standard deviation of this population over this period.

Year	Population (millions)	Year	Population (millions)
2015	75	2040	83
2020	76	2045	84
2025	78	2050	86
2030	80	2055	88
2035	82	2060	89

Source: U.S. Census Bureau

53. *Public school enrollments* The following table gives the enrollments in U.S. public schools, in thousands, for selected years from 1899 and projected to 2022.

(a) What is the mean public school enrollment for these years?

(b) What is the standard deviation of the public school enrollment for these years?

School Year	Enrollment (1000s)	School Year	Enrollment (1000s)
1899–1900	15,503	1969–1970	45,550
1909–1910	17,814	1979–1980	41,651
1919–1920	21,578	1989–1990	40,543
1929–1930	25,678	1999–2000	46,857
1939–1940	25,434	2009–2010	49,373
1949–1950	25,111	2020–2021	52,688
1959–1960	35,182	2021–2022	53,113

Source: National Center for Education Statistics, Department of Education

54. *Private school enrollments* The table gives the private school enrollments as percents of total school enrollment (actual and projected) for selected school years from 1899–1900 to 2021–2022. Find the mean and standard deviation of the percents of private school enrollments for the given school years.

School Year	% Private	School Year	% Private
1899–1900	8.0	1969–1970	10.8
1909–1910	8.0	1979–1980	10.7
1919–1920	7.3	1989–1990	12.1
1929–1930	9.4	1999–2000	11.4
1939–1940	9.3	2009–2010	9.8
1949–1950	11.9	2020–2021	9.1
1959–1960	13.9	2021–2022	9.1

Source: U.S. Department of Education

SECTION 8.3

Discrete Probability Distributions; The Binomial Distribution

OBJECTIVES

- To verify that a table or formula describes a discrete probability distribution
- To compute the mean and expected value of a discrete probability distribution
- To make decisions using expected value
- To find the variance and standard deviation of a discrete probability distribution
- To find the mean and standard deviation of a binomial distribution
- To expand a binomial to a power, using the binomial formula

APPLICATION PREVIEW

The T. J. Cooper Insurance Company insures 100,000 automobiles. Company records over a 5-year period give the following payouts and their probabilities during each 6-month period.

Payment	$500,000	$250,000	$125,000	$25,000	$5000
Probability	0.0001	0.001	0.002	0.008	0.02

The company can determine how much to charge each driver by finding the expected value of the discrete probability distribution determined by this table. (See Example 3.)

A special discrete probability distribution, the binomial probability distribution, can be used to find the expected value for binomial experiments. For example, clinical studies have shown that 5% of photorefractive keratectomy procedures are unsuccessful in correcting nearsightedness. Because each eye operation is independent, the number of failures follows the binomial distribution, and we can easily find the expected number of unsuccessful operations per 1000 operations. (See Example 7.) In this section, we will determine if a table or formula describes a probability distribution, compute the mean and standard deviation of a binomial distributions, and make decisions using expected value.

Discrete Probability Distribution

If a player rolls a die and receives $1 for each dot on the face she rolls, the amount of money won on one roll can be represented by the variable x. If the die is rolled once, the following table gives the possible outcomes of the experiment and their probabilities.

x	1	2	3	4	5	6
$Pr(x)$	1/6	1/6	1/6	1/6	1/6	1/6

Note that we have used the variable x to denote the possible numerical outcomes of this experiment. Because x results from a probability experiment, we call x a **random variable,** and because there are a finite number of possible values of x, we say that x is a discrete random variable. Whenever all possible values of a random variable can be listed (or counted), the random variable is a **discrete random variable.**

If x represents the possible number of heads that can occur in the toss of four coins, we can use the sample space {0, 1, 2, 3, 4} to list the possible numerical values of x. Table 8.1 shows the values the random variable of the coin-tossing experiment can assume and how the probability is distributed over these values.

TABLE 8.1

x	$Pr(x)$
0	1/16
1	1/4
2	3/8
3	1/4
4	1/16

Discrete Probability Distribution

A table, graph, or formula that assigns to each value of a **discrete random variable** x a probability $Pr(x)$ describes a **discrete probability distribution** if the following two conditions hold.

(i) $0 \leq Pr(x) \leq 1$, for any value of x.
(ii) The sum of all the probabilities is 1. We use Σ to denote "the sum of" and write $\Sigma Pr(x) = 1$ where the sum is taken over all values of x.

EXAMPLE 1 ## Discrete Probability Distribution

An experiment consists of selecting a ball from a bag containing 15 balls, each with a number 1 through 5. If the probability of selecting a ball with the number x on it is $\Pr(x) = x/15$, where x is an integer and $1 \leq x \leq 5$, verify that $f(x) = \Pr(x) = x/15$ describes a discrete probability distribution for the random variable x.

Solution

For each integer x, with $1 \leq x \leq 5$, $\Pr(x) = x/15$ satisfies $0 \leq \Pr(x) \leq 1$.

$$\Sigma \Pr(x) = \Pr(1) + \Pr(2) + \Pr(3) + \Pr(4) + \Pr(5)$$

$$= \frac{1}{15} + \frac{2}{15} + \frac{3}{15} + \frac{4}{15} + \frac{5}{15} = 1$$

Hence $\Pr(x) = x/15$ describes a discrete probability distribution.

Probability Density Histograms

We can visualize the possible values of a discrete random variable and their associated probabilities by constructing a graph. This graph, called a **probability density histogram,** is designed so that centered over each value of the discrete random variable x along the horizontal axis is a bar having width equal to 1 unit and height (and thus, area) equal to $\Pr(x)$. Figure 8.13 gives the probability density histogram for the experiment described in Example 1.

Figure 8.13

Mean and Expected Value

We found the **mean** of a set of n numbers grouped into k classes by using the formula

$$\frac{\Sigma[x \cdot f(x)]}{n}, \text{ or with } \Sigma\left[x \cdot \frac{f(x)}{n}\right]$$

We can find the **theoretical mean** of a probability distribution by using the values x of the random variable and the probabilities that those values will occur. This mean is called the **expected value** of x.

Mean and Expected Value

If x is a discrete random variable with values $x_1, x_2, \ldots, x_n$, then the **mean, μ,** of the distribution is the **expected value of x,** denoted by **$E(x)$,** and is given by

$$\mu = E(x) = \Sigma[x\Pr(x)] = x_1\Pr(x_1) + x_2\Pr(x_2) + \cdots + x_n\Pr(x_n)$$

EXAMPLE 2	**Testing**

A series of five-question multiple choice quizzes has 5 possible answers to each question. If a student guesses the answer to each question, the possible numbers of answers she could get correct and the probability of getting each number are given in the table. What is the expected number of answers she will get correct per quiz?

x	Pr(x)
0	1024/3125
1	256/625
2	128/625
3	32/625
4	4/625
5	1/3125

Solution

The expected value of this distribution is

$$E(x) = 0 \cdot \frac{1024}{3125} + 1 \cdot \frac{256}{625} + 2 \cdot \frac{128}{625} + 3 \cdot \frac{32}{625} + 4 \cdot \frac{4}{625} + 5 \cdot \frac{1}{3125} = 1$$

This means that a student can expect to get 1 answer correct per quiz if she guesses at every answer.

Many decisions in business and science are made on the basis of what the outcomes of specific decisions will be, so expected value is very important in decision making and planning.

EXAMPLE 3	**Insurance**	APPLICATION PREVIEW	

The T. J. Cooper Insurance Company insures 100,000 cars. Company records over a 5-year period indicate that during each 6-month period, it will pay out the following amounts for accidents.

$500,000 with probability 0.0001 $25,000 with probability 0.008
$250,000 with probability 0.001 $5000 with probability 0.02
$125,000 with probability 0.002 $0 with probability 0.9689

How could the company use the expected payout per car for each 6-month period to help determine its rates?

Solution

The expected value of the company's payments is

$$\$500{,}000(0.0001) + \$250{,}000(0.001) + \$125{,}000(0.002) + \$25{,}000(0.008)$$
$$+ \$5000(0.02) = \$50 + \$250 + \$250 + \$200 + \$100 = \$850$$

Thus the average premium the company would charge each driver per car for a 6-month period would be

$$\$850 + \text{operating costs} + \text{profit} + \text{reserve for bad years}$$

CHECKPOINT

1. Consider a game in which you roll a die and receive $1 for each spot that occurs.
   (a) What are the expected winnings from this game?
   (b) If you paid $4 to play this game, how much would you lose, on average, each time you played the game?
2. An experiment has the following possible outcomes for the random variable x: 1, 2, 3, 4, 6, 7, 8, 9, 10. The probability that the value x occurs is $x/50$. Find the expected value of x for the experiment.

Note that for constants a and b, it can be shown that

$$E(ax + b) = aE(x) + b.$$

EXAMPLE 4   Pricing

An appliance dealer sells three different models of upright freezers, with 13.5, 15.9, and 19.1 cubic feet of storage space. Let X represent the storage space of a freezer purchased by any customer and $\Pr(X)$ the probability that the freezer purchased has X cubic feet. Suppose X has the following probability distribution.

X	13.5	15.9	19.1
$\Pr(X)$	0.2	0.5	0.3

(a) Find and interpret $E(X)$.
(b) If the price (in dollars) of a freezer with capacity X cubic feet is $22.5X - 8.5$, find the expected price paid for the average freezer purchased.

Solution

(a) $E(X) = (13.5)(0.2) + (15.9)(0.5) + (19.1)(0.3) = 16.38$

This means that the mean cubic feet of freezer space on any sale is 16.38 cubic feet.

(b) On average, the price of a freezer is

$$P = 22.5X - 8.5$$

Because the expected size of any freezer sold is 16.38 cubic feet, the expected price is found as follows:

$$E(P) = E(22.5X - 8.5) = 22.5E(X) - 8.5$$

$$= 22.5(16.38) - 8.5 \approx 360(\text{dollars})$$

Measures of Dispersion   Figure 8.14 shows two probability histograms that have the same mean (expected value). However, these histograms look very different. This is because the histograms differ in the **dispersion,** or **variation,** of the values of the random variables.

$$\mu = E(x) = 4\left(\frac{2}{10}\right) + 5\left(\frac{6}{10}\right) + 6\left(\frac{2}{10}\right)$$

$$= \frac{8 + 30 + 12}{10} = 5$$

$$\mu = E(x) = 1\left(\frac{2}{10}\right) + 2\left(\frac{1}{10}\right) + 4\left(\frac{1}{10}\right)$$

$$+ 5\left(\frac{2}{10}\right) + 6\left(\frac{1}{10}\right) + 8\left(\frac{1}{10}\right) + 9\left(\frac{2}{10}\right)$$

$$= \frac{2 + 2 + 4 + 10 + 6 + 8 + 18}{10} = 5$$

Figure 8.14   (a)   (b)

Thus we need a way to indicate how distributions with the same mean, such as the ones above, differ. We can find the **variance** of a probability distribution by finding the mean of the *squares* of these deviations. The square root of this measure, called the **standard deviation,** is very useful in describing how the values of x are concentrated about the mean of the probability distribution.

Variance and Standard Deviation	If x is a discrete random variable with values $x_1, x_2, \ldots, x_n$ and mean μ, then the **variance** σ^2 of the distribution of x is

$$\sigma^2 = \Sigma[(x - \mu)^2 \Pr(x)]$$

The **standard deviation** from the mean μ is

$$\sigma = \sqrt{\sigma^2} = \sqrt{\Sigma[(x-\mu)^2 \Pr(x)]}$$

EXAMPLE 5   Standard Deviations of Distributions

Find the standard deviations of the distributions described in
(a) Figure 8.14(a)   (b) Figure 8.14(b).

Solution

(a) $\sigma^2 = \Sigma[(x - \mu)^2 \Pr(x)]$

$$= (4 - 5)^2 \cdot \frac{2}{10} + (5 - 5)^2 \cdot \frac{6}{10} + (6 - 5)^2 \cdot \frac{2}{10} = 0.4$$

$$\sigma = \sqrt{0.4} \approx 0.632$$

(b) $\sigma^2 = (1 - 5)^2 \cdot \frac{2}{10} + (2 - 5)^2 \cdot \frac{1}{10} + (4 - 5)^2 \cdot \frac{1}{10} + (5 - 5)^2 \cdot \frac{2}{10}$

$$+ (6 - 5)^2 \cdot \frac{1}{10} + (8 - 5)^2 \cdot \frac{1}{10} + (9 - 5)^2 \cdot \frac{2}{10} = 8.4$$

$$\sigma = \sqrt{8.4} \approx 2.898$$

As we can see by referring to Figure 8.14 and to the standard deviations calculated in Example 5, smaller values of σ indicate that the values of x are clustered nearer μ (as is true with sample mean and standard deviation). When σ is large, the values of x are more widely dispersed from μ. As we saw for sample data in Section 8.2, a large standard deviation s indicates that the data are widely dispersed from the sample mean $\bar{x}$.

The Binomial Distribution   A special discrete probability distribution is the **binomial probability distribution,** which describes all possible outcomes of a binomial experiment with their probabilities. Table 8.2 gives the binomial probability distribution for the experiment of tossing a fair coin 6 times, with x equal to the number of heads.

TABLE 8.2

x	$\Pr(x)$	x	$\Pr(x)$
0	$\binom{6}{0}\left(\frac{1}{2}\right)^0\left(\frac{1}{2}\right)^6 = \frac{1}{64}$	4	$\binom{6}{4}\left(\frac{1}{2}\right)^4\left(\frac{1}{2}\right)^2 = \frac{15}{64}$
1	$\binom{6}{1}\left(\frac{1}{2}\right)^1\left(\frac{1}{2}\right)^5 = \frac{6}{64}$	5	$\binom{6}{5}\left(\frac{1}{2}\right)^5\left(\frac{1}{2}\right)^1 = \frac{6}{64}$
2	$\binom{6}{2}\left(\frac{1}{2}\right)^2\left(\frac{1}{2}\right)^4 = \frac{15}{64}$	6	$\binom{6}{6}\left(\frac{1}{2}\right)^6\left(\frac{1}{2}\right)^0 = \frac{1}{64}$
3	$\binom{6}{3}\left(\frac{1}{2}\right)^3\left(\frac{1}{2}\right)^3 = \frac{20}{64}$		

Binomial Probability Distribution	If x is a variable that assumes the values $0, 1, 2, \ldots, r, \ldots, n$ with probabilities $$\binom{n}{0}p^0 q^n, \ \binom{n}{1}p^1 q^{n-1}, \ \binom{n}{2}p^2 q^{n-2}, \ \ldots, \ \binom{n}{r}p^r q^{n-r}, \ \ldots, \ \binom{n}{n}p^n q^0,$$ respectively, where p is the probability of success and $q = 1 - p$ is the probability of failure, then x is called a **binomial variable.** The values of x and their corresponding probabilities described above form the **binomial probability distribution.**

Recall that $\binom{n}{r} = {}_nC_r$ can be evaluated easily on a graphing calculator.

CHECKPOINT

3. Show that the values of x and the associated probabilities in Table 8.2 satisfy the conditions for a discrete probability distribution.

Mean and Standard Deviation

The expected value of the number of successes (heads) for the coin toss experiment in Table 8.2 on the previous page is given by

$$E(x) = 0 \cdot \frac{1}{64} + 1 \cdot \frac{6}{64} + 2 \cdot \frac{15}{64} + 3 \cdot \frac{20}{64} + 4 \cdot \frac{15}{64} + 5 \cdot \frac{6}{64} + 6 \cdot \frac{1}{64} = \frac{192}{64} = 3$$

This expected number of successes seems reasonable. If the probability of success is $1/2$, we would expect to succeed on half of the 6 trials. We could also use the formula for expected value to see that the expected number of heads in 100 tosses is $100(1/2) = 50$. For any binomial distribution, the expected number of successes is given by np, where n is the number of trials and p is the probability of success.

Mean of a Binomial Distribution	The theoretical **mean** (or **expected value**) of any binomial distribution is $$\mu = np$$ where n is the number of trials in the corresponding binomial experiment and p is the probability of success on each trial.

A simple formula can be developed for the standard deviation of a binomial distribution.

Standard Deviation of a Binomial Distribution	The **standard deviation** of a binomial distribution is $$\sigma = \sqrt{npq}$$ where n is the number of trials, p is the probability of success on each trial, and $q = 1 - p$.

The standard deviation of the binomial distribution corresponding to the number of heads resulting when a coin is tossed 16 times is

$$\sigma = \sqrt{16 \cdot \frac{1}{2} \cdot \frac{1}{2}} = \sqrt{4} = 2$$

EXAMPLE 6   **Nursing Homes**

According to the *New England Journal of Medicine,* there is a 43% chance that a person 65 years or older will enter a nursing home sometime in his or her lifetime. Of 100 people in this age group, what is the expected number of people who will eventually enter a nursing home, and what is the standard deviation?

Solution
The number of people who will eventually enter a nursing home follows a binomial distribution, with the probability that any one person in this group will enter a home equal to $p = 0.43$ and the probability that he or she will not equal to $q = 0.57$. Thus the expected number out of 100 that will eventually enter a nursing home is

$$E(x) = np = 100(0.43) = 43$$

The standard deviation of this distribution is

$$\sigma = \sqrt{npq} = \sqrt{(100)(0.43)(0.57)} \approx 4.95$$

EXAMPLE 7   **Eye Surgery** | APPLICATION PREVIEW |

Clinical studies have shown that 5% of patients operated on for nearsightedness with photorefractive keratectomy (PRK) still need to wear glasses. Find the expected number of unsuccessful operations (patients still wearing glasses) per 1000 operations.

Solution
Each operation is independent, so the number of failures follows the binomial distribution. The probability of an unsuccessful operation is $p = 0.05$ and $n = 1000$. Thus the expected number of unsuccessful operations in 1000 operations is

$$E(x) = \mu = 1000(0.05) = 50$$

CHECKPOINT

4. A fair cube is colored so that 4 faces are green and 2 are red. The cube is tossed 9 times. If success is defined as a red face being up, find
    (a) the mean number of red faces.
    (b) the standard deviation of the number of red faces that occur.

Binomial Formula

The binomial probability distribution is closely related to the powers of a binomial. For example, if a binomial experiment has 3 trials with probability of success p on each trial, then the binomial probability distribution is given in Table 8.3, with the values of x written from 3 to 0. Compare this with the expansion of $(p + q)^3$, which we introduced in Chapter 0, "Algebraic Concepts."

$$(p + q)^3 = p^3 + 3p^2q + 3pq^2 + q^3$$

The formula we can use to expand a binomial $(a + b)$ to any positive integer power n is as follows.

TABLE 8.3

x	$Pr(x)$
3	$\binom{3}{3}p^3q^0 = p^3$
2	$\binom{3}{2}p^2q = 3p^2q$
1	$\binom{3}{1}pq^2 = 3pq^2$
0	$\binom{3}{0}p^0q^3 = q^3$

Binomial Formula

$$(a + b)^n = \binom{n}{n}a^n + \binom{n}{n-1}a^{n-1}b + \binom{n}{n-2}a^{n-2}b^2 + \cdots$$

$$+ \binom{n}{2}a^2b^{n-2} + \binom{n}{1}ab^{n-1} + \binom{n}{0}b^n$$

EXAMPLE 8   Binomial Formula

Expand $(x + y)^4$.

Solution

$$(x + y)^4 = \binom{4}{4}x^4 + \binom{4}{3}x^3y + \binom{4}{2}x^2y^2 + \binom{4}{1}xy^3 + \binom{4}{0}y^4$$

$$= x^4 + 4x^3y + 6x^2y^2 + 4xy^3 + y^4$$

CHECKPOINT ANSWERS

1. (a) $E(x) = \$3.50$
   (b) You would lose $0.50, on average, from each play.
2. $E(x) = 7.2$
3. Each value of the random variable x has a probability, with $0 \le \Pr(x) \le 1$, and with $\Sigma \Pr(x) = 1$. Thus the conditions of a probability distribution are satisfied.
4. (a) $\mu = 3$
   (b) $\sigma = \sqrt{2}$

EXERCISES 8.3

Determine whether each table in Problems 1–4 describes a discrete probability distribution. Explain.

1.
x	Pr(x)
1	−1/5
2	1/4
3	5/10
4	9/20

2.
x	Pr(x)
0	−4/5
1	2/5
2	3/5
3	4/5

3.
x	Pr(x)
−1	1/4
1	3/8
2	1/4
4	1/8

4.
x	Pr(x)
0	1/3
4	1/6
8	1/2
12	0

Determine whether each formula in Problems 5–8 describes a discrete probability distribution. Explain.

5. $\Pr(x) = \dfrac{x}{21}; \quad x = 0, 1, 2, 3, 4, 5, 6$

6. $\Pr(x) = \dfrac{x}{10}; \quad x = 1, 2, 3, 4$

7. $\Pr(x) = \dfrac{10 - x}{10}; \quad x = 1, 2, 3, 4, 5$

8. $\Pr(x) = \dfrac{x + 1}{15}; \quad x = 1, 2, 3, 4$

Each of the tables in Problems 9–12 defines a discrete probability distribution. Find the expected value of each distribution.

9.
x	0	1	2	3
Pr(x)	1/8	1/4	1/4	3/8

10.
x	1	2	3	4
Pr(x)	1/10	1/5	3/10	2/5

11.
x	4	5	6	7
Pr(x)	1/3	1/3	1/3	0

12.
x	1	2	3	4
Pr(x)	1/15	4/15	1/5	7/15

In Problems 13–16, find the mean, variance, and standard deviation for each probability distribution.

13.

x	Pr(x)
0	1/4
1	1/4
2	1/8
3	3/8

14.

x	Pr(x)
3	1/4
4	1/4
5	1/4
6	1/4

15. $Pr(x) = \dfrac{x}{21}$; $x = 0, 1, 2, 3, 4, 5, 6$

16. $Pr(x) = \dfrac{x}{10}$; $x = 2, 3, 5$

17. Suppose an experiment has five possible outcomes for x: 0, 1, 2, 3, 4. The probability that each of these outcomes occurs is $x/10$. What is the expected value of x for the experiment?

18. Suppose an experiment has six possible outcomes for x: 0, 1, 2, 3, 4, 5. The probability that each of these outcomes occurs is $x/15$. What is the expected value of x for the experiment?

19. Five slips of paper containing the numbers 0, 1, 2, 3, 4 are placed in a hat. If the experiment consists of drawing one number and if the experiment is repeated a large number of times, what is the expected value of the number drawn?

20. An experiment consists of rolling a die once. If the experiment is repeated a large number of times, what is the expected value of the number rolled?

21. A die is rolled 3 times, and success is rolling a 5.
    (a) Construct the binomial distribution that describes this experiment.
    (b) Find the mean of this distribution.
    (c) Find the standard deviation of this distribution.

22. A die is rolled 3 times. Success is rolling a number divisible by 3.
    (a) Construct the binomial distribution that describes this experiment.
    (b) Find the mean of this distribution.
    (c) Find the standard deviation of this distribution.

23. A variable x has a binomial distribution with probability of success 0.7 for each trial. For a total of 60 trials, what are
    (a) the mean and
    (b) the standard deviation of the distribution?

24. A variable x has a binomial distribution with probability of success equal to 0.8 for each trial with a total of 40 trials. What are
    (a) the mean and
    (b) the standard deviation of the distribution?

25. A coin is "loaded" so that the probability of tossing a head is 3/5. If it is tossed 50 times, what are
    (a) the mean and
    (b) the standard deviation of the number of heads that occur?

26. Suppose a pair of dice is thrown 1200 times. How many times would we expect a sum of 7 to occur?

27. Suppose a pair of dice is thrown 900 times. How many times would we expect a sum of 6 to occur?

28. Suppose a die is "loaded" so that the probability of getting each even number is 1/4 and the probability of getting each odd number is 1/12. If it is rolled 240 times, how many times would we expect to get a 3?

29. Expand $(a + b)^6$.

30. Expand $(x + y)^5$.

31. Expand $(x + h)^4$.

32. Write the general expression for $(x + h)^n$.

APPLICATIONS

33. *Animal relocation* In studying endangered species, scientists have found that when animals are relocated, it takes x years without offspring before the first young are born, where x and the probability of x are given in the table. What is the expected number of years before the first young are born?

x	0	1	2	3	4
Pr(x)	0.04	0.35	0.38	0.18	0.05

34. *Lottery scandal* The Pennsylvania Daily Number is a three-digit number game that costs $1 per "number" and has a winning ticket payoff of $500. On April 24, 1980, the winning number was 666. Several weeks later it was discovered that the April 24 drawing had been fixed. Exposure of the scandal revealed that all balls except those with 4 or 6 had been altered so that the winning number would contain only those digits. If you purchased a $1 ticket for each possible 3-digit number that consisted of only 4s or 6s, find the expected payoff on:
    (a) April 24, 1980. (First list all possible 3-digit numbers that consist of only 4s or 6s.)
    (b) a day when the lottery was not fixed.

35. *Campaigning* A candidate must decide whether he should spend his time and money on funding TV commercials or making personal appearances. His staff determines that by using TV, he can reach 100,000 people with probability 0.01, 50,000 people with probability 0.47, and 25,000 people with probability 0.52. By making personal appearances, he can reach 80,000 people with probability 0.02, 50,000 people with probability 0.47, and 20,000 people with probability 0.51. In the tables, x represents the number of people reached by each choice. In each case, find the expected value of x to decide which method will reach more people.

TV Commercials		Personal Appearances	
x	Pr(x)	x	Pr(x)
100,000	0.01	80,000	0.02
50,000	0.47	50,000	0.47
25,000	0.52	20,000	0.51

36. *Genetics* If the probability that a newborn child is a male is 1/2, what is the expected number of male children in a family having 4 children?

37. *Raffle* A nonprofit organization sells chances for a $40,000 classic Mustang at $100 per ticket. It sells 1500 tickets and offers four prizes, summarized in the table. What are the expected winnings (or loss) for each ticket?

Prizes	Amount
First	$40,000
Second	5,000
Third	2,500
Fourth	1,500

Source: Automobile

38. *Lottery* A charity sells raffle tickets for $1 each. First prize is $500, second prize is $100, third prize is $10. If you buy one of the 1000 tickets sold, what are your expected winnings?

39. *Gambling* Suppose a student is offered a chance to draw a card from an ordinary deck of 52 playing cards and win $15 for an ace, $10 for a king, and $1 for a queen. If the student pays $4 to play the game, what is the amount the student expects to win each time?

40. *Revenue* The Rent-to-Own Company estimates that 35% of its rentals result in the sale of the product, with an average revenue of 100% of revenue R, 56% of the rentals are returned in good condition, with an average revenue of 35% of R on these rentals, and the remainder of the rentals are stolen or returned in poor condition, with a loss of 15% of R on these rentals. If these estimates are accurate, what is the expected percent of revenue for this company?

41. *Sales* A young man plans to sell umbrellas at the city's Easter Parade. He knows that he can sell 180 umbrellas at $10 each if it rains hard, he can sell 50 if it rains lightly, and he can sell 10 if it doesn't rain at all. Past records show it rains hard 25% of the time on Easter, rains lightly 20% of the time, and does not rain at all 55% of the time. If he can buy 0, 100, or 200 umbrellas at $4 each and return the unsold ones for $2 each, how many should he buy?

42. *Advertising* A candidate must decide whether he should spend his advertising dollars on print advertising or on telemarketing. His staff determines that by using print advertising, he can reach 80,000 people with probability 0.01, reach 40,000 people with probability 0.47, and reach 25,000 with probability 0.52; by using telemarketing, he can reach 70,000 people with probability 0.04, reach 50,000 people with probability 0.38, and reach 30,000 with probability 0.58. Which method will reach more people?

43. *Insurance* A car owner must decide whether she should take out a $500-deductible collision policy in addition to her liability insurance policy. Records show that each year in her area, 8% of the drivers have one accident that is their fault or for which no fault is assigned and that the average cost of repairs for these types of accidents is $5000. If the $500-deductible collision policy costs $350 per year, would she save money in the long run by buying the insurance or "taking the chance"? *Hint:* Find the expected values if she has the policy and if she doesn't have the policy and compare them.

44. *Altimeters* Suppose a company manufactures altimeters so that they are accurate at an average height of 1000 feet. Is the accuracy of this single measurement sufficient to ensure the safety of the passengers and crew of planes using these altimeters? Explain.

45. *Machining* A machinist makes pipes with an average diameter of 2 in. If he machines 100 pipes with an average diameter of 2 in., does this mean that all of them are usable? (A pipe is usable if its diameter is within 0.01 in. of 2 in.) Explain.

46. *Budgeting* Suppose a youth has a part-time job in an ice cream shop. He receives $80 if he is called to work a full day and $40 if he is called to work a half-day. Over the past year, he has been called to work a full day an average of 8 days per month and a half-day an average of 14 days per month. How much can he expect to earn *per day* during a 30-day month?

47. *Health care* Suppose that 10% of the patients who have a certain disease will die from it.
   (a) If 100 people have the disease, how many would we expect to die from it?
   (b) What is the standard deviation of the number of deaths that could occur?

48. *Cancer research* Suppose it has been determined that the probablity is 0.6 that a rat injected with cancerous cells will live. If 35 rats are injected, how many would be expected to die?

49. *Voting* A candidate claims that 60% of the voters in his district will vote for him.
   (a) If his district contains 100,000 voters, how many votes does he expect to get from his district?
   (b) What is the standard deviation of the number of these votes?
   (c) If the number of votes the candidate gets is 2 standard deviations below what he expected, approximately how many votes will he get?

50. *Genetics* In a family with 2 children, the probability that both children will be boys is 1/4. Suppose 1200 families with two children are selected at random.
   (a) How many of the families would we expect to have 2 boys?
   (b) What is the standard deviation of the number of families with 2 boys?
   (c) Suppose that of the 1200 families, 315 families have two boys. How many standard deviations above the mean is this number (315) of families?

51. *Testing* A multiple-choice test has 20 questions and 5 choices for each question. If a student is totally unprepared and guesses on each question, the mean is the number of questions she can expect to answer correctly.
    (a) How many questions can she expect to answer correctly?
    (b) What is the standard deviation of the distribution?

52. *Birth control* Suppose a birth control pill is 99% effective in preventing pregnancy. What number of women would be expected to get pregnant out of 100 women using this pill?

53. *Quality control* A certain calculator circuit board is manufactured in lots of 200. If 1% of the boards are defective, find the mean and standard deviation of the number of defects in each lot.

54. *CPA exam* Forty-eight percent of accountants taking a CPA exam fail the first time. If 1000 candidates take the exam for the first time, what is the expected number that will pass?

55. *Seed germination* A certain type of corn seed has an 85% germination rate. If 2000 seeds were planted, how many seeds would be expected not to germinate?

56. *Quality control* The probability that a manufacturer produces a defective faucets is 0.001. What is the expected number of defective faucets in a shipment of 3000?

57. *Oil drilling* Suppose that when an oil company drills a well, there is a 15% chance that it will produce oil.

Assume that the outcomes of the drillings are independent and the company drills 12 wells.
    (a) Find the mean and standard deviation of the number of successful wells.
    (b) Find the probability that at most 3 wells produce oil.
    (c) Suppose the company has fixed costs of $28,000 for the entire drilling project, each productive well costs $24,000 to drill, and each unproductive well costs $15,000 to drill. Write the function that expresses the total cost of drilling x successful wells and find the company's expected total cost for the 12 wells.

58. *Warranties* A home improvement warehouse, HIW, has 15 sump pumps in stock. The company sells these pumps for $150 each, with a double-your-money-back guarantee for any defective pump. Suppose the probability of any pump being defective is 0.08 and each pump's quality is independent.
    (a) Find the mean and standard deviation of the number of defective pumps.
    (b) Find the probability that at least 2 pumps are defective.
    (c) Let x represent the number of defective pumps. Write an expression in x for HIW's net revenue from the sale of all 15 pumps (including the money back guarantee of returns of defective ones). Then find HIW's expected net revenue.

SECTION 8.4

Normal Probability Distribution

OBJECTIVES

- To calculate the probability that a random variable following the standard normal distribution has values in a certain interval
- To convert normal distribution values to standard normal values (z-scores)
- To find the probability that normally distributed values lie in a certain interval

APPLICATION PREVIEW

Discrete probability distributions are important, but they do not apply to many kinds of measurements. For example, the weights of people, the heights of trees, and other measures occurring in nature cannot be measured with whole numbers because the values cannot be listed or counted, as is possible for a discrete random variable. Many of these measurements follow a special continuous probability distribution called the normal distribution.

IQ scores follow the normal distribution with a mean of 100 and a standard deviation of 15. The graph of this normal distribution is a bell-shaped curve that is symmetric about the mean of 100. We can use this information to find the probability that a person picked at random will have an IQ between 100 and 124. (See Example 4.)

The **normal distribution** is perhaps the most important probability distribution because so many measurements that occur in nature follow this particular distribution.

Normal Distribution

The **normal distribution** has the following properties.

1. Its graph is a bell-shaped curve like that in Figure 8.15. The graph is called the **normal curve.** It approaches but never touches the horizontal axis as it extends in both directions. The figure shows the percent of scores that lie under the curve and within given intervals.*

Figure 8.15   Normal distribution

2. The curve is symmetric about a vertical center line that passes through the value that is the mean, the median, *and* the mode of the distribution. That is, the mean, median, and mode are the same for a normal distribution. (That is why all of these are sometimes called average.)
3. A normal distribution is completely determined when its mean μ and its standard deviation σ are known.
4. Approximately 68% of all scores lie within 1 standard deviation of the mean. Approximately 95% of all scores lie within 2 standard deviations of the mean. More than 99.5% of all scores will lie within 3 standard deviations of the mean.

As mentioned in the Application Preview, IQ scores follow a normal distribution with mean 100 and standard deviation 15. Thus, 34% of IQ scores will be between 100 and 115, 95% will be between 70 and 130, and 2.5% will be greater than 130. [See Figure 8.16(a).]

The percent of scores in a given interval from x_1 to x_2 is also the area under the normal curve from x_1 to x_2, and both represent the *probability* that a score will lie between x_1 and x_2. This means that a person chosen at random will have probability 0.34 of having an IQ between 100 and 115, probability 0.95 of having an IQ between 70 and 130, and probability 0.025 of having an IQ greater than 130.

Figure 8.16   (a)   (b)

EXAMPLE 1 **Quality control**

A machine dispenses juice into bottles and the fill levels are normally distributed with a mean of 1 liter (1000 milliliters) and a standard deviation of 20 milliliters. See Figure 8.16(b).
(a) Within what interval of fill levels will 68% the bottles be filled?
(b) Below what fill level will 16% of the bottles be filled?

*Percents shown are approximate.

Solution

(a) Figure 8.16(b) shows the normal distribution of the fill levels from the machine. Sixty-eight percent of the fill levels lie within 1 standard deviation (20 milliliters) of the mean (1000 milliliters), so 68% of the bottles will contain between 980 milliliters and 1020 milliliters.

(b) Figure 8.16(b) shows that 16% of the fill levels will be less than 980 milligrams, which is 1 standard deviation (20 milliliters) below the mean (1000 milliliters). ◼

CHECKPOINT

1. The mean of a normal distribution is 25, and the standard deviation is 3.
   (a) What percent of the scores will be between 22 and 28?
   (b) What is the probability that a score chosen at random will be between 22 and 28?

---

z-Scores

Because the probability of obtaining a score from a normal distribution is always related to how many standard deviations the score is away from the mean, we will show how to express all scores from a normal distribution as **standard scores,** or **z-scores.**

The distribution of z-scores will always be a normal distribution with mean 0 and standard deviation 1. This distribution is called the **standard normal distribution.** (See Figure 8.17.) The total area under the curve is 1, with 0.5 on either side of the mean 0.

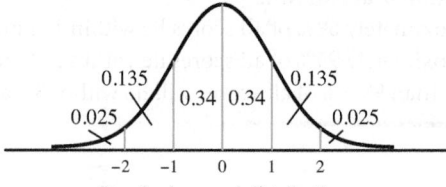

Figure 8.17   Standard normal distribution

By comparing Figure 8.17 with Figure 8.15, we see that each unit from 0 in the standard normal distribution corresponds to 1 standard deviation from the mean of the normal distribution.

We can use a table to determine more accurately the area under the standard normal curve between two z-scores. Appendix C gives the area under the standard normal curve from $z = 0$ to $z = z_0$ for values of z_0 from 0 to 3.86. As with the normal curve, the area under the curve from $z = 0$ to $z = z_0$ is the probability that a z-score lies between 0 and z_0.

EXAMPLE 2   Standard Normal Distribution

(a) Find the area under the standard normal curve from $z = 0$ to $z = 1.50$.
(b) Find $\Pr(0 \leq z \leq 1.50)$.

Solution

(a) Looking in the column headed by z in Appendix C, we see 1.50. Across from 1.50 in the column headed by A is 0.4332. Thus the area under the standard normal curve between $z = 0$ and $z = 1.50$ is $A_{1.50} = 0.4432$. (See Figure 8.18.)

(b) The area under the curve from 0 to 1.50 equals the probability that z lies between 0 and 1.50. Thus

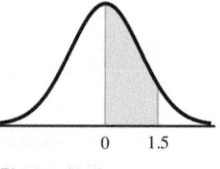

Figure 8.18

$$\Pr(0 \leq z \leq 1.50) = A_{1.50} = 0.4332$$

The following facts, which are direct results of the symmetry of the standard normal curve about μ, are useful in calculating probabilities using Appendix C.

1. $\Pr(-z_0 \leq z \leq 0) = \Pr(0 \leq z \leq z_0) = A_{z0}$
2. $\Pr(z \geq 0) = \Pr(z \leq 0) = 0.5$

EXAMPLE 3 **Probabilities with z-Scores**

Find the following probabilities for the random variable z with standard normal distribution.
(a) $\Pr(-1 \le z \le 0)$
(b) $\Pr(-1 \le z \le 1.5)$
(c) $\Pr(1 \le z \le 1.5)$
(d) $\Pr(z > 2)$
(e) $\Pr(z < 1.35)$

Solution
(a) $\Pr(-1 \le z \le 0) = \Pr(0 \le z \le 1) = A_1 = 0.3413$
(b) We find $\Pr(-1 \le z \le 1.5)$ by using A_1 and $A_{1.5}$ follows:

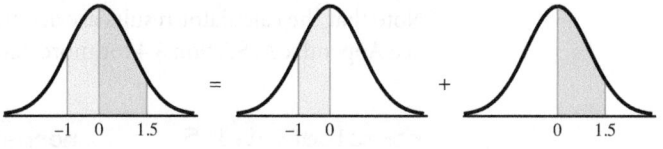

$$
\begin{aligned}
\Pr(-1 \le z \le 1.5) &= \Pr(-1 \le z \le 0) &+ \Pr(0 \le z \le 1.5)\\
&= A_1 &+ A_{1.5}\\
&= 0.3413 &+ 0.4332\\
&= 0.7745
\end{aligned}
$$

(c) We find $\Pr(1 \le z \le 1.5)$ by using A_1 and $A_{1.5}$ follows:

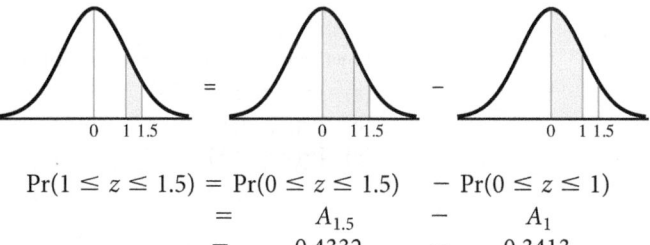

$$
\begin{aligned}
\Pr(1 \le z \le 1.5) &= \Pr(0 \le z \le 1.5) &- \Pr(0 \le z \le 1)\\
&= A_{1.5} &- A_1\\
&= 0.4332 &- 0.3413\\
&= 0.0919
\end{aligned}
$$

(d) We find $\Pr(z > 2)$ by using 0.5 and A_2 as follows:

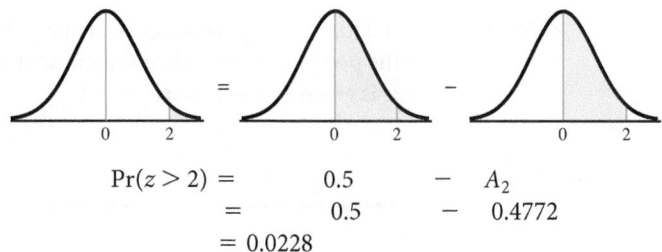

$$
\begin{aligned}
\Pr(z > 2) &= 0.5 &- A_2\\
&= 0.5 &- 0.4772\\
&= 0.0228
\end{aligned}
$$

(e) We find $\Pr(z < 1.35)$ by using 0.5 and $A_{1.35}$ as follows:

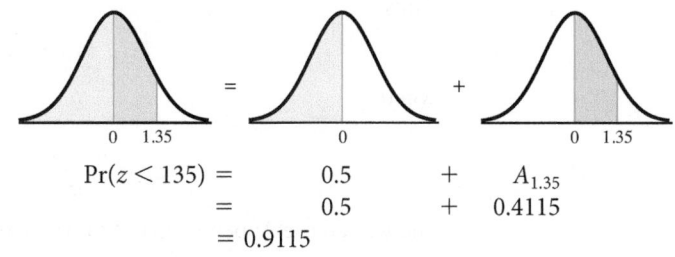

$$
\begin{aligned}
\Pr(z < 135) &= 0.5 &+ A_{1.35}\\
&= 0.5 &+ 0.4115\\
&= 0.9115
\end{aligned}
$$

Notice in Appendix C that the last entry has $z_0 = 3.86$ and $A = 0.4999$; this means that $\Pr(0 \le z \le 3.86) = 0.4999$ and, thus, $\Pr(z > 3.86) = 0.0001$. For z-scores that are significantly greater than 3.86, say $z = 10$, it is common practice to use $\Pr(z > 10) = 0$. (Similarly, $\Pr(-10 < z) = 0$.)

Calculator Note   The area under the standard normal distribution curve between $z = a$ and $z = b$, or $\Pr(a \le z \le b)$, can be found on a graphing calculator by evaluating normalcdf(a, b), found in the DISTR menu. For example, $\Pr(-1 \le z \le 1.5)$, found in Example 3(b), is found as follows.

$$\Pr(-1 \le z \le 1.5) = \text{normalcdf}(-1, 1.5) \approx 0.7745 \quad \text{[See Figure 8.19(a).]}$$

We can find $\Pr(z > 2)$, found in Example 3(d), by evaluating $\Pr(2 < z \le 10)$ as follows.

$$\Pr(z > 2) \approx \Pr(2 < z \le 10) = \text{normalcdf}(2, 10) \approx 0.0228 \quad \text{[See Figure 8.19(b).]}$$

Note that the calculator results are accurate to more decimal places than the table values. See Appendix A, Section 8.4 for more details. ∎

Figure 8.19   (a)   (b)

CHECKPOINT

2. For the standard normal distribution, find the following probabilities.
    (a) $\Pr(0 \le z \le 2.5)$
    (b) $\Pr(z > 2.5)$
    (c) $\Pr(z \le 2.5)$

If a population follows a normal distribution, but with mean and/or standard deviation different from 0 and 1, respectively, we can convert the scores to standard scores, or z-scores, using the following formula.

z-Scores   If data for a population are normally distributed and σ is the standard deviation of the population data, then the number of standard deviations that x is from the mean μ is given by the **z-score**

$$z = \frac{x - \mu}{\sigma}$$

This formula enables us to convert scores from any normal distribution to a distribution of z-scores with no units of measurement.
Thus

$$\Pr(a \le x \le b) = \Pr(z_a \le z \le z_b)$$

where

$$z_a = \frac{a - \mu}{\sigma} \quad \text{and} \quad z_b = \frac{b - \mu}{\sigma}$$

and we can use Appendix C to find these probabilities.

EXAMPLE 4   IQ Scores | APPLICATION PREVIEW |

The normal distribution of IQ scores has mean $\mu = 100$ and standard deviation $\sigma = 15$.
(a) Find the z-scores for $x = 100$ and $x = 124$.
(b) Find the probability that an IQ score is between 100 and 124.

Solution

(a) The z-scores for $x = 100$ and $x = 124$ are

Figure 8.20

$$\text{for } 100\text{: } z = \frac{100 - 100}{15} = 0 \qquad \text{for } 124\text{: } z = \frac{124 - 100}{15} = 1.6$$

A z-score of 1.6 indicates that 124 is 1.6 standard deviations above the mean. (See Figure 8.20.)

(b) Using Appendix C, the probability that an IQ score is between 100 and 124 is

$$\Pr(100 \le x \le 124) = \Pr(0 \le z \le 1.6) = A_{1.6} = 0.4452$$

EXAMPLE 5   Height

If the height of a population of students is normally distributed with mean $\mu = 68$ inches and standard deviation $\sigma = 4$ inches, what is the probability that a person chosen at random from the population will be between
(a) 68 and 76 inches tall?   (b) 65 and 74 inches tall?

Solution

(a) To find $\Pr(68 \le x \le 76)$, we convert 68 and 76 to z-scores.

$$\text{For } 68\text{: } z = \frac{68 - 68}{4} = 0 \qquad \text{For } 76\text{: } z = \frac{76 - 68}{4} = 2$$

Thus

$$\Pr(68 \le x \le 76) = \Pr(0 \le z \le 2) = A_2 = 0.4772$$

(b) The z-scores for 65 and 74 are

$$\text{For } 65\text{: } z = \frac{65 - 68}{4} = -0.75 \qquad \text{For } 74\text{: } z = \frac{74 - 68}{4} = 1.5$$

Thus

$$\Pr(65 \le x \le 74) = \Pr(-0.75 \le z \le 1.5)$$
$$= A_{0.75} + A_{1.5}$$
$$= 0.2734 + 0.4332 = 0.7066$$

Calculator Note   Normal probabilities such as those in Example 5 can be calculated using the calculator command 2:normalcdf(lowerbound, upperbound, μ, σ) under DISTR. Figure 8.21 shows that probability $\Pr(65 \le x \le 74)$ from Example 5 can be found using normalcdf(65, 74, 68, 4). Details are given in Appendix A, Section 8.4.

```
normalcdf(65,74,
68,4)
      .7065654918
```

Figure 8.21

Spreadsheet Note   We can use Excel to find the normal probability that a score x is less than the value a by using the command =normdist(a, μ, σ, true). See the following spreadsheet for the normal probability calculations with $\mu = 6$ and $\sigma = 2$.

1. $\Pr(x < 5)$ uses =normdist(5,6,2,true) in cell B2.
2. $\Pr(x < 8)$ uses =normdist(8,6,2,true) in cell B3.
3. $\Pr(5 < x < 8)$ uses =B3–B2 in cell B4.
For additional information, see Appendix B, Section 8.4, or the Online Excel Guide.

	A	B
1	MU = 6	STD = 2
2	Pr(x<5)	0.308537539
3	Pr(x<8)	0.841344746
4	Pr(5<x<8)	0.532807207

CHECKPOINT

3. For the normal distribution with mean 70 and standard deviation 5, find the following probabilities.
   (a) $\Pr(70 \le x \le 77)$
   (b) $\Pr(68 \le x \le 73)$
   (c) $\Pr(x > 75)$

EXAMPLE 6   Demand

Recessionary pressures have forced an electrical supplies distributor to consider reducing its inventory. It has determined that over the past year, the daily demand for 48 inch fluorescent light fixtures is normally distributed with a mean of 432 and a standard deviation of 86.1. If the distributor decides to reduce its daily inventory to 500 units, what percent of the time will its inventory be insufficient to meet the demand? Will this cost the distributor business?

Solution

The probability we seek is $\Pr(x > 500)$, and because the distribution is normal, we can use the normalcdf command on a graphing calculator. As noted previously, $\Pr(z > 10)$ is essentially 0, so we can find $\Pr(x > 500)$ by calculating $\Pr(500 < x < M)$ where M is the number (upper limit) corresponding to $z = 10$. This number M can be found as follows:

$$z = \frac{x - \mu}{\sigma} \Rightarrow 10 = \frac{M - 432}{86.1} \Rightarrow M = 10(86.1) + 432 = 1293$$

As Figure 8.22 shows,

$$\Pr(x > 500) \approx \Pr(500 < x < 1293) = \text{normalcdf}(500,1293,432,86.1) \approx 0.2148.$$

Thus the distributor will have insufficient inventory about 21.48% of the time. This may result in a loss of customers, so the distributor should not decrease inventory to 500 units per day.

```
normalcdf(500,12
93,432,86.1)
      .2148282603
```

Figure 8.22

Sometimes we want to find a score that corresponds to a given probability (area) rather than find the probability from a given score. Example 7 illustrates how this is done.

EXAMPLE 7 | Scholarships

A college will give a partial scholarship to the top 5% of the graduates of a local high school, as measured by the students' GPAs. If the GPAs of a graduating class are normally distributed with mean of 3.2 and standard deviation of 0.25, find the smallest GPA eligible for a scholarship.

Solution

We seek the GPA, x, which corresponds to the number z_0 satisfying $\Pr(z > z_0) = 0.05$. From Appendix C, we see that $\Pr(0 < z < 1.645) = 0.45$, so $\Pr(z > 1.645) = 0.05$, and $z_0 = 1.645$. The smallest GPA that satisfies this condition is then found by solving for x in

$$1.645 = \frac{x - 3.2}{0.25}$$

This gives

$$0.411 = x - 3.2, \quad \text{or} \quad x = 3.611$$

so the minimum GPA eligible for a scholarship is 3.6.

Calculator Note We can also use a graphing calculator to solve problems such as Example 7. Given an area A under a normal curve with given μ and σ, we can find x_0 so that $\Pr(x \le x_0) = A$ by using the command invNorm(A, μ, σ) in the DISTR menu.

Thus in Example 7, evaluating $x_0 = $ invNorm(0.95, 3.2, 0.25) gives the threshold GPA, x_0, for which $\Pr(x \le x_0) = 0.95$ [or equivalently $\Pr(x > x_0) = 0.05$]. Figure 8.23 shows (as Example 7 did) that the minimum GPA to be eligible for a scholarship is $x_0 = 3.611$.

```
invNorm(0.95,3.2
,0.25)
        3.611213406
```

Figure 8.23

EXAMPLE 8 | Graphs of Normal Distributions

The function

$$f(x) = \frac{1}{\sigma\sqrt{2\pi}} e^{-(x-\mu)^2/(2\sigma^2)}$$

gives the equation for a normal curve with mean μ and standard deviation σ.

(a) Graph the following normal curves to see how different means yield different distributions.

$$\mu = 0, \sigma = 1, y = \frac{1}{\sqrt{2\pi}} e^{-x^2/2} \quad \text{and}$$

$$\mu = 3, \sigma = 1, y = \frac{1}{\sqrt{2\pi}} e^{-(x-3)^2/2}$$

If the standard deviations are the same, how does increasing the size of the mean affect the graph of the distribution?

(b) To see how normal distributions differ for different standard deviations, graph the normal distributions with

$$\mu = 0, \sigma = 3 \quad \text{and}$$
$$\mu = 0, \sigma = 2$$

What happens to the height of the curve as the standard deviation decreases? Do the data appear to be clustered nearer the mean when the standard deviation is smaller?

Solution

(a) The graphs are shown in Figure 8.24. The graphs are the same size but are centered over different means. A different mean causes the graph to shift to the right or left.

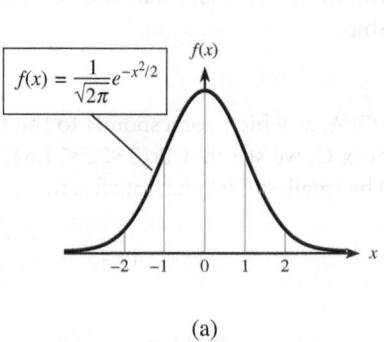

Figure 8.24   (a)   (b)

(b) The graphs are shown in Figure 8.25 on the next page. The height of the graph will be larger if the standard deviation decreases. Yes, the data will be clustered closer to the mean when the standard deviation is smaller.

 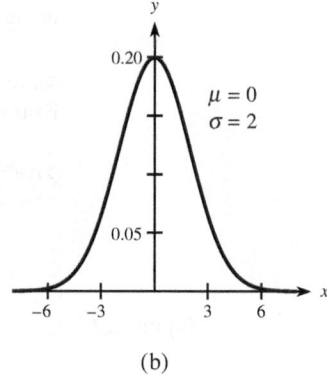

Figure 8.25   (a)   (b)

CHECKPOINT ANSWERS	1. (a) 68% lie in this range.	(b) 0.68	
	2. (a) 0.4938	(b) 0.0062	(c) 0.9938
	3. (a) 0.4192	(b) 0.3812	(c) 0.1587

EXERCISES 8.4

Find the probability that a z-score from the standard normal distribution will lie within each of the intervals in Problems 1–14.

1. $0 \leq z \leq 1.8$ 2. $0 \leq z \leq 2.4$
3. $-0.6 \leq z \leq 0$ 4. $-3 \leq z \leq 0$
5. $-1.5 \leq z \leq 2.1$ 6. $-1.25 \leq z \leq 3$
7. $-1.9 \leq z \leq -1.1$ 8. $-2.45 \leq z \leq -1.45$
9. $2.1 \leq z \leq 3.0$ 10. $1.85 \leq z \leq 2.85$
11. $z > 2$ 12. $z > 1.5$
13. $z < 1.2$ 14. $z > -1.6$

Suppose a population of scores x is normally distributed with $\mu = 20$ and $\sigma = 5$. In Problems 15–18, use the standard normal distribution to find the probabilities indicated.

15. $\Pr(20 \leq x \leq 22.5)$ 16. $\Pr(20 \leq x \leq 21.25)$
17. $\Pr(13.75 \leq x \leq 20)$ 18. $\Pr(18.5 \leq x \leq 20)$

Suppose a population of scores x is normally distributed with $\mu = 50$ and $\sigma = 10$. In Problems 19–22, use the standard normal distribution to find the probabilities indicated.

19. $\Pr(45 \leq x \leq 55)$ 20. $\Pr(42 \leq x \leq 58)$
21. $\Pr(35 \leq x \leq 60)$ 22. $\Pr(32 \leq x \leq 68)$

Suppose a population of scores x is normally distributed with $\mu = 110$ and $\sigma = 12$. In Problems 23–26, use the standard normal distribution to find the probabilities indicated.

23. $\Pr(x < 134)$ 24. $\Pr(x < 88)$
25. $\Pr(x > 128)$ 26. $\Pr(x > 96)$
27. Find the number A that satisfies $\Pr(z > A) = 0.95$ for the standard normal z-score.

28. Find the number A that satisfies $\Pr(-A < z < A) = 0.8664$ for the standard normal z-score.
29. The random variable x has a normal distribution with $\mu = -3$ and $\sigma = 4$. Find B so that $\Pr(x < B) = 0.75$
30. The random variable x has a normal distribution with $\mu = 40$ and $\sigma = 5$. Find B so that $\Pr(x > B) = 0.12$

APPLICATIONS

31. *Growth* The Fish Commission states that the lengths of all fish in Spring Run are normally distributed, with mean $\mu = 15$ cm and standard deviation $\sigma = 4$ cm. What is the probability that a fish caught in Spring Run will be between
    (a) 15 and 19 cm long?   (b) 10 and 15 cm long?
32. *Butterfat* A quart of Parker's milk contains a mean of 39 g of butterfat, with a standard deviation of 2 g. If the butterfat is normally distributed, find the probability that a quart of this brand of milk chosen at random will contain between
    (a) 39 and 43 g of butterfat.
    (b) 36 and 39 g of butterfat.
33. *Growth* The heights of a certain species of plant are normally distributed, with mean $\mu = 20$ cm and standard deviation $\sigma = 4$ cm. What is the probability that a plant chosen at random will be between 10 and 30 cm tall?
34. *Mating calls* The durations of the mating calls of a population of tree toads are normally distributed, with mean 189 milliseconds (msec) and standard deviation 32 msec. What proportion of these calls would be expected to last between
    (a) 157 and 221 msec?   (b) 205 and 253 msec?
35. *Growth* The mean weight of a group of boys is 160 lb, with a standard deviation of 15 lb. If the weights are normally distributed, find the probability that one of the boys picked at random from the group weighs
    (a) between 160 and 181 lb.
    (b) more than 190 lb.
    (c) between 181 and 190 lb.
    (d) between 130 and 181 lb.
36. *Testing* The Scholastic Aptitude Test (SAT) scores in mathematics at a certain high school are normally distributed, with a mean of 500 and a standard deviation of 100. What is the probability that an individual chosen at random has a score
    (a) greater than 700?   (b) less than 300?
    (c) between 550 and 600?
37. *Mileage* A certain model of automobile has its gas mileage (in miles per gallon, or mpg) normally distributed, with a mean of 28 mpg and a standard deviation of 4 mpg. Find the probability that a car selected at random has gas mileage
    (a) less than 22 mpg.   (b) greater than 30 mpg.
    (c) between 26 and 30 mpg.
38. *Quality control* A machine precision-cuts tubing such that $\mu = 40.00$ in. and $\sigma = 0.03$ in. If the lengths are normally distributed, find the probability that a piece of tubing selected at random measures
    (a) greater than 40.05 in.
    (b) less than 40.045 in.
    (c) between 39.95 and 40.05 in.
39. *Blood pressure* Systolic blood pressure for a group of women is normally distributed, with a mean of 120 and a standard deviation of 12. Find the probability that a woman selected at random has blood pressure
    (a) greater than 140.   (b) less than 110.
    (c) between 110 and 130.
40. *Industrial waste* In a certain state, the daily amounts of industrial waste are normally distributed, with a mean of 8000 tons and a standard deviation of 2000 tons. Find the probability that on a randomly selected day, the amount of industrial waste is
    (a) greater than 11,000 tons.
    (b) less than 6000 tons.
    (c) between 9000 and 11,000 tons.
41. *Reaction time* Reaction time is normally distributed, with a mean of 0.7 sec and a standard deviation of 0.1 sec. Find the probability that an individual selected at random has a reaction time
    (a) greater than 0.9 sec.
    (b) less than 0.6 sec.
    (c) between 0.6 and 0.9 sec.
42. *Inventory* Suppose that the electrical supplies distributor in Example 6 wants to reduce its daily inventory but wants to limit to 5% the number of days it will have an insufficient inventory of 48-in. fluorescent lightbulbs to meet daily demand. At what level should it maintain its daily inventory? (Recall that the daily demand over the past year had a mean of 432 and a standard deviation of 86.1.)
43. *Test results* At a major university, exam scores, x, in a large enrollment course are normally distributed with a mean score of 78 and standard deviation of 6. If the test is curved so that the top 10% of scores get a grade of A, find the minimum score to receive an A.
44. *Budgeting* The amount spent monthly, x, for maintenance and repairs at XONIX, LLC, is normally distributed with a mean of $2000 and standard deviation of $120. If x is the amount budgeted for next month, find x to the nearest $10 so that the probability of being over-budget for maintenance and repairs is 0.05.
45. *Quality control* The milk machine at a large dairy can be set to fill containers of various sizes. The fill amounts are normally distributed with the mean equal to the fill amount setting and a standard deviation of 0.3 oz. Find the fill amount setting so that the machine underfills a gallon container (128 oz) 1% of the time.
46. *Manufacturing* A textile manufacturer produces bolts of fabric with widths that are normally distributed with a mean of 48" and standard deviation of 0.25". Find the tolerance x so that 92% of the time the width of a randomly selected bolt is within x inches of 48".

47. *College standards* At a certain college, GPAs are normally distributed with a mean GPA of 2.48 and a standard deviation of 0.9. If the college wants to limit the number of academic suspensions to at most 15% of its students, find the academic suspension threshold GPA so that at most 15% of students fall below this GPA.

The Normal Curve Approximation to the Binomial Distribution

OBJECTIVE

- To use a normal approximation to compute a binomial probability

APPLICATION PREVIEW

An insurance company has 20,000 houses insured for fire damage in a certain city. If the probability that any one of these insured houses will have fire damage is 0.003, what is the probability that more than 50 of them will have fire damage? (See Example 2.) In this section, we discuss how to apply a normal approximation of a binomial distribution to solve a problem such as this.

Binomial probability calculations can be tedious when a large number of trials are involved (especially if we do not use technology). For example, to compute the probability requested in the Application Preview using the binomial probability distribution, we would have to compute the sum of 19,950 terms that use $i = 51$ through $i = 20,000$, which we represent by

$$Pr(x > 50) = \sum_{i=51}^{20,000} (_{20,000}C_i)(0.003)^i(0.997)^{20,000-i}$$

In general, normal curves can be used to approximate binomial probabilities closely if the number of trials is sufficiently large. This is because the histograms of binomial distributions more closely fit the shape of the area under a normal curve as the number of trials increases. To illustrate this, consider the binomial distributions with $p = 0.25$ and $n = 10$, $n = 25$, and $n = 50$. (See Figure 8.26.)

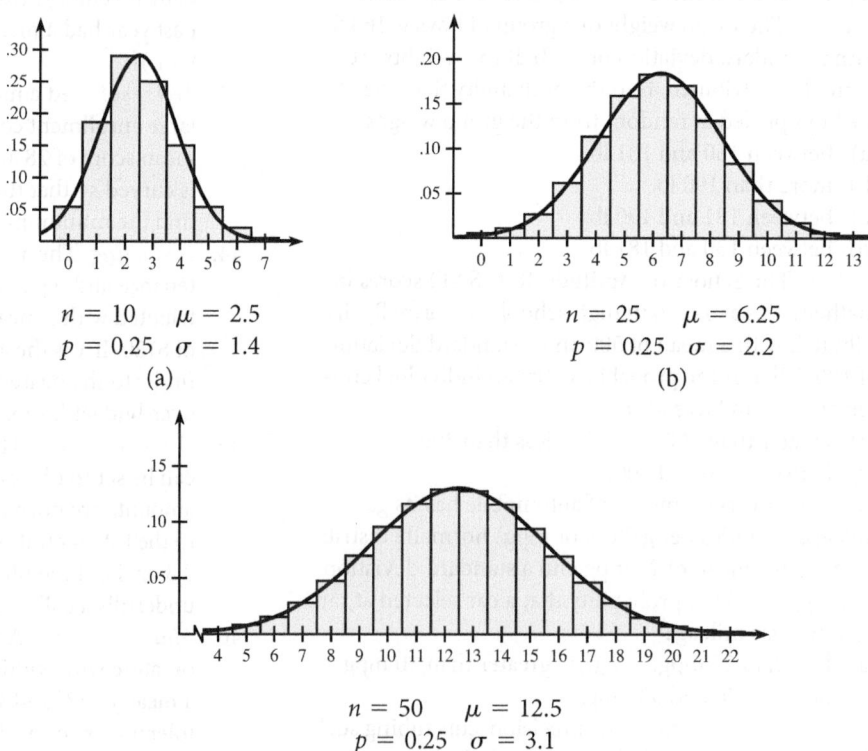

$n = 10$ $\mu = 2.5$	$n = 25$ $\mu = 6.25$
$p = 0.25$ $\sigma = 1.4$	$p = 0.25$ $\sigma = 2.2$
(a)	(b)

$n = 50$ $\mu = 12.5$
$p = 0.25$ $\sigma = 3.1$
(c)

Figure 8.26

Normal distributions can be used to approximate binomial probabilities under the following conditions.

Normal Approximation to the Binomial

For a binomial probability experiment with n trials and with the probability of success on each trial equal to p and probability of failure equal to $q = 1 - p$:

1. If $np \geq 5$ and $nq \geq 5$, then probabilities from a binomial probability distribution can be approximated accurately using a normal distribution with mean $\mu = np$ and standard deviation $\sigma = \sqrt{npq}$.
2. Because a binomial distribution uses only nonnegative integers and the normal distribution is continuous, the binomial probability that the integer x occurs is approximated by finding the normal probability over the interval $[x - 0.5, x + 0.5]$. This is referred to as the continuity correction.

Under these conditions, we can approximate a binomial probability as follows.

NORMAL APPROXIMATION OF A BINOMIAL PROBABILITY

Procedure	Example
To find a binomial probability with a normal approximation:	Sam will win $5000 if he rolls a die 18 times and gets a number divisible by 3 on exactly 12 of the rolls. What is the probability that he will win the $5000?
1. Confirm that $np \geq 5$ and $nq \geq 5$ so that probabilities from a binomial probability distribution can be approximated using a normal distribution.	1. Because $n = 18$ and the probability of rolling a number divisible by 3 is $p = 2/6 = 1/3$, we have $$np = 18 \cdot \frac{1}{3} = 6 \geq 5 \text{ and } nq = 18 \cdot \frac{2}{3} = 12 \geq 5$$
2. Compute the mean $\mu = np$ and the standard deviation $\sigma = \sqrt{npq}$ for use in the normal approximation.	2. $\mu = np = 6$ and $\sigma = \sqrt{npq} = \sqrt{4} = 2$
3. Use the continuity correction to convert the binomial range of values to the corresponding interval of normal distribution values.	3. We find the probability that x is in the continuous interval from $12 - 0.5 = 11.5$ to $12 + 0.05 = 12.5$. We approximate $\Pr(x = 12)$ by finding the normal probability approximation $\Pr(11.5 \leq x \leq 12.5)$.
4. Convert the x-values of the normal distribution to standard distribution z-scores and find the probabilities.	4. Computing the z-scores gives $$z_{11.5} = \frac{x - \mu}{\sigma} = \frac{11.5 - 6}{2} = \frac{5.5}{2} = 2.75 \text{ and}$$ $$z_{12.5} = \frac{12.5 - 6}{2} = \frac{6.5}{2} = 3.25$$ So $$\Pr(2.75 \leq z \leq 3.25) = A_{3.25} - A_{2.75}$$ $$= 0.4994 - 0.4970 = 0.0024$$ Thus the probability is approximately 0.0024.

The probability found above approximates the binomial probability

$$\Pr(x = 12) = {}_{18}C_{12}\left(\frac{1}{3}\right)^{12}\left(\frac{2}{3}\right)^{6} \approx 0.0031$$

The normal approximation would be closer if the number of trials (rolls) were larger. This binomial probability is found directly with relative ease, so the normal approximation is not particularly useful here. But it is very useful and gives an excellent approximation in solving the following problem.

EXAMPLE 1   Centenarians

Figure 8.27 shows that 80% of U.S. centenarians are women (*Source*: U.S. Bureau of the Census, "PCT3 Sex by Age," factfinder.census.gov). In a group of 6000 centenarians belonging to AARP, what is the probability that no more than 4750 will be women?

Thousands

40

4

Years of age
☐ 105 or older
☐ 100 to 104

37

10
1

9

Women   Men

Note: Components do not add to total because of rounding.

Figure 8.27

Solution

The problem is a binomial experiment with $n = 6000$ and $p = 0.80$. Because $np = 6000(0.80) = 4800$ and $nq = 6000(0.20) = 1200$, we can apply the normal approximation using

$$\mu = np = 4800 \quad \text{and} \quad \sigma = \sqrt{npq} = \sqrt{6000(0.80)(0.20)} \approx 30.984$$

We find the binomial probability $\Pr(x \le 4750)$ by using the normal approximation $\Pr(x \le 4750.5)$. The z-score for 4750.5 is

$$z = \frac{4750.5 - 4800}{30.984} \approx -1.60$$

Thus the probability that no more than 4750 of the centenarians will be women is

$$\Pr(x \le 4750.5) = \Pr(z \le -1.60) = 0.5 - A_{1.60} = 0.5 - 0.4452 = 0.0548$$

EXAMPLE 2   Fire Insurance | APPLICATION PREVIEW |

In a certain city, an insurance company has 20,000 houses insured for fire damage. If the probability that any one of these insured houses will have fire damage is 0.003, what is the probability that more than 50 of them will have fire damage?

Solution

We seek the binomial probability $\Pr(x > 50)$, where $n = 20{,}000$ and $p = 0.003$. First note that $\mu = np = 20{,}000(0.003) = 60$, $nq = 20{,}000(0.997) = 19{,}940$, and $\sigma = \sqrt{20{,}000(0.003)(0.997)} \approx 7.73$. Because np and nq are both significantly greater than 5, we are confident that the normal approximation will be very close to the binomial probability.

In the normal approximation, we find $\Pr(x \ge 50.5)$ because this gives an interval with $x > 50$. The z-score for 50.5 is

$$z = \frac{50.5 - 60}{7.73} \approx -1.23$$

and the probability is

$$\Pr(x \ge 50.5) = \Pr(z \ge -1.23) = 0.5 + A_{1.23} = 0.5 + 0.3907 = 0.8907$$

Thus the approximate probability that more than 50 of these houses will have fire damage is 0.89.

CHECKPOINT

1. Which of the following binomial probability distributions can be approximated accurately with a normal distribution?
   (a) $n = 22$, $p = 0.09$ (b) $n = 22$, $p = 0.3$
2. Suppose a binomial probability experiment has $p = \Pr(\text{Success}) = 0.4$, $n = 600$ trials, and k is the number of successes. Use a normal approximation to estimate $\Pr(k \le 252)$.

EXAMPLE **3** ### Centenarians

If 0.15% of the U.S. population lives to be 100 years of age (*Source:* U.S. Bureau of the Census), what is the probability that between 8 and 12 (inclusive) of the 3400 citizens of Springfield will live to be centenarians?

Solution

The problem is a binomial experiment with $n = 3400$ and $p = 0.0015$. Because $np = 3400(0.0015) = 5.1$ and $nq = 3400(0.9985) = 3394.9$, we can apply the normal approximation, using

$$\mu = np = 5.1 \quad \text{and} \quad \sigma = \sqrt{npq} = \sqrt{3400(0.0015)(0.9985)} \approx 2.257$$

We seek the binomial probability $\Pr(8 \le x \le 12)$ and approximate it with the normal approximation by finding $\Pr(7.5 \le x \le 12.5)$. The z-scores for 7.5 and 12.5 are

$$z_{7.5} = \frac{7.5 - 5.1}{2.257} \approx 1.06 \quad \text{and} \quad z_{12.5} = \frac{12.5 - 5.1}{2.257} \approx 3.28$$

Thus the probability that between 8 and 12 of the citizens will become centenarians is

$$\Pr(7.5 \le x \le 12.5) = \Pr(1.06 \le z \le 3.28) = A_{3.28} - A_{1.06} = 0.4995 - 0.3554 = 0.1441$$

CHECKPOINT
ANSWERS

1. (a) No, $np \not\geq 5$.   (b) Yes.
2. $\Pr(k \le 252) \approx 0.8508$

EXERCISES 8.5

In Problems 1–4, indicate which of the binomial distributions can be approximated by a normal distribution.

1. $n = 28, p = 0.3$
2. $n = 45, p = 0.1$
3. $n = 12, p = 0.3$
4. $n = 200, p = 0.005$

For the binomial experiments in Problems 5–18, find the normal approximation of the probability of

5. 91 successes in 150 trials if $p = 0.6$.
6. 740 successes in 900 trials if $p = 0.8$.
7. 96 successes in 180 trials if $p = 0.4$.
8. 17 successes in 87 trials if $p = 0.2$.
9. between 75 and 80 successes (inclusive) in 150 trials if $p = 0.6$.
10. between 65 and 70 successes (inclusive) in 120 trials if $p = 0.5$.
11. more than 80 successes in 100 trials if $p = 0.7$.
12. more than 120 successes in 200 trials if $p = 0.6$.
13. no more than 80 successes in 100 trials if $p = 0.7$.
14. no more than 450 successes in 1000 trials if $p = 0.4$.
15. at least 95 successes in 500 trials if $p = 0.2$.
16. at least 423 successes in 6000 trials if $p = 0.07$.
17. fewer than 70 successes in 180 trials if $p = 0.4$.
18. fewer than 22 successes in 87 trials if $p = 0.2$.

APPLICATIONS

In the following problems, use a normal approximation to the binomial.

19. *Gambling* If a die is rolled 300 times, what is the probability that a 6 will occur 55 times?
20. *Gambling* If a fair coin is tossed 100 times, what is the probability that 50 heads will occur?
21. *Gambling* If a fair coin is tossed 100 times, what is the probability that no more than 50 heads will occur?
22. *Gambling* If a die is rolled 300 times, what is the probability that a 6 will occur at least 55 times?
23. *Management* Circuitown buys plasma televisions in lots of 1000. If one brand of set is defective with probability 0.01, what is the probability that at least 8 sets will be defective in a lot?
24. *Management* The manager of a wholesale buyers' club has been told by the home office that 40% of all customers favor a new policy that gives nearly immediate checkout (by moving to the front of the line) for members paying a 20% premium on their annual dues. If this is true, what is the probability that at most 380 of 1000 members the manager surveyed will favor the new policy?
25. *Management* An airport announced a plan to make a special security checkpoint so that first-class passengers

would have priority passing through security. Airlines supported this plan, assuming that 25% of passengers would like the idea and it would lead to the sale of more first-class tickets. If this is true, what is the probability that more than 2800 of 10,800 passengers who were surveyed will favor the new policy?

26. *Management* Suppose that AudioMart has a secret sale released only on the Internet because management thinks that word-of-mouth publicity about the sale will result in 5% of U.S. households recognizing the company name. If this is true, what is the probability that 60 of 1200 people surveyed recognize the company name?

27. *Human resources* A report by *U.S. News & World Report* stated that 35% of all employee credentials examined had been falsified. If this is true, what is the probability that at least 75 of 200 employees hired during a year have falsified their credentials?

28. *Sales* A smoking cessation program advertises that 60% of all participants in its program quit smoking for at least 6 months. Suppose *Consumer Checkup* surveyed 400 "graduates" of the program and found that 220 had not smoked for 6 months following the end of the program. What is the probability that this will happen if the advertising claim is true?

29. *Genetics* If the ratio of boys born to girls born is 105 to 100, what is the probability that out of 2000 babies born in Santa Clara, 1030 will be girls?

30. *Biology* It has been determined empirically that the probability that a certain cell will survive for a given period of time is 0.3. What is the probability that 600 of 2000 of these cells will survive for this period of time?

31. *Insurance* Empirical records show that the probability is 0.06 that a driver insured with Riders Insurance Company will have an accident during 2019 in which he or she is at fault. If the company has 12,000 drivers insured in Century City, what is the probability that at most 800 will have an at-fault accident in 2019?

32. *Revenue* The Rent-to-Own Company estimates that 40% of its rentals result in a sale of the product. If the company rents 15,000 of its products in a year, what is the probability that it will sell at most 6100 of its products?

33. *Testing* Suppose a final exam contains 120 multiple-choice questions with 5 choices for each answer, and a poorly prepared student knows the answers to 60 questions and guesses on the other 60. What is the probability that she will answer 60% of the questions correctly? More than 60% correctly?

34. *Drugs* The probability that a certain drug will lower cholesterol significantly is 0.82. If the drug is administered to 1000 patients, what is the probability that more than 800 will have significantly lower cholesterol?

35. *Testing* A standardized exam for admission to a special program has been passed by 53% of the students taking it over the last five years.
    (a) Suppose that 1120 of 2000 students taking the test this year pass. What is the probability that at least 1120 will pass if the pass rate is 53%?
    (b) Does this suggest something is different? If so, what could have happened?

36. *TV ratings* A television show rating of 6.2 means that 6.2% of the 110 million TV households watched the show. If a sample of 100 local TV households were queried, what is the probability that more than 10 would have watched the show?

37. *Knee operations* The probability is 0.025 that a knee operation at Memorial Hospital has complications that warrant reopening the knee. If the hospital performs 1300 knee operations in a year, what is the probability that 45 or more of the operations will result in complications?

38. *Genetics* According to one of Mendel's hybridization experiments, when peas with green pods are crossed with peas with yellow pods, 25% of the offspring pods should be yellow. What is the probability that at least 152 of 580 offspring peas will have yellow pods?

CHAPTER SUMMARY & REVIEW

KEY TERMS AND FORMULAS

Section 8.1

Binomial probability experiment (p. 486)

$$Pr(x) = \binom{n}{x} p^x q^{n-x}$$

Section 8.2

Frequency histogram (p. 492)
Mode (p. 492)
Median (p. 493)

Mean (p. 494)

$$\bar{x} = \frac{\Sigma x}{n}$$

Mean for grouped data (p. 494)

$$\bar{x} = \frac{\Sigma(x \cdot f(x))}{\Sigma f(x)}$$

Range (p. 496)
Sample variance (p. 496)

$$s^2 = \frac{\Sigma(x - \bar{x})^2}{n - 1}$$

Sample standard deviation (p. 496)

$$s = \sqrt{\frac{\Sigma(x - \bar{x})^2}{n - 1}}$$

Section 8.3

Random variable (p. 502)
Discrete probability distribution (p. 502)
Probability density histogram (p. 503)
Mean and expected value (p. 503)
$\quad \mu = E(x) = \Sigma[x \Pr(x)]$
Variance (p. 506)
$\quad \sigma^2 = \Sigma(x - \mu)^2 \Pr(x)$
Standard deviation (p. 506)
$\quad \sigma = \sqrt{\sigma^2}$
Binomial probability distribution (p. 507)

Mean
$\quad \mu = np$
Standard deviation
$\quad \sigma = \sqrt{npq}$
Binomial formula (p. 509)

$$(a + b)^n = \binom{n}{n}a^n + \binom{n}{n-1}a^{n-1}b$$

$$+ \cdots + \binom{n}{1}ab^{n-1} + \binom{n}{0}b^n$$

Section 8.4

Normal distribution (p. 513)
$\quad$ Normal curve
Standard normal distribution (p. 514)

z-scores (p. 516)

$$z = \frac{x - \mu}{\sigma}$$

Section 8.5

Normal approximation to the binomial
$\quad$ distribution (p. 522)
$\quad np \geq 5$ and $nq \geq 5$

$\Pr(x)$ uses interval $[x - 0.5, x + 0.5]$
Procedure (p. 523)

REVIEW EXERCISES

Section 8.1

1. If the probability of success on each trial of an experiment is 0.4, what is the probability of 5 successes in 7 trials?

2. A bag contains 5 black balls and 7 white balls. If we draw 4 balls, with each one replaced before the next is drawn, what is the probability that
   (a) 2 balls are black?
   (b) at least 2 balls are black?

3. If a die is rolled 4 times, what is the probability that a number greater than 4 is rolled at least 2 times?

Section 8.2

Use the data in the frequency table in Problems 4–7.
4. Construct a frequency histogram for the data.
5. What is the mode of the data?
6. What is the mean of the data?
7. What is the median of the data?
8. Construct a frequency histogram for the following set of test scores: 14, 16, 15, 14, 17, 16, 12, 12, 13, 14.

Score	Frequency
1	4
2	6
3	8
4	3
5	5

9. What is the median of the scores in Problem 8?
10. What is the mode of the scores in Problem 8?
11. What is the mean of the scores in Problem 8?
12. Find the mean, variance, and standard deviation of the following sample data: 4, 3, 4, 6, 8, 0, 2.
13. Find the mean, variance, and standard deviation of the following sample data: 3, 2, 1, 5, 1, 4, 0, 2, 1, 1.

Section 8.3

14. For the following probability distribution, find the expected value $E(x)$.

x	$\Pr(x)$
1	0.2
2	0.3
3	0.4
4	0.1

Determine whether each function or table in Problems 15–18 represents a discrete probability distribution.

15. $\Pr(x) = x/15, x = 1, 2, 3, 4, 5$

16. $\Pr(x) = x/55$, $x = 1, 2, 3, 4, 5, 6, 7, 8, 9$

17.
x	Pr(x)
3	1/6
4	1/3
5	1/3
6	1/6

18.
x	Pr(x)
2	1/2
3	1/4
4	−1/4
5	1/2

19. For the probability distribution shown, find the expected value $E(x)$.

x	1	2	3	4
Pr(x)	0.4	0.3	0.2	0.1

20. For the discrete probability distribution described by $\Pr(x) = x/16$, $x = 1, 2, 3, 4, 6$, find the
    (a) mean.
    (b) variance.
    (c) standard deviation.

21. For the probability distribution shown, find the
    (a) mean.
    (b) variance.
    (c) standard deviation.

x	Pr(x)
1	1/12
2	1/6
3	1/3
4	5/12

22. A coin has been altered so that the probability that a head will occur is 2/3. If the coin is tossed 6 times, give the mean and standard deviation of the distribution of the number of heads.

23. Suppose a pair of dice is thrown 18 times. How many times would we expect a sum of 7 to occur?

24. Expand $(x + y)^5$.

Section 8.4

25. What is the area under the standard normal curve between $z = -1.6$ and $z = 1.9$?

26. If z is a standard normal score, find $\Pr(-1 \le z \le -0.5)$.

27. Find $\Pr(1.23 \le z \le 2.55)$.

28. If a variable x is normally distributed, with $\mu = 25$ and $\sigma = 5$, find $\Pr(25 \le x \le 30)$.

29. If a variable x is normally distributed, with $\mu = 25$ and $\sigma = 5$, find $\Pr(20 \le x \le 30)$.

30. If a variable x is normally distributed, with $\mu = 25$ and $\sigma = 5$, find $\Pr(30 \le x \le 35)$.

31. Find the number A so that $\Pr(-A < z < A) = 0.98$ for the standard normal z-score.

Section 8.5

For the binomial distributions in Problems 32 and 33, will the normal distribution be a good approximation if

32. $n = 25$, $p = 0.15$?
33. $n = 15$, $p = 0.4$?

For the binomial experiments in Problems 34–37, find the normal approximation for the probability of

34. 50 successes in 200 trials when $p = 0.2$.

35. at least 43 successes in 60 trials when $p = 0.8$.
36. between 19 and 36 successes (inclusive) in 80 trials when $p = 0.4$.
37. no more than 132 successes in 250 trials when $p = 0.6$.

APPLICATIONS

Section 8.1

38. *Genetics* Suppose the probability that a certain couple will have a blond child is 1/4. If they have 6 children, what is the probability that 2 of them will be blond?

39. *Sampling* Suppose 70% of a population opposes a proposal and a sample of size 5 is drawn from the population. What is the probability that the majority of the sample will favor the proposal?

40. *Crime* Suppose 20% of the population are victims of crime. Out of 5 people selected at random, find the probability that 2 are crime victims.

41. *Disease* One person in 100,000 develops a certain disease. Calculate
    (a) Pr(exactly 1 person in 100,000 has the disease).
    (b) Pr(at least 1 person in 100,000 has the disease).

Section 8.2

Farm families **The distribution of farm families (as a percent of the population) in a 50-county survey is given in the table. Use these sample data in Problems 42–44.**

Percent	Number of Counties
10–19	5
20–29	16
30–39	25
40–49	3
50–59	1

42. Make a frequency histogram for these data.
43. Use class marks to find the mean percent of farm families in these 50 counties.
44. Use class marks to find the standard deviation of the percent of farm families in these 50 counties.

Section 8.3

45. *Cancer testing* The probability that a man with prostate cancer will test positive with the prostate specific antigen (PSA) test is 0.91. If 500 men with prostate cancer are tested, how many would we expect to test positive?

46. *Fraud* A company selling substandard drugs to developing countries sold 2,000,000 capsules with 60,000 of them empty (*Source: 60 Minutes*). If a person gets 100 randomly chosen capsules from this company, what is the expected number of empty capsules this person will get?

47. *Racing* Suppose you paid $2 for a bet on a horse and, as a result, you will win $100 if your horse wins a given race. Find the expected value of the bet if the odds that the horse will win are 3 to 12.

48. *Lotteries* A state lottery pays $500 to anyone who selects the correct 3-digit number from a random drawing. If it costs $1 to play, then the probability distribution for the amount won is given in the table. What are the expected winnings of a person who plays?

x	Pr(x)
−1	0.999
499	0.001

49. *Crime* Refer to Problem 40.
    (a) What is the expected number of people in this sample that are crime victims?
    (b) Find the probability that exactly the expected number of people in this sample are victims of crime.

Section 8.4

50. *Testing* Suppose the mean SAT score for students admitted to a university is 1500, with a standard deviation of 300. Suppose that a student is selected at random. If the scores are normally distributed, find the probability that the student's SAT score is
    (a) between 1500 and 2100.
    (b) between 1800 and 2100.
    (c) greater than 2100.

51. *Net worth* Suppose the mean net worth of the residents of Sun City, a retirement community, is $611,000 (*Source: The Island Packet*). If their net worth is normally distributed with a standard deviation of $96,000,

what percent of the residents have net worths between $700,000 and $800,000?

52. *Testing* The length of time it takes to complete a college placement test is normally distributed with a mean of 39 minutes and a standard deviation of 6 minutes. How much time (to the nearest minute) is needed so that 90% of the test takers have time to finish.

Section 8.5

In Problems 53–56, use a normal approximation.

53. *Genetics* The ratio of females to males in the U.S. population is 51 to 49. If 100 people are selected at random from the population, find the probability that at least 53 will be female.

54. *Quality control* Records over 10 years indicate that 5% of Acer televisions will have some defective components. If the latest models have the same number of defects, what is the probability that 6 or more of 100 sets will have defective components?

55. *Management* Suppose that a particular Walgreens estimates that it will earn 10% of the printer ink business by offering an ink cartridge refill program. If the estimate is correct, what is the probability that more than 800 of the 7500 persons who need ink will use this Walgreens program?

56. *Revenue* Islands Realty estimates that 5% of the families who inquire about time-share villas will purchase one. If this is true, what is the probability that no more than 20 of 500 families who inquire about time-share villas will make a purchase?

8 CHAPTER TEST

1. If a coin is "loaded" so that the probability that a head will occur on each toss is 1/3, what is the probability that
   (a) 3 heads will result from 5 tosses of the coin?
   (b) at least 3 heads will occur in 5 tosses of the coin?

2. Suppose the coin in Problem 1 is tossed 12 times.
   (a) What is the expected number of heads?
   (b) Find the mean, variance, and standard deviation of the distribution of heads.

3. If x is a random variable, what properties must Pr(x) satisfy to be a discrete probability distribution function?

4. Find the expected value of the variable x for the probability distribution given in the table.

x	3	4	5	6	7	8
Pr(x)	0.2	0.3	0.1	0.1	0.2	0.1

5. For the probability distribution shown, find the mean, variance, and standard deviation.

x	10	12	15	18	20	25
Pr(x)	0.1	0.3	0.1	0.2	0.1	0.2

6. For the sample data in the table, find the mean, median, and mode.

Score	Frequency
20	5
21	7
22	3
23	4
24	2

7. If the variable x is normally distributed, with a mean of 16 and a standard deviation of 6, find the following probabilities.
   (a) $\Pr(14 \leq x \leq 22)$
   (b) $\Pr(x \leq 22)$
   (c) $\Pr(22 \leq x \leq 24)$

8. For the normal distribution with mean 70 and standard deviation 12, find:
   (a) $\Pr(73 \leq x \leq 97)$
   (b) $\Pr(65 \leq x \leq 84)$
   (c) $\Pr(x > 84)$

9. The random variable x has a normal distribution with mean 22 and standard deviation 8. Find B so that $\Pr(x > B) = 0.02$.

10. Use a normal approximation to a binomial distribution to find the probability that $x \geq 10$ if $n = 50$ and $p = 0.3$.

11. Use a normal approximation to a binomial distribution to find the probability that $x \leq 25$ if $n = 120$ and $p = 0.2$.

The table gives the ages of a sample of householders in primary families. Use this table in Problems 12 and 13.

Age of Householder (years)	Number (thousands)
15–24	3395
25–34	13,347
35–44	17,547
45–54	18,119
55–64	13,462
65+	12,978

Source: U.S. Bureau of the Census

12. Construct a histogram of the data.

13. Use class marks and the given number (frequency) in each class to find the mean and standard deviation of the ages of the householders. Use 74 as the class mark for the 65+ class.

14. The table gives the projected 2020 population of the United States.
   (a) Use the class marks and the given number (frequency) in each class to find the mean age.
   (b) In third world countries where the birth rate is higher and the life span is shorter, which group—under 30, 30–59, or 60 and over—would be most likely to be the smallest? How would this affect a third world country's mean age relative to that of the United States?

Age	Class Mark	Number (millions)
Under 15	7	68.1
15–29	22	67.3
30–44	37	66.8
45–59	52	63.3
60–74	67	53.3
Over 75	82	22.5

Source: U.S. Bureau of the Census

15. The table summarizes the number of mobile phones per 100 people in the population of each of the 64 countries with the largest number of phones.
   (a) Use class marks and the number of countries (frequency) to find the mean number of mobile phones per 100 people in the population for these countries.
   (b) Should we expect this mean to increase or decrease in the future?

Number of Mobile Phones per 100 People Population	Number of Countries
0–19	2
20–39	1
40–59	0
60–79	10
80–99	7
100–119	20
120–139	14
140–159	6
160–179	2
180–199	1
200–219	1

Source: www.cia.gov/library/publications/the-world-factbook

16. Suppose that 2% of the computer chips shipped to an assembly plant are defective.
   (a) What is the probability that 10 of 100 chips chosen from the shipment will be defective?
   (b) What is the expected number of defective chips in the shipment if it contains 1500 chips?

The table gives the percent of women who become pregnant during 1 year of use with different types of contraceptives. The "Typical Use" column includes failures from incorrect or inconsistent use. Use this table in Problems 17–19.

Failure Rates Over 1 Year

Contraceptive Type	Correct and Consistent Use	Typical Use
Spermicides	6%	21%
Diaphragm	6	18
Male latex condom	3	12
Unprotected	N/A	85

Source: R. A. Hatcher, J. Trussel, F. Stewart, et al., *Contraceptive Technology*, Irvington Pub.

17. If a group of 30 women use diaphragms correctly and consistently, how many of these 30 women could be expected to become pregnant in a year?

18. If a group of 30 women use diaphragms typically, how many of these 30 women could be expected to become pregnant in a year?

19. If spermicides and male latex condoms are used correctly by a group of 30 couples, how many of the 30 women could be expected to become pregnant in a year? Assume that these uses are independent events.

20. A new light bulb has an expected life of 18,620 hours, with a standard deviation of 4012 hours. If the hours of life of these bulbs are normally distributed, find the probability that one of these bulbs chosen at random will last
    (a) less than 10,000 hours.
    (b) more than 24,000 hours.
    (c) between 15,000 and 21,000 hours.

21. Hargray Communications offered a bundled package of television cable, broadband Internet, and basic telephone service for $99.99 for the first 3 months. If the company expects that 1% of the viewers of the ad will purchase the service, what is the probability that at least 120 of 11,000 viewers of the ad will make the purchase?

22. A juice manufacturer sells several kinds of juice in 59-oz containers. A machine fills the containers, and the amount dispensed by the machine is normally distributed with a mean of 59 oz and standard deviation of 0.5 oz. Overfilling the container wastes juice, and underfilling it risks consumer dissatisfaction. What filling tolerance t guarantees that 95% of the time the machine fills within t oz of 59 oz? *Hint:* This means that 2.5% of the time the machine dispenses more than $59 + t$ oz and 2.5% of the time it dispenses less than $59 - t$ oz.

8 EXTENDED APPLICATIONS & GROUP PROJECTS

I. Lotteries

One of the reasons the Powerball Lottery (offered by 44 states, Puerto Rico, the U.S. Virgin Islands, and the District of Columbia) is so large is that the odds of winning are so small and the pot continues to grow until someone wins. To win the Powerball Jackpot, a player's 5 game balls and 1 red powerball must match those chosen. Since Powerball began on April 19, 1992, the game has been changed. Each change has lowered the probability of winning by placing more balls in play. See the table, which compares the original and the 2015 Powerball games.

Type of Game	Original Powerball	2015 Powerball
Game	5-of-45	5-of-69
Powerballs	1-of-45	1-of-26

Source: powerball.com

1. Use the information in the table to find the probability of winning the original 5-of-45 game and that of winning the 2015 5-of-69 game. Note that the order in which the first five numbers occur does not matter and that the Powerball is not used in this game.

2. Use the information in the table to find the probability of winning the Powerball Jackpot in the original game and in the 2015 game. Note that the order in which the first five numbers occur does not matter. Approximate odds for 2015 Powerball can be found at www.powerball.com.

The minimum payoff for the Jackpot has increased from $5 million to $20 million, and the table gives the payoffs for each game.

Payoffs

Match	Original Game Payout	2015 Game Payout
5 + powerball	Jackpot	Jackpot
5	$100,000	$1,000,000
4 + powerball	5,000	50,000
4	100	100
3 + powerball	100	100
3	5	7
2 + powerball	5	7
1 + powerball	2	4
Powerball	1	4

Source: powerball.com

3. Assuming that a share of the Jackpot is $40 million, find the expected winnings from one ticket in the original game and in the 2015 game. The sponsors of the Powerball game claim that making the probability lower improves the game. How do they justify that claim?

II. Statistics in Medical Research; Hypothesis Testing

Bering Research Laboratories is involved in a national study organized by the National Centers for Disease Control to determine whether a new birth control pill affects the blood pressures of women who are using it. A random sample of 100 women using the pill was selected, and the participants' blood pressures were measured. The mean blood pressure was $\bar{x} = 112.5$. If the blood pressures of all women are normally distributed, with mean $\mu = 110$ and standard deviation $\sigma = 12$, is the mean of this sample sufficiently far from the mean of the population of all women to indicate that the birth control pill affects blood pressure?

To answer this question, researchers at Bering Labs first need to know how the means of samples drawn from a normal population are distributed. As a result of the **Central Limit Theorem,** if all possible samples of size n are drawn from a normal population that has mean μ and standard deviation σ, then the distribution of the means of these samples will be normally distributed with mean μ but with standard deviation given by

$$\sigma_{\bar{x}} = \frac{\sigma}{\sqrt{n}}$$

To conclude whether women using this birth control pill have blood pressures that are significantly different from those of all women in the population, researchers must decide whether the mean $\bar{x}$ of their sample is so far from the population mean μ that it is unlikely that the sample was chosen from the population.

In this statistical test, the researchers will assume that the sample has been drawn from the population of women with mean $\mu = 110$ unless the blood pressures collected in the sample are so different from those of the population that it is not reasonable to make this assumption. In statistics, we can say that the assumption is unreasonable if the probability that the sample mean, $\bar{x} = 112.5$, could be drawn from this population, with mean 110, is less than 0.05. If this probability is less than 0.05, we say that the sample is drawn from a population with a mean different from 110, which strongly suggests that the women who have taken the birth control pill have, on average, blood pressures different from those of the women who are not using the pill. That is, there is statistically significant evidence that the pill affects the blood pressures of women.

Because 95% of all normally distributed data points lie within 2 standard deviations of the mean, researchers at Bering Labs need to determine whether the sample mean $\bar{x} = 112.5$ is more than 2 standard deviations from $\mu = 110$. To determine how many standard deviations $\bar{x} = 112.5$ is from $\mu = 110$, they compute the z-score for $\bar{x}$ with the formula

$$z_{\bar{x}} = \frac{\bar{x} - \mu}{\sigma/\sqrt{n}}$$

Use this to determine whether there is sufficient evidence that the new birth control pill affects blood pressure.

Derivatives

9

If a firm receives $90,000 in revenue during a 30-day month, its average revenue per day is $90,000/30 = $3000. This does not necessarily mean the actual revenue was $3000 on any one day, just that the average was $3000 per day. Similarly, if a person drove 50 miles in one hour, the average velocity was 50 miles per hour, but the driver still could have received a speeding ticket for traveling 70 miles per hour.

The smaller the time interval, the nearer the average velocity will be to the instantaneous velocity (the speedometer reading). Similarly, changes in revenue over a smaller number of units can give information about the instantaneous rate of change of revenue. The mathematical bridge from average rates of change to instantaneous rates of change is the limit.

This chapter is concerned with limits and rates of change. We will see that the derivative of a function can be used to determine instantaneous rates of change.

The topics and some representative applications discussed in this chapter include the following.

Prerequisite Problem Type	For Section	Answer	Section for Review
If $f(x) = \dfrac{x^2 - x - 6}{x + 2}$, then find: (a) $f(-2.1)$ (b) $f(-2)$	**9.1–9.9**	(a) -5.1 (b) undefined	1.2 Function notation
Let $f(x) = \begin{cases} x^2 + 1 & \text{if } x \le 1 \\ x + 2 & \text{if } x > 1 \end{cases}$, find: (a) $f(0.99)$ (b) $f(1.01)$	**9.1**	(a) 1.9801 (b) 3.01	2.4 Piecewise defined functions
Factor: (a) $x^2 - x - 6$ (b) $x^2 - 4$ (c) $x^2 + 3x + 2$	**9.1** **9.7**	(a) $(x + 2)(x - 3)$ (b) $(x - 2)(x + 2)$ (c) $(x + 1)(x + 2)$	0.6 Factoring
Write as a power: (a) $\sqrt{t}$ (b) $\dfrac{1}{x}$ (c) $\dfrac{1}{\sqrt[3]{x^2 + 1}}$	**9.4–9.8**	(a) $t^{1/2}$ (b) x^{-1} (c) $(x^2 + 1)^{-1/3}$	0.3, 0.4 Exponents and radicals
Simplify: (a) $\dfrac{4(x + h)^2 - 4x^2}{h}$ if $h \ne 0$ (b) $(2x^3 + 3x + 1)(2x) + (x^2 + 4)(6x^2 + 3)$ (c) $\dfrac{x(3x^2) - x^3(1)}{x^2}$ if $x \ne 0$	**9.3** **9.5** **9.7**	(a) $8x + 4h$ (b) $10x^4 + 33x^2 + 2x + 12$ (c) $2x$	0.5 Simplifying algebraic expressions
Simplify: (a) $\dfrac{x^2 - x - 6}{x + 2}$ if $x \ne -2$ (b) $\dfrac{x^2 - 4}{x - 2}$ if $x \ne 2$	**9.1** **9.7**	(a) $x - 3$ (b) $x + 2$	0.7 Simplifying fractions
If $f(x) = 3x^2 + 2x$, find $\dfrac{f(x + h) - f(x)}{h}$ if $h \ne 0$	**9.3**	$6x + 3h + 2$	1.2 Function notation
Find the slope of the line passing through $(1, 2)$ and $(2, 4)$.	**9.3**	2	1.3 Slopes
Write the equation of the line passing through $(1, 5)$ with slope 8.	**9.3** **9.4** **9.6**	$y = 8x - 3$	1.3 Point-slope equation of a line

SECTION 9.1   Limits

OBJECTIVES

- To use graphs and numerical tables to find limits of functions when they exist
- To find limits of polynomial functions
- To find limits of rational functions
- To find limits of piecewise defined functions

APPLICATION PREVIEW

Although everyone recognizes the value of eliminating pollution from smokestack emissions of factories, company owners are concerned about the cost of removing this pollution. Suppose that USA Steel has shown that the daily cost C of removing p percent of the particulate pollution from the emissions at one of its plants is

$$C = C(p) = \frac{7300p}{100 - p} \quad \text{(dollars)}$$

To investigate the cost of removing as much of the pollution as possible, we can evaluate the limit as p (the percent) approaches 100 from values less than 100. (See Example 6.) Using a limit is important in this case because this function is undefined at $p = 100$. (It is impossible to remove 100% of the pollution.)

In various applications, we have seen the importance of the slope of a line as a rate of change. In particular, the slope of a linear total cost, total revenue, or profit function for a product tells us the marginals or rates of change of these functions. When these functions are not linear, how do we define marginals (and slope)?

We can get an idea about how to extend the concept of slope (and rate of change) to functions that are not linear. Observe that for many curves, if we take a very close (or "zoom-in") view near a point, the curve appears straight. (See Figure 9.1.) We can think of the slope of the "straight" line as the slope of the curve at the point. The mathematical process that achieves this is the process of taking limits. The concept of limit is essential to the study of calculus.

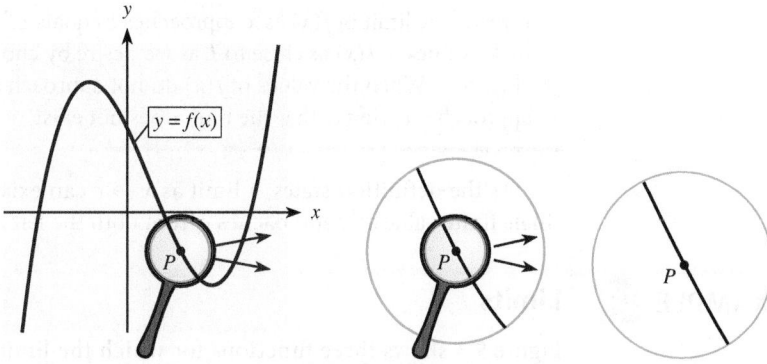

Figure 9.1   When we zoom in near point P, the curve appears straight.

Concept of a Limit   We have used the notation $f(c)$ to indicate the value of a function $f(x)$ at $x = c$. If we need to discuss a value that $f(x)$ approaches as x approaches c, we use the idea of a **limit**. For example, if

$$f(x) = \frac{x^2 - x - 6}{x + 2}$$

then we know that $x = -2$ is not in the domain of $f(x)$, so $f(-2)$ does not exist even though $f(x)$ exists for every value of $x \neq -2$. Figure 9.2 on the next page shows the graph of $y = f(x)$ with an open circle where $x = -2$. The open circle indicates that $f(-2)$ does not exist but shows that points near $x = -2$ have functional values that lie on the line on either side of the open circle. Even though $f(-2)$ is not defined, the figure shows that as x approaches -2 from either side of -2, the graph approaches the open circle at $(-2, -5)$ and the values of $f(x)$ approach -5. Thus -5 is the limit of $f(x)$ as x approaches -2, and we write

$$\lim_{x \to -2} f(x) = -5, \quad \text{or} \quad f(x) \to -5 \quad \text{as} \quad x \to -2$$

TABLE 9.1

LEFT OF −2

x	$f(x) = \dfrac{x^2 - x - 6}{x + 2}$
−3.000	−6.000
−2.500	−5.500
−2.100	−5.100
−2.010	−5.010
−2.001	−5.001

RIGHT OF −2

x	$f(x) = \dfrac{x^2 - x - 6}{x + 2}$
−1.000	−4.000
−1.500	−4.500
−1.900	−4.900
−1.990	−4.990
−1.999	−4.999

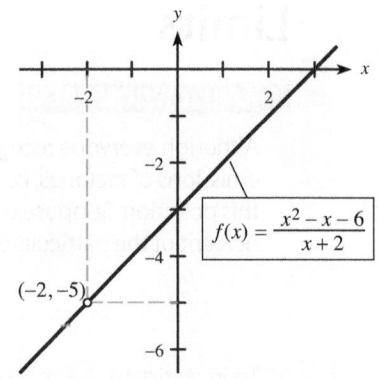

Figure 9.2

This conclusion is fairly obvious from the graph, but it is not so obvious from the equation for $f(x)$.

We can use the values near $x = -2$ in Table 9.1 to help verify that $f(x) \to -5$ as $x \to -2$. Note that to the left of −2, the values of $f(x)$ get very close to −5 as x gets very close to −2, and to the right of −2, the values of $f(x)$ get very close to −5 as x gets very close to −2. Hence, Table 9.1 and Figure 9.2 indicate that the value of $f(x)$ approaches −5 as x approaches −2 from both sides of $x = -2$.

From our discussion of the graph in Figure 9.2 and Table 9.1, we see that as x approaches −2 from either side of −2, the limit of the function is the value L that the function approaches. This limit L is not necessarily the value of the function at $x = -2$. This leads to our intuitive definition of **limit.**

Limit

Let $f(x)$ be a function defined on an open interval containing c, except perhaps at c. Then

$$\lim_{x \to c} f(x) = L$$

is read "the limit of $f(x)$ as x approaches c equals L." The number L exists if we can make values of $f(x)$ as close to L as we desire by choosing values of x sufficiently close to c. When the values of $f(x)$ do not approach a single finite value L as x approaches c, we say that the limit does not exist.

As the definition states, a limit as $x \to c$ can exist only if the function approaches a single finite value as x approaches c from both the left and right of c.

EXAMPLE 1   Limits

Figure 9.3 shows three functions for which the limit exists as x approaches 2. Use this figure to find the following.

(a) $\lim_{x \to 2} f(x)$ and $f(2)$ (if it exists)

(b) $\lim_{x \to 2} g(x)$ and $g(2)$ (if it exists)

(c) $\lim_{x \to 2} h(x)$ and $h(2)$ (if it exists)

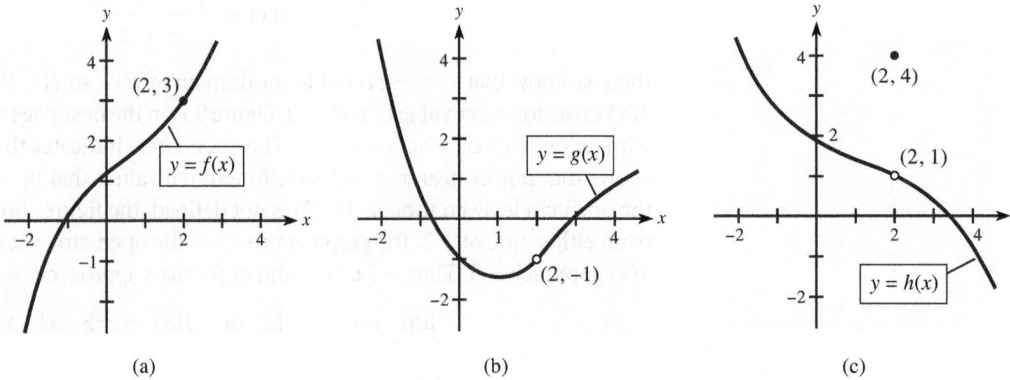

(a)   (b)   (c)

Figure 9.3

Solution

(a) From the graph in Figure 9.3(a), we see that as x approaches 2 from both the left and the right, the graph approaches the point $(2, 3)$. Thus $f(x)$ approaches the single value 3. That is,

$$\lim_{x \to 2} f(x) = 3$$

The value of $f(2)$ is the y-coordinate of the point on the graph at $x = 2$. Thus $f(2) = 3$.

(b) Figure 9.3(b) shows that as x approaches 2 from both the left and the right, the graph approaches the open circle at $(2, -1)$. Thus

$$\lim_{x \to 2} g(x) = -1$$

The figure also shows that at $x = 2$, there is no point on the graph. Thus $g(2)$ is undefined.

(c) Figure 9.3(c) shows that

$$\lim_{x \to 2} h(x) = 1$$

The figure also shows that at $x = 2$, there is a point on the graph at $(2, 4)$. Thus $h(2) = 4$, and we see that $\lim_{x \to 2} h(x) \neq h(2)$.

As Example 1 shows, the limit of the function as x approaches c may or may not be the same as the value of the function at $x = c$.

In Example 1, we saw that the limit as x approaches 2 meant the limit as x approaches 2 from both the left and the right. We also can consider limits from only the left or only the right; these are called **one-sided limits.**

One-Sided Limits

Limit from the Right: $\lim_{x \to c^+} f(x) = L$
means that the values of $f(x)$ approach the value L as $x \to c$ but $x > c$.

Limit from the Left: $\lim_{x \to c^-} f(x) = M$
means that the values of $f(x)$ approach the value M as $x \to c$ but $x < c$.

Note that when one or both one-sided limits fail to exist, then the limit does not exist. Also, when the one-sided limits differ, such as if $L \neq M$ above, then the values of $f(x)$ do not approach a *single* value as x approaches c, and $\lim_{x \to c} f(x)$ does not exist.

EXAMPLE **2**   **One-Sided Limits**

Using the functions graphed in Figure 9.4, determine why the limit as $x \to 2$ does not exist for each function

(a) $f(x)$ (b) $g(x)$ (c) $h(x)$

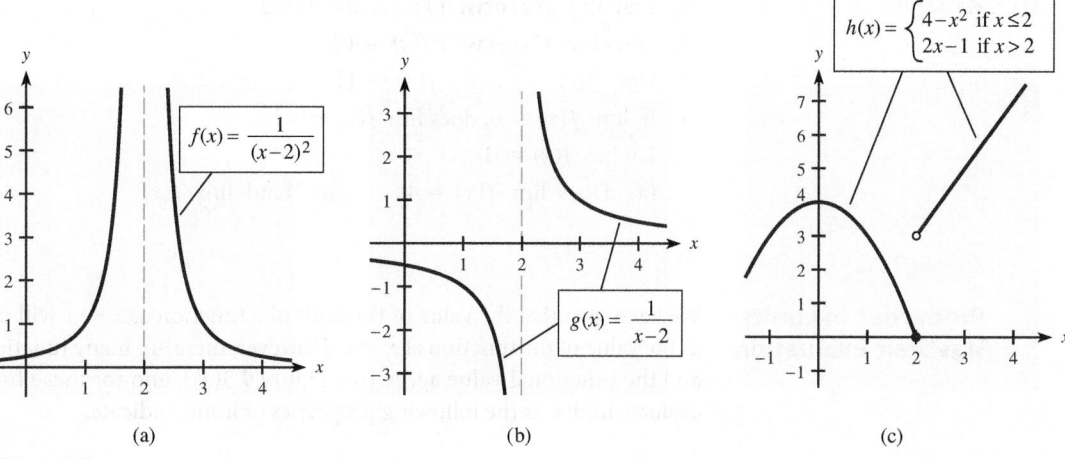

(a)   (b)   (c)

Figure 9.4

Solution

(a) As $x \to 2$ from both the left side and the right side of $x = 2$, $f(x)$ increases without bound, which we denote by saying that $f(x)$ approaches ∞ as $x \to 2$. In this case, $\lim\limits_{x \to 2} f(x)$ does not exist [denoted by $\lim\limits_{x \to 2} f(x)$ DNE] because $f(x)$ does not approach a finite value as $x \to 2$. In this case, we write

$$f(x) \to \infty \text{ as } x \to 2$$

The graph has a vertical asymptote at $x = 2$.

(b) As $x \to 2$ from the left, $g(x)$ approaches $-\infty$, and as $x \to 2$ from the right, $g(x)$ approaches ∞, so $g(x)$ does not approach a finite value as $x \to 2$. Therefore, the limit does not exist. The graph of $y = g(x)$ has a vertical asymptote at $x = 2$.
In this case, we summarize by writing

$$\lim\limits_{x \to 2^-} g(x) \text{ DNE} \qquad \text{or} \qquad g(x) \to -\infty \text{ as } x \to 2^-$$

$$\lim\limits_{x \to 2^+} g(x) \text{ DNE} \qquad \text{or} \qquad g(x) \to \infty \text{ as } x \to 2^+$$

and

$$\lim\limits_{x \to 2} g(x) \text{ DNE}$$

(c) As $x \to 2$ from the left, the graph approaches the point at $(2, 0)$, so $\lim\limits_{x \to 2^-} h(x) = 0$. As $x \to 2$ from the right, the graph approaches the open circle at $(2, 3)$, so $\lim\limits_{x \to 2^+} h(x) = 3$. Because these one-sided limits differ, $\lim\limits_{x \to 2} h(x)$ does not exist. ■

Examples 1 and 2 illustrate the following two important facts regarding limits.

The Limit

1. The limit $\lim\limits_{x \to c} f(x) = L$ only if the following two conditions are satisfied:

   (a) The limit L is a finite value (real number).
   (b) The limit as x approaches c from the left equals the limit as x approaches c from the right. That is, we must have

   $$\lim\limits_{x \to c^-} f(x) = \lim\limits_{x \to c^+} f(x)$$

   Figure 9.4 and Example 2 illustrate cases where $\lim\limits_{x \to c} f(x)$ does not exist.

2. The limit $\lim\limits_{x \to c} f(x)$ and the function value $f(c)$ are independent. When $\lim\limits_{x \to c} f(x)$ exists, $f(c)$ may be (i) the same as the limit, (ii) undefined, or (iii) defined but different from the limit. (See Figure 9.3 and Example 1.)

CHECKPOINT

1. Can $\lim\limits_{x \to c} f(x)$ exist if $f(c)$ is undefined?
2. Does $\lim\limits_{x \to c} f(x)$ exist if $f(c) = 0$?
3. Does $f(c) = 1$ if $\lim\limits_{x \to c} f(x) = 1$?
4. If $\lim\limits_{x \to c^-} f(x) = 0$, does $\lim\limits_{x \to c} f(x)$ exist?
5. Let $\lim\limits_{x \to c} f(x) = 4$.
   (a) Does $\lim\limits_{x \to c^+} f(x) = 4$?   (b) Find $\lim\limits_{x \to c^-} f(x)$.

Properties of Limits; Algebraic Evaluation

We have seen that the value of the limit of a function as $x \to c$ will not always be the same as the value of the function at $x = c$. However, there are many functions for which the limit and the functional value agree [see Figure 9.3(a)], and for these functions, we can easily evaluate limits, as the following properties of limits indicate.

Properties of Limits

If k is a constant, $\lim_{x \to c} f(x) = L$, and $\lim_{x \to c} g(x) = M$, then the following are true.

I. $\lim_{x \to c} k = k$

II. $\lim_{x \to c} x = c$

III. $\lim_{x \to c} [f(x) \pm g(x)] = L \pm M$

IV. $\lim_{x \to c} [f(x) \cdot g(x)] = LM$

V. $\lim_{x \to c} \dfrac{f(x)}{g(x)} = \dfrac{L}{M}$ if $M \neq 0$

VI. $\lim_{x \to c} \sqrt[n]{f(x)} = \sqrt[n]{\lim_{x \to c} f(x)} = \sqrt[n]{L}$,

provided $L > 0$ when n is even.

If f is a polynomial function, then Properties I–IV imply that $\lim_{x \to c} f(x)$ can be found by evaluating $f(c)$. Moreover, if h is a rational function whose denominator is not zero at $x = c$, then Property V implies that $\lim_{x \to c} h(x)$ can be found by evaluating $h(c)$. The following summarizes these observations and recalls the definitions of polynomial and rational functions.

Function	Definition	Limit
Polynomial function	The function $f(x) = a_n x^n + a_{n-1} x^{n-1} + \cdots + a_1 x + a_0,$ where $a_n \neq 0$ and n is a positive integer, is called a **polynomial function** of degree n.	$\lim_{x \to c} f(x) = f(c)$ for all values c (by Properties I–IV)
Rational function	The function $$h(x) = \frac{f(x)}{g(x)}$$ where both $f(x)$ and $g(x)$ are polynomial functions, is called a **rational function.**	$\lim_{x \to c} h(x) = \lim_{x \to c} \dfrac{f(x)}{g(x)} = \dfrac{f(c)}{g(c)}$ when $g(c) \neq 0$ (by Property V)

EXAMPLE 3   Limits

Find the following limits, if they exist.

(a) $\lim_{x \to -1} (x^3 - 2x)$ (b) $\lim_{x \to 4} \dfrac{x^2 - 4x}{x - 2}$

Solution

(a) Note that $f(x) = x^3 - 2x$ is a polynomial, so

$$\lim_{x \to -1} f(x) = f(-1) = (-1)^3 - 2(-1) = 1$$

Figure 9.5(a) on the next page shows the graph of $f(x) = x^3 - 2x$.

(b) Note that this limit has the form

$$\lim_{x \to c} \frac{f(x)}{g(x)}$$

where $f(x)$ and $g(x)$ are polynomials and $g(c) \neq 0$. Therefore, we have

$$\lim_{x \to 4} \frac{x^2 - 4x}{x - 2} = \frac{4^2 - 4(4)}{4 - 2} = \frac{0}{2} = 0$$

Figure 9.5(b) shows the graph of $g(x) = \dfrac{x^2 - 4x}{x - 2}$.

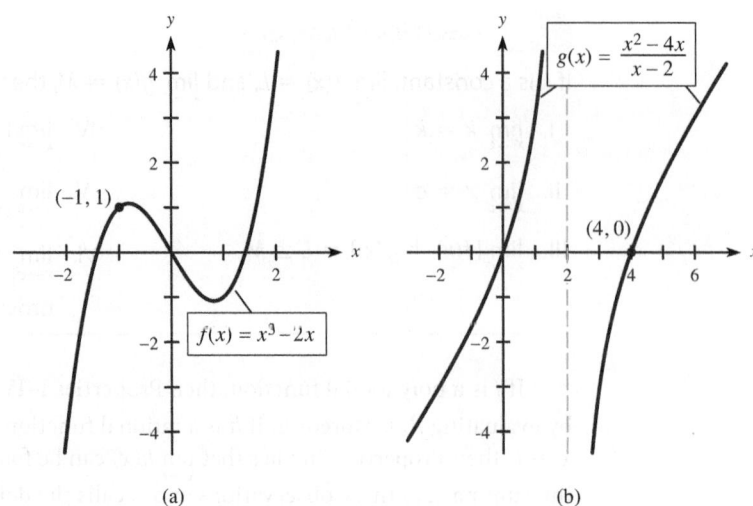

Figure 9.5   (a)   (b)

We have seen that we can use Property V to find the limit of a rational function $f(x)/g(x)$ as long as the denominator is *not* zero. If the limit of the denominator of $f(x)/g(x)$ is zero, then there are two possible cases.

Rational Functions: Evaluating Limits of the Form $\lim\limits_{x\to c} \dfrac{f(x)}{g(x)}$ where $\lim\limits_{x\to c} g(x) = 0$	**Type I.** If $\lim\limits_{x\to c} f(x) = 0$ and $\lim\limits_{x\to c} g(x) = 0$, then $\lim\limits_{x\to c} \dfrac{f(x)}{g(x)}$ has the **0/0 indeterminate form** at $x = c$. We can factor $x - c$ from $f(x)$ and $g(x)$, reduce the fraction, and then find the limit of the resulting expression, if it exists. **Type II.** If $\lim\limits_{x\to c} f(x) \neq 0$ and $\lim\limits_{x\to c} g(x) = 0$, then $\lim\limits_{x\to c} \dfrac{f(x)}{g(x)}$ does not exist. In this case, the values of $f(x)/g(x)$ become unbounded as x approaches c; the line $x = c$ is a vertical asymptote.

EXAMPLE 4   0/0 Indeterminate Form

Evaluate the following limits, if they exist.

(a) $\lim\limits_{x\to 2} \dfrac{x^2 - 4}{x - 2}$ (b) $\lim\limits_{x\to 1} \dfrac{x^2 - 3x + 2}{x^2 - 1}$

Solution

(a) This limit has the 0/0 indeterminate form at $x = 2$ because both the numerator and denominator equal zero when $x = 2$. Thus we can factor $x - 2$ from both the numerator and the denominator and reduce the fraction. (We can divide by $x - 2$ because $x - 2 \neq 0$ while $x \to 2$.)

$$\lim_{x\to 2} \frac{x^2 - 4}{x - 2} = \lim_{x\to 2} \frac{(x - 2)(x + 2)}{x - 2} = \lim_{x\to 2} (x + 2) = 4$$

Figure 9.6(a) shows the graph of $f(x) = (x^2 - 4)/(x - 2)$. Note the open circle at $(2, 4)$.

(b) By substituting 1 for x in $(x^2 - 3x + 2)/(x^2 - 1)$, we see that the expression has the 0/0 indeterminate form at $x = 1$, so $x - 1$ is a factor of both the numerator and the denominator. (We can then reduce the fraction because $x - 1 \neq 0$ while $x \to 1$.)

$$\lim_{x\to 1} \frac{x^2 - 3x + 2}{x^2 - 1} = \lim_{x\to 1} \frac{(x - 1)(x - 2)}{(x - 1)(x + 1)} = \lim_{x\to 1} \frac{x - 2}{x + 1}$$
$$= \frac{1 - 2}{1 + 1} = \frac{-1}{2} \qquad \text{(by Property V)}$$

Figure 9.6(b) shows the graph of $g(x) = (x^2 - 3x + 2)/(x^2 - 1)$. Note the open circle at $(1, -\frac{1}{2})$.

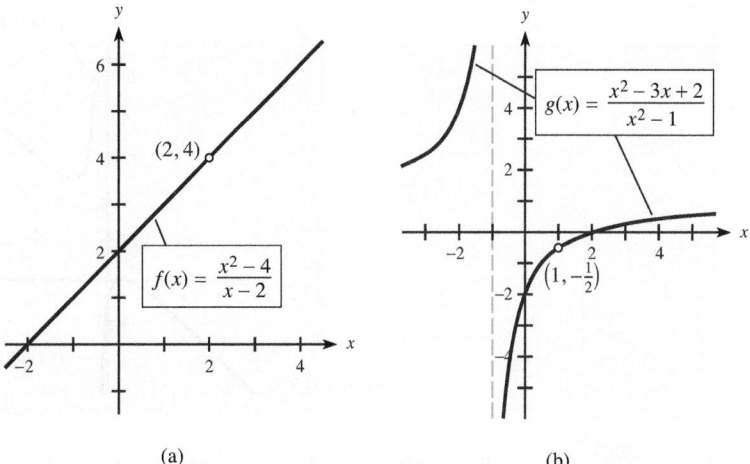

Figure 9.6   (a)   (b)

Note that although both problems in Example 4 had the 0/0 indeterminate form, they had different answers.

EXAMPLE 5   Limit with $a/0$ Form

Find $\displaystyle \lim_{x \to 1} \frac{x^2 + 3x + 2}{x - 1}$, if it exists.

Solution

Substituting 1 for x in the function results in $6/0$, so this limit has the form $a/0$, with $a \neq 0$, and is like the Type II form discussed previously. Hence the limit does not exist. Because the numerator is not zero when $x = 1$, we know that $x - 1$ is *not* a factor of the numerator, and we cannot divide numerator and denominator as we did in Example 4. Table 9.2 confirms that this limit does not exist, because the values of the expression become unbounded as x approaches 1.

TABLE 9.2

Left of $x = 1$		Right of $x = 1$	
x	$\dfrac{x^2 + 3x + 2}{x - 1}$	x	$\dfrac{x^2 + 3x + 2}{x - 1}$
0.5	-7.5	1.5	17.5
0.7	-15.3	1.2	35.2
0.9	-55.1	1.1	65.1
0.99	-595.01	1.01	605.01
0.999	-5995.001	1.001	6005.001
0.9999	$-59{,}995.0001$	1.0001	60,005.0001
$\displaystyle \lim_{x \to 1^-} \frac{x^2 + 3x + 2}{x - 1}$ DNE		$\displaystyle \lim_{x \to 1^+} \frac{x^2 + 3x + 2}{x - 1}$ DNE	
$(f(x) \to -\infty$ as $x \to 1^-)$		$(f(x) \to \infty$ as $x \to 1^+)$	

The left-hand and right-hand limits do not exist. Thus $\displaystyle \lim_{x \to 1} \frac{x^2 + 3x + 2}{x - 1}$ does not exist.

In Example 5, even though the left-hand and right-hand limits do not exist (see Table 9.2), knowledge that the functional values are unbounded (that is, they become infinite) is helpful in graphing. The graph is shown in Figure 9.7 on the next page. We see that $x = 1$ is a vertical asymptote.

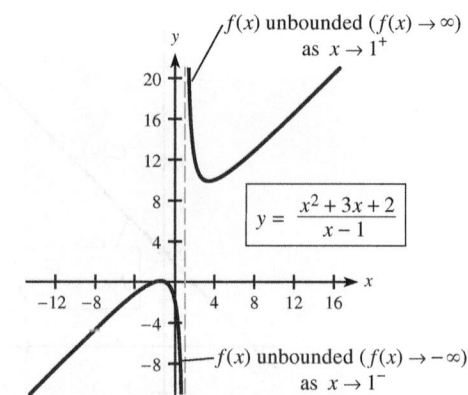

Figure 9.7

$f(x)$ unbounded ($f(x) \to \infty$) as $x \to 1^+$

$$y = \frac{x^2 + 3x + 2}{x - 1}$$

$f(x)$ unbounded ($f(x) \to -\infty$) as $x \to 1^-$

EXAMPLE 6   Cost-Benefit | APPLICATION PREVIEW |

USA Steel has shown that the daily cost C of removing p percent of the particulate pollution from the smokestack emissions at one of its plants is

$$C = C(p) = \frac{7300p}{100 - p}$$

Investigate the cost of removing as much of the pollution as possible.

Solution

First note that the costs of removing 90% and 99% of the pollution are found as follows:

Removing 90%: $C(90) = \dfrac{7300(90)}{100 - 90} = \dfrac{657{,}000}{10} = 65{,}700$ (dollars)

Removing 99%: $C(99) = \dfrac{7300(99)}{100 - 99} = \dfrac{722{,}700}{1} = 722{,}700$ (dollars)

The cost of removing 100% of the pollution is undefined because the denominator of the function is 0 when $p = 100$. To see what the cost approaches as p approaches 100 from values smaller than 100, we evaluate $\displaystyle\lim_{x \to 100^-} \frac{7300p}{100 - p}$. This limit has the Type II form for rational functions. Thus $\dfrac{7300p}{100 - p} \to \infty$ as $x \to 100^-$, which means that as the amount of pollution that is removed approaches 100%, the cost increases without bound. (That is, it is cost prohibitive to remove 100% of the pollution.)

CHECKPOINT

6. Evaluate the following limits (if they exist).

(a) $\displaystyle\lim_{x \to -3} \frac{2x^2 + 5x - 3}{x^2 - 9}$ (b) $\displaystyle\lim_{x \to 5} \frac{x^2 - 3x - 3}{x^2 - 8x + 1}$ (c) $\displaystyle\lim_{x \to -3/4} \frac{4x}{4x + 3}$

In Problems 7–10, assume that f, g, and h are polynomials.

7. Does $\displaystyle\lim_{x \to c} f(x) = f(c)$?

8. Does $\displaystyle\lim_{x \to c} \frac{g(x)}{h(x)} = \frac{g(c)}{h(c)}$?

9. If $g(c) = 0$ and $h(c) = 0$, can we be certain that

(a) $\displaystyle\lim_{x \to c} \frac{g(x)}{h(x)} = 0$?   (b) $\displaystyle\lim_{x \to c} \frac{g(x)}{h(x)}$ exists?

10. If $g(c) \neq 0$ and $h(c) = 0$, what can be said about $\displaystyle\lim_{x \to c} \frac{g(x)}{h(x)}$ and $\displaystyle\lim_{x \to c} \frac{h(x)}{g(x)}$?

Limits of Piecewise Defined Functions

As we noted in Section 2.4, "Special Functions and Their Graphs," many applications are modeled by piecewise defined functions. To see how we evaluate a limit involving a piecewise defined function, consider the following example.

EXAMPLE 7 Limits of a Piecewise Defined Function

Find $\lim\limits_{x \to 1^-} f(x)$, $\lim\limits_{x \to 1^+} f(x)$, and $\lim\limits_{x \to 1} f(x)$, if they exist, for

$$f(x) = \begin{cases} x^2 + 1 & \text{if } x \leq 1 \\ x + 2 & \text{if } x > 1 \end{cases}$$

Solution

Because $f(x)$ is defined by $x^2 + 1$ when $x < 1$,

$$\lim_{x \to 1^-} f(x) = \lim_{x \to 1^-} (x^2 + 1) = 2$$

Because $f(x)$ is defined by $x + 2$ when $x > 1$,

$$\lim_{x \to 1^+} f(x) = \lim_{x \to 1^+} (x + 2) = 3$$

And because

$$2 = \lim_{x \to 1^-} f(x) \neq \lim_{x \to 1^+} f(x) = 3$$

$\lim\limits_{x \to 1} f(x)$ does not exist. Table 9.3 and Figure 9.8 show these results numerically and graphically.

TABLE 9.3	
LEFT OF 1	
x	$f(x) = x^2 + 1$
0.9	1.81
0.99	1.98
0.999	1.998
0.9999	1.9998
RIGHT OF 1	
x	$f(x) = x + 2$
1.01	3.01
1.001	3.001
1.0001	3.0001
1.00001	3.00001

Figure 9.8

Calculator Note

We have used graphical, numerical, and algebraic methods to understand and evaluate limits. Graphing calculators can be especially effective when exploring limits graphically or numerically. See the following example and Appendix A, Section 9.1, for details.

EXAMPLE 8 Limits: Graphically, Numerically, and Algebraically

Consider the following limits.

(a) $\lim\limits_{x \to 5} \dfrac{x^2 + 2x - 35}{x^2 - 6x + 5}$ (b) $\lim\limits_{x \to -1} \dfrac{2x}{x + 1}$

Investigate each limit by using the following methods.

(i) Graphically: Graph the function with a graphing calculator and trace near the limiting x-value.

(ii) Numerically: Use the table feature of a graphing calculator to evaluate the function very close to the limiting x-value.

(iii) Algebraically: Use properties of limits and algebraic techniques.

Solution

(a) $\lim\limits_{x\to5} \dfrac{x^2 + 2x - 35}{x^2 - 6x + 5}$

   (i) Figures 9.9(a) and 9.9(b) show the graph of $y = (x^2 + 2x - 35)/(x^2 - 6x + 5)$. Tracing near $x = 5$ will show y-values getting close to 3.

   (ii) Figure 9.9(c) shows a table for $y_1 = (x^2 + 2x - 35)/(x^2 - 6x + 5)$ with x-values approaching 5 from both sides. (Note that the function is undefined at $x = 5$.) Again, the y-values approach 3 as x approaches 5 from both sides.

   Both (i) and (ii) strongly suggest $\lim\limits_{x\to5} \dfrac{x^2 + 2x - 35}{x^2 - 6x + 5} = 3$.

   (iii) Algebraic evaluation of this limit confirms what the graph and the table suggest.

$$\lim\limits_{x\to5} \dfrac{x^2 + 2x - 35}{x^2 - 6x + 5} = \lim\limits_{x\to5} \dfrac{(x + 7)(x - 5)}{(x - 1)(x - 5)} = \lim\limits_{x\to5} \dfrac{x + 7}{x - 1} = \dfrac{12}{4} = 3$$

X	Y₁
4.9	3.0513
4.99	3.005
4.999	3.0005
5	ERROR
5.001	2.9995
5.01	2.995
5.1	2.9512

X=4.9

Figure 9.9   (a)   (b)   (c)

(a)

X	Y₁
-1.1	22
-1.01	202
-1.001	2002
-1	ERROR
-.999	-1998
-.99	-198
-.9	-18

X=-.9

(b)

Figure 9.10

(b) $\lim\limits_{x\to-1} \dfrac{2x}{x + 1}$

   (i) Figure 9.10(a) shows the graph of $y = 2x/(x + 1)$; it indicates a break in the graph near $x = -1$. Evaluation confirms that the break occurs at $x = -1$ and suggests that the function becomes unbounded near $x = -1$. In addition, we can see that as x approaches -1 from opposite sides, the function is headed in different directions. All this indicates that the limit does not exist.

   (ii) Figure 9.10(b) shows a graphing calculator table of values for $y_1 = 2x/(x + 1)$ and with x-values approaching $x = -1$ from both sides. The table reinforces our preliminary conclusion from the graph that the limit does not exist, because the function values are not approaching a single value and are becoming unbounded near $x = -1$.

   (iii) Algebraically, we see that this limit has the form $-2/0$. Thus $\lim\limits_{x\to-1} \dfrac{2x}{x + 1}$ DNE.

Spreadsheet Note The Excel spreadsheet indicates that $\lim\limits_{x\to2} \dfrac{x^2 - 4}{x - 2} = 4$. See Appendix B, Sections 9.1 and 9.2, or the Online Excel Guide for details.

	A	B	C	D
1	x	f (x)	x	f (x)
2	2.1	4.1	1.9	3.9
3	2.05	4.05	1.95	3.95
4	2.01	4.01	1.99	3.99
5	2.001	4.001	1.999	3.999

**CHECKPOINT
ANSWERS**

1. Yes. See Figure 9.2 and Table 9.1.
2. Not necessarily. See Figure 9.4(c).
3. Not necessarily. See Figure 9.3(c).
4. Not necessarily. See Figure 9.4(c).
5. (a) Yes (b) 4
6. (a) $\lim\limits_{x \to -3} \dfrac{2x^2 + 5x - 3}{x^2 - 9} = \dfrac{7}{6}$

   (b) $\lim\limits_{x \to 5} \dfrac{x^2 - 3x - 3}{x^2 - 8x + 1} = -\dfrac{1}{2}$

   (c) $\lim\limits_{x \to -3/4} \dfrac{4x}{4x + 3}$ does not exist.
7. Yes. Properties I–IV yield this result.
8. Not necessarily. If $h(c) \neq 0$, then this is true. Otherwise, it is not true.
9. For both (a) and (b), $g(x)/h(x)$ has the 0/0 indeterminate form at $x = c$. In this case, we can make no general conclusion about the limit.
10. $\lim\limits_{x \to c} \dfrac{g(x)}{h(x)}$ does not exist, and $\lim\limits_{x \to c} \dfrac{h(x)}{g(x)} = 0$

EXERCISES 9.1

In Problems 1–6, a graph of $y = f(x)$ is shown and a c-value is given. For each problem, use the graph to find the following, whenever they exist.
(a) $\lim\limits_{x \to c} f(x)$ and (b) $f(c)$

In Problems 7–10, use the graph of $y = f(x)$ and the given c-value to find the following, whenever they exist.
(a) $\lim\limits_{x \to c^-} f(x)$ (b) $\lim\limits_{x \to c^+} f(x)$
(c) $\lim\limits_{x \to c} f(x)$ (d) $f(c)$

1. $c = 6$

2. $c = 4$

7. $c = 2$

8. $c = -10$

3. $c = -10$

4. $c = 20$

9. $c = 2$

10. $c = -4\frac{1}{2}$

5. $c = -2$

6. $c = -8$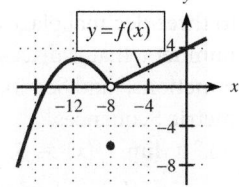

In Problems 11–14, complete each table and predict the limit, if it exists.

11. $f(x) = \dfrac{2 - x - x^2}{x - 1}$

$\lim\limits_{x \to 1} f(x) = ?$

x	$f(x)$
0.9	
0.99	
0.999	
1.001	
1.01	
1.1	

12. $f(x) = \dfrac{2x + 1}{\frac{1}{4} - x^2}$

$\lim\limits_{x \to -0.5} f(x) = ?$

x	$f(x)$
-0.51	
-0.501	
-0.5001	
-0.4999	
-0.499	
-0.49	

13. $f(x) = \begin{cases} 5x - 1 & \text{for } x < 1 \\ 8 - 2x - x^2 & \text{for } x \ge 1 \end{cases}$

$\lim\limits_{x \to 1} f(x) = ?$

x	$f(x)$
0.9	
0.99	
0.999	
1.001	
1.01	
1.1	

14. $f(x) = \begin{cases} 4 - x^2 & \text{for } x \le -2 \\ x^2 + 2x & \text{for } x > -2 \end{cases}$

$\lim\limits_{x \to -2} f(x) = ?$

x	$f(x)$
-2.1	
-2.01	
-2.001	
-1.999	
-1.99	

In Problems 15–40, use properties of limits and algebraic methods to find the limits, if they exist.

15. $\lim\limits_{x \to 80} (82 - x)$

16. $\lim\limits_{x \to -35} (34 + x)$

17. $\lim\limits_{x \to 3} (2x^3 - 12x^2 + 5x + 3)$

18. $\lim\limits_{x \to -1} (4x^3 - 2x^2 + 2)$

19. $\lim\limits_{x \to -1/3} \dfrac{1 - 3x}{9x^2 + 1}$

20. $\lim\limits_{x \to -1/2} \dfrac{4x - 2}{4x^2 + 1}$

21. $\lim\limits_{x \to -4} \dfrac{x^2 - 16}{x + 4}$

22. $\lim\limits_{x \to 3} \dfrac{x^2 - 9}{x - 3}$

23. $\lim\limits_{x \to -5} \dfrac{x^2 + 8x + 15}{x^2 + 5x}$

24. $\lim\limits_{x \to 7} \dfrac{x^2 - 8x + 7}{x^2 - 6x - 7}$

25. $\lim\limits_{x \to -1/4} \dfrac{x + 4x^2}{x^2 - 1/16}$

26. $\lim\limits_{x \to 1/2} \dfrac{8x^2 - 4x}{x - 1/2}$

27. $\lim\limits_{x \to 10} \dfrac{3x^2 - 30x}{x^2 - 100}$

28. $\lim\limits_{x \to -6} \dfrac{2x^2 - 72}{3x^2 + 18x}$

29. $\lim\limits_{x \to -2} \dfrac{x^2 + 4x + 4}{x^2 + 3x + 2}$

30. $\lim\limits_{x \to 10} \dfrac{x^2 - 8x - 20}{x^2 - 11x + 10}$

31. $\lim\limits_{x \to 3} f(x)$, where $f(x) = \begin{cases} 10 - 2x & \text{if } x < 3 \\ x^2 - x & \text{if } x \ge 3 \end{cases}$

32. $\lim\limits_{x \to 5} f(x)$, where $f(x) = \begin{cases} 7x - 10 & \text{if } x < 5 \\ 25 & \text{if } x \ge 5 \end{cases}$

33. $\lim\limits_{x \to -1} f(x)$, where $f(x) = \begin{cases} x^2 + \dfrac{4}{x} & \text{if } x \le -1 \\ 3x^3 - x - 1 & \text{if } x > -1 \end{cases}$

34. $\lim\limits_{x \to 2} f(x)$, where $f(x) = \begin{cases} \dfrac{x^3 - 4}{x - 3} & \text{if } x \le 2 \\ \dfrac{3 - x^2}{x} & \text{if } x > 2 \end{cases}$

35. $\lim\limits_{x \to 2} \dfrac{x^2 + 6x + 9}{x - 2}$

36. $\lim\limits_{x \to 5} \dfrac{x^2 - 6x + 8}{x - 5}$

37. $\lim\limits_{x \to -1} \dfrac{x^2 + 5x + 6}{x + 1}$

38. $\lim\limits_{x \to 3} \dfrac{x^2 + 2x - 3}{x - 3}$

39. $\lim\limits_{h \to 0} \dfrac{(x + h)^3 - x^3}{h}$

40. $\lim\limits_{h \to 0} \dfrac{2(x + h)^2 - 2x^2}{h}$

In Problems 41–44, graph each function with a graphing calculator and use it to predict the limit. Check your work either by using the table feature of the calculator or by finding the limit algebraically.

41. $\lim\limits_{x \to 10} \dfrac{x^2 - 19x + 90}{3x^2 - 30x}$

42. $\lim\limits_{x \to -3} \dfrac{x^4 + 3x^3}{2x^4 - 18x^2}$

43. $\lim\limits_{x \to -1} \dfrac{x^3 - x}{x^2 + 2x + 1}$

44. $\lim\limits_{x \to 5} \dfrac{x^2 - 7x + 10}{x^2 - 10x + 25}$

In Problems 45–48, use the table feature of a graphing calculator to predict each limit. Check your work by using either a graphical or an algebraic approach.

45. $\lim\limits_{x \to -2} \dfrac{x^4 - 4x^2}{x^2 + 8x + 12}$

46. $\lim\limits_{x \to -4} \dfrac{x^3 + 4x^2}{2x^2 + 7x - 4}$

47. $\lim\limits_{x \to 4} f(x)$, where $f(x) = \begin{cases} 12 - \dfrac{3}{4}x & \text{if } x \le 4 \\ x^2 - 7 & \text{if } x > 4 \end{cases}$

48. $\lim\limits_{x \to 7} f(x)$, where $f(x) = \begin{cases} 2 + x - x^2 & \text{if } x \le 7 \\ 13 - 9x & \text{if } x > 7 \end{cases}$

49. Use values 0.1, 0.01, 0.001, 0.0001, and 0.00001 to approximate

$$\lim\limits_{a \to 0} (1 + a)^{1/a}$$

to three decimal places. This limit equals the special number e that is discussed in Section 5.1, "Exponential Functions," and Section 6.2, "Compound Interest; Geometric Sequences."

50. (a) If $\lim\limits_{x \to 2^+} f(x) = 5$, $\lim\limits_{x \to 2^-} f(x) = 5$, and $f(2) = 0$, find $\lim\limits_{x \to 2} f(x)$, if it exists. Explain your conclusions.

(b) If $\lim_{x \to 0^+} f(x) = 3$, $\lim_{x \to 0^-} f(x) = 0$, and $f(0) = 0$, find $\lim_{x \to 0} f(x)$, if it exists. Explain your conclusions.

51. If $\lim_{x \to 3} f(x) = 4$ and $\lim_{x \to 3} g(x) = -2$, find
   (a) $\lim_{x \to 3} [f(x) + g(x)]$ (b) $\lim_{x \to 3} [f(x) - g(x)]$

   (c) $\lim_{x \to 3} [f(x) \cdot g(x)]$ (d) $\lim_{x \to 3} \dfrac{g(x)}{f(x)}$

52. If $\lim_{x \to -2} f(x) = 6$ and $\lim_{x \to -2} g(x) = 3$, find
   (a) $\lim_{x \to -2} [5f(x) - 4g(x)]$ (b) $\lim_{x \to -2} [g(x)]^2$

   (c) $\lim_{x \to -2} [4 - xf(x)]$ (d) $\lim_{x \to -2} \left[\dfrac{f(x)}{g(x)}\right]$

53. If $\lim_{x \to 2} [f(x) + g(x)] = 5$ and $\lim_{x \to 2} g(x) = 11$, find
   (a) $\lim_{x \to 2} f(x)$
   (b) $\lim_{x \to 2} \{[f(x)]^2 - [g(x)]^2\}$
   (c) $\lim_{x \to 2} \dfrac{3g(x)}{f(x) - g(x)}$

54. If $\lim_{x \to 5} [f(x) - g(x)] = 8$ and $\lim_{x \to 5} g(x) = 2$, find
   (a) $\lim_{x \to 5} f(x)$ (b) $\lim_{x \to 5} \{[g(x)]^2 - f(x)\}$

   (c) $\lim_{x \to 5} \left[\dfrac{2xg(x)}{4 - f(x)}\right]$

APPLICATIONS

55. *Revenue* The total revenue for a product is given by
$$R(x) = 1600x - x^2$$
where x is the number of units sold. What is $\lim_{x \to 100} R(x)$?

56. *Profit* If the profit function for a product is given by
$$P(x) = 92x - x^2 - 1760$$
find $\lim_{x \to 40} P(x)$.

57. *Sales and training* The average monthly sales volume (in thousands of dollars) for a firm depends on the number of hours x of training of its sales staff, according to
$$S(x) = \frac{4}{x} + 30 + \frac{x}{4}, \quad 4 \le x \le 100$$
   (a) Find $\lim_{x \to 4^+} S(x)$.   (b) Find $\lim_{x \to 100} S(x)$.

58. *Sales and training* During the first 4 months of employment, the monthly sales S (in thousands of dollars) for a new salesperson depend on the number of hours x of training as follows:
$$S = S(x) = \frac{9}{x} + 10 + \frac{x}{4}, \quad x \ge 4$$
   (a) Find $\lim_{x \to 4^+} S(x)$.   (b) Find $\lim_{x \to 10} S(x)$.

59. *Advertising and sales* Suppose that the daily sales S (in dollars) t days after the end of an advertising campaign are
$$S = S(t) = 400 + \frac{2400}{t + 1}$$
   (a) Find $S(0)$.   (b) Find $\lim_{t \to 7} S(t)$.
   (c) Find $\lim_{t \to 14} S(t)$.

60. *Advertising and sales* Sales y (in thousands of dollars) are related to advertising expenses x (in thousands of dollars) according to
$$y = y(x) = \frac{200x}{x + 10}, \quad x \ge 0$$
   (a) Find $\lim_{x \to 10} y(x)$.   (b) Find $\lim_{x \to 0} y(x)$.

61. *Productivity* During an 8-hour shift, the rate of change of productivity (in units per hour) of infant activity centers assembled after t hours on the job is
$$r(t) = \frac{128(t^2 + 6t)}{(t^2 + 6t + 18)^2}, \quad 0 \le t \le 8$$
   (a) Find $\lim_{t \to 4} r(t)$.   (b) Find $\lim_{t \to 8^-} r(t)$.
   (c) Is the rate of productivity higher near the lunch break (at $t = 4$) or near quitting time (at $t = 8$)?

62. *Revenue* If the revenue for a product is $R(x) = 100x - 0.1x^2$ and the average revenue per unit is
$$\overline{R}(x) = \frac{R(x)}{x}, \quad x > 0$$
find (a) $\lim_{x \to 100} \dfrac{R(x)}{x}$ and   (b) $\lim_{x \to 0^+} \dfrac{R(x)}{x}$

63. *Cost-benefit* Suppose that the cost C of obtaining water that contains p percent impurities is given by
$$C(p) = \frac{120{,}000}{p} - 1200$$
   (a) Find $\lim_{p \to 100^-} C(p)$, if it exists. Interpret this result.
   (b) Find $\lim_{p \to 0^+} C(p)$, if it exists.
   (c) Is complete purity possible? Explain.

64. *Cost-benefit* Suppose that the cost C of removing p percent of the particulate pollution from the smokestacks of an industrial plant is given by
$$C(p) = \frac{730{,}000}{100 - p} - 7300$$
   (a) Find $\lim_{p \to 80} C(p)$.
   (b) Find $\lim_{p \to 100^-} C(p)$, if it exists.
   (c) Can 100% of the particulate pollution be removed? Explain.

65. *Federal income tax* The following table shows part of a tax rate schedule for single filers. Use this schedule and create a table of values that could be used to find the following limits, if they exist. Let x represent the amount of taxable income and let $T(x)$ represent the tax due.

(a) $\lim\limits_{x \to 36,900^-} T(x)$ (b) $\lim\limits_{x \to 36,900^+} T(x)$

(c) $\lim\limits_{x \to 36,900} T(x)$

Single Filers

If taxable income is over—	But not over—	The tax is:
$0	$9075	10% of the amount over $0
$9075	$36,900	$907.50 plus 15% of the amount over 9075
$36,900	$89,350	$5081.25 plus 25% of the amount over 36,900
$89,350	$186,350	$18,193.75 plus 28% of the amount over 89,350

Source: Internal Revenue Service

66. *Parking costs* The Ace Parking Garage charges $5.00 for parking for 2 hours or less and $1.50 for each extra hour or part of an hour after the 2-hour minimum. The parking charges for the first 5 hours could be written as a function of the time as follows:

$$f(t) = \begin{cases} \$5.00 & \text{if } 0 < t \le 2 \\ \$6.50 & \text{if } 2 < t \le 3 \\ \$8.00 & \text{if } 3 < t \le 4 \\ \$9.50 & \text{if } 4 < t \le 5 \end{cases}$$

(a) Find $\lim\limits_{t \to 1} f(t)$, if it exists.

(b) Find $\lim\limits_{t \to 2} f(t)$, if it exists.

67. *Municipal water rates* The Corner Water Corp. of Springfield has the following rates per 1000 gallons of water used.

Usage (x)	Cost per 1000 Gallons ($C(x)$)
First 10,000 gallons	$15.96
Next 110,000 gallons	13.56
Over 120,000 gallons	Additional 11.04

If Corner Water has a monthly service fee of $12.76, write a function $C = C(x)$ that models the charges (where x is thousands of gallons) and find $\lim\limits_{x \to 10} C(x)$ (that is, as usage approaches 10,000 gallons).

68. *Airport parking* The Hourly Parking Garage at BWI International Airport in Baltimore costs $2 per half hour during the first hour and $4 for each hour or part of an hour for more than 1 hour and up to 5 hours. If $C = C(t)$ is the total charge for t hours in BWI's Hourly Parking Garage, write a piecewise function that describes $C(t)$ for $t < 3$. Use $C(t)$ to find the following limits, if they exist.

(a) $\lim\limits_{t \to 0.5^-} C(t)$ (b) $\lim\limits_{t \to 0.5^+} C(t)$

(c) $\lim\limits_{t \to 0.5} C(t)$ (d) $\lim\limits_{t \to 2.5} C(t)$

Dow Jones Industrial Average **The graph in the figure shows the Dow Jones Industrial Average (DJIA) on a particularly tumultuous day. Use the graph for Problems 69 and 70, with t as the time of day and $D(t)$ as the DJIA at time t.**

69. Estimate $\lim\limits_{t \to 9:30\text{AM}^+} D(t)$, if it exists. Explain what this limit corresponds to.

70. Estimate $\lim\limits_{t \to 4:00\text{PM}^-} D(t)$, if it exists. Explain what this limit corresponds to.

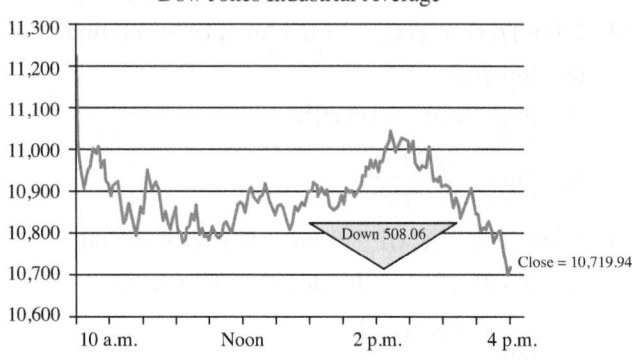

Dow Jones Industrial Average

Down 508.06

Close = 10,719.94

Source: Google Finance

Obesity **Obesity (BMI ≥ 30) is a serious problem in the United States and is expected to get worse. Being overweight increases the risk of diabetes, heart disease, and many other ailments, but the severely obese (BMI ≥ 40) are most at risk and the most expensive to treat. The following table shows the percent of obese Americans who are severely obese for selected years from 1990 and projected to 2030.**

Percent Obese Who Are Severely Obese

Year	1990	2000	2010	2015	2020	2025	2030
Percent	6.30	9.95	15.9	18.6	21.1	23.8	26.3

Source: American Journal of Preventive Medicine 42 (June 2012): 563–570. ajpmonline.org

The percent of obese American adults who are severely obese can be modeled by the function

$$S(x) = \frac{0.264x^2 + 10.7x - 66.9}{-0.00850x^2 + 1.25x + 0.854}$$

where x is the number of years after 1980. Use this function in Problems 71 and 72.

71. (a) Find $\lim\limits_{x \to 60} S(x)$, if it exists.

(b) What does this limit predict?

(c) Does this prediction seem plausible? Explain.

72. (a) Find $\lim\limits_{x \to 40} S(x)$, if it exists.

(b) What does this limit estimate?

(c) Is the function accurate as $x \to 40$? Explain.

SECTION 9.2

Continuous Functions; Limits at Infinity

OBJECTIVES

- To determine whether a function is continuous or discontinuous at a point
- To determine where a function is discontinuous
- To find limits at infinity and horizontal asymptotes

APPLICATION PREVIEW

Suppose that a friend of yours and her husband have a taxable income of $151,900 and she tells you that she doesn't want to make any more money because that would put them in a higher tax bracket. She makes this statement because the tax rate schedule for married taxpayers filing a joint return (part of which is shown in the table) appears to have a jump in taxes for taxable income at $151,900.

Married Filing Jointly or Qualifying Widow(er)

Taxable Income Over	But Not Over	Tax Rate
$0	$18,550	10%
$18,550	$75,300	$1,855.00 plus 15% of the amount over $18,550
$75,300	$151,900	$10,367.50 plus 25% of the amount over $75,300
$151,900	$231,450	$29,517.50 plus 28% of the amount over $151,900
$231,450	$413,350	$51,791.50 plus 33% of the amount over $231,450
$413,350	$466,950	$111,818.50 plus 35% of the amount over $413,350

Source: Internal Revenue Service

To see whether the couple's taxes would jump to a higher level, we will write the function that gives income tax for married taxpayers with taxable incomes up to $466,950 as a function of taxable income and show that the function is continuous. (See Example 3.) That is, we will see that the tax paid does not jump at $151,900 even though the tax on income above $151,900 is collected at a higher rate. In this section, we will show how to determine whether a function is continuous and will investigate some different types of discontinuous functions.

In addition, we will find limits at infinity and horizontal asymptotes.

Continuous Functions

We have found that $f(c)$ is the same as the limit as $x \to c$ for any polynomial function $f(x)$ and any real number c. Any function for which this special property holds is called a **continuous function.** The graphs of such functions can be drawn without lifting the pencil from the paper, and graphs of others may have holes, vertical asymptotes, or jumps that make it impossible to draw them without lifting the pencil. In general, we define continuity of a function at the value $x = c$ as follows.

Continuity at a Point

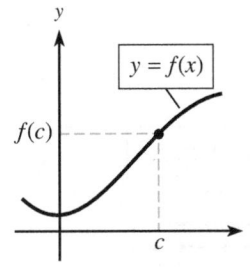

The function f is **continuous at $x = c$** if *all* of the following conditions are satisfied.

1. $f(c)$ exists   2. $\lim\limits_{x \to c} f(x)$ exists   3. $\lim\limits_{x \to c} f(x) = f(c)$

The figure at the left illustrates these three conditions.
If one or more of the conditions above do not hold, we say that the function is **discontinuous at $x = c$.**

If a function is discontinuous at one or more points, it is called a **discontinuous function.** Figure 9.11 on the next page shows graphs of some functions that are discontinuous at $x = 2$.

(a) $f(x) = \dfrac{1}{x-2}$

$\lim\limits_{x \to 2} f(x)$ and $f(2)$ do not exist.

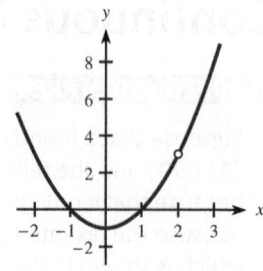

(b) $f(x) = \dfrac{x^3 - 2x^2 - x + 2}{x - 2}$

$f(2)$ does not exist.

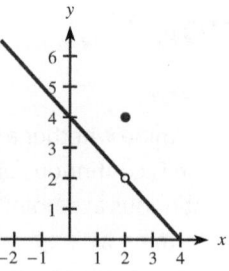

(c) $f(x) = \begin{cases} 4 - x & \text{if } x \neq 2 \\ 4 & \text{if } x = 2 \end{cases}$

$\lim\limits_{x \to 2} f(x) = 2 \neq 4 = f(2)$

Figure 9.11

We have seen that $\lim\limits_{x \to c} f(x) = f(c)$ for every real number c if $f(x)$ is a polynomial, and that

$$\lim_{x \to c} h(x) = h(c) \text{ if } h(x) = \frac{f(x)}{g(x)} \text{ is a rational function and } g(c) \neq 0. \text{ So we have the following.}$$

Polynomial and Rational Functions

Every polynomial function is continuous for all real numbers.
Every rational function is continuous at all values of x except those that make the denominator 0.

EXAMPLE 1   Discontinuous Functions

For what values of x, if any, are the following functions continuous?

(a) $h(x) = \dfrac{3x + 2}{4x - 6}$ (b) $f(x) = \dfrac{x^2 - x - 2}{x^2 - 4}$

Solution

(a) This is a rational function, so it is continuous for all values of x except those that make the denominator, $4x - 6$, equal to 0. Because $4x - 6 = 0$ at $x = 3/2$, $h(x)$ is continuous for all real numbers except $x = 3/2$. Figure 9.12(a) shows a vertical asymptote at $x = 3/2$.

(b) This is a rational function, so it is continuous everywhere except where the denominator is 0. To find the zeros of the denominator, we factor $x^2 - 4$.

$$f(x) = \frac{x^2 - x - 2}{x^2 - 4} = \frac{x^2 - x - 2}{(x - 2)(x + 2)}$$

Because the denominator is 0 for $x = 2$ and $x = -2$, $f(2)$ and $f(-2)$ do not exist (because division by 0 is undefined). Thus the function is continuous except at $x = 2$ and $x = -2$. The graph of this function [see Figure 9.12(b)] shows a hole at $x = 2$ and a vertical asymptote at $x = -2$.

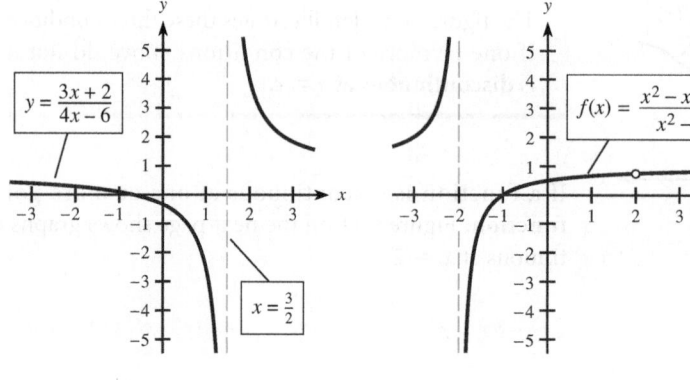

Figure 9.12   (a)   (b)

1. Find any x-values where the following functions are discontinuous.

   (a) $f(x) = x^3 - 3x + 1$ (b) $g(x) = \dfrac{x^3 - 1}{(x - 1)(x + 2)}$

If the pieces of a piecewise defined function are polynomials, the only values of x where the function might be discontinuous are those at which the definition of the function changes.

EXAMPLE 2   Piecewise Defined Functions

Determine the values of x, if any, for which the following functions are discontinuous.

(a) $g(x) = \begin{cases} (x + 2)^3 + 1 & \text{if } x \le -1 \\ 3 & \text{if } x > -1 \end{cases}$ (b) $f(x) = \begin{cases} 4 - x^2 & \text{if } x < 2 \\ x - 2 & \text{if } x \ge 2 \end{cases}$

Solution

(a) $g(x)$ is a piecewise defined function in which each part is a polynomial. Thus, to see whether a discontinuity exists, we need only check the value of x for which the definition of the function changes—that is, at $x = -1$. Note that $x = -1$ satisfies $x \le -1$, so $g(-1) = (-1 + 2)^3 + 1 = 2$. Because $g(x)$ is defined differently for $x < -1$ and $x > -1$, we use left- and right-hand limits.

For $x \to -1^-$, we know that $x < -1$, so $g(x) = (x + 2)^3 + 1$:

$$\lim_{x \to -1^-} g(x) = \lim_{x \to -1^-} [(x + 2)^3 + 1] = (-1 + 2)^3 + 1 = 2$$

Similarly, for $x \to -1^+$, we know that $x > -1$, so $g(x) = 3$:

$$\lim_{x \to -1^+} g(x) = \lim_{x \to -1^+} 3 = 3$$

Because the left- and right-hand limits differ, $\lim_{x \to -1} g(x)$ does not exist, so $g(x)$ is discontinuous at $x = -1$. This result is confirmed by examining the graph of g, shown in Figure 9.13.

(b) As with $g(x)$, $f(x)$ is continuous everywhere except perhaps at $x = 2$, where the definition of $f(x)$ changes. Because $x = 2$ satisfies $x \ge 2$, $f(2) = 2 - 2 = 0$. The left- and right-hand limits are

Left: $\lim_{x \to 2^-} f(x) = \lim_{x \to 2^-} (4 - x^2) = 4 - 2^2 = 0$

Right: $\lim_{x \to 2^+} f(x) = \lim_{x \to 2^+} (x - 2) = 2 - 2 = 0$

Because the right- and left-hand limits are equal, we conclude that $\lim_{x \to 2} f(x) = 0$. The limit is equal to the functional value:

$$\lim_{x \to 2} f(x) = f(2)$$

We conclude that f is continuous at $x = 2$, and thus f is continuous for all values of x. This result is confirmed by the graph of f, shown in Figure 9.14.

$g(x) = \begin{cases} (x + 2)^3 + 1 & \text{if } x \le -1 \\ 3 & \text{if } x > -1 \end{cases}$

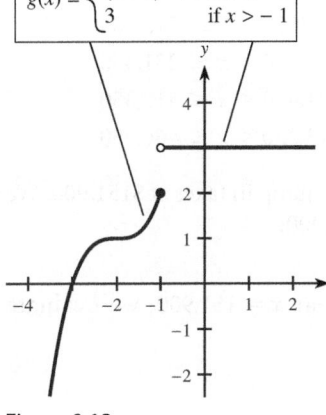

Figure 9.13

$f(x) = \begin{cases} 4 - x^2 & \text{if } x < 2 \\ x - 2 & \text{if } x \ge 2 \end{cases}$

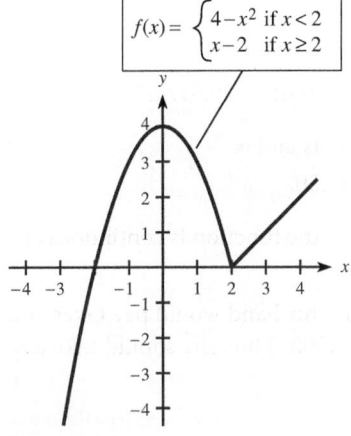

Figure 9.14

EXAMPLE 3   Taxes | APPLICATION PREVIEW |

A partial tax rate schedule for married taxpayers filing a joint return (shown in the table) appears to have a jump in taxes for taxable income at $151,900.

Married Filing Jointly or Qualifying Widow(er)

Taxable Income over	But not over	Tax Rate
$0	$18,550	10%
$18,550	$75,300	$1,855.00 plus 15% of the amount over $18,550
$75,300	$151,900	$10,367.50 plus 25% of the amount over $75,300
$151,900	$231,450	$29,517.50 plus 28% of the amount over $151,900
$231,450	$413,350	$51,791.50 plus 33% of the amount over $231,450
$413,350	$466,950	$111,818.50 plus 35% of the amount over $413,350

Source: Internal Revenue Service

(a) Use the table and write the function that gives income tax for married taxpayers in each income range as a function of taxable income, x.

(b) Is the function in part (a) continuous at $x = 151{,}900$?

(c) A married friend of yours and her husband have a taxable income of $151,900, and she tells you that she doesn't want to make any more money because doing so would put her in a higher tax bracket. What will you tell her to do if she is offered a raise?

Solution

(a) The function that gives the tax due for married taxpayers with $0 \leq x \leq 466{,}950$ is

$$T(x) = \begin{cases} 0.10x & \text{if } 0 \leq x \leq 18{,}550 \\ 1{,}855.00 + 0.15(x - 18{,}550) & \text{if } 18{,}550 < x \leq 75{,}300 \\ 10{,}367.50 + 0.25(x - 75{,}300) & \text{if } 75{,}300 < x \leq 151{,}900 \\ 29{,}517.50 + 0.28(x - 151{,}900) & \text{if } 151{,}900 < x \leq 231{,}450 \\ 51{,}791.50 + 0.33(x - 231{,}450) & \text{if } 231{,}450 < x \leq 413{,}350 \\ 111{,}818.50 + 0.35(x - 413{,}350) & \text{if } 413{,}350 < x \leq 466{,}950 \end{cases}$$

(b) If this function is continuous at $x = 151{,}900$, there is no jump in taxes at $151,900. We examine the three conditions for continuity at $x = 151{,}900$:

(i) $T(151{,}900) = 29{,}517.50$, so $T(151{,}900)$ exists.

(ii) Because the function is piecewise defined near $x = 151{,}900$, we evaluate $\lim_{x \to 151{,}900} T(x)$ by evaluating one-sided limits.

From the left, we evaluate $\lim_{x \to 151{,}900^-} T(x)$:

$$\lim_{x \to 151{,}900^-} [10{,}367.50 + 0.25(x - 75{,}300)] = 29{,}517.50$$

From the right, we evaluate $\lim_{x \to 151{,}900^+} T(x)$:

$$\lim_{x \to 151{,}900^+} [29{,}517.50 + 0.28(x - 151{,}900)] = 29{,}517.50$$

Because these one-sided limits agree, the limit exists and is

$$\lim_{x \to 151{,}900} T(x) = 29{,}517.50.$$

(iii) Because $\lim_{x \to 151{,}900} T(x) = T(151{,}900) = 29{,}517.50$, the function is continuous at $x = 151{,}900$.

(c) If your friend earned more than $151,900, she and her husband would pay taxes at a higher rate *only* on the amount of money *above* $151,900. Thus she should take any raise that is offered.

CHECKPOINT

2. If $f(x)$ and $g(x)$ are polynomials, $h(x) = \begin{cases} f(x) & \text{if } x \leq a \\ g(x) & \text{if } x > a \end{cases}$

is continuous everywhere except perhaps at _____.

Limits at Infinity   We have seen that the graph of $y = 1/x$ has a vertical asymptote at $x = 0$ [shown in Figure 9.15(a)]. By graphing $y = 1/x$ and evaluating the function for very large x-values, we can see that $y = 1/x$ never becomes negative for positive x-values regardless of how large the x-value is. Although no value of x makes $1/x$ equal to 0, it is easy to see that $1/x$ approaches 0 as x gets very large. This is denoted by

$$\lim_{x \to \infty} \frac{1}{x} = 0$$

and means that the line $y = 0$ (the x-axis) is a horizontal asymptote for $y = 1/x$. We also see that $y = 1/x$ approaches 0 as x decreases without bound, and we denote this by

$$\lim_{x \to -\infty} \frac{1}{x} = 0$$

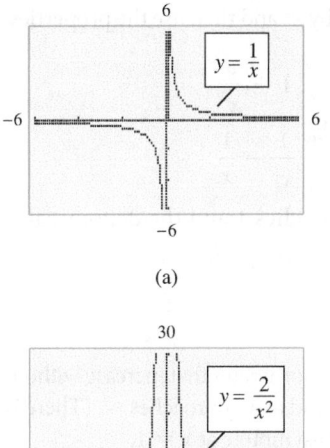

(a)

(b)

Figure 9.15

These limits for $f(x) = 1/x$ can also be established using numerical tables.

x	$f(x) = 1/x$	x	$f(x) = 1/x$
100	0.01	-100	-0.01
100,000	0.00001	$-100,000$	-0.00001
100,000,000	0.00000001	$-100,000,000$	-0.00000001
$\downarrow$	$\downarrow$	$\downarrow$	$\downarrow$
∞	0	$-\infty$	0
$\lim\limits_{x \to \infty} \dfrac{1}{x} = 0$		$\lim\limits_{x \to -\infty} \dfrac{1}{x} = 0$	

We can use the graph of $y = 2/x^2$ in Figure 9.15(b) to see that the x-axis ($y = 0$) is a horizontal asymptote and that

$$\lim_{x \to \infty} \frac{2}{x^2} = 0 \quad \text{and} \quad \lim_{x \to -\infty} \frac{2}{x^2} = 0$$

By using graphs and/or tables of values, we can generalize the results for the functions shown in Figure 9.15 and conclude the following.

Limits at Infinity

If c is any constant, then

1. $\lim\limits_{x \to \infty} c = c$ and $\lim\limits_{x \to -\infty} c = c$.

2. $\lim\limits_{x \to \infty} \dfrac{c}{x^p} = 0$, where $p > 0$.

3. $\lim\limits_{x \to -\infty} \dfrac{c}{x^n} = 0$, where $n > 0$ is any integer.

To use these properties for finding the limits of rational functions as x approaches ∞ or $-\infty$, we first divide each term of the numerator and denominator by the highest power of x present and then determine the limit of the resulting expression.

EXAMPLE 4   **Limits at Infinity**

Find each of the following limits, if they exist.

(a) $\lim\limits_{x \to \infty} \dfrac{2x - 1}{x + 2}$ (b) $\lim\limits_{x \to -\infty} \dfrac{x^2 + 3}{1 - x}$

Solution

(a) The highest power of x present is x^1, so we divide each term in the numerator and denominator by x and then use the properties for limits at infinity.

$$\lim_{x \to \infty} \frac{2x - 1}{x + 2} = \lim_{x \to \infty} \frac{\dfrac{2x}{x} - \dfrac{1}{x}}{\dfrac{x}{x} + \dfrac{2}{x}} = \lim_{x \to \infty} \frac{2 - \dfrac{1}{x}}{1 + \dfrac{2}{x}}$$

$$= \frac{2 - 0}{1 + 0} = 2 \quad \text{(by Properties 1 and 2)}$$

Figure 9.16(a) on the next page shows the graph of this function with the y-coordinates of the graph approaching 2 as x approaches ∞ and as x approaches $-\infty$. That is, $y = 2$ is a horizontal asymptote. Note also that there is a discontinuity (vertical asymptote) where $x = -2$.

(b) We divide each term in the numerator and denominator by x^2 and then use the properties.

$$\lim_{x \to -\infty} \frac{x^2 + 3}{1 - x} = \lim_{x \to -\infty} \frac{\dfrac{x^2}{x^2} + \dfrac{3}{x^2}}{\dfrac{1}{x^2} - \dfrac{x}{x^2}} = \lim_{x \to -\infty} \frac{1 + \dfrac{3}{x^2}}{\dfrac{1}{x^2} - \dfrac{1}{x}}$$

This limit does not exist because the numerator approaches 1 and the denominator approaches 0 through positive values. Thus

$$\frac{x^2 + 3}{1 - x} \to \infty \text{ as } x \to -\infty$$

The graph of this function, shown in Figure 9.16(b), has y-coordinates that increase without bound as x approaches $-\infty$ and that decrease without bound as x approaches ∞. (There is no horizontal asymptote.) Note also that there is a vertical asymptote at $x = 1$.

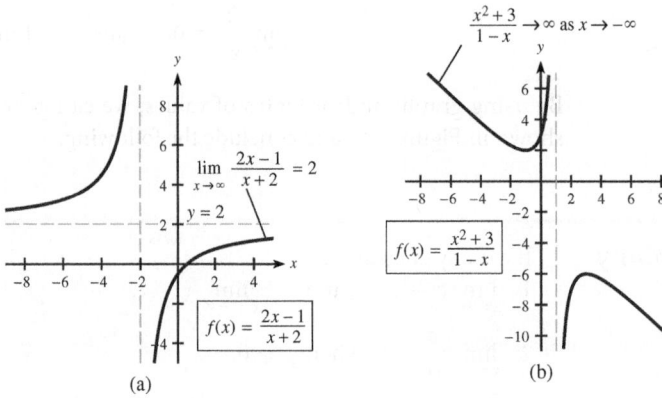

Figure 9.16   (a)   (b)

In our work with limits at infinity, we have mentioned horizontal asymptotes several times. The connection between these concepts follows.

Limits at Infinity and Horizontal Asymptotes

If $\lim_{x \to \infty} f(x) = b$ or $\lim_{x \to -\infty} f(x) = b$, where b is a constant, then the line $y = b$ is a horizontal asymptote for the graph of $y = f(x)$. Otherwise, $y = f(x)$ has no horizontal asymptotes.

CHECKPOINT

3. (a) Evaluate $\lim_{x \to \infty} \dfrac{x^2 - 4}{2x^2 - 7}$.

   (b) What does part (a) say about horizontal asymptotes for
   $f(x) = (x^2 - 4)/(2x^2 - 7)$?

Calculator Note   We can use the graphing and table features of a graphing calculator to help locate and investigate discontinuities and limits at infinity (horizontal asymptotes). A graphing calculator can be used to focus our attention on a possible discontinuity and to support or suggest appropriate algebraic calculations. See the following example.

EXAMPLE 5 **Limits with Technology**

Use a graphing calculator to investigate the continuity of the following functions.

(a) $f(x) = \dfrac{x^2 + 1}{x + 1}$

(b) $g(x) = \dfrac{x^2 - 2x - 3}{x^2 - 1}$

(c) $h(x) = \dfrac{|x + 1|}{x + 1}$

(d) $k(x) = \begin{cases} \dfrac{-x^2}{2} - 2x & \text{if } x \leq -1 \\ \dfrac{x}{2} + 2 & \text{if } x > -1 \end{cases}$

Solution

(a) Figure 9.17(a) shows that $f(x)$ has a discontinuity (vertical asymptote) near $x = -1$. Because $f(-1)$ DNE, we know that $f(x)$ is not continuous at $x = -1$.

(b) Figure 9.17(b) shows that $g(x)$ is discontinuous (vertical asymptote) near $x = 1$, and this looks like the only discontinuity. However, the denominator of $g(x)$ is zero at $x = 1$ and $x = -1$, so $g(x)$ must have discontinuities at both of these x-values. Evaluating or using the table feature confirms that $x = -1$ is a discontinuity (a hole, or missing point). The figure also shows a horizontal asymptote; evaluation of $\lim\limits_{x \to \infty} g(x)$ confirms that this is the line $y = 1$.

(c) Figure 9.17(c) shows a discontinuity (jump) at $x = -1$. We also see that $h(-1)$ DNE, which confirms the observations from the graph.

(d) The graph in Figure 9.17(d) appears to be continuous. The only "suspicious" x-value is $x = -1$, where the formula for $k(x)$ changes. Evaluating $k(-1)$ and examining a table near $x = -1$ indicates that $k(x)$ is continuous there. Algebraic evaluations of the two one-sided limits confirm this.

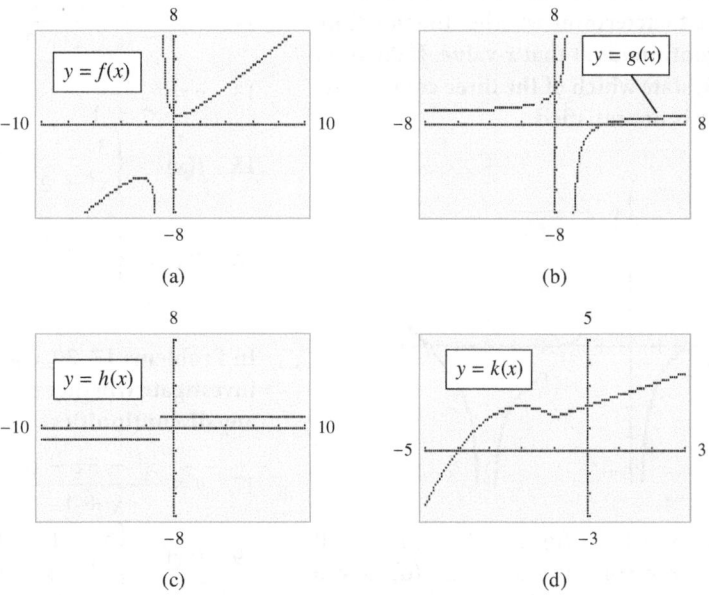

Figure 9.17

(a)   (b)   (c)   (d)

Continous Functions and Limits at Infinity

- The following information is useful in discussing continuity of functions.

    A. A polynomial function is continuous everywhere.

    B. A rational function is a function of the form $\dfrac{f(x)}{g(x)}$, where $f(x)$ and $g(x)$ are polynomials.

    1. If $g(x) \neq 0$ at any value of x, the function is continuous everywhere.

    2. If $g(c) = 0$, the function is discontinuous at $x = c$.

        (a) If $g(c) = 0$ and $f(c) \neq 0$ then there is a vertical asymptote at $x = c$.

        (b) If $g(c) = 0$ and $\lim\limits_{x \to c} \dfrac{f(x)}{g(x)} = L$, then the graph has a missing point at (c, L).

    C. A piecewise defined function may have a discontinuity at any x-value where the function changes its formula. One-sided limits must be used to see whether the limit exists.

- The following steps are useful when we are evaluating limits at infinity for a rational function $f(x) = p(x)/q(x)$.

    1. Divide both $p(x)$ and $q(x)$ by the highest power of x found in either polynomial.

    2. Use the properties of limits at infinity to complete the evaluation.

1. (a) This is a polynomial function, so it is continuous at all values of x (discontinuous at none).

   (b) This is a rational function. It is discontinuous at $x = 1$ and $x = -2$ because these values make its denominator 0.

2. $x = a$

3. (a) $\lim\limits_{x \to \infty} \dfrac{x^2 - 4}{2x^2 - 7} = \dfrac{1}{2}$

   (b) The line $y = 1/2$ is a horizontal asymptote.

EXERCISES 9.2

In Problems 1 and 2, refer to the figure. For each given x-value, use the figure to determine whether the function is continuous or discontinuous at that x-value. If the function is discontinuous, state which of the three conditions that define continuity is not satisfied.

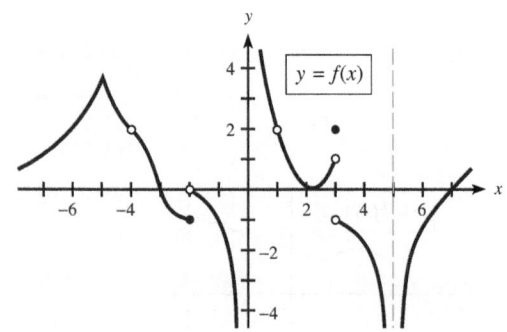

1. (a) $x = -5$ (b) $x = 1$ (c) $x = 3$ (d) $x = 0$
2. (a) $x = 2$ (b) $x = -4$ (c) $x = -2$ (d) $x = 5$

In Problems 3–8, determine whether each function is continuous or discontinuous at the given x-value. Examine the three conditions in the definition of continuity.

3. $f(x) = \dfrac{x^2 - 4}{x - 2}, \qquad x = -2$

4. $y = \dfrac{x^2 - 9}{x + 3}, \qquad x = 3$

5. $y = \dfrac{x^2 - x - 12}{x^2 + 3x}, \qquad x = -3$

6. $f(x) = \dfrac{x^2 - 6x + 8}{x^2 + x - 20}, \qquad x = 4$

7. $f(x) = \begin{cases} x - 3 & \text{if } x \le 2 \\ 4x - 7 & \text{if } x > 2 \end{cases}, \qquad x = 2$

8. $f(x) = \begin{cases} x^2 + 1 & \text{if } x \le 1 \\ 2x^2 - 1 & \text{if } x > 1 \end{cases}, \qquad x = 1$

In Problems 9–16, determine whether the given function is continuous. If it is not, identify where it is discontinuous and which condition fails to hold. You can verify your conclusions by graphing each function with a graphing utility.

9. $f(x) = 4x^2 - 1$ 10. $y = 5x^2 - 2x$

11. $g(x) = \dfrac{4x^2 + 3x + 2}{x + 2}$ 12. $y = \dfrac{4x^2 + 4x + 1}{x + 1/2}$

13. $y = \dfrac{x}{x^2 + 1}$ 14. $y = \dfrac{2x - 1}{x^2 + 3}$

15. $f(x) = \begin{cases} 3 & \text{if } x \le 1 \\ x^2 + 2 & \text{if } x > 1 \end{cases}$

16. $f(x) = \begin{cases} x^3 + 10 & \text{if } x \le -2 \\ 2 & \text{if } x > -2 \end{cases}$

In Problems 17–20, use a graphing calculator to investigate whether each of the following functions has any discontinuities.

17. $y = \dfrac{x^2 - 5x - 6}{x + 1}$ 18. $y = \dfrac{x^2 - 5x + 4}{x - 4}$

19. $f(x) = \begin{cases} x - 4 & \text{if } x \le 3 \\ x^2 - 8 & \text{if } x > 3 \end{cases}$

20. $f(x) = \begin{cases} x^2 + 4 & \text{if } x \ne 4 \\ 8 & \text{if } x = 4 \end{cases}$

Each of Problems 21–24 contains a function and its graph. For each problem, answer parts (a) and (b).
(a) Use the graph to determine, as well as you can,
   (i) vertical asymptotes. (ii) $\lim\limits_{x \to \infty} f(x)$.
   (iii) $\lim\limits_{x \to -\infty} f(x)$.   (iv) horizontal asymptotes.
(b) Check your conclusions in (a) by using the functions to determine items (i)–(iv) analytically.

21. $f(x) = \dfrac{8}{x + 2}$ 22. $f(x) = \dfrac{x - 3}{x - 2}$

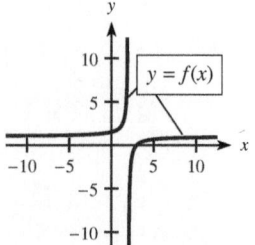

23. $f(x) = \dfrac{2(x + 1)^3(x + 5)}{(x - 3)^2(x + 2)^2}$ 24. $f(x) = \dfrac{4x^2}{x^2 - 4x + 4}$

In Problems 25–32, complete (a) and (b).
(a) Use analytic methods to evaluate each limit.
(b) What does the result from part (a) tell you about horizontal asymptotes?

You can verify your conclusions by graphing the functions with a graphing calculator.

25. $\displaystyle\lim_{x \to \infty} \dfrac{3}{x + 1}$

26. $\displaystyle\lim_{x \to \infty} \dfrac{4}{x^2 - 2x}$

27. $\displaystyle\lim_{x \to -\infty} \dfrac{x^3 - 1}{x^3 + 4}$

28. $\displaystyle\lim_{x \to -\infty} \dfrac{3x^2 + 2}{x^2 - 4}$

29. $\displaystyle\lim_{x \to -\infty} \dfrac{5x^3 - 4x}{3x^3 - 2}$

30. $\displaystyle\lim_{x \to \infty} \dfrac{4x^2 + 5x}{x^2 - 4x}$

31. $\displaystyle\lim_{x \to \infty} \dfrac{3x^2 + 5x}{6x + 1}$

32. $\displaystyle\lim_{x \to -\infty} \dfrac{5x^3 - 8}{4x^2 + 5x}$

In Problems 33 and 34, use a graphing calculator to complete (a) and (b).
(a) Graph each function using a window with $0 \le x \le 300$ and $-2 \le y \le 2$. What does the graph indicate about $\displaystyle\lim_{x \to \infty} f(x)$?
(b) Use the table feature with x-values larger than 10,000 to investigate $\displaystyle\lim_{x \to \infty} f(x)$. Does the table support your conclusions in part (a)?

33. $f(x) = \dfrac{x^2 - 4}{3 + 2x^2}$

34. $f(x) = \dfrac{5x^3 - 7x}{1 - 3x^3}$

In Problems 35 and 36, complete (a)–(c). Use analytic methods to find (a) any points of discontinuity and (b) limits as $x \to \infty$ and $x \to -\infty$. (c) Then explain why, for these functions, a graphing calculator is better as a support tool for the analytic methods than as the primary tool for investigation.

35. $f(x) = \dfrac{1000x - 1000}{x + 1000}$

36. $f(x) = \dfrac{3000x}{4350 - 2x}$

For Problems 37 and 38, let

$$f(x) = \dfrac{a_n x^n + a_{n-1} x^{n-1} + \cdots + a_1 x + a_0}{b_m x^m + b_{m-1} x^{m-1} + \cdots + b_1 x + b_0}$$

be a rational function.

37. If $m = n$, show that $\displaystyle\lim_{x \to \infty} f(x) = \dfrac{a_n}{b_n}$ and hence that $y = \dfrac{a_n}{b_n}$ is a horizontal asymptote.

38. (a) If $m > n$, show that $\displaystyle\lim_{x \to \infty} f(x) = 0$ and hence that $y = 0$ is a horizontal asymptote.
    (b) If $m < n$, find $\displaystyle\lim_{x \to \infty} f(x)$. What does this say about horizontal asymptotes?

APPLICATIONS

39. *Sales volume* Suppose that the weekly sales volume (in thousands of units) for a product is given by

$$y = \dfrac{32}{(p + 8)^{2/5}}$$

where p is the price in dollars per unit. Is this function continuous
(a) for all values of p?   (b) at $p = 24$?
(c) for all $p \ge 0$?
(d) What is the domain for this application?

40. *Worker productivity* Suppose that the average number of minutes M that it takes a new employee to assemble one unit of a product is given by

$$M = \dfrac{40 + 30t}{2t + 1}$$

where t is the number of days on the job. Is this function continuous
(a) for all values of t?   (b) at $t = 14$?
(c) for all $t \ge 0$?
(d) What is the domain for this application?

41. *Demand* Suppose that the demand for a product is defined by the equation

$$p = \dfrac{200{,}000}{(q + 1)^2}$$

where p is the price and q is the quantity demanded.
(a) Is this function discontinuous at any value of q? What value?
(b) Because q represents quantity, we know that $q \ge 0$. Is this function continuous for $q \ge 0$?

42. *Advertising and sales* The sales volume y (in thousands of dollars) is related to advertising expenditures x (in thousands of dollars) according to

$$y = \dfrac{200x}{x + 10}$$

(a) Is this function discontinuous at any points?
(b) Advertising expenditures x must be nonnegative. Is this function continuous for these values of x?

43. *Annuities* If an annuity can make an unending number of equal payments at the end of the interest periods, it is called a **perpetuity.** If a lump sum investment of A_n

is needed to result in n periodic payments of R when the interest rate per period is i, then

$$A_n = R \left[\frac{1 - (1 + i)^{-n}}{i} \right]$$

(a) Evaluate $\lim_{n \to \infty} A_n$ to find a formula for the lump sum payment for a perpetuity.
(b) Find the lump sum investment needed to make payments of \$100 per month in perpetuity if interest is 12% compounded monthly.

44. *Response to adrenalin* Experimental evidence suggests that the response y of the body to the concentration x of injected adrenalin is given by

$$y = \frac{x}{a + bx}$$

where a and b are experimental constants.
(a) Is this function continuous for all x?
(b) On the basis of your conclusion in part (a) and the fact that in the context of the application $x \geq 0$ and $y \geq 0$, must a and b both be positive, both be negative, or have opposite signs?

45. *Cost-benefit* Suppose that the cost C of removing p percent of the impurities from the wastewater in a manufacturing process is given by

$$C(p) = \frac{9800p}{101 - p}$$

Is this function continuous for all those p-values for which the problem makes sense?

46. *Pollution* Suppose that the cost C of removing p percent of the particulate pollution from the exhaust gases at an industrial site is given by

$$C(p) = \frac{8100p}{100 - p}$$

Describe any discontinuities for $C(p)$. Explain what each discontinuity means.

47. *Pollution* The percent p of particulate pollution that can be removed from the smokestacks of an industrial plant by spending C dollars is given by

$$p = \frac{100C}{7300 + C}$$

Find the percent of the pollution that could be removed if spending C were allowed to increase without bound. Can 100% of the pollution be removed? Explain.

48. *Cost-benefit* The percent p of impurities that can be removed from the wastewater of a manufacturing process at a cost of C dollars is given by

$$p = \frac{100C}{8100 + C}$$

Find the percent of the impurities that could be removed if cost were no object (that is, if cost were allowed to increase without bound). Can 100% of the impurities be removed? Explain.

49. *Electrical usage costs* The monthly charge in dollars for x kilowatt-hours (kWh) of electricity used by a residential consumer of Excelsior Electric Membership Corporation from November through June is given by the function

$$C(x) = \begin{cases} 20 + 0.188x & \text{if} & 0 \leq x \leq 100 \\ 38.80 + 0.15(x - 100) & \text{if} & 100 < x \leq 500 \\ 98.80 + 0.10(x - 500) & \text{if} & x > 500 \end{cases}$$

(a) What is the monthly charge if 1100 kWh of electricity is consumed in a month?
(b) Find $\lim_{x \to 100} C(x)$ and $\lim_{x \to 500} C(x)$, if the limits exist.
(c) Is C continuous at $x = 100$ and at $x = 500$?

50. *Calories and temperature* Suppose that the number of calories of heat required to raise 1 g of water (or ice) from $-40°C$ to $x°C$ is given by

$$f(x) = \begin{cases} \frac{1}{2}x + 20 & \text{if} -40 \leq x < 0 \\ x + 100 & \text{if } 0 \leq x \end{cases}$$

(a) What can be said about the continuity of the function $f(x)$?
(b) What happens to water at $0°C$ that accounts for the behavior of the function at $0°C$?

51. *Modeling U.S. workforce* Since 1950, the U.S. workforce has seen the arrival of the baby boomers and the changing role of women, among other influences. The data in the table show the millions of men and women in the U.S. workforce for selected years from 1950 and projected to 2050. Complete the following to explore the dynamics of the changing roles of men and women in the workforce.
(a) With x representing the number of years past 1950, use the data in the table to find a linear model for the number of men in the workforce, $m(x)$, and a model for the number of women in the workforce, $w(x)$. Report each model with three significant digits.
(b) Use the results from part (a) to find the function $r(x)$ that gives the ratio of men to women in the U.S. workforce.
(c) Find $\lim_{x \to 0} r(x)$ and $\lim_{x \to 100} r(x)$ and interpret their meanings.
(d) Find $\lim_{x \to \infty} r(x)$ and interpret its meaning.

	Workforce (in millions)	
Year	Men	Women
1950	43.8	18.4
1960	46.4	23.2
1970	51.2	31.5
1980	61.5	45.5
1990	69.0	56.8
2000	75.2	65.7
2010	82.2	75.5
2015	84.2	78.6
2020	85.4	79.3
2030	88.5	81.6
2040	94.0	86.5
2050	100.3	91.5

Source: U.S. Bureau of Labor Statistics

52. *U.S. smart phones* Using data from 2010 to 2016, the fraction of U.S. cell phone users who are smart phone users can be modeled by the function

$$f(t) = \frac{21.35t + 69.59}{4.590t + 233.1}$$

where t is equal to the number of years after 2010 (*Source:* emarketer.com).
(a) Is the function continuous for years from 2010 onward?
(b) Evaluate $\lim_{t \to \infty} f(t)$ if it exists to find a horizontal asymptote.
(c) When can we be sure this model is no longer valid for this application?
(d) Does the $\lim_{t \to \infty} f(t)$ give the long-term projection of the fraction of smart phone users?

SECTION 9.3 Rates of Change and Derivatives

OBJECTIVES

- To define and find average rates of change
- To define the derivative as a rate of change
- To use the definition of derivative to find derivatives of functions
- To use derivatives to find slopes of tangents to curves
- To understand the relationship between continuity and differentiablility of a function

APPLICATION PREVIEW

In Chapter 1, "Linear Equations and Functions," we studied linear revenue functions and defined the marginal revenue for a product as the rate of change of the revenue function. For linear revenue functions, this rate is also the slope of the line that is the graph of the revenue function. In this section, we will define marginal revenue as the rate of change of the revenue function, even when the revenue function is not linear.

Thus if an oil company's revenue (in thousands of dollars) is given by

$$R = 100x - x^2, \quad x \geq 0$$

where x is the number of thousands of barrels of oil sold per day, we can find and interpret the marginal revenue when 20,000 barrels are sold. (See Example 4.)

We will discuss the relationship between the *instantaneous rate of change* of a function at a given point and the slope of the line tangent to the graph of the function at that point. We will see how the derivative of a revenue function can be used to find both the slope of its tangent line and its marginal revenue.

Average Rates of Change For linear functions, we have seen that the slope of the line measures the average rate of change of the function and it can be found from any two points on the line. However, for a function that is not linear, the slope between different pairs of points no longer always gives the same number, but it can be interpreted as an **average rate of change.**

Average Rate of Change

The **average rate of change** of a function $y = f(x)$ from $x = a$ to $x = b$ is defined by

$$\text{Average rate of change} = \frac{f(b) - f(a)}{b - a}$$

The figure shows that this average rate is the same as the slope of the segment (or secant line) joining the points $(a, f(a))$ and $(b, f(b))$.

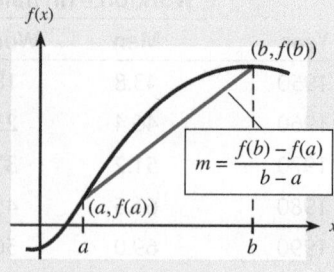

EXAMPLE 1   Total Cost

Suppose a company's total cost in dollars to produce x units of its product is given by

$$C(x) = 0.01x^2 + 25x + 1500$$

Find the average rate of change of total cost for the second 100 units produced (from $x = 100$ to $x = 200$).

Solution

The average rate of change of total cost from $x = 100$ to $x = 200$ units is

$$\frac{C(200) - C(100)}{200 - 100} = \frac{[0.01(200)^2 + 25(200) + 1500] - [0.01(100)^2 + 25(100) + 1500]}{100}$$

$$= \frac{6900 - 4100}{100} = \frac{2800}{100} = 28 \text{ dollars per unit}$$

EXAMPLE 2   Elderly in the Workforce

Figure 9.18 shows the percents of elderly men and elderly women in the workforce in selected years from 1970 and projected to 2040. Find and interpret the average rate of change of the percent of (a) elderly men in the workforce and (b) elderly women in the workforce from 1970 to 2040.

Elderly in the Workforce, 1970–2040

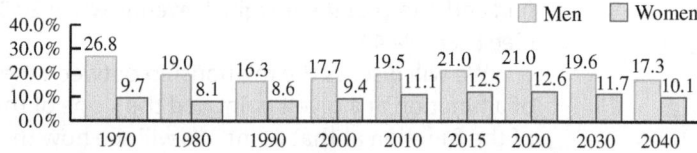

Figure 9.18   *Source:* Bureau of the Census, U.S. Department of Commerce

Solution

(a) From 1970 to 2040, the annual average rate of change in the percent of elderly men in the workforce is

$$\frac{\text{Change in men's percent}}{\text{Change in years}} = \frac{17.3 - 26.8}{2040 - 1970} = \frac{-9.5}{70} \approx -0.136 \text{ percentage points per year}$$

This means that from 1970 to 2040, *on average*, the percent of elderly men in the workforce dropped by 0.136 percentage points per year.

(b) Similarly, the average rate of change for women is

$$\frac{\text{Change in women's percent}}{\text{Change in years}} = \frac{10.1 - 9.7}{2040 - 1970} = \frac{0.4}{70} \approx 0.0057 \text{ percentage points per year}$$

This means that from 1970 to 2040, *on average*, the percent of elderly women in the workforce increased by 0.0057 percentage points each year. ◼

Instantaneous Rates of Change: Velocity

Another common rate of change is velocity. For instance, if we travel 200 miles in our car over a 4-hour period, we know that we averaged 50 mph. However, during that trip, there may have been times when we were traveling on an interstate at faster than 50 mph and times when we were stopped at a traffic light. Thus, for the trip, we have not only an average velocity but also instantaneous velocities (or instantaneous speeds as displayed on the speedometer). Let's see how average velocity can lead us to instantaneous velocity.

Suppose a ball is thrown straight upward at 64 feet per second from a spot 96 feet above ground level. The equation that describes the height y of the ball after x seconds is

$$y = f(x) = 96 + 64x - 16x^2$$

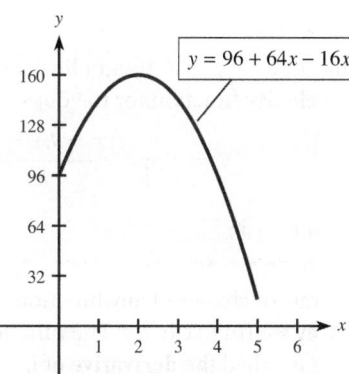

Figure 9.19 shows the graph of this function for $0 \le x \le 5$. The average velocity of the ball over a given time interval is the change in the height divided by the length of time that has passed. Table 9.4 shows some average velocities over time intervals beginning at $x = 1$.

Figure 9.19

TABLE 9.4

AVERAGE VELOCITIES

Time (seconds)			Height (feet)			Average Velocity (ft/sec)
Beginning	Ending	Change (Δx)	Beginning	Ending	Change (Δy)	($\Delta y/\Delta x$)
1	2	1	144	160	16	16/1 = 16
1	1.5	0.5	144	156	12	12/0.5 = 24
1	1.1	0.1	144	147.04	3.04	3.04/0.1 = 30.4
1	1.01	0.01	144	144.3184	0.3184	0.3184/0.01 = 31.84

In Table 9.4, the smaller the time interval, the more closely the average velocity approximates the instantaneous velocity at $x = 1$. Thus the instantaneous velocity at $x = 1$ is closer to 31.84 feet per second than to 30.4 feet per second.

If we represent the change in time by h, then the average velocity from $x = 1$ to $x = 1 + h$ approaches the instantaneous velocity at $x = 1$ as h approaches 0. (Note that h can be positive or negative.) This is illustrated in the following example.

EXAMPLE   3   Velocity

Suppose a ball is thrown straight upward so that its height $f(x)$ (in feet) is given by the equation

$$f(x) = 96 + 64x - 16x^2$$

where x is time (in seconds).

(a) Find the average velocity from $x = 1$ to $x = 1 + h$.

(b) Find the instantaneous velocity at $x = 1$.

Solution

(a) Let h represent the change in x (time) from 1 to $1 + h$. Then the corresponding change in $f(x)$ (the height) is

$$f(1 + h) - f(1) = [96 + 64(1 + h) - 16(1 + h)^2] - [96 + 64 - 16]$$
$$= 96 + 64 + 64h - 16(1 + 2h + h^2) - 144$$
$$= 16 + 64h - 16 - 32h - 16h^2 = 32h - 16h^2$$

The average velocity V_{av} is the change in height divided by the change in time.

$$V_{av} = \frac{f(1 + h) - f(1)}{1 + h - 1} = \frac{32h - 16h^2}{h} = 32 - 16h$$

(b) The instantaneous velocity V is the limit of the average velocity as h approaches 0.

$$V = \lim_{h \to 0} V_{av} = \lim_{h \to 0} (32 - 16h) = 32 \text{ feet per second}$$

Note that average velocity is found over a time interval. Instantaneous velocity is usually called **velocity,** and it can be found at any time x, as follows.

Velocity

Suppose that an object moving in a straight line has its position y at time x given by $y = f(x)$. Then the **velocity** function for the object at time x is

$$V = \lim_{h \to 0} \frac{f(x + h) - f(x)}{h}$$

provided that this limit exists.

The instantaneous rate of change of any function (commonly called *rate of change*) can be found in the same way we find velocity. The function that gives this instantaneous rate of change of a function f is called the **derivative** of f.

Derivative

If f is a function given by $y = f(x)$, then the **derivative** of $f(x)$ at any value x, denoted $f'(x)$, is a new function defined by

$$f'(x) = \lim_{h \to 0} \frac{f(x + h) - f(x)}{h}$$

if this limit exists. If $f'(c)$ exists, we say that f is **differentiable** at c.

The following procedure illustrates how to find the derivative of a function $y = f(x)$ at any value x.

DERIVATIVE USING THE DEFINITION

Procedure	Example
To find the derivative of $y = f(x)$ at any value x:	Find the derivative of $f(x) = 4x^2$.
1. Let h represent the change in x from x to $x + h$.	1. The change in x from x to $x + h$ is h.
2. The corresponding change in $y = f(x)$ is $$f(x + h) - f(x)$$	2. The change in $f(x)$ is $$f(x + h) - f(x) = 4(x + h)^2 - 4x^2$$ $$= 4(x^2 + 2xh + h^2) - 4x^2$$ $$= 4x^2 + 8xh + 4h^2 - 4x^2$$ $$= 8xh + 4h^2$$

(Continued)

3. Form the **difference quotient** $\dfrac{f(x + h) - f(x)}{h}$ and simplify.

3. $\dfrac{f(x + h) - f(x)}{h} = \dfrac{8xh + 4h^2}{h}$

$$= 8x + 4h$$

4. Find $\lim\limits_{h \to 0} \dfrac{f(x + h) - f(x)}{h}$ to determine $f'(x)$, the derivative of $f(x)$.

4. $f'(x) = \lim\limits_{h \to 0} \dfrac{f(x + h) - f(x)}{h}$

$$f'(x) = \lim\limits_{h \to 0} (8x + 4h) = 8x$$

Note that in the example above, we could have found the derivative of the function $f(x) = 4x^2$ at a particular value of x (for example, $x = 3$) by evaluating the derivative formula at that value:

$$f'(x) = 8x \quad \text{so} \quad f'(3) = 8(3) = 24$$

In addition to $f'(x)$, the derivative of $y = f(x)$ may be denoted by

$$\frac{dy}{dx}, \quad y', \quad \frac{d}{dx} f(x), \quad D_x y, \quad \text{or} \quad D_x f(x)$$

We can, of course, use variables other than x and y to represent functions and their derivatives. For example, we can represent the derivative of the function $p = 2q^2 - 1$ by dp/dq.

CHECKPOINT

1. Find the average rate of change of $f(x) = 30 - x - x^2$ over $[1, 4]$.

2. For the function $y = f(x) = x^2 - x + 1$, find each of the following.

   (a) $f(x + h) - f(x)$

   (b) $\dfrac{f(x + h) - f(x)}{h}$

   (c) $f'(x) = \lim\limits_{h \to 0} \dfrac{f(x + h) - f(x)}{h}$

   (d) $f'(2)$

For linear functions, we defined the **marginal revenue** for a product as the rate of change of the total revenue function for the product. If the total revenue function for a product is not linear, we define the marginal revenue for the product as the instantaneous rate of change, or the derivative, of the revenue function.

Marginal Revenue

Suppose that the total revenue function for a product is given by $R = R(x)$, where x is the number of units sold. Then the **marginal revenue** at x units is

$$\overline{MR} = R'(x) = \lim\limits_{h \to 0} \dfrac{R(x + h) - R(x)}{h}$$

provided that the limit exists.

Note that the marginal revenue (derivative of the revenue function) can be found by using the steps in the Procedure/Example box beginning on the preceding page. These steps also can be combined, as they are in Example 4.

| EXAMPLE | 4 | **Revenue** | APPLICATION PREVIEW | |

Suppose that an oil company's revenue (in thousands of dollars) is given by the equation

$$R = R(x) = 100x - x^2, \quad x \geq 0$$

where x is the number of thousands of barrels of oil sold each day.

(a) Find the function that gives the marginal revenue at any value of x.
(b) Find the marginal revenue when 20,000 barrels are sold (that is, at $x = 20$).

Solution

(a) The marginal revenue function is the derivative of $R(x)$.

$$R'(x) = \lim_{h \to 0} \frac{R(x + h) - R(x)}{h} = \lim_{h \to 0} \frac{[100(x + h) - (x + h)^2] - (100x - x^2)}{h}$$

$$= \lim_{h \to 0} \frac{100x + 100h - (x^2 + 2xh + h^2) - 100x + x^2}{h}$$

$$= \lim_{h \to 0} \frac{100h - 2xh - h^2}{h} = \lim_{h \to 0} (100 - 2x - h) = 100 - 2x$$

Thus the marginal revenue function is $\overline{MR} = R'(x) = 100 - 2x$.

(b) The function found in part (a) gives the marginal revenue at *any* value of x. To find the marginal revenue when 20 thousand barrels are sold, we evaluate $R'(20)$.

$$R'(20) = 100 - 2(20) = 60$$

Hence the marginal revenue at $x = 20$ is 60 thousand dollars per thousand barrels of oil. Because the marginal revenue is used to approximate the revenue from the sale of one additional unit, we interpret $R'(20) = 60$ to mean that the expected revenue from the sale of the next thousand barrels (after 20,000) will be approximately $60,000. [*Note:* The actual revenue from this sale is $R(21) - R(20) = 1659 - 1600 = 59$ thousand dollars.]

Tangent to a Curve

Just as average rates of change are connected with slopes, so are instantaneous rates (derivatives). In fact, the slope of the graph of a function at any point is the same as the derivative at that point. To show this, we define the slope of a curve at a point on the curve as the slope of the line tangent to the curve at the point.

In geometry, a **tangent** to a circle is defined as a line that has one point in common with the circle. [See Figure 9.20(a).] This definition does not apply to all curves, as Figure 9.20(b) shows. Many lines can be drawn through the point A that touch the curve only at A. One of the lines, line l, looks like it is tangent to the curve, in the same sense as a line is tangent to a circle.

Figure 9.20   (a)   (b)

In Figure 9.21, the line l represents the tangent line to the curve at point A and shows that secant lines (s_1, s_2, etc.) through A approach line l as the second points (Q_1, Q_2, etc.) approach A. (For points and secant lines to the left of A, there would be a similar figure and conclusion.) This means that as we choose points on the curve closer and closer to A (from both sides of A), the limiting position of the secant lines through A is the **tangent line** to the curve at A.

Figure 9.21

Figure 9.22

From Figure 9.22, we see that the slope of an arbitrary secant line through $A(x_1, f(x_1))$ and $Q(x_1 + h, f(x_1 + h))$ is given by

$$m_{AQ} = \frac{f(x_1 + h) - f(x_1)}{h}$$

Thus, as Q approaches A, the slope of the secant line AQ approaches the **slope of the tangent** line at A, and we have the following.

Slope of the Tangent

The **slope of the tangent** to the graph of $y = f(x)$ at point $A(x_1, f(x_1))$ is

$$m = \lim_{h \to 0} \frac{f(x_1 + h) - f(x_1)}{h}$$

if this limit exists. That is, $m = f'(x_1)$, the derivative at $x = x_1$.

EXAMPLE 5   Slope of the Tangent

Find the slope of $y = f(x) = x^2$ at the point $A(2, 4)$.

Solution
The formula for the slope of the tangent to $y = f(x)$ at $(2, 4)$ is

$$m = f'(2) = \lim_{h \to 0} \frac{f(2 + h) - f(2)}{h}$$

Thus for $f(x) = x^2$, we have

$$m = f'(2) = \lim_{h \to 0} \frac{(2 + h)^2 - 2^2}{h}$$

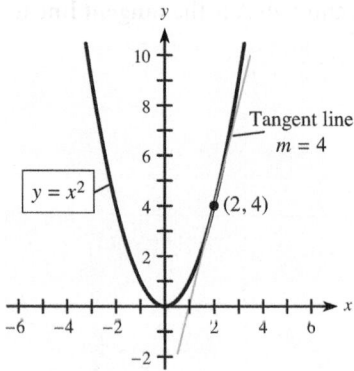

Figure 9.23

Taking the limit immediately would result in both the numerator and the denominator approaching 0. To avoid this, we simplify the fraction before taking the limit.

$$m = \lim_{h \to 0} \frac{4 + 4h + h^2 - 4}{h} = \lim_{h \to 0} \frac{4h + h^2}{h} = \lim_{h \to 0} (4 + h) = 4$$

Thus the slope of the tangent to $y = x^2$ at $(2, 4)$ is 4. (See Figure 9.23.)

The statement "the slope of the tangent to the curve at $(2, 4)$ is 4" is frequently simplified to the statement "the slope of the curve at $(2, 4)$ is 4." Knowledge that the slope is a positive number on an interval tells us that the function is increasing on that interval, which means that a point moving along the graph of the function rises as it moves to the right on that interval. If the derivative (and thus the slope) is negative on an interval, the curve is decreasing on the interval; that is, a point moving along the graph falls as it moves to the right on that interval.

EXAMPLE 6 Tangent Line

Given $y = f(x) = 3x^2 + 2x + 11$, find

(a) the derivative of $f(x)$ at any point $(x, f(x))$.
(b) the slope of the tangent to the curve at $(1, 16)$.
(c) the equation of the line tangent to $y = 3x^2 + 2x + 11$ at $(1, 16)$.

Solution
(a) The derivative of $f(x)$ at any value x is denoted by $f'(x)$ and is

$$y' = f'(x) = \lim_{h \to 0} \frac{f(x + h) - f(x)}{h}$$

$$= \lim_{h \to 0} \frac{[3(x + h)^2 + 2(x + h) + 11] - (3x^2 + 2x + 11)}{h}$$

$$= \lim_{h \to 0} \frac{3(x^2 + 2xh + h^2) + 2x + 2h + 11 - 3x^2 - 2x - 11}{h}$$

$$= \lim_{h \to 0} \frac{6xh + 3h^2 + 2h}{h} = \lim_{h \to 0} (6x + 3h + 2) = 6x + 2$$

(b) The derivative is $f'(x) = 6x + 2$, so the slope of the tangent to the curve at $(1, 16)$ is $f'(1) = 6(1) + 2 = 8$.
(c) The equation of the tangent line uses the given point $(1, 16)$ and the slope $m = 8$. Using $y - y_1 = m(x - x_1)$ gives $y - 16 = 8(x - 1)$, or $y = 8x + 8$.

The discussion in this section indicates that the derivative of a function has several interpretations.

Interpretations of the Derivative

For a given function, each of the following means "find the **derivative**."

1. Find the **velocity** of an object moving in a straight line.
2. Find the **instantaneous rate of change** of a function.
3. Find the **marginal revenue** for a given revenue function.
4. Find the **slope of the tangent** to the graph of a function.

That is, all the terms printed in boldface are mathematically the same, and all are found with the same technique.

Note in Figure 9.23 that near the point of tangency at (2, 4), the tangent line and the function look coincident. In fact, if we graphed both with a graphing calculator and repeatedly zoomed in near the point (2, 4), the two graphs would eventually appear as one. (Try this for yourself.) Thus the derivative of $f(x)$ at the point where $x = a$ can be approximated by finding the slope between $(a, f(a))$ and a second point that is nearby.

In addition, we know that the slope of the tangent to $f(x)$ at $x = a$ is defined by

$$f'(a) = \lim_{h \to 0} \frac{f(a + h) - f(a)}{h}$$

Hence we also could estimate $f'(a)$ (that is, the slope of the tangent at $x = a$) by evaluating

$$\frac{f(a + h) - f(a)}{h} \quad \text{when } h \approx 0 \text{ and } h \neq 0$$

EXAMPLE 7 Approximating the Slope of the Tangent Line

(a) Let $f(x) = 2x^3 - 6x^2 + 2x - 5$. Use $\dfrac{f(a + h) - f(a)}{h}$ and two values of h to make estimates of the slope of the tangent to $f(x)$ at $x = 1$ on opposite sides of $x = 1$.

(b) Use the following table of values of x and $g(x)$ to estimate $g'(3)$.

x	1	1.9	2.7	2.9	2.999	3	3.002	3.1	4	5
$g(x)$	1.6	4.3	11.4	10.8	10.513	10.5	10.474	10.18	6	-5

Solution

A graphing calculator can facilitate the following calculations.

(a) We can use $h = 0.0001$ and $h = -0.0001$ as follows:

With $h = 0.0001$: $\quad f'(1) \approx \dfrac{f(1 + 0.0001) - f(1)}{0.0001} = \dfrac{f(1.0001) - f(1)}{0.0001} \approx -4$

With $h = -0.0001$: $\quad f'(1) \approx \dfrac{f(1 + (-0.0001)) - f(1)}{-0.0001} = \dfrac{f(0.9999) - f(1)}{-0.0001} \approx -4$

Thus $f'(1) \approx 4$.

(b) We use the given table and measure the slope between (3, 10.5) and another point that is nearby (the closer, the better). Using (2.999, 10.513), we obtain

$$g'(3) \approx \frac{y_2 - y_1}{x_2 - x_1} = \frac{10.5 - 10.513}{3 - 2.999} = \frac{-0.013}{0.001} = -13$$

Spreadsheet Note

Excel can be used to approximate the value of a derivative at a given value of x by approximating the limit in the definition of derivative. See Appendix B, Sections 9.3–9.7, or the Online Excel Guide for details.

Differentiability and Continuity

So far we have talked about how the derivative is defined, what it represents, and how to find it. However, there are functions for which derivatives do not exist at every value of x. Figure 9.24 on the next page shows some common cases where $f'(c)$ does not exist but $f'(x)$ exists for all other values of x. These cases occur where there is a discontinuity, a corner, or a vertical tangent line.

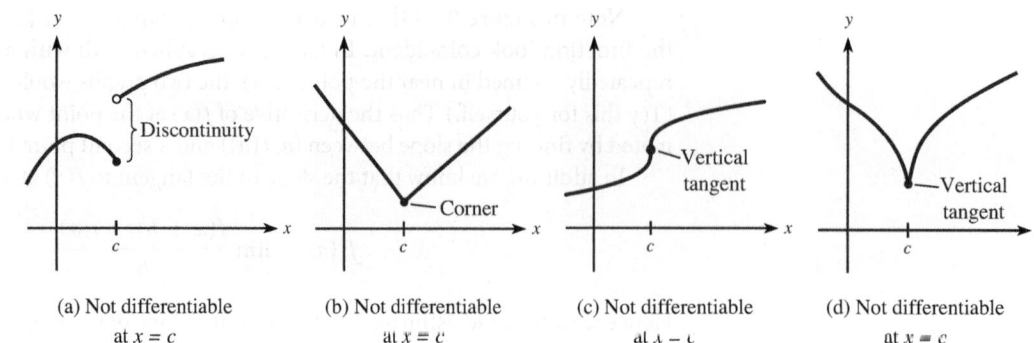

Figure 9.24

(a) Not differentiable at $x = c$

(b) Not differentiable at $x = c$

(c) Not differentiable at $x = c$

(d) Not differentiable at $x = c$

From Figure 9.24, we see that a function may be continuous at $x = c$ even though $f'(c)$ does not exist. Thus continuity does not imply differentiability at a point. However, differentiability does imply continuity.

Differentiability Implies Continuity

If a function f is differentiable at $x = c$, then f is continuous at $x = c$.

CHECKPOINT

3. Which of the following are given by $f'(c)$?
   (a) The slope of the tangent when $x = c$
   (b) The y-coordinate of the point where $x = c$
   (c) The instantaneous rate of change of $f(x)$ at $x = c$
   (d) The marginal revenue at $x = c$ if $f(x)$ is the revenue function

4. Must a graph that has no discontinuity, corner, or cusp at $x = c$ be differentiable at $x = c$?

Calculator Note

We can use a graphing calculator to explore the relationship between secant lines and tangent lines. Figure 9.25 illustrates the secant lines from the point $(1, 1)$ on $y = x^2$ for three different choices for a second point $(a, b) = (a, a^2)$.

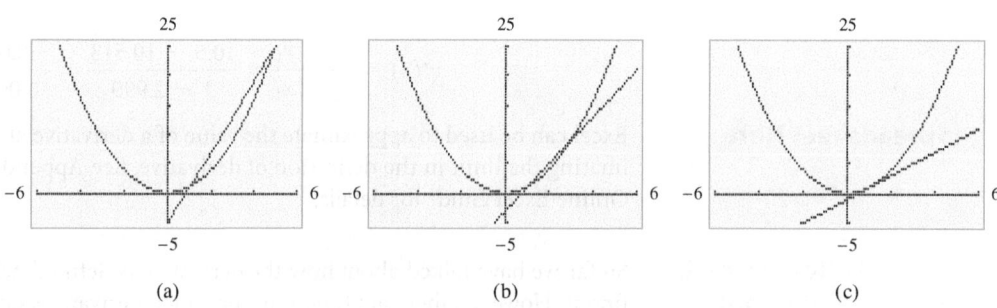

Figure 9.25

(a)

(b)

(c)

We see that as $a \to 1$, the point (a, a^2) moves closer to $(1, 1)$ and the slopes of the secant lines approach the following limit.

$$\lim_{a \to 1} \frac{a^2 - 1}{a - 1} = \lim_{a \to 1} (a + 1) = 2$$

This limit, 2, is the slope of the tangent line at (1, 1) and the derivative of $y = x^2$ at (1, 1). ∎

CHECKPOINT ANSWERS

1. -6

2. (a) $f(x + h) - f(x) = 2xh + h^2 - h$

   (b) $\dfrac{f(x + h) - f(x)}{h} = 2x + h - 1$

   (c) $f'(x) = 2x - 1$

   (d) $f'(2) = 3$

3. Parts (a), (c), and (d) are given by $f'(c)$. The y-coordinate where $x = c$ is given by $f(c)$.

4. No. See Figure 9.24(c).

EXERCISES 9.3

In Problems 1–4, for each given function, find the average rate of change over each specified interval.

1. $f(x) = x^2 + x - 12$ over (a) [0, 5] and (b) [−3, 10]
2. $f(x) = 6 - x - x^2$ over (a) [−1, 2] and (b) [1, 10]
3. For $f(x)$ given by the table, over (a) [2, 5] and (b) [3.8, 4]

x	0	2	2.5	3	3.8	4	5
$f(x)$	14	20	22	19	17	16	30

4. For $f(x)$ given in the table, over (a) [3, 3.5] and (b) [2, 6]

x	1	2	3	3.5	3.7	6
$f(x)$	40	25	18	15	18	38

5. Given $f(x) = 2x - x^2$, find the average rate of change of $f(x)$ over each of the following pairs of intervals.
   (a) [2.9, 3] and [2.99, 3]   (b) [3, 3.1] and [3, 3.01]
   (c) What do the calculations in parts (a) and (b) suggest the instantaneous rate of change of $f(x)$ at $x = 3$ might be?

6. Given $f(x) = x^2 + 3x + 7$, find the average rate of change of $f(x)$ over each of the following pairs of intervals.
   (a) [1.9, 2] and [1.99, 2]
   (b) [2, 2.1] and [2, 2.01]
   (c) What do the calculations in parts (a) and (b) suggest the instantaneous rate of change of $f(x)$ at $x = 2$ might be?

7. In the Procedure/Example box in this section, we were given $f(x) = 4x^2$ and found $f'(x) = 8x$. Find
   (a) the instantaneous rate of change of $f(x)$ at $x = 4$.
   (b) the slope of the tangent to the graph of $y = f(x)$ at $x = 4$.
   (c) the point on the graph of $y = f(x)$ at $x = 4$.

8. In Example 6 in this section, we were given $f(x) = 3x^2 + 2x + 11$ and found $f'(x) = 6x + 2$. Find
   (a) the instantaneous rate of change of $f(x)$ at $x = 6$.
   (b) the slope of the tangent to the graph of $y = f(x)$ at $x = 6$.
   (c) the point on the graph of $y = f(x)$ at $x = 6$.

9. Let $f(x) = 3x^2 - 2x$.
   (a) Use the definition of derivative and the Procedure/Example box on page 562 to verify that $f'(x) = 6x - 2$.
   (b) Find the instantaneous rate of change of $f(x)$ at $x = -1$.
   (c) Find the slope of the tangent to the graph of $y = f(x)$ at $x = -1$.
   (d) Find the point on the graph of $y = f(x)$ at $x = -1$.

10. Let $f(x) = 9 - \dfrac{1}{2}x^2$.
    (a) Use the definition of derivative and the Procedure/Example box on page 562 to verify that $f'(x) = -x$.
    (b) Find the instantaneous rate of change of $f(x)$ at $x = 2$.
    (c) Find the slope of the tangent to the graph of $y = f(x)$ at $x = 2$.
    (d) Find the point on the graph of $y = f(x)$ at $x = 2$.

In Problems 11–14, the tangent line to the graph of $f(x)$ at $x = 1$ is shown. On the tangent line, P is the point of tangency and A is another point on the line.
   (a) Find the coordinates of the points P and A.
   (b) Use the coordinates of P and A to find the slope of the tangent line.
   (c) Find $f'(1)$.
   (d) Find the instantaneous rate of change of $f(x)$ at P.

11.

12.

13.

14.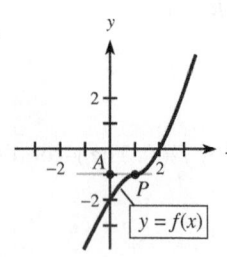

For each function in Problems 15–18, find
(a) the derivative using the definition.
(b) the instantaneous rate of change of the function at any value and at the given value.
(c) the slope of the tangent at the given value.

15. $f(x) = 5x^2 + 6x - 11$; $x = -2$
16. $f(x) = 16x^2 - 4x + 2$; $x = 1$
17. $p(q) = 2q^2 + q + 5$; $q = 10$
18. $p(q) = 2q^2 - 4q + 5$; $q = 2$

For each function in Problems 19–22, approximate $f'(a)$ in the following ways.

(a) Use $\dfrac{f(a + h) - f(a)}{h}$ with $h = 0.0001$.

(b) Graph the function on a graphing calculator. Then zoom in near the point until the graph appears straight, pick two points, and find the slope of the line you see.

19. $f'(2)$ for $f(x) = 3x^4 - 7x - 5$
20. $f'(-1)$ for $f(x) = 2x^3 - 11x + 9$
21. $f'(4)$ for $f(x) = (2x - 1)^3$
22. $f'(3)$ for $f(x) = \dfrac{3x + 1}{2x - 5}$

In Problems 23 and 24, use the given tables to approximate $f'(a)$ as accurately as you can.

23.

x	12.0	12.99	13	13.1	$a = 13$
f(x)	1.41	17.42	17.11	22.84	

24.

x	−7.4	−7.50	−7.51	−7	$a = -7.5$
f(x)	22.12	22.351	22.38	24.12	

In the figures given in Problems 25 and 26, at each point A and B, draw an approximate tangent line and then use it to complete parts (a) and (b).
(a) Is $f'(x)$ greater at point A or at point B? Explain.
(b) Estimate $f'(x)$ at point B.

25.

26.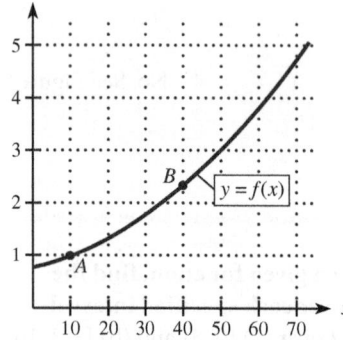

In Problems 27 and 28, a point (a, b) on the graph of $y = f(x)$ is given, as is the equation of the line tangent to the graph of $f(x)$ at (a, b). In each case, find $f'(a)$ and $f(a)$.
27. $(4, -11)$; $7x - 3y = 61$
28. $(-1, 6)$; $x + 10y = 59$
29. If the instantaneous rate of change of $f(x)$ at $(2, -4)$ is 5, write the equation of the line tangent to the graph of $f(x)$ at $x = 2$.
30. If the instantaneous rate of change of $g(x)$ at $(-1, -2)$ is $1/2$, write the equation of the line tangent to the graph of $g(x)$ at $x = -1$.

Because the derivative of a function represents both the slope of the tangent to the curve and the instantaneous rate of change of the function, it is possible to use information about one to gain information about the other. In Problems 31 and 32, use the graph of the function $y = f(x)$ given in Figure 9.26.

Figure 9.26

31. (a) Over what interval(s) (a) through (d) is the rate of change of $f(x)$ positive?

(b) Over what interval(s) (a) through (d) is the rate of change of $f(x)$ negative?

(c) At what point(s) A through E is the rate of change of $f(x)$ equal to zero?

32. (a) At what point(s) A through E does the rate of change of $f(x)$ change from positive to negative?

(b) At what point(s) A through E does the rate of change of $f(x)$ change from negative to positive?

33. Given the graph of $y = f(x)$ in Figure 9.27, determine for which x-values A, B, C, D, or E the function is
(a) continuous.   (b) differentiable.

34. Given the graph of $y = f(x)$ in Figure 9.27, determine for which x-values F, G, H, I, or J the function is
(a) continuous.   (b) differentiable.

Figure 9.27

In Problems 35–38, (a) find the slope of the tangent to the graph of $f(x)$ at any point, (b) find the slope of the tangent at the given point, (c) write the equation of the line tangent to the graph of $f(x)$ at the given point, and (d) graph both $f(x)$ and its tangent line (use a graphing utility).

35. $f(x) = x^2 + x; (2, 6)$

36. $f(x) = x^2 + 3x; (-1, -2)$

37. $f(x) = x^3 + 3; (1, 4)$

38. $f(x) = 5x^3 + 2; (-1, -3)$

APPLICATIONS

39. *Total cost* Suppose total cost in dollars from the production of x printers is given by

$$C(x) = 0.0001x^3 + 0.005x^2 + 28x + 3000$$

Find the average rate of change of total cost when production changes
(a) from 100 to 300 printers.
(b) from 300 to 600 printers.
(c) Interpret the results from parts (a) and (b).

40. *Average velocity* If an object is thrown upward at 64 feet per second from a height of 20 feet, its height S after t seconds is given by

$$S(x) = 20 + 64t - 16t^2$$

What is the average velocity in the
(a) first 2 seconds after it is thrown?
(b) next 2 seconds?

41. *Demand* If the demand for a product is given by

$$D(p) = \frac{1000}{\sqrt{p}} - 1$$

what is the average rate of change of demand when p increases from
(a) 1 to 25?   (b) 25 to 100?

42. *Revenue* If the total revenue function for a blender is

$$R(x) = 36x - 0.01x^2$$

where x is the number of units sold, what is the average rate of change in revenue $R(x)$ as x increases from 10 to 20 units?

43. *Total cost* Suppose the figure shows the total cost graph for a company. Arrange the average rates of change of total cost from A to B, B to C, and A to C from smallest to greatest and explain your choice.

44. *Foreign-born population* The figure shows the percent of the U.S. population that was foreign-born for selected years from 1910 and projected to 2020.
(a) Use the figure to find the average rate of change in the percent of the U.S. population that was foreign-born from 1960 to 2020. Interpret your result.
(b) From the figure, determine for which two consecutive data points the average rate of change in the percent of foreign-born was (i) closest to zero and (ii) furthest from zero.

Foreign-Born Population Percent: 1910–2020

Source: U.S. Bureau of the Census

45. *Marginal revenue* The revenue function for a home theater system is

$$R(x) = 300x - x^2 \text{ dollars}$$

where x denotes the number of units sold.
(a) What is the function that gives marginal revenue?
(b) What is the marginal revenue if 50 units are sold, and what does it mean?
(c) What is the marginal revenue if 140 units are sold, and what does it mean?

(d) What is the marginal revenue if 150 units are sold?

(e) As the number of units sold passes through 150, what happens to revenue?

46. *Marginal revenue* Suppose the total revenue function for a blender is

$$R(x) = 36x - 0.01x^2 \text{ dollars}$$

where x is the number of units sold.

(a) What function gives the marginal revenue?

(b) What is the marginal revenue when 600 units are sold, and what does it mean?

(c) What is the marginal revenue when 2000 units are sold, and what does it mean?

(d) What is the marginal revenue when 1800 units are sold, and what does it mean?

47. *Labor force and output* The monthly output at the Olek Carpet Mill is

$$Q(x) = 15,000 + 2x^2 \text{ units}, \qquad (40 \le x \le 60)$$

where x is the number of workers employed at the mill. If there are currently 50 workers, find the instantaneous rate of change of monthly output with respect to the number of workers. That is, find $Q'(50)$.

48. *Consumer expenditure* Suppose that the demand for x units of a product is

$$x = 10,000 - 100p$$

where p dollars is the price per unit. Then the consumer expenditure for the product is

$$E(p) = px = p(10,000 - 100p) = 10,000p - 100p^2$$

What is the instantaneous rate of change of consumer expenditure with respect to price at

(a) any price p? (b) $p = 5$? (c) $p = 20$?

49. *Profit* Suppose that the profit function for the monthly sales of a car by a dealership is

$$P(x) = 500x - x^2 - 100$$

where x is the number of cars sold. What is the instantaneous rate of change of profit when

(a) 200 cars are sold? Explain its meaning.

(b) 300 cars are sold? Explain its meaning.

50. *Profit* If the total revenue function and the total cost function for a toy are

$$R(x) = 2x \quad \text{and} \quad C(x) = 100 + 0.2x^2 + x$$

what is the instantaneous rate of change of profit if 10 units are produced and sold? Explain its meaning.

51. *Heat index* The highest recorded temperature in the state of Alaska was 100°F, occurring on June 27, 1915, at Fort Yukon. The *heat index* is the apparent temperature of the air at a given temperature and humidity level. If x denotes the relative humidity (in percent), then the heat index (in degrees Fahrenheit) for an air temperature of 100°F can be approximated by the function

$$f(x) = 0.009x^2 + 0.139x + 91.875$$

(a) At what rate is the heat index changing when the humidity is 50%?

(b) Write a sentence that explains the meaning of your answer in part (a).

52. *Receptivity* In learning theory, receptivity is defined as the ability of students to understand a complex concept. Receptivity is highest when the topic is introduced and tends to decrease as time passes in a lecture. Suppose that the receptivity of a group of students in a mathematics class is given by

$$g(t) = -0.2t^2 + 3.1t + 32$$

where t is minutes after the lecture begins.

(a) At what rate is receptivity changing 10 minutes after the lecture begins?

(b) Write a sentence that explains the meaning of your answer in part (a).

53. *Marginal revenue* Suppose the graph shows a manufacturer's total revenue, in thousands of dollars, from the sale of x smart phones to dealers.

(a) Is the marginal revenue greater at 300 smart phones or at 700? Explain.

(b) Use part (a) to decide whether the sale of the 301st smart phone or the 701st brings in more revenue. Explain.

54. *Social Security beneficiaries* The graph shows a model for the number of millions of Social Security beneficiaries projected to 2030. The model was developed with data from the Social Security Trustees Report.

(a) Was the instantaneous rate of change of the number of beneficiaries with respect to the year greater in 1960 or in 1980? Justify your answer.

(b) Is the instantaneous rate of change of the number of beneficiaries projected to be greater in 2000 or 2030? Justify your answer.

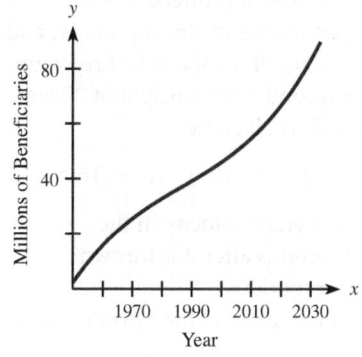

SECTION 9.4   Derivative Formulas

OBJECTIVES

- To find derivatives of powers of x
- To find derivatives of constant functions
- To find derivatives of functions involving constant coefficients
- To find derivatives of sums and differences of functions

APPLICATION PREVIEW

For more than 50 years, U.S. total personal income has experienced steady growth. With U.S. Bureau of Labor Statistics data for selected years from 1960 and projected to 2024, U.S. total personal income I, in billions of current dollars, can be modeled by

$$I = I(t) = 6.12t^2 - 49.7t + 620$$

where t is the number of years past 1960. We can find the rate of growth of total U.S. personal income in 2020 by using the derivative $I'(t)$ of the total personal income function. (See Example 8.)

As we discussed in the previous section, the derivative of a function can be used to find the rate of change of the function. In this section, we will develop formulas that make it easier to find certain derivatives.

Derivative of $f(x) = x^n$

We can use the definition of derivative to show the following.

$$\text{If } f(x) = x^2, \text{ then } f'(x) = 2x.$$
$$\text{If } f(x) = x^3, \text{ then } f'(x) = 3x^2.$$
$$\text{If } f(x) = x^4, \text{ then } f'(x) = 4x^3.$$
$$\text{If } f(x) = x^5, \text{ then } f'(x) = 5x^4.$$

Do you recognize a pattern here? We can use the definition of derivative and the binomial formula to verify the pattern and find a formula for the derivative of $f(x) = x^n$. If n is a positive integer, then

$$f'(x) = \lim_{h \to 0} \frac{f(x + h) - f(x)}{h} = \lim_{h \to 0} \frac{(x + h)^n - x^n}{h}$$

Because we are assuming that n is a positive integer, we can use the binomial formula, developed in Section 8.3, to expand $(x + h)^n$. This formula can be stated as follows:

$$(x + h)^n = x^n + nx^{n-1}h + \frac{n(n - 1)}{1 \cdot 2} x^{n-2} h^2 + \cdots + h^n$$

Thus the derivative formula yields

$$f'(x) = \lim_{h \to 0} \frac{\left[x^n + nx^{n-1}h + \dfrac{n(n - 1)}{1 \cdot 2} x^{n-2}h^2 + \cdots + h^n \right] - x^n}{h}$$

$$= \lim_{h \to 0} \left[nx^{n-1} + \frac{n(n - 1)}{1 \cdot 2} x^{n-2}h + \cdots + h^{n-1} \right]$$

Note that each term after nx^{n-1} contains h as a factor, so all terms except nx^{n-1} will approach 0 as $h \to 0$. Thus

$$f'(x) = nx^{n-1}$$

Even though we proved this derivative rule only for the case when n is a positive integer, the rule applies for any real number n.

Powers of x Rule

If $f(x) = x^n$, where n is a real number, then $f'(x) = nx^{n-1}$.

EXAMPLE 1   **Powers of x Rule**

Find the derivatives of the following functions.

(a) $y = x^{14}$ (b) $f(x) = x^{-2}$ (c) $y = x$ (d) $g(x) = x^{1/3}$

Solution

(a) If $y = x^{14}$, then $dy/dx = 14x^{14-1} = 14x^{13}$.

(b) The Powers of x Rule applies for all real values. Thus for $f(x) = x^{-2}$, we have

$$f'(x) = -2x^{-2-1} = -2x^{-3} = \frac{-2}{x^3}$$

(c) If $y = x$, then $dy/dx = 1x^{1-1} = x^0 = 1$. (Note that $y = x$ is a line with slope 1.)

(d) The Powers of x Rule applies to $y = x^{1/3}$.

$$g'(x) = \frac{1}{3}x^{1/3-1} = \frac{1}{3}x^{-2/3} = \frac{1}{3x^{2/3}}$$

In Example 1, we took the derivative with respect to x of *both sides* of each equation. We denote the operation "take the derivative with respect to x" by $\dfrac{d}{dx}$. Thus for $y = x^{14}$ in part (a), we can use this notation on both sides of the equation.

$$\frac{d}{dx}(y) = \frac{d}{dx}(x^{14}) \quad \text{gives} \quad \frac{dy}{dx} = 14x^{13}$$

Similarly, we can use this notation to indicate the derivative of an expression.

$$\frac{d}{dx}(x^{-2}) = -2x^{-3}$$

The differentiation rules are stated and proved for the independent variable x, but they also apply to other independent variables. The following examples illustrate differentiation involving variables other than x and y.

EXAMPLE 2   **Derivatives**

Find the derivatives of the following functions.

(a) $u(s) = s^8$ (b) $p = q^{2/3}$ (c) $C(t) = \sqrt{t}$ (d) $s = \dfrac{1}{\sqrt{t}}$

Solution

(a) If $u(s) = s^8$, then $u'(s) = 8s^{8-1} = 8s^7$.

(b) If $p = q^{2/3}$, then

$$\frac{dp}{dq} = \frac{2}{3}q^{2/3-1} = \frac{2}{3}q^{-1/3} = \frac{2}{3q^{1/3}}$$

(c) Writing $\sqrt{t}$ in its equivalent form, $t^{1/2}$, using the derivative formula, and writing the derivative in radical form give $C'(t) = \dfrac{1}{2}t^{1/2-1} = \dfrac{1}{2}t^{-1/2} = \dfrac{1}{2}\cdot\dfrac{1}{t^{1/2}} = \dfrac{1}{2\sqrt{t}}$

(d) Writing $\dfrac{1}{\sqrt{t}}$ as $\dfrac{1}{t^{1/2}} = t^{-1/2}$, taking the derivative, and writing the derivative in a form similar to that of the original function give

$$\frac{ds}{dt} = -\frac{1}{2}t^{-1/2-1} = -\frac{1}{2}t^{-3/2} = -\frac{1}{2}\cdot\frac{1}{t^{3/2}} = -\frac{1}{2\sqrt{t^3}}$$

EXAMPLE 3 Tangent Line

Write the equation of the tangent line to the graph of $y = x^3$ at $x = 1$.

Solution

Writing the equation of the tangent line to $y = x^3$ at $x = 1$ involves three steps.

1. Evaluate the function to find the point of tangency.
   At $x = 1$: $y = (1)^3 = 1$, so the point is $(1, 1)$

2. Evaluate the derivative to find the slope of the tangent.
   At any point: $m_{tan} = y' = 3x^2$
   At $x = 1$: $m_{tan} = y'\big|_{x=1} = 3(1^2) = 3$

3. Use $y - y_1 = m(x - x_1)$ with the point $(1, 1)$ and slope $m = 3$.

$$y - 1 = 3(x - 1) \Rightarrow y = 3x - 3 + 1 \Rightarrow y = 3x - 2$$

Figure 9.28 shows the graph of $y = x^3$ and the tangent line at $x = 1$.

Figure 9.28

Derivative of a Constant

A function of the form $y = f(x) = c$, where c is a constant, is called a **constant function.** We can show that the derivative of a constant function is 0, as follows:

$$f'(x) = \lim_{h \to 0} \frac{f(x + h) - f(x)}{h} = \lim_{h \to 0} \frac{c - c}{h} = \lim_{h \to 0} 0 = 0$$

We can state this rule formally.

Constant Function Rule   If $f(x) = c$, where c is a constant, then $f'(x) = 0$.

EXAMPLE 4 Derivative of a Constant

Find the derivative of the function defined by $y = 4$.

Solution

Because 4 is a constant, $\dfrac{dy}{dx} = 0$.

Recall that the function defined by $y = 4$ has a horizontal line as its graph. Thus the slope of the line (and the derivative of the function) is 0.

Derivative of $y = c \cdot u(x)$

We now can take derivatives of constant functions and powers of x. But we do not yet have a rule for taking derivatives of functions of the form $f(x) = 4x^5$ or $g(t) = \frac{1}{2}t^2$. The following rule provides a method for handling functions of this type.

Coefficient Rule   If $f(x) = c \cdot u(x)$, where c is a constant and $u(x)$ is a differentiable function of x, then $f'(x) = c \cdot u'(x)$.

The Coefficient Rule says that the derivative of a constant times a function is the constant times the derivative of the function.

Using Properties of Limits II and IV (from Section 9.1, "Limits"), we can show

$$\lim_{h \to 0} c \cdot g(h) = c \cdot \lim_{h \to 0} g(h)$$

We can use this result to verify the Coefficient Rule. If $f(x) = c \cdot u(x)$, then

$$f'(x) = \lim_{h \to 0} \frac{f(x + h) - f(x)}{h} = \lim_{h \to 0} \frac{c \cdot u(x + h) - c \cdot u(x)}{h}$$

$$= \lim_{h \to 0} c \cdot \left[\frac{u(x + h) - u(x)}{h} \right] = c \cdot \lim_{h \to 0} \frac{u(x + h) - u(x)}{h}$$

so $f'(x) = c \cdot u'(x)$.

EXAMPLE 5 **Coefficient Rule for Derivatives**

Find the derivatives of the following functions.

(a) $f(x) = 4x^5$ (b) $g(t) = \frac{1}{2}t^2$ (c) $p = \frac{5}{\sqrt{q}}$

Solution
(a) $f'(x) = 4(5x^4) = 20x^4$
(b) $g'(t) = \frac{1}{2}(2t) = t$
(c) $p = \frac{5}{\sqrt{q}} = 5q^{-1/2}$,   so $\frac{dp}{dq} = 5\left(-\frac{1}{2}q^{-3/2}\right) = -\frac{5}{2\sqrt{q^3}}$

EXAMPLE 6 **Internet Users in Latin America**

Like the rest of the world, the increase in the number of Internet users has slowed in Latin America during the second decade of the 21st century. Using data from 2013 and projected to 2019, the number of Internet users (in millions) in Latin America can be modeled by

$$y = 201x^{0.30}$$

with x equal to the number of years after 2010 (*Source:* eMarketer).

(a) Name the function that models the rate of change in the number of Internet users in Latin America.
(b) Find the function from part (a).
(c) Predict the rate of change in the number of Internet users in Latin America in 2025.

Solution
(a) The rate of change in the number of Internet users in Latin America is modeled by the derivative.

(b) $\dfrac{dy}{dx} = 201(0.30x^{0.30 - 1}) = 60.3x^{-0.7}$

(c) $\dfrac{dy}{dx}\Big|_{x = 15} = 60.3(15)^{-0.7} \approx 9.06$

Thus the model predicts that the number of Internet users in Latin America will increase by about 9.06 million between 2025 and 2026.

Derivatives of Sums and Differences   In Example 6 of Section 9.3, "Rates of Change and Derivatives," we found the derivative of $f(x) = 3x^2 + 2x + 11$ to be $f'(x) = 6x + 2$. This result, along with the results of several of the derivatives calculated in the exercises for that section, suggest that we can find the derivative of a function by finding the derivatives of its terms and combining them. The following rules state this formally.

Sum Rule   If $f(x) = u(x) + v(x)$, where u and v are differentiable functions of x, then
$f'(x) = u'(x) + v'(x)$.

We can prove this rule as follows:

If $f(x) = u(x) + v(x)$, then

$$f'(x) = \lim_{h \to 0} \frac{f(x + h) - f(x)}{h} = \lim_{h \to 0} \frac{[u(x + h) + v(x + h)] - [u(x) + v(x)]}{h}$$

$$= \lim_{h \to 0} \left[\frac{u(x + h) - u(x)}{h} + \frac{v(x + h) - v(x)}{h} \right]$$

$$= \lim_{h \to 0} \frac{u(x + h) - u(x)}{h} + \lim_{h \to 0} \frac{v(x + h) - v(x)}{h} = u'(x) + v'(x)$$

A similar rule applies to the difference of functions.

Difference Rule

If $f(x) = u(x) - v(x)$, where u and v are differentiable functions of x, then
$f'(x) = u'(x) - v'(x)$.

EXAMPLE 7 | **Sum and Difference Rules**

Find the derivatives of the following functions.

(a) $y = 3x + 5$ (b) $f(x) = 4x^3 - 2x^2 + 5x - 3$
(c) $p = \frac{1}{3}q^3 + 2q^2 - 3$ (d) $u(x) = 5x^4 + x^{1/3}$
(e) $y = 4x^3 + \sqrt{x}$ (f) $s = 5t^6 - \dfrac{1}{t^2}$

Solution

(a) $y' = 3 \cdot 1 + 0 = 3$

(b) The rules regarding the derivatives of sums and differences of two functions also apply if more than two functions are involved. We may think of the functions that are added and subtracted as terms of the function f. Then it would be correct to say that we may take the derivative of a function term by term. Thus

$$f'(x) = 4(3x^2) - 2(2x) + 5(1) - 0 = 12x^2 - 4x + 5$$

(c) $\dfrac{dp}{dq} = \frac{1}{3}(3q^2) + 2(2q) - 0 = q^2 + 4q$

(d) $u'(x) = 5(4x^3) + \frac{1}{3}x^{-2/3} = 20x^3 + \dfrac{1}{3x^{2/3}}$

(e) We may write the function as $y = 4x^3 + x^{1/2}$, so

$$y' = 4(3x^2) + \frac{1}{2}x^{-1/2} = 12x^2 + \dfrac{1}{2x^{1/2}} = 12x^2 + \dfrac{1}{2\sqrt{x}}$$

(f) We may write $s = 5t^6 - 1/t^2$ as $s = 5t^6 - t^{-2}$, so

$$\dfrac{ds}{dt} = 5(6t^5) - (-2t^{-3}) = 30t^5 + 2t^{-3} = 30t^5 + \dfrac{2}{t^3}$$

Each derivative in Example 7 has been *simplified*. This means that the final form of the derivative contains no negative exponents and the use of radicals or fractional exponents matches the original problem.

Also in part (a) of Example 7, we saw that the derivative of $y = 3x + 5$ is 3. Because the slope of a line is the same at all points on the line, it is reasonable that the derivative of a linear equation is a constant. In particular, the slope of the graph of the equation $y = mx + b$ is m at all points on its graph because the derivative of $y = mx + b$ is $y' = f'(x) = m$.

EXAMPLE 8   **Personal Income** | APPLICATION PREVIEW |

Total personal income in the United States has risen steadily over the past decades, from 4.9 trillion U.S. dollars in 1990 to 15.3 trillion U.S. dollars in 2015. This personal income I (in billions of dollars) from 1960 and projected to 2024 can be modeled by

$$I = I(t) = 6.12t^2 - 49.7t + 620$$

where t is the number of years after 1960 (*Source:* U.S. Bureau of Labor Statistics). For 2020, find the model's prediction for

(a) the total U.S. personal income.
(b) the rate of change of the total U.S. personal income.

Solution
(a) For 2020, $t = 60$ and

$$I(60) = 6.12(60)^2 - 49.7(60) + 620 = 19{,}670 \text{ billion dollars}$$

(b) The rate of change of total U.S. personal income is given by

$$I'(t) = 12.24t - 49.7$$

The predicted rate of change for 2020 is

$$I'(60) = 12.24(60) - 49.7 = 684.7 \text{ billion dollars per year}$$

This predicts that total U.S. personal income will increase about $684.7 billion from 2020 to 2021.

CHECKPOINT

1. True or false: The derivative of a constant times a function is equal to the constant times the derivative of the function.
2. True or false: The derivative of the sum of two functions is equal to the sum of the derivatives of the two functions.
3. True or false: The derivative of the difference of two functions is equal to the difference of the derivatives of the two functions.
4. Does the Coefficient Rule apply to $f(x) = x^n/c$, where c is a constant? Explain.
5. Find the derivative of each of the following functions.

   (a) $f(x) = x^{10} - 10x + 5$ (b) $s = \dfrac{1}{t^5} - 10^7 + 1$

6. Find the slope of the line tangent to $f(x) = x^3 - 4x^2 + 1$ at $x = -1$.

EXAMPLE 9   **Horizontal Tangents**

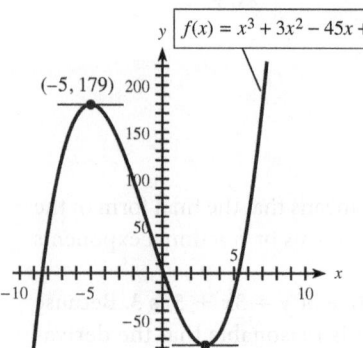

Find all points on the graph of $f(x) = x^3 + 3x^2 - 45x + 4$ where the tangent line is horizontal.

Solution
A horizontal line has slope equal to 0. Thus, to find the desired points, we solve $f'(x) = 0$.

$$f'(x) = 3x^2 + 6x - 45$$

We solve $3x^2 + 6x - 45 = 0$ as follows:

$$3x^2 + 6x - 45 = 0 \Rightarrow 3(x^2 + 2x - 15) = 0 \Rightarrow 3(x + 5)(x - 3) = 0$$

Solving $3(x + 5)(x - 3) = 0$ gives $x = -5$ and $x = 3$. The y-coordinates for these x-values come from $f(x)$. The desired points are $(-5, f(-5)) = (-5, 179)$ and $(3, f(3)) = (3, -77)$. Figure 9.29 shows the graph of $y = f(x)$ with these points and the tangent lines at them indicated.

Figure 9.29

Marginal Revenue   The marginal revenue $R'(x)$ is used to estimate the change in revenue caused by the sale of one additional unit.

EXAMPLE 10   Revenue

Suppose that a manufacturer of a product knows that because of the demand for this product, his revenue is given by

$$R(x) = 1500x - 0.02x^2, \qquad 0 \le x \le 1000$$

where x is the number of units sold and $R(x)$ is in dollars.

(a) Find the marginal revenue at $x = 500$.
(b) Find the change in revenue caused by the increase in sales from 500 to 501 units.

Solution
(a) The marginal revenue for any value of x is

$$R'(x) = 1500 - 0.04x$$

The marginal revenue at $x = 500$ is

$$R'(500) = 1500 - 20 = 1480 \,(\text{dollars per unit})$$

We can interpret this to mean that the approximate revenue from the sale of the 501st unit will be \$1480.

(b) The revenue at $x = 500$ is $R(500) = 745{,}000$, and the revenue at $x = 501$ is $R(501) = 746{,}479.98$, so the change in revenue is

$$R(501) - R(500) = 746{,}479.98 - 745{,}000 = 1479.98 \,(\text{dollars})$$

Notice that the marginal revenue at $x = 500$ is a good estimate of the revenue from the 501st unit.

Calculator Note   Most graphing calculators have a feature called the **numerical derivative** that can approximate the derivative of a function at a point. To find the numerical derivative of $f(x)$ at $x = c$ using a graphing calculator, choose the MATH menu and select 8:nDeriv. Next enter the function, x, and the value c, so that the display shows nDeriv($f(x)$, x, c); then press ENTER. The numerical derivative will appear. The numerical derivative of $R(x) = 1500x - 0.02x^2$ with respect to x at $x - 500$ can be found using:

$$\text{nDeriv}(1500x - 0.02x^2, x, 500) = 1480$$

Note that this result agrees with the solution in Example 10(a). See Appendix A, Sections 9.4–9.7, for details.

EXAMPLE 11   Comparing f(x) and f'(x)

(a) Graph $f(x) = x^3 - 3x + 3$ and its derivative $f'(x)$ on the same set of axes so that all values of x that make $f'(x) = 0$ are in the x-range.
(b) Investigate the graph of $y = f(x)$ near values of x where $f'(x) = 0$. Does the graph of $y = f(x)$ appear to turn at values where $f'(x) = 0$?
(c) Compare the interval of x values where $f'(x) < 0$ with the interval where the graph of $y = f(x)$ is decreasing from left to right.
(d) What is the relationship between the intervals where $f'(x) > 0$ and where the graph of $y = f(x)$ is increasing from left to right?

Solution

(a) The graphs of $f(x) = x^3 - 3x + 3$ and $f'(x) = 3x^2 - 3$ are shown in Figure 9.30.

(b) The values where $f'(x) = 0$ are the x-intercepts, $x = -1$ and $x = 1$. The graph of $y = x^3 - 3x + 3$ appears to turn at both these values.

(c) $f'(x) < 0$ where the graph of $y = f'(x)$ is below the x-axis, for $-1 < x < 1$. The graph of $y = f(x)$ appears to be decreasing on this interval.

(d) They appear to be the same intervals.

Figure 9.30

CHECKPOINT
ANSWERS

1. True, by the Coefficient Rule
2. True, by the Sum Rule
3. True, by the Difference Rule
4. Yes. $f(x) = x^n/c = (1/c)x^n$, so the coefficient is $(1/c)$.
5. (a) $f'(x) = 10x^9 - 10$

    (b) $\dfrac{ds}{dt} = \dfrac{-5}{t^6}$

6. The slope of the tangent at $x = -1$ is $f'(-1) = 11$.

EXERCISES 9.4

Find the derivatives of the functions in Problems 1–14.

1. $y = 4$
2. $f(s) = 6$
3. $f(t) = t$
4. $s = t^2$
5. $y = 6 - 8x + 2x^2$
6. $y = 12 + 2x - 7x^3$
7. $f(x) = 3x^4 - x^6$
8. $f(x) = 3x^4 - x^9$
9. $y = 10x^5 - 3x^3 + 5x - 11$
10. $y = 3x^5 - 5x^3 - 8x + 8$
11. $w = z^7 - 3z^6 + 13$
12. $u = 2t^{10} - 5t^5 - 9$
13. $g(x) = 2x^{12} - 5x^6 + 9x^4 + x - 5$
14. $h(x) = 12x^{20} + 8x^{10} - 2x^7 + 17x - 9$

In Problems 15–18, at the indicated points, find
(a) the slope of the tangent to the curve.
(b) the instantaneous rate of change of the function.

15. $y = 7x^2 + 2x + 1, \quad x = 2$
16. $C(x) = 3x^2 - 5, \quad (3, 22)$
17. $P(x) = x^3 - 6x, \quad (2, -4)$
18. $R(x) = 16x + x^2, \quad x = 1$

In Problems 19–26, find the derivative of each function.

19. $y = x^{-5} + x^{-8} - 3$
20. $y = x^{-1} - x^{-2} + 13$
21. $z = 3t^{11/3} - 2t^{7/4} - t^{1/2} + 8$
22. $w = 5u^{8/5} - 3u^{5/6} + u^{1/3} + 5$

23. $f(x) = 5x^{-4/5} + 2x^{-4/3}$
24. $f(x) = 6x^{-8/3} - x^{-2/3}$
25. $g(x) = \dfrac{3}{x^5} + \dfrac{2}{x^4} + 6\sqrt[3]{x}$
26. $h(x) = \dfrac{7}{x^7} - \dfrac{3}{x^3} + 8\sqrt{x}$

In Problems 27–30, write the equation of the tangent line to each curve at the indicated point. As a check, graph both the function and the tangent line.

27. $y = x^3 - 5x^2 + 7 \quad$ at $x = 1$
28. $y = x^4 - 4x^3 - 2 \quad$ at $x = 2$
29. $f(x) = 4x^2 - \dfrac{1}{x} \quad$ at $x = -\dfrac{1}{2}$
30. $f(x) = \dfrac{x^3}{3} - \dfrac{3}{x^3} \quad$ at $x = -1$

In Problems 31–34, find the coordinates of points where the graph of $f(x)$ has horizontal tangents. As a check, graph $f(x)$ and see whether the points you found look as though they have horizontal tangents.

31. $f(x) = -x^3 + 9x^2 - 15x + 6$
32. $f(x) = \dfrac{1}{3}x^3 - 3x^2 - 16x + 8$

33. $f(x) = x^4 - 4x^3 + 9$
34. $f(x) = 3x^5 - 5x^3 + 2$

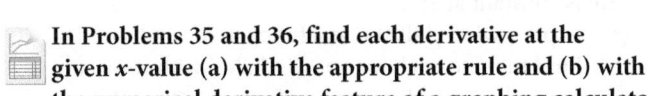
In Problems 35 and 36, find each derivative at the given x-value (a) with the appropriate rule and (b) with the numerical derivative feature of a graphing calculator.
35. $y = 5 - 2\sqrt{x}$ at $x = 4$
36. $y = 1 + 3x^{2/3}$ at $x = -8$

In Problems 37–40, complete the following.
(a) **Find the derivative of each function and evaluate it at the given x-value.**
(b) **Use the numerical derivative feature of a graphing calculator to check your evaluation from part (a).**
37. $f(x) = 2x^3 + 5x - \pi^4 + 8$ at $x = 2$
38. $f(x) = 3x^2 - 8x + 2^5 - 20$ at $x = 4$
39. $h(x) = \dfrac{10}{x^3} - \dfrac{10}{\sqrt[5]{x^2}} + x^2 + 1$ at $x = -1$
40. $g(x) = \dfrac{5}{x^{10}} + \dfrac{4}{\sqrt[4]{x^3}} + x^5 - 4$ at $x = 1$

The tangent line to a curve at a point closely approximates the curve near the point. In fact, for x-values close enough to the point of tangency, the function and its tangent line are virtually indistinguishable. Problems 41 and 42 explore this relationship. Use each given function and the indicated point to complete the following.
(a) **Write the equation of the tangent line to the curve at the indicated point.**
(b) **Use a graphing calculator to graph both the function and its tangent line. Be sure your graph shows the point of tangency.**
(c) **Repeatedly zoom in on the point of tangency. Do the function and the tangent line eventually become indistinguishable?**
41. $f(x) = 3x^2 + 2x$ at $x = 1$
42. $f(x) = 4x - x^2$ at $x = 5$

For each function in Problems 43–46, do the following.
(a) **Find $f'(x)$.**
(b) **Graph both $f(x)$ and $f'(x)$ using a graphing calculator.**
(c) **Use the graph of $f'(x)$ to identify x-values where $f'(x) = 0$, $f'(x) > 0$, and $f'(x) < 0$.**
(d) **Use the graph of $f(x)$ to identify x-values where $f(x)$ has a maximum or minimum point, where the graph of $f(x)$ is rising, and where the graph of $f(x)$ is falling.**
43. $f(x) = 8 - 2x - x^2$
44. $f(x) = x^2 + 4x - 12$
45. $f(x) = x^3 - 12x - 5$
46. $f(x) = 7 - 3x^2 - \dfrac{x^3}{3}$

APPLICATIONS

47. *Revenue* Suppose that a wholesaler expects that his monthly revenue, in dollars, for an electronic game will be
$$R(x) = 100x - 0.1x^2, \quad 0 \le x \le 800$$
where x is the number of units sold. Find his marginal revenue and interpret it when the quantity sold is
(a) $x = 300$. (b) $x = 600$.

48. *Revenue* The total revenue, in dollars, for a commodity is described by the function
$$R = 300x - 0.02x^2$$
(a) What is the marginal revenue when 40 units are sold?
(b) Interpret your answer to part (a).

49. *Metabolic rate* According to Kleiber's law, the metabolic rate q of the vast majority of animals is related to the animal's mass M according to
$$q = kM^{3/4}$$
where k is a constant. This means that a cat, with mass about 100 times that of a mouse, has a metabolism about $100^{3/4} \approx 32$ times greater than that of a mouse. Find the function that describes the rate of change of the metabolic rate with respect to mass.

50. *Capital investment and output* The monthly output of a certain product is
$$Q(x) = 800x^{5/2}$$
where x is the capital investment in millions of dollars. Find dQ/dx, which can be used to estimate the effect on the output if an additional capital investment of $1 million is made.

51. *Demand* The demand for q units of a product depends on the price p (in dollars) according to
$$q = \dfrac{1000}{\sqrt{p}} - 1, \quad \text{for } p > 0$$
Find and explain the meaning of the instantaneous rate of change of demand with respect to price when the price is
(a) $25. (b) $100.

52. *Demand* Suppose that the demand for a product depends on the price p according to
$$D(p) = \dfrac{50{,}000}{p^2} - \dfrac{1}{2}, \quad p > 0$$
where p is in dollars. Find and explain the meaning of the instantaneous rate of change of demand with respect to price when
(a) $p = 50$. (b) $p = 100$.

53. *Cost and average cost* Suppose that the total cost function, in dollars, for the production of x units of a product is given by
$$C(x) = 4000 + 55x + 0.1x^2$$

Then the average cost of producing x items is

$$\overline{C(x)} = \frac{\text{total cost}}{x} = \frac{4000}{x} + 55 + 0.1x$$

(a) Find the instantaneous rate of change of average cost with respect to the number of units produced at any level of production.
(b) Find the level of production at which this rate of change equals zero.
(c) At the value found in part (b), find the instantaneous rate of change of cost and find the average cost. What do you notice?

54. *Cost and average cost* Suppose that the total cost function, in dollars, for a certain commodity is given by

$$C(x) = 40{,}500 + 190x + 0.2x^2$$

where x is the number of units produced.
(a) Find the instantaneous rate of change of the average cost

$$\overline{C} = \frac{40{,}500}{x} + 190 + 0.2x$$

for any level of production.
(b) Find the level of production where this rate of change equals zero.
(c) At the value found in part (b), find the instantaneous rate of change of cost and find the average cost. What do you notice?

55. *Cost-benefit* Suppose that for a certain city, the cost C, in dollars, of obtaining drinking water that contains p percent impurities (by volume) is given by

$$C = \frac{120{,}000}{p} - 1200$$

(a) Find the rate of change of cost with respect to p when impurities account for 10% (by volume).
(b) Write a sentence that explains the meaning of your answer in part (a).

56. *Cost-benefit* Suppose that the cost C, in dollars, of processing the exhaust gases at an industrial site to ensure that only p percent of the particulate pollution escapes is given by

$$C(p) = \frac{8100(100 - p)}{p}$$

(a) Find the rate of change of cost C with respect to the percent of particulate pollution that escapes when $p = 2$ (percent).
(b) Write a sentence interpreting your answer to part (a).

57. *Wind chill* One form of the formula that meteorologists use to calculate wind chill temperature WC is

$$WC = 35.74 + 0.6215t - 35.75s^{0.16} + 0.4275t\, s^{0.16}$$

where s is the wind speed in mph and t is the actual air temperature in degrees Fahrenheit. Suppose temperature is constant at $15°$.
(a) Express wind chill WC as a function of wind speed s.
(b) Find the rate of change of wind chill with respect to wind speed when the wind speed is 25 mph.
(c) Interpret your answer to part (b).

58. *Allometric relationships—crabs* Data for fiddler crabs analyzed by Thompson in *On Growth and Form* show that the allometric relationship between the weight C of the claw and the weight W of the body is given by

$$C = 0.11W^{1.54}$$

Find the function that gives the rate of change of claw weight with respect to body weight.

Recall that for all modeling problems, use the unrounded model for any calculations unless instructed otherwise.

59. Modeling *Consumer price index* The table below gives the U.S. consumer price index (CPI) for selected years from 2012 and projected to 2050. With the reference year as 2012, a 2020 CPI $= 120.56$ means that goods and services costing $100.00 in 2012 are expected to cost $120.56 in 2020.
(a) Find the quadratic function that is the best fit for the data, with x as the number of years past 2010 and y as the CPI in dollars. Report the model as $y = f(x)$ with three significant digit coefficients.
(b) Use the data to find the average rate of change of the CPI from 2012 to 2020.
(c) Find the derivative of the reported model found in part (a).
(d) Find the instantaneous rate of change of the CPI for the year 2020.
(e) Use the rate of change from part (d) to predict the CPI for 2022.

Year	CPI	Year	CPI
2012	100.00	2030	158.90
2014	104.00	2035	182.43
2016	108.58	2040	209.44
2018	114.09	2045	240.45
2020	120.56	2050	276.05
2025	138.41		

Source: Social Security Administration

60. Modeling *Renewable electric power* The following table gives the total U.S. renewable electric power generation, in billions of kilowatt-hours, for selected years from 2012 and projected to 2040.
(a) Model these data with a power function $P(t)$, where t is the number of years past 2000. Report the model with three significant digit coefficients.

(b) Use the reported model from part (a) to find the function that models the rate of change of U.S. renewable electric power generation.

(c) Use the result from part (b) to find and interpret the rate of change of U.S. renewable electric power generation in 2020.

Renewable Electric Power Generation

Year	Kilowatt-hours (billions)	Year	Kilowatt-hours (billions)
2012	502	2028	730
2016	629	2032	764
2020	667	2036	800
2024	700	2040	851

Source: U.S. Department of Energy

61. Modeling *U.S. population* The table gives the U.S. population to the nearest million for selected years from 1950 and projected to 2050.

Year	Total	Year	Total
1950	160	2010	315
1960	190	2015	328
1970	215	2020	343
1980	235	2030	370
1990	260	2040	391
2000	288	2050	409

Source: Social Security Administration

(a) Find a cubic function $P(t)$ that models these data, where P is the U.S. population in millions and t is the number of years past 1950. Report the model with three significant digit coefficients.

(b) Use the part (a) result to find the function that models the instantaneous rate of change of the U.S. population.

(c) Find and interpret the instantaneous rates of change in 2000 and 2025.

62. Modeling *Gross domestic product* The table shows U.S. gross domestic product (GDP) in billions of dollars for selected years from 2000 to 2070 (actual and projected).

Year	GDP	Year	GDP
2000	9143	2040	79,680
2005	12,145	2045	103,444
2010	16,174	2050	133,925
2015	21,270	2055	173,175
2020	27,683	2060	224,044
2025	35,919	2065	290,042
2030	46,765	2070	375,219
2035	61,100		

Source: Social Security Administration Trustees Report

(a) Model these data with a cubic function $g = g(t)$, where g is in billions of dollars and t represents the number of years past 2000. Report the model with three significant digit coefficients.

(b) Use the reported model to find the predicted instantaneous rate of change of the GDP in 2025.

(c) Interpret your answer to part (b).

SECTION **9.5**

The Product Rule and the Quotient Rule

OBJECTIVES

- To use the Product Rule to find the derivatives of certain functions
- To use the Quotient Rule to find the derivatives of certain functions

APPLICATION PREVIEW

When medicine is administered, reaction (measured in change of blood pressure or temperature) can be modeled by

$$R = m^2\left(\frac{c}{2} - \frac{m}{3}\right)$$

where c is a positive constant and m is the amount of medicine absorbed into the blood.[*] The rate of change of R with respect to m is the sensitivity of the body to medicine. To find an expression for sensitivity as a function of m, we calculate dR/dm. We can find this derivative with the Product Rule for derivatives. (See Example 5.)

[*]Source: R. M. Thrall et al., *Some Mathematical Models in Biology,* U.S. Department of Commerce, 1967.

Product Rule We have simple formulas for finding the derivatives of the sums and differences of functions. But we are not so lucky with products. The derivative of a product is *not* the product of the derivatives. To see this, we consider the function $f(x) = x \cdot x$. Because this function is $f(x) = x^2$, its derivative is $f'(x) = 2x$. But the product of the derivatives of x and x would give $1 \cdot 1 = 1 \neq 2x$. Thus we need a different formula to find the derivative of a product. This formula is given by the **Product Rule.**

Product Rule If $f(x) = u(x) \cdot v(x)$, where u and v are differentiable functions of x, then

$$f'(x) = u(x) \cdot v'(x) + v(x) \cdot u'(x)$$

Thus the derivative of a product of two functions is the first function times the derivative of the second plus the second function times the derivative of the first.

We can prove the Product Rule as follows: If $f(x) = u(x) \cdot v(x)$, then

$$\lim_{h \to 0} \frac{f(x + h) - f(x)}{h} = \lim_{h \to 0} \frac{u(x + h) \cdot v(x + h) - u(x) \cdot v(x)}{h}$$

Subtracting and adding $u(x + h) \cdot v(x)$ in the numerator gives

$$f'(x) = \lim_{h \to 0} \frac{u(x + h) \cdot v(x + h) - u(x + h) \cdot v(x) + u(x + h) \cdot v(x) - u(x) \cdot v(x)}{h}$$

$$= \lim_{h \to 0} \left\{ u(x + h) \left[\frac{v(x + h) - v(x)}{h} \right] + v(x) \left[\frac{u(x + h) - u(x)}{h} \right] \right\}$$

Properties III and IV of limits (from Section 9.1, "Limits") give

$$f'(x) = \lim_{h \to 0} u(x + h) \cdot \lim_{h \to 0} \frac{v(x + h) - v(x)}{h} + \lim_{h \to 0} v(x) \cdot \lim_{h \to 0} \frac{u(x + h) - u(x)}{h}$$

Because u is differentiable and hence continuous, it follows that $\lim_{h \to 0} u(x + h) = u(x)$, so we have the formula

$$f'(x) = u(x) \cdot v'(x) + v(x) \cdot u'(x)$$

EXAMPLE 1 Product Rule

(a) Find dy/dx if $y = (2x^3 + 3x + 1)(x^2 + 4)$.
(b) At the point where $x = 1$, find the slope of the tangent to the graph of

$$y = f(x) = (4x^3 + 5x^2 - 6x + 5)(x^3 - 4x^2 + 1)$$

Solution

(a) Using the Product Rule with $u(x) = 2x^3 + 3x + 1$ and $v(x) = x^2 + 4$, we have

$$\frac{dy}{dx} = (2x^3 + 3x + 1)(2x) + (x^2 + 4)(6x^2 + 3)$$

$$= 4x^4 + 6x^2 + 2x + 6x^4 + 3x^2 + 24x^2 + 12$$

$$= 10x^4 + 33x^2 + 2x + 12$$

(b) $f'(x) = (4x^3 + 5x^2 - 6x + 5)(3x^2 - 8x) + (x^3 - 4x^2 + 1)(12x^2 + 10x - 6)$
If we substitute $x = 1$ into $f'(x)$, we find that the slope of the curve at $x = 1$ is
$f'(1) = 8(-5) + (-2)(16) = -72.$

Quotient Rule For a quotient of two functions, we might be tempted to take the derivative of the numerator divided by the derivative of the denominator, but this is incorrect. With the example $f(x) = x^3/x$ (which equals x^2 if $x \neq 0$), this approach would give $3x^2/1 = 3x^2$ as the derivative, rather than $2x$. Thus finding the derivative of a function that is the quotient of two functions requires the **Quotient Rule.**

Quotient Rule

If $f(x) = \dfrac{u(x)}{v(x)}$, where u and v are differentiable functions of x, with $v(x) \neq 0$, then

$$f'(x) = \frac{v(x) \cdot u'(x) - u(x) \cdot v'(x)}{[v(x)]^2}$$

The preceding formula says that the derivative of a quotient is the denominator times the derivative of the numerator minus the numerator times the derivative of the denominator, all divided by the square of the denominator.

To see that this rule is reasonable, again consider the function $f(x) = x^3/x,\ x \neq 0$. Using the Quotient Rule, with $u(x) = x^3$ and $v(x) = x$, we get

$$f'(x) = \frac{x(3x^2) - x^3(1)}{x^2} = \frac{3x^3 - x^3}{x^2} = \frac{2x^3}{x^2} = 2x$$

We see that $f'(x) = 2x$ is the correct derivative. The proof of the Quotient Rule is left for the student in the exercises in this section.

EXAMPLE 2   Quotient Rule

(a) If $f(x) = \dfrac{x^2 - 4x}{x + 5}$, find $f'(x)$.

(b) If $f(x) = \dfrac{x^3 - 3x^2 + 2}{x^2 - 4}$, find the instantaneous rate of change of $f(x)$ at $x = 3$.

Solution

(a) Using the Quotient Rule with $u(x) = x^2 - 4x$ and $v(x) = x + 5$, we get

$$f'(x) = \frac{(x + 5)(2x - 4) - (x^2 - 4x)(1)}{(x + 5)^2}$$

$$= \frac{2x^2 + 6x - 20 - x^2 + 4x}{(x + 5)^2} = \frac{x^2 + 10x - 20}{(x + 5)^2}$$

(b) To find the desired rate of change, we evaluate $f'(x)$ at $x = 3$. Using the Quotient Rule with $u(x) = x^3 - 3x^2 + 2$ and $v(x) = x^2 - 4$, we get

$$f'(x) = \frac{(x^2 - 4)(3x^2 - 6x) - (x^3 - 3x^2 + 2)(2x)}{(x^2 - 4)^2}$$

$$= \frac{(3x^4 - 6x^3 - 12x^2 + 24x) - (2x^4 - 6x^3 + 4x)}{(x^2 - 4)^2} = \frac{x^4 - 12x^2 + 20x}{(x^2 - 4)^2}$$

Thus the instantaneous rate of change at $x = 3$ is $f'(3) = 33/25 = 1.32$.

EXAMPLE 3   Quotient Rule

Use the Quotient Rule to find the derivative of $y = 1/x^3$.

Solution

Letting $u(x) = 1$ and $v(x) = x^3$, we get

$$y' = \frac{x^3(0) - 1(3x^2)}{(x^3)^2} = -\frac{3x^2}{x^6} = -\frac{3}{x^4}$$

Note that we could have found the derivative more easily by rewriting y.

$$y = 1/x^3 = x^{-3} \quad \text{gives} \quad y' = -3x^{-4} = -\frac{3}{x^4}$$

Recall that we proved the Powers of x Rule for positive integer powers and assumed that it was true for all real number powers. In Problem 38 of the exercises in this section, you will be asked to use the Quotient Rule to show that the Powers of x Rule applies to negative integers.

It is not necessary to use the Quotient Rule when the denominator of the function in question contains only a constant. For example, the function $y = (x^3 - 3x)/3$ can be written $y = \frac{1}{3}(x^3 - 3x)$, so the derivative is $y' = \frac{1}{3}(3x^2 - 3) = x^2 - 1$.

Calculator Note   We mentioned that graphing calculators have a numerical derivative feature that can be used to estimate the derivative of a function at a specific value of x. This feature can also be used to check the derivative of a function that has been computed with a formula. We graph both the derivative calculated with a formula and the numerical derivative. If the two graphs lie on top of each other, the computed derivative agrees with the numerical derivative. Figure 9.31 illustrates this idea for the derivative of $f(x) = \dfrac{x^3 - 3x^2 + 2}{x^2 - 4}$ from Example 2(b). Figure 9.31(a) shows $f'(x) = \dfrac{x^4 - 12x^2 + 20x}{(x^2 - 4)^2}$ as Y_1 and the calculator's numerical derivative of $f(x)$ as Y_2. Figure 9.31(b) shows the graphs of both Y_1 and Y_2. (The graphs are coincident.) See Appendix A, Section 9.4, for details. ■

Figure 9.31   (a)   (b)

CHECKPOINT

1. True or false: The derivative of the product of two functions is equal to the product of the derivatives of the two functions.
2. True or false: The derivative of the quotient of two functions is equal to the quotient of the derivatives of the two functions.
3. Find $f'(x)$ for each of the following.
    (a) $f(x) = (x^{12} + 8x^5 - 7)(10x^7 - 4x + 19)$ Do not simplify.

    (b) $f(x) = \dfrac{2x^4 + 3}{3x^4 + 2}$ Simplify.

4. If $y = \frac{4}{3}(x^2 + 3x - 4)$, does finding y' require the Product Rule? Explain.
5. If $y = f(x)/c$, where c is a constant, does finding y' require the Quotient Rule? Explain.

EXAMPLE 4   Marginal Revenue

Suppose that the revenue function for a flash drive is given by

$$R(x) = 10x + \frac{100x}{3x + 5}$$

where x is the number of flash drives sold per day and R is in dollars.

(a) Find the marginal revenue function.
(b) Find the marginal revenue when $x = 15$.

Solution

(a) We must use the Quotient Rule to find the marginal revenue (the derivative).

$$\overline{MR} = R'(x) = 10 + \frac{(3x + 5)(100) - 100x(3)}{(3x + 5)^2}$$

$$= 10 + \frac{300x + 500 - 300x}{(3x + 5)^2} = 10 + \frac{500}{(3x + 5)^2}$$

(b) The marginal revenue when $x = 15$ is $R'(15)$.

$$R'(15) = 10 + \frac{500}{[(3)(15) + 5]^2} = 10 + \frac{500}{(50)^2} = 10.20 \text{ (dollars per unit)}$$

Recall that $R'(15)$ estimates the revenue from the sale of the 16th flash drive.

$R'(15) = \$10.20$

EXAMPLE | 5 | **Sensitivity to a Drug** | APPLICATION PREVIEW |

When medicine is administered, reaction (measured in change of blood pressure or temperature) can be modeled by

$$R = m^2 \left(\frac{c}{2} - \frac{m}{3} \right)$$

where c is a positive constant and m is the amount of medicine absorbed into the blood. The rate of change of R with respect to m is the sensitivity of the body to medicine. Find an expression for sensitivity s as a function of m.

Solution

The sensitivity is the rate of change of R with respect to m, or the derivative. Thus

$$s = \frac{dR}{dm} = m^2 \left(0 - \frac{1}{3} \right) + \left(\frac{c}{2} - \frac{1}{3}m \right)(2m)$$

$$= -\frac{1}{3}m^2 + mc - \frac{2}{3}m^2 = mc - m^2$$

CHECKPOINT
ANSWERS

1. False. The derivative of a product is $\dfrac{d}{dx}(fg) = f \cdot \dfrac{dg}{dx} + g \cdot \dfrac{df}{dx}$

2. False. The derivative of a quotient is $\dfrac{d}{dx}\left(\dfrac{f}{g}\right) = \dfrac{g \cdot f' - f \cdot g'}{g^2}$

3. (a) $f'(x) = (x^{12} + 8x^5 - 7)(70x^6 - 4) + (10x^7 - 4x + 19)(12x^{11} + 40x^4)$

   (b) $f'(x) = \dfrac{-20x^3}{(3x^4 + 2)^2}$

4. No. y' can be found with the Coefficient Rule: $y' = \dfrac{4}{3}(2x + 3)$

5. No. y' can be found with the Coefficient Rule: $y' = \left(\dfrac{1}{c}\right)f'(x)$

EXERCISES 9.5

In Problems 1–4, find the derivative and simplify.

1. $s = (t^4 + 1)(t^3 - 1)$
2. $y = (5x + 3)(x^2 - 2x)$
3. $y = (3x^7 + 4)(8x^6 - 6x^4 - 9)$
4. $f(x) = (x^{12} + 3x^4 + 4)(2x^3 - 1)$

In Problems 5–8, find the derivative but do not simplify your answer.

5. $y = (7x^6 - 5x^4 + 2x^2 - 1)(4x^9 + 3x^7 - 5x^2 + 3x)$
6. $y = (9x^9 - 7x^7 - 6x)(3x^5 - 4x^4 + 3x^3 - 8)$
7. $y = (\sqrt[5]{x} - 2\sqrt[4]{x} + 1)(x^3 - 5x - 7)$
8. $y = (x^2 + x + 1)(\sqrt[3]{x} - 2\sqrt{x} + 5)$

In Problems 9 and 10, at each indicated point, find
(a) the slope of the tangent line.
(b) the instantaneous rate of change of the function.

9. $y = (x^2 + 1)(x^3 - 4x)$ at $(-2, 0)$
10. $y = (x^3 - 3)(x^2 - 4x + 1)$ at $(2, -15)$

In Problems 11–20, find the indicated derivatives and simplify.

11. $\dfrac{dp}{dq}$ for $p = \dfrac{q^2 + 3}{2q - 1}$

12. $C'(x)$ for $C(x) = \dfrac{2x^3}{3x^4 + 2}$

13. $\dfrac{dy}{dx}$ for $y = \dfrac{1 - 2x^2}{x^4 - 2x^2 + 5}$

14. $\dfrac{ds}{dt}$ for $s = \dfrac{t^3 - 4}{t^3 - 2t^2 - t - 5}$

15. $\dfrac{dz}{dx}$ for $z = x^2 + \dfrac{x^2}{1 - x - 2x^2}$

16. $\dfrac{dy}{dx}$ for $y = 200x - \dfrac{100x}{3x + 1}$

17. $\dfrac{dp}{dq}$ for $p = \dfrac{3\sqrt[3]{q}}{1 - q}$

18. $\dfrac{dy}{dx}$ for $y = \dfrac{2\sqrt{x} - 1}{1 - 4\sqrt{x^3}}$

19. y' for $y = \dfrac{x(x^2 + 4)}{x - 2}$

20. $f'(x)$ for $f(x) = \dfrac{(x + 1)(x - 2)}{x^2 + 1}$

In Problems 21 and 22, at the indicated point for each function, find
(a) the slope of the tangent line.
(b) the instantaneous rate of change of the function.

21. $y = \dfrac{x^2 + 1}{x + 3}$ at $(2, 1)$

22. $y = \dfrac{x^2 - 4x}{x^2 + 2x}$ at $\left(2, -\dfrac{1}{2}\right)$

In Problems 23–26, write the equation of the tangent line to the graph of the function at the indicated point. Check the reasonableness of your answer by graphing both the function and the tangent line.

23. $y = (9x^2 - 6x + 1)(1 + 2x)$ at $x = 1$
24. $y = (4x^2 + 4x + 1)(7 - 2x)$ at $x = 2$
25. $y = \dfrac{3x^4 - 2x - 1}{4 - x^2}$ at $x = 1$
26. $y = \dfrac{x^2 - 4x}{2x - x^3}$ at $x = 2$

In Problems 27–30, use the numerical derivative feature of a graphing calculator to find the derivative of each function at the given x-value.

27. $y = \left(4\sqrt{x} + \dfrac{3}{x}\right)\left(3\sqrt[3]{x} - \dfrac{5}{x^2} - 25\right)$ at $x = 1$

28. $y = (3\sqrt[4]{x^5} + \sqrt[5]{x^4} - 1)\left(\dfrac{2}{x^3} - \dfrac{1}{\sqrt{x}}\right)$ at $x = 1$

29. $f(x) = \dfrac{4x - 4}{3x^{2/3}}$ at $x = 1$

30. $f(x) = \dfrac{3\sqrt[3]{x} + 1}{x + 2}$ at $x = -1$

In Problems 31–34, complete the following.
(a) Find the derivative of each function and check your work by graphing both your calculated derivative and the numerical derivative of the function.
(b) Use your graph of the derivative to find points where the original function has horizontal tangent lines.
(c) Use a graphing calculator to graph the function and indicate the points found in part (b) on the graph.

31. $f(x) = (x^2 + 4x + 4)(x - 7)$
32. $f(x) = (x^2 - 14x + 49)(2x + 1)$

33. $y = \dfrac{x^2}{x - 2}$ 34. $y = \dfrac{x^2 - 7}{4 - x}$

In Problems 35 and 36,
(a) find $f'(x)$.
(b) graph both $f(x)$ and $f'(x)$ with a graphing calculator.
(c) identify the x-values where $f'(x) = 0, f'(x) > 0$, and $f'(x) < 0$.
(d) identify x-values where $f(x)$ has a maximum point or a minimum point, where $f(x)$ is increasing, and where $f(x)$ is decreasing.

35. $f(x) = \dfrac{10x^2}{x^2 + 1}$ 36. $f(x) = \dfrac{8 - x^2}{x^2 + 4}$

37. Prove the Quotient Rule for differentiation. (*Hint:* Add $[-u(x) \cdot v(x) + u(x) \cdot v(x)]$ to the expanded numerator and use steps similar to those used to prove the Product Rule.)

38. Use the Quotient Rule to show that the Powers of x Rule applies to negative integer powers. That is, show that $(d/dx)x^n = nx^{n-1}$ when $n = -k, k > 0$, by finding the derivative of $f(x) = 1/(x^k)$.

APPLICATIONS

39. *Cost-benefit* If the cost C (in dollars) of removing p percent of the particulate pollution from the exhaust gases at an industrial site is given by

$$C(p) = \frac{8100p}{100 - p}$$

    find the rate of change of C with respect to p.
40. *Cost-benefit* If the cost C (in dollars) of removing p percent of the impurities from the wastewater in a manufacturing process is given by

$$C(p) = \frac{9800p}{101 - p}$$

    find the rate of change of C with respect to p.
41. *Revenue* Suppose the revenue (in dollars) from the sale of x units of a product is given by

$$R(x) = \frac{60x^2 + 74x}{2x + 2}$$

    Find the marginal revenue when 49 units are sold. Interpret your result.
42. *Revenue* The revenue (in dollars) from the sale of x units of a product is given by

$$R(x) = \frac{3000}{2x + 2} + 80x - 1500$$

    Find the marginal revenue when 149 units are sold. Interpret your result.
43. *Revenue* A travel agency will plan a group tour for groups of size 25 or larger. If the group contains exactly 25 people, the cost is $300 per person. If each person's cost is reduced by $10 for each additional person above the 25, then the revenue is given by

$$R(x) = (25 + x)(300 - 10x)$$

    where x is the number of additional people above 25. Find the marginal revenue if the group contains 30 people. Interpret your result.
44. *Revenue* McRobert's Electronics sells 200 TVs per month at a price of $400 per unit. Market research indicates that the store can sell one additional TV for each $1 it reduces the price. In this case, the total revenue is

$$R(x) = (200 + x)(400 - x)$$

    where x is the number of additional TVs beyond the 200. If the store sells a total of 250 TVs, find the marginal revenue. Interpret your result.

45. *Response to a drug* The reaction R to an injection of a drug is related to the dosage x (in milligrams) according to

$$R(x) = x^2\left(500 - \frac{x}{3}\right)$$

    where 1000 mg is the maximum dosage. If the rate of reaction with respect to the dosage defines the sensitivity to the drug, find the sensitivity.
46. *Nerve response* The number of action potentials produced by a nerve, t seconds after a stimulus, is given by

$$N(t) = 25t + \frac{4}{t^2 + 2} - 2$$

    Find the rate at which the action potentials are produced by the nerve.
47. *Test reliability* If a test having reliability r is lengthened by a factor n, the reliability of the new test is given by

$$R = \frac{nr}{1 + (n - 1)r}, \quad 0 < r \le 1$$

    Find the rate at which R changes with respect to n.
48. *Advertising and sales* The sales of a product s (in thousands of dollars) are related to advertising expenses (in thousands of dollars) by

$$s = \frac{200x}{x + 10}$$

    Find and interpret the meaning of the rate of change of sales with respect to advertising expenses when
    (a) $x = 10$.   (b) $x = 20$.
49. *Candidate recognition* Suppose that the proportion P of voters who recognize a candidate's name t months after the start of the campaign is given by

$$P(t) = \frac{13t}{t^2 + 100} + 0.18$$

    (a) Find the rate of change of P when $t = 6$ and explain its meaning.
    (b) Find the rate of change of P when $t = 12$ and explain its meaning.
    (c) One month prior to the election, is it better for $P'(t)$ to be positive or negative? Explain.
50. *Endangered species population* It is determined that a wildlife refuge can support a group of up to 120 of a certain endangered species. If 75 are introduced onto the refuge and their population after t years is given by

$$p(t) = 75\left(1 + \frac{4t}{t^2 + 16}\right)$$

    find the rate of population growth after t years. Find the rate after each of the first 7 years.
51. *Wind chill* Each winter the so-called "polar vortex" of deep frigid air plunges into the United States and sometimes brings record cold and dangerous wind chills. If s

is the wind speed in miles per hour and $s \geq 5$, then the wind chill (in degrees Fahrenheit) for an air temperature of $0°F$ can be approximated by the function

$$f(s) = \frac{289.173 - 58.5731s}{s + 1}$$

(a) At what rate is the wind chill changing when the wind speed is 20 mph?
(b) Explain the meaning of your answer to part (a).

52. *Response to injected adrenalin* Experimental evidence has shown that the response y of a muscle is related to the concentration of injected adrenaline x according to the equation

$$y = \frac{x}{a + bx}$$

where a and b are constants. Find the rate of change of response with respect to the concentration.

53. *Social Security beneficiaries* The table gives the number of millions of Social Security beneficiaries (actual and projected) for selected years from 1950 through 2030.

Year	Number of Beneficiaries (millions)	Year	Number of Beneficiaries (millions)
1950	2.9	2000	44.8
1960	14.3	2010	53.3
1970	25.2	2020	68.8
1980	35.1	2030	82.7
1990	39.5		

Source: Social Security Trustees Report

With $B(t)$ representing the number of beneficiaries (in millions) t years past 1950, these data can be modeled by the function

$$B(t) = (0.01t + 3)(0.0238t^2 - 9.79t + 3100) - 9290$$

(a) Find the function that gives the instantaneous rate of change of the number of beneficiaries.
(b) Find and interpret the instantaneous rate of change in 2020.
(c) Use the data to determine which of the average rates of change (from 2010 to 2020, from 2020 to 2030, or from 2010 to 2030) best approximates the instantaneous rate from part (b).

54. *Emissions* The table shows data for sulfur dioxide emissions from electricity generation (in millions of short tons) for selected years from 2000 and projected to 2035. These data can be modeled by the function

$$E(x) = (0.001x - 0.062)(-0.18x^2 + 8.2x - 200)$$

where x is the number of years past 2000.
(a) Find the function that models the rate of change of these emissions.
(b) Find and interpret $E'(20)$.

Year	Short Tons (in millions)
2000	11.4
2005	10.2
2008	7.6
2015	4.7
2020	4.2
2025	3.8
2030	3.7
2035	3.8

Source: U.S. Department of Energy

55. *Females in the workforce* For selected years from 1950 and with projections to 2050, the table shows the percent of total U.S. workers who were female.

Year	% Female	Year	% Female
1950	29.6	2010	47.9
1960	33.4	2015	48.3
1970	38.1	2020	48.1
1980	42.5	2030	48.0
1990	45.2	2040	47.9
2000	46.6	2050	47.7

Source: U.S. Bureau of the Census

Assume that these data can be modeled with the function

$$p(t) = \frac{78.6t + 2090}{1.38t + 64.1}$$

where $p(t)$ is the percent of the U.S. workforce that is female and t is the number of years past 1950.
(a) Find the function that models the instantaneous rate of change of the percent of U.S. workers who were female.
(b) Use the function from part (a) to find the instantaneous rates of change in 2005 and 2020.
(c) Interpret each of the rates of change in part (b).

56. *Alzheimer's* As the baby boomer generation ages and the proportion of the U.S population over 65 increases, the number of Americans with Alzheimer's disease and other dementia is projected to grow each year. With data from the Social Security Administration and the Alzheimer's Association for selected years from 2000 and projected to 2050, the percent of the U.S. population with Alzheimer's can be modeled with the function

$$A(t) = \frac{0.34t^2 + 1.3t + 450}{-0.012t^2 + 3.3t + 260}$$

where t is the number of years past 1990.
(a) Find the function that gives the instantaneous rate of change of $A(t)$.
(b) Use your answer in part (a) to find and interpret the instantaneous rate of change of the percent of the U.S. population with Alzheimer's in 2025.

The Chain Rule and the Power Rule

OBJECTIVES

- To use the Chain Rule to differentiate functions
- To use the Power Rule to differentiate functions

APPLICATION PREVIEW

The demand x for a product is given by

$$x = \frac{98}{\sqrt{2p+1}} - 1$$

where p is the price per unit. To find how fast demand is changing when price is $24, we take the derivative of x with respect to p. If we write this function with a power rather than a radical, it has the form

$$x = 98(2p+1)^{-1/2} - 1$$

The formulas learned so far cannot be used to find this derivative. We use a new formula, the Power Rule, to find this derivative. (See Example 6.) In this section, we will discuss the Chain Rule and the Power Rule, which is one of the results of the Chain Rule, and we will use these formulas to solve applied problems.

Composite Functions

Recall from Section 1.2, "Functions," that if f and g are functions, then the composite functions g of f (denoted $g \circ f$) and f of g (denoted $f \circ g$) are defined as follows:

$$(g \circ f)(x) = g(f(x)) \quad \text{and} \quad (f \circ g)(x) = f(g(x))$$

EXAMPLE 1 Composite Function

If $f(x) = 3x^2$ and $g(x) = 2x - 1$, find $F(x) = f(g(x))$.

Solution

Substituting $g(x) = 2x - 1$ for x in $f(x)$ gives

$$f(g(x)) = f(2x - 1) = 3(2x - 1)^2 \quad \text{so} \quad F(x) = 3(2x - 1)^2$$

Chain Rule

We could find the derivative of the function $F(x) = 3(2x - 1)^2$ by expanding the expression $3(2x - 1)^2$. Then

$$F(x) = 3(4x^2 - 4x + 1) = 12x^2 - 12x + 3$$

so $F'(x) = 24x - 12$. But we can use a very powerful rule, called the **Chain Rule,** to find derivatives of composite functions. If we write the composite function $y = f(g(x))$ in the form $y = f(u)$, where $u = g(x)$, we state the Chain Rule as follows.

Chain Rule

If f and g are differentiable functions with $y = f(u)$ and $u = g(x)$, then y is a differentiable function of x, and

$$\frac{dy}{dx} = f'(u) \cdot g'(x)$$

or, equivalently,

$$\frac{dy}{dx} = \frac{dy}{du} \cdot \frac{du}{dx}$$

Note that dy/du represents the derivative of $y = f(u)$ *with respect to* u and du/dx represents the derivative of $u = g(x)$ *with respect to* x. For example, if $y = 3(2x - 1)^2$, then the outside function, f, is the squaring function and the inside function, g, is $2x - 1$, so we may write $y = f(u) = 3u^2$, where $u = g(x) = 2x - 1$. Then the derivative is

$$\frac{dy}{dx} = \frac{dy}{du} \cdot \frac{du}{dx} = 6u \cdot 2 = 12u$$

To write this derivative in terms of x, we substitute $2x - 1$ for u. Thus

$$\frac{dy}{dx} = 12(2x - 1) = 24x - 12$$

Note that we get the same result by using the Chain Rule as we did by expanding $f(x) = 3(2x - 1)^2$. The Chain Rule is important because it is not always possible to rewrite the function as a polynomial. Consider the following example.

EXAMPLE 2   Chain Rule

If $y = \sqrt{x^2 - 1}$, find $\dfrac{dy}{dx}$.

Solution

If we write this function as $y = f(u) = \sqrt{u} = u^{1/2}$, with $u = x^2 - 1$, we can find the derivative.

$$\frac{dy}{dx} = \frac{dy}{du} \cdot \frac{du}{dx} = \frac{1}{2} \cdot u^{-1/2} \cdot 2x = u^{-1/2} \cdot x = \frac{1}{\sqrt{u}} \cdot x = \frac{x}{\sqrt{u}}$$

To write this derivative in terms of x alone, we substitute $x^2 - 1$ for u. Then

$$\frac{dy}{dx} = \frac{x}{\sqrt{x^2 - 1}}$$

Note that we could not find the derivative of a function like that of Example 2 by the methods discussed previously.

EXAMPLE 3   Allometric Relationships

The relationship between the length L (in meters) and weight W (in kilograms) of a species of fish in the Pacific Ocean is given by $W = 10.375L^3$. The rate of growth in length is given by $\dfrac{dL}{dt} = 0.36 - 0.18L$, where t is measured in years.

(a) Determine a formula for the rate of growth in weight $\dfrac{dW}{dt}$ in terms of L.

(b) If a fish weighs 30 kilograms, approximate its rate of growth in weight using the formula found in part (a).

Solution

(a) The rate of change uses the Chain Rule, as follows:

$$\frac{dW}{dt} = \frac{dW}{dL} \cdot \frac{dL}{dt} = 31.125L^2 (0.36 - 0.18L) = 11.205L^2 - 5.6025L^3$$

(b) From $W = 10.375L^3$ and $W = 30$ kg, we can find L by solving

$$30 = 10.375L^3$$

$$\frac{30}{10.375} = L^3 \quad \text{so} \quad L = \sqrt[3]{\frac{30}{10.375}} \approx 1.4247 \text{ m}$$

Hence, the rate of growth in weight is

$$\frac{dW}{dt} \approx 11.205(1.4247)^2 - 5.6025(1.4247)^3 \approx 6.542 \text{ kilograms/year}$$

Power Rule   The Chain Rule is very useful and will be extremely important with functions we will study later. A special case of the Chain Rule, called the **Power Rule,** is useful for the algebraic functions we have studied so far—composite functions where the outside function is a power.

| Power Rule | If $y = u^n$, where u is a differentiable function of x, then |

$$\frac{dy}{dx} = nu^{n-1} \cdot \frac{du}{dx}$$

EXAMPLE 4 Power Rule

(a) If $y = (x^2 - 4x)^6$, find $\frac{dy}{dx}$.   (b) If $p = \frac{4}{3q^2 + 1}$, find $\frac{dp}{dq}$.

Solution

(a) This has the form $y = u^n = u^6$, with $u = x^2 - 4x$. Thus by the Power Rule,

$$\frac{dy}{dx} = nu^{n-1} \cdot \frac{du}{dx} = 6u^5 (2x - 4)$$

Substituting $x^2 - 4x$ for u gives

$$\frac{dy}{dx} = 6(x^2 - 4x)^5 (2x - 4) = (12x - 24)(x^2 - 4x)^5$$

(b) We can use the Power Rule to find dp/dq if we write the equation in the form

$$p = 4(3q^2 + 1)^{-1}$$

Then

$$\frac{dp}{dq} = 4[-1(3q^2 + 1)^{-2} (6q)] = \frac{-24q}{(3q^2 + 1)^2}$$

The derivative of the function in Example 4(b) can also be found by using the Quotient Rule, but the Power Rule provides a more efficient method.

EXAMPLE 5 Power Rule with Radicals

Find the derivatives of (a) $y = 3\sqrt[3]{x^2 - 3x + 1}$ and (b) $g(x) = \frac{1}{\sqrt{(x^2 + 1)^3}}$.

Solution

(a) Because $y = 3(x^2 - 3x + 1)^{1/3}$, we can make use of the Power Rule with $u = x^2 - 3x + 1$.

$$y' = 3\left(nu^{n-1} \frac{du}{dx} \right) = 3\left[\frac{1}{3} u^{-2/3} (2x - 3) \right]$$

$$= (x^2 - 3x + 1)^{-2/3} (2x - 3) = \frac{2x - 3}{(x^2 - 3x + 1)^{2/3}}$$

(b) Writing $g(x)$ as a power gives $g(x) = (x^2 + 1)^{-3/2}$. Then

$$g'(x) = -\frac{3}{2} (x^2 + 1)^{-5/2}(2x) = -3x \cdot \frac{1}{(x^2 + 1)^{5/2}} = \frac{-3x}{\sqrt{(x^2 + 1)^5}}$$

CHECKPOINT

1. (a) If $f(x) = (3x^4 + 1)^{10}$, does $f'(x) = 10(3x^4 + 1)^9$?

   (b) If $f(x) = (2x + 1)^5$, does $f'(x) = 10(2x + 1)^4$?

   (c) If $f(x) = \dfrac{[u(x)]^n}{c}$, where c is a constant, does $f'(x) = \dfrac{n[u(x)]^{n-1} \cdot u'(x)}{c}$?

2. (a) If $f(x) = \dfrac{12}{2x^2 - 1}$, find $f'(x)$ by using the Power Rule (not the Quotient Rule).

   (b) If $f(x) = \dfrac{\sqrt{x^3 - 1}}{3}$, find $f'(x)$ by using the Power Rule (not the Quotient Rule).

EXAMPLE 6 **Demand** | APPLICATION PREVIEW |

The demand for x hundred units of a product is given by

$$x = 98(2p + 1)^{-1/2} - 1$$

where p is the price per unit in dollars. Find the rate of change of the demand with respect to price when $p = 24$.

Solution

The rate of change of demand with respect to price is

$$\frac{dx}{dp} = 98\left[-\frac{1}{2}(2p + 1)^{-3/2}(2)\right] = -98(2p + 1)^{-3/2}$$

When $p = 24$, the rate of change is

$$\left.\frac{dx}{dp}\right|_{p=24} = -98(48 + 1)^{-3/2} = -98 \cdot \frac{1}{49^{3/2}} = -\frac{2}{7}$$

This means that when the price is $24, demand is changing at the rate of $-2/7$ hundred units per dollar, or if the price changes by $1, demand will change by about $-200/7$ units.

CHECKPOINT ANSWERS

1. (a) No. $f'(x) = 10(3x^4 + 1)^9 (12x^3)$ (b) Yes   (c) Yes

2. (a) $f'(x) = \dfrac{-48x}{(2x^2 - 1)^2}$ (b) $f'(x) = \dfrac{x^2}{2\sqrt{x^3 - 1}}$

EXERCISES 9.6

In Problems 1 and 2, find $\dfrac{dy}{du}, \dfrac{du}{dx}$, and $\dfrac{dy}{dx}$.

1. (a) $y = u^3$ and $u = x^2 + 1$
   (b) $y = u^4$ and $u = 4x^2 - x + 8$
2. (a) $y = u^4$ and $u = x^2 + 4x$
   (b) $y = u^{10}$ and $u = x^2 + 5x$

Differentiate the functions in Problems 3–20.

3. $f(x) = (3x^5 - 2)^{20}$
4. $g(x) = (3 - 2x)^{10}$
5. $h(x) = \frac{3}{4}(x^5 - 2x^3 + 5)^8$

6. $k(x) = \frac{5}{7}(2x^3 - x + 6)^{14}$
7. $s(t) = 5t - 3(2t^4 + 7)^3$
8. $p(q) = 4(3q^2 - 1)^4 - 13q$
9. $g(x) = (x^4 - 5x)^{-2}$ 10. $p = (q^3 + 1)^{-5}$
11. $f(s) = \dfrac{3}{(2s^5 + 1)^4}$ 12. $g(t) = \dfrac{1}{4t^3 + 1}$
13. $g(x) = \dfrac{1}{(2x^3 + 3x + 5)^{3/4}}$
14. $y = \dfrac{1}{(3x^3 + 4x + 1)^{3/2}}$
15. $y = \sqrt{3x^2 + 4x + 9}$ 16. $y = \sqrt{x^2 + 3x}$

17. $y = \dfrac{11(x^3 - 7)^6}{9}$ 18. $y = \dfrac{5\sqrt{1 - x^3}}{6}$

19. $z = \dfrac{(3w + 1)^5 - 3w}{7}$ 20. $y = \dfrac{\sqrt{2x - 1} - \sqrt{x}}{2}$

At the indicated point, for each function in Problems 21–24, find
(a)   the slope of the tangent line.
(b)   the instantaneous rate of change of the function.
21. $y = (x^3 + 2x)^4$ at $x = 2$
22. $y = \sqrt{5x^2 + 2x}$ at $x = 1$
23. $y = \sqrt{x^3 + 1}$ at $(2, 3)$
24. $y = (4x^3 - 5x + 1)^3$ at $(1, 0)$

In Problems 25–28, write the equation of the line tangent to the graph of each function at the indicated point. As a check, graph both the function and the tangent line you found to see whether it looks correct.
25. $y = (x^2 - 3x + 3)^3$ at $(2, 1)$
26. $y = (x^2 + 1)^3$ at $(2, 125)$
27. $y = \sqrt{3x^2 - 2}$ at $x = 3$
28. $y = \dfrac{1}{(x^3 - x)^3}$ at $x = 2$

In Problems 29 and 30, complete the following for each function.
(a)   Find $f'(x)$.
(b)   Check your result in part (a) by graphing both it and the numerical derivative of the function.
(c)   Find x-values for which the slope of the tangent is 0.
(d)   Find points (x, y) where the slope of the tangent is 0.
(e)   Use a graphing utility to graph the function and locate the points found in part (d).
29. $f(x) = (x^2 - 4)^3 + 12$
30. $f(x) = 10 - (x^2 - 2x - 8)^2$

In Problems 31 and 32, do the following for each function $f(x)$.
(a)   Find $f'(x)$.
(b)   Graph both $f(x)$ and $f'(x)$ with a graphing utility.
(c)   Determine x-values where
      $f'(x) = 0, f'(x) > 0, f'(x) < 0$.
(d)   Determine x-values for which $f(x)$ has a maximum or minimum point, where the graph is increasing, and where it is decreasing.
31. $f(x) = 12 - 3(1 - x^2)^{4/3}$
32. $f(x) = 3 + \dfrac{1}{16}(x^2 - 4x)^4$

In Problems 33 and 34, find the derivative of each function.
33. (a) $y = \dfrac{2x^3}{3}$ (b) $y = \dfrac{2}{3x^3}$

(c) $y = \dfrac{(2x)^3}{3}$ (d) $y = \dfrac{2}{(3x)^3}$

34. (a) $y = \dfrac{3}{(5x)^5}$ (b) $y = \dfrac{3x^5}{5}$

(c) $y = \dfrac{3}{5x^5}$ (d) $y = \dfrac{(3x)^5}{5}$

APPLICATIONS

35. *Ballistics* Ballistics experts are able to identify the weapon that fired a certain bullet by studying the markings on the bullet. Tests are conducted by firing into a bale of paper. If the distance s, in inches, that the bullet travels into the paper is given by
$$s = 27 - (3 - 10t)^3$$
for $0 \le t \le 0.3$ second, find the velocity of the bullet one-tenth of a second after it hits the paper.

36. *Population of microorganisms* Suppose that the population of a certain microorganism at time t (in minutes) is given by
$$P = 1000 - 1000(t + 10)^{-1}$$
Find the rate of change of population.

37. *Revenue* The revenue from the sale of a product is
$$R = 1500x + 3000(2x + 3)^{-1} - 1000 \text{ dollars}$$
where x is the number of units sold. Find the marginal revenue when 100 units are sold. Interpret your result.

38. *Revenue* The revenue from the sale of x units of a product is
$$R = 15(3x + 1)^{-1} + 50x - 15 \text{ dollars}$$
Find the marginal revenue when 40 units are sold. Interpret your result.

39. *Pricing and sales* Suppose that the weekly sales volume y (in thousands of units sold) depends on the price per unit (in dollars) of the product according to
$$y = 32(3p + 1)^{-2/5}, \quad p > 0$$
(a)   What is the rate of change in sales volume when the price is $21?
(b)   Interpret your answer to part (a).

40. *Pricing and sales* A chain of auto service stations has found that its monthly sales volume S (in thousands of dollars) is related to the price p (in dollars) of an oil change according to
$$S = \dfrac{98}{\sqrt{p + 5}}, \quad p > 10$$
(a)   What is the rate of change of sales volume when the price is $44?
(b)   Interpret your answer to part (a).

41. *Demand* Suppose that the demand for q units of a product priced at p per unit is described by
$$p = \dfrac{200{,}000}{(q + 1)^2}$$

(a) What is the rate of change of price with respect to the quantity demanded when $q = 49$?

(b) Interpret your answer to part (a).

Stimulus-response **The relation between the magnitude of a sensation y and the magnitude of the stimulus x is given by**

$$y = k(x - x_0)^n$$

where k is a constant, x_0 is the threshold of effective stimulus, and n depends on the type of stimulus. Find the rate of change of sensation with respect to the amount of stimulus for each of Problems 42–44.

42. For the stimulus of visual brightness $y = k(x - x_0)^{1/3}$

43. For the stimulus of warmth $y = k(x - x_0)^{8/5}$

44. For electrical stimulation $y = k(x - x_0)^{7/2}$

45. *Demand* If the demand for q units of a product priced at $\$p$ per unit is described by the equation

$$p = \frac{100}{\sqrt{2q + 1}}$$

find the rate of change of p with respect to q.

46. *Advertising and sales* The daily sales S (in thousands of dollars) attributed to an advertising campaign are given by

$$S = 1 + \frac{3}{t + 3} - \frac{18}{(t + 3)^2}$$

where t is the number of weeks the campaign runs. What is the rate of change of sales at

(a) $t = 8$?   (b) $t = 10$?

(c) Should the campaign be continued after the 10th week? Explain.

47. *Body-heat loss* The description of body-heat loss due to convection involves a coefficient of convection, K_c, which depends on wind velocity according to the following equation.

$$K_c = 4\sqrt{4v + 1}$$

Find the rate of change of the coefficient with respect to the wind velocity.

48. *Data entry speed* The data entry speed (in entries per minute) of a data clerk trainee is

$$S = 10\sqrt{0.8x + 4}, \quad 0 \le x \le 100$$

where x is the number of hours of training he has had. What is the rate at which his speed is changing, and what does this rate mean when he has had

(a) 15 hours of training?

(b) 40 hours of training?

49. *Investments* If an IRA is a variable-rate investment for 20 years at rate r percent per year, compounded monthly, then the future value S that accumulates from an initial investment of $\$1000$ is

$$S = 1000\left[1 + \frac{0.01r}{12}\right]^{240}$$

What is the rate of change of S with respect to r, and what does it tell us if the interest rate is

(a) 6%?   (b) 12%?

50. *Concentration of body substances* The concentration C of a substance in the body depends on the quantity of the substance Q and the volume V through which it is distributed. For a static substance, this is given by

$$C = \frac{Q}{V}$$

For a situation like that in the kidneys, where the fluids are moving, the concentration is the ratio of the rate of change of quantity with respect to time and the rate of change of volume with respect to time.

(a) Formulate the equation for concentration of a moving substance.

(b) Show that this is equal to the rate of change of quantity with respect to volume.

51. *National health expenditures* The following table shows the total national expenditures for health (in billions of dollars) for selected years from 2002 and projected to 2024. (These data include expenditures for medical research and medical facilities construction.)

Year	Amount	Year	Amount
2002	1602	2014	3080
2004	1855	2016	3403
2006	2113	2018	3786
2008	2414	2020	4274
2010	2604	2022	4825
2012	2817	2024	5425

Source: U.S. Centers for Medicare and Medicaid Services

Assume that these data can be modeled with the function

$$A(t) = 333(0.1t + 1)^3 - 1830(0.1t + 1)^2$$
$$+ 4510(0.1t + 1) - 1750$$

where $A(t)$ is in billions of dollars and t is the number of years after 2000.

(a) Find the function that models the instantaneous rate of change of total national health care expenditures.

(b) Use the model from part (a) to find and interpret the instantaneous rate of change of national health care expenditures in 2012 and 2020.

(c) Use the data to find an average rate of change from 2018 to 2022 that approximates the instantaneous rate of change for 2020.

52. *Energy use* Energy use per dollar of GDP indexed to 1980 means that energy use for any year is viewed as a percent of the use per dollar of GDP in 1980. The following data show the energy use per dollar of GDP, as a percent, for selected years from 1985 and projected to 2035.

Energy Use per Dollar of GDP

Year	Percent	Year	Percent
1985	83	2015	51
1990	79	2020	45
1995	75	2025	41
2000	67	2030	37
2005	60	2035	34
2010	56		

Source: U.S. Department of Energy

These data can be modeled with the function

$$E(t) = 0.0039(0.4t + 2)^3 - 0.13(0.4t + 2)^2$$
$$- 1.4(0.4t + 2) + 91$$

where $E(t)$ is the energy use per dollar of GDP (indexed to 1980) and t is the number of years past 1980.
(a) Find $E'(t)$.
(b) Use this model to find and interpret the instantaneous rates of change of energy use per dollar of GDP in 2000 and 2025.
(c) Use the data in the table to find an average rate of change that approximates the 2025 instantaneous rate.
53. *Gross domestic product* The table shows U.S. gross domestic product (GDP) in billions of dollars for selected years from 2000 to 2070 (actual and projected).

Year	GDP	Year	GDP
2000	9143	2040	79,680
2005	12,145	2045	103,444
2010	16,174	2050	133,925
2015	21,270	2055	173,175
2020	27,683	2060	224,044
2025	35,919	2065	290,042
2030	46,765	2070	375,219
2035	61,100		

Source: Social Security Administration Trustees Report

Assume that the GDP can be modeled with the function

$$G(t) = 213(0.2t + 5)^3 - 5020(0.2t + 5)^2$$
$$+ 8810t + 104,000$$

where $G(t)$ is in billions of dollars and t is the number of years past 2000.
(a) Use the model to find and interpret the instantaneous rates of change of the GDP in 2015 and 2025.
(b) Use the data in the table to find the average rate of change of the GDP from 2015 to 2025.
(c) How well does your answer from part (b) approximate the instantaneous rate of change of GDP in 2020?

54. *Diabetes* The figure shows the percent of the U.S. population with diabetes (diagnosed and undiagnosed) for selected years from 2010 and projections to 2050. Assume that this percent can be modeled by

$$y = 6.97(0.5x + 5)^{0.495}$$

where y is the percent and x is the number of years past 2010.

Percent with Diabetes*

*Estimated

Source: Centers for Disease Control and Prevention

(a) Use the figure to find the average rate of change from 2010 to 2050.
(b) Use the model to find the instantaneous rate of change of the U.S. population with diabetes in 2020. Is the average rate found in part (a) a good approximation of the 2020 instantaneous rate?
(c) Use the model to find and interpret the instantaneous rate of change of the percent of the U.S. population with diabetes in 2050.

SECTION 9.7 — **Using Derivative Formulas**

OBJECTIVE

- To use derivative formulas separately and in combination with each other

APPLICATION PREVIEW

Suppose the weekly revenue function for a product is given by

$$R(x) = \frac{36,000,000x}{(2x + 500)^2}$$

where $R(x)$ is the dollars of revenue from the sale of x units. We can find marginal revenue by finding the derivative of the revenue function. This revenue function contains both a quotient and a power, so its derivative is found by using both the Quotient Rule and the Power Rule, but in which order are these rules applied? (See Example 4.) In this section, we consider functions whose derivatives require more than one derivative formula and discuss how we decide the order in which to apply the formulas.

We have used the Power Rule to find the derivatives of functions like

$$y = (x^3 - 3x^2 + x + 1)^5$$

but we have not found the derivatives of functions like

$$y = [(x^2 + 1)(x^3 + x + 1)]^5$$

This function is different because the function u (which is raised to the fifth power) is the product of two functions, $(x^2 + 1)$ and $(x^3 + x + 1)$. The equation is of the form $y = u^5$, where $u = (x^2 + 1)(x^3 + x + 1)$. This means that the Product Rule should be used to find du/dx. Then

$$\frac{dy}{dx} = 5u^4 \cdot \frac{du}{dx}$$

$$= 5[(x^2 + 1)(x^3 + x + 1)]^4 [(x^2 + 1)(3x^2 + 1) + (x^3 + x + 1)(2x)]$$

$$= 5[(x^2 + 1)(x^3 + x + 1)]^4 (5x^4 + 6x^2 + 2x + 1)$$

$$= (25x^4 + 30x^2 + 10x + 5)[(x^2 + 1)(x^3 + x + 1)]^4$$

A different type of problem involving the Power Rule and the Product Rule is finding the derivative of $y = (x^2 + 1)^5 (x^3 + x + 1)$. We may think of y as the *product* of two functions, one of which is a power. Thus the fundamental formula we should use is the Product Rule. The two functions are $u(x) = (x^2 + 1)^5$ and $v(x) = x^3 + x + 1$. The Product Rule gives

$$\frac{dy}{dx} = u(x) \cdot v'(x) + v(x) \cdot u'(x)$$

$$= (x^2 + 1)^5 (3x^2 + 1) + (x^3 + x + 1)[5(x^2 + 1)^4(2x)]$$

Note that the Power Rule was used to find $u'(x)$ since $u(x) = (x^2 + 1)^5$.
We can simplify dy/dx by factoring $(x^2 + 1)^4$ from both terms:

$$\frac{dy}{dx} = (x^2 + 1)^4[(x^2 + 1)(3x^2 + 1) + (x^3 + x + 1) \cdot 5 \cdot 2x]$$

$$= (x^2 + 1)^4(13x^4 + 14x^2 + 10x + 1)$$

EXAMPLE 1 Power of a Quotient

If $y = \left(\dfrac{x^2}{x - 1}\right)^5$, find y'.

Solution
We again have an equation of the form $y = u^n$, but this time u is a quotient. Thus we will need the Quotient Rule to find du/dx.

$$y' = nu^{n-1} \cdot \frac{du}{dx} = 5u^4 \frac{(x - 1) \cdot 2x - x^2 \cdot 1}{(x - 1)^2}$$

Substituting for u and simplifying give

$$y' = 5\left(\frac{x^2}{x - 1}\right)^4 \cdot \frac{2x^2 - 2x - x^2}{(x - 1)^2} = \frac{5x^8(x^2 - 2x)}{(x - 1)^6} = \frac{5x^{10} - 10x^9}{(x - 1)^6}$$

EXAMPLE 2 Quotient of Two Powers

Find $f'(x)$ if $f(x) = \dfrac{(x - 1)^2}{(x^4 + 3)^3}$.

Solution

This function is the quotient of two functions, $(x - 1)^2$ and $(x^4 + 3)^3$, so we must use the Quotient Rule to find the derivative of $f(x)$. However, taking the derivatives of both $(x - 1)^2$ and $(x^4 + 3)^3$ will require the Power Rule.

$$f'(x) = \frac{[v(x) \cdot u'(x) - u(x) \cdot v'(x)]}{[v(x)]^2}$$

$$= \frac{(x^4 + 3)^3[2(x - 1)(1)] - (x - 1)^2[3(x^4 + 3)^2 \, 4x^3]}{[(x^4 + 3)^3]^2}$$

$$= \frac{2(x^4 + 3)^3(x - 1) - 12x^3(x - 1)^2(x^4 + 3)^2}{(x^4 + 3)^6}$$

We see that 2, $(x^4 + 3)^2$, and $(x - 1)$ are all factors in both terms of the numerator, so we can factor them from both terms and reduce the fraction.

$$f'(x) = \frac{2(x^4 + 3)^2(x - 1)[(x^4 + 3) - 6x^3(x - 1)]}{(x^4 + 3)^6}$$

$$= \frac{2(x - 1)(-5x^4 + 6x^3 + 3)}{(x^4 + 3)^4}$$

EXAMPLE | 3 | **Product with a Power**

Find $f'(x)$ if $f(x) = (x^2 - 1)\sqrt{3 - x^2}$.

Solution

The function is the product of two functions, $x^2 - 1$ and $\sqrt{3 - x^2}$. Therefore, we will use the Product Rule to find the derivative of $f(x)$, but the derivative of $\sqrt{3 - x^2} = (3 - x^2)^{1/2}$ will require the Power Rule.

$$f'(x) = u(x) \cdot v'(x) + v(x) \cdot u'(x)$$

$$= (x^2 - 1)\left[\frac{1}{2}(3 - x^2)^{-1/2}(-2x)\right] + (3 - x^2)^{1/2}(2x)$$

$$= (x^2 - 1)[-x(3 - x^2)^{-1/2}] + (3 - x^2)^{1/2}(2x)$$

$$= \frac{-x^3 + x}{(3 - x^2)^{1/2}} + 2x(3 - x^2)^{1/2}$$

We can combine these terms over the common denominator $(3 - x^2)^{1/2}$ as follows:

$$f'(x) = \frac{-x^3 + x}{(3 - x^2)^{1/2}} + \frac{2x(3 - x^2)^1}{(3 - x^2)^{1/2}} = \frac{-x^3 + x + 6x - 2x^3}{(3 - x^2)^{1/2}} = \frac{-3x^3 + 7x}{\sqrt{3 - x^2}}$$

We should note that in Example 3, we could have written $f'(x)$ in the form

$$f'(x) = (-x^3 + x)(3 - x^2)^{-1/2} + 2x(3 - x^2)^{1/2}$$

Now the factor $(3 - x^2)$, to different powers, is contained in both terms of the expression. Thus we can factor $(3 - x^2)^{-1/2}$ from both terms. (We choose the $-1/2$ power because it is the smaller of the two powers.) Dividing $(3 - x^2)^{-1/2}$ into the first term gives $(-x^3 + x)$, and dividing it into the second term gives $2x(3 - x^2)^1$. Thus we have

$$f'(x) = (3 - x^2)^{-1/2}[(-x^3 + x) + 2x(3 - x^2)] = \frac{-3x^3 + 7x}{(3 - x^2)^{1/2}}$$

which agrees with our previous answer.

CHECKPOINT

1. If a function has the form $y = [u(x)]^n \cdot v(x)$, where n is a constant, we begin to find the derivative by using the _____ Rule and then use the _____ Rule to find the derivative of $[u(x)]^n$.
2. If a function has the form $y = [u(x)/v(x)]^n$, where n is a constant, we begin to find the derivative by using the _____ Rule and then use the _____ Rule.
3. Find the derivative of each of the following and simplify.

   (a) $f(x) = 3x^4(2x^4 + 7)^5$ (b) $g(x) = \dfrac{(4x + 3)^7}{2x - 9}$

EXAMPLE **4** **Revenue** | APPLICATION PREVIEW |

Suppose that the weekly revenue function for a product is given by

$$R(x) = \frac{36{,}000{,}000x}{(2x + 500)^2}$$

where $R(x)$ is the dollars of revenue from the sale of x units.

(a) Find the marginal revenue function.
(b) Find the marginal revenue when 50 units are sold.

Solution
(a) $\overline{MR} = R'(x)$

$$= \frac{(2x + 500)^2(36{,}000{,}000) - 36{,}000{,}000x[2(2x + 500)^1(2)]}{(2x + 500)^4}$$

$$= \frac{36{,}000{,}000(2x + 500)(2x + 500 - 4x)}{(2x + 500)^4} = \frac{36{,}000{,}000(500 - 2x)}{(2x + 500)^3}$$

(b) $\overline{MR}(50) = R'(50) = \dfrac{36{,}000{,}000(500 - 100)}{(100 + 500)^3} = \dfrac{36{,}000{,}000(400)}{(600)^3} = \dfrac{200}{3} \approx 66.67$

The marginal revenue is \$66.67 when 50 units are sold. That is, the predicted revenue from the sale of the 51st unit is approximately \$66.67.

It may be helpful to review the formulas needed to find the derivatives of various types of functions. Table 9.5 presents examples of different types of functions and the formulas needed to find their derivatives.

TABLE 9.5

SUMMARY OF DERIVATIVE FORMULAS

Examples	Formulas
$f(x) = 14$	If $f(x) = c$, then $f'(x) = 0$.
$y = x^4$	If $f(x) = x^n$, then $f'(x) = nx^{n-1}$.
$g(x) = 5x^3$	If $g(x) = cf(x)$, then $g'(x) = cf'(x)$.
$y = 3x^2 + 4x$	If $f(x) = u(x) + v(x)$, then $f'(x) = u'(x) + v'(x)$.

$y = (x^2 - 2)(x + 4)$ If $f(x) = u(x) \cdot v(x)$, then $f'(x) = u(x) \cdot v'(x) + v(x) \cdot u'(x)$.

$f(x) = \dfrac{x^3}{x^2 + 1}$ If $f(x) = \dfrac{u(x)}{v(x)}$ then $f'(x) = \dfrac{v(x) \cdot u'(x) - u(x) \cdot v'(x)}{[v(x)]^2}$.

$y = (x^3 - 4x)^{10}$ If $y = u^n$ and $u = g(x)$, then $\dfrac{dy}{dx} = nu^{n-1} \cdot \dfrac{du}{dx}$.

$y = \left(\dfrac{x-1}{x^2 + 3}\right)^3$ Power Rule, then Quotient Rule to find $\dfrac{du}{dx}$, where $u = \dfrac{x-1}{x^2+3}$.

$y = (x + 1)\sqrt{x^3 + 1}$ Product Rule, then Power Rule to find $v'(x)$, where $v(x) = \sqrt{x^3 + 1}$.

$y = \dfrac{(x^2 - 3)^4}{x + 1}$ Quotient Rule, then Power Rule to find the derivative of the numerator.

CHECKPOINT
ANSWERS

1. Product, Power
2. Power, Quotient
3. (a) $f'(x) = 12x^3(12x^4 + 7)(2x^4 + 7)^4$

   (b) $g'(x) = \dfrac{2(24x - 129)(4x + 3)^6}{(2x - 9)^2}$

EXERCISES 9.7

Find the derivatives of the functions in Problems 1–32. Simplify and express the answer using positive exponents only.

1. $f(x) = \pi^4$

2. $f(x) = \dfrac{1}{4}$

3. $g(x) = \dfrac{4}{x^4}$

4. $y = \dfrac{x^4}{4}$

5. $g(x) = 5x^3 + \dfrac{4}{x}$

6. $y = 3x^2 + 4\sqrt{x}$

7. $y = (x^2 - 2)(x + 4)$

8. $y = (x^3 - 5x^2 + 1)(x^3 - 3)$

9. $f(u) = \dfrac{u^3 + 1}{u^2}$

10. $C(w) = \dfrac{1 + w^2 - w^4}{1 + w^4}$

11. $y = \dfrac{(x^3 - 4x)^{10}}{10}$

12. $y = \dfrac{5}{2}(3x^4 - 6x^2 + 2)^5$

13. $y = \dfrac{5}{3}x^3(4x^5 - 5)^3$

14. $y = 3x^4(2x^5 + 1)^7$

15. $y = (x - 1)^2(x^2 + 1)$

16. $f(x) = (5x^3 + 1)(x^4 + 5x)^2$

17. $y = \dfrac{(x^2 - 4)^3}{x^2 + 1}$

18. $y = \dfrac{(x^2 - 3)^4}{x}$

19. $p = [(q + 1)(q^3 - 3)]^3$

20. $s = [(4 - t^2)(t^2 + 5t)]^4$

21. $R(x) = [x^2(x^2 + 3x)]^4$

22. $c(x) = [x^3(x^2 + 1)]^{-3}$

23. $y = \left(\dfrac{2x - 1}{x^2 + x}\right)^4$

24. $y = \left(\dfrac{5 - x^2}{x^4}\right)^3$

25. $g(x) = (8x^4 + 3)^2(x^3 - 4x)^3$

26. $y = (3x^3 - 4x)^3(4x^2 - 8)^2$

27. $f(x) = \dfrac{\sqrt[3]{x^2 + 5}}{4 - x^2}$

28. $g(x) = \dfrac{\sqrt[3]{2x - 1}}{2x + 1}$

29. $y = x^2 \sqrt[4]{4x - 3}$

30. $y = 3x\sqrt[3]{4x^4 + 3}$

31. $c(x) = 2x\sqrt{x^3 + 1}$

32. $R(x) = x\sqrt[3]{3x^3 + 2}$

In Problems 33 and 34, find the derivative of each function.

33. (a) $F_1(x) = \dfrac{3(x^4 + 1)^5}{5}$

    (b) $F_2(x) = \dfrac{3}{5(x^4 + 1)^5}$

    (c) $F_3(x) = \dfrac{(3x^4 + 1)^5}{5}$

    (d) $F_4(x) = \dfrac{3}{(5x^4 + 1)^5}$

34. (a) $G_1(x) = \dfrac{2(x^3 - 5)^3}{3}$

    (b) $G_2(x) = \dfrac{(2x^3 - 5)^3}{3}$

    (c) $G_3(x) = \dfrac{2}{3(x^3 - 5)^3}$

    (d) $G_4(x) = \dfrac{2}{(3x^3 - 5)^3}$

APPLICATIONS

35. *Physical output* The total physical output P of workers is a function of the number of workers, x. The

function $P = f(x)$ is called the physical productivity function. Suppose that the physical productivity of x construction workers is given by

$$P = 10(3x + 1)^3 - 10$$

Find the marginal physical productivity, dP/dx.

36. *Revenue* Suppose that the revenue function for a certain product is given by

$$R(x) = 15(2x + 1)^{-1} + 30x - 15$$

where x is in thousands of units and R is in thousands of dollars.
   (a) Find the marginal revenue when 2000 units are sold.
   (b) How is revenue changing when 2000 units are sold?

37. *Revenue* Suppose that the revenue in dollars from the sale of x campers is given by

$$R(x) = 60,000x + 40,000(10 + x)^{-1} - 4000$$

   (a) Find the marginal revenue when 10 units are sold.
   (b) How is revenue changing when 10 units are sold?

38. *Production* Suppose that the production of x items of a new line of products is given by

$$x = 200[(t + 10) - 400(t + 40)^{-1}]$$

where t is the number of weeks the line has been in production. Find the rate of production, dx/dt.

39. *National consumption* If the national consumption function is given by

$$C(y) = 2(y + 1)^{1/2} + 0.4y + 4$$

where y is the national disposable income, find the marginal propensity to consume, dC/dy.

40. *Demand* Suppose that the demand function for q units of an appliance priced at $\$p$ per unit is given by

$$p = \frac{400(q + 1)}{(q + 2)^2}$$

Find the rate of change of price with respect to the number of appliances.

41. *Volume* When squares of side x inches are cut from the corners of a 12-inch-square piece of cardboard, an open-top box can be formed by folding up the sides. The volume of this box is given by

$$V = x(12 - 2x)^2$$

Find the rate of change of volume with respect to the size of the squares.

42. *Advertising and sales* Suppose that sales (in thousands of dollars) are directly related to an advertising campaign according to

$$S = 1 + \frac{3t - 9}{(t + 3)^2}$$

where t is the number of weeks of the campaign.
   (a) Find the rate of change of sales after 3 weeks.
   (b) Interpret the result in part (a).

43. *Advertising and sales* An inferior product with an extensive advertising campaign does well when it is released, but sales decline as people discontinue use of the product. If the sales S (in thousands of dollars) after t weeks are given by

$$S(t) = \frac{200t}{(t + 1)^2}, \quad t \geq 0$$

what is the rate of change of sales when $t = 9$? Interpret your result.

44. *Advertising and sales* An excellent film with a very small advertising budget must depend largely on word-of-mouth advertising. If attendance at the film after t weeks is given by

$$A = \frac{100t}{(t + 10)^2}$$

what is the rate of change in attendance and what does it mean when (a) $t = 10$? (b) $t = 20$?

45. *Per capita expenditures for U.S. health care* The following table shows the amount spent per person for health care in the United States for selected years from 2002 and projected to 2024. These data can be modeled by

$$y = \frac{4.6(x + 10)^2 - 49(x + 10) + 1600}{0.0026x + 0.28}$$

where x is the number of years after 2000 and y is per capita expenditures for health care.
   (a) Find the instantaneous rate of change of per capita health care expenditures (to the nearest dollar) for 2010 and 2020.
   (b) Interpret the rate of change for 2020 found in part (a).
   (c) Use the data to find the average rate of change from 2018 to 2020. How well does this approximate the rate of change in 2020?

Year	$ per Person	Year	$ per Person
2002	5563	2014	9695
2004	6331	2016	10,527
2006	7091	2018	11,499
2008	7944	2020	12,741
2010	8428	2022	14,129
2012	8996	2024	15,618

Source: U.S. Centers for Medicare and Medicaid Services

Higher-Order Derivatives

OBJECTIVES

- To find and interpret second derivatives of certain functions
- To find higher-order derivatives

APPLICATION PREVIEW

Since cell phones were introduced, their popularity has increased enormously. Figure 9.32(a) shows a graph of the billions of worldwide cellular subscribers (actual and projected) as a function of the number of years past 1990 (*Source: International Telecommunications Union and Key Global Telecom Indicators*). Note that the number of subscribers is always increasing and that the rate of change of that number (as shown by tangent lines to the graph) is always positive. However, the tangent lines shown in Figure 9.32(b) indicate that the rate of change of the number of subscribers is greater at *B* than at either *A* or *C*.

Furthermore, the rate of change of the number of subscribers (the slopes of tangents) increases from *A* to *B* and then decreases from *B* to *C*. To learn how the rate of change of the number of subscribers is changing, we are interested in finding the derivative of the rate of change of the number of subscribers—that is, the derivative of the derivative of the number of subscribers. (See Example 4.) This is called the second derivative. In this section, we will discuss second and higher-order derivatives.

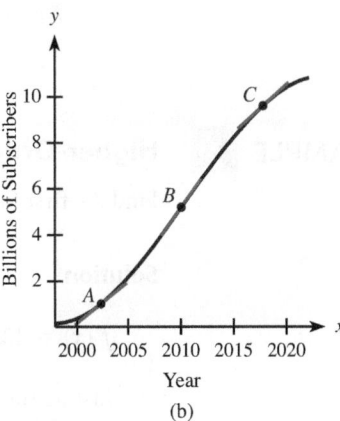

Figure 9.32   (a)   (b)

Second Derivatives Because the derivative of a function is itself a function, we can take a derivative of the derivative. The derivative of a first derivative is called a **second derivative.** We can find the second derivative of a function *f* by differentiating it twice. If f' represents the first derivative of a function, then f'' represents the second derivative of that function.

EXAMPLE 1   Second Derivative

(a) Find the second derivative of $y = x^4 - 3x^2 + x^{-2}$.
(b) If $f(x) = 3x^3 - 4x^2 + 5$, find $f''(x)$.

Solution

(a) The first derivative is $y' = 4x^3 - 6x - 2x^{-3}$.
    The second derivative, denoted by y'', is the derivative of y':

$$y'' = 12x^2 - 6 + 6x^{-4}$$

(b) The first derivative is $f'(x) = 9x^2 - 8x$.
    The second derivative is the derivative of $f'(x)$:

$$f''(x) = 18x - 8$$

It is also common to use $\dfrac{d^2y}{dx^2}$ and $\dfrac{d^2f(x)}{dx^2}$ to denote the second derivative of a function.

EXAMPLE 2 **Second Derivative**

If $y = \sqrt{2x - 1}$, find d^2y/dx^2.

Solution

The first derivative is

$$\frac{dy}{dx} = \frac{1}{2}(2x - 1)^{-1/2}(2) = (2x - 1)^{-1/2}$$

The second derivative is

$$\frac{d^2y}{dx^2} = -\frac{1}{2}(2x - 1)^{-3/2}(2) = -(2x - 1)^{-3/2}$$

$$= \frac{-1}{(2x - 1)^{3/2}} = \frac{-1}{\sqrt{(2x - 1)^3}}$$

Higher-Order Derivatives   We can also find third, fourth, fifth, and higher derivatives, continuing indefinitely. The third, fourth, and fifth derivatives of a function f are denoted by f''', $f^{(4)}$, and $f^{(5)}$, respectively. Other notations for the third and fourth derivatives include

$$y''' = \frac{d^3y}{dx^3} = \frac{d^3f(x)}{dx^3}, \qquad y^{(4)} = \frac{d^4y}{dx^4} = \frac{d^4f(x)}{dx^4}$$

EXAMPLE 3 **Higher-Order Derivatives**

Find the first four derivatives of $f(x) = 4x^3 + 5x^2 + 3$.

Solution

$$f'(x) = 12x^2 + 10x, \qquad f''(x) = 24x + 10, \qquad f'''(x) = 24, \qquad f^{(4)}(x) = 0$$

Just as the first derivative, $f'(x)$, can be used to determine the rate of change of a function $f(x)$, the second derivative, $f''(x)$, can be used to determine the rate of change of $f'(x)$.

EXAMPLE 4 **Worldwide Cellular Subscriberships** | APPLICATION PREVIEW |

By using International Telecommunications Union and Key Global Telecom Indicators data from 1990 and projected to 2020, the billions of world cell phone subscriberships can be modeled by the function

$$C(t) = -0.000728t^3 + 0.0414t^2 - 0.296t + 0.340$$

where t is the number of years past 1990.

(a) Find the instantaneous rate of change of world cell phone subscriberships.
(b) Find the instantaneous rate of change of the function found in part (a).
(c) For what t-value does the second derivative of $C(t)$ equal zero?
(d) Find the instantaneous rate of change of the world cell phone subscriberships in 2005 and in 2018.
(e) Use the second derivative to approximate how fast the instantaneous rate of change of world cell phone subscriberships is changing in 2005 and in 2018.
(f) Explain the meaning of $C'(28)$ and $C''(28)$.

Solution

(a) The instantaneous rate of change of $C(t)$ is

$$C'(t) = -0.002184t^2 + 0.0828t - 0.296$$

(b) The instantaneous rate of change of $C'(t)$ is

$$C''(t) = -0.004368t + 0.0828$$

(c) To find the t-value when $C''(t) = -0.004368t + 0.0828 = 0$, we solve as follows:

$$0.0828 = 0.004368t \Rightarrow t = \frac{0.0828}{0.004368} \approx 18.96$$

Thus $C''(t) = 0$ in 2009.

(d) We find these rates of change by evaluating the derivative

In 2005: $C'(15) = -0.002184(15)^2 + 0.0828(15) - 0.296 \approx 0.455$ billion per year

In 2018: $C'(28) = -0.002184(28)^2 + 0.0828(28) - 0.296 \approx 0.310$ billion per year

(e) In 2005: $C''(15) = -0.004368(15) + 0.0828 \approx 0.0173$ billion per year per year

In 2018: $C''(28) = -0.004368(28) + 0.0828 \approx -0.0395$ billion per year per year

(f) In 2018, the number of world cell phone subscriberships increased at a rate of about 0.310 billion per year, but the rate of change decreased at a rate of about 0.0395 billion per year per year. Thus in 2018 the number of world cell phone subscriberships was increasing but at a decreasing (slower) rate. (See Figure 9.32 on page 603.)

EXAMPLE 5   **Rate of Change of a Derivative**

Let $f(x) = 3x^4 + 6x^3 - 3x^2 + 4$.

(a) How fast is $f(x)$ changing at $(1, 10)$?
(b) How fast is $f'(x)$ changing at $(1, 10)$?
(c) Is $f'(x)$ increasing or decreasing at $(1, 10)$?

Solution

(a) Because $f'(x) = 12x^3 + 18x^2 - 6x$, we have

$$f'(1) = 12 + 18 - 6 = 24$$

Thus the rate of change of $f(x)$ at $(1, 10)$ is 24 (y units per x unit).

(b) Because $f''(x) = 36x^2 + 36x - 6$, we have

$$f''(1) = 66$$

Thus the rate of change of $f'(x)$ at $(1, 10)$ is 66 (y units per x unit) per x unit.

(c) Because $f''(1) = 66 > 0, f'(x)$ is increasing at $(1, 10)$.

EXAMPLE 6   **Acceleration**

Suppose that a particle travels according to the equation

$$s = 100t - 16t^2 + 200$$

where s is the distance in feet and t is the time in seconds. Then ds/dt is the velocity, and $d^2s/dt^2 = dv/dt$ is the acceleration of the particle. Find the acceleration.

Solution

The velocity is $v = ds/dt = 100 - 32t$ feet per second, and the acceleration is

$$\frac{dv}{dt} = \frac{d^2s}{dt^2} = -32 \text{ (feet/second)/second} = -32 \text{ feet/second}^2$$

CHECKPOINT

Suppose that the distance a particle travels is given by

$$s = 4x^3 - 12x^2 + 6$$

where s is in feet and x is in seconds.
1. Find the function that describes the velocity of this particle.
2. Find the function that describes the acceleration of this particle.
3. Is the acceleration always positive?
4. When does the *velocity* of this particle increase?

Calculator Note

We can use the numerical derivative feature of a graphing calculator to find the second derivative of a function at a point. Figure 9.33 shows how the numerical derivative feature of a graphing calculator can be used to find $f''(1)$ for the function $f(x) = 3x^4 + 6x^3 - 3x^2 + 4$. The second derivative of this function at $x = 1$ was found to be 66 in Example 5, so the numerical derivative approximation is quite accurate. See Appendix A, Section 9.8, for details.

```
nDeriv(nDeriv(3X
^4+6X^3-3X2+4,X,
X),X,1)
          66.000024
```

Figure 9.33

CHECKPOINT
ANSWERS

1. The velocity is described by $s'(x) = 12x^2 - 24x$.
2. The acceleration is described by $s''(x) = 24x - 24$.
3. No. Acceleration is negative when $x < 1$ second, zero when $x = 1$ second, and positive when $x > 1$ second.
4. The velocity increases when the acceleration is positive, after 1 second.

EXERCISES 9.8

In Problems 1–6, find the second derivative.
1. $f(x) = 2x^{10} - 18x^5 - 12x^3 + 4$
2. $y = 6x^5 - 3x^4 + 12x^2$
3. $g(x) = x^3 - \dfrac{1}{x}$
4. $h(x) = x^2 - \dfrac{1}{x^2}$
5. $y = x^3 - \sqrt{x}$
6. $y = 3x^2 - \sqrt[3]{x^2}$

In Problems 7–12, find the third derivative.
7. $y = x^5 - 16x^3 + 12$
8. $y = 6x^3 - 12x^2 + 6x$
9. $f(x) = 2x^9 - 6x^6$
10. $f(x) = 3x^5 - x^6$
11. $y = 1/x$
12. $y = 1/x^2$

In Problems 13–24, find the indicated derivative.
13. If $y = x^5 - x^{1/2}$, find $\dfrac{d^2y}{dx^2}$.
14. If $y = x^4 + x^{1/3}$, find $\dfrac{d^2y}{dx^2}$.

15. If $f(x) = \sqrt{x + 1}$, find $f'''(x)$.
16. If $f(x) = \sqrt{x - 5}$, find $f'''(x)$.
17. Find $\dfrac{d^4y}{dx^4}$ if $y = 4x^3 - 16x$.
18. Find $y^{(4)}$ if $y = x^6 - 15x^3$.
19. Find $f^{(4)}(x)$ if $f(x) = \sqrt{x}$.
20. Find $f^{(4)}(x)$ if $f(x) = 1/x$.
21. Find $y^{(4)}$ if $y' = \sqrt{4x - 1}$.
22. Find $y^{(5)}$ if $\dfrac{d^2y}{dx^2} = \sqrt[3]{3x + 2}$.
23. Find $f^{(6)}(x)$ if $f^{(4)}(x) = x(x + 1)^{-1}$.
24. Find $f^{(3)}(x)$ if $f'(x) = \dfrac{x^2}{x^2 + 1}$.
25. If $f(x) = 16x^2 - x^3$, what is the rate of change of $f'(x)$ at $(1, 15)$?

26. If $y = 36x^2 - 6x^3 + x$, what is the rate of change of y' at $(1, 31)$?

In Problems 27–30, use the numerical derivative feature of a graphing calculator to approximate the given second derivatives.

27. $f''(3)$ for $f(x) = x^3 - \dfrac{27}{x}$

28. $f''(-1)$ for $f(x) = \dfrac{x^2}{4} - \dfrac{4}{x^2}$

29. $f''(21)$ for $f(x) = \sqrt{x^2 + 4}$

30. $f''(3)$ for $f(x) = \dfrac{1}{\sqrt{x^2 + 7}}$

In Problems 31 and 32, do the following for each function $f(x)$.
(a) Find $f'(x)$ and $f''(x)$.
(b) Graph $f(x)$, $f'(x)$, and $f''(x)$ with a graphing utility.
(c) Identify x-values where $f''(x) = 0$, $f''(x) > 0$, and $f''(x) < 0$.
(d) Identify x-values where $f'(x)$ has a maximum point or a minimum point, where $f'(x)$ is increasing, and where $f'(x)$ is decreasing.
(e) When $f(x)$ has a maximum point, is $f''(x) > 0$ or $f''(x) < 0$?
(f) When $f(x)$ has a minimum point, is $f''(x) > 0$ or $f''(x) < 0$?

31. $f(x) = x^3 - 3x^2 + 5$ 32. $f(x) = 2 + 3x - x^3$

APPLICATIONS

33. *Acceleration* A particle travels as a function of time according to the formula
$$s = 100 + 10t + 0.01t^3$$
where s is in meters and t is in seconds. Find the acceleration of the particle when $t = 2$.

34. *Acceleration* If the formula describing the distance s (in feet) an object travels as a function of time (in seconds) is
$$s = 100 + 160t - 16t^2$$
what is the acceleration of the object when $t = 4$?

35. *Revenue* The revenue (in dollars) from the sale of x units of a certain product can be described by
$$R(x) = 100x - 0.01x^2$$
Find the instantaneous rate of change of the marginal revenue.

36. *Revenue* Suppose that the revenue (in dollars) from the sale of a product is given by
$$R = 70x + 0.5x^2 - 0.001x^3$$
where x is the number of units sold. How fast is the marginal revenue $\overline{MR}$ changing when $x = 100$?

37. *Sensitivity* When medicine is administered, reaction (measured in change of blood pressure or temperature) can be modeled by
$$R = m^2\left(\frac{c}{2} - \frac{m}{3}\right)$$
where c is a positive constant and m is the amount of medicine absorbed into the blood (*Source:* R. M. Thrall et al., *Some Mathematical Models in Biology*, U.S. Department of Commerce, 1967). The sensitivity to the medication is defined to be the rate of change of reaction R with respect to the amount of medicine m absorbed in the blood.
(a) Find the sensitivity.
(b) Find the instantaneous rate of change of sensitivity with respect to the amount of medicine absorbed in the blood.
(c) Which order derivative of reaction gives the rate of change of sensitivity?

38. *Photosynthesis* The amount of photosynthesis that takes place in a certain plant depends on the intensity of light x according to the equation
$$f(x) = 145x^2 - 30x^3$$
(a) Find the rate of change of photosynthesis with respect to the intensity.
(b) What is the rate of change when $x = 1$? When $x = 3$?
(c) How fast is the rate found in part (a) changing when $x = 1$? When $x = 3$?

39. *Revenue* The revenue (in thousands of dollars) from the sale of a product is
$$R = 15x + 30(4x + 1)^{-1} - 30$$
where x is the number of units sold.
(a) At what rate is the marginal revenue $\overline{MR}$ changing when the number of units being sold is 25?
(b) Interpret your result in part (a).

40. *Advertising and sales* The sales of a product S (in thousands of dollars) are given by
$$S = \frac{600x}{x + 40}$$
where x is the advertising expenditure (in thousands of dollars).
(a) Find the rate of change of sales with respect to advertising expenditure.
(b) Use the second derivative to find how this rate is changing at $x = 20$.
(c) Interpret your result in part (b).

41. *Advertising and sales* The daily sales S (in thousands of dollars) that are attributed to an advertising campaign are given by
$$S = 1 + \frac{3}{t + 3} - \frac{18}{(t + 3)^2}$$

where t is the number of weeks the campaign runs.
(a) Find the rate of change of sales at any time t.
(b) Use the second derivative to find how this rate is changing at $t = 15$.
(c) Interpret your result in part (b).

42. *Advertising and sales* A product with a large advertising budget has its sales S (in millions of dollars) given by

$$S = \frac{500}{t + 2} - \frac{1000}{(t + 2)^2}$$

where t is the number of months the product has been on the market.
(a) Find the rate of change of sales at any time t.
(b) What is the rate of change of sales at $t = 2$?
(c) Use the second derivative to find how this rate is changing at $t = 2$.
(d) Interpret your results from parts (b) and (c).

43. *Average annual wage* Using Social Security Administration data for selected years from 2012 and projected to 2050, the U.S. average annual wage, in thousands of dollars, can be modeled by

$$W(t) = 0.0212t^{2.11}$$

where t is the number of years past 1975.
(a) Use the model to find a function that models the instantaneous rate of change of W.
(b) Find a function that models the rate at which the instantaneous rate from part (a) is changing.
(c) Find and interpret $W(50)$, $W'(50)$, and $W''(50)$.

44. *Demographics* The makeup of various groups within the U.S. population may reshape the electorate in ways that could change political representation and policies. By using U.S. Department of Labor data from 1980 and projected to 2050 for the civilian non-institutional population ages 16 or older, in millions, the population of those who are non-White or Hispanic can be modeled by the function

$$P(t) = 0.707t^{1.17} + 20.0$$

where t is the number of years past 1970.
(a) Find the function that models the instantaneous rate of change of the population of non-Whites or Hispanics.
(b) Find the function that models how fast the rate found in part (a) changes.
(c) Find and interpret $P(55)$, $P'(55)$, and $P''(55)$.

45. *Modeling Economic dependency ratio* The economic dependency ratio is defined as the number of persons in the total population who are not in the workforce per 100 in the workforce. Since 1960, baby boomers in the workforce coupled with a decrease in the birth rate have caused a significant decrease in the economic dependency ratio.

The table shows the economic dependency ratio for selected years from 1960 and projected to 2050.

Year	Ratio	Year	Ratio
1960	150.4	2015	91.9
1970	140.4	2020	97.4
1980	108.9	2030	106.4
1990	98.3	2040	109.0
2000	93.9	2050	111.4
2010	90.3		

Source: U.S. Bureau of Labor Statistics

(a) Model these data with a cubic function, $R(x)$, where $R(x)$ is the economic dependency ratio and x is the number of years past 1950. Report the model with three significant digit coefficients.
(b) Use the reported model from part (a) to find the function that models the rate of change of $R(x)$.
(c) Find the function that gives the rate of change of $R'(x)$.
(d) Find and interpret $R'(90)$ and $R''(90)$.

46. **Modeling *U.S. population*** The table gives the U.S. population to the nearest million for selected years from 1950 and projected to 2050.

Year	Total	Year	Total
1950	160	2010	315
1960	190	2015	328
1970	215	2020	343
1980	235	2030	370
1990	260	2040	391
2000	288	2050	409

Source: Social Security Administration

(a) Find a cubic function $P(t)$ that models these data, where P is the U.S. population in millions and t is the number of years past 1950. Report the model with three significant digit coefficients.
(b) Use the reported model to find the function that models the instantaneous rate of change of the U.S. population.
(c) Use the second derivative to determine how fast this rate was changing in 2000 and 2020.
(d) Write sentences that explain the meanings of $P'(70)$ and $P''(70)$.

47. *Income by age* The median income $f(x)$, in thousands of dollars, is a function of the age of workers ages 20–62, x, and can be modeled by

$$f(x) = 0.000864x^3 - 0.128x^2 + 6.61x - 62.6$$

(a) Find the instantaneous rate of change of the median income function.
(b) Find the instantaneous rate of change of the median income for 25-year-old and 55-year-old workers.

(c) Find the second derivative of the median income function.

(d) Use the second derivative to determine how fast the instantaneous rate of change in the median income

of workers is changing for 25-year-old and 55-year-old workers.

(e) Explain the meaning of $f'(55)$ and $f''(55)$.

<table>
<tr><td>SECTION 9.9</td></tr>
</table>

Applications: Marginals and Derivatives

OBJECTIVES

- To find the marginal cost and marginal revenue at different levels of production
- To find the marginal profit function, given information about cost and revenue

APPLICATION PREVIEW

If the total cost in dollars to produce x kitchen blenders is given by

$$C(x) = 0.001x^3 - 0.3x^2 + 32x + 2500$$

what is the marginal cost function and what does it tell us about how costs are changing when $x = 80$ and $x = 200$ blenders are produced? (See Example 3.)

In Section 1.6, "Applications of Functions in Business and Economics," we defined the marginals for linear total cost, total revenue, and profit functions as the rate of change or slope of the respective function. In Section 9.3, we extended the notion of marginal revenue to nonlinear total revenue functions by defining marginal revenue as the derivative of total revenue. In this section, we extend the notion of marginal to nonlinear functions for any total cost or profit function.

Marginal Revenue   As we saw earlier, the instantaneous rate of change (the derivative) of the revenue function gives the **marginal revenue function.**

Marginal Revenue

If $R = R(x)$ is the total revenue function for a commodity, then the **marginal revenue function** is $\overline{MR} = R'(x)$.

Recall that if the demand function for a product in a monopoly market is $p = f(x)$, then the total revenue from the sale of x units is

$$R(x) = px = f(x) \cdot x$$

EXAMPLE 1   Revenue and Marginal Revenue

If the demand for a product in a monopoly market is given by

$$p = 16 - 0.02x$$

where x is the number of units and p is the price per unit, (a) find the total revenue function and (b) find the marginal revenue for this product at $x = 40$.

Solution

(a) The total revenue function is

$$R(x) = px = (16 - 0.02x)x = 16x - 0.02x^2$$

(b) The marginal revenue function is

$$\overline{MR} = R'(x) = 16 - 0.04x$$

At $x = 40$, $R'(40) = 16 - 1.6 = 14.40$ dollars per unit. Thus the 41st item sold will increase the total revenue by approximately \$14.40.

The marginal revenue is an approximation or estimate of the revenue gained from the sale of 1 additional unit. We used marginal revenue in Example 1 to find that the revenue from the sale of the 41st item will be approximately $14.40. The actual increase in revenue from the sale of the 41st item is

$$R(41) - R(40) = 622.38 - 608.00 = \$14.38$$

Marginal revenue (and other marginals) can be used to predict for more than one additional unit. For instance, in Example 1, $\overline{MR}(40) = \$14.40$ per unit means that the expected or approximate revenue for the 41st through the 45th items sold would be 5($14.40) = \$72.00. The actual revenue for these 5 items is $R(45) - R(40) = \$679.50 - \$608.00 = \$71.50$.

EXAMPLE 2   Maximum Revenue

Use the graphs in Figure 9.34 to determine the x-value where the total revenue function has its maximum. What is happening to the marginal revenue at and near this x-value?

Solution
Figure 9.34(a) shows that the total revenue function has a maximum value at $x = 400$. After that, the total revenue function decreases. This means that the total revenue will be reduced each time a unit is sold if more than 400 are produced and sold. The graph of the marginal revenue function in Figure 9.34(b) shows that the marginal revenue is positive to the left of 400. This indicates that the rate at which the total revenue is changing is positive until 400 units are sold; thus the total revenue is increasing. Then at 400 units, the rate of change is 0. After 400 units are sold, the marginal revenue is negative, which indicates that the total revenue is now decreasing. It is clear from looking at either graph that 400 units should be produced and sold to maximize the total revenue function $R(x)$. That is, the total revenue function has its maximum at $x = 400$.

Figure 9.34

(a) Total revenue function   (b) Marginal revenue function

Marginal Cost   As with marginal revenue, the derivative of a total cost function gives the **marginal cost function.**

Marginal Cost   If $C = C(x)$ is a total cost function for a commodity, then its derivative, $\overline{MC} = C'(x)$, is the **marginal cost function.**

Notice that the linear total cost function with equation

$$C(x) = 300 + 6x \qquad \text{(in dollars)}$$

has marginal cost $6 per unit because its slope is 6. Taking the derivative of $C(x)$ also gives

$$\overline{MC} = C'(x) = 6$$

which verifies that the marginal cost is $6 per unit at all levels of production.

EXAMPLE 3 **Marginal Cost** | APPLICATION PREVIEW |

Suppose the daily total cost in dollars for a certain factory to produce x kitchen blenders is

$$C(x) = 0.001x^3 - 0.3x^2 + 32x + 2500$$

(a) Find the marginal cost function for these blenders.
(b) Find and interpret the marginal cost when $x = 80$ and $x = 200$.

Solution
(a) The marginal cost function is the derivative of $C(x)$.

$$\overline{MC} = C'(x) = 0.003x^2 - 0.6x + 32$$

(b) $C'(80) = 0.003(80)^2 - 0.6(80) + 32 = 3.2$ dollars per unit
$C'(200) = 0.003(200)^2 - 0.6(200) + 32 = 32$ dollars per unit

These values for the marginal cost can be used to *estimate* the amount that total cost would change if production were increased by one blender. Thus

$$C'(80) = 3.2$$

means that total cost would increase by *about* $3.20 if an 81st blender were produced. Note that

$$C(81) - C(80) = 3.141 \approx \$3.14$$

is the actual increase in total cost for an 81st blender.

Also, $C'(200) = 32$ means that total cost would increase by *about* $32 if a 201st blender were produced.

Whenever $C'(x)$ is positive, it means that an additional unit produced adds to or increases the total cost. In addition, the value of the derivative (or marginal cost) measures how fast $C(x)$ is increasing. Thus, our calculations above indicate that $C(x)$ is increasing faster at $x = 200$ than at $x = 80$. The graphs of the total cost function and the marginal cost function in Figure 9.35(a) and (b) also illustrate these facts. ■

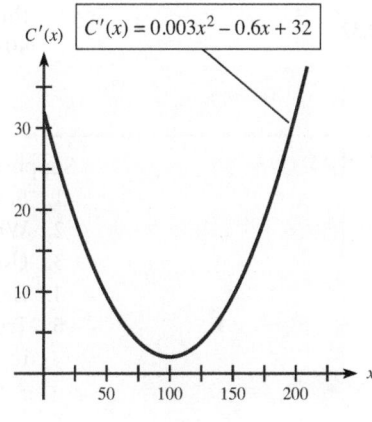

Figure 9.35   (a) Total cost   (b) Marginal cost

The graphs of many marginal cost functions tend to be U-shaped; they eventually will rise, even though there may be an initial interval where they decrease. Looking at the marginal cost graph in Figure 9.35(b) on the previous page, we see that marginal cost reaches its minimum near $x = 100$. We can also see this in Figure 9.35(a) by noting that tangent lines drawn to the total cost graph would have slopes that decrease until about $x = 100$ and then would increase.

Because producing more units can never reduce the total cost of production, the following properties are valid for total cost functions.

1. The total cost can never be negative. If there are fixed costs, the cost of producing 0 units is positive; otherwise, the cost of producing 0 units is 0.
2. The total cost function is always increasing; the more units produced, the higher the total cost. Thus the marginal cost is always positive.
3. There may be limitations on the units produced, such as those imposed by plant space.

EXAMPLE 4 Total and Marginal Cost

Suppose the graph in Figure 9.36 shows the monthly total cost for producing a product.

(a) Estimate the total cost of producing 400 items.
(b) Estimate the cost of producing the 401st item.
(c) Will producing the 151st item cost more or less than producing the 401st item?

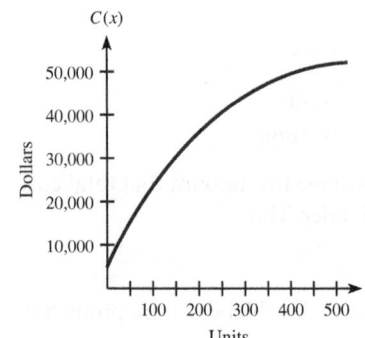

Figure 9.36

Solution

(a) The total cost of producing 400 items is the height of the total cost graph when $x = 400$, or about $50,000.

(b) The approximate cost of the 401st item is the marginal cost when $x = 400$, or the slope of the tangent line drawn to the graph at $x = 400$. Figure 9.37 shows the total cost graph with a tangent line at $x = 400$.

Note that the tangent line passes through the point $(0, 40,000)$, so we can find the slope by using the points $(0, 40,000)$ and $(400, 50,000)$.

$$m = \frac{y_2 - y_1}{x_2 - x_1} = \frac{50,000 - 40,000}{400 - 0} = \frac{10,000}{400} = 25$$

Thus the marginal cost at $x = 400$ is 25 dollars per item, so the approximate cost of the 401st item is $25.

(c) From Figure 9.37, we can see that if a tangent line to the graph were drawn where $x = 150$, it would be steeper than the one at $x = 400$. Because the slope of the tangent is the marginal cost and the marginal cost predicts the cost of the next item, this means that it would cost more to produce the 151st item than to produce the 401st.

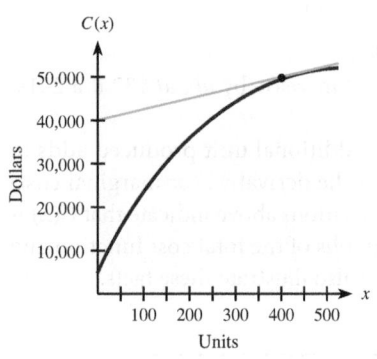

Figure 9.37

CHECKPOINT

Suppose the total cost function for a commodity is $C(x) = 0.01x^3 - 0.9x^2 + 33x + 3000$.
1. Find the marginal cost function.
2. What is the marginal cost if $x = 50$ units are produced?
3. Use marginal cost to estimate the cost of producing the 51st unit.
4. Calculate $C(51) - C(50)$ to find the actual cost of producing the 51st unit.
5. True or false: For products that have linear cost functions, the actual cost of producing the $(x + 1)$st unit is equal to the marginal cost at x.

Marginal Profit   As with marginal cost and marginal revenue, the derivative of a profit function for a commodity will give us the **marginal profit function** for the commodity.

Marginal profit

> If $P = P(x)$ is the profit function for a commodity, then the **marginal profit function** is $\overline{MP} = P'(x)$.

EXAMPLE 5   Marginal Profit

If the profit for a product is given by $P(x) = 20\sqrt{x + 1} - 2x - 22$ thousand dollars, what is the marginal profit at a production level of 15 units?

Solution
The marginal profit function is

$$\overline{MP} = P'(x) = 20 \cdot \frac{1}{2}(x + 1)^{-1/2} - 2 = \frac{10}{\sqrt{x + 1}} - 2$$

If 15 units are produced, the marginal profit is

$$P'(15) = \frac{10}{\sqrt{15 + 1}} - 2 = \frac{1}{2} = 0.5$$

This means that the profit from the sale of the 16th unit is approximately 0.5 (thousand dollars), or $500.

In a **competitive market,** each firm is so small that its actions in the market cannot affect the price of the product. The price of the product is determined in the market by the intersection of the market demand curve (from all consumers) and the market supply curve (from all firms that supply this product). The firm can sell as little or as much as it desires at the given market price, which it cannot change.

Therefore, a firm in a competitive market has a total revenue function given by $R(x) = px$, where p is the market equilibrium price for the product and x is the quantity sold.

EXAMPLE 6   Profit in a Competitive Market

A firm in a competitive market must sell its product for $200 per unit. The cost per unit (per day) is $80 + x$, where x represents the number of units sold per day. Find the marginal profit function.

Solution
If the cost per unit is $80 + x$, then the total cost of x units is given by the equation $C(x) = (80 + x)x = 80x + x^2$. The revenue per unit is $200, so the total revenue is given by $R(x) = 200x$. Thus the profit function is

$$P(x) = R(x) - C(x) = 200x - (80x + x^2), \quad \text{or} \quad P(x) = 120x - x^2$$

The marginal profit is $P'(x) = 120 - 2x$.

The marginal profit in Example 6 is not always positive, so producing and selling a certain number of items will maximize profit. Note that the marginal profit will be negative (that is, profit will decrease) if more than 60 items per day are produced. We will discuss methods of maximizing total revenue and profit, and of minimizing average cost, in the next chapter.

CHECKPOINT

If the total profit function for a product is $P(x) = 20\sqrt{x + 1} - 2x - 22$, then the marginal profit and its derivative are

$$\overline{MP} = P'(x) = \frac{10}{\sqrt{x + 1}} - 2 \quad \text{and} \quad P''(x) = \frac{-5}{\sqrt{(x + 1)^3}}$$

6. Is $P''(x) < 0$ for all values of $x \geq 0$?
7. Is the marginal profit decreasing for all $x \geq 0$?

EXAMPLE 7   Marginal Profit

Figure 9.38 shows graphs of a company's total revenue and total cost functions.

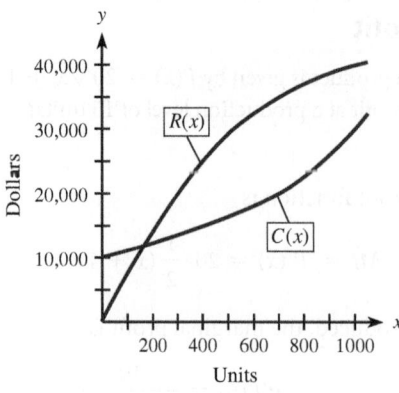

Figure 9.38

(a) If 100 units are being produced and sold, will producing the 101st item increase or decrease the profit?
(b) If 300 units are being produced and sold, will producing the 301st item increase or decrease the profit?
(c) If 1000 units are being produced and sold, will producing the 1001st item increase or decrease the profit?

Solution

At a given x-value, the slope of the tangent line to each function gives the marginal at that x-value.

(a) At $x = 100$, we can see that the graph of $R(x)$ is steeper than the graph of $C(x)$. Thus the tangent line to $R(x)$ will be steeper than the tangent line to $C(x)$. Hence $\overline{MR}(100) > \overline{MC}(100)$, which means that the revenue from the 101st item will exceed the cost. Therefore profit will increase when the 101st item is produced. Note that at $x = 100$, total costs are greater than total revenue, so the company is losing money but should still sell the 101st item because it will reduce the amount of loss.
(b) At $x = 300$, we can see that the tangent line to $R(x)$ again will be steeper than the tangent line to $C(x)$. Hence $\overline{MR}(300) > \overline{MC}(300)$, which means that the revenue from the 301st item will exceed the cost. Therefore profit will increase when the 301st item is produced.
(c) At $x = 1000$, we can see that the tangent line to $C(x)$ will be steeper than the tangent line to $R(x)$. Hence $\overline{MC}(1000) > \overline{MR}(1000)$, which means that the cost of the 1001st item will exceed the revenue. Therefore profit will decrease when the 1001st item is produced. ▪

EXAMPLE 8   Profit and Marginal Profit

In Example 5, we found that the profit (in thousands of dollars) for a company's products is given by $P(x) = 20\sqrt{x + 1} - 2x - 22$ and its marginal profit is given by $P'(x) = \dfrac{10}{\sqrt{x + 1}} - 2.$

(a) Use the graphs of $P(x)$ and $P'(x)$ to determine the relationship between the two functions.
(b) When is the marginal profit 0? What is happening to profit at this level of production?

Solution

(a) By comparing the graphs of the two functions (shown in Figure 9.39), we see that for $x > 0$, profit $P(x)$ is increasing over the interval where the marginal profit $P'(x)$ is positive and profit is decreasing over the interval where the marginal profit $P'(x)$ is negative.

(b) By using ZERO or SOLVER, or by using algebra, we see that $P'(x) = 0$ when $x = 24$. This level of production ($x = 24$) is where profit is maximized, at 30 (thousand dollars). ▪

Figure 9.39

CHECKPOINT	1. $\overline{MC} = C'(x) = 0.03x^2 - 1.8x + 33$
ANSWERS	2. $C'(50) = 18$
	3. The 51st unit will cost approximately \$18 to produce.
	4. $C(51) - C(50) = 18.61$
	5. True 6. Yes 7. Yes, because $P''(x) < 0$ for $x \geq 0$

EXERCISES 9.9

MARGINAL REVENUE, COST, AND PROFIT

In Problems 1–8, total revenue is in dollars and x is the number of units.

1. (a) If the total revenue function for a product is $R(x) = 4x$, what is the marginal revenue function for that product?
   (b) What does this marginal revenue function tell us?

2. If the total revenue function for a product is $R(x) = 32x$, what is the marginal revenue for the product? What does this mean?

3. Suppose that the total revenue function for a commodity is $R = 64x - 0.02x^2$.
   (a) Find $R(100)$ and tell what it represents.
   (b) Find the marginal revenue function.
   (c) Find the marginal revenue at $x = 100$ and tell what it predicts about the sale of the next unit and the next 3 units.
   (d) Find $R(101) - R(100)$ and explain what this value represents.

4. Suppose that the total revenue function for a commodity is $R(x) = 44x - 0.05x^2$.
   (a) Find $R(50)$ and tell what it represents.
   (b) Find the marginal revenue function.
   (c) Find the marginal revenue at $x = 50$ and tell what it predicts about the sale of the next unit and the next 2 units.
   (d) Find $R(51) - R(50)$ and explain what this value represents.

5. Suppose that demand for local cable TV service is given by

$$p = 120 - 0.4x$$

where p is the monthly price per subscriber in dollars and x is the number of subscribers (in hundreds).
   (a) Find the total revenue as a function of the number of subscribers (in hundreds).
   (b) Find the number of subscribers when the company charges \$80 per month for cable service. Then find the total revenue for $p = \$80$.
   (c) How could the company attract more subscribers?
   (d) Find and interpret the marginal revenue when the price is \$80 per month. What does this suggest about the monthly charge to subscribers?

6. Suppose that in a monopoly market, the demand function for a product is given by

$$p = 160 - 0.1x$$

where x is the number of units and p is the price in dollars.
   (a) Find the total revenue from the sale of 500 units.
   (b) Find and interpret the marginal revenue at 500 units.
   (c) Is more revenue expected from the 501st unit sold or from the 701st? Explain.

7. Suppose the total revenue for a certain product is given by $R(x) = 36x - 0.01x^2$.
   (a) Graph the marginal revenue function for this product.
   (b) At what value of x will total revenue be maximized?
   (c) What is the maximum revenue?

8. Suppose the total revenue for a certain product is given by $R(x) = 25x - 0.05x^2$.
   (a) Graph the marginal revenue function for this product.
   (b) Determine the number of units that must be sold to maximize total revenue.
   (c) What is the maximum revenue?

In Problems 9–16, cost is in dollars and x is the number of units. Find the marginal cost functions for the given cost functions.

9. $C(x) = 40 + 8x$
10. $C(x) = 200 + 16x$
11. $C(x) = 500 + 13x + x^2$
12. $C(x) = 300 + 10x + 0.01x^2$
13. $C = x^3 - 6x^2 + 24x + 10$
14. $C = 0.1x^3 - 1.5x^2 + 9x + 15$
15. $C = 400 + 27x + x^3$
16. $C(x) = 50 + 48x + x^3$
17. Suppose that the cost function for a commodity is

$$C(x) = 40 + x^2 \quad \text{dollars}$$

(a) Find the marginal cost at $x = 5$ units and tell what this predicts about the cost of producing 1 additional unit.
(b) Calculate $C(6) - C(5)$ to find the actual cost of producing 1 additional unit.

18. Suppose that the cost function for a commodity is

$$C(x) = 300 + 6x + 0.05x^2 \, \text{dollars}$$

(a) Find the marginal cost at $x = 8$ units and tell what this predicts about the cost of producing 1 additional unit.
(b) Calculate $C(9) - C(8)$ to find the actual cost of producing 1 additional unit.

19. If the cost function for a commodity is

$$C(x) = x^3 - 4x^2 + 30x + 20 \quad \text{dollars}$$

find the marginal cost at $x = 4$ units and tell what this predicts about the cost of producing 1 additional unit and 3 additional units.

20. If the cost function for a commodity is

$$C(x) = \tfrac{1}{90}x^3 + 4x^2 + 4x + 10 \quad \text{dollars}$$

find the marginal cost at $x = 3$ units and tell what this predicts about the cost of producing 1 additional unit and 2 additional units.

21. If the cost function for a commodity is

$$C(x) = 300 + 4x + x^2$$

graph the marginal cost function.

22. If the cost function for a commodity is

$$C(x) = x^3 - 12x^2 + 63x + 15$$

graph the marginal cost function.

In each of Problems 23 and 24, the graph of a company's total cost function is shown. For each problem, use the graph to answer the following questions.
(a) **Will the 101st item or the 501st item cost more to produce? Explain.**
(b) **Does this total cost function represent a manufacturing process that is getting more efficient or less efficient? Explain.**

23.

24.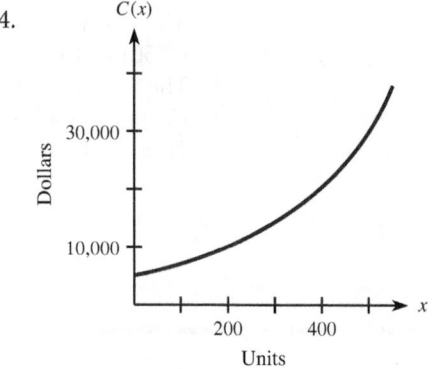

In Problems 25–28, cost, revenue, and profit are in dollars and x is the number of units.

25. If the total profit function is $P(x) = 5x - 25$, find the marginal profit. What does this mean?
26. If the total profit function is $P(x) = 16x - 32$, find the marginal profit. What does this mean?
27. Suppose that the total revenue function for a product is $R(x) = 50x$ and that the total cost function is $C(x) = 1900 + 30x + 0.01x^2$.
   (a) Find the profit from the production and sale of 500 units.
   (b) Find the marginal profit function.
   (c) Find $\overline{MP}$ at $x = 500$ and explain what it predicts.
   (d) Find $P(501) - P(500)$ and explain what this value represents.
28. Suppose that the total revenue function is given by

$$R(x) = 46x$$

   and that the total cost function is given by

$$C(x) = 100 + 30x + 0.1x^2$$

   (a) Find $P(100)$.
   (b) Find the marginal profit function.
   (c) Find $\overline{MP}$ at $x = 100$ and explain what it predicts.
   (d) Find $P(101) - P(100)$ and explain what this value represents.

In each of Problems 29 and 30, the graphs of a company's total revenue function and total cost function are shown. For each problem, use the graph to answer the following questions.

(a) From the sale of 100 items, 400 items, and 700 items, rank from smallest to largest the amount of profit received. Explain your choices and note whether any of these scenarios results in a loss.

(b) From the sale of the 101st item, the 401st item, and the 701st item, rank from smallest to largest the amount of profit received. Explain your choices, and note whether any of these scenarios results in a loss.

29.

30.

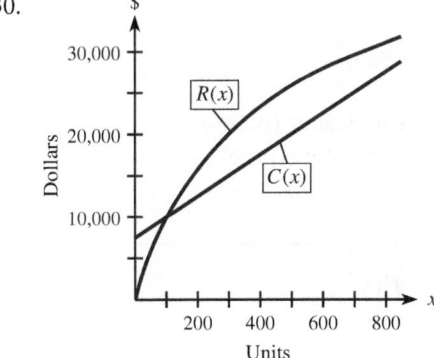

In each of Problems 31 and 32, the graph of a company's profit function is shown. For each problem, use the graph to answer the following questions about points *A*, *B*, and *C*.

(a) Rank from smallest to largest the amounts of profit received at these points. Explain your choices, and note whether any point results in a loss.

(b) Rank from smallest to largest the marginal profit at these points. Explain your choices, and note whether any marginal is negative and what this means.

31.

32.

33. (a) Graph the marginal profit function for the profit function $P(x) = 30x - x^2 - 200$, where $P(x)$ is in thousands of dollars and x is hundreds of units.

(b) What level of production and sales will give a 0 marginal profit?

(c) At what level of production and sales will profit be at a maximum?

(d) What is the maximum profit?

34. (a) Graph the marginal profit function for the profit function $P(x) = 16x - 0.1x^2 - 100$, where $P(x)$ is in hundreds of dollars and x is hundreds of units.

(b) What level of production and sales will give a 0 marginal profit?

(c) At what level of production and sales will profit be at a maximum?

(d) What is the maximum profit?

35. The price of a product in a competitive market is $300. If the cost per unit of producing the product is $160 + 0.1x$ dollars, where x is the number of units produced per month, how many units should the firm produce and sell to maximize its profit?

36. The cost per unit of producing a product is $60 + 0.2x$ dollars, where x represents the number of units produced per week. If the equilibrium price determined by a competitive market is $220, how many units should the firm produce and sell each week to maximize its profit?

37. If the daily cost per unit of producing a product by the Ace Company is $10 + 0.1x$ dollars and the price on the competitive market is $70, what is the maximum daily profit the Ace Company can expect on this product?

38. The Mary Ellen Candy Company produces chocolate Easter bunnies at a cost per unit of $0.40 + 0.005x$ dollars, where x is the number produced. If the price on the competitive market for a bunny this size is $10.00, how many should the company produce to maximize its profit?

9 CHAPTER SUMMARY & REVIEW

KEY TERMS AND FORMULAS

Section 9.1

Limit (p. 536)
One-sided limits (p. 537)
Properties of limits (p. 538)
Polynomial functions (p. 539)

Limits of rational functions (p. 540)
   $0/0$ indeterminate form
Limits of piecewise defined functions (p. 543)

Section 9.2

Continuous function (p. 549)
Limit at infinity (p. 553)

Vertical asymptote (p. 553)
Horizontal asymptote (p. 554)

Section 9.3

Average rate of change of f over $[a, b]$ (p. 560)

$$\frac{f(b) - f(a)}{b - a}$$

Average velocity (p. 561)
Instantaneous rate of change (p. 561)
Velocity (p. 561)
Derivative of $f(x)$ (p. 562)

$$f'(x) = \lim_{h \to 0} \frac{f(x + h) - f(x)}{h}$$

Derivative notation (p. 562)

$$y', f'(x), \frac{dy}{dx}, \frac{df(x)}{dx}$$

Marginal revenue (p. 563)
$$\overline{MR} = R'(x)$$
Slope of a tangent (p. 565)
Tangent line (p. 565)
Interpretations of the derivative (p. 566)
Differentiability and continuity (p. 567)

Section 9.4

Powers of x Rule (p. 573)

$$\frac{d(x^n)}{dx} = nx^{n-1}$$

Constant Function Rule (p. 575)

$$\frac{d(c)}{dx} = 0 \quad \text{for constant } c$$

Coefficient Rule (p. 575)

$$\frac{d}{dx}[c \cdot f(x)] = c \cdot f'(x)$$

Sum Rule (p. 576)

$$\frac{d}{dx}(u + v) = \frac{du}{dx} + \frac{dv}{dx}$$

Difference Rule (p. 577)

$$\frac{d}{dx}(u - v) = \frac{du}{dx} - \frac{dv}{dx}$$

Section 9.5

Product Rule (p. 584)

$$\frac{d}{dx}(uv) = uv' + vu'$$

Quotient Rule (p. 585)

$$\frac{d}{dx}\left(\frac{u}{v}\right) = \frac{vu' - uv'}{v^2}$$

Section 9.6

Composite function (p. 591)
Chain Rule (p. 591)

$$\frac{dy}{dx} = \frac{dy}{du} \cdot \frac{du}{dx}$$

Power Rule (p. 592)

$$\frac{d}{dx}(u^n) = nu^{n-1}\frac{du}{dx}$$

Section 9.7

Derivative formulas summary (p. 600)

Section 9.8

Second derivative of $f(x)$ (p. 603)

$$f''(x) = \frac{d}{dx}(f'(x))$$

Higher-order derivatives (p. 603)

Acceleration (p. 605)

Section 9.9

Marginal revenue function (p. 609)

$$\overline{MR} = R'(x)$$

Marginal cost function (p. 610)

$$\overline{MC} = C'(x)$$

Marginal profit function (p. 612)

$$\overline{MP} = P'(x)$$

REVIEW EXERCISES

Section 9.1

In Problems 1–6, use the graph of $y = f(x)$ in Figure 9.40 to find the functional values and limits, if they exist.

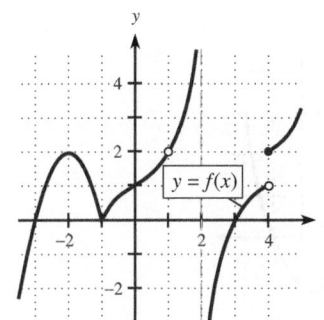

Figure 9.40

1. (a) $f(-2)$
   (b) $\lim_{x \to -2} f(x)$
2. (a) $f(-1)$
   (b) $\lim_{x \to -1} f(x)$
3. (a) $f(4)$
   (b) $\lim_{x \to 4^-} f(x)$
4. (a) $\lim_{x \to 4^+} f(x)$
   (b) $\lim_{x \to 4} f(x)$
5. (a) $f(1)$
   (b) $\lim_{x \to 1} f(x)$
6. (a) $f(2)$
   (b) $\lim_{x \to 2} f(x)$

In Problems 7–20, find each limit, if it exists.

7. $\lim_{x \to 4} (3x^2 + x + 3)$

8. $\lim_{x \to 4} \dfrac{x^2 - 16}{x + 4}$

9. $\lim_{x \to -1} \dfrac{x^2 - 1}{x + 1}$

10. $\lim_{x \to 5} \dfrac{x^2 - 6x + 5}{x^2 - 5x}$

11. $\lim_{x \to 2} \dfrac{4x^3 - 8x^2}{4x^3 - 16x}$

12. $\lim_{x \to -\frac{1}{2}} \dfrac{x^2 - \frac{1}{4}}{6x^2 + x - 1}$

13. $\lim_{x \to 3} \dfrac{x^2 - 16}{x - 3}$

14. $\lim_{x \to -3} \dfrac{x^2 - x - 12}{2x - 6}$

15. $\lim_{x \to 1} \dfrac{x^2 - 9}{x - 3}$

16. $\lim_{x \to 2} \dfrac{x^2 - 8}{x - 2}$

17. $\lim_{x \to 1} f(x)$ where $f(x) = \begin{cases} 4 - x^2 & \text{if } x < 1 \\ 4 & \text{if } x = 1 \\ 2x + 1 & \text{if } x > 1 \end{cases}$

18. $\lim_{x \to -2} f(x)$ where $f(x) = \begin{cases} x^3 - x & \text{if } x < -2 \\ 2 - x^2 & \text{if } x \geq -2 \end{cases}$

19. $\lim_{h \to 0} \dfrac{3(x + h)^2 - 3x^2}{h}$

20. $\lim_{h \to 0} \dfrac{[(x + h) - 2(x + h)^2] - (x - 2x^2)}{h}$

In Problems 21 and 22, use tables to investigate each limit. Check your result analytically or graphically.

21. $\lim_{x \to 2} \dfrac{x^2 + 10x - 24}{x^2 - 5x + 6}$

22. $\lim_{x \to -\frac{1}{2}} \dfrac{x^2 + \frac{1}{6}x - \frac{1}{6}}{x^2 + \frac{5}{6}x + \frac{1}{6}}$

Section 9.2

Use the graph of $y = f(x)$ in Figure 9.40 to answer the questions in Problems 23 and 24.

23. Is $f(x)$ continuous at
    (a) $x = -1$?
    (b) $x = 1$?
24. Is $f(x)$ continuous at
    (a) $x = -2$?
    (b) $x = 2$?

In Problems 25–30, suppose that

$$f(x) = \begin{cases} x^2 + 1 & \text{if } x \leq 0 \\ x & \text{if } 0 < x < 1 \\ 2x^2 - 1 & \text{if } x \geq 1 \end{cases}$$

25. What is $\lim_{x \to -1} f(x)$?
26. What is $\lim_{x \to 0} f(x)$, if it exists?
27. What is $\lim_{x \to 1} f(x)$, if it exists?
28. Is $f(x)$ continuous at $x = 0$?
29. Is $f(x)$ continuous at $x = 1$?
30. Is $f(x)$ continuous at $x = -1$?

For the functions in Problems 31–34, determine which are continuous. Identify discontinuities for those that are not continuous.

31. $y = \dfrac{x^2 + 25}{x - 5}$

32. $y = \dfrac{x^2 - 3x + 2}{x - 2}$

33. $f(x) = \begin{cases} x + 2 & \text{if } x \leq 2 \\ 5x - 6 & \text{if } x > 2 \end{cases}$

34. $y = \begin{cases} x^4 - 3 & \text{if } x \leq 1 \\ 2x - 3 & \text{if } x > 1 \end{cases}$

In Problems 35 and 36, use the graphs to find (a) the points of discontinuity, (b) $\lim_{x \to \infty} f(x)$, and (c) $\lim_{x \to -\infty} f(x)$.

35.

36.

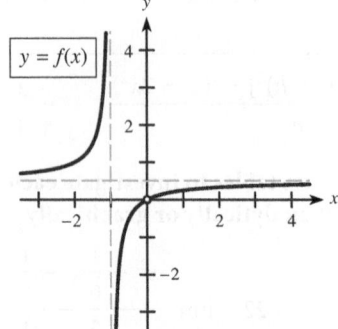

In Problems 37 and 38, evaluate the limits, if they exist. Then state what each limit tells about any horizontal asymptotes.

37. $\lim_{x \to -\infty} \dfrac{2x^2}{1 - x^2}$

38. $\lim_{x \to \infty} \dfrac{3x^{2/3}}{x + 1}$

Section 9.3

39. Find the average rate of change of

$$f(x) = 2x^4 - 3x + 7 \text{ over } [-1, 2]$$

In Problems 40 and 41, decide whether the statements are true or false.

40. $\lim_{h \to 0} \dfrac{f(x + h) - f(x)}{h}$ gives the formula for the slope of the tangent and the instantaneous rate of change of $f(x)$ at any value of x.

41. $\lim_{h \to 0} \dfrac{f(c + h) - f(c)}{h}$ gives the equation of the tangent line to $f(x)$ at $x = c$.

42. Use the definition of derivative to find $f'(x)$ for $f(x) = 3x^2 + 2x - 1$.

43. Use the definition of derivative to find $f'(x)$ if $f(x) = x - x^2$.

Use the graph of $y = f(x)$ in Figure 9.40 on the previous page to answer the questions in Problems 44–46.

44. Explain which is greater: the average rate of change of f over $[-3, 0]$ or over $[-1, 0]$.

45. Is $f(x)$ differentiable at
   (a) $x = -1$?   (b) $x = 1$?

46. Is $f(x)$ differentiable at
   (a) $x = -2$?   (b) $x = 2$?

47. Let $f(x) = \dfrac{\sqrt[3]{4x}}{(3x^2 - 10)^2}$. Approximate $f'(2)$
   (a) by using the numerical derivative feature of a graphing calculator.
   (b) by evaluating $\dfrac{f(2 + h) - f(2)}{h}$ with $h = 0.0001$.

48. Use the given table of values for $g(x)$ to
   (a) find the average rate of change of $g(x)$ over $[2, 5]$.
   (b) approximate $g'(4)$ as accurately as possible.

x	2	2.3	3.1	4	4.3	5
$g(x)$	13.2	12.1	9.7	12.2	14.3	18.1

Use the following graph of $f(x)$ to complete Problems 49 and 50.

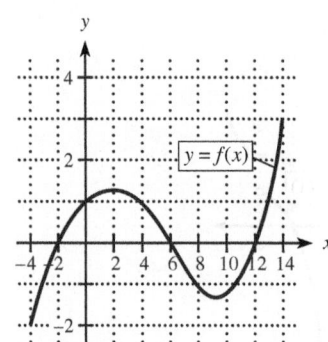

49. Estimate $f'(4)$.

50. Rank the following from smallest to largest and explain.

   $A: f'(2)$ $B: f'(6)$
   $C:$ the average rate of change of $f(x)$ over $[2, 10]$

Section 9.4

51. If $c = 4x^5 - 6x^3$, find c'.

52. If $f(x) = 10x^9 - 5x^6 + 4x - 2^7 + 19$, find $f'(x)$.

53. If $p = q + \sqrt{7}$, find dp/dq.

54. If $y = \sqrt{x}$, find y'.

55. If $f(z) = \sqrt[3]{2^4}$, find $f'(z)$.

56. If $v(x) = 4/\sqrt[3]{x}$, find $v'(x)$.

57. If $y = \dfrac{1}{x} - \dfrac{1}{\sqrt{x}}$, find y'.

58. If $f(x) = \dfrac{3}{2x^2} - \sqrt[3]{x} + 4^5$, find $f'(x)$.

59. Write the equation of the line tangent to the graph of $y = 3x^5 - 6$ at $x = 1$.

60. Write the equation of the line tangent to the curve $y = 3x^3 - 2x$ at the point where $x = 2$.

In Problems 61 and 62, (a) find all x-values where the slope of the tangent equals zero, (b) find points (x, y) where the slope of the tangent equals zero, and (c) use a graphing utility to graph the function and label the points found in part (b).

61. $f(x) = x^3 - 3x^2 + 1$ 62. $f(x) = x^6 - 6x^4 + 8$

Section 9.5

63. If $f(x) = (3x - 1)(x^2 - 4x)$, find $f'(x)$.

64. Find y' if $y = (x^4 + 3)(3x^3 + 1)$.

65. If $p = \dfrac{5q^3}{2q^3 + 1}$, find $\dfrac{dp}{dq}$.

66. Find $\dfrac{ds}{dt}$ if $s = \dfrac{\sqrt{t}}{(3t + 1)}$.

67. Find $\dfrac{dy}{dx}$ for $y = \sqrt{x}\,(3x + 2)$.

68. Find $\dfrac{dC}{dx}$ for $C = \dfrac{5x^4 - 2x^2 + 1}{x^3 + 1}$.

Section 9.6

69. If $y = (x^3 - 4x^2)^3$, find y'.

70. If $y = (5x^6 + 6x^4 + 5)^6$, find y'.

71. If $y = (2x^4 - 9)^9$, find $\dfrac{dy}{dx}$.

72. Find $g'(x)$ if $g(x) = \dfrac{1}{\sqrt{x^3 - 4x}}$.

Section 9.7

73. Find $f'(x)$ if $f(x) = x^2(2x^4 + 5)^8$.

74. Find S' if $S = \dfrac{(3x + 1)^2}{x^2 - 4}$.

75. Find $\dfrac{dy}{dx}$ if $y = [(3x + 1)(2x^3 - 1)]^{12}$.

76. Find y' if $y = \left(\dfrac{x + 1}{1 - x^2}\right)^3$.

77. Find y' if $y = x\sqrt{x^2 - 4}$.

78. Find $\dfrac{dy}{dx}$ if $y = \dfrac{x}{\sqrt[3]{3x - 1}}$.

Section 9.8

In Problems 79 and 80, find the second derivatives.

79. $y = \sqrt{x} - x^2$ 80. $y = x^4 - \dfrac{1}{x}$

In Problems 81 and 82, find the fifth derivatives.

81. $y = (2x + 1)^4$ 82. $y = \dfrac{(1 - x)^6}{24}$

83. If $\dfrac{dy}{dx} = \sqrt{x^2 - 4}$, find $\dfrac{d^3y}{dx^3}$.

84. If $\dfrac{d^2y}{dx^2} = \dfrac{x}{x^2 + 1}$, find $\dfrac{d^4y}{dx^4}$.

APPLICATIONS

Sections 9.1 and 9.2

Cost, revenue, and profit **In Problems 85–88, assume that a company's monthly total revenue and total cost (both in dollars) are given by**

$$R(x) = 140x - 0.01x^2 \quad \text{and} \quad C(x) = 60x + 70{,}000$$

where x is the number of units. Let $P(x)$ denote the profit function.

85. Find (a) $\lim\limits_{x \to 4000} R(x)$, (b) $\lim\limits_{x \to 4000} C(x)$, and (c) $\lim\limits_{x \to 4000} P(x)$.

86. Find and interpret (a) $\lim\limits_{x \to 0^+} C(x)$ and (b) $\lim\limits_{x \to 1000} P(x)$.

87. If $\overline{R}(x) = \dfrac{R(x)}{x}$ and $\overline{C}(x) = \dfrac{C(x)}{x}$ are, respectively, the company's average revenue per unit and average cost per unit, find

    (a) $\lim\limits_{x \to 0^+} \overline{R}(x)$.   (b) $\lim\limits_{x \to 0^+} \overline{C}(x)$.

88. Evaluate and explain the meanings of

    (a) $\lim\limits_{x \to \infty} C(x)$.   (b) $\lim\limits_{x \to \infty} \overline{C}(x) = \lim\limits_{x \to \infty} \dfrac{C(x)}{x}$.

Section 9.3

Elderly in the workforce **The graph shows the percent of elderly men and women in the workforce for selected years from 1970 and projected to 2040. Use this graph in Problems 89 and 90.**

89. For the period from 1990 to 2030, find and interpret the annual average rate of change of
    (a) elderly men in the workforce.
    (b) elderly women in the workforce.

90. (a) Find the annual average rate of change of the percent of elderly men in the workforce from 1970 to 1980 and from 2030 to 2040.
    (b) Find the annual average rate of change of the percent of elderly women in the workforce from 1970 to 1980 and from 2030 to 2040.

Elderly in the Workforce, 1970–2040

Source: Bureau of the Census, U.S. Department of Commerce

Section 9.4

91. *Demand* Suppose that the demand for x units of a product is given by $x = (100/p) - 1$, where p is the price per unit of the product. Find and interpret the rate of change of demand with respect to price if the price is
    (a) $10.   (b) $20.

92. *Severe weather ice makers* Thunderstorms severe enough to produce hail develop when an upper-level low (a pool of cold air high in the atmosphere) moves through a region where there is warm, moist air at the surface. These storms create an updraft that draws the moist air into subfreezing air above 10,000 feet. Data from the National Weather Service indicate that the strength of the updraft, as measured by its speed s in mph, affects the size of the hail according to

$$h - 0.000595s^{1.922}$$

where h is the diameter of the hail (in inches). Find and interpret $h(100)$ and $h'(100)$.

93. *Revenue* The graph shows the revenue function for a commodity. Will the $(A + 1)$st item sold or the $(B + 1)$st item sold produce more revenue? Explain.

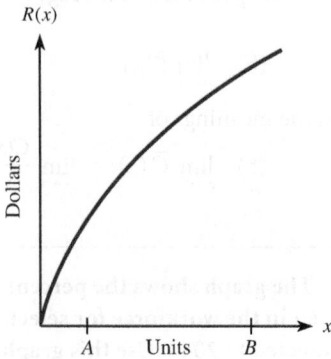

Section 9.5

94. *Revenue* In a 100-unit apartment building when the price charged per apartment rental is $(830 + 30x)$ dollars, the number of apartments rented is $100 - x$ and the total revenue for the building is

$$R(x) = (830 + 30x)(100 - x)$$

where x is the number of $30 rent increases (and the resulting number of unrented apartments). Find the marginal revenue when $x = 10$. Does this tell you that the rent should be raised (causing more vacancies) or lowered? Explain.

95. *Productivity* Suppose the productivity of a worker (in units per hour) after x hours of training and time on the job is given by

$$P(x) = 3 + \frac{70x^2}{x^2 + 1000}$$

(a) Find and interpret $P(20)$.
(b) Find and interpret $P'(20)$.

Section 9.6

96. *Demand* The demand q for a product at price p is given by

$$q = 10,000 - 50\sqrt{0.02p^2 + 500}$$

Find the rate of change of demand with respect to price.

97. *Supply* The number of units x of a product that is supplied at price p is given by

$$x = \sqrt{p - 1}, \quad p \geq 1$$

If the price p is $10, what is the rate of change of the supply with respect to the price, and what does it tell us?

Section 9.8

98. *Acceleration* Suppose an object moves so that its distance to a sensor, in feet, is given by

$$s(t) = 16 + 140t + 8\sqrt{t}$$

where t is the time in seconds. Find the acceleration at time $t = 4$ seconds.

99. *Profit* Suppose a company's profit (in dollars) is given by

$$P(x) = 70x - 0.1x^2 - 5500$$

where x is the number of units. Find and interpret $P'(300)$ and $P''(300)$.

Section 9.9

In Problems 100–107, cost, revenue, and profit are in dollars and x is the number of units.

100. *Cost* If the cost function for a particular good is $C(x) = 3x^2 + 6x + 600$, what is the
   (a) marginal cost function?
   (b) marginal cost if 30 units are produced?
   (c) interpretation of your answer in part (b)?

101. *Cost* If the total cost function for a commodity is $C(x) = 400 + 5x + x^3$, what is the marginal cost when 4 units are produced, and what does it mean?

102. *Revenue* The total revenue function for a commodity is $R = 40x - 0.02x^2$, with x representing the number of units.
   (a) Find the marginal revenue function.
   (b) At what level of production will marginal revenue be 0?

103. *Profit* If the total revenue function for a product is given by $R(x) = 60x$ and the total cost function is given by $C = 200 + 10x + 0.1x^2$, what is the marginal profit at $x = 10$? What does the marginal profit at $x = 10$ predict?

104. *Revenue* The total revenue function for a commodity is given by $R = 80x - 0.04x^2$.
   (a) Find the marginal revenue function.
   (b) What is the marginal revenue at $x = 100$?
   (c) Interpret your answer in part (b).

105. *Revenue* If the revenue function for a product is

$$R(x) = \frac{60x^2}{2x + 1}$$

find the marginal revenue.

106. *Profit* A firm has monthly costs given by

$$C = 45{,}000 + 100x + x^3$$

where x is the number of units produced per month. The firm can sell its product in a competitive market for \$4600 per unit. Find the marginal profit.

107. *Profit* A small business has weekly costs of

$$C = 100 + 30x + \frac{x^2}{10}$$

where x is the number of units produced each week. The competitive market price for this business's product is \$46 per unit. Find the marginal profit.

108. *Cost, revenue, and profit* The graph shows the total revenue and total cost functions for a company. Use the graph to decide (and justify) at which of points A, B, and C
   (a) the revenue from the next item will be least.
   (b) the profit will be greatest.
   (c) the profit from the sale of the next item will be greatest.
   (d) the next item sold will reduce the profit.

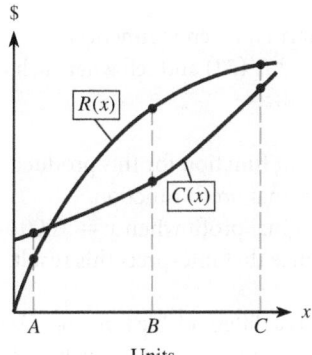

9 CHAPTER TEST

In Problems 1–4, evaluate the limits, if they exist. Use algebraic methods.

1. $\displaystyle\lim_{x \to -2} \frac{4x - x^2}{4x - 8}$

2. $\displaystyle\lim_{x \to \infty} \frac{8x^2 - 4x + 1}{2 + x - 5x^2}$

3. $\displaystyle\lim_{x \to 7} \frac{x^2 - 5x - 14}{x^2 - 6x - 7}$

4. $\displaystyle\lim_{x \to -5} \frac{5x - 25}{x + 5}$

5. (a) Write the limit definition for $f'(x)$.
    (b) Use the definition from (a) to find $f'(x)$ for $f(x) = 3x^2 - x + 9$.

6. Let $f(x) = \dfrac{4x}{x^2 - 8x}$. Identify all x-values where $f(x)$ is *not* continuous.

In Problems 7–13, use derivative formulas to find the derivative of each function. Simplify, except for Problem 10.

7. $B = 0.523W - 5176$

8. $p = 9t^{10} - 6t^7 - 17t + 23$

9. $y = \dfrac{3x^3}{2x^7 + 11}$

10. $f(x) = (3x^5 - 2x + 3)(4x^{10} + 10x^4 - 17)$

11. $g(x) = \frac{3}{4}(2x^5 + 7x^3 - 5)^{12}$

12. $y = (x^2 + 3)(2x + 5)^6$

13. $f(x) = 12\sqrt{x} - \dfrac{10}{x^2} + 17$

14. Find $\dfrac{d^3y}{dx^3}$ for $y = x^3 - x^{-3}$.

15. Let $f(x) = x^3 - 3x^2 - 24x - 10$.
    (a) Write the equation of the line tangent to the graph of $y = f(x)$ at $x = -1$.
    (b) Find all points (both x- and y-coordinates) where $f'(x) = 0$.

16. Find the average rate of change of $f(x) = 4 - x - 2x^2$ over $[1, 6]$.

17. Use the given tables to evaluate the following limits, if they exist.
    (a) $\displaystyle\lim_{x \to 5} f(x)$ (b) $\displaystyle\lim_{x \to 5} g(x)$ (c) $\displaystyle\lim_{x \to 5^-} g(x)$

x	4.99	4.999	$\to 5 \leftarrow$	5.001	5.01
$f(x)$	2.01	2.001	$\to ? \leftarrow$	1.999	1.99

x	4.99	4.999	$\to 5 \leftarrow$	5.001	5.01
$g(x)$	-3.99	-3.999	$\to ? \leftarrow$	6.999	6.99

18. Use the definition of continuity to investigate whether $g(x)$ is continuous at $x = -2$. Show your work.

$$g(x) = \begin{cases} 6 - x & \text{if } x \le -2 \\ x^3 & \text{if } x > -2 \end{cases}$$

In Problems 19 and 20, suppose a company has its total cost for a product given by $C(x) = 200x + 10,000$ dollars and its total revenue given by $R(x) = 250x - 0.01x^2$ dollars, where x is the number of units produced and sold.

19. (a) Find the marginal revenue function.
    (b) Find $R(72)$ and $R'(72)$ and tell what each represents or predicts.

20. (a) Form the profit function for this product.
    (b) Find the marginal profit function.
    (c) Find the marginal profit when $x = 1000$ and then write a sentence that interprets this result.

21. Suppose that $f(x)$ is a differentiable function. Use the table of values to approximate $f'(3)$ as accurately as possible.

x	2	2.5	2.999	3	3.01	3.1
$f(x)$	0	18.4	44.896	45	46.05	56.18

22. Use the graph to perform the evaluations (a)–(f) and to answer (g)–(i). If no value exists, so indicate.

    (a) $f(1)$
    (b) $\lim\limits_{x \to 6} f(x)$
    (c) $\lim\limits_{x \to 3^-} f(x)$
    (d) $\lim\limits_{x \to -4} f(x)$
    (e) $\lim\limits_{x \to -\infty} f(x)$
    (f) Estimate $f'(4)$.
    (g) Find all x-values where $f'(x)$ does not exist.
    (h) Find all x-values where $f(x)$ is not continuous.
    (i) Rank from smallest to largest: $f'(-2), f'(2)$, and the average rate of change of $f(x)$ over $[-2, 2]$.

Graph of $y = f(x)$

23. Given that the line $y = \frac{2}{3}x - 8$ is tangent to the graph of $y = f(x)$ at $x = 6$, find
    (a) $f'(6)$.
    (b) $f(6)$.
    (c) the instantaneous rate of change of $f(x)$ with respect to x at $x = 6$.

24. The graph shows the total revenue and total cost functions for a company. Use the graph to decide (and justify) at which of points A, B, and C
    (a) profit is the greatest.
    (b) there is a loss.
    (c) producing and selling another item will increase profit.
    (d) the next item sold will decrease profit.

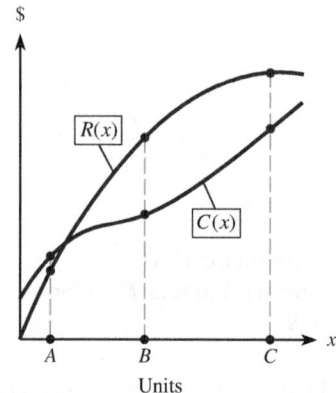

9 　EXTENDED APPLICATIONS & GROUP PROJECTS

I. Marginal Return to Sales

A tire manufacturer studying the effectiveness of television advertising and other promotions on sales of its GRIPPER-brand tires attempted to fit data it had gathered to the equation

$$S = a_0 + a_1x + a_2x^2 + b_1y$$

where S is sales revenue in millions of dollars, x is millions of dollars spent on television advertising, y is millions of dollars spent on other promotions, and $a_0, a_1, a_2,$ and b_1 are constants. The data, gathered in two different regions of the country where expenditures for other promotions were kept constant (at B_1 and B_2), resulted in the following quadratic equations relating TV advertising and sales.

$$\text{Region 1:}\quad S_1 = 30 + 20x - 0.4x^2 + B_1$$

$$\text{Region 2:}\quad S_2 = 20 + 36x - 1.3x^2 + B_2$$

The company wants to know how to make the best use of its advertising dollars in the regions and whether the current allocation could be improved. Advise management about current advertising effectiveness, allocation of additional expenditures, and reallocation of current advertising expenditures by answering the following questions.

1. In the analysis of sales and advertising, **marginal return to sales** is usually used, and it is given by dS_1/dx for Region 1 and dS_2/dx for Region 2.

   (a) Find $\dfrac{dS_1}{dx}$ and $\dfrac{dS_2}{dx}$.

   (b) If $10 million is being spent on TV advertising in each region, what is the marginal return to sales in each region?

2. Which region would benefit more from additional advertising expenditure if $10 million is currently being spent in each region?

3. If any additional money is made available for advertising, in which region should it be spent?

4. How could money already being spent be reallocated to produce more sales revenue?

II. Energy from Crude Oil (Modeling)

The table shows the total energy supply from crude oil products, in quadrillion BTUs, for the years from 2010 and projected through 2040.

1. Find the cubic function that models the data, with x equal to the number of years past 2010 and y equal to the number of quadrillion BTUs of energy. Report the model as $y = f(x)$ with three significant digit coefficients.
2. Graph the unrounded model and the data points on the same axes, with x representing the years from 2010 to 2040.
3. Use the reported model $y = f(x)$ for $x = -5$ through $x = 33$.
   (a) Graph $y = f(x)$ for this x-range.
   (b) Find the quadrillion BTUs of energy when $x = 9.0$.
   (c) Find the quadrillion BTUs of energy when $x = 9.16$.
   (d) Find the quadrillion BTUs of energy when $x = 9.3$.
4. What can we conclude about the point (9.16, 15.933) on the graph of $y = f(x)$?
5. Find the rate of change of the reported function $y = f(x)$.
6. Graph $y = f'(x)$ for x-values -5 through 33.
7. (a) What is the value of $y = f'(x)$ at $x = 9.16$?

   (b) Is the value of $y = f'(x)$ positive or negative at $x = 9.0$?
   (c) Is the value of $y = f'(x)$ positive or negative at $x = 9.3$?
8. What can we conclude about the derivative on either side of the x-coordinate of the point (9.16, 15.933)?
9. What can we conclude about the point (25.36, 12.958) on the graph of $y = f(x)$?
10. What can we conclude about the derivative on either side of the x-coordinate of the point (25.36, 12.958)?

Total Energy Supply from Crude Oil Products, in Quadrillion BTUs

Year	BTUs	Year	BTUs	Year	BTUs
2010	11.59	2021	15.75	2032	13.51
2011	12.16	2022	15.42	2033	13.56
2012	13.58	2023	15.09	2034	13.52
2013	14.61	2024	14.74	2035	13.40
2014	15.35	2025	14.50	2036	13.07
2015	15.58	2026	14.11	2037	13.52
2016	16.08	2027	13.91	2038	12.94
2017	16.03	2028	14.71	2039	13.11
2018	16.02	2029	13.54	2040	13.12
2019	16.10	2030	13.47		
2020	15.95	2031	13.52		

Source: www.eia.gov

III. Tangent Lines and Optimization in Business and Economics

In business and economics, common questions of interest include how to maximize profit or revenue, how to minimize average costs, and how to maximize average productivity. For questions such as these, the description of how to obtain the desired maximum or minimum represents an optimal (or best possible) solution to the problem. And the process of finding an optimal solution is called optimization. Answering these questions often involves tangent lines. In this project, we examine how tangent lines can be used to minimize average costs.

Suppose that Wittage, Inc., manufactures paper shredders for home and office use and that its weekly total costs (in dollars) for x shredders are given by

$$C(x) = 0.03x^2 + 12.75x + 6075$$

The average cost per unit for x units [denoted by $\overline{C}(x)$] is the total cost divided by the number of units. Thus the average cost function for Wittage, Inc., is

$$\overline{C}(x) = \frac{C(x)}{x} = \frac{0.03x^2 + 12.75x + 6075}{x}$$

$$= \frac{0.03x^2}{x} + \frac{12.75x}{x} + \frac{6075}{x}$$

$$\overline{C}(x) = 0.03x + 12.75 + \frac{6075}{x}$$

Wittage, Inc., would like to know how the company can use marginal costs to gain information about minimizing average costs. To investigate this relationship, answer the following questions.

1. Find Wittage's marginal cost function; then complete the following table.

x	100	200	300	400	500	600
$\overline{C}(x)$						
$\overline{MC}(x)$						

2. (a) For what x-values in the table is $\overline{C}$ getting smaller?
   (b) For these x-values, is $\overline{MC} < \overline{C}, \overline{MC} > \overline{C}$, or $\overline{MC} = \overline{C}$?

3. (a) For what x-values in the table is $\overline{C}$ getting larger?
   (b) For these x-values, is $\overline{MC} < \overline{C}, \overline{MC} > \overline{C}$, or $\overline{MC} = \overline{C}$?

4. Between what pair of consecutive x-values in the table will $\overline{C}$ reach its minimum?

5. Interpret (a) $\overline{C}$ (200) and $\overline{MC}$(200) and (b) $\overline{C}$ (400) and $\overline{MC}$(400).

6. On the basis of what $\overline{C}$ and $\overline{MC}$ tell us and the work so far, complete the following statements by filling in the blank with *increase, decrease,* or *stay the same.* Explain your reasoning.
   (a) $\overline{MC} < \overline{C}$ means that if Wittage makes one more unit, then $\overline{C}$ will _____.
   (b) $\overline{MC} > \overline{C}$ means that if Wittage makes one more unit, then $\overline{C}$ will _____.

7. (a) On the basis of your answers to Question 6, how will $\overline{C}$ and $\overline{MC}$ be related when $\overline{C}$ is minimized? Write a careful statement.
   (b) Use your idea from part (a) to find x where $\overline{C}$ is minimized. Then check your calculations by graphing $\overline{C}$ and locating the minimum from the graph.

Next, let's examine graphically the relationship that emerged in Question 7 to see whether it is true in general. Figure 9.41 shows a typical total cost function (Wittage's total cost function has a similar shape) and an arbitrary point on the graph.

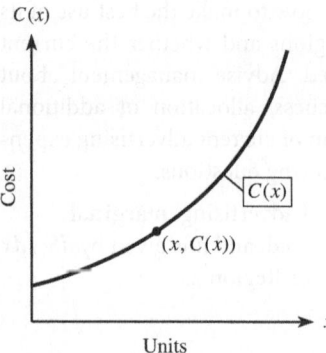

Figure 9.41

8. (a) Measure the slope of the line joining the point (x, C(x)) and the origin.
   (b) How is this slope related to the function $\overline{C}$ at (x, C(x))?

9. Figure 9.42(a) show.s a typical total cost function with several points labeled.
   (a) Explain how you can tell at a glance that $\overline{C}(x)$ is decreasing as the level of production moves from A to B to C to D.
   (b) Explain how you can tell at a glance that $\overline{C}(x)$ is increasing as the level of production moves from Q to R to S to T.

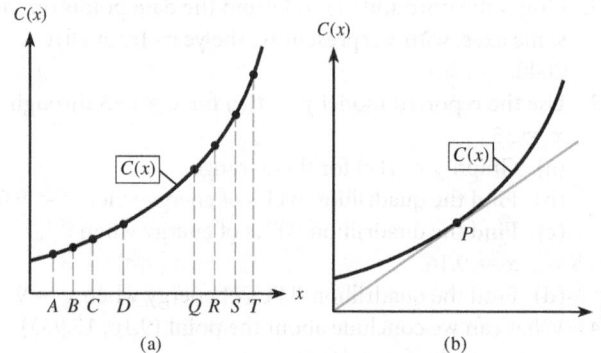

Figure 9.42

10. In Figure 9.42(b), a line from (0, 0) is drawn tangent to C(x) and the point of tangency is labeled P. At point P in Figure 9.42(b), what represents
    (a) the average cost, $\overline{C}(x)$?
    (b) the marginal cost, $\overline{MC}(x)$?
    (c) Explain how Figure 9.42 confirms that $\overline{C}(x)$ is minimized when $\overline{MC}(x) = \overline{C}(x)$.

On the basis of the numerical approach for Wittage's total cost function and the general graphical approach, what recommendation would you give Wittage about determining the number of units that will minimize average costs (even if the total cost function changes)?

Martin Charles Hatch/Shutterstock

Applications of Derivatives

10

The derivative can be used to determine where a function has a "turning point" on its graph so that we can determine where the graph reaches its highest or lowest point within a particular interval. These points are called the relative maxima and relative minima, respectively, and are useful in sketching the graph of the function. The techniques for finding these points are also useful in solving applied problems such as finding the maximum profit, the minimum average cost, and the maximum productivity. The second derivative can be used to find points of inflection of the graph of a function and to find the point of diminishing returns in certain applications.

The topics and some representative applications discussed in this chapter include the following.

Prerequisite Problem Type	For Section	Answer	Section for Review
Write $\frac{1}{3}(x^2 - 1)^{-2/3}(2x)$ with positive exponents.	**10.2**	$\dfrac{2x}{3(x^2 - 1)^{2/3}}$	0.3, 0.4 Exponents and radicals
Factor: (a) $x^3 - x^2 - 6x$ (b) $8000 - 80x - 3x^2$	**10.1–10.3**	(a) $x(x - 3)(x + 2)$ (b) $(40 - x)(200 + 3x)$	0.6 Factoring
(a) For what values of x is $\dfrac{2}{3\sqrt[3]{x + 2}}$ undefined? (b) For what values of x is $\frac{1}{3}(x^2 - 1)^{-2/3}(2x)$ undefined?	**10.1–10.2** **10.5**	(a) $x = -2$ (b) $x = -1, x = 1$	1.2 Domains of functions
If $f(x) = \frac{1}{3}x^3 - x^2 - 3x + 2$, and $f'(x) = x^2 - 2x - 3$, (a) find $f(-1)$. (b) find $f'(-2)$.	**10.1**	(a) $\dfrac{11}{3}$ (b) 5	1.2 Function notation
(a) Solve $0 = x^2 - 2x - 3$. (b) If $f'(x) = 3x^2 - 3$, what values of x make $f'(x) = 0$?	**10.1–10.5**	(a) $x = -1, x = 3$ (b) $x = -1, x = 1$	2.1 Solving quadratic equations
Does $\lim\limits_{x \to -2} \dfrac{2x - 4}{3x + 6}$ exist?	**10.5**	No; unbounded	9.1 Limits
(a) Find $f''(x)$ if $f(x) = x^3 - 4x^2 + 3$. (b) Find $P''(x)$ if $P(x) = 48x - 1.2x^2$.	**10.2**	(a) $f''(x) = 6x - 8$ (b) $P''(x) = -2.4$	9.8 Higher-order derivatives
Find the derivatives: (a) $y = \frac{1}{3}x^3 - x^2 - 3x + 2$ (b) $f = x + 2\left(\dfrac{80,000}{x}\right)$ (c) $p(t) = 1 + \dfrac{4t}{t^2 + 16}$ (d) $y = (x + 2)^{2/3}$ (e) $y = \sqrt[3]{x^2 - 1}$	**10.1–10.4**	(a) $y' = x^2 - 2x - 3$ (b) $f' = 1 - \dfrac{160,000}{x^2}$ (c) $p'(t) = \dfrac{64 - 4t^2}{(t^2 + 16)^2}$ (d) $y' = \dfrac{2}{3(x + 2)^{1/3}}$ (e) $y' = \dfrac{2x}{3(x^2 - 1)^{2/3}}$	9.4, 9.5, 9.6 Derivatives

Relative Maxima and Minima: Curve Sketching

OBJECTIVES

- To use the derivative of a function to determine where it is increasing or decreasing
- To find relative maxima and minima and horizontal points of inflection of functions
- To sketch graphs of functions by using information about maxima, minima, and horizontal points of inflection

APPLICATION PREVIEW

When a company initiates an advertising campaign, there is typically a surge in weekly sales. As the effect of the campaign lessens, sales attributable to it usually decrease. For example, suppose a company models its weekly sales revenue during an advertising campaign by

$$S = \frac{100t}{t^2 + 100}$$

where t is the number of weeks since the beginning of the campaign. The company would like to determine accurately when the revenue function is increasing, when it is decreasing, and when sales revenue is maximized. (See Example 4.)

In this section, we will use the derivative of a function to decide whether the function is increasing or decreasing on an interval and to find where the function has relative maximum points and relative minimum points. We will use the information about derivatives of functions to graph the functions and to solve applied problems.

Recall that we can find the maximum value or the minimum value of a quadratic function by finding the vertex of its graph. But for functions of higher degree, the special features of their graphs may be harder to find accurately, even when a graphing utility is used. In addition to intercepts and asymptotes, we can use the first derivative as an aid in graphing. The first derivative identifies the "turning points" of the graph, which help us determine the general shape of the graph and choose a viewing window that includes the interesting points of the graph. Note that for a quadratic function $f(x) = ax^2 + bx + c$, the solution to $f'(x) = 2ax + b = 0$ is $x = -b/2a$. This solution is the x-coordinate of the vertex (turning point) of $f(x)$, found in Section 2.2.

In Figure 10.1(a) on the next page, we see that the graph of $y = \frac{1}{3}x^3 - x^2 - 3x + 2$ has two "turning points," at $(-1, \frac{11}{3})$ and $(3, -7)$. The curve has a relative maximum at $(-1, \frac{11}{3})$ because this point is higher than any other point "near" it on the curve; the curve has a relative minimum at $(3, -7)$ because this point is lower than any other point "near" it on the curve. A formal definition follows.

Relative Maxima and Minima

The point $(x_1, f(x_1))$ is a **relative maximum point** of the function f if there is an interval around x_1 on which $f(x_1) \geq f(x)$ for all x in the interval. In this case, we say that the relative maximum *occurs* at $x = x_1$ and the relative maximum is $f(x_1)$.

The point $(x_2, f(x_2))$ is a **relative minimum point** of the function f if there is an interval around x_2 on which $f(x_2) \leq f(x)$ for all x in the interval. In this case, we say that the relative minimum *occurs* at $x = x_2$ and the relative minimum is $f(x_2)$.

To determine whether a turning point of a function is a maximum point or a minimum point, it is frequently helpful to know what the graph of the function does in intervals on either side of the turning point. We say that a function is **increasing** on an interval if the values of the function increase as the x-values increase (that is, if the graph rises as we move from left to right on the interval). Similarly, a function is **decreasing** on an interval if the values of the function decrease as the x-values increase (that is, if the graph falls as we move from left to right on the interval).

We have seen that if the slope of a line is positive, then the linear function is increasing and its graph is rising. Similarly, if $f(x)$ is differentiable over an interval and if each tangent line to the curve over that interval has positive slope, then the curve is rising over the interval and the function is increasing. Because the derivative of the function gives the slope of the tangent to the curve, we see that if $f'(x) > 0$ on an interval, then $f(x)$ is increasing on that interval. A similar conclusion can be reached when the derivative is negative on the interval.

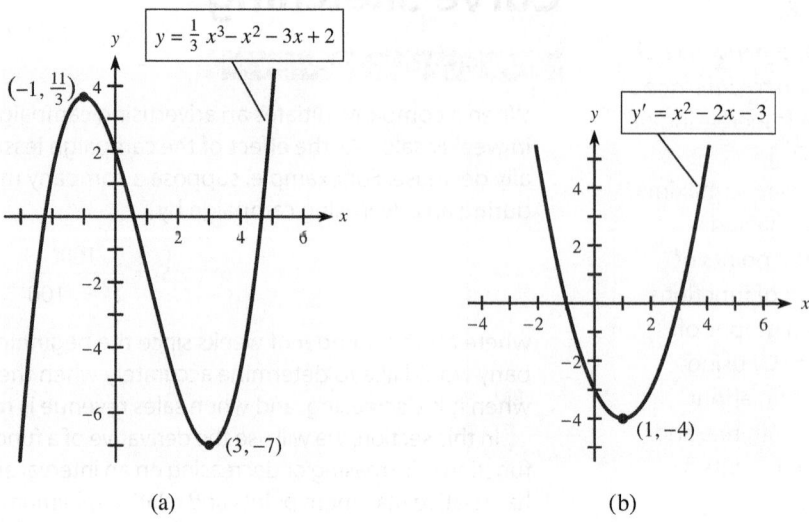

Figure 10.1   (a)   (b)

Increasing and Decreasing Functions

Let f be a function that is differentiable on an interval (a, b).

If $f'(x) > 0$ for all x in (a, b), then f is increasing on (a, b).

If $f'(x) < 0$ for all x in (a, b), then f is decreasing on (a, b).

Figure 10.1(a) shows the graph of a function, and Figure 10.1(b) shows the graph of its derivative. The figures show that the graph of $y = f(x)$ is increasing for the same x-values for which the graph of $y' = f'(x)$ is above the x-axis [when $f'(x) > 0$]. Similarly, the graph of $y = f(x)$ is decreasing for the same x-values ($-1 < x < 3$) for which the graph of $y' = f'(x)$ is below the x-axis [when $f'(x) < 0$].

The derivative $f'(x)$ can change signs only at values of x at which $f'(x) = 0$ or $f'(x)$ is undefined. We call these values of x **critical values**. The point corresponding to a critical value for x is a **critical point**.* Because a curve changes from increasing to decreasing at a relative maximum and from decreasing to increasing at a relative minimum [see Figure 10.1(a)], we have the following.

Relative Maximum and Minimum

If f has a relative maximum or a relative minimum at $x = x_0$, then $f'(x_0) = 0$ or $f'(x_0)$ is undefined.

Figure 10.2 shows a function with two relative maxima, one at $x = x_1$ and the second at $x = x_3$, and one relative minimum at $x = x_2$. At $x = x_1$ and $x = x_2$, we see that $f'(x) = 0$, and at $x = x_3$ the derivative does not exist.

Figure 10.2

*There may be some critical values at which both $f'(x)$ and $f(x)$ are undefined. Critical points do not occur at these values, but studying the derivative on either side of such values may be of interest.

Thus we can find relative maxima and minima for a curve by finding values of x for which the function has critical points. The behavior of the derivative to the left and right of (and near) these points will tell us whether they are relative maxima, relative minima, or neither.

Because the critical values are the only values at which the graph can have turning points, the derivative cannot change sign anywhere except at a critical value. Thus, in an interval between two critical values, the sign of the derivative at any value in the interval will be the sign of the derivative at all values in the interval.

Using the critical values of $f(x)$ and the sign of $f'(x)$ between those critical values, we can create a **sign diagram for $f'(x)$**. The sign diagram for the graph in Figure 10.2 is shown in Figure 10.3. This sign diagram was created from the graph of f, but it is also possible to predict the shape of a graph from a sign diagram.

Direction of graph of $f(x)$:

signs and values of $f'(x)$:

x-axis with critical values:

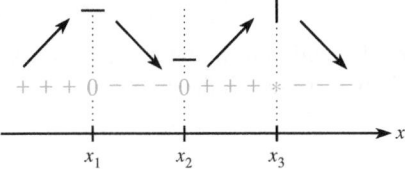

Figure 10.3   *means that $f'(x_3)$ is undefined

Figure 10.4 shows two ways that a function can have a relative maximum at a critical point, and Figure 10.5 shows two ways for a relative minimum.

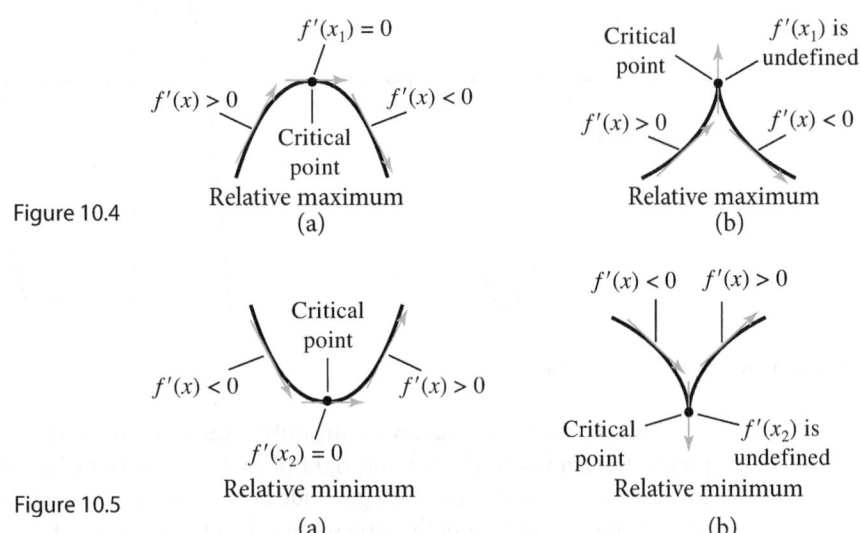

Figure 10.4

Figure 10.5

The preceding discussion suggests the following procedure for finding relative maxima and minima of a function.

FIRST-DERIVATIVE TEST

Procedure	Example
To find relative maxima and minima of a function:	Find the relative maxima and minima of $f(x) = \frac{1}{3}x^3 - x^2 - 3x + 2$.
1. Find the first derivative of the function.	1. $f'(x) = x^2 - 2x - 3$
2. Set the derivative equal to 0 and solve for values of x that satisfy $f'(x) = 0$. These are called **critical values.** Values that make $f'(x)$ undefined are also critical values.	2. $0 = x^2 - 2x - 3 = (x + 1)(x - 3)$ has solutions $x = -1, x = 3$. No values of x make $f'(x) = x^2 - 2x - 3$ undefined. Critical values are -1 and 3.

(Continued)

3. Substitute the critical values into the *original function* to find the **critical points**.

3. $f(-1) = \frac{11}{3}$ $f(3) = -7$
   The critical points are $(-1, \frac{11}{3})$ and $(3, -7)$.

4. Evaluate $f'(x)$ at a value of x to the left and one to the right of each critical point to develop a sign diagram.
   (a) If $f'(x) > 0$ to the left and $f'(x) < 0$ to the right of the critical value, the critical point is a relative maximum point.
   (b) If $f'(x) < 0$ to the left and $f'(x) > 0$ to the right of the critical value, the critical point is a relative minimum point.

4. $f'(-2) = 5 > 0$ and $f'(0) = -3 < 0$
   Thus $(-1, 11/3)$ is a relative maximum point.
   $f'(2) = -3 < 0$ and $f'(4) = 5 > 0$
   Thus $(3, -7)$ is a relative minimum point. The sign diagram for $f'(x)$ is

5. Use the information from the sign diagram and selected points to sketch the graph.

5. The information from this sign diagram is shown in Figure 10.6(a). Plotting additional points gives the graph of the function, which is shown in Figure 10.6(b).

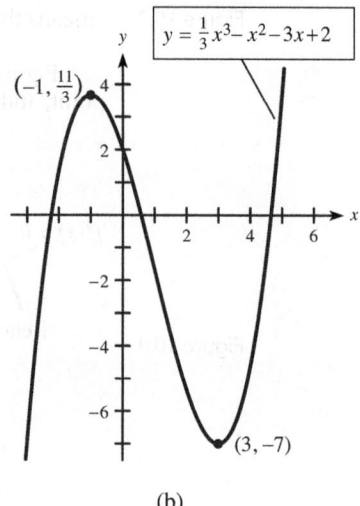

Figure 10.6   (a)   (b)

Because the critical values are the only x-values at which the graph can have turning points, we can test to the left and right of each critical value by testing to the left of the smallest critical value, then testing a value *between* each two successive critical values, and then testing to the right of the largest critical value. The following example illustrates this procedure.

EXAMPLE 1   Maxima and Minima

Find the relative maxima and minima of $f(x) = \frac{1}{4}x^4 - \frac{1}{3}x^3 - 3x^2 + 8$, and sketch its graph.

Solution

1. $f'(x) = x^3 - x^2 - 6x$
2. Setting $f'(x) = 0$ gives $0 = x^3 - x^2 - 6x$. Solving for x gives

$$0 = x(x - 3)(x + 2)$$

$x = 0$	$x - 3 = 0$	$x + 2 = 0$
	$x = 3$	$x = -2$

Thus the critical values are $x = 0$, $x = 3$, and $x = -2$.

3. Substituting the critical values into the original function gives the critical points:

$$f(-2) = \tfrac{8}{3}, \quad \text{so } \left(-2, \tfrac{8}{3}\right) \text{ is a critical point.}$$
$$f(0) = 8, \quad \text{so } (0, 8) \text{ is a critical point.}$$
$$f(3) = -\tfrac{31}{4}, \quad \text{so } \left(3, -\tfrac{31}{4}\right) \text{ is a critical point.}$$

4. Testing $f'(x)$ to the left of the smallest critical value, then between the critical values, and finally to the right of the largest critical value will give the sign diagram. Evaluating $f'(x)$ at the test values $x = -3$, $x = -1$, $x = 1$, and $x = 4$ gives the signs to determine relative maxima and minima.

   The sign diagram for $f'(x)$ is

   Thus we have

   $\left(-2, \tfrac{8}{3}\right)$ is a relative minimum.

   $(0, 8)$ is a relative maximum.

   $\left(3, -\tfrac{31}{4}\right)$ is a relative minimum.

5. Figure 10.7(a) shows the graph of the function near the critical points, and Figure 10.7(b) shows the graph of the function.

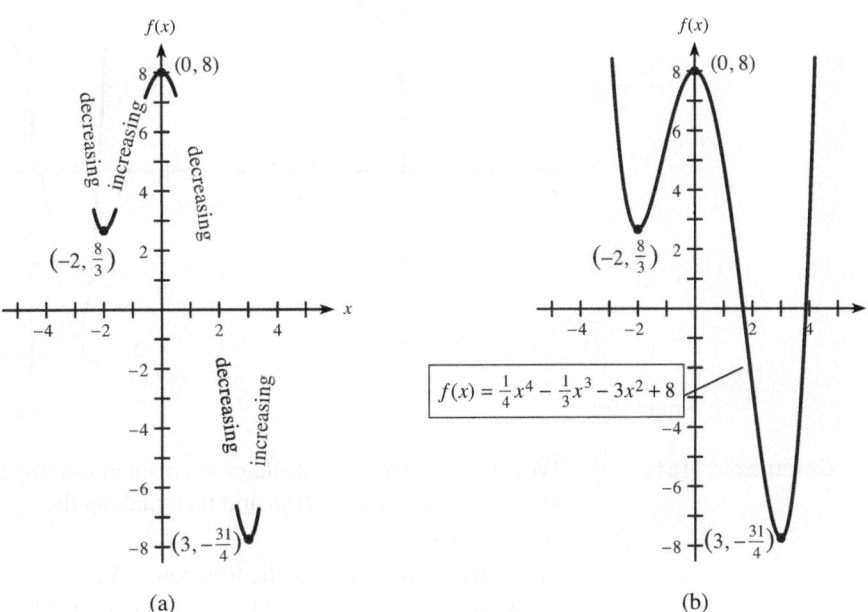

Figure 10.7

(a)

(b)

$$f(x) = \tfrac{1}{4}x^4 - \tfrac{1}{3}x^3 - 3x^2 + 8$$

Note that we substitute the critical values into the *original function* $f(x)$ to find the y-values of the critical points, but we test for relative maxima and minima by substituting values near the critical values into the *derivative of the function*, $f'(x)$.

Only four values were needed to test three critical points in Example 1. This method will work *only if* the critical values are tested in order from smallest to largest.

If the first derivative of f is 0 at x_0 but does not change from positive to negative or from negative to positive as x passes through x_0, then the critical point at x_0 is neither a relative maximum nor a relative minimum. In this case, we say that f has a **horizontal point of inflection** (abbreviated HPI) at x_0.

EXAMPLE 2   **Maxima, Minima, and Horizontal Points of Inflection**

Find the relative maxima, relative minima, and horizontal points of inflection of $h(x) = \frac{1}{4}x^4 - \frac{2}{3}x^3 - 2x^2 + 8x + 4$, and sketch its graph.

Solution

1. $h'(x) = x^3 - 2x^2 - 4x + 8$
2. $0 = x^3 - 2x^2 - 4x + 8$ or $0 = x^2(x-2) - 4(x-2)$. Therefore, we have $0 = (x-2)(x^2-4)$. Thus $x = -2$ and $x = 2$ are solutions.
3. The critical points are $\left(-2, -\frac{32}{3}\right)$ and $\left(2, \frac{32}{3}\right)$.
4. Using test values such as $x = -3$, $x = 0$, and $x = 3$ gives the sign diagram for $h'(x)$.

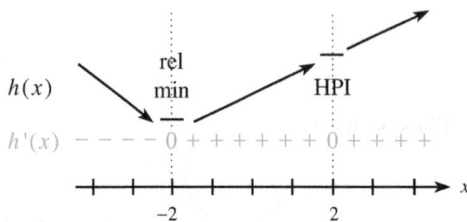

5. Figure 10.8(a) shows the graph of the function near the critical points, and Figure 10.8(b) shows the graph of the function.

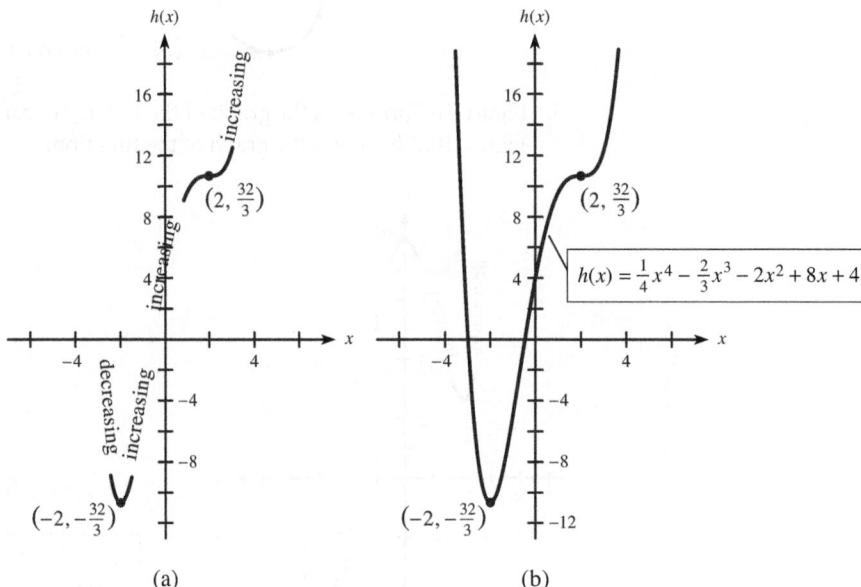

Figure 10.8   (a)   (b)

Calculator Note   We can use a graphing calculator as an aid in locating the x-values where $f'(x) = 0$, which are the critical values of $f(x)$, and then making the sign diagram used to classify these critical values, as follows.

1. Enter the derivative of the function in Y_1.
2. Graph Y_1 and use ZERO to determine the x-values where $Y_1 = 0$; this gives the critical values.
3. Use TABLE to evaluate the derivative to the left and right of each critical value. This creates a sign diagram for $f'(x)$ which can be used to determine whether each critical value is a relative maximum, a relative minimum, or neither.
4. Enter the function in Y_2 and use TABLE to evaluate the function at each critical value to find the y-coordinates of the critical points.

Figure 10.9 on the next page illustrates steps (2) and (3) above for $f(x) = \dfrac{1}{3}x^3 - 4x$,

which has derivative $f'(x) = x^2 - 4$. See Appendix A, Section 10.1, for details.

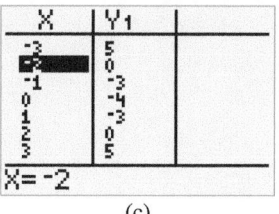

Figure 10.9   (a)   (b)   (c)

Spreadsheet Note   Excel can be used to find the relative maxima and relative miinima of a function. For the function $f(x) = \dfrac{x^3}{3} - 4x$, we can use *GoalSeek*, found under *Data>What-If-Analysis>Goal Seek*, to find that $f'(x) = x^2 - 4 = 0$ has solutions $x = -2$ and $x = 2$.

We can then test values of $f'(x) = x^2 - 4$ near the critical values $x = -2$ and $x = 2$ to determine relative maxima and relative minima. The following spreadsheet shows that the relative maximum is at $(-2, \frac{16}{3})$ and the relative minimum is at $(2, -\frac{16}{3})$. For more details, see Appendix B, Section 10.1, or the Online Excel Guide.

	A	B	C
1	x	f(x)=x^3/3–4x	f'(x)=x^2–4
2	−4	-5.333333333	12
3	−3	3	5
4	−2	5.333333333	0
5	−1	3.666666667	-3
6	0	0	-4
7	1	-3.666666667	-3
8	2	-5.333333333	0
9	3	-3	5
10	4	5.333333333	12

EXAMPLE 3   **Undefined Derivatives**

Find the relative maxima and minima (if any) of the graph of $y = (x + 2)^{2/3}$.

Solution

1. $y' = f'(x) = \dfrac{2}{3}(x + 2)^{-1/3} = \dfrac{2}{3\sqrt[3]{x + 2}}$

2. $0 = \dfrac{2}{3\sqrt[3]{x + 2}}$ has no solutions; $f'(x)$ is undefined at $x = -2$.

3. $f(-2) = 0$, so the critical point is $(-2, 0)$.

4. The sign diagram for $f'(x)$ is

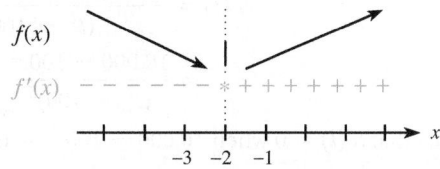

*means that $f'(-2)$ is undefined.

Thus a relative minimum occurs at $(-2, 0)$.

5. Figure 10.10(a) shows the graph of the function near the critical points, and Figure 10.10(b) shows the graph of the function.

y

4

decreasing $\quad$ increasing

2

x

-6 $\quad$ -4 $\quad$ -2 $\quad$ 2 $\quad$ 4

(-2, 0)

(a)

y

$y = (x+2)^{2/3}$

4

2

x

-6 $\quad$ -4 $\quad$ -2 $\quad$ 2 $\quad$ 4

(-2, 0)

(b)

Figure 10.10

CHECKPOINT

1. The x-values of critical points are found where $f'(x)$ is _____ or _____.
2. Decide whether the following are true or false.
   (a) If $f'(1) = 7$, then $f(x)$ is increasing at $x = 1$.
   (b) If $f'(-2) = 0$, then a relative maximum or a relative minimum occurs at $x = -2$.
   (c) If $f'(-3) = 0$ and $f'(x)$ changes from positive on the left to negative on the right of $x = -3$, then a relative minimum occurs at $x = -3$.
3. If $f(x) = 7 + 3x - x^3$, then $f'(x) = 3 - 3x^2$. Use these functions to decide whether the following statements are true or false.
   (a) The only critical value is $x = 1$.
   (b) The critical points are $(1, 0)$ and $(-1, 0)$.
4. If $f'(x)$ has the following partial sign diagram, make a "stick-figure" sketch of $f(x)$ and label where any maxima and minima occur. Assume that $f(x)$ is defined for all real numbers.

   $f'(x) \quad + + + 0 - - - * + + + + + + 0 + + +$

   -1 $\qquad$ 0 $\qquad$ 2 $\qquad$ x

   *means that $f'(0)$ is undefined.

EXAMPLE $\boxed{4}$ **Advertising** | APPLICATION PREVIEW |

The weekly sales S of a product during an advertising campaign are given by

$$S = \frac{100t}{t^2 + 100}, \qquad 0 \le t \le 20$$

where t is the number of weeks since the beginning of the campaign and S is in thousands of dollars.

(a) Over what interval are sales increasing? Decreasing?
(b) What are the maximum weekly sales?
(c) Sketch the graph for $0 \le t \le 20$.

Solution

(a) To find where S is increasing, we first find $S'(t)$.

$$S'(t) = \frac{(t^2 + 100)100 - (100t)2t}{(t^2 + 100)^2}$$

$$= \frac{10,000 - 100t^2}{(t^2 + 100)^2}$$

We see that $S'(t) = 0$ when $10,000 - 100t^2 = 0$, or

$$100(100 - t^2) = 0$$
$$100(10 + t)(10 - t) = 0$$
$$t = -10 \quad \text{or} \quad t = 10$$

Because $S'(t)$ is never undefined ($t^2 + 100 \neq 0$ for any real t) and because $0 \leq t \leq 20$, our only critical value is $t = 10$. Testing $S'(t)$ to the left and right of $t = 10$ gives the sign diagram.

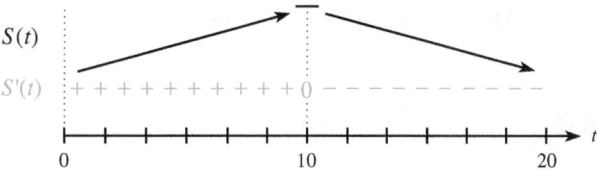

Hence, S is increasing on the interval $[0, 10)$ and decreasing on the interval $(10, 20]$.

(b) Because S is increasing to the left of $t = 10$ and S is decreasing to the right of $t = 10$, the maximum value of S occurs at $t = 10$ and is

$$S = S(10) = \frac{100(10)}{10^2 + 100} = \frac{1000}{200} = 5 \text{ (thousand dollars)}$$

(c) Plotting some additional points gives the graph; see Figure 10.11.

Figure 10.11

Calculator Note With a graphing calculator, choosing an appropriate viewing window is the key to understanding the graph of a function. To find an appropriate window, set the x-min of the window to the left of the smallest critical value and the x-max to the right of the largest critical value, and set the y-min and y-max to contain the y-coordinates of the critical points. See Example 5 and Appendix A, Section 10.1, for details.

   EXAMPLE   5   **Critical Points and Viewing Windows**

Find the critical values of $f(x) = 0.0001x^3 + 0.003x^2 - 3.6x + 5$. Use them to determine an appropriate viewing window. Then sketch the graph.

Solution

The critical points are helpful in graphing the function. We begin by finding $f'(x)$.

$$f'(x) = 0.0003x^2 + 0.006x - 3.6$$

Now we solve $f'(x) = 0$ to find the critical values.

$$0 = 0.0003x^2 + 0.006x - 3.6$$
$$0 = 0.0003(x^2 + 20x - 12,000)$$
$$0 = 0.0003(x + 120)(x - 100)$$
$$x = -120 \quad \text{or} \quad x = 100$$

We choose a window that includes $x = -120$ and $x = 100$ and use TABLE to find $f(-120) = 307.4$ and $f(100) = -225$. We then graph $y = f(x)$ in a window that includes $y = -225$ and $y = 307.4$. (See Figure 10.12.) On this graph, we can see that $(-120, 307.4)$ is a relative maximum and that $(100, -225)$ is a relative minimum.

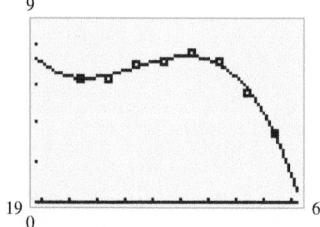

Figure 10.12

EXAMPLE 6 **Aging workers**

The table shows the millions of Americans who are working full-time at selected ages from 27 to 62.

(a) Find a cubic model that gives the number of Americans working full-time, y (in millions), as a function of their age, x. Report the model with three significant digits in the coefficients.

(b) Find the relative maximum and minimum of the reported function.

Age	Millions Working Full-Time	Age	Millions Working Full-Time
27	6.30	47	7.52
32	6.33	52	7.10
37	6.96	57	5.58
42	7.07	62	3.54

Source: Wall Street Journal

Figure 10.13

Solution

(a) A cubic function that models these data is

$$f(x) = -0.000362x^3 + 0.0401x^2 - 1.39x + 21.7$$

Figure 10.13 shows a graph of the model with the data.

(b) We use $f'(x) = -0.001086x^2 + 0.0802x - 1.39$ and solve $f'(x) = 0$ to find the critical values. We can solve

$$-0.001086x^2 + 0.0802x - 1.39 = 0$$

with the quadratic formula or with a graphing calculator. The two solutions are approximately

$$x = 27.8 \quad \text{and} \quad x = 46.1$$

The sign diagram shows that $x = 27.8$ gives a relative minimum and $x = 46.1$ gives a relative maximum.

Thus the model indicates a relative minimum of $f(27.8) \approx 6.3$ (million) full-time workers at age 27.8 and a relative maximum of $f(46.1) \approx 7.4$ (million) full-time workers at age 46.1.

Spreadsheet Note Excel can be used to create sign diagrams that determine the maxima and minima of functions. Details are given in Appendix B, Section 10.1, and the Online Excel Guide.

CHECKPOINT
ANSWERS

1. $f'(x) = 0$ or $f'(x)$ is undefined.
2. (a) True. $f(x)$ is increasing when $f'(x) > 0$.
   (b) False. See Figure 10.8.
   (c) False. A relative maximum occurs at $x = -3$.
3. (a) False. Critical values are $x = 1$ and $x = -1$.
   (b) False. Critical points are $(1, 9)$ and $(-1, 5)$.
4.

EXERCISES 10.1

In Problems 1 and 2, use the indicated points on the graph of $y = f(x)$ to identify points at which $f(x)$ has (a) a relative maximum, (b) a relative minimum, and (c) a horizontal point of inflection.

1.

2.

3. Use the graph of $y = f(x)$ in Problem 1 to identify at which of the indicated points the derivative $f'(x)$ (a) changes from positive to negative, (b) changes from negative to positive, and (c) does not change sign.

4. Use the graph of $y = f(x)$ in Problem 2 to identify at which of the indicated points the derivative $f'(x)$ (a) changes from positive to negative, (b) changes from negative to positive, and (c) does not change sign.

In Problems 5 and 6, use the sign diagram for $f'(x)$ to determine (a) the critical values of $f(x)$, (b) intervals on which $f(x)$ increases, (c) intervals on which $f(x)$ decreases, (d) x-values at which relative maxima occur, and (e) x-values at which relative minima occur.

5. $f'(x)$ $\quad - - - 0 + + + + + 0 - - -$

   $\qquad\qquad\quad 3 \qquad\quad 7$

6. $f'(x)$ $\quad + + + + 0 + + + + + + 0 - - - -$

   $\qquad\qquad -5 \qquad\quad 8$

In Problems 7–10, (a) find the critical values of the function and (b) make a sign diagram and determine the relative maxima and minima.

7. $y = 2x^3 - 12x^2 + 6$ 8. $y = x^3 - 3x^2 + 6x + 1$
9. $y = 2x^5 + 5x^4 - 11$ 10. $y = 15x^3 - x^5 + 7$

For each function and graph in Problems 11–14
(a) estimate the coordinates of the relative maxima, relative minima, or horizontal points of inflection by observing the graph.
(b) use $y' = f'(x)$ to find the critical values.
(c) find the critical points.
(d) Do the results in part (c) confirm your estimates in part (a)?

11. $y = x^3 - 3x + 4$ 12. $y = x - \frac{1}{3}x^3$

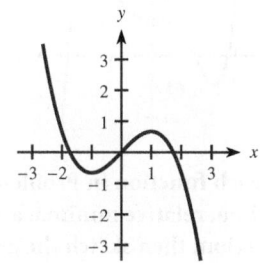

13. $y = x^3 + 3x^2 + 3x - 2$ 14. $y = x^3 - 6x^2 + 12x + 1$

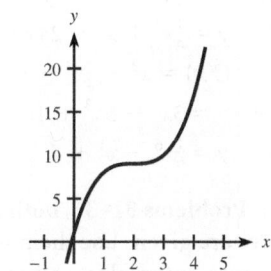

For each function in Problems 15–20
(a) find $y' = f'(x)$.
(b) find the critical values.
(c) find the critical points.
(d) find intervals of x-values where the function is increasing and where it is decreasing.
(e) classify the critical points as relative maxima, relative minima, or horizontal points of inflection. In each case, check your conclusions with a graphing calculator.

15. $y = \frac{1}{2}x^2 - x$

16. $y = x^2 + 4x$

17. $y = \frac{x^3}{3} + \frac{x^2}{2} - 2x + 1$

18. $y = \frac{x^4}{4} - \frac{x^3}{3} - 2$

19. $y = x^{2/3}$

20. $y = -(x - 3)^{2/3}$

For each function and graph in Problems 21–24
(a) use the graph to identify x-values for which $y' > 0$, $y' < 0$, $y' = 0$, and y' does not exist.
(b) use the derivative to check your conclusions.

21. $y = 6 - x - x^2$

22. $y = \frac{1}{2}x^2 - 4x + 1$

23. $y = 6 + x^3 - \frac{1}{15}x^5$

24. $y = x^4 - 2x^2 - 1$

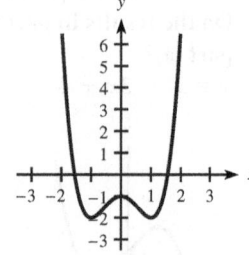

For each function in Problems 25–30, find the relative maxima, relative minima, and horizontal points of inflection; then sketch the graph. Check your graph with a graphing utility.

25. $y = \frac{1}{3}x^3 - x^2 + x + 1$

26. $y = \frac{1}{4}x^4 - \frac{2}{3}x^3 + \frac{1}{2}x^2 - 2$

27. $y = \frac{1}{3}x^3 + x^2 - 24x + 20$

28. $C(x) = x^3 - \frac{3}{2}x^2 - 18x + 5$

29. $y = 3x^5 - 5x^3 + 1$

30. $y = \frac{1}{6}x^6 - x^4 + 7$

In Problems 31–36, both a function and its derivative are given. Use them to find critical values, critical points, intervals on which the function is increasing and decreasing, relative maxima, relative minima, and horizontal points of inflection; sketch the graph of each function.

31. $y = (x^2 - 2x)^2$ $\qquad \frac{dy}{dx} = 4x(x - 1)(x - 2)$

32. $f(x) = (x^2 - 4)^2$ $\qquad f'(x) = 4x(x + 2)(x - 2)$

33. $y = \frac{x^3(x - 5)^2}{27}$ $\qquad \frac{dy}{dx} = \frac{5x^2(x - 3)(x - 5)}{27}$

34. $y = \frac{x^2(x - 5)^3}{27}$ $\qquad \frac{dy}{dx} = \frac{5x(x - 2)(x - 5)^2}{27}$

35. $f(x) = x^{2/3}(x - 5)$ $\qquad f'(x) = \frac{5(x - 2)}{3x^{1/3}}$

36. $f(x) = x - 3x^{2/3}$ $\qquad f'(x) = \frac{x^{1/3} - 2}{x^{1/3}}$

In Problems 37–42, use the derivative to locate critical points and determine a viewing window that shows all features of the graph. Use a graphing calculator to sketch a complete graph.

37. $f(x) = x^3 - 225x^2 + 15{,}000x - 12{,}000$

38. $f(x) = x^3 - 15x^2 - 16{,}800x + 80{,}000$

39. $f(x) = x^4 - 160x^3 + 7200x^2 - 40{,}000$

40. $f(x) = x^4 - 240x^3 + 16{,}200x^2 - 60{,}000$

41. $y = 7.5x^4 - x^3 + 2$

42. $y = 7 + 3x^5 - 5x^6$

In each of Problems 43–46, a graph of $f'(x)$ is given. Use the graph to determine the critical values of $f(x)$, where $f(x)$ is increasing, where it is decreasing, and where it has relative maxima, relative minima, and horizontal points of inflection. In each case, sketch a possible graph for $f(x)$ that passes through $(0, 0)$.

43. $f'(x) = x^2 - x - 2$ 44. $\qquad f'(x) = 4x - x^2$

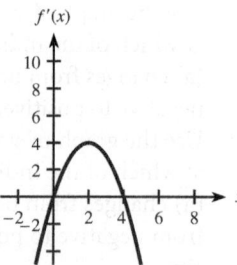

45. $f'(x) = x^3 - 3x^2$ 46. $\qquad f'(x) = x(x - 2)^2$

In Problems 47 and 48, two graphs are given. One is the graph of f, and the other is the graph of f'. Decide which is which and explain your reasoning.

47.

48.

 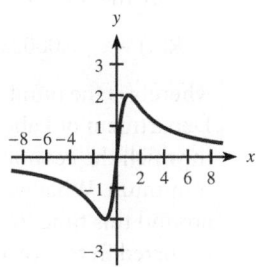

APPLICATIONS

49. *Advertising and sales* Suppose that the daily sales (in dollars) t days after the end of an advertising campaign are given by

$$S = 1000 + \frac{400}{t + 1}, \quad t \geq 0$$

Does S increase for all $t \geq 0$, decrease for all $t \geq 0$, or change direction at some point?

50. *Pricing and sales* Suppose that a chain of auto service stations, Quick-Oil, Inc., has found that its monthly sales volume y (in thousands of dollars) is related to the price p (in dollars) of an oil change by

$$y = \frac{90}{\sqrt{p + 5}}, \quad p > 10$$

Is y increasing or decreasing for all values of $p > 10$?

51. *Productivity* A time study showed that, on average, the productivity of a worker after t hours on the job can be modeled by

$$P(t) = 27t + 6t^2 - t^3, \quad 0 \leq t \leq 8$$

where P is the number of units produced per hour.
(a) Find the critical values of this function.
(b) Which critical value makes sense in this model?
(c) For what values of t is P increasing?
(d) Graph the function for $0 \leq t \leq 8$.

52. *Production* Analysis of daily output of a factory shows that, on average, the number of units per hour y produced after t hours of production is

$$y = 70t + 0.5t^2 - t^3, \quad 0 \leq t \leq 8$$

(a) Find the critical values of this function.
(b) Which critical values make sense in this particular problem?
(c) For which values of t, for $0 \leq t \leq 8$, is y increasing?
(d) Graph this function.

53. *Production costs* Suppose that the average cost, in dollars, of producing a shipment of a certain product is

$$\overline{C} = 5000x + \frac{125,000}{x}, \quad x > 0$$

where x is the number of machines used in the production process.
(a) Find the critical values of this function.
(b) Over what interval does the average cost decrease?
(c) Over what interval does the average cost increase?

54. *Average costs* Suppose the average costs of a mining operation depend on the number of machines used and average costs, in dollars, are given by

$$\overline{C}(x) = 2900x + \frac{1,278,900}{x}, \quad x > 0$$

where x is the number of machines used.
(a) Find the critical values of $\overline{C}(x)$ that lie in the domain of the problem.
(b) Over what interval in the domain do average costs decrease?
(c) Over what interval in the domain do average costs increase?
(d) How many machines give minimum average costs?
(e) What is the minimum average cost?

55. *Marginal revenue* Suppose the weekly marginal revenue function for selling x units of a product is given by the graph in the figure.

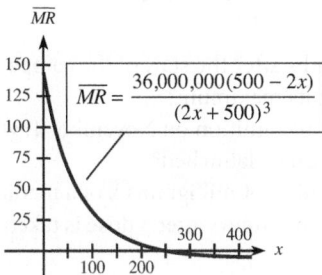

(a) At each of $x = 150$, $x = 250$, and $x = 350$, what is happening to revenue?
(b) Over what interval is revenue increasing?
(c) How many units must be sold to maximize revenue?

56. *Earnings* Suppose that the rate of change $f'(x)$ of the average annual earnings of new car salespersons is shown in the figure.

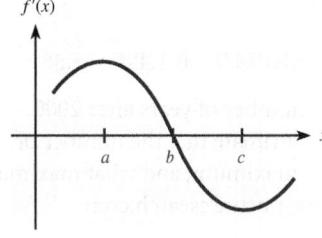

(a) If a, b, and c represent certain years, what is happening to $f(x)$, the average annual earnings of the salespersons, at a, b, and c?

(b) Over what interval (involving a, b, or c) is there an increase in $f(x)$, the average annual earnings of the salespersons?

57. *Revenue* The weekly revenue of a certain recently released film is given by

$$R(t) = \frac{50t}{t^2 + 36}, \quad t \geq 0$$

where R is in millions of dollars and t is in weeks.

(a) Find the critical values.

(b) For how many weeks will weekly revenue increase?

58. *Medication* Suppose that the concentration C of a medication in the bloodstream t hours after an injection is given by

$$C(t) = \frac{0.2t}{t^2 + 1}$$

(a) Determine the number of hours before C attains its maximum.

(b) Find the maximum concentration.

59. *Candidate recognition* Suppose that the proportion P of voters who recognize a candidate's name t months after the start of the campaign is given by

$$P(t) = \frac{13t}{t^2 + 100} + 0.18$$

(a) How many months after the start of the campaign is recognition at its maximum?

(b) To have greatest recognition on November 1, when should a campaign be launched?

60. *Medication* The number of milligrams x of a medication in the bloodstream t hours after a dose is taken can be modeled by

$$x(t) = \frac{2000t}{t^2 + 16}$$

(a) For what t-values is x increasing?

(b) Find the t-value at which x is maximum.

(c) Find the maximum value of x.

61. *Worldwide cell phone subscriberships* In 2013, worldwide cell phone subscriberships surpassed the world's total population of 6.8 billion. Using data from 2009 and projected to 2020, the billions of subscriberships can be modeled by

$$C(t) = 0.000286t^3 - 0.0443t^2 + 1.49t - 5.36$$

where t is equal to the number of years after 2000. When does this model estimate that the number of subscribers reached its maximum, and what maximum does it estimate? *Source:* portioresearch.com

62. *Economic dependency ratio* The economic dependency ratio is defined as the number of persons in the total population who are not in the workforce per 100 in the workforce. Since 1960, baby boomers in the workforce and a decrease in the birth rate have caused a significant decrease in the economic dependency ratio. With data for selected years from 1960 and projected to 2050, the economic dependency ratio R can be modeled by the function

$$R(x) = 0.0002x^3 + 0.052x^2 - 1.06x + 192$$

where x is the number of years past 1950 (*Source:* U.S. Department of Labor). Use this model to find the year in which the economic dependency ratio reached its minimum. What was happening in the United States around this time that helps explain why the minimum occurred in this year?

63. *Modeling China's labor pool* The following table shows the millions of individuals, ages 15–59, in China's labor pool for selected years from 1975 and projected to 2050.

(a) Find the cubic function $L(t)$ that best models the size of this labor pool, where t is the number of years after 1970. Report the model with three significant digit coefficients.

(b) Use the reported model to estimate the maximum size of this labor pool before it begins to shrink and the year when the maximum occurs.

Year	Labor Pool (millions)	Year	Labor Pool (millions)
1975	490	2015	920
1980	560	2020	920
1985	650	2025	905
1990	730	2030	875
1995	760	2035	830
2000	800	2040	820
2005	875	2045	800
2010	910	2050	670

Source: United Nations

64. *Modeling Energy from crude oil* The table shows the total energy supply from crude oil products, in quadrillion BTUs, for selected years from 2010 and projected to 2040.

(a) Find the cubic function that is the best model for the data. Use x as the number of years after 2010 and $C(x)$ as the quadrillion BTUs of energy from crude oil products. Report the model with three significant digit coefficients.

(b) Find the critical values of the reported model.

(c) Find the reported model's critical points and classify them.

(d) Do you think this model will be valid for years past 2040? Explain.

Total Energy Supply from Crude Oil Products (in quadrillion BTUs)

Year	BTUs	Year	BTUs
2010	11.6	2030	13.5
2015	15.6	2035	13.4
2020	16.0	2040	13.1
2025	14.5		

Source: U.S. Energy Information Administration

65. **Modeling** *Employment in manufacturing* The table shows the total employment in U.S. manufacturing, in millions, for selected years from 2010 and projected to 2040.
    (a) Find the cubic function that is the best model for the data. Use *t* as the number of years after 2010

and $M(t)$ as the millions employed in U.S. manufacturing. Report the model with three significant digit coefficients.

(b) Find the reported model's critical points and classify them.

(c) Do you think this model will be accurate for years between the critical points? Explain.

U.S. Employment in Manufacturing (in millions)

Year	Employment	Year	Employment
2010	11.5	2030	12.5
2015	12.4	2035	11.8
2020	12.8	2040	11.0
2025	12.9		

Source: U.S. Department of Energy

SECTION 10.2 Concavity; Points of Inflection

OBJECTIVES

- To determine the concavity of the graph of a function at a point
- To find points of inflection of graphs of functions
- To use the second-derivative test to graph functions

APPLICATION PREVIEW

Suppose that a retailer wants to sell his store and uses the graph in Figure 10.14 to show how profits have increased since he opened the store and the potential for profit in the future. Can we conclude that profits will continue to grow, or should we be concerned about future earnings?

Note that although profits are still increasing in 2020, they seem to be increasing more slowly than in previous years. Indeed, they appear to have been growing at a decreasing rate since about 2018. We can analyze this situation more carefully by identifying the point at which profit begins to grow more slowly—that is, the *point of diminishing returns*. (See Example 3.)

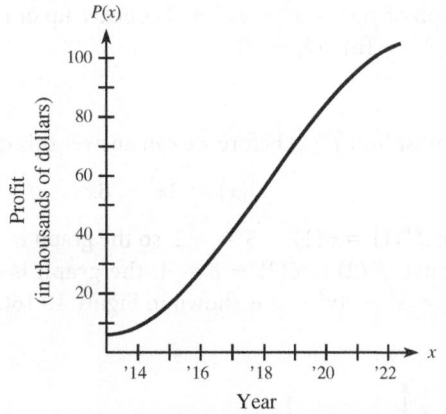

Figure 10.14

Just as we used the first derivative to determine whether a curve was increasing or decreasing on a given interval, we can use the second derivative to determine whether the curve is concave up or concave down on an interval.

Concavity

A curve is said to be **concave up** on an interval (a, b) if at each point on the interval the curve is above its tangent at the point. [See Figure 10.15(a).] If the curve is below all its tangents on a given interval, it is **concave down** on the interval [Figure 10.15(b)].

Looking at Figure 10.15(a), we see that the *slopes* of the tangent lines increase over the interval where the graph is concave up. Because $f'(x)$ gives the slopes of those tangents, it follows that $f'(x)$ is increasing over the interval where $f(x)$ is concave up. However, we know that $f'(x)$ is increasing when its derivative, $f''(x)$, is positive. That is, if the second derivative is positive, the curve is concave up.

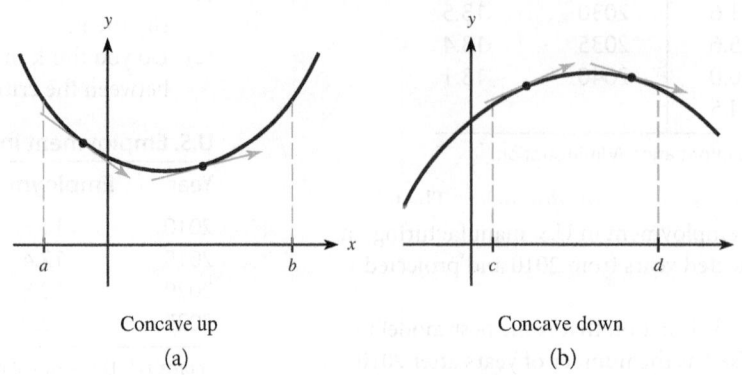

Concave up	Concave down
(a)	(b)

Figure 10.15

Similarly, if the second derivative of a function is negative over an interval, the slopes of the tangents to the graph decrease over that interval. This happens when the tangent lines are above the graph, as in Figure 10.15(b), so the graph must be concave down on this interval.

Thus we see that the second derivative can be used to determine the concavity of a curve.

Concave Up and Concave Down

Assume that the first and second derivatives of function f exist.
The function f is **concave up** on an interval I if $f''(x) > 0$ on I and **concave up** at the point $(a, f(a))$ if $f''(a) > 0$.
The function f is **concave down** on an interval I if $f''(x) < 0$ on I and **concave down** at the point $(a, f(a))$ if $f''(a) < 0$.

EXAMPLE | 1 | **Concavity at a Point**

Is the graph of $f(x) = x^3 - 4x^2 + 3$ concave up or down at the point
(a) $(1, 0)$?   (b) $(2, -5)$?

Solution
(a) We must find $f''(x)$ before we can answer this question.

$$f'(x) = 3x^2 - 8x \qquad f''(x) = 6x - 8$$

Then $f''(1) = 6(1) - 8 = -2$, so the graph is concave down at $(1, 0)$.
(b) Because $f''(2) = 6(2) - 8 = 4$, the graph is concave up at $(2, -5)$. The graph of $f(x) = x^3 - 4x^2 + 3$ is shown in Figure 10.16(a).

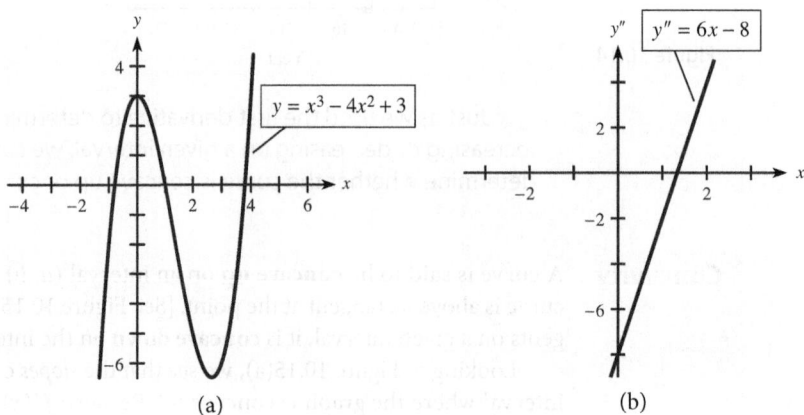

Figure 10.16   (a)   (b)

Points of Inflection Looking at the graph of $y = x^3 - 4x^2 + 3$ [Figure 10.16(a)], we see that the curve is concave down on the left and concave up on the right. Thus it has changed from concave down to concave up, and from Example 1, we would expect the concavity to change somewhere between $x = 1$ and $x = 2$. Figure 10.16(b) shows the graph of $y'' = f''(x) = 6x - 8$, and we can see that $y'' = 0$ when $x = \frac{4}{3}$ and that $y'' < 0$ for $x < \frac{4}{3}$ and $y'' > 0$ for $x > \frac{4}{3}$. Thus the second derivative changes sign at $x = \frac{4}{3}$, so the concavity of the graph of $y = f(x)$ changes at $x = \frac{4}{3}$, $y = -\frac{47}{27}$. The point where concavity changes is called a **point of inflection.**

Point of Inflection A point (x_0, y_0) on the graph of a function f is called a **point of inflection** if the curve is concave up on one side of the point and concave down on the other side. The second derivative at this point, $f''(x_0)$, will be 0 or undefined.

In general, we can find points of inflection and information about concavity as follows.

FINDING POINTS OF INFLECTION AND CONCAVITY

Procedure	Example
To find the point(s) of inflection of a curve and intervals where it is concave up and where it is concave down:	Find the points of inflection and concavity of the graph of $$y = \frac{x^4}{2} - x^3 + 5.$$
1. Find the second derivative of the function.	1. $y' = f'(x) = 2x^3 - 3x^2$ $y'' = f''(x) = 6x^2 - 6x$
2. Set the second derivative equal to 0 and solve for x. Potential points of inflection occur at these values of x or at values of x where $f(x)$ is defined and $f''(x)$ is undefined.	2. $0 = 6x^2 - 6x = 6x(x - 1)$ has solutions $x = 0, x = 1$. $f''(x)$ is defined everywhere.
3. Find the potential points of inflection.	3. $(0, 5)$ and $\left(1, \frac{9}{2}\right)$ are potential points of inflection.
4. If the second derivative has opposite signs on the two sides of one of these values of x, a point of inflection occurs. The curve is concave up where $f''(x) > 0$ and concave down where $f''(x) < 0$. The changes in the sign of $f''(x)$ correspond to changes in concavity and occur at points of inflection.	4. A **sign diagram for $f''(x)$** is 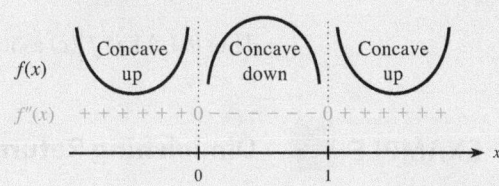 $(0, 5)$ and $\left(1, \frac{9}{2}\right)$ are points of inflection.

See the graph in Figure 10.17.

The graph of $y = \frac{1}{2}x^4 - x^3 + 5$ is shown in Figure 10.17. Note the points of inflection at $(0, 5)$ and $\left(1, \frac{9}{2}\right)$. The point of inflection at $(0, 5)$ is a horizontal point of inflection because $f'(x)$ is also 0 at $x = 0$.

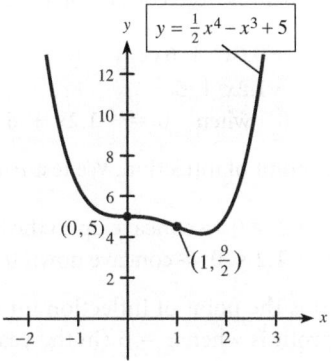

Figure 10.17

EXAMPLE 2 **Water Purity**

Suppose that a real estate developer wants to remove pollution from a small lake so that she can sell lakefront homes on a "crystal clear" lake. The graph in Figure 10.18 shows the relation between dollars spent on cleaning the lake and the purity of the water. The point of inflection on the graph is called the **point of diminishing returns** on her investment because it is where the *rate* of return on her investment changes from increasing to decreasing. Show that the rate of change in the purity of the lake, $f'(x)$, is maximized at this point, $x = c$. Assume that $f(c)$, $f'(c)$, and $f''(c)$ are defined.

Figure 10.18

Solution

Because $x = c$ is a point of inflection for $f(x)$, we know that the concavity must change at $x = c$. From the figure, we see the following.

$$x < c: \quad f(x) \text{ is concave up, so } f''(x) > 0.$$
$$f''(x) > 0 \text{ means that } f'(x) \text{ is increasing.}$$
$$x > c: \quad f(x) \text{ is concave down, so } f''(x) < 0.$$
$$f''(x) < 0 \text{ means that } f'(x) \text{ is decreasing.}$$

Thus $f'(x)$ has $f'(c)$ as its relative maximum.

EXAMPLE 3 **Diminishing Returns** | APPLICATION PREVIEW |

Suppose the annual profit for a store (in thousands of dollars) is given by

$$P(x) = -0.2x^3 + 3x^2 + 6$$

where x is the number of years past 2013. If this model is accurate, find the point of diminishing returns for the profit (where profit begins to grow more slowly).

Solution

The point of diminishing returns occurs at the point of inflection. Thus we seek the point where the graph of this function changes from concave up to concave down, if such a point exists.

$$P'(x) = -0.6x^2 + 6x$$
$$P''(x) = -1.2x + 6$$
$$P''(x) = 0 \quad \text{when} \quad 0 = -1.2x + 6 \quad \text{or} \quad \text{when } x = 5$$

Thus $x = 5$ is a possible point of inflection. We test $P''(x)$ to the left and right of $x = 5$.

$$P''(4) = 1.2 > 0 \Rightarrow \text{concave up to the left of } x = 5$$
$$P''(6) = -1.2 < 0 \Rightarrow \text{concave down to the right of } x = 5$$

Thus $(5, P(5)) = (5, 56)$ is the point of inflection for the graph, and the point of diminishing returns for the profit is when $x = 5$ (in the year 2018) and is $P(5) = 56$ thousand dollars. Figure 10.19 shows the graphs of $P(x)$, $P'(x)$, and $P''(x)$. At $x = 5$, we see that the point of diminishing returns on the graph of $P(x)$ corresponds to the maximum point of the graph of $P'(x)$ and the zero (or x-intercept) of the graph of $P''(x)$.

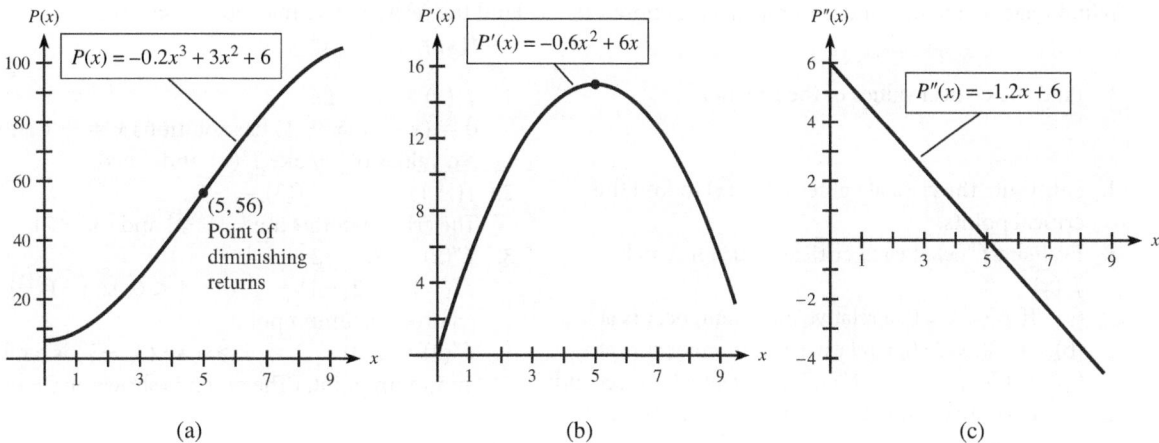

Figure 10.19   (a)   (b)   (c)

CHECKPOINT

1. If $f''(x) > 0$, then $f(x)$ is concave _____.
2. At what value of x does the graph $y = \frac{1}{3}x^3 - 2x^2 + 2x$ have a point of inflection?
3. On the graph below, locate any points of inflection (approximately) and label where the curve satisfies $f''(x) > 0$ and $f''(x) < 0$.

4. Determine whether the following is true or false. If $f''(0) = 0$, then $f(x)$ has a point of inflection at $x = 0$.

Second-Derivative Test   We can use information about points of inflection and concavity to help sketch graphs. For example, if we know that the curve is concave up at a critical point where $f'(x) = 0$, then the point must be a relative minimum because the tangent to the curve is horizontal at the critical point, and only a point at the bottom of a "concave up" curve could have a horizontal tangent. [See Figure 10.20(a).]

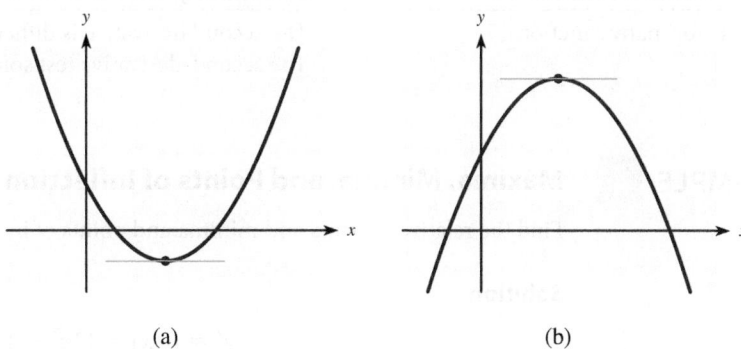

Figure 10.20   (a)   (b)

On the other hand, if the curve is concave down at a critical point where $f'(x) = 0$, then the point is a relative maximum. [See Figure 10.20(b).]

Thus we can use the **second-derivative test** to determine whether a critical point where $f'(x) = 0$ is a relative maximum or minimum.

SECOND-DERIVATIVE TEST

Procedure	Example
To find relative maxima and minima of a function:	Find the relative maxima and minima of $y = f(x) = \frac{1}{3}x^3 - x^2 - 3x + 2$.
1. Find the critical values of the function.	1. $f'(x) = x^2 - 2x - 3$ $0 = (x - 3)(x + 1)$ has solutions $x = -1$ and $x = 3$. No values of x make $f'(x)$ undefined.
2. Substitute the critical values into $f(x)$ to find the critical points.	2. $f(-1) = \frac{11}{3}$ $f(3) = -7$ The critical points are $\left(-1, \frac{11}{3}\right)$ and $(3, -7)$.
3. Evaluate $f''(x)$ at each critical value for which $f'(x) = 0$. (a) If $f''(x_0) < 0$, a relative maximum occurs at x_0. (b) If $f''(x_0) > 0$, a relative minimum occurs at x_0. (c) If $f''(x_0) = 0$, or $f''(x_0)$ is undefined, the second-derivative test fails; use the first-derivative test.	3. $f''(x) = 2x - 2$ $f''(-1) = 2(-1) - 2 = -4 < 0$, so $\left(-1, \frac{11}{3}\right)$ is a relative maximum point. $f''(3) = 2(3) - 2 = 4 > 0$, so $(3, -7)$ is a relative minimum point. (The graph is shown in Figure 10.21.)

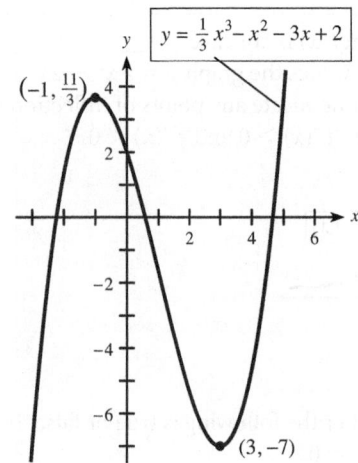

Figure 10.21

Because the second-derivative test (just shown) and the first-derivative test (in Section 10.1) are both methods for classifying critical values, let's compare the advantages and disadvantages of the second-derivative test.

Advantage of the Second-Derivative Test	Disadvantages of the Second-Derivative Test
It is quick and easy for many functions.	The second derivative is difficult to find for some functions. The second-derivative test sometimes fails to give results.

EXAMPLE 4 Maxima, Minima, and Points of Inflection

Find the relative maxima and minima and points of inflection of $y = 3x^4 - 4x^3 - 2$.

Solution

$$y' = f'(x) = 12x^3 - 12x^2$$

Solving $0 = 12x^3 - 12x^2 = 12x^2(x - 1)$ gives $x = 1$ and $x = 0$. Thus the critical points are $(1, -3)$ and $(0, -2)$.

$$y'' = f''(x) = 36x^2 - 24x$$

$f''(1) = 12 > 0 \Rightarrow (1, -3)$ is a relative minimum point.
$f''(0) = 0 \Rightarrow$ the second-derivative test fails.

Because the second-derivative test fails, we must use the first-derivative test at the critical point $(0, -2)$. A sign diagram for $f'(x)$ shows that $(0,-2)$ is a horizontal point of inflection.

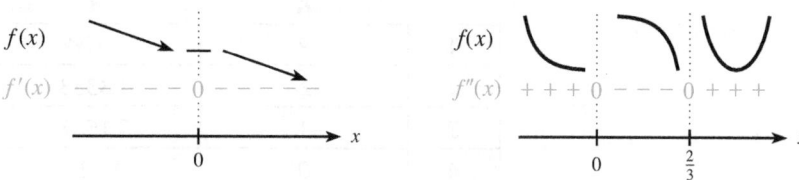

We look for points of inflection by setting $f''(x) = 0$ and solving for x. We find that $0 = 36x^2 - 24x$ has solutions $x = 0$ and $x = \frac{2}{3}$. The sign diagram for $f''(x)$ shows points of inflection at both of these x-values, that is at the points $(0, -2)$ and $\left(\frac{2}{3}, -\frac{70}{27}\right)$. The point $(0, -2)$ is a special point, where the curve changes concavity *and* has a horizontal tangent. (See Figure 10.22.)

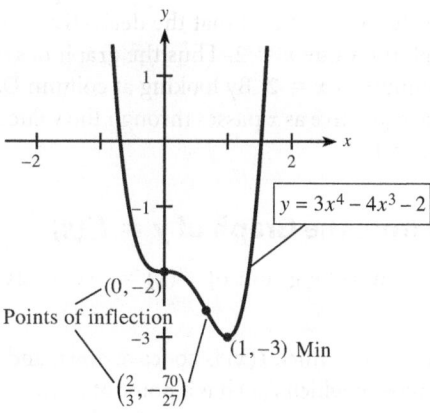

$$y = 3x^4 - 4x^3 - 2$$

$(0,-2)$
Points of inflection
$(1,-3)$ Min
$\left(\frac{2}{3}, -\frac{70}{27}\right)$

Figure 10.22

Calculator Note We can use a graphing calculator to explore the relationships among f, f', and f'', as we did in the previous section for f and f'. See Appendix A, Section 10.2, for details.

EXAMPLE 5 **Concavity from the Graph of $y = f(x)$**

Figure 10.23 shows the graph of $f(x) = \frac{1}{6}(2x^3 - 3x^2 - 12x + 12)$.

(a) From the graph, estimate points where $f''(x) = 0$.
(b) From the graph, observe intervals where $f''(x) > 0$ and where $f''(x) < 0$.
(c) Check the conclusions from parts (a) and (b) by calculating $f''(x)$ and graphing it.

Figure 10.23

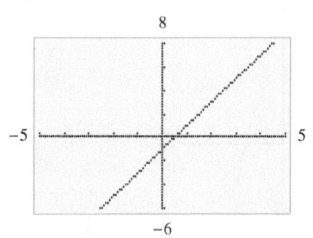

Figure 10.24

Solution

(a) From Figure 10.23, the point of inflection appears to be near $x = \frac{1}{2}$, so we expect $f''(x) = 0$ at (or very near) $x = \frac{1}{2}$.

(b) We see that the graph is concave down [so $f''(x) < 0$] to the left of the point of inflection. That is, $f''(x) < 0$ when $x < \frac{1}{2}$. Similarly, $f''(x) > 0$ when $x > \frac{1}{2}$.

(c) $f(x) = \frac{1}{6}(2x^3 - 3x^2 - 12x + 12)$
$f'(x) = \frac{1}{6}(6x^2 - 6x - 12) = x^2 - x - 2$
$f''(x) = 2x - 1$
Thus $f''(x) = 0$ when $x = \frac{1}{2}$.
Figure 10.24 shows the graph of $f''(x) = 2x - 1$. We see that the graph crosses the x-axis ($f''(x) = 0$) when $x = \frac{1}{2}$ is below the x-axis ($f''(x) < 0$) when $x < \frac{1}{2}$ and is above the x-axis ($f''(x) > 0$) when $x > \frac{1}{2}$. This verifies our conclusions from parts (a) and (b).

Spreadsheet Note

We can investigate the function in Example 5 by using Excel to find the outputs of $f(x) = \frac{1}{6}(2x^3 - 3x^2 - 12x + 12)$, $f'(x)$, and $f''(x)$ for values of x at and near the critical points, including values where $f''(x) = 0$. The following Excel spreadsheet illustrates how we extend the Appendix B, Section 10.1, technique for relative maxima and minima by adding a column for $f''(x)$.

	A	B	C	D
	x	f(x)	f'(x)	f''(x)
1	x	f(x)	f'(x)	f''(x)
2	−2	1.3333	4	−5
3	−1	3.1667	0	−3
4	0	2	−2	−1
5	1/2	0.9167	−2.25	0
6	1	−0.1667	−2	1
7	2	−1.3333	0	3
8	3	0.5	4	5

By looking at column C, we see that $f'(x)$ changes from positive to negative as x passes through the value $x = -1$ and that the derivative changes from negative to positive as x passes through the value $x = 2$. Thus the graph has a relative maximum at $x = -1$ and a relative minimum at $x = 2$. By looking at column D, we can also see that $f''(x)$ changes from negative to positive as x passes through the value $x = 1/2$, so the graph has a point of inflection at $x = 1/2$.

EXAMPLE 6

Concavity from the Graph of $y = f'(x)$

Figure 10.25 shows the graph of $f'(x) = -x^2 - 2x$. Use the graph of $f'(x)$ to do the following.

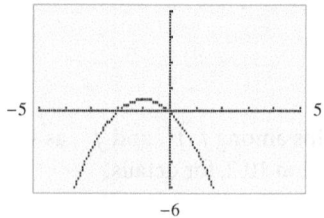

Figure 10.25

(a) Find intervals on which $f(x)$ is concave down and concave up.
(b) Find x-values at which $f(x)$ has a point of inflection.
(c) Check the conclusions from parts (a) and (b) by finding $f''(x)$ and graphing it.
(d) For $f(x) = \frac{1}{3}(9 - x^3 - 3x^2)$, calculate $f'(x)$ to verify that this could be $f(x)$.

Solution

(a) Concavity for $f(x)$ can be found from the sign of $f''(x)$. Because $f''(x)$ is the first derivative of $f'(x)$, wherever the graph of $f'(x)$ is increasing, it follows that $f''(x) > 0$. Thus $f''(x) > 0$ and $f(x)$ is concave up when $x < -1$. Similarly, $f''(x) < 0$, and $f(x)$ is concave down, when $f'(x)$ is decreasing—that is, when $x > -1$.

(b) From (a), we know that $f''(x)$ changes sign at $x = -1$, so $f(x)$ has a point of inflection at $x = -1$. Note that $f'(x)$ has its maximum at the x-value where $f(x)$ has a point of inflection. In fact, points of inflection for $f(x)$ will correspond to relative extrema for $f'(x)$.

(c) For $f'(x) = -x^2 - 2x$, we have $f''(x) = -2x - 2$. Figure 10.26 shows the graph of $y = f''(x)$ and verifies our conclusions from (a) and (b).

(d) If $f(x) = \frac{1}{3}(9 - x^3 - 3x^2)$, then $f'(x) = \frac{1}{3}(-3x^2 - 6x) = -x^2 - 2x$. Figure 10.27 shows the graph of $f(x) = \frac{1}{3}(9 - x^3 - 3x^2)$. Note that the point of inflection and the concavity correspond to what we discovered in parts (a) and (b).

Figure 10.26

Figure 10.27

The relationships among $f(x)$, $f'(x)$, and $f''(x)$ that we explored in Example 6 can be summarized as follows.

$f''(x)$	positive (+)	negative (−)	(+) to (−)	(−) to (+)
$f'(x)$	increasing	decreasing	maximum	minimum
$f(x)$	concave up	concave down	point of inflection	

CHECKPOINT
ANSWERS

1. Up
2. At $x = 2$
3. Points of inflection at A, B, and C
   $f''(x) < 0$ to the left of A and between B and C
   $f''(x) > 0$ between A and B and to the right of C

4. (a) False. Consider $f(x) = x^4$.

EXERCISES 10.2

In Problems 1–4, determine whether each function is concave up or concave down at the indicated points.

1. $f(x) = x^3 - 3x^2 + 1$ at (a) $x = -2$ (b) $x = 3$
2. $f(x) = x^3 + 6x - 4$ at (a) $x = -5$ (b) $x = 7$
3. $g(x) = 2x^4 - 5x^3 + 11x - 4$ at (a) $x = 3$ (b) $x = \frac{1}{2}$
4. $g(x) = 7 - 8x^3 + 4x^5$ at (a) $x = 4$ (b) $x = \frac{1}{2}$

In Problems 5–10, use the indicated x-values on the graph of $y = f(x)$ to find the following.

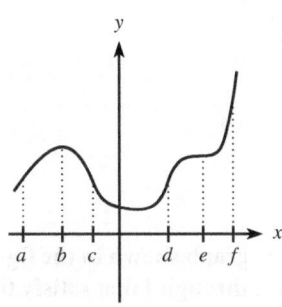

5. Find intervals over which the graph is concave down.
6. Find intervals over which the graph is concave up.
7. Find intervals where $f''(x) > 0$.
8. Find intervals where $f''(x) < 0$.
9. Find the x-coordinates of three points of inflection.
10. Find the x-coordinate of a horizontal point of inflection.

In Problems 11–14, a function and its graph are given. Use the second derivative to determine intervals on which the function is concave up, to determine intervals on which it is concave down, and to locate points of inflection. Check these results against the graph shown.

11. $f(x) = x^3 - 6x^2 + 5x + 6$

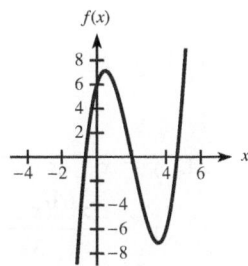

12. $y = x^3 - 9x^2$

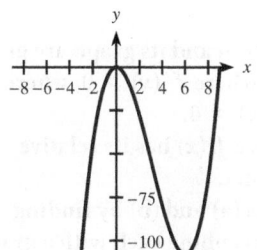

13. $f(x) = \frac{1}{4}x^4 + \frac{1}{2}x^3 - 3x^2 + 3$

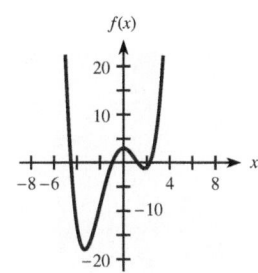

14. $y = 2x^4 - 6x^2 + 4$

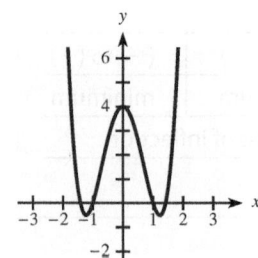

Find the relative maxima, relative minima, and points of inflection and sketch the graphs of the functions in Problems 15–20.

15. $y = x^2 - 4x + 2$
16. $y = x^3 - x^2$

17. $y = \frac{1}{3}x^3 - 2x^2 + 3x + 2$

18. $y = x^3 - 3x^2 + 6$
19. $y = x^4 - 16x^2$

20. $y = x^4 - 8x^3 + 16x^2$

In Problems 21–24, a function and its first and second derivatives are given. Use these to find relative maxima, relative minima, and points of inflection; sketch the graph of each function.

21. $f(x) = 3x^5 - 20x^3$
   $f'(x) = 15x^2(x - 2)(x + 2)$
   $f''(x) = 60x(x^2 - 2)$

22. $f(x) = x^5 - 5x^4$
   $f'(x) = 5x^3(x - 4)$
   $f''(x) = 20x^2(x - 3)$

23. $y = x^{1/3}(x - 4)$

$y' = \dfrac{4(x - 1)}{3x^{2/3}}$

$y'' = \dfrac{4(x + 2)}{9x^{5/3}}$

24. $y = x^{4/3}(x - 7)$

$y' = \dfrac{7x^{1/3}(x - 4)}{3}$

$y'' = \dfrac{28(x - 1)}{9x^{2/3}}$

In Problems 25 and 26, a function and its graph are given.

(a) From the graph, estimate where $f''(x) > 0$, where $f''(x) < 0$, and where $f''(x) = 0$.

(b) Use part (a) to decide where $f'(x)$ has its relative maxima and relative minima.

(c) Verify your results in parts (a) and (b) by finding $f'(x)$ and $f''(x)$ and then graphing each with a graphing utility.

25. $f(x) = -\frac{1}{3}x^3 + x^2 + 8x - 12$

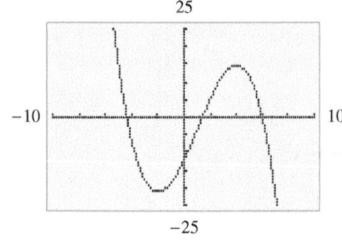

26. $f(x) = \frac{1}{3}x^3 + 2x^2 - 12x - 20$

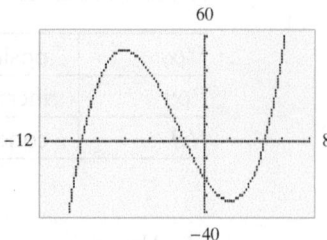

In Problems 27 and 28, $f'(x)$ and its graph are given. Use the graph of $f'(x)$ to determine the following.

(a) Where is the graph of $f(x)$ concave up, and where is it concave down?

(b) Where does $f(x)$ have any points of inflection?

(c) Find $f''(x)$ and graph it. Then use that graph to check your conclusions from parts (a) and (b).

(d) Sketch a possible graph of $f(x)$.

27. $f'(x) = 4x - x^2$

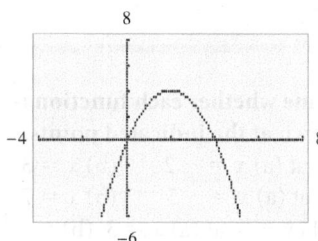

28. $f'(x) = x^2 - x - 2$

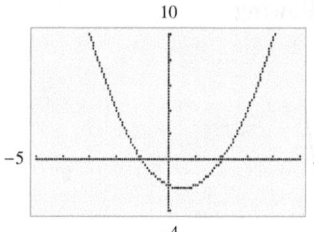

In Problems 29 and 30, use the graph shown in the figure and identify points from A through I that satisfy the given conditions.

29. (a) $f'(x) > 0$ and $f''(x) > 0$
   (b) $f'(x) < 0$ and $f''(x) < 0$
   (c) $f'(x) = 0$ and $f''(x) > 0$
   (d) $f'(x) > 0$ and $f''(x) = 0$
   (e) $f'(x) = 0$ and $f''(x) = 0$

30. (a) $f'(x) > 0$ and $f''(x) < 0$
   (b) $f'(x) < 0$ and $f''(x) > 0$
   (c) $f'(x) = 0$ and $f''(x) < 0$
   (d) $f'(x) < 0$ and $f''(x) = 0$

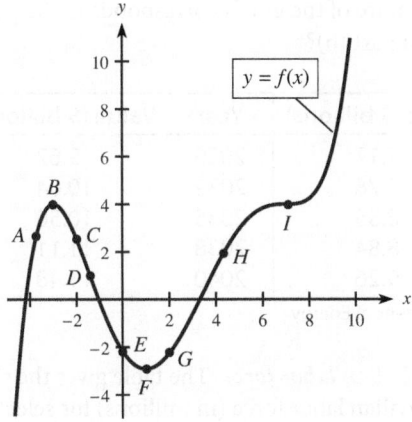

In Problems 31 and 32, a graph is given. Tell where $f(x)$ is concave up, where it is concave down, and where it has points of inflection on the interval $-2 < x < 2$ if the given graph is the graph of
(a) $f(x)$.   (b) $f'(x)$.   (c) $f''(x)$.

31.

32.

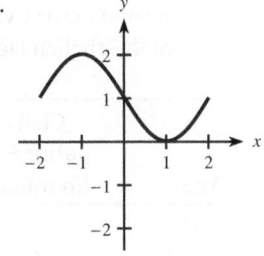

APPLICATIONS

33. *Productivity—diminishing returns* The figure is a typical graph of worker productivity as a function of time on the job.

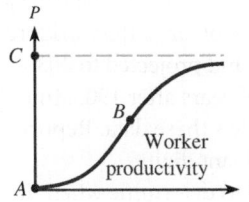

(a) If P represents the productivity and t represents the time, write a mathematical symbol that represents the rate of change of productivity with respect to time.
(b) Which of A, B, and C is the critical point for the rate of change found in part (a)? This point actually corresponds to the point at which the rate of production is maximized, or the point for maximum worker efficiency. In economics, this is called the point of diminishing returns.
(c) Which of A, B, and C corresponds to the upper limit of worker productivity?

34. *Population growth* The figure shows the growth of a population as a function of time.

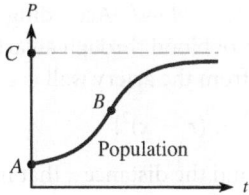

(a) If P represents the population and t represents the time, write a mathematical symbol that represents the rate of change (growth *rate*) of the population with respect to time.
(b) Which of A, B, and C corresponds to the point at which the growth *rate* attains its maximum?
(c) Which of A, B, and C corresponds to the upper limit of population?

35. *Advertising and sales* The figure shows the daily sales volume S as a function of time t since an ad campaign began.

(a) Which of A, B, and C is the point of inflection for the graph?
(b) On which side of C is $d^2S/dt^2 > 0$?
(c) Does the *rate of change* of sales volume attain its minimum at C?

36. *Oxygen purity* The figure shows the oxygen level P (for purity) in a lake t months after an oil spill.

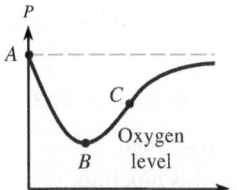

(a) Which of A, B, and C is the point of inflection for the graph?
(b) On which side of C is $d^2P/dt^2 < 0$?
(c) Does the *rate of change* of purity attain its maximum at C?

37. *Production* Suppose that the total number of units produced by a worker in t hours of an 8-hour shift can be modeled by the production function $P(t)$:

$$P(t) = 27t + 12t^2 - t^3$$

(a) Find the number of hours before production is maximized.
(b) Find the number of hours before the rate of production is maximized. That is, find the point of diminishing returns.

38. *Poiseuille's law—velocity of blood* According to Poiseuille's law, the speed S of blood through an artery of radius r at a distance x from the artery wall is given by

$$S = k[r^2 - (r - x)^2]$$

where k is a constant. Find the distance x that maximizes the speed.

39. *Advertising and sales—diminishing returns* Suppose that a company's daily sales volume attributed to an advertising campaign is given by

$$S(t) = \frac{3}{t + 3} - \frac{18}{(t + 3)^2} + 1$$

(a) Find how long it will be before sales volume is maximized.
(b) Find how long it will be before the rate of change of sales volume is minimized. That is, find the point of diminishing returns.

40. *Oxygen purity—diminishing returns* Suppose that the oxygen level P (for purity) in a body of water t months after an oil spill is given by

$$P(t) = 500\left[1 - \frac{4}{t + 4} + \frac{16}{(t + 4)^2}\right]$$

(a) Find how long it will be before the oxygen level reaches its minimum.
(b) Find how long it will be before the rate of change of P is maximized. That is, find the point of diminishing returns.

41. *Energy use* Energy use per capita indexed to 1995 means that per capita energy use for any year is viewed as a percent of per capita use in 1995. Using U.S. Department of Energy data for selected years from 1985 and projected to 2035, the per capita energy use, as a percent of the use in 1995, can be modeled by the function

$$E(t) = 0.000772t^3 - 0.0760t^2 + 1.83t + 87.3$$

where t is the number of years past 1980.
(a) Find the critical points for this function.
(b) Use the second-derivative test to classify and interpret these critical points.

42. *Modeling Industrial shipments* The following table gives the value (in billions of dollars) of U.S. industrial shipments for selected years from 2014 and projected to 2040.
(a) Find a cubic function that models these data, with x as the number of years after 2010 and y as the billions of dollars of U.S. industrial shipments. Report your model with two significant digit coefficients.
(b) Use the reported model to find the point at which the rate of change of the value of U.S. industrial shipments begins to increase.
(c) Interpret the result found in part (b).

(d) What feature of the graph corresponds to the point found in part (b)?

Year	Value ($ billions)	Year	Value ($ billions)
2014	7.17	2029	9.62
2017	7.78	2032	10.04
2020	8.35	2035	10.56
2023	8.84	2038	11.11
2026	9.26	2040	11.48

Source: U.S. Department of Energy

43. *Modeling Civilian labor force* The table gives the size of the U.S. civilian labor force (in millions) for selected years from 1950 and projected to 2050.
(a) Find a cubic function that models these data, with x equal to the number of years after 1950 and y equal to the labor force in millions. Report the model with three significant digit coefficients.
(b) Use the reported model to find the year when the second derivative predicts that the rate of change of the civilian labor force begins to decrease.

Year	Civilian Labor Force (in millions)	Year	Civilian Labor Force (in millions)
1950	62.2	2010	157.7
1960	69.6	2015	162.8
1970	82.8	2020	164.7
1980	106.9	2030	170.1
1990	125.8	2040	180.5
2000	140.9	2050	191.8

Source: U.S. Bureau of Labor Statistics

44. *Modeling Elderly men in the workforce* The table gives the percent of men 65 years or older in the workforce for selected years from 1920 and projected to 2030.
(a) With x as the number of years after 1900, find the cubic function that models these data. Report the model with three significant digits.
(b) Use the reported model to determine when the rate of change of the percent of elderly men in the workforce reached its minimum.
(c) On the graph of this model, to what does the result in part (b) correspond?

Year	Percent	Year	Percent
1920	55.6	1980	19.0
1930	54.0	1990	16.3
1940	41.8	2000	17.7
1950	45.8	2010	22.6
1960	33.1	2020	27.2
1970	21.8	2030	27.6

Source: U.S. Bureau of the Census

45. Modeling *Home health care* The table gives the annual cost per person age 65 or older for home health care from 2006 and projected through 2021. While these annual costs per person may seem modest, the majority of older Americans live healthy, active lives and require no special care.
    (a) With t equal to the number of years past 2005, find a cubic function $C(t)$ that models the annual cost per person age 65 or older for home health care. Report the model with three significant digits.
    (b) Find the point of inflection of the reported model. Examine the function on either side of the point of inflection and interpret your results.

Year	Cost (in $)	Year	Cost (in $)
2006	1418	2014	1967
2007	1529	2015	2045
2008	1589	2016	2122
2009	1673	2017	2203
2010	1764	2018	2305
2011	1787	2019	2416
2012	1841	2020	2532
2013	1883	2021	2653

Source: Centers for Medicare and Medicaid Services

46. Modeling CO_2 *emissions* The following table gives the millions of metric tons of carbon dioxide emissions from biomass energy combustion in the United States for selected years from 2010 and projected to 2032.
    (a) Create a cubic function that models these data, with x as the number of years past 2010 and y as the millions of metric tons of carbon dioxide emissions. Report your model with two significant digit coefficients.
    (b) The data show that carbon dioxide emissions are increasing during the period from 2010 to 2032. Use the reported model to find the point at which the rate of increase begins to decrease.
    (c) Interpret the result found in part (b).
    (d) What feature of the graph corresponds to the point found in part (b)?

Year	2010	2012	2014	2016	2018	2020
CO_2 Emissions	338.5	364.5	396.1	425.8	453.1	498.4

Year	2022	2024	2026	2028	2030	2032
CO_2 Emissions	556.2	590.9	629.7	663.1	701.1	743.7

Source: U.S. Department of Energy

SECTION 10.3   Optimization in Business and Economics

OBJECTIVES

- To find absolute maxima and minima
- To maximize revenue, given the total revenue function
- To minimize the average cost, given the total cost function
- To find the maximum profit from total cost and total revenue functions, or from a profit function

APPLICATION PREVIEW

Suppose a travel agency charges $300 per person for a certain tour when the tour group has 25 people, but will reduce the price by $10 per person for each additional person above the 25. To determine the group size that will maximize the revenue, the agency must create a model for the revenue. With such a model, the techniques of calculus can be useful in determining the maximum revenue. (See Example 2.)

Most companies (such as the travel agency) are interested in obtaining the greatest possible revenue or profit. Similarly, manufacturers of products are concerned about producing their products for the lowest possible average cost per unit. Therefore, rather than finding just the relative maxima or relative minima of a function, we will consider where the absolute maximum or absolute minimum of a function occurs in a given interval.

In this section, we will discuss techniques to find the absolute extrema of a function and then use them to solve applications involving revenue, cost, and profit.

As the name implies, **absolute extrema** are the functional values that are the largest or smallest values over the entire domain of the function or over the interval of interest.

Absolute Extrema   The value $f(a)$ is the **absolute maximum** of f if $f(a) \geq f(x)$ for all x in the domain of f or over the interval of interest.
The value $f(b)$ is the **absolute minimum** of f if $f(b) \leq f(x)$ for all x in the domain of f or over the interval of interest.

We begin by considering the graph of $y = (x - 1)^2$, shown in Figure 10.28(a). This graph has a relative minimum at $(1, 0)$. Note that the relative minimum is the lowest point on the graph. In this case, the point $(1, 0)$ is an **absolute minimum point** and 0 is the absolute minimum for the function. Similarly, when there is a point that is the highest point on the graph over the domain of the function, we call the point an **absolute maximum point** of the graph of the function.

In Figure 10.28(a), we see that there is no relative maximum. However, if the domain of the function is restricted to the interval $\left[\frac{1}{2}, 2\right]$, then we get the graph shown in Figure 10.28(b). In this case, there is an absolute maximum of 1 at the point $(2, 1)$ and the absolute minimum of 0 is still at $(1, 0)$.

If the domain of $y = (x - 1)^2$ is restricted to the interval $[2, 3]$, the resulting graph is that shown in Figure 10.28(c). In this case, the absolute minimum is 1 and occurs at the point $(2, 1)$ and the absolute maximum is 4 and occurs at $(3, 4)$.

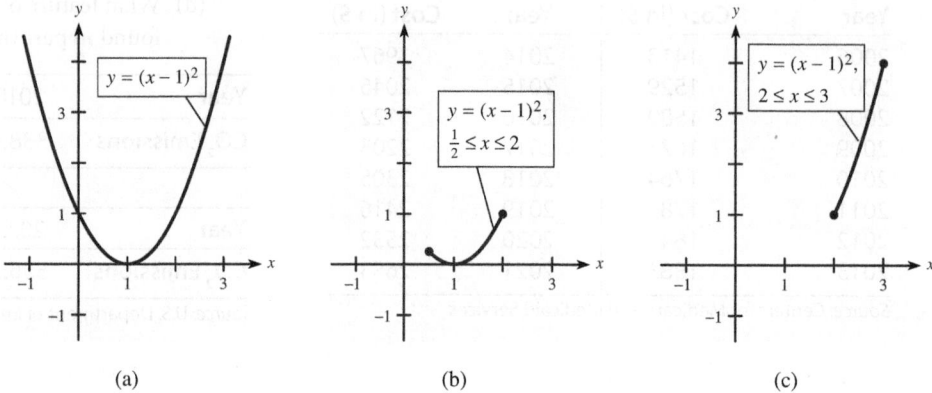

Figure 10.28   (a)   (b)   (c)

As the preceding discussion indicates, if the domain of a continuous function is limited to a closed interval, the absolute maximum or minimum may occur at an endpoint of the domain. In testing functions with limited domains for absolute maxima and minima, we must compare the function values at the endpoints of the domain with the function values at the critical values found by taking derivatives. In the management, life, and social sciences, a limited domain occurs often because many quantities are required to be positive, or at least nonnegative.

Maximizing Revenue   Because the marginal revenue is the first derivative of the total revenue, the total revenue function will have a critical point at the point where the marginal revenue equals 0. With the total revenue function $R(x) = 16x - 0.02x^2$, the point where $R'(x) = 0$ is clearly a maximum because $R(x)$ is a parabola that opens downward. But the domain may be limited, the revenue function may not always be a parabola, or the critical point may not always be a maximum, so it is important to verify where the maximum value occurs.

EXAMPLE 1   Revenue

The total revenue in dollars for a firm is given by

$$R(x) = 8000x - 40x^2 - x^3$$

where x is the number of units sold per day. If only 50 units can be sold per day, find the number of units that must be sold to maximize revenue. Find the maximum revenue.

Solution

This revenue function is limited to x in the interval $[0, 50]$. Thus the maximum revenue will occur at a critical value in this interval or at an endpoint. $R'(x) = 8000 - 80x - 3x^2$, so we must solve $8000 - 80x - 3x^2 = 0$ for x:

Thus $(40 - x)(200 + 3x) = 0$ means $40 - x = 0$ or $200 + 3x = 0$ so

$$x = 40 \quad \text{or} \quad x = -\frac{200}{3}$$

The negative value of x is not relevant, so for $x = 40$ we use either the second-derivative test or the first-derivative test with a sign diagram.

Second-Derivative Test	First-Derivative Test
$R''(x) = -80 - 6x$, $R''(40) = -320 < 0$, so $x = 40$ gives a relative maximum.	$R(x)$ $R'(x)$ $+ + + + + + + + + 0 - - - - - - -$ at 40

These tests show that a relative maximum occurs at $x = 40$, giving revenue $R(40) = \$192{,}000$. Checking the endpoints $x = 0$ and $x = 50$ gives $R(0) = \$0$ and $R(50) = \$175{,}000$. Thus $R = \$192{,}000$ at $x = 40$ is the (absolute) maximum revenue.

CHECKPOINT

1. True or false: If $R(x)$ is the total revenue function for a product, we find all possible points where $R(x)$ could be maximized by solving $\overline{MR} = 0$ for x.

EXAMPLE 2   Revenue | APPLICATION PREVIEW |

A travel agency will plan tours for groups of 25 or larger. If the group contains exactly 25 people, the price is $300 per person. However, the price per person is reduced by $10 for each additional person above the 25. What size group will produce the largest revenue for the agency?

Solution

The total revenue is

$$R = (\text{number of people})(\text{price per person})$$

The table shows how the revenue is changed by increases in the size of the group.

Number in Group	Price per Person	Revenue
25	300	7500
25 + 1	300 − 10	7540
25 + 2	300 − 20	7560
⋮	⋮	⋮
25 + x	300 − 10x	(25 + x)(300 − 10x)

Thus when x is the number of people added to the 25, the total revenue will be

$$R = R(x) = (25 + x)(300 - 10x) \quad \text{or} \quad R(x) = 7500 + 50x - 10x^2$$

This is a quadratic function, so its graph is a parabola that is concave down. Thus a maximum will occur at its vertex, where $R'(x) = 0$.

$R'(x) = 50 - 20x$, and the solution to $0 = 50 - 20x$ is $x = 2.5$. Thus adding 2.5 people to the group should maximize the total revenue. But we cannot add half a person, so we will test the total revenue function for 27 people and 28 people. This will determine the optimal group size.

For $x = 2$ (27 people) we get $R(2) = 7500 + 50(2) - 10(2)^2 = 7560$. For $x = 3$ (28 people) we get $R(3) = 7500 + 50(3) - 10(3)^2 = 7560$. Note that both 27 and 28 people give the same total revenue and that this revenue is greater than the revenue for 25 people. Thus the revenue is maximized at either 27 or 28 people in the group. (See Figure 10.29.)

Figure 10.29

Minimizing Average Cost   Because the total cost function is always increasing for $x \geq 0$, the number of units that will make the total cost a minimum is always $x = 0$ units, which gives an absolute minimum. However, it is more useful to find the number of units that will make the **average cost** per unit a minimum.

Average Cost   If the total cost function is $C = C(x)$, then the per unit **average cost function** is

$$\overline{C} = \frac{C(x)}{x}$$

Note that the average cost per unit is undefined if no units are produced.

We can use derivatives to find the minimum of the average cost function, as the next example shows.

EXAMPLE 3   Average Cost

If the total cost function for a commodity is given by $C = \frac{1}{4}x^2 + 4x + 100$ dollars, where x represents the number of units produced, producing how many units will result in a minimum *average cost* per unit? Find the minimum average cost.

Solution
Begin by finding the average cost function and its derivative.

$$\overline{C} = \frac{\frac{1}{4}x^2 + 4x + 100}{x} = \frac{1}{4}x + 4 + \frac{100}{x}$$

$$\overline{C}' = \overline{C}'(x) = \frac{1}{4} - \frac{100}{x^2}$$

Setting $\overline{C}' = 0$ gives

$$0 = \frac{1}{4} - \frac{100}{x^2} \quad \text{so} \quad 0 = x^2 - 400 \quad \text{and} \quad x = \pm 20$$

Because the quantity produced must be positive, 20 units should minimize the average cost per unit. We show that it is an absolute minimum by using the second derivative to show that $\overline{C}$ is concave up for all positive x.

$$\overline{C}''(x) = \frac{200}{x^3} \quad \text{so} \quad \overline{C}''(x) > 0 \quad \text{when } x > 0$$

Thus the minimum average cost per unit occurs if 20 units are produced. The graph of the average cost per unit is shown in Figure 10.30. The minimum average cost per unit is $\overline{C}(20) = \$14$.

Figure 10.30

$$\overline{C} = \frac{x}{4} + 4 + \frac{100}{x}$$

(20, 14) Min

CHECKPOINT

2. If $C(x) = 0.01x^2 + 20x + 2500$, form $\overline{C}(x)$, the average cost function, and find the minimum average cost.

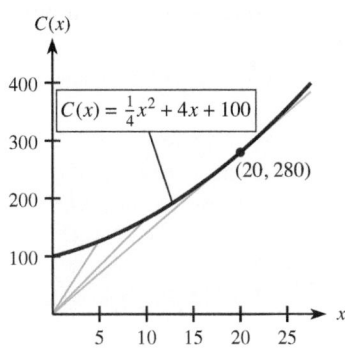

$C(x) = \frac{1}{4}x^2 + 4x + 100$

(20, 280)

Figure 10.31

The graph of the cost function for the commodity in Example 3 is shown in Figure 10.31, along with several lines that join $(0, 0)$ to a point of the form $(x, C(x))$ on the total cost graph. Note that the slope of each of these lines has the form

$$m = \frac{y_2 - y_1}{x_2 - x_1} = \frac{C(x) - 0}{x - 0} = \frac{C(x)}{x}$$

Thus the slope of each of these lines is the *average cost* for the given number of units at the point on $C(x)$. Note that the line from the origin to the point on the curve where $x = 20$ is tangent to the total cost curve. Hence, when $x = 20$, the slope of this line represents both the derivative of the cost function (the *marginal cost*) and the *average cost*. All lines from the origin to points with x-values larger than 20 or smaller than 20 are steeper (and therefore have greater slopes) than the line to the point where $x = 20$. Thus the minimum average cost occurs where the average cost equals the marginal cost. You will be asked to show this analytically in Problems 23 and 24 of the 10.3 Exercises.

Maximizing Profit   We have defined the marginal profit function as the derivative of the profit function. That is,

$$\overline{MP} = P'(x)$$

In this chapter, we have seen how to use the derivative to find maxima and minima for various functions. Now we can apply those same techniques in the context of **profit maximization.** We can use marginal profit to maximize profit functions.

If there is a physical limitation on the number of units that can be produced in a given period of time, then the endpoints of the interval caused by these limitations should also be checked.

EXAMPLE **4**   **Profit**

Suppose that the production capacity for a certain commodity cannot exceed 30 units per week. If the profit for this commodity is

$$P(x) = 4x^3 - 210x^2 + 3600x - 200 \quad \text{dollars}$$

where x is the number of units sold, find the number of items that will maximize profit.

Solution

The restrictions on capacity mean that $P(x)$ is restricted by $0 \leq x \leq 30$. The marginal profit function is

$$P'(x) = 12x^2 - 420x + 3600$$

Setting $P'(x)$ equal to 0, we get

$$0 = 12(x - 15)(x - 20)$$

so $P'(x) = 0$ at $x = 15$ *and* $x = 20$. A sign diagram for $P'(x)$ tests these critical values.

Thus the total profit function has a *relative* maximum at (15, 20,050), but we must check the endpoints (0 and 30) before deciding whether it is the absolute maximum.

$$P(0) = -200 \quad \text{and} \quad P(30) = 26,800$$

Thus the absolute maximum profit is \$26,800 per week, and it occurs at the endpoint, $x = 30$. Figure 10.32 shows the graph of the profit function.

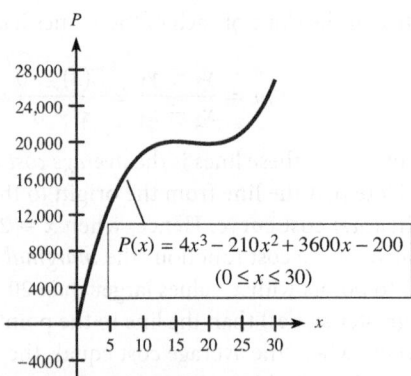

Figure 10.32

In a **monopolistic market,** the seller who has a monopoly controls the supply of a product and can force the price higher by limiting supply.

If the demand function for the product is $p = f(x)$, total revenue for the sale of x units is $R(x) = px = f(x) \cdot x$. Note that the price p is fixed by the market in a competitive market but varies with output for the monopolist.

If $\overline{C} = \overline{C}(x)$ represents the average cost per unit sold, then the total cost for the x units sold is $C = \overline{C} \cdot x = \overline{C}x$. Because we have both total cost and total revenue as a function of the quantity, x, we can maximize the profit function, $P(x) = px - \overline{C}x$, where p represents the demand function $p = f(x)$ and $\overline{C}$ represents the average cost function $\overline{C} = \overline{C}(x)$.

EXAMPLE 5 Profit in a Monopoly Market

MONOPOLY

The price of a product in dollars is related to the number of units x demanded daily by

$$p = 168 - 0.2x$$

A monopolist finds that the daily average cost for this product is

$$\overline{C} = 120 + x \quad \text{dollars}$$

(a) How many units must be sold daily to maximize profit?
(b) What is the selling price at this "optimal" level of production?
(c) What is the maximum possible daily profit?

Solution

(a) The total revenue function for the product is

$$R(x) = px = (168 - 0.2x)x = 168x - 0.2x^2$$

One big player controls supply and dictates pricing.

© Eric Isselée/Shutterstock.com

and the total cost function is

$$C(x) = \overline{C} \cdot x = (120 + x)x = 120x + x^2$$

Thus the profit function is

$$P(x) = R(x) - C(x) = 168x - 0.2x^2 - (120x + x^2) = 48x - 1.2x^2$$

Then $P'(x) = 48 - 2.4x$, so $P'(x) = 0$ when $x = 20$. We see that $P''(20) = -2.4$, so by the second-derivative test, $P(x)$ has a maximum at $x = 20$. That is, selling 20 units will maximize profit.

(b) The selling price is determined by $p = 168 - 0.2x$, so the price that will result from supplying 20 units per day is $p = 168 - 0.2(20) = 164$. That is, the "optimal" selling price is $164 per unit.

(c) The profit at $x = 20$ is $P(20) = 48(20) - 1.2(20)^2 = 960 - 480 = 480$. Thus the maximum possible profit is $480 per day.

COMPETITION

Several players are so small that individual actions cannot affect product price, so supply and demand dictate price.

In a **competitive market,** each firm is so small that its actions in the market cannot affect the price of the product. The price of the product is determined in the market by the intersection of the market demand curve (from all consumers) and market supply curve (from all firms that supply the product). The firm can sell as little or as much as it desires at the market equilibrium price.

Therefore, a firm in a competitive market has a total revenue function given by $R(x) = px$, where p is the market equilibrium price for the product and x is the quantity sold.

EXAMPLE   6   Profit in a Competitive Market

A firm in a competitive market must sell its product for $200 per unit. The average cost per unit (per week) is $\overline{C} = 80 + x$, where x is the number of units sold per week. How many units should be sold to maximize profit?

Solution

If the average cost per unit is $\overline{C} = 80 + x$, then the total cost of x units is given by $C(x) = (80 + x)x = 80x + x^2$. The revenue per unit is $200, so the total revenue is given by $R(x) = 200x$. Thus the profit function is

$$P(x) = R(x) - C(x) = 200x - (80x + x^2), \quad \text{or} \quad P(x) = 120x - x^2$$

Then $P'(x) = 120 - 2x$. Setting $P'(x) = 0$ and solving for x gives $x = 60$. Because $P''(60) = -2$, the profit is maximized when the firm sells 60 units per week.

CHECKPOINT

3. (a) If $p = 5000 - x$ gives the demand function in a monopoly market, find $R(x)$, if it is possible with this information.

(b) If $p = 5000 - x$ gives the demand function in a competitive market, find $R(x)$, if it is possible with this information.

4. If $R(x) = 400x - 0.25x^2$ and $C(x) = 150x + 0.25x^2 + 8500$ are the total revenue and total cost (both in dollars) for x units of a product, find the number of units that gives maximum profit and find the maximum profit.

Calculator Note   As we have seen, graphing calculators can be used to locate maximum values. In addition, if it is difficult to determine critical values algebraically, we may be able to approximate them graphically. For example, if

$$P(x) = 2500 - \frac{3000}{x + 1} - 12x - x^2 \qquad \text{then} \qquad P'(x) = \frac{3000}{(x + 1)^2} - 12 - 2x$$

Finding the critical values by solving $P'(x) = 0$ is difficult unless we use a graphing approach. Figure 10.33(a) shows the graph of $P(x)$, and Figure 10.33(b) shows the graph of $P'(x)$. These figures indicate that the maximum occurs near $x = 10$.

By adjusting the viewing window for $P'(x)$, we obtain the graph in Figure 10.34. This shows that $P'(x) = 0$ when $x = 9$. The maximum is $P(9) = 2500 - 300 - 108 - 81 = 2011$. See Appendix A, Section 10.3, for additional details. ◼

Figure 10.33   (a)   (b)   Figure 10.34

Spreadsheet Note   To find optimal values of functions, use the Solver feature of Excel, found under *Data>Analysis>Solver*, and follow the instructions. See Appendix B, Section 10.3 and 10.4, or the Online Excel Guide for detailed steps. ◼

CHECKPOINT ANSWERS

1. False. $\overline{MR} = R'(x)$, but there may also be critical points where $R'(x)$ is undefined, or $R(x)$ may be maximized at endpoints of a restricted domain.

2. $\overline{C}(x) = \dfrac{C(x)}{x} = 0.01x + 20 + \dfrac{2500}{x}$

   The minimum average cost per unit is $\overline{C}(500) = 30$ dollars per unit.

3. (a) $R(x) = p \cdot x = 5000x - x^2$
   (b) In a competitive market, we need to know the supply function and find the equilibrium price before we can form $R(x)$.

4. The (absolute) maximum profit occurs when $x = 250$ and is $P(250) = \$22,750$.

EXERCISES 10.3

In Problems 1–6, find the absolute maxima and minima for $f(x)$ on the interval $[a, b]$.

1. $f(x) = x^3 - 2x^2 - 4x + 2,\ [-1, 3]$
2. $f(x) = x^3 - 3x + 3,\ [-3, 1.5]$
3. $f(x) = x^3 + x^2 - x + 1,\ [-2, 0]$
4. $f(x) = x^3 - 3x^2 - 24x + 7,\ [-3, 6]$
5. $f(x) = 2x^3 - 3x^2 - 12x - 5,\ [-10, 10]$
6. $f(x) = 9 + 6x^2 - x^3,\ [-3, 10]$

MAXIMIZING REVENUE

7. (a) If the total revenue function for a hammer is $R = 36x - 0.01x^2$, then sales of how many hammers, x, will maximize the total revenue in dollars? Find the maximum revenue.

(b) Find the maximum revenue if production is limited to at most 1500 hammers.

8. (a) If the total revenue function for a blender is $R(x) = 25x - 0.05x^2$, sales of how many units, x, will provide the maximum total revenue in dollars? Find the maximum revenue.

(b) Find the maximum revenue if production is limited to at most 200 blenders.

9. If the total revenue function for a computer is $R(x) = 2000x - 20x^2 - x^3$, find the level of sales, x, that maximizes revenue and find the maximum revenue in dollars.

10. A firm has total revenues given by

$$R(x) = 2800x - 8x^2 - x^3 \text{ dollars}$$

for x units of a product. Find the maximum revenue from sales of that product.

11. An agency charges $100 per person for a trip to a concert if 70 people travel in a group. But for each person above the 70, the charge will be reduced by $1. How many people will maximize the total revenue for the agency if the trip is limited to at most 90 people?

12. A company handles an apartment building with 70 units. Experience has shown that if the rent for each of the units is $1080 per month, all the units will be filled, but 1 unit will become vacant for each $20 increase in the monthly rate. What rent should be charged to maximize the total revenue from the building if the upper limit on the rent is $1300 per month?

13. A cable TV company has 4000 customers paying $110 each month. If each $1 reduction in price attracts 50 new customers, find the price that yields maximum revenue. Find the maximum revenue.

14. If club members charge $5 admission to a classic car show, 1000 people will attend, and for each $1 increase in price, 100 fewer people will attend. What price will give the maximum revenue for the show? Find the maximum revenue.

15. The function $\overline{R}(x) = R(x)/x$ defines the average revenue for selling x units. For

$$R(x) = 2000x + 20x^2 - x^3$$

   (a) find the maximum average revenue.
   (b) show that $\overline{R}(x)$ attains its maximum at an x-value where $\overline{R}(x) = \overline{MR}$.

16. For the revenue function given by

$$R(x) = 2800x + 8x^2 - x^3$$

   (a) find the maximum average revenue.
   (b) show that $\overline{R}(x)$ attains its maximum at an x-value where $\overline{R}(x) = \overline{MR}$.

MINIMIZING AVERAGE COST

17. If the total cost function for a lamp is $C(x) = 250 + 33x + 0.1x^2$ dollars, producing how many units, x, will result in a minimum average cost per unit? Find the minimum average cost.

18. If the total cost function for a product is $C(x) = 300 + 10x + 0.03x^2$ dollars, producing how many units, x, will result in a minimum average cost per unit? Find the minimum average cost.

19. If the total cost function for a product is $C(x) = 810 + 0.1x^2$ dollars, producing how many units, x, will result in a minimum average cost per unit? Find the minimum average cost.

20. If the total cost function for a product is $C(x) = 250 + 6x + 0.1x^2$ dollars, producing how many units, x,

will minimize the average cost? Find the minimum average cost.

21. If the total cost function for a product is $C(x) = 100(0.02x + 4)^3$ dollars, where x represents the number of hundreds of units produced, producing how many units will minimize average cost? Find the minimum average cost.

22. If the total cost function for a product is $C(x) = (x + 5)^3$ dollars, where x represents the number of hundreds of units produced, producing how many units will minimize average cost? Find the minimum average cost.

23. For the cost function $C(x) = 25 + 13x + x^2$, show that average costs are minimized at the x-value where

$$\overline{C}(x) = \overline{MC}$$

24. For the cost function $C(x) = 300 + 10x + 0.03x^2$, show that average costs are minimized at the x-value where

$$\overline{C}(x) = \overline{MC}$$

The graphs in Problems 25 and 26 show total cost functions. For each problem
(a) explain how to use the total cost graph to determine the level of production at which average cost is minimized.
(b) determine that level of production.

25.

26.

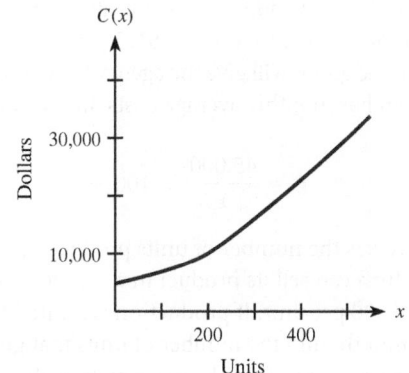

MAXIMIZING PROFIT

27. If the profit function for a product is $P(x) = 5600x + 85x^2 - x^3 - 200,000$ dollars, selling how many items, x, will produce a maximum profit? Find the maximum profit.

28. If the profit function for a commodity is $P = 6400x - 18x^2 - \frac{1}{3}x^3 - 40,000$ dollars, selling how many units, x, will result in a maximum profit? Find the maximum profit.

29. A manufacturer estimates that its product can be produced at a total cost of $C(x) = 45,000 + 100x + x^3$ dollars. If the manufacturer's total revenue from the sale of x units is $R(x) = 4600x$ dollars, determine the level of production x that will maximize the profit. Find the maximum profit.

30. A product can be produced at a total cost $C(x) = 800 + 100x^2 + x^3$ dollars, where x is the number produced. If the total revenue is given by $R(x) = 60,000x - 50x^2$ dollars, determine the level of production, x, that will maximize the profit. Find the maximum profit.

31. A firm can produce only 1000 units per month. The monthly total cost is given by $C(x) = 300 + 200x$ dollars, where x is the number produced. If the total revenue is given by $R(x) = 250x - \frac{1}{100}x^2$ dollars, how many items, x, should the firm produce for maximum profit? Find the maximum profit.

32. A firm can produce 100 units per week. If its total cost function is $C = 500 + 1500x$ dollars and its total revenue function is $R = 1600x - x^2$ dollars, how many units, x, should it produce to maximize its profit? Find the maximum profit.

33. A company handles an apartment building with 50 units. Experience has shown that if the rent for each of the units is $720 per month, all of the units will be filled, but 1 unit will become vacant for each $20 increase in this monthly rate. If the monthly cost of maintaining the apartment building is $12 per rented unit, what rent should be charged per month to maximize the profit?

34. A travel agency will plan a tour for groups of size 25 or larger. If the group contains exactly 25 people, the cost is $500 per person. However, each person's cost is reduced by $10 for each additional person above the 25. If the travel agency incurs a cost of $125 per person for the tour, what size group will give the agency the maximum profit?

35. A firm has monthly average costs, in dollars, given by

$$\overline{C} = \frac{45,000}{x} + 100 + x$$

where x is the number of units produced per month. The firm can sell its product in a competitive market for $1600 per unit. If production is limited to 600 units per month, find the number of units that gives maximum profit, and find the maximum profit.

36. A small business has weekly average costs, in dollars, of

$$\overline{C} = \frac{100}{x} + 30 + \frac{x}{10}$$

where x is the number of units produced each week. The competitive market price for this business's product is $46 per unit. If production is limited to 150 units per week, find the level of production that yields maximum profit, and find the maximum profit.

37. The weekly demand function for x units of a product sold by only one firm is $p = 600 - \frac{1}{2}x$ dollars, and the average cost of production and sale is $\overline{C} = 300 + 2x$ dollars.
    (a) Find the quantity that will maximize profit.
    (b) Find the selling price at this optimal quantity.
    (c) What is the maximum profit?

38. The monthly demand function for x units of a product sold by a monopoly is $p = 8000 - x$ dollars, and its average cost is $\overline{C} = 4000 + 5x$ dollars.
    (a) Determine the quantity that will maximize profit.
    (b) Determine the selling price at the optimal quantity.
    (c) Determine the maximum profit.

39. The monthly demand function for a product sold by a monopoly is $p = 1960 - \frac{1}{3}x^2$ dollars, and the average cost is $\overline{C} = 1000 + 2x + x^2$ dollars. Production is limited to 1000 units, and x is in hundreds of units.
    (a) Find the quantity that will give maximum profit.
    (b) Find the maximum profit.

40. The monthly demand function for x units of a product sold by a monopoly is $p = 5900 - \frac{1}{2}x^2$ dollars, and its average cost is $\overline{C} = 3020 + 2x$ dollars. If production is limited to 100 units, find the number of units that maximizes profit. Will the maximum profit result in a profit or loss?

41. An industry with a monopoly on a product has its average weekly costs, in dollars, given by

$$\overline{C} = \frac{10,000}{x} + 60 - 0.03x + 0.00001x^2$$

The weekly demand for x units of the product is given by $p = 120 - 0.015x$ dollars. Find the price the industry should set and the number of units it should produce to obtain maximum profit. Find the maximum profit.

42. A large corporation with monopolistic control in the marketplace has its average daily costs, in dollars, given by

$$\overline{C} = \frac{800}{x} + 100x + x^2$$

The daily demand for x units of its product is given by $p = 60,000 - 50x$ dollars. Find the quantity that gives maximum profit and find the maximum profit. What selling price should the corporation set for its product?

43. Coastal Soda Sales has been granted exclusive market rights to the upcoming Beaufort Seafood Festival. This means that during the festival, Coastal will have a monopoly, and it is anxious to take advantage of this position in its pricing strategy. The daily demand function is

$$p = 2 - 0.0004x$$

and the daily total cost function is

$$C(x) = 800 + 0.2x + 0.0001x^2$$

where x is the number of units.
   (a) Determine Coastal's total revenue and profit functions.
   (b) What profit-maximizing price per soda should Coastal charge, how many sodas per day would it expect to sell at this price, and what would be the daily profits?
   (c) If the festival organizers wanted to set an economically efficient price of $1.25 per soda, how would this change the results from part (b)? Would Coastal be willing to provide sodas for the festival at this regulated price? Why or why not?

44. A retiree from a large Atlanta financial services firm decides to keep busy and supplement her retirement income by opening a small upscale folk art company near Charleston, South Carolina. The company, Sand Dollar Art, manufactures and sells in a purely competitive market, and the following monthly market information for x units at p dollars per unit applies:

$$\text{Demand:} \quad p = 2000 - 4.5x$$
$$\text{Supply:} \quad p = 100 + 0.25x$$

   (a) Find the market equilibrium quantity and price for this market.
   (b) If Sand Dollar Art's monthly cost function is

$$C(x) = 400 + 100x + x^2$$

   find the profit-maximizing monthly quantity. What are the total monthly revenues and total monthly costs? What monthly profit does Sand Dollar Art earn?
   (c) Assuming that Sand Dollar Art is representative of firms in this competitive market, what is its market share?

MISCELLANEOUS APPLICATIONS

45. *Marginal revenue and marginal cost* The figure shows the graph of a quadratic revenue function and a linear cost function.
   (a) At which of the four x-values shown is the distance between the revenue and the cost greatest?
   (b) At which of the four x-values shown is the profit largest?

   (c) At which of the four x-values shown is the slope of the tangent to the revenue curve equal to the slope of the cost line?
   (d) What is the relationship between marginal cost and marginal revenue when profit is at its maximum value?

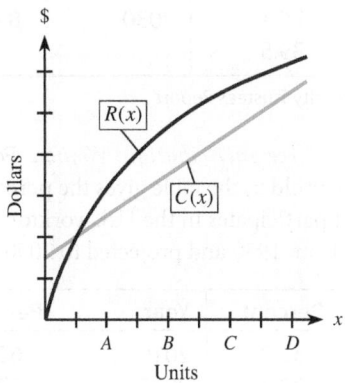

46. *Marginal revenue and marginal cost* The figure shows the graph of revenue function $y = R(x)$ and cost function $y = C(x)$.
   (a) At which of the four x-values shown is the profit largest?
   (b) At which of the four x-values shown is the slope of the tangent to the revenue curve equal to the slope of the tangent to the cost curve?
   (c) What is the relationship between marginal cost and marginal revenue when profit is at its maximum value?

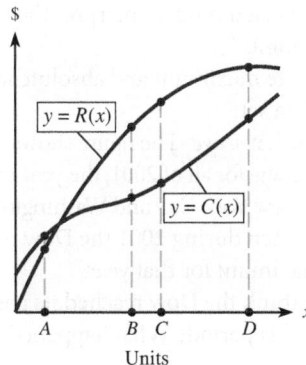

47. Modeling *Social Security beneficiaries* The numbers of millions of Social Security beneficiaries for selected years from 1950 and projected to 2030 are given in the following table.
   (a) Find the cubic function that models these data, with x equal to the number of years past 1950. Report the model with 3 significant digits.
   (b) Find the point of inflection of the graph of the reported model for $x > 0$.
   (c) Graph this function and discuss what the point of inflection indicates.

	Number of Beneficiaries		Number of Beneficiaries
Year	(millions)	Year	(millions)
1950	2.9	2000	45.2
1960	14.3	2010	53.4
1970	25.2	2020	69.1
1980	35.1	2030	84.7
1990	39.5		

Source: Social Security Trustees Report

48. Modeling *Workforce participation: Women* For women age 16 or older, the table gives the percent of this group that participates in the U.S. workforce for selected years from 1950 and projected to 2050.

Year	Percent	Year	Percent
1950	33.9	2010	62.2
1960	37.7	2015	62.1
1970	43.3	2020	60.3
1980	51.5	2030	57.4
1990	57.5	2040	56.7
2000	60.2	2050	56.6

Source: U.S. Bureau of the Census

(a) With *x* as the number of years past 1940, find a quartic function that models the data. Report the model with three significant digit coefficients.

(b) For the years from 1950 to 2050, determine all critical points of the reported model.

(c) Find the absolute maximum and absolute minimum of the reported model. Interpret the coordinates of each point.

(d) Find the absolute maximum and absolute minimum of the data set.

49. *Dow Jones Industrial Average* The figure shows the Dow Jones Industrial Average for all of 2001, the year of the terrorist attacks on New York City and Washington, D.C.

(a) Approximate when during 2001 the Dow reached its absolute maximum for that year.

(b) When do you think the Dow reached its absolute minimum for this period? What happened to trigger this?

Dow Jones Industrial Average

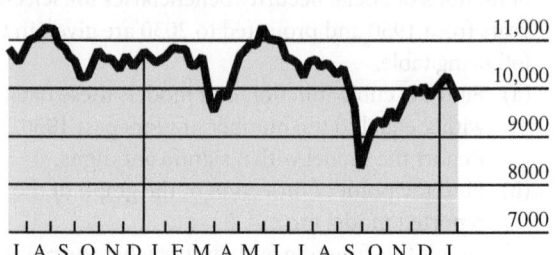

J A S O N D J F M A M J J A S O N D J
2000   2001

Source: From *The Wall Street Journal,* January 17, 2002. Copyright © 2002 by Dow Jones & Co. Reprinted by permission of Dow Jones & Co. via Copyright Clearance Center.

50. *Dow Jones averages* The figure shows the daily Dow Jones Industrial Average (DJIA) and its 30-day moving average from late July to early November. Use the figure to complete the following.

(a) Approximate the absolute maximum point and absolute minimum point for the daily DJIA.

(b) Approximate the absolute maximum point and absolute minimum point for the DJIA 30-day moving average.

$INDU (Dow Jones Industrial Average) INDX

Aug 6   13 20 27 **Sep**10 17 24 **Oct** 8   15 22 29 **Nov**12

Source: stockcharts.com

51. *Social Security support* The graph shows the number of workers, $W = f(t)$, still in the workforce per Social Security beneficiary (historically and projected into the future) as a function of time *t*, in calendar years with $1950 \le t \le 2050$. Use the graph to answer the following.

(a) What is the absolute maximum of $f(t)$?

(b) What is the absolute minimum of $f(t)$?

Source: Social Security Administration

SECTION 10.4

Applications of Maxima and Minima

OBJECTIVES

- To apply the procedures for finding maxima and minima to solve problems from the management, life, and social sciences

APPLICATION PREVIEW

Suppose that a company needs 1,000,000 items during a year and that preparation costs are $800 for each production run. Suppose further that it costs the company $6 to produce each item and $1 to store each item for up to a year. Find the number of units that should be produced in each production run so that the total costs of production and storage are minimized. This question is answered using an inventory cost model. (See Example 4.)

This inventory-cost determination is a typical example of the kinds of questions and important business applications that require the use of the derivative for finding maxima and minima. As managers, workers, or consumers, we may be interested in such things as maximum revenue, maximum profit, minimum cost, maximum medical dosage, and maximum utilization of resources.

If we have functions that model cost, revenue, or population growth, we can apply the methods of this chapter to find the maxima and minima of those functions.

EXAMPLE 1

Company Growth

Suppose that a new company begins production in 2017 with eight employees and the growth of the company over the next 10 years is predicted by

$$N = N(t) = 8\left(1 + \frac{160t}{t^2 + 16}\right), \quad 0 \le t \le 10$$

where N is the number of employees t years after 2017.

Determine in what year the number of employees will be maximized and the maximum number of employees.

Solution

This function will have a relative maximum when $N'(t) = 0$.

$$N'(t) = 8\left[\frac{(t^2 + 16)(160) - (160t)(2t)}{(t^2 + 16)^2}\right]$$

$$= 8\left[\frac{160t^2 + 2560 - 320t^2}{(t^2 + 16)^2}\right]$$

$$= 8\left[\frac{2560 - 160t^2}{(t^2 + 16)^2}\right]$$

Because $N'(t) = 0$ when its numerator is 0 (note that this denominator is never 0), we must solve

$$2560 - 160t^2 = 0$$
$$160(4 + t)(4 - t) = 0$$

so
$$t = -4 \text{ or } t = 4$$

We are interested only in positive t-values, so we test $t = 4$.

$$\left.\begin{array}{l} N'(0) = 8\left[\dfrac{2560}{256}\right] > 0 \\[3mm] N'(10) = 8\left[\dfrac{-13{,}440}{(116)^2}\right] < 0 \end{array}\right\} \Rightarrow \text{relative maximum}$$

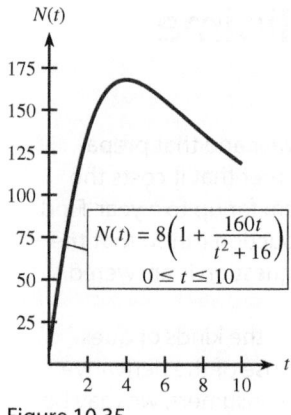

Figure 10.35

The relative maximum is

$$N(4) = 8\left(1 + \frac{640}{32}\right) = 168$$

At $t = 0$, the number of employees is $N(0) = 8$, and it increases to $N(4) = 168$. After $t = 4$ (in 2021), $N(t)$ decreases to $N(10) = 118$ (approximately), so $N(4) = 168$ is the maximum number of employees. Figure 10.35 verifies these conclusions.

Sometimes we must develop the function we need from the statement of the problem. In this case, it is important to understand what is to be maximized or minimized and to express that quantity as a function of *one* variable.

EXAMPLE 2 Minimizing Cost

A farmer needs to enclose a rectangular pasture containing 1,600,000 square feet. Suppose that along the road adjoining his property he wants to use a more expensive fence and that he needs no fence on one side perpendicular to the road because a river bounds his property on that side. If the fence costs $15 per foot along the road and $10 per foot along the two remaining sides that must be fenced, what dimensions of his rectangular field will minimize his cost?

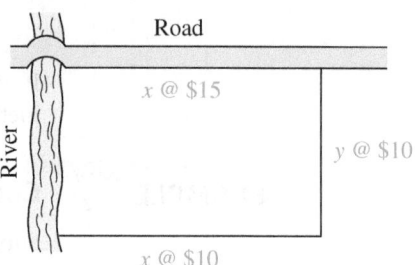

Figure 10.36

Solution

In Figure 10.36, x represents the length of the pasture along the road (and parallel to the road) and y represents the width. The cost function for the fence used is

$$C = 15x + 10y + 10x = 25x + 10y$$

We cannot use a derivative to find where C is minimized unless we write C as a function of x or y only. Because the area of the rectangular field must be 1,600,000 square feet, we have

$$A = xy = 1,600,000$$

Solving for y in terms of x and substituting give C as a function of x.

$$y = \frac{1,600,000}{x}$$

$$C = 25x + 10\left(\frac{1,600,000}{x}\right) = 25x + \frac{16,000,000}{x}$$

To find $C'(x)$, we first rewrite: $C = 25x + 16,000,000x^{-1}$. Then

$$C'(x) = 25 - 16,000,000x^{-2} = 25 - \frac{16,000,000}{x^2}$$

We find the critical values of C by solving $C'(x) = 0$ as follows:

$$0 = 25 - \frac{16,000,000}{x^2}$$

$$0 = 25x^2 - 16,000,000 \qquad \text{(Multiply both sides by } x^2.)$$

$$25x^2 = 16,000,000$$

$$x^2 = 640,000 \Rightarrow x = \pm\sqrt{640,000} = \pm 800$$

We use $x = 800$ feet because $x = -800$ is meaningless in this application. Testing to see whether $x = 800$ gives the minimum cost, we find

$$C''(x) = \frac{32,000,000}{x^3}$$

$C''(x) > 0$ for $x > 0$, so $C(x)$ is concave up for all positive x. Thus $x = 800$ gives the absolute minimum, and $C(800) = 40,000$ is the minimum cost. The other dimension of the rectangular field is $y = 1,600,000/800 = 2000$ feet. Figure 10.37 verifies that $C(x)$ reaches its minimum (of 40,000) at $x = 800$.

Figure 10.37

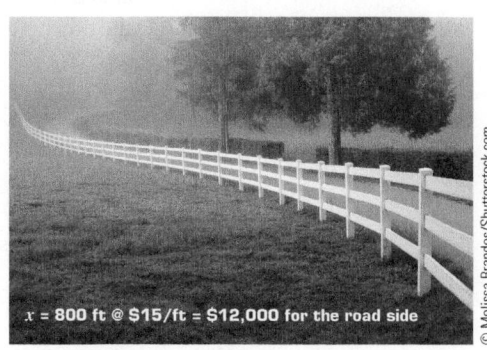

$x = 800$ ft @ $15/ft = $12,000 for the road side

EXAMPLE 3   Postal Restrictions

Postal restrictions limit the size of packages sent through the mail. If the restrictions are that the length plus the girth may not exceed 108 inches, find the volume of the largest box with square cross section that can be mailed.

Solution

Let l equal the length of the box and let s equal a side of the square end. (See Figure 10.38.) The volume we seek to maximize is given by

$$V = s^2 l$$

We can use the restriction that girth plus length equals 108

$$4s + l = 108$$

to express V as a function of s or l. Because $l = 108 - 4s$, the equation for V becomes

$$V = s^2(108 - 4s) = 108s^2 - 4s^3$$

We solve $dV/ds = 0$ to find the critical values.

$$\frac{dV}{ds} = 216s - 12s^2$$

$$0 = s(216 - 12s)$$

The critical values are $s = 0$, $s = \frac{216}{12} = 18$. The critical value $s = 0$ will not maximize the volume, for in this case, $V = 0$. Testing to the left and right of $s = 18$ gives

$$V'(17) > 0 \quad \text{and} \quad V'(19) < 0$$

Thus $s = 18$ inches and $l = 108 - 4(18) = 36$ inches yield a maximum volume of 11,664 cubic inches. Once again, we can verify our results graphically. Figure 10.39 shows that $V = 108s^2 - 4s^3$ achieves its maximum when $s = 18$.

Girth = distance around

Figure 10.38

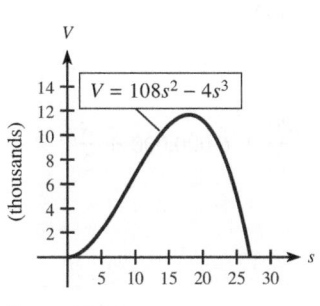

Figure 10.39

CHECKPOINT

Suppose we want to find the minimum value of $C = 5x + 2y$ and we know that x and y must be positive and that $xy = 1000$.

1. What equation do we differentiate to solve this problem?
2. Find the critical values.
3. Find the minimum value of C.

We next consider **inventory cost models,** in which x items are produced in each production run and items are removed from inventory at a fixed constant rate. Because items are removed at a constant rate, the average number stored at any time is $x/2$. Also, when $x = 0$, new items must be added to inventory from a production run. Thus the number of units in storage changes with time and is illustrated in Figure 10.40. In these models, costs are associated with both production and storage, but lowering one of these costs means increasing the other. To see how inventory cost models work, consider the following example.

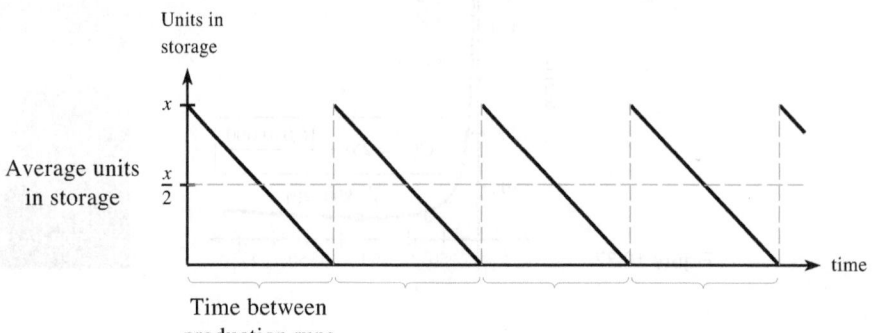

Figure 10.40

EXAMPLE 4 **Inventory Cost Model** | APPLICATION PREVIEW |

Suppose that a company needs 1,000,000 items during a year and that preparation costs are $800 for each production run. Suppose further that it costs the company $6 to produce each item and $1 to store an item for up to a year. If each production run consists of x items, find x so that the total costs of production and storage are minimized.

Solution

The total production costs are given by

$$\binom{\text{No. of}}{\text{runs}}\binom{\text{cost}}{\text{per run}} + \binom{\text{no. of}}{\text{items}}\binom{\text{cost}}{\text{per item}} = \left(\frac{1{,}000{,}000}{x}\right)(\$800) + (1{,}000{,}000)(\$6)$$

The total storage costs are

$$\binom{\text{Average}}{\text{no. stored}}\binom{\text{storage cost}}{\text{per item}} = \left(\frac{x}{2}\right)(\$1)$$

Thus the total costs of production and storage are

$$C = \left(\frac{1{,}000{,}000}{x}\right)(800) + 6{,}000{,}000 + \frac{x}{2} = \frac{800{,}000{,}000}{x} + 6{,}000{,}000 + \frac{x}{2}$$

We want to find x so that C is minimized.

$$C' = \frac{-800{,}000{,}000}{x^2} + \frac{1}{2}$$

If $x > 0$, critical values occur when $C' = 0$.

$$0 = \frac{-800{,}000{,}000}{x^2} + \frac{1}{2}$$

$$\frac{800{,}000{,}000}{x^2} = \frac{1}{2}$$

$$1{,}600{,}000{,}000 = x^2$$

$$x = \pm 40{,}000$$

Because x must be positive, we test $x = 40{,}000$ with the second derivative.

$$C''(x) = \frac{1{,}600{,}000{,}000}{x^3}, \text{ so } C''(40{,}000) > 0$$

Note that $x = 40{,}000$ yields an absolute minimum value of C, because $C'' > 0$ for all $x > 0$. That is, production runs of 40,000 items yield minimum total costs for production and storage.

Technology Note Problems of the types we've studied in this section could also be solved (at least approximately) with a graphing calculator or Excel. With this approach, our first goal is still to express the quantity to be maximized or minimized as a function of one variable. Then that function can be graphed, and the (at least approximate) optimal value can be obtained from the graph. This method is especially useful with problems that have critical values that are difficult to find algebraically, like the one in Example 5.

 EXAMPLE 5 **Property Development**

A developer of a campground must pay for utility line installation to the community center from a transformer on the street at the corner of her property. Because of local restrictions, the lines must be underground on her property. Suppose that the costs are \$50 per meter along the street and \$100 per meter underground. How far from the transformer should the line enter the property to minimize installation costs? (See Figure 10.41.)

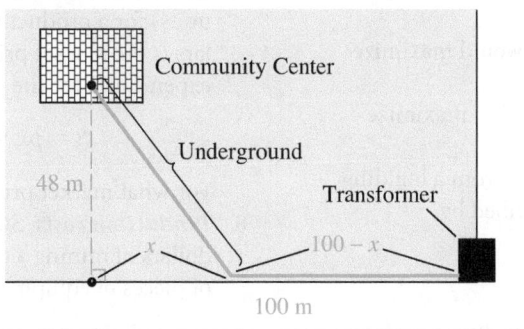

Figure 10.41

Solution

If the developer had the cable placed underground from the community center perpendicular to the street and then to the transformer, then $x = 0$ in Figure 10.41 and the cost would be

$$\$100(48) + \$50(100) = \$9800$$

It may be possible to save some money by placing the cable on a diagonal to the street, but then only $x \leq 100$ makes sense. By using the Pythagorean Theorem, we find that the length of the underground cable that meets the street x meters closer to the transformer is

$$\sqrt{48^2 + x^2} = \sqrt{2304 + x^2} \quad \text{meters}$$

Thus the cost C of installation is given by

$$C = 100\sqrt{2304 + x^2} + 50(100 - x) \quad \text{dollars}$$

Figure 10.42 shows the graph of this function over an interval for x that contains $0 \leq x \leq 100$. Because any extrema must occur in this interval, we can find the minimum by using MIN on a graphing calculator or Excel. See Appendices A and B, Section 10.4, or the Online Excel Guide for the steps. The minimum cost is \$9156.92, when $x = 27.7$ meters (that is, when the cable meets the street 72.3 meters from the transformer).

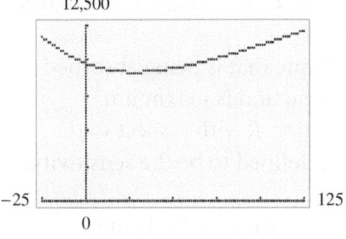

Figure 10.42

EXERCISES 10.4

APPLICATIONS

1. *Return to sales* The manufacturer of GRIPPER tires modeled its return to sales from television advertising expenditures in two regions as follows:

Region 1: $S_1 = 30 + 20x_1 - 0.4x_1^2$
Region 2: $S_2 = 20 + 36x_2 - 1.3x_2^2$

where S_1 and S_2 are the sales revenue in millions of dollars and x_1 and x_2 are millions of dollars of expenditures for television advertising.
(a) What advertising expenditures would maximize sales revenue in each district?
(b) How much money will be needed to maximize sales revenue in both districts?

2. *Projectiles* A ball thrown into the air from a building 100 ft high travels along a path described by
$$y = \frac{-x^2}{110} + x + 100$$
where y is its height in feet and x is the horizontal distance from the building in feet. What is the maximum height the ball will reach?

3. *Profit* The profit per acre from a grove of orange trees is given by $x(200 - x)$ dollars, where x is the number of orange trees per acre. How many trees per acre will maximize the profit?

4. *Reaction rates* The velocity v of an autocatalytic reaction can be represented by the equation
$$v = x(a - x)$$
where a is the amount of material originally present and x is the amount that has been decomposed at any given time. Find the maximum velocity of the reaction.

5. *Productivity* Analysis of daily output of a factory during an 8-hour shift shows that the hourly number of units y produced after t hours of production is
$$y = 70t + \tfrac{1}{2}t^2 - t^3, \quad 0 \le t \le 8$$
(a) After how many hours will the hourly number of units be maximized?
(b) What is the maximum hourly output?

6. *Productivity* A time study showed that, on average, the productivity of a worker after t hours on the job can be modeled by
$$P = 27t + 6t^2 - t^3, \quad 0 \le t \le 8$$
where P is the number of units produced per hour. After how many hours will productivity be maximized? What is the maximum productivity?

7. *Consumer expenditure* Suppose that the demand x (in units) for a product is $x = 10{,}000 - 100p$, where p dollars is the market price per unit. Then the consumer expenditure for the product is
$$E = px = 10{,}000p - 100p^2$$
For what market price will expenditure be greatest?

8. *Production costs* Suppose that the monthly cost in dollars of mining a certain ore is related to the number of pieces of equipment used according to
$$C = 25{,}000x + \frac{870{,}000}{x}, \quad x > 0$$
where x is the number of pieces of equipment used. Using how many pieces of equipment will minimize the cost?

Medication **For Problems 9 and 10, consider that when medicine is administered, reaction (measured in change of blood pressure or temperature) can be modeled by**
$$R = m^2 \left(\frac{c}{2} - \frac{m}{3} \right)$$
where c is a positive constant and m is the amount of medicine absorbed into the blood (*Source:* R. M. Thrall et al., *Some Mathematical Models in Biology,* U.S. Department of Commerce, 1967).

9. Find the amount of medicine that is being absorbed into the blood when the reaction is maximum.

10. The rate of change of reaction R with respect to the amount of medicine m is defined to be the sensitivity.
(a) Find the sensitivity, S.
(b) Find the amount of medicine that is being absorbed into the blood when the sensitivity is maximum.

11. *Advertising and sales* An inferior product with a large advertising budget sells well when it is introduced, but sales fall as people discontinue use of the product. Suppose that the weekly sales S are given by

$$S = \frac{200t}{(t + 1)^2}, \quad t \geq 0$$

where S is in millions of dollars and t is in weeks. After how many weeks will sales be maximized?

12. *Revenue* A newly released film has its weekly revenue given by

$$R(t) = \frac{50t}{t^2 + 36}, \quad t \geq 0$$

where R is in millions of dollars and t is in weeks.
(a) After how many weeks will the weekly revenue be maximized?
(b) What is the maximum weekly revenue?

13. *News impact* Suppose that the percent p (as a decimal) of people who could correctly identify two of eight defendants in a drug case t days after their trial began is given by

$$p(t) = \frac{6.4t}{t^2 + 64} + 0.05$$

Find the number of days before the percent is maximized and find the maximum percent.

14. *Candidate recognition* Suppose that in an election year, the proportion p of voters who recognize a certain candidate's name t months after the campaign started is given by

$$p(t) = \frac{7.2t}{t^2 + 36} + 0.2$$

After how many months is the proportion maximized?

15. *Minimum fence* Two equal rectangular lots are to be enclosed by fencing the perimeter of a rectangular lot and then putting a fence across its middle. If each lot is to contain 1200 square feet, what is the minimum amount of fence needed to enclose the lots (include the fence across the middle)?

16. *Minimum fence* The running yard for a dog kennel must contain at least 900 square feet. If a 20-foot side of the kennel is used as part of one side of a rectangular yard with 900 square feet, what dimensions will require the least amount of fencing?

17. *Minimum cost* A rectangular field with one side along a river is to be fenced. Suppose that no fence is needed along the river, the fence on the side opposite the river costs $40 per foot, and the fence on the other sides costs $10 per foot. If the field must contain 45,000 square feet, what dimensions will minimize costs?

18. *Minimum cost* From a tract of land, a developer plans to fence a rectangular region and then divide it into two identical rectangular lots by putting a fence down the middle. Suppose that the fence for the outside boundary costs $20 per foot and the fence for the middle costs $8 per foot.

If each lot contains 13,500 square feet, find the dimensions of each lot that yield the minimum cost for the fence.

19. *Optimization at a fixed cost* A rectangular area is to be enclosed and divided into thirds. The family has $800 to spend for the fencing material. The outside fence costs $10 per foot installed, and the dividers cost $20 per foot installed. What are the dimensions that will maximize the area enclosed? (The answer contains a fraction.)

20. *Minimum cost* A 4-pen kennel of 640 square feet is to be constructed as shown. The cost is $20 per foot for the sides and $5 per foot for the ends and dividers. What are the dimensions of the kennel that will minimize the cost?

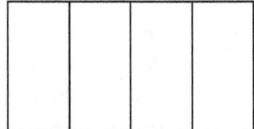

21. *Minimum cost* The base of a rectangular box is to be twice as long as it is wide. The volume of the box is 256 cubic inches. The material for the top costs $0.50 per square inch, and the material for the sides and bottom costs $0.25 per square inch. Find the dimensions that will make the cost a minimum.

22. *Velocity of air during a cough* According to B. F. Visser, the velocity v of air in the trachea during a cough is related to the radius r of the trachea according to

$$v = ar^2(r_0 - r)$$

where a is a constant and r_0 is the radius of the trachea in a relaxed state. Find the radius r that produces the maximum velocity of air in the trachea during a cough.

23. *Inventory cost model* Suppose that a company needs 1,500,000 items during a year and that preparation for each production run costs $600. Suppose also that it costs $15 to produce each item and $2 per year to store an item. Use the inventory cost model to find the number of items in each production run so that the total costs of production and storage are minimized.

24. *Inventory cost model* Suppose that a company needs 60,000 items during a year and that preparation for each production run costs $800. Suppose further that it costs $8 to produce each item and $1.50 to store an item for one year. Use the inventory cost model to find the number of items in each production run that will minimize the total costs of production and storage.

25. *Inventory cost model* A company needs 150,000 items per year. It costs the company $720 to prepare a production run of these items and $14 to produce each item. If it also costs the company $1.50 per year for each item stored, find the number of items that should be produced in each run so that total costs of production and storage are minimized.

26. *Inventory cost model* A company needs 450,000 items per year. Production costs are $1000 to prepare for a production run and $20 for each item produced. Inventory costs are $4 per item per year. Find the number of

items that should be produced in each run so that the total costs of production and storage are minimized.

27. *Volume* A rectangular box with a square base is to be

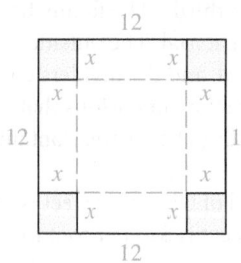

formed from a square piece of metal with 12-inch sides. If a square piece with side x is cut from each corner of the metal and the sides are folded up to form an open box, the volume of the box is $V = (12 - 2x)^2x$. What value of x will maximize the volume of the box?

28. *Volume*
   (a) A square piece of cardboard 36 centimeters on a side is to be formed into a rectangular box by cutting squares with length x from each corner and folding up the sides. What is the maximum volume possible for the box?
   (b) Show that if the piece of cardboard is k centimeters on each side, cutting squares of size $k/6$ and folding up the sides gives the maximum volume.

29. *Revenue* The owner of an orange grove must decide when to pick one variety of oranges. She can sell them for $24 a bushel if she sells them now, with each tree yielding an average of 5 bushels. The yield increases by half a bushel per week for the next 5 weeks, but the price per bushel decreases by $1.50 per bushel each week. When should the oranges be picked for maximum return?

30. *Minimum material*
   (a) A box with an open top and a square base is to be constructed to contain 4000 cubic inches. Find the dimensions that will require the minimum amount of material to construct the box.
   (b) A box with an open top and a square base is to be constructed to contain k cubic inches. Show that the minimum amount of material is used to construct the box when each side of the base is $x = (2k)^{1/3}$ and the height is $y = (k/4)^{1/3}$

31. *Minimum cost* A printer has a contract to print 100,000 posters for a political candidate. He can run the posters by using any number of plates from 1 to 30 on his press. If he uses x metal plates, they will produce x copies of the poster with each impression of the press. The metal plates cost $20 to prepare, and it costs $125 per hour to run the press. If the press can make 1000 impressions per hour, how many metal plates should the printer make to minimize costs?

32. *Shortest time* A vacationer on an island 8 miles offshore from a point that is 48 miles from town must travel to town occasionally. (See the figure.) The vacationer has a boat capable of traveling 30 mph and can go by auto along the coast at 55 mph. At what point should the car be left to minimize the time it takes to get to town?

33. *U.S. oil reserves* By using U.S. Department of Energy data for selected years from 2011 and projected to 2040, the U.S. onshore oil reserves in the lower 48 states (in billions of barrels) can be modeled by the function

$$R(t) = -0.00044t^3 + 0.0042t^2 + 0.52t + 19$$

where t is the number of years past 2010.
   (a) In what year does the model predict the onshore oil reserves in the lower 48 states will reach a maximum? Find the predicted maximum. Is this the absolute maximum for the period from 2011 to 2040?
   (b) Find the absolute minimum point for the period from 2011 to 2040.
   (c) Find the t-value of the point of inflection for $R(t)$. At that t-value, is the rate of change of these oil reserves maximum or minimum? Explain.

SECTION 10.5   Rational Functions: More Curve Sketching

OBJECTIVES

- To locate horizontal asymptotes
- To locate vertical asymptotes
- To sketch graphs of functions that have vertical and/or horizontal asymptotes

APPLICATION PREVIEW

Suppose that the total cost of producing a shipment of a product is

$$C(x) = 5000x + \frac{125,000}{x}, \quad x > 0$$

where x is the number of machines used in the production process. To find the number of machines that will minimize the total cost, we find the minimum value of this rational function. (See Example 3.) The graph of this function contains a vertical asymptote at $x = 0$. We will discuss graphs and applications involving asymptotes in this section.

The procedures for using the first-derivative test and the second-derivative test are given in previous sections, but none of the graphs discussed in those sections contains vertical asymptotes or horizontal asymptotes. In this section, we consider how to use information about asymptotes along with the first and second derivatives, and we present a unified approach to curve sketching.

Asymptotes   In Section 2.4, "Special Functions and Their Graphs," we first discussed asymptotes and saw that they are important features of the graphs that have them. Then in our discussion of limits in Sections 9.1 and 9.2, we discovered the relationship between certain limits and asymptotes. The formal definition of **vertical asymptotes** uses limits.

Vertical Asymptote

The line $x = x_0$ is a **vertical asymptote** of the graph of $y = f(x)$ if the values of $f(x)$ approach ∞ or $-\infty$ as x approaches x_0 (from the left or the right).

From our work with limits, recall that a vertical asymptote will occur on the graph of a function at an x-value at which the denominator (but not the numerator) of the function is equal to zero. These observations allow us to determine where vertical asymptotes occur.

Vertical Asymptote of a Rational Function

The graph of the rational function

$$h(x) = \frac{f(x)}{g(x)}$$

has a vertical asymptote at $x = c$ if $g(c) = 0$ and $f(c) \neq 0$.

Because a **horizontal asymptote** tells us the behavior of the values of the function (y-coordinates) when x increases or decreases without bound, we use limits at infinity to determine the existence of horizontal asymptotes.

Horizontal Asymptote

The graph of a rational function $y = f(x)$ will have a **horizontal asymptote** at $y = b$, for a constant b, if

$$\lim_{x \to \infty} f(x) = b \quad \text{or} \quad \lim_{x \to -\infty} f(x) = b$$

Otherwise, the graph has no horizontal asymptote.

For a rational function f, $\lim_{x \to \infty} f(x) = b$ if and only if $\lim_{x \to -\infty} f(x) = b$, so we only need to find one of these limits to locate a horizontal asymptote. In Problems 37 and 38 in the 9.2 Exercises, the following statements regarding horizontal asymptotes of the graphs of rational functions were proved.

Horizontal Asymptotes of Rational Functions

Consider the rational function $y = \dfrac{f(x)}{g(x)} = \dfrac{a_n x^n + \cdots + a_1 x + a_0}{b_m x^m + \cdots + b_1 x + b_0}$.

1. If $n < m$ (that is, if the degree of the numerator is less than that of the denominator), a horizontal asymptote occurs at $y = 0$ (the x-axis).
2. If $n = m$ (that is, if the degree of the numerator equals that of the denominator), a horizontal asymptote occurs at $y = \dfrac{a_n}{b_m}$ (the ratio of the leading coefficients).
3. If $n > m$ (that is, if the degree of the numerator is greater than that of the denominator), there is no horizontal asymptote.

EXAMPLE 1 **Vertical and Horizontal Asymptotes**

Find any vertical and horizontal asymptotes for

(a) $f(x) = \dfrac{2x - 1}{x + 2}$ (b) $f(x) = \dfrac{x^2 + 3}{1 - x}$ (c) $g(x) = \dfrac{10x}{x^2 + 9}$

Solution

(a) The denominator of this function is 0 at $x = -2$, and because this value does not make the numerator 0, there is a vertical asymptote at $x = -2$. Because the function is rational, with the degree of the numerator equal to that of the denominator and with the ratio of the leading coefficients equal to 2, the graph of the function has a horizontal asymptote at $y = 2$. The graph is shown in Figure 10.43(a).

(b) At $x = 1$, the denominator of $f(x)$ is 0 and the numerator is not, so a vertical asymptote occurs at $x = 1$. The function is rational with the degree of the numerator greater than that of the denominator, so there is no horizontal asymptote. The graph is shown in Figure 10.43(b).

(c) The denominator of this function is never zero ($x^2 + 9 \geq 9$ for every real number). Therefore, there is no vertical asymptote. This is a rational function with the degree of the numerator less than that of the denominator; thus $y = 0$ (the x-axis) is a horizontal asymptote. The graph is shown in Figure 10.43(c).

Figure 10.43   (a)   (b)   (c)

More Curve Sketching   We now extend our first- and second-derivative techniques of curve sketching to include functions that have asymptotes.

In general, the following steps are helpful when we sketch the graph of a function.

Graphing Guidelines

1. Determine the domain of the function. The domain may be restricted by the nature of the problem or by the equation.
2. Look for vertical asymptotes, especially if the function is a rational function.
3. Look for horizontal asymptotes, especially if the function is a rational function.
4. Find the relative maxima and minima by using the first-derivative test or the second-derivative test.
5. Use the second derivative to find the points of inflection if this derivative is easily found.
6. Use other information (intercepts, for example) and plot additional points to complete the sketch of the graph.

EXAMPLE 2 **Graphing with Asymptotes**

Sketch the graph of the function $f(x) = \dfrac{x^2}{(x + 1)^2}$.

Solution

1. This is a rational function, and the domain is the set of all real numbers except $x = -1$ (which makes the denominator equal to 0).

2. Because $x = -1$ makes the denominator 0 and does not make the numerator 0, there is a vertical asymptote at $x = -1$.

3. Because
$$\frac{x^2}{(x+1)^2} = \frac{x^2}{x^2 + 2x + 1}$$
we see that the degree of the numerator of the function is equal to that of the denominator and the ratio of the leading coefficients is 1. Hence, the graph of the function has a horizontal asymptote at $y = 1$.

4. To find any maxima and minima, we first find $f'(x)$.
$$f'(x) = \frac{(x+1)^2(2x) - x^2[2(x+1)]}{(x+1)^4} = \frac{2x(x+1)[(x+1) - x]}{(x+1)^4} = \frac{2x}{(x+1)^3}$$

Thus $f'(x) = 0$ when $x = 0$ (and $y = 0$), and $f'(x)$ is undefined at $x = -1$ (where the vertical asymptote occurs). Using $x = 0$ and $x = -1$ gives the following sign diagram for $f'(x)$. The sign diagram shows that the critical point $(0, 0)$ is a relative minimum and shows how the graph approaches the vertical asymptote at $x = -1$.

*$x = -1$ is a vertical asymptote.

5. The second derivative is
$$f''(x) = \frac{(x+1)^3(2) - 2x[3(x+1)^2]}{(x+1)^6}$$
Factoring $(x+1)^2$ from the numerator and simplifying give
$$f''(x) = \frac{2 - 4x}{(x+1)^4}$$

We can see that $f''(0) = 2 > 0$, so the second-derivative test also shows that $(0, 0)$ is a relative minimum. We see that $f''(x) = 0$ when $x = \frac{1}{2}$. Checking $f''(x)$ between $x = -1$ (where it is undefined) and $x = \frac{1}{2}$ shows that the graph is concave up on this interval.

Note also that $f''(x) < 0$ for $x > \frac{1}{2}$, so the point $\left(\frac{1}{2}, \frac{1}{9}\right)$ is a point of inflection. Also see the sign diagram for $f''(x)$.

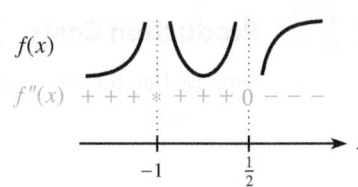

*$x = -1$ is a vertical asymptote.

6. To see how the graph approaches the horizontal asymptote, we check $f(x)$ for large values of $|x|$
$$f(-100) = \frac{(-100)^2}{(-99)^2} = \frac{10,000}{9,801} > 1, \quad f(100) = \frac{100^2}{101^2} = \frac{10,000}{10,201} < 1$$

Thus the graph has the characteristics shown in Figure 10.44(a). The graph is shown in Figure 10.44(b).

(a)

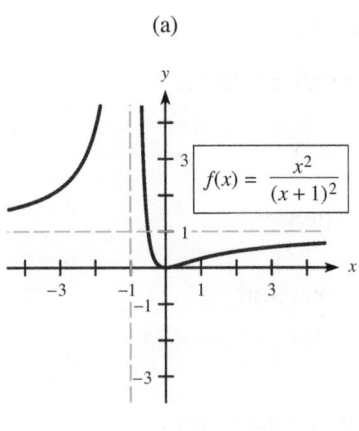

(b)

Figure 10.44

When we want to learn about a function $f(x)$ or sketch its graph, it is important to understand what information we obtain from $f(x)$, from $f'(x)$, and from $f''(x)$. The following summary may be helpful.

DERIVATIVES AND GRAPHS

Source	Information Provided
$f(x)$	y-coordinates; horizontal asymptotes, vertical asymptotes; domain restrictions
$f'(x)$	Increasing [$f'(x) > 0$]; decreasing [$f'(x) < 0$]; critical points [$f'(x) = 0$ or $f'(x)$ undefined]; sign-diagram tests for maxima and minima
$f''(x)$	Concave up [$f''(x) > 0$]; concave down [$f''(x) < 0$]; possible points of inflection [$f''(x) = 0$ or $f''(x)$ undefined]; sign-diagram tests for points of inflection; second-derivative test for maxima and minima

CHECKPOINT

1. Let $f(x) = \dfrac{2x + 10}{x - 1}$ and decide whether the following are true or false.
   (a) $f(x)$ has a vertical asymptote at $x = 1$.
   (b) $f(x)$ has $y = 2$ as its horizontal asymptote.

2. Let $f(x) = \dfrac{x^3 - 16}{x} + 1$; then $f'(x) = \dfrac{2x^3 + 16}{x^2}$ and $f''(x) = \dfrac{2x^3 - 32}{x^3}$.
   Use these to determine whether the following are true or false.
   (a) There are no asymptotes.
   (b) $f'(x) = 0$ when $x = -2$
   (c) A partial sign diagram for $f'(x)$ is

   *means that $f'(0)$ is undefined.

   (d) There is a relative minimum at $x = -2$.
   (e) A partial sign diagram for $f''(x)$ is

   *means that $f''(0)$ is undefined.

   (f) There are points of inflection at $x = 0$ and $x = \sqrt[3]{16}$.

EXAMPLE 3 **Production Costs** | APPLICATION PREVIEW |

Suppose that the total cost of producing a shipment of a certain product is

$$C(x) = 5000x + \frac{125{,}000}{x}, \quad x > 0$$

where x is the number of machines used in the production process.

(a) Determine any asymptotes for $C(x)$.
(b) How many machines should be used to minimize the total cost?
(c) Graph this total cost function.

Solution

(a) Writing this function with all terms over a common denominator gives

$$C(x) = 5000x + \frac{125{,}000}{x} = \frac{5000x^2 + 125{,}000}{x}$$

The domain of $C(x)$ does not include 0, and $C \to \infty$ as $x \to 0^+$, so there is a vertical asymptote at $x = 0$. Thus the cost increases without bound as the number of machines used in the process approaches zero. Because the numerator has a higher degree than the denominator, there is no horizontal asymptote.

(b) Finding the derivative of $C(x)$ gives

$$C'(x) = 5000 - \frac{125{,}000}{x^2} = \frac{5000x^2 - 125{,}000}{x^2}$$

Setting $C'(x) = 0$ and solving for x gives the critical values of x.

$$0 = \frac{5000(x + 5)(x - 5)}{x^2}$$

$$x = 5 \quad \text{or} \quad x = -5$$

Because $C''(x) = 250{,}000 x^{-3} = \dfrac{250{,}000}{x^3}$ is positive for all $x > 0$, using 5 machines minimizes the cost at $C(5) = 50{,}000$.

(c) The graph is shown in Figure 10.45.

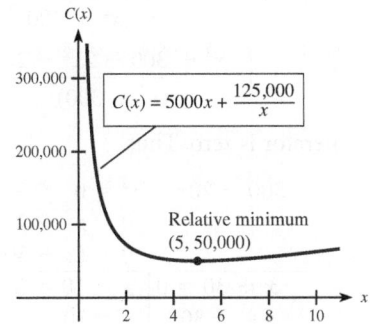

Figure 10.45

$C(x)$

$C(x) = 5000x + \dfrac{125{,}000}{x}$

Relative minimum
(5, 50,000)

EXAMPLE   4

Horizontal and Vertical Asymptotes

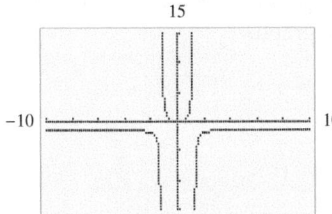

Figure 10.46

Figure 10.46 shows the graph of $f(x) = \dfrac{71x^2}{28(3 - 2x^2)}$.

(a) Determine whether the function has horizontal or vertical asymptotes and estimate where they occur.

(b) Check your conclusions to part (a) analytically.

Solution

(a) The graph appears to have a horizontal asymptote somewhere between $y = -1$ and $y = -2$, perhaps near $y = -1.5$. Also, there are two vertical asymptotes located approximately at $x = 1.25$ and $x = -1.25$.

(b) The function

$$f(x) = \frac{71x^2}{28(3 - 2x^2)} = \frac{71x^2}{84 - 56x^2}$$

is a rational function with the degree of the numerator equal to that of the denominator and with the ratio of the leading coefficients equal to $-71/56$. Thus the graph of the function has a horizontal asymptote at $y = -71/56 \approx -1.27$.

Vertical asymptotes occur at x-values where $28(3 - 2x^2) = 0$. Solving gives

$$3 - 2x^2 = 0 \quad \text{or} \quad 3 = 2x^2 \quad \text{so} \quad \frac{3}{2} = x^2$$

Thus $\qquad \pm\sqrt{\dfrac{3}{2}} = x \quad \text{or} \quad x \approx \pm 1.225$

Calculator Note

The procedures previously outlined in this section are necessary to generate a complete and accurate graph. The graph of a function is easily generated with a graphing calculator, as long as the viewing window is appropriate. We frequently need information provided by derivatives to obtain a window that shows all features of a graph. See Example 5 and Appendix A, Section 10.5, for details. ▪

EXAMPLE 5 Graphing with Technology

The standard viewing window of the graph of $f(x) = \dfrac{x + 10}{x^2 + 300}$ appears blank (check and see). Find any asymptotes, maxima, and minima, and determine an appropriate viewing window. Sketch the graph.

Solution

Because $x^2 + 300 = 0$ has no real solution, there are no vertical asymptotes. The function is rational with the degree of the numerator less than that of the denominator, so the horizontal asymptote is $y = 0$, which is the x-axis.

We then find an appropriate viewing window by locating the critical points.

$$f'(x) = \frac{(x^2 + 300)(1) - (x + 10)(2x)}{(x^2 + 300)^2}$$

$$= \frac{x^2 + 300 - 2x^2 - 20x}{(x^2 + 300)^2} = \frac{300 - 20x - x^2}{(x^2 + 300)^2}$$

$f'(x) = 0$ when the numerator is zero. Thus

$$300 - 20x - x^2 = 0$$
$$0 = x^2 + 20x - 300$$
$$0 = (x + 30)(x - 10)$$

$$\begin{array}{c|c} x + 30 = 0 & x - 10 = 0 \\ x = -30 & x = 10 \end{array}$$

The critical points are $x = -30$, $y \approx -0.01666667$ and $x = 10$, $y = 0.05$. See the sign diagram for $f'(x)$.

Without using the information above, a graphing calculator may not give a useful graph. An x-range that includes -30 and 10 is needed. Because $y = 0$ is a horizontal asymptote, these relative extrema are absolute, and the y-range must be quite small for the shape of the graph to be seen clearly. Figure 10.47 shows the graph. ▪

Figure 10.47

EXERCISES 10.5

In Problems 1–4, a function and its graph are given. Use the graph to find each of the following, if they exist. Then confirm your results analytically.

(a) vertical asymptotes

(b) $\lim\limits_{x \to \infty} f(x)$

(c) $\lim\limits_{x \to -\infty} f(x)$

(d) horizontal asymptotes

1. $f(x) = \dfrac{x - 4}{x - 2}$

2. $f(x) = \dfrac{8}{x + 2}$

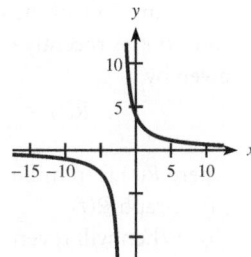

3. $f(x) = \dfrac{3(x^4 + 2x^3 + 6x^2 + 2x + 5)}{(x^2 - 4)^2}$

4. $f(x) = \dfrac{x^2}{(x - 2)^2}$

In Problems 5–10, find any horizontal and vertical asymptotes for each function.

5. $y = \dfrac{2x}{x - 3}$

6. $y = \dfrac{3x - 1}{x + 5}$

7. $y = \dfrac{x + 1}{x^2 - 4}$

8. $y = \dfrac{4x}{9 - x^2}$

9. $y = \dfrac{3x^3 - 6}{x^2 + 4}$

10. $y = \dfrac{6x^3}{4x^2 + 9}$

For each function in Problems 11–18, find any horizontal and vertical asymptotes, and use information from the first derivative to sketch the graph.

11. $f(x) = \dfrac{2x + 2}{x - 3}$

12. $f(x) = \dfrac{5x - 15}{x + 2}$

13. $y = \dfrac{x^2 + 4}{x}$

14. $y = \dfrac{x^2 + 4}{x^2}$

15. $y = \dfrac{27x^2}{(x + 1)^3}$

16. $y = \left(\dfrac{x + 2}{x - 3}\right)^2$

17. $f(x) = \dfrac{16x}{x^2 + 1}$

18. $f(x) = \dfrac{4x^2}{x^4 + 1}$

In Problems 19–24, a function and its first and second derivatives are given. Use these to find any horizontal and vertical asymptotes, critical points, relative maxima, relative minima, and points of inflection. Then sketch the graph of each function.

19. $y = \dfrac{x}{(x - 1)^2}$

$y' = -\dfrac{x + 1}{(x - 1)^3}$

$y'' = \dfrac{2x + 4}{(x - 1)^4}$

20. $y = \dfrac{(x - 1)^2}{x^2}$

$y' = \dfrac{2(x - 1)}{x^3}$

$y'' = \dfrac{6 - 4x}{x^4}$

21. $y = x + \dfrac{3}{\sqrt[3]{x - 3}}$

$y' = 1 - \dfrac{1}{(x - 3)^{4/3}}$

$y'' = \dfrac{4}{3(x - 3)^{7/3}}$

22. $y = 3\sqrt[3]{x} + \dfrac{1}{x}$

$y' = \dfrac{x^{4/3} - 1}{x^2}$

$y'' = \dfrac{6 - 2x^{4/3}}{3x^3}$

23. $f(x) = \dfrac{9(x - 2)^{2/3}}{x^2}$

$f'(x) = \dfrac{12(3 - x)}{x^3(x - 2)^{1/3}}$

$f''(x) = \dfrac{4(7x^2 - 42x + 54)}{x^4(x - 2)^{4/3}}$

24. $f(x) = \dfrac{3x^{2/3}}{x + 1}$

$f'(x) = \dfrac{2 - x}{x^{1/3}(x + 1)^2}$

$f''(x) = \dfrac{2(2x^2 - 8x - 1)}{3x^{4/3}(x + 1)^3}$

In Problems 25–28, a function and its graph are given.

(a) Use the graph to estimate the locations of any horizontal or vertical asymptotes.

(b) Use the function to determine precisely the locations of any asymptotes.

25. $f(x) = \dfrac{9x}{17 - 4x}$ 26. $f(x) = \dfrac{5 - 13x}{3x + 20}$

27. $f(x) = \dfrac{20x^2 + 98}{9x^2 - 49}$ 28. $f(x) = \dfrac{15x^2 - x}{7x^2 - 35}$

For each function in Problems 29–34, complete the following steps.

(a) **Use a graphing calculator to graph the function in the standard viewing window.**

(b) **Analytically determine the location of any asymptotes and extrema.**

(c) **Graph the function in a viewing window that shows all features of the graph. State the ranges for x-values and y-values for your viewing window.**

29. $f(x) = \dfrac{x + 25}{x^2 + 1400}$ 30. $f(x) = \dfrac{x - 50}{x^2 + 1100}$

31. $f(x) = \dfrac{100(9 - x^2)}{x^2 + 100}$ 32. $f(x) = \dfrac{200x^2}{x^2 + 100}$

33. $f(x) = \dfrac{1000x - 4000}{x^2 - 10x - 2000}$

34. $f(x) = \dfrac{900x + 5400}{x^2 - 30x - 1800}$

APPLICATIONS

35. *Cost-benefit* The percent p of particulate pollution that can be removed from the smokestacks of an industrial plant by spending C dollars is given by

$$p = \dfrac{100C}{7300 + C}$$

(a) Find any C-values at which the rate of change of p with respect to C does not exist. Make sure that these make sense in the problem.
(b) Find C-values for which p is increasing.
(c) If there is a horizontal asymptote, find it.
(d) Can 100% of the pollution be removed?

36. *Cost-benefit* The percent p of impurities that can be removed from the wastewater of a manufacturing process at a cost of C dollars is given by

$$p = \dfrac{100C}{8100 + C}$$

(a) Find any C-values at which the rate of change of p with respect to C does not exist. Make sure that these make sense in the problem.
(b) Find C-values for which p is increasing.
(c) Find any horizontal asymptotes.
(d) Can 100% of the pollution be removed?

37. *Revenue* A recently released film has its weekly revenue given by

$$R(t) = \dfrac{50t}{t^2 + 36}, \quad t \ge 0$$

where $R(t)$ is in millions of dollars and t is in weeks.

(a) Graph $R(t)$.
(b) When will revenue be maximized?
(c) Suppose that if revenue decreases for 4 consecutive weeks, the film will be removed from theaters and will be released as a video 12 weeks later. When will the video come out?

38. *Minimizing average cost* If the total daily cost, in dollars, of producing plastic rafts for swimming pools is given by

$$C(x) = 500 + 8x + 0.05x^2$$

where x is the number of rafts produced per day, then the average cost per raft produced is given by $\overline{C}(x) = C(x)/x$, for $x > 0$.

(a) Graph this function.
(b) Discuss what happens to the average cost as the number of rafts decreases, approaching 0.
(c) Find the level of production that minimizes average cost.

39. *Wind chill* If x is the wind speed in miles per hour and is greater than or equal to 5, then the wind chill (in degrees Fahrenheit) for an air temperature of 0°F can be approximated by the function

$$f(x) = \dfrac{289.173 - 58.5731x}{x + 1}, \quad x \ge 5$$

(a) Ignoring the restriction $x \ge 5$, does $f(x)$ have a vertical asymptote? If so, what is it?
(b) Does $f(x)$ have a vertical asymptote within its domain?
(c) Does $f(x)$ have a horizontal asymptote? If so, what is it?
(d) In the context of wind chill, does $\lim\limits_{x \to \infty} f(x)$ have a physical interpretation? If so, what is it, and is it meaningful?

40. *Profit* An entrepreneur starts new companies and sells them when their growth is maximized. Suppose that the annual profit for a new company is given by

$$P(x) = 42 - \frac{1}{2}x - \frac{18}{x+1}$$

where P is in thousands of dollars and x is the number of years after the company is formed. If she wants to sell the company before profits begin to decline, after how many years should she sell it?

41. *Productivity* The figure is a typical graph of worker productivity per hour P as a function of time t on the job.
    (a) What is the horizontal asymptote?
    (b) What is $\lim\limits_{x \to \infty} P(t)$?
    (c) What is the horizontal asymptote for $P'(t)$?
    (d) What is $\lim\limits_{x \to \infty} P'(t)$?

42. *Sales volume* The figure shows a typical curve that gives the volume of sales S as a function of time t after an ad campaign.
    (a) What is the horizontal asymptote?
    (b) What is $\lim\limits_{t \to \infty} S(t)$?
    (c) What is the horizontal asymptote for $S'(t)$?
    (d) What is $\lim\limits_{t \to \infty} S'(t)$?

43. *Females in the workforce* For selected years from 1950 and projected to 2050, the table shows the percent of total U.S. workers who were female.

Year	% Female	Year	% Female
1950	29.6	2010	47.9
1960	33.4	2015	48.3
1970	38.1	2020	48.1
1980	42.5	2030	48.0
1990	45.2	2040	47.9
2000	46.6	2050	47.7

Source: U.S. Bureau of Labor Statistics

Assume that these data can be modeled with the function

$$p(t) = \frac{78.6t + 2090}{1.38t + 64.1}$$

where $p(t)$ is the percent of the U.S. workforce that is female and t is the number of years past 1950.
    (a) Find $\lim\limits_{t \to \infty} P(t)$.
    (b) Interpret your answer to part (a).
    (c) Does $p(t)$ have any vertical asymptotes within its domain $t \geq 0$?
    (d) Whenever $p(t) < 0$ or $p(t) > 100$, the model would be inappropriate. Determine whether the model is ever inappropriate for $t \geq 0$.

44. *Modeling Obesity* Obesity (BMI $\geq$ 30) is a serious problem in the United States and expected to get worse. Being overweight increases the risk of diabetes, heart disease, and many other ailments, but the severely obese (BMI $\geq$ 40) are most at risk and are the most expensive to treat. The percent of Americans who are obese and severely obese from 1990 projected to 2030 are shown in the table below. Report the following models with 3 significant digits.
    (a) Find the linear function, $O(x)$, that models the percent of Americans who are obese, with x equal to the number of years past 1980.
    (b) Find the linear function, $S(x)$, that models the percent of Americans who are severely obese, with x equal to the number of years past 1980.
    (c) Form the rational function $F(x)$ that gives the fraction of obese Americans who are severely obese.
    (d) Find $\lim\limits_{x \to \infty} F(x)$ and tell what it means in terms of these data.
    (e) What does part (d) tell us about the graph of $y = F(x)$?
    (f) Does $F(x)$ have any vertical asymptotes for $x > 0$?

Year	1990	2000	2010	2015	2020	2025	2030
% Obese	12.7	22.1	30.9	34.5	37.4	39.9	42.2
% Severely Obese	0.8	2.2	4.9	6.4	7.9	9.5	11.1

Source: American Journal of Preventive Medicine 42 (June 2012) 563–70, ajpmonline.org

45. *Barometric pressure* The figure shows a barograph readout of the barometric pressure as recorded by Georgia Southern University's meteorological equipment. The figure shows a tremendous drop in barometric pressure on March 13, 1993.
    (a) If $B(t)$ is barometric pressure expressed as a function of time, as shown in the figure, did $B(t)$ have a vertical asymptote sometime after 8 A.M. on March 13, 1993? Explain why or why not.
    (b) Consult Google or another search engine to find out what happened in Georgia (and in the eastern United States) on March 13, 1993, to cause such a dramatic drop in barometric pressure.

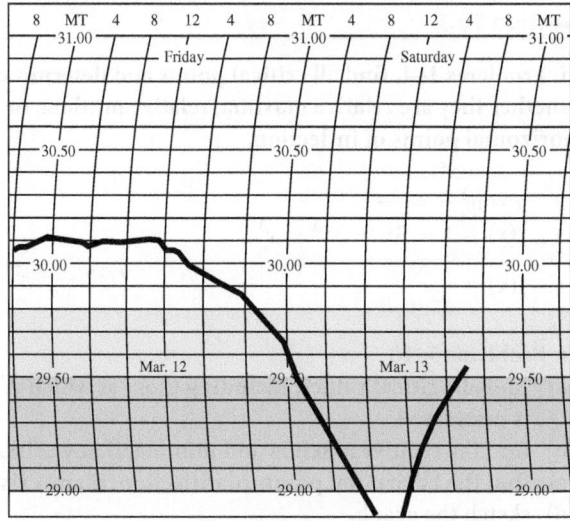

Source: Statesboro Herald, March 14, 1993.

10 CHAPTER SUMMARY & REVIEW

Section 10.1

Relative maxima and minima (p. 629)
Increasing (p. 630)
$f'(x) > 0$
Decreasing (p. 630)
$f'(x) < 0$

Critical points (p. 631)
$f'(x) = 0$ or $f'(x)$ undefined
Sign diagram for $f'(x)$ (p. 632)
First-derivative test (p. 632)
Horizontal point of inflection (p. 634)

Section 10.2

Concave up (p. 644)
$f''(x) > 0$
Concave down (p. 644)
$f''(x) < 0$

Point of inflection (p. 645)
May occur where $f''(x) = 0$ or $f''(x)$ undefined
Sign diagram for $f''(x)$ (p. 645)
Diminishing returns (p. 646)
Second-derivative test (p. 647)

Section 10.3

Absolute extrema (p. 655)
Maximizing revenue (p. 656)
Average cost (p. 658)
$\overline{C}(x) = C(x)/x$

Profit maximization (p. 659)
Monopolistic market (p. 660)
$R(x) = p \cdot x$ where $p = f(x)$ is the demand function
Competitive market (p. 661)
$R(x) = p \cdot x$ where $p =$ equilibrium price

Section 10.4

Inventory cost models (p. 670)

Section 10.5

Asymptotes for $f(x)/g(x)$ (p. 675)
  Vertical: $x = c$ if $g(c) = 0$ and $f(c) \neq 0$
  y unbounded near $x = c$

Horizontal: $y = b$
  $f(x) \to b$ as $x \to \infty$ or $x \to -\infty$
  Use the highest power terms of $f(x)$ and $g(x)$
Graphing guidelines (p. 676)
Derivatives and graphs (p. 678)

REVIEW EXERCISES

Section 10.1

In Problems 1–4, find all critical points and determine whether they are relative maxima, relative minima, or horizontal points of inflection.

1. $y = -x^2$
2. $p = q^2 - 4q - 5$
3. $f(x) = 1 - 3x + 3x^2 - x^3$
4. $f(x) = \dfrac{3x}{x^2 + 1}$

In Problems 5–10
(a) find all critical values, including those at which $f'(x)$ is undefined.
(b) find the relative maxima and minima, if any exist.
(c) find the horizontal points of inflection, if any exist.
(d) sketch the graph.

5. $y = x^3 + x^2 - x - 1$
6. $f(x) = 4x^3 - x^4$
7. $f(x) = x^3 - \dfrac{15}{2}x^2 - 18x + \dfrac{3}{2}$
8. $y = 5x^7 - 7x^5 - 1$
9. $y = x^{2/3} - 1$
10. $y = x^{2/3}(x - 4)^2$

Section 10.2

11. Is the graph of $y = x^4 - 3x^3 + 2x - 1$ concave up or concave down at $x = 2$?
12. Find intervals on which the graph of $y = x^4 - 2x^3 - 12x^2 + 6$ is concave up and intervals on which it is concave down, and find points of inflection.
13. Find the relative maxima, relative minima, and points of inflection of the graph of $y = x^3 - 3x^2 - 9x + 10$.

In Problems 14 and 15, find any relative maxima, relative minima, and points of inflection, and sketch each graph.

14. $y = x^3 - 12x$

15. $y = 2 + 5x^3 - 3x^5$

Section 10.3

16. Given $R = 280x - x^2$, find the absolute maximum and minimum for R when (a) $0 \le x \le 200$ and (b) $0 \le x \le 100$.

17. Given $y = 6400x - 18x^2 - \dfrac{x^3}{3}$, find the absolute maximum and minimum for y when (a) $0 \le x \le 50$ and (b) $0 \le x \le 100$.

Section 10.5

In Problems 18 and 19, use the graphs to find the following items.
(a) vertical asymptotes
(b) horizontal asymptotes
(c) $\lim\limits_{x \to \infty} f(x)$
(d) $\lim\limits_{x \to -\infty} f(x)$

18.

19.

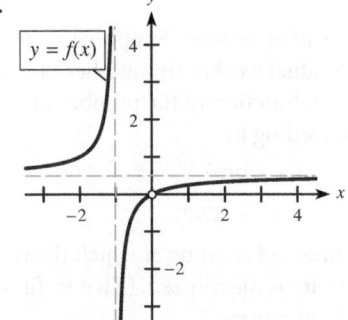

In Problems 20 and 21, find any horizontal asymptotes and any vertical asymptotes.

20. $y = \dfrac{3x + 2}{2x - 4}$

21. $y = \dfrac{x^2}{1 - x^2}$

In Problems 22–24
(a) find any horizontal and vertical asymptotes.
(b) find any relative maxima and minima.
(c) sketch each graph.

22. $y = \dfrac{3x}{x + 2}$

23. $y = \dfrac{8(x - 2)}{x^2}$

24. $y = \dfrac{x^2}{x - 1}$

Sections 10.1 and 10.2

In Problems 25 and 26, a function and its graph are given.
(a) Use the graph to determine (estimate) x-values where $f'(x) > 0$, where $f'(x) < 0$, and where $f'(x) = 0$.
(b) Use the graph to determine x-values where $f''(x) > 0$, where $f''(x) < 0$, and where $f''(x) = 0$.
(c) Check your conclusions to (a) by finding $f'(x)$ and graphing it with a graphing calculator.
(d) Check your conclusions to (b) by finding $f''(x)$ and graphing it with a graphing calculator.

25. $f(x) = x^3 - 4x^2 + 4x$

26. $f(x) = 0.0025x^4 + 0.02x^3 - 0.48x^2 + 0.08x + 4$

In Problems 27 and 28, $f'(x)$ and its graph are given.
(a) Use the graph of $f'(x)$ to determine (estimate) where the graph of $f(x)$ is increasing, where it is decreasing, and where it has relative extrema.
(b) Use the graph of $f'(x)$ to determine where $f''(x) > 0$, where $f''(x) < 0$, and where $f''(x) = 0$.
(c) Verify that the given $f(x)$ has $f'(x)$ as its derivative, and graph $f(x)$ to check your conclusions in part (a).
(d) Calculate $f''(x)$ and graph it to check your conclusions in part (b).

27. $f'(x) = x^2 + 4x - 5 \quad \left(\text{for } f(x) = \dfrac{x^3}{3} + 2x^2 - 5x\right)$

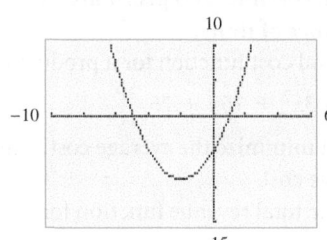

28. $f'(x) = 6x^2 - x^3$ $\left(\text{for } f(x) = 2x^3 - \dfrac{x^4}{4}\right)$

In Problems 29 and 30, $f''(x)$ and its graph are given.
(a) Use the graph to determine (estimate) where the graph of $f(x)$ is concave up, where it is concave down, and where it has points of inflection.
(b) Verify that the given $f(x)$ has $f''(x)$ as its second derivative, and graph $f(x)$ to check your conclusions in part (a).

29. $f''(x) = 4 - x$ $\left(\text{for } f(x) = 2x^2 - \dfrac{x^3}{6}\right)$

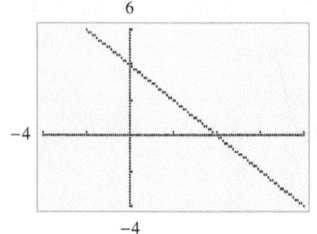

30. $f''(x) = 6 - x - x^2$ $\left(\text{for } f(x) = 3x^2 - \dfrac{x^3}{6} - \dfrac{x^4}{12}\right)$

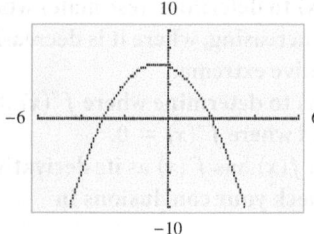

APPLICATIONS

Sections 10.1–10.3

In Problems 31–36, cost, revenue, and profit are in dollars and x is the number of units.

31. *Cost* Suppose the total cost function for a product is

$$C(x) = 3x^2 + 15x + 75$$

How many units will minimize the average cost? Find the minimum average cost.

32. *Revenue* Suppose the total revenue function for a product is given by

$$R(x) = 32x - 0.01x^2$$

(a) How many units will maximize the total revenue? Find the maximum revenue.

(b) If production is limited to 1500 units, how many units will maximize the total revenue? Find the maximum revenue.

33. *Profit* Suppose the profit function for a product is

$$P(x) = 1080x + 9.6x^2 - 0.1x^3 - 50,000$$

Find the maximum profit.

34. *Profit* How many units (x) will maximize profit if $R(x) = 46x - 0.01x^2$ and $C(x) = 0.05x^2 + 10x + 1100$?

35. *Profit* A product can be produced at a total cost of $C(x) - 800 + 4x$, where x is the number produced and is limited to at most 150 units. If the total revenue is given by $R(x) = 80x - \frac{1}{4}x^2$, determine the level of production that will maximize the profit.

36. *Average cost* The total cost function for a product is $C = 2x^2 + 54x + 98$. How many units must be produced to minimize average cost?

37. *Marginal profit* The figure shows the graph of a marginal profit function for a company. At what level of sales will profit be maximized? Explain.

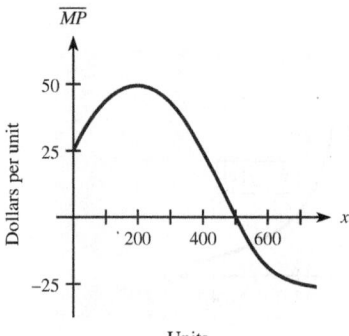

Units

38. *Productivity—diminishing returns* Suppose the productivity P of an individual worker (in number of items produced per hour) is a function of the number of hours of training t according to

$$P(t) = 5 + \dfrac{95t^2}{t^2 + 2700}$$

Find the number of hours of training at which the rate of change of productivity is maximized. (That is, find the point of diminishing returns.)

39. *Output* The following figure shows a typical graph of output y (in thousands of dollars) as a function of capital investment I (also in thousands of dollars).

(a) Is the point of diminishing returns closest to the point at which $I = 20$, $I = 60$, or $I = 120$? Explain.

(b) The average output per dollar of capital investment is defined as the total output divided by the amount of capital investment; that is,

$$\text{Average output} = \dfrac{f(I)}{I}$$

Calculate the slope of a line from $(0, 0)$ to an arbitrary point $(I, f(I))$ on the output graph. How is this slope related to the average output?

(c) Is the maximum average output attained when the capital investment is closest to $I = 40$, to $I = 70$, or to $I = 140$? Explain.

40. *Revenue* MMR II Extreme Bike Shop sells 54 of its most popular mountain bikes per month at a price of $3080 each. Market research indicates that MMR II could sell one more of these bikes for each $20 price reduction. At what selling price will MMR II maximize the revenue from these bikes?

41. *Profit* If in Problem 40 the mountain bikes cost the shop $1360 each, at what selling price will MMR II's profit be a maximum?

42. *Profit* Suppose that for a product in a competitive market, the demand function is $p = 1200 - 2x$ and the supply function is $p = 200 + 2x$, where x is the number of units and p is in dollars. A firm's average cost function for this product is

$$\overline{C}(x) = \frac{12{,}000}{x} + 50 + x$$

Find the maximum profit. (*Hint:* First find the equilibrium price.)

43. *Profit* The monthly demand function for x units of a product sold at p per unit by a monopoly is $p = 800 - x$, and its average cost is $\overline{C} = 200 + x$.
(a) Determine the quantity that will maximize profit.
(b) Find the selling price at the optimal quantity.

44. *Profit* Suppose that in a monopolistic market, the demand function for a commodity is

$$p = 7000 - 10x - \frac{x^2}{3}$$

where x is the number of units and p is in dollars. If a company's average cost function for this commodity is

$$\overline{C}(x) = \frac{40{,}000}{x} + 600 + 8x$$

find the maximum profit.

Section 10.4

45. *Reaction to a drug* The reaction R to an injection of a drug is related to the dose x (in milligrams) according to

$$R(x) = x^2\left(500 - \frac{x}{3}\right)$$

Find the dose that yields the maximum reaction.

46. *Productivity* The number of parts produced per hour by a worker is given by

$$N = 4 + 3t^2 - t^3$$

where t is the number of hours on the job without a break. If the worker starts at 8 A.M., when will she be at maximum productivity during the morning?

47. *Population* Population estimates show that the equation $P = 300 + 10t - t^2$ represents the size of the graduating class of a high school, where t represents the number of years after 2017, $0 \le t \le 10$. What will be the largest graduating class in the next 10 years?

48. *Night brightness* Suppose that an observatory is to be built between cities A and B, which are 30 miles apart. For the best viewing, the observatory should be located where the night brightness from these cities is minimum. If the night brightness of city A is 8 times that of city B, then the night brightness b between the two cities and x miles from A is given by

$$b = \frac{8k}{x^2} + \frac{k}{(30 - x)^2}$$

where k is a constant. Find the best location for the observatory; that is, find x that minimizes b.

49. *Product design* A playpen manufacturer wants to make a rectangular enclosure with maximum play area. To remain competitive, he wants the perimeter of the base to be only 16 feet. What dimensions should the playpen have?

50. *Printing design* A page is to contain 56 square inches of print and have a $\frac{3}{4}$-inch margin at the bottom and 1-inch margins at the top and on both sides. Find the dimensions that minimize the size of the page (and hence the costs for paper).

51. *Drug sensitivity* The reaction R to an injection of a drug is related to the dose x, in milligrams, according to

$$R(x) = x^2\left(500 - \frac{x}{3}\right)$$

The sensitivity to the drug is defined by dR/dx. Find the dose that maximizes sensitivity.

52. *Per capita health care costs* For the years from 2002 and projected to 2024, the U.S. per capita out-of-pocket cost for health care C (in dollars) can be modeled by the function

$$C(t) = 0.908t^3 - 25.3t^2 + 549t + 4540$$

where t is the number of years past 2000 (*Source:* U.S. Centers for Medicare and Medicaid Services).
(a) When does the rate of change of health care costs per capita reach its minimum?
(b) On a graph of $C(t)$, what feature occurs at the t-value found in part (a)?

53. *Inventory cost model* A company needs to produce 288,000 items per year. Production costs are $1500 to prepare for a production run and $30 for each item

produced. Inventory costs are $1.50 per year for each item stored. Find the number of items that should be produced in each run so that the total costs of production and storage are minimum.

Section 10.5

54. *Average cost* Suppose the total cost of producing x units of a product is given by

$$C(x) = 4500 + 120x + 0.05x^2 \quad \text{dollars}$$

(a) Find any asymptotes of the average cost function $\overline{C}(x) = C(x)/x$.
(b) Graph the average cost function.

55. *Market share* Suppose a company's percent share of the market (actual and projected) for a new product t quarters after its introduction is given by

$$M(t) = \frac{3.8t^2 + 3}{0.1t^2 + 1}$$

(a) Find the company's market share when the product is introduced.
(b) Find any horizontal asymptote of the graph of $M(t)$ and write a sentence that explains the meaning of this asymptote.

---

10 CHAPTER TEST

Find the relative maxima, relative minima, points of inflection, and asymptotes, if they exist, for each of the functions in Problems 1–3. Graph each function.

1. $f(x) = x^3 + 6x^2 + 9x + 3$

2. $y = 4x^3 - x^4 - 10$

3. $y = \dfrac{x^2 - 3x + 6}{x - 2}$

In Problems 4–6, use the function $y = 3x^5 - 5x^3 + 2$.
4. Over what intervals is the graph of this function concave up?

5. Find the points of inflection of this function.

6. Find the relative maxima and minima of this function.

7. Find the absolute maximum and minimum for $f(x) = 2x^3 - 15x^2 + 3$ on the interval $[-2, 8]$.

8. Find all horizontal and vertical asymptotes of the function

$$f(x) = \frac{200x - 500}{x + 300}.$$

9. Use the following graph of $y = f(x)$ and the indicated points to complete the chart. Enter $+$, $-$, or 0 according to whether f, f', and f'' are positive, negative, or zero at each point.

Point	f	f'	f''
A			
B			
C			

10. Use the following figure to complete parts (a)–(c).
(a) $\lim\limits_{x \to -\infty} f(x) = ?$
(b) What is the vertical asymptote?
(c) Find the horizontal asymptote.

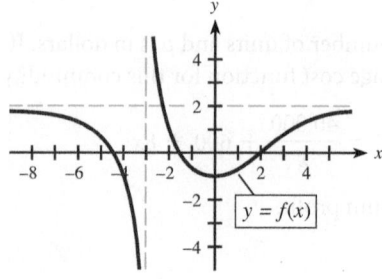

11. If $f(6) = 10, f'(6) = 0$, and $f''(6) = -3$, what can we conclude about the point on the graph of $y = f(x)$ where $x = 6$? Explain.

12. The aged dependency ratio is defined as the number of individuals age 65 or older per 100 individuals ages 20–64. The aging of the baby boomer generation along with medical advancements and lifestyle changes for all individuals have caused this ratio to rise, shaping society's plans for the needs of a greater number of older individuals. By using Social Security Administration data for selected years from 1990 and projected to 2045, the aged dependency ratio can be modeled by the function

$$A(t) = -0.000497t^3 + 0.0449t^2 - 0.669t + 22.3$$

where t is the number of years past 1990.
   (a) Find the critical points for this model, and classify them as relative maxima or relative minima.
   (b) Interpret the points found in part (a)

13. The revenue function for a product is $R(x) = 164x$ dollars and the cost function for the product is

$$C(x) = 0.01x^2 + 20x + 300 \text{ dollars}$$

where x is the number of units produced and sold.
   (a) How many units of the product should be sold to obtain maximum profit?
   (b) What is the maximum possible profit?

14. The cost of producing x units of a product is given by

$$C(x) = 100 + 20x + 0.01x^2 \text{ dollars}$$

How many units should be produced to minimize average cost?

15. A firm sells 100 TVs per month at $300 each, but market research indicates that it can sell 1 more TV per month for each $2 reduction of the price. At what price will the revenue be maximized?

16. An open-top box is made by cutting squares from the corners of a piece of tin and folding up the sides. If the piece of tin was originally 20 cm on a side, how long should the sides of the removed squares be to maximize the resulting volume?

17. A company estimates that it will need 784,000 items during the coming year. It costs $420 to manufacture each item, $2500 to prepare for each production run, and $5 per year for each item stored. How many units should be in each production run so that the total costs of production and storage are minimized?

18. **Modeling** The table gives the number of women age 16 years or older (in millions) in the U.S. civilian workforce for selected years from 1950 and projected to 2050.
   (a) Use x as the number of years past 1950 to create a cubic model using these data. Report the model with three significant digit coefficients.
   (b) During what year does the reported model indicate that the rate of change of the number of women in the workforce reached its maximum?
   (c) What feature of the graph of the function found in part (a) is the result found in part (b)?

Year	Millions of Women in the Workforce
1950	18.4
1960	23.2
1970	31.5
1980	45.5
1990	56.8
2000	65.6
2010	75.5
2015	78.6
2020	79.2
2030	81.6
2040	86.5
2050	91.5

Source: U.S. Bureau of Labor Statistics

10 EXTENDED APPLICATIONS & GROUP PROJECTS

I. Production Management

Metal Containers, Inc., is reviewing the way it submits bids on U.S. Army contracts. The army often requests open-top boxes with square bases and of specified volumes. The army also specifies the materials for the boxes, and the base is usually made of a different material than the sides. The box is assembled by riveting a bracket at each of the eight corners. For Metal Containers, the total cost of producing a box is the sum of the cost of the materials for the box and the labor costs associated with affixing each bracket.

Instead of estimating each job separately, the company wants to develop an overall approach that will allow it to cost out proposals more easily. To accomplish this, company managers need you to devise a formula for the total cost of producing each box and determine the dimensions that allow a box of specified volume to be produced at minimum cost. Use the following notation to help you solve this problem.

Cost of the material for the base = A per square unit

Cost of the material for the sides = B per square unit

Cost of each bracket = C

Cost to affix each bracket = D

Length of the sides of the base = x

Height of the box = h

Volume specified by the army = V

1. Write an expression for the company's total cost in terms of these quantities.
2. At the time an order is received for boxes of a specified volume, the costs of the materials and labor will be fixed and only the dimensions will vary. Find a formula for each dimension of the box so that the total cost is a minimum.
3. The army requests bids on boxes of 48 cubic feet with base material costing the container company $12 per square foot and side material costing $8 per square foot. Each bracket costs $5, and the associated labor cost is $1 per bracket. Use your formulas to find the dimensions of the box that meet the army's requirements at a minimum cost. What is this cost?

Metal Containers asks you to determine how best to order the brackets it uses on its boxes. You are able to obtain the following information: The company uses approximately 100,000 brackets a year, and the purchase price of each is $5. It buys the same number of brackets (say, n) each time it places an order with the supplier, and it costs $60 to process each order. Metal Containers also has additional costs associated with storing, insuring, and financing its inventory of brackets. These carrying costs amount to 15% of the average value of inventory annually. The brackets are used steadily and deliveries are made just as inventory reaches zero so that inventory fluctuates between zero and n brackets.

4. If the total annual cost associated with the bracket supply is the sum of the annual purchasing cost and the annual carrying costs, what order size n would minimize the total cost?
5. In the general case of the bracket-ordering problem, the order size n that minimizes the total cost of the bracket supply is called the economic order quantity, or EOQ. Use the following notations to determine a general formula for the EOQ.

Fixed cost per order = F

Unit cost = C

Quantity purchased per year = P

Carrying cost (as a decimal rate) = r

II. Room Pricing in the Off-Season (Modeling)

The data in the table, from a survey of hotels with comparable rates on Hilton Head Island, show that room occupancy during the off-season (November through February) is related to the price charged for a basic room.

Price per Day	Occupancy Rate, %
$104	53
134	47
143	46
149	45
164	40
194	32

The goal is to use these data to help answer the following questions.

A. What price per day will maximize the daily off-season revenue for a typical hotel in this group if it has 200 rooms available?
B. Suppose that for this typical hotel, the daily cost is $5510 plus $30 per occupied room. What price will maximize the profit for this hotel in the off-season?

The price per day that will maximize the off-season profit for this typical hotel applies to this group of hotels. To find the room price per day that will maximize the daily revenue and the room price per day that will maximize the profit for this hotel (and thus the group of hotels) in the off-season, complete the following.

1. Multiply each occupancy rate by 200 to get the hypothetical room occupancy. Create the revenue data points that compare the price with the revenue, R, which is equal to price times the room occupancy.
2. Find an equation that models the revenue, R, as a function of the price per day, x.
3. Use maximization techniques to find the price that these hotels should charge to maximize the daily revenue.
4. Find a model for the occupancy as a function of the price, and use the occupancy function to create a daily cost function.
5. Form the profit function.
6. Use maximization techniques to find the price that will maximize the profit.

Milifertz/Shutterstock

Derivatives Continued

In this chapter, we develop derivative formulas for logarithmic and exponential functions, focusing primarily on base e exponentials and logarithms. We will apply logarithmic and exponential functions and use their derivatives to solve maximization and minimization problems in the management and life sciences.

We will also develop methods for finding the derivative of one variable with respect to another even when the first variable is not a function of the other. This method is called implicit differentiation. We will use implicit differentiation with respect to time to solve problems involving rates of change of two or more variables. These problems are called related-rates problems.

The topics and some representative applications discussed in this chapter include the following.

Prerequisite Problem Type	For Section	Answer	Section for Review
(a) Simplify: $\dfrac{1}{(3x)^{1/2}} \cdot \dfrac{1}{2}(3x)^{-1/2} \cdot 3$ (b) Write with a positive exponent: $\sqrt{x^2 - 1}$	**11.1**	(a) $\dfrac{1}{2x}$ (b) $(x^2 - 1)^{1/2}$	0.4 Rational exponents
(a) Vertical lines have _____ slopes. (b) Horizontal lines have _____ slopes.	**11.3**	(a) Undefined (b) 0	1.3 Slopes
Write the equation of the line passing through $(-2, -2)$ with slope 5.	**11.3**	$y = 5x + 8$	1.3 Equations of lines
Solve $x^2 + y^2 - 9 = 0$ for y.	**11.3**	$y = \pm\sqrt{9 - x^2}$	2.1 Quadratic equations
(a) Write $\log_a (x + h) - \log_a x$ as an expression involving one logarithm. (b) Does $\ln x^4 = 4 \ln x$? (c) Does $\dfrac{x}{h} \log_a\left(\dfrac{x + h}{x}\right) = \log_a\left(1 + \dfrac{h}{x}\right)^{x/h}$? (d) Expand $\ln (xy)$ to separate x and y. (e) If $y = a^x$, then $x =$ _____. (f) Simplify $\ln e^x$.	**11.1–11.2**	(a) $\log_a\left(\dfrac{x + h}{x}\right)$ (b) Yes (c) Yes (d) $\ln x + \ln y$ (e) $\log_a y$ (f) x	5.2 Logarithms
Find the derivative of (a) $y = x^2 - 2x - 2$ (b) $T(q) = 400q - \dfrac{4}{3}q^2$ (c) $y = \sqrt{9 - x^2}$	**11.1–11.5**	(a) $y' = 2x - 2$ (b) $T'(q) = 400 - \dfrac{8}{3}q$ (c) $y' = -x(9 - x^2)^{-1/2}$	9.4–9.6 Derivatives
If $\dfrac{dy}{dx} = \dfrac{-1}{2\sqrt{x}}$, find the slope of the tangent to $y = f(x)$ at $x = 4$.	**11.3**	Slope $= -\dfrac{1}{4}$	9.3–9.7 Derivatives

SECTION 11.1 # Derivatives of Logarithmic Functions

OBJECTIVES

- To find derivatives of natural logarithmic functions
- To find derivatives of logarithmic functions with bases other than e

APPLICATION PREVIEW

The table shows the expected life spans at birth for people born in certain years in the United States, with projections to 2050. These data can be modeled by the function $l(x) = 8.7744 + 14.907 \ln x$, where x is the number of years past 1900. The graph of this function is shown in Figure 11.1. If we wanted to use this model to find the rate of change of life span with respect to the number of years past 1900, we would need the derivative of this function and hence the derivative of the logarithmic function $\ln x$. (See Example 4.)

Year	Life Span (years)	Year	Life Span (years)
1920	54.1	1990	75.4
1930	59.7	2000	76.8
1940	62.9	2010	78.7
1950	68.2	2020	80.2
1960	69.7	2030	81.7
1970	70.8	2040	83.0
1980	73.7	2050	84.4

Source: National Center for Health Statistics

$l(x) = 8.7744 + 14.907 \ln x$

Figure 11.1

Logarithmic Functions   Recall that we define the **logarithmic function** $y = \log_a x$ as follows.

Logarithmic Function

For $a > 0$ and $a \neq 1$, the **logarithmic function**

$$y = \log_a x \qquad \text{(logarithmic form)}$$

has domain $x > 0$, base a, and is defined by

$$a^y = x \qquad \text{(exponential form)}$$

The a is called the **base** in both $\log_a x = y$ and $a^y = x$, and y is the *logarithm* in $\log_a x = y$ and the *exponent* in $a^y = x$. Thus **a logarithm is an exponent.** Although logarithmic functions can have any base a, where $a > 0$ and $a \neq 1$, most problems in calculus and many of the applications to the management, life, and social sciences involve logarithms with base e, called **natural logarithms.** In this section, we'll see why this base is so important. Recall that the natural logarithmic function ($y = \log_e (x)$) is written $y = \ln x$; see Figure 11.2 for its graph.

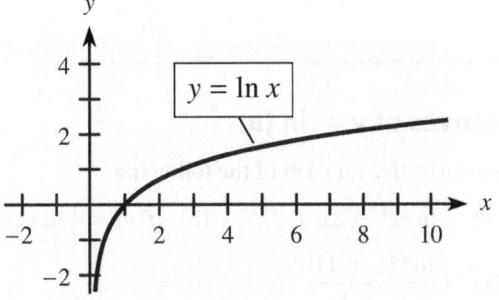

Figure 11.2

Derivative of $y = \ln x$ From Figure 11.2, we see that for $x > 0$, the graph of $y = \ln x$ is always increasing, so the slope of the tangent line to any point must be positive. This means that the derivative of $y = \ln x$ is always positive. Figure 11.3 shows the graph of $y = \ln x$ with tangent lines drawn at several points with their slopes indicated. Note in Figure 11.3 that at each point where a tangent line is drawn, the slope of the tangent line is the reciprocal of the x-coordinate. In fact, this is true for every point on $y = \ln x$, so the slope of the tangent at any point is given by $1/x$.

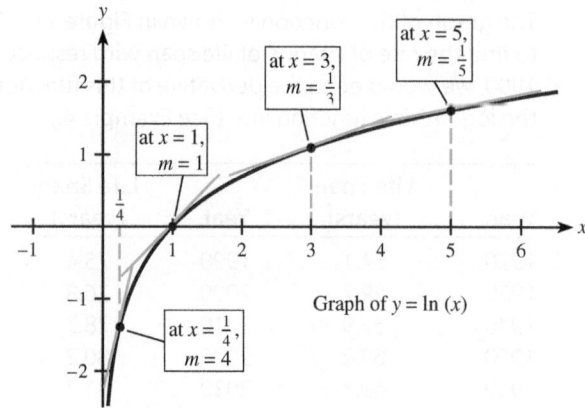

Figure 11.3

At the end of this section, we will prove the following formula for the derivative of $y = \ln x$.

Derivative of $y = \ln x$ If $y = \ln x$, then $\dfrac{dy}{dx} = \dfrac{1}{x}$.

EXAMPLE   1   **Derivatives Involving $\ln x$**

(a) If $y = x^3 + 3 \ln x$, find dy/dx.   (b) If $y = x^2 \ln x$, find y'.

Solution

(a) $\dfrac{dy}{dx} = 3x^2 + 3\left(\dfrac{1}{x}\right) = 3x^2 + \dfrac{3}{x}$

(b) By the Product Rule,

$$y' = x^2 \cdot \dfrac{1}{x} + (\ln x)(2x) = x + 2x \ln x$$

We can use the Chain Rule to find the formula for the derivative of $y = \ln u$, where $u = f(x)$.

Derivatives of Natural Logarithmic Functions   If $y = \ln u$, where u is a differentiable function of x, then

$$\dfrac{dy}{dx} = \dfrac{1}{u} \cdot \dfrac{du}{dx}$$

EXAMPLE   2   **Derivatives of $y = \ln (u)$**

Find the derivative for each of the following.

(a) $f(x) = \ln (x^4 - 3x + 7)$ (b) $f(x) = \frac{1}{3} \ln (2x^6 - 3x + 2)$

(c) $g(x) = \dfrac{\ln (2x + 1)}{2x + 1}$

Solution

(a) $f'(x) = \dfrac{1}{x^4 - 3x + 7}(4x^3 - 3) = \dfrac{4x^3 - 3}{x^4 - 3x + 7}$

(b) $f'(x)$ is $\frac{1}{3}$ of the derivative of $\ln(2x^6 - 3x + 2)$.

$$f'(x) = \frac{1}{3} \cdot \frac{1}{2x^6 - 3x + 2}(12x^5 - 3)$$

$$= \frac{4x^5 - 1}{2x^6 - 3x + 2}$$

(c) We begin with the Quotient Rule.

$$g'(x) = \frac{(2x+1)\dfrac{1}{2x+1}(2) - [\ln(2x+1)]2}{(2x+1)^2}$$

$$= \frac{2 - 2\ln(2x+1)}{(2x+1)^2}$$

CHECKPOINT

1. If $y = \ln(3x^2 + 2)$, find y'.
2. If $y = \ln x^6$, find y'.

Using Properties of Logarithms A logarithmic function of products, quotients, or powers, such as $y = \ln[x(x^5 - 2)^{10}]$, can be rewritten with properties of logarithms so that finding the derivative is much easier. The properties of logarithms, which were introduced in Section 5.2, are stated here for logarithms with an arbitrary base a (with $a > 0$ and $a \ne 1$) and for natural logarithms.

PROPERTIES OF LOGARITHMS

Let M, N, p, and a be real numbers with $M > 0$, $N > 0$, $a > 0$, and $a \ne 1$.

Base a Logarithms	*Natural Logarithms*
I. $\log_a(a^x) = x$ (for any real x)	I. $\ln(e^x) = x$
II. $a^{\log_a(x)} = x$ (for $x > 0$)	II. $e^{\ln x} = x$
III. $\log_a(MN) = \log_a M + \log_a N$	III. $\ln(MN) = \ln M + \ln N$
IV. $\log_a\left(\dfrac{M}{N}\right) = \log_a M - \log_a N$	IV. $\ln\left(\dfrac{M}{N}\right) = \ln M - \ln N$
V. $\log_a(M^p) = p\log_a M$	V. $\ln(M^p) = p\ln M$

For example, to find the derivative of $f(x) = \ln\sqrt[3]{2x^6 - 3x + 2}$, it is easier to rewrite this as follows:

$$f(x) = \ln[(2x^6 - 3x + 2)^{1/3}] = \tfrac{1}{3}\ln(2x^6 - 3x + 2)$$

Then take the derivative, as in Example 2(b).

EXAMPLE ‖ 3 ‖ **Logarithm Properties and Derivatives**

Use logarithm properties to find the derivatives for

(a) $y = \ln[x(x^5 - 2)^{10}]$. (b) $f(x) = \ln\left(\dfrac{\sqrt[3]{3x + 5}}{x^2 + 11}\right)^4$.

Solution

(a) We use logarithm Properties III and V to rewrite the function.

$$y = \ln x + \ln (x^5 - 2)^{10} \qquad \text{Property III}$$
$$y = \ln x + 10 \ln (x^5 - 2) \qquad \text{Property V}$$

We now take the derivative.

$$\frac{dy}{dx} = \frac{1}{x} + 10 \cdot \frac{1}{x^5 - 2} \cdot 5x^4$$

$$= \frac{1}{x} + \frac{50x^4}{x^5 - 2}$$

(b) Again, we begin by using logarithm properties.

$$f(x) = \ln \left(\frac{\sqrt[3]{3x + 5}}{x^2 + 11} \right)^4 = 4 \ln \left(\frac{\sqrt[3]{3x + 5}}{x^2 + 11} \right) \qquad \text{Property V}$$

$$f(x) = 4 \left[\tfrac{1}{3} \ln (3x + 5) - \ln (x^2 + 11) \right] \qquad \text{Properties IV and V}$$

We now take the derivative.

$$f'(x) = 4 \left(\frac{1}{3} \cdot \frac{1}{3x + 5} \cdot 3 - \frac{1}{x^2 + 11} \cdot 2x \right)$$

$$= 4 \left(\frac{1}{3x + 5} - \frac{2x}{x^2 + 11} \right) = \frac{4}{3x + 5} - \frac{8x}{x^2 + 11}$$

CHECKPOINT

3. If $y = \ln \sqrt[3]{x^2 + 1}$, find y'.

4. Find $f'(x)$ for $f(x) = \ln \left[\dfrac{2x^4}{(5x + 7)^5} \right]$.

EXAMPLE 4 **Life Span** | APPLICATION PREVIEW |

Assume that the average life span (in years) for people born from 1920 and projected to 2050 can be modeled by

$$l(x) = 8.7744 + 14.907 \ln x$$

where x is the number of years past 1900.
(a) Find the function that models the rate of change of life span.
(b) Does $l(x)$ have a maximum value for $x > 0$?
(c) Evaluate $\lim_{x \to \infty} l'(x)$.
(d) What do the results of parts (b) and (c) tell us about the average life span?

Solution

(a) The rate of change of life span is given by the derivative.

$$l'(x) = 0 + 14.907 \left(\frac{1}{x} \right) = \frac{14.907}{x}$$

(b) For $x > 0$, we see that $l'(x) > 0$. Hence $l(x)$ is increasing for all values of $x > 0$, and $l(x)$ never achieves a maximum value. That is, there is no maximum life span.

(c) $\lim_{x \to \infty} l'(x) = \lim_{x \to \infty} \frac{14.907}{x} = 0$

(d) If this model is accurate, life span will continue to increase, but at an ever slower rate.

EXAMPLE 5 Cost

Suppose the total cost function for manufacturing x skateboards is given by

$$C(x) = 18{,}250 + 615 \ln (4x + 10)$$

where $C(x)$ is in dollars. Find the marginal cost when 100 units are produced, and explain what it means.

Solution

Marginal cost is given by $C'(x)$.

$$\overline{MC} = C'(x) = 615\left(\frac{1}{4x + 10}\right)(4) = \frac{2460}{4x + 10}$$

$$\overline{MC}(100) = \frac{2460}{4(100) + 10} = \frac{2460}{410} = 6$$

When 100 units are produced, the marginal cost is 6. This means that the approximate cost of producing the 101st skateboard is $6.

Derivative of
$y = \log_a (x)$

So far we have found derivatives of natural logarithmic functions. If we have a logarithmic function with a base other than e, then we can use the **change-of-base formula.**

Change-of-Base Formula

To express a logarithm base a as a natural logarithm, use

$$\log_a x = \frac{\ln x}{\ln a}$$

We can apply this change-of-base formula to find the derivative of a logarithm with any base, as the following example illustrates.

EXAMPLE 6 Derivative of $y = \log_a (u)$

If $y = \log_4 (x^3 + 1)$, find dy/dx.

Solution

By using the change-of-base formula, we have

$$y = \log_4 (x^3 + 1) = \frac{\ln (x^3 + 1)}{\ln 4} = \frac{1}{\ln 4} \cdot \ln (x^3 + 1)$$

Thus

$$\frac{dy}{dx} = \frac{1}{\ln 4} \cdot \frac{1}{x^3 + 1} \cdot 3x^2 = \frac{3x^2}{(x^3 + 1) \ln 4}$$

Note that this formula means that logarithms with bases other than e will have the *constant* $1/(\ln a)$ as a factor in their derivatives (as Example 6 had $1/\ln 4$ as a factor). This means that derivatives involving natural logarithms have a simpler form, and we see why base e logarithms are used more frequently in calculus.

EXAMPLE 7 Critical Values

Let $f(x) = x \ln x - x$. Use the graph of the derivative of $f(x)$ for $x > 0$ to answer the following questions.

(a) At what value a does the graph of $f'(x)$ cross the x-axis [that is, where is $f'(x) = 0$]?
(b) What value a is a critical value for $y = f(x)$?
(c) Does $f(x)$ have a relative maximum or a relative minimum at $x = a$?

Solution

$f'(x) = x \cdot \dfrac{1}{x} + \ln x - 1 = \ln x$. The graph of $f'(x) = \ln x$ is shown in Figure 11.4(a).

(a) The graph crosses the x-axis at $x = 1$, so $f'(a) = 0$ if $a = 1$.
(b) $a = 1$ is a critical value of $f(x)$.
(c) Because $f'(x)$ is negative for $x < 1$, $f(x)$ is decreasing for $x < 1$.
Because $f'(x)$ is positive for $x > 1$, $f(x)$ is increasing for $x > 1$.
Therefore, $f(x)$ has a relative minimum at $x = 1$.
The graph of $f(x) = x \ln x - x$ is shown in Figure 11.4(b). It has a relative minimum at the point $(1, -1)$.

Figure 11.4   (a)   (b)

Calculator Note As with polynomial functions, critical values involving logarithmic functions can be found by using the SOLVER feature of a graphing calculator. Figure 11.5 shows the steps used to find the two critical values of $y = x^2 - 8 \ln x$ by solving $y' = 2x - \dfrac{8}{x} = 0$ with SOLVER to obtain the critical values $x = 2$ and $x = -2$. See Appendix A, Section 11.1, for details. ▨

Figure 11.5

Spreadsheet Note We can use *Data > Analysis > Solver* to find relative maxima and minima for functions involving logarithms just as we did with polynomial functions. See Appendix B, Sections 10.3 and 10.4, or the Online Excel Guide for detailed steps.

Proof That $\dfrac{d}{dx}(\ln x) = \dfrac{1}{x}$ For completeness, we now include the formal proof that if $y = \ln x$, then $dy/dx = 1/x$.

$$\dfrac{dy}{dx} = \lim_{h \to 0} \dfrac{f(x + h) - f(x)}{h}$$

$$= \lim_{h \to 0} \dfrac{\ln(x + h) - \ln x}{h}$$

$$= \lim_{h \to 0} \dfrac{\ln\left(\dfrac{x + h}{x}\right)}{h} \qquad \text{Property IV}$$

$$= \lim_{h \to 0} \dfrac{x}{x} \cdot \dfrac{1}{h} \ln\left(\dfrac{x + h}{x}\right) \qquad \text{Introduce } \dfrac{x}{x}$$

$$= \lim_{h \to 0} \dfrac{1}{x} \cdot \dfrac{x}{h} \ln\left(1 + \dfrac{h}{x}\right)$$

$$= \lim_{h \to 0} \dfrac{1}{x} \ln\left(1 + \dfrac{h}{x}\right)^{x/h} \qquad \text{Property V}$$

$$= \frac{1}{x} \lim_{h \to 0} \left[\ln \left(1 + \frac{h}{x} \right)^{x/h} \right]^{*}$$

$$= \frac{1}{x} \ln \left[\lim_{h \to 0} \left(1 + \frac{h}{x} \right)^{x/h} \right]$$

If we let $a = \dfrac{h}{x}$, then $h \to 0$ means $a \to 0$, and we have

$$\frac{dy}{dx} = \frac{1}{x} \ln \left[\lim_{a \to 0} (1 + a)^{1/a} \right]$$

In Problem 49 in the 9.1 Exercises, we saw that $\lim_{a \to 0} (1 + a)^{1/a} = e$. Hence,

$$\frac{dy}{dx} = \frac{1}{x} \ln e = \frac{1}{x}$$

*The next step uses a new limit property for continuous composite functions. In particular, $\lim_{x \to c} \ln (f(x)) = \ln [\lim_{x \to c} f(x)]$ when $\lim_{x \to c} f(x)$ exists and is positive.

CHECKPOINT
ANSWERS

1. $y' = \dfrac{6x}{3x^2 + 2}$

2. $y' = \dfrac{6}{x}$

3. $y' = \dfrac{2x}{3(x^2 + 1)}$

4. $f'(x) = \dfrac{4}{x} - \dfrac{25}{5x + 7}$

EXERCISES 11.1

Find the derivatives of the functions in Problems 1–10.

1. $f(x) = 4 \ln x$
2. $y = 3 \ln x$
3. $y = \ln 8x$
4. $y = \ln 5x$
5. $y = \ln x^4$
6. $f(x) = \ln x^3$
7. $f(x) = \ln (4x + 9)$
8. $y = \ln (6x + 1)$
9. $y = \ln (2x^2 - x) + 3x$
10. $y = \ln (8x^3 - 2x) - 2x$
11. Find dp/dq if $p = \ln (q^2 + 1)$.

12. Find $\dfrac{ds}{dq}$ if $s = \ln \left(\dfrac{q^2}{4} + 1 \right)$.

In each of Problems 13–18, find the derivative of the function in part (a). Then find the derivative of the function in part (b) or show that the function in part (b) is the same function as that in part (a).

13. (a) $y = \ln x - \ln (x - 1)$

    (b) $y = \ln \dfrac{x}{x - 1}$

14. (a) $y = \ln (x - 1) + \ln (2x + 1)$

    (b) $y = \ln [(x - 1)(2x + 1)]$

15. (a) $y = \frac{1}{3} \ln (x^2 - 1)$ 16. (a) $y = 3 \ln (x^4 - 1)$

    (b) $y = \ln \sqrt[3]{x^2 - 1}$ (b) $y = \ln (x^4 - 1)^3$

17. (a) $y = \ln (4x - 1) - 3 \ln x$

    (b) $y = \ln \left(\dfrac{4x - 1}{x^3} \right)$

18. (a) $y = 3 \ln x - \ln (x + 1)$

    (b) $y = \ln \left(\dfrac{x^3}{x + 1} \right)$

19. Find $\dfrac{dp}{dq}$ if $p = \ln \left(\dfrac{q^2 - 1}{q} \right)$.

20. Find $\dfrac{ds}{dt}$ if $s = \ln [t^3(t^2 - 1)]$.

21. Find $\dfrac{dy}{dt}$ if $y = \ln \left(\dfrac{t^2 + 3}{\sqrt{1 - t}} \right)$.

22. Find $\dfrac{dy}{dx}$ if $y = \ln \left(\dfrac{3x + 2}{x^2 - 5} \right)^{1/4}$.

23. Find $\dfrac{dy}{dx}$ if $y = \ln (x^3 \sqrt{x + 1})$.

24. Find $\dfrac{dy}{dx}$ if $y = \ln [x^2(x^4 - x + 1)]$.

In Problems 25–38, find y'.

25. $y = x - \ln x$
26. $y = x^2 \ln (2x + 3)$
27. $y = \dfrac{\ln x}{x}$
28. $y = \dfrac{1 + \ln x}{x^2}$
29. $y = \ln (x^4 + 3)^2$
30. $y = \ln (3x + 1)^{1/2}$
31. $y = (\ln x)^4$
32. $y = (\ln x)^{-1}$
33. $y = [\ln (x^4 + 3)]^2$
34. $y = \sqrt{\ln (3x + 1)}$
35. $y = \log_4 x$
36. $y = \log_5 x$
37. $y = \log_6 (x^4 - 4x^3 + 1)$
38. $y = \log_2 (1 - x - x^2)$

In Problems 39–42, find the relative maxima and relative minima, and sketch the graph with a graphing calculator to check your results.

39. $y = x \ln x$

40. $y = x^2 \ln x$

41. $y = x^2 - 8 \ln x$

42. $y = \ln x - x$

APPLICATIONS

43. *Marginal cost* Suppose that the total cost (in dollars) for a product is given by

$$C(x) = 1500 + 200 \ln (2x + 1)$$

where x is the number of units produced.
   (a) Find the marginal cost function.
   (b) Find the marginal cost when 200 units are produced and interpret your result.
   (c) Total cost functions always increase because producing more items costs more. What then must be true of the marginal cost function? Does it apply in this problem?

44. *Investment* If money is invested at the constant rate r, the time to increase the investment by a factor x is

$$t = \frac{\ln x}{r}$$

   (a) At what rate $\dfrac{dt}{dx}$ is the time changing at $x = 2$?

   (b) What happens to $\dfrac{dt}{dx}$ as x gets very large? Interpret this result.

45. *Marginal revenue* The total revenue, in dollars, from the sale of x units of a product is given by

$$R(x) = \frac{2500x}{\ln (10x + 10)}$$

   (a) Find the marginal revenue function.
   (b) Find the marginal revenue when 100 units are sold and interpret your result.

46. *Supply* Suppose that the supply of x units of a product at price p dollars per unit is given by

$$p = 10 + 50 \ln (3x + 1)$$

   (a) Find the rate of change of supply price with respect to the number of units supplied.
   (b) Find the rate of change of supply price when the number of units is 33.
   (c) Approximate the price increase associated with the number of units supplied changing from 33 to 34.

47. *Demand* The demand function for a product is given by $p = 4000/\ln (x + 10)$, where p is the price per unit in dollars when x units are demanded.
   (a) Find the rate of change of price with respect to the number of units sold when 40 units are sold.

   (b) Find the rate of change of price with respect to the number of units sold when 90 units are sold.
   (c) Find the second derivative to see whether the rate at which the price is changing at 40 units is increasing or decreasing.

48. *pH level* The pH of a solution is given by

$$pH = -\log [H^+]$$

where $[H^+]$ is the concentration of hydrogen ions (in gram atoms per liter). What is the rate of change of pH with respect to $[H^+]$?

49. *Drug concentration* Concentration (in mg/ml) in the bloodstream of a certain drug is related to the time t (in minutes) after an injection and can be calculated using y in the equation

$$y = A \ln (t) - Bt + C$$

where A, B, and C are positive constants. In terms of A and B, find t at which y (and hence the drug concentration) reaches its maximum.

50. *Decibels* The loudness of sound (L, measured in decibels) perceived by the human ear depends on intensity levels (I) according to

$$L = 10 \log (I/I_0)$$

where I_0 is the standard threshold of audibility. If $x = I/I_0$, then using the change-of-base formula, we get

$$L = \frac{10 \ln (x)}{\ln 10}$$

At what rate is the loudness changing with respect to x when the intensity is 100 times the standard threshold of audibility (that is, when $x = 100$)?

51. *Richter scale* The Richter scale reading, R, used for measuring the magnitude of an earthquake with intensity I is determined by

$$R = \frac{\ln (I/I_0)}{\ln 10}$$

where I_0 is a standard minimum threshold of intensity. If $I_0 = 1$, what is the rate of change of the Richter scale reading with respect to intensity?

52. *Women in the workforce* From 1950 and projected to 2050, the percent of women in the workforce can be modeled by

$$w(x) = 9.42 + 8.70 \ln x$$

where x is the number of years past 1940 (*Source: U.S. Bureau of Labor Statistics*). If this model is accurate, at what rate will the percent be changing in 2020?

53. *Modeling Obesity* Obesity (BMI $\geq$ 30) is a serious problem in the United States and is expected to get worse. Being overweight increases the risk of diabetes, heart disease, and many other ailments. The table gives the percent of Americans who are obese for selected years from 1990 and projected to 2030.

Year	1990	2000	2010	2015	2020	2025	2030
% Obese	12.7	22.1	30.9	34.5	37.4	39.9	42.2

Source: American Journal of Preventive Medicine 42 (June 2012).

   (a) Find a logarithmic function that models the data, with *x* equal to the number of years after 1980 and *y* equal to the percent. Report the model with 3 significant digits.

   (b) Use the reported model to find the instantaneous rate of change of obesity.

   (c) At what rate is obesity projected to increase in 2020?

54. **Modeling *Diabetes*** The following table gives the percent of adult Americans with diabetes for selected years from 2010 and projected to 2050.

   (a) Find a logarithmic function that models the data, with *x* equal to the number of years after 2000 and *y* equal to the percent of the adult American population with diabetes. Report the model with 3 significant digits.

   (b) Use the reported model to find the instantaneous rate of change of the percent of Americans with diabetes.

   (c) At what rate is the percent of Americans with diabetes projected to increase in 2030?

Year	Percent	Year	Percent
2010	15.7	2035	29.0
2015	18.9	2040	31.4
2020	21.1	2045	32.1
2025	24.2	2050	34.3
2030	27.2		

Source: Centers for Disease Control and Prevention

SECTION 11.2 — Derivatives of Exponential Functions

OBJECTIVE

- To find derivatives of exponential functions

APPLICATION PREVIEW

We saw in Chapter 6, "Mathematics of Finance," that the amount that accrues when $100 is invested at 8% compounded continuously is

$$S(t) = 100e^{0.08t}$$

where *t* is the number of years. If we want to find the rate at which the money in this account is growing at the end of 1 year, then we need to find the derivative of this exponential function. (See Example 4.)

Derivative of $y = e^x$ Just as base *e* logarithms are most convenient, we begin by focusing on base *e* exponentials. Figure 11.6(a) shows the graph of $f(x) = e^x$, and Figure 11.6(b) shows the same graph with tangent lines drawn to several points.

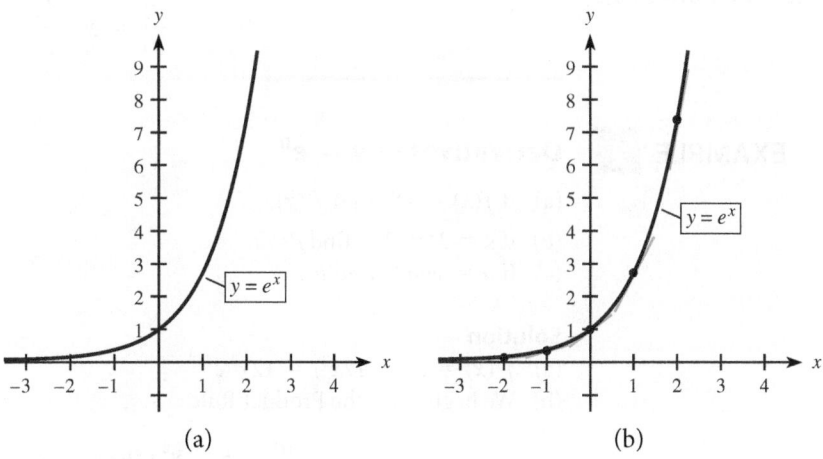

Figure 11.6   (a)   (b)

Note in Figure 11.6(b) that when $x < 0$, tangent lines have slopes near 0, much like the *y*-coordinates of $f(x) = e^x$. Furthermore, as *x* increases to $x = 0$ and for $x > 0$, the slopes of the tangents increase just as the values of the function do. This suggests that the function that gives the slope of the tangent to the graph of $f(x) = e^x$ (that is, the derivative) is similar to the function itself. In fact, the derivative of $f(x) = e^x$ is exactly the function itself, which we prove as follows:

From logarithms Property I, we know that

$$\ln e^x = x$$

Taking the derivative, with respect to x, of both sides of this equation, we have

$$\frac{d}{dx}(\ln e^x) = \frac{d}{dx}(x)$$

Using the Chain Rule for logarithms gives

$$\frac{1}{e^x} \cdot \frac{d}{dx}(e^x) = 1$$

and solving for $\frac{d}{dx}(e^x)$ yields

$$\frac{d}{dx}(e^x) = e^x$$

Thus we can conclude the following.

Derivative of $y = e^x$ If $y = e^x$, then $\dfrac{dy}{dx} = e^x$.

EXAMPLE 1   Derivative of an Exponential Function

If $y = 3e^x + 4x - 11$, find $\dfrac{dy}{dx}$.

Solution

$$\frac{dy}{dx} = 3e^x + 4$$

Derivative of $y = e^u$ As with logarithmic functions, the Chain Rule permits us to expand our derivative formulas.

Derivatives of Exponential Functions   If $y = e^u$, where u is a differentiable function of x, then

$$\frac{dy}{dx} = e^u \cdot \frac{du}{dx}$$

EXAMPLE 2   Derivatives of $y = e^u$

(a) If $f(x) = e^{4x^3}$ find $f'(x)$.
(b) If $s = 3te^{3t^2 + 5t}$, find ds/dt.
(c) If $u = w/e^{3w}$, find u'.

Solution
(a) $f'(x) = e^{4x^3} \cdot (12x^2) = 12x^2 e^{4x^3}$
(b) We begin with the Product Rule.

$$\begin{aligned}
\frac{ds}{dt} &= 3t \cdot e^{3t^2 + 5t}(6t + 5) + e^{3t^2 + 5t} \cdot 3 \\
&= (18t^2 + 15t)e^{3t^2 + 5t} + 3e^{3t^2 + 5t} \\
&= 3e^{3t^2 + 5t}(6t^2 + 5t + 1)
\end{aligned}$$

(c) The function is a quotient. Using the Quotient Rule gives

$$u' = \frac{(e^{3w})(1) - (w)(e^{3w} \cdot 3)}{(e^{3w})^2} = \frac{e^{3w} - 3we^{3w}}{e^{6w}} = \frac{1 - 3w}{e^{3w}}$$

EXAMPLE 3   **Derivatives and Logarithmic Properties**

If $y = e^{\ln x^2}$, find y'.

Solution

$$y' = e^{\ln x^2} \cdot \frac{1}{x^2} \cdot 2x = \frac{2}{x} e^{\ln x^2}$$

By logarithm Property II (see the previous section), $e^{\ln u} = u$, and we can simplify the derivative to

$$y' = \frac{2}{x} \cdot x^2 = 2x$$

Note that if we had used this property *before* taking the derivative, we would have had

$$y = e^{\ln x^2} = x^2$$

and the derivative would be $y' = 2x$.

CHECKPOINT   1. If $y = 2e^{4x}$, find y'.   2. If $y = e^{x^2 + 6x}$, find y'.   3. If $s = te^{t^2}$, find ds/dt.

EXAMPLE 4   **Future Value** | APPLICATION PREVIEW |

When $100 is invested at 8% compounded continuously, the amount that accrues after t years, which is called the future value, is $S(t) = 100e^{0.08t}$. At what rate is the money in this account growing
(a) at the end of 1 year?   (b) at the end of 10 years?

Solution
The rate of growth of the money is given by

$$S'(t) = 100e^{0.08t}(0.08) = 8e^{0.08t}$$

(a) The rate of growth of the money at the end of 1 year is

$$S'(1) = 8e^{0.08} \approx 8.666$$

Thus the future value will change by about $8.67 during the second year.
(b) The rate of growth of the money at the end of 10 years is

$$S'(10) = 8e^{0.08(10)} \approx 17.804$$

Thus the future value will change by about $17.80 during the eleventh year.

EXAMPLE 5   **Revenue**

North Forty, Inc., is a manufacturer of wilderness camping equipment. The revenue function for its best-selling tent, the Sierra, can be modeled by the function

$$R(x) = 250xe^{(1 - 0.01x)}$$

where $R(x)$ is the revenue in thousands of dollars from the sale of x thousand Sierra tents. Find the marginal revenue when 75,000 tents are sold and explain what it means.

Solution
The marginal revenue function is given by $R'(x)$, and to find this derivative, we use the Product Rule.

$$R'(x) = \overline{MR} = 250x[e^{(1-0.01x)} \cdot (-0.01)] + e^{(1-0.01x)}(250)$$
$$\overline{MR} = 250e^{(1-0.01x)}(1 - 0.01x)$$

To find the marginal revenue when 75,000 tents are sold, we use $x = 75$.

$$\overline{MR}(75) = 250e^{(1-0.75)}(1 - 0.75) \approx 80.25$$

This means that the sale of one (thousand) more Sierra tents will yield approximately $80.25 (thousand) in additional revenue.

CHECKPOINT

4   If the sales of a product are given by $S = 1000e^{-0.2x}$, where x is the number of days after the end of an advertising campaign, what is the rate of change in sales 20 days after the end of the campaign?

Derivative of $y = a^u$ In a manner similar to that used to find the derivative of $y = e^x$, we can develop a formula for the derivative of $y = a^x$ for any base $a > 0$ and $a \neq 1$.

Derivative of $y = a^u$ If $y = a^x$, with $a > 0$, $a \neq 1$, then

$$\frac{dy}{dx} = a^x \ln a$$

If $y = a^u$, with $a > 0$, $a \neq 1$, where u is a differentiable function of x, then

$$\frac{dy}{dx} = a^u \frac{du}{dx} \ln a$$

EXAMPLE   6   Derivatives of $y = a^u$

(a) If $y = 4^x$, find dy/dx.   (b) If $y = 5^{x^2+x}$, find y'.

Solution

(a) $\dfrac{dy}{dx} = 4^x \ln 4$

(b) $y' = 5^{x^2+x}(2x + 1) \ln 5$

Calculator Note   As with other functions, we can make use of a graphing calculator to check derivatives of functions involving exponentials. See Appendix A, Section 11.2, for details.

EXAMPLE   7   Technology and Critical Values

For the function $y = e^x - 3x^2$, complete the following.

(a) Approximate the critical values of the function to four decimal places.
(b) Determine whether relative maxima or relative minima occur at the critical values.

Solution

(a) The derivative is $y' = e^x - 6x$. Using the ZERO feature of a graphing calculator, we find that $y' = 0$ at $x \approx 0.2045$ [see Figure 11.7(a)] and at $x \approx 2.8331$.
(b) From the graph of $y' = e^x - 6x$ in Figure 11.7(a), we can observe where $y' > 0$ and where $y' < 0$. From this, we can make a sign diagram to determine relative maxima and relative minima.

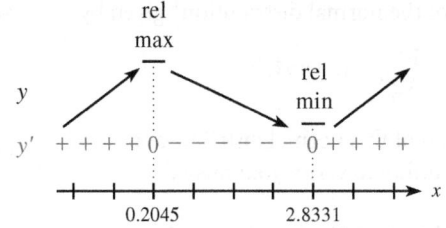

The graph of $y = e^x - 3x^2$ in Figure 11.7(b) shows that the relative maximum point is (0.2045, 1.1015) and that the relative minimum point is (2.8331, −7.0813).

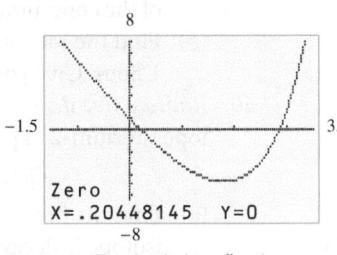

Graph of $y' = e^x - 6x$

Graph of $y = e^x - 3x^2$

Figure 11.7   (a)   (b)

Calculator Note   As with other functions, the SOLVER feature of a graphing calculator can also be used to find maxima and minima of functions involving exponentials. See Appendix A, Section 11.2, for details.

CHECKPOINT ANSWERS

1. $y' = 8e^{4x}$
2. $y' = (2x + 6)e^{x^2 + 6x}$
3. $\dfrac{ds}{dt} = e^{t^2} + 2t^2 e^{t^2}$
4. The rate of change is given by $S'(20) = -200e^{-4} \approx -3.663$ sales/day.

EXERCISES 11.2

Find the derivatives of the functions in Problems 1–34.

1. $y = 5e^x - x$
2. $y = x^2 - 3e^x$
3. $f(x) = e^x - x^e$
4. $f(x) = 4e^x - \ln x$
5. $g(x) = 500(1 - e^{-0.1x})$
6. $h(x) = 750e^{0.04x}$
7. $y = e^{x^3}$
8. $y = e^{x^2 - 1}$
9. $y = 6e^{3x^2}$
10. $y = 1 - 2e^{-x^3}$
11. $y = 2e^{(x^2 + 1)^3}$
12. $y = e^{\sqrt{x^2 - 9}}$
13. $y = e^{\ln x^3}$
14. $y = e^3 + e^{\ln x}$
15. $y = e^{-1/x}$
16. $y = 2e^{\sqrt{x}}$
17. $y = e^{-1/x^2} + e^{-x^2}$
18. $y = \dfrac{2}{e^{2x}} + \dfrac{e^{2x}}{2}$
19. $s = t^2 e^t$
20. $p = 4qe^{q^3}$
21. $y = e^{x^4} - (e^x)^4$
22. $y = 4(e^x)^3 - 4e^{x^3}$
23. $y = \ln(e^{4x} + 2)$
24. $y = \ln(e^{2x} + 1)$
25. $y = e^{-3x} \ln(2x)$
26. $y = e^{2x^2} \ln(4x)$
27. $y = \dfrac{1 + e^{5x}}{e^{3x}}$
28. $y = \dfrac{x}{1 + e^{2x}}$
29. $y = (e^{3x} + 4)^{10}$
30. $y = \dfrac{e^x - e^{-x}}{e^x + e^{-x}}$
31. $y = 6^x$
32. $y = 3^x$
33. $y = 4^{x^2}$
34. $y = 5^{2x - 1}$

35. (a) What is the slope of the line tangent to $y = xe^{-x}$ at $x = 1$?
    (b) Write the equation of the line tangent to the graph of $y = xe^{-x}$ at $x = 1$.

36. (a) What is the slope of the line tangent to $y = e^{-x}/(1 + e^{-x})$ at $x = 0$?
    (b) Write the equation of the line tangent to the graph of $y = e^{-x}/(1 + e^{-x})$ at $x = 0$.

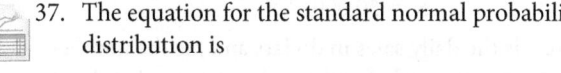 37. The equation for the standard normal probability distribution is

$$y = \frac{1}{\sqrt{2\pi}} e^{-z^2/2}$$

    (a) At what value of z will the curve be at its highest point?
    (b) Graph this function with a graphing utility to verify your answer.

38. (a) Find the mode of the normal distribution* given by

$$y = \frac{1}{\sqrt{2\pi}} e^{-(x-10)^2/2}$$

    (b) What is the mean of this normal distribution?
    (c) Use a graphing utility to verify your answer.

In Problems 39–42, find any relative maxima and minima. Use a graphing utility to check your results.

39. $y = \dfrac{e^x}{x}$ 40. $y = \dfrac{x}{e^x}$

41. $y = x - e^x$ 42. $y = \dfrac{x^2}{e^x}$

APPLICATIONS

43. *Future value* If P is invested for n years at 10% compounded continuously, the future value that results after n years is given by the function

$$S = Pe^{0.1n}$$

    (a) At what rate is the future value growing at any time (for any nonnegative n)?
    (b) At what rate is the future value growing after 1 year ($n = 1$)?
    (c) Is the rate of growth of the future value after 1 year greater than 10%? Explain.

44. *Future value* The future value that accrues when $700 is invested at 9% compounded continuously is

$$S(t) = 700e^{0.09t}$$

    where t is the number of years.
    (a) At what rate is the money in this account growing when $t = 4$?
    (b) At what rate is it growing when $t = 10$?

45. *Sales decay* After the end of an advertising campaign, the sales of a product are given by

$$S = 100{,}000e^{-0.5t}$$

    where S is weekly sales in dollars and t is the number of weeks since the end of the campaign.
    (a) Find the rate of change of S (that is, the rate of *sales decay*).
    (b) From looking at the function and its derivative, explain how you know sales are decreasing.

46. *Sales decay* The sales decay for a product is given by

$$S = 50{,}000e^{-0.8t}$$

    where S is the daily sales in dollars and t is the number of days since the end of a promotional campaign. Find the rate of sales decay.

47. *Marginal cost* Suppose that the total cost in dollars of producing x units of a product is given by

$$C(x) = 10{,}000 + 20xe^{x/600}$$

Find the marginal cost when 600 units are produced.

48. *Marginal revenue* Suppose that the revenue in dollars from the sale of x units of a product is given by

$$R(x) = 1000xe^{-x/50}$$

Find the marginal revenue function.

49. *Drugs in a bloodstream* The percent concentration y of a certain drug in the bloodstream at any time t (in hours) is given by

$$y = 100(1 - e^{-0.462t})$$

    (a) What function gives the instantaneous rate of change of the concentration of the drug in the bloodstream?
    (b) Find the rate of change of the concentration after 1 hour. Give your answer to three decimal places.

50. *Radioactive decay* The amount of the radioactive isotope thorium-234 present at time t in years is given by

$$Q(t) = 100e^{-0.02828t}$$

    (a) Find the function that describes how rapidly the isotope is decaying.
    (b) Find the rate of radioactive decay of the isotope after 10 years.

51. *Pollution* Pollution levels in Lake Sagamore have been modeled by the equation

$$x = 0.05 + 0.18e^{-0.38t}$$

    where x is the volume of pollutants (in cubic kilometers) and t is the time (in years). What is the rate of change of x with respect to time?

52. *Drug concentration* Suppose the concentration $C(t)$, in mg/ml, of a drug in the bloodstream t minutes after an injection is given by

$$C(t) = 20te^{-0.04t}$$

    (a) Find the instantaneous rate of change of the concentration after 10 minutes.
    (b) Find the maximum concentration and when it occurs.

53. *National health care* With U.S. Department of Health and Human Services data from 2002 and projected to 2024, the total public expenditures for health care H can be modeled by

$$H = 1500e^{0.053t}$$

    where t is the number of years past 2000 and H is in billions of dollars. If this model is accurate, at what rate will health care expenditures change in 2022?

54. *Personal consumption* Using U.S. Bureau of Labor Statistics data for selected years from 1994 and projected to 2024, the billions of dollars spent for personal consumption in the United States can be modeled by

$$P = 6010e^{0.0252t}$$

    where t is the number of years after 1990. If this model is accurate, find and interpret the rate of change of personal consumption in 2022.

55. *Richter scale* The intensity of an earthquake is related to the Richter scale reading R by

$$\frac{I}{I_0} = 10^R$$

---

*The mode occurs at the highest point on normal curves and equals the mean.

where I_0 is a standard minimum intensity. If $I_0 = 1$, what is the rate of change of the intensity I with respect to the Richter scale reading?

56. *Decibel readings* The intensity level of sound, I, is given by

$$\frac{I}{I_0} = 10^{L/10}$$

where L is the decibel reading and I_0 is the standard threshold of audibility. If $I/I_0 = y$, at what rate is y changing with respect to L when $L = 20$?

57. *Consumer Price Index* Using Social Security Administration data for selected years from 2012 and projected to 2050, the U.S. Consumer Price Index (CPI) can be modeled by the function

$$C(t) = 92.7 e^{0.0271t}$$

where t is the number of years past 2010. With the reference year as 2012, a 2015 CPI $= 106.15$ means that goods and services costing $100.00 in 2012 cost $106.15 in 2015.

(a) Find the function that describes how fast the CPI model $C(t)$ is changing.

(b) Find the instantaneous rate of change of the CPI model in 2010 and 2025.

(c) From part (b), interpret the rate for 2025.

58. *Blood pressure* Medical research has shown that between heartbeats, the pressure in the aorta of a normal adult is a function of time in seconds and can be modeled by the equation

$$P = 95 e^{-0.491t}$$

(a) Use the derivative to find the rate at which the pressure is changing at any time t.

(b) Use the derivative to find the rate at which the pressure is changing after 0.1 second.

(c) Is the pressure increasing or decreasing?

59. *Spread of disease* Suppose that the spread of a disease through the student body at an isolated college campus can be modeled by

$$y = \frac{10{,}000}{1 + 9999 e^{-0.99t}}$$

where y is the total number affected at time t (in days). Find the rate of change of y.

60. *Spread of a rumor* The number of people $N(t)$ in a community who are reached by a particular rumor at time t (in days) is given by

$$N(t) = \frac{50{,}500}{1 + 100 e^{-0.7t}}$$

Find the rate of change of $N(t)$.

61. *Population* Using Social Security Administration data for selected years from 1950 and projected to 2050, the population of Americans ages 20–64 can be modeled by the function

$$P(t) = \frac{250}{1 + 1.91 e^{-0.0280t}}$$

where t is the number of years after 1950 and $P(t)$ is in millions.

(a) Find and interpret $P'(45)$.

(b) At what rate is this population projected to increase in 2040?

(c) What does this tell us about this population after 2040?

62. *Carbon dioxide emissions* Using U.S. Department of Energy data for selected years from 2010 and projected to 2032, the millions of metric tons of carbon dioxide (CO_2) emissions from biomass energy combustion in the United States can be modeled with the function

$$E(t) = \frac{1310}{1 + 2.95 e^{-0.0619t}}$$

where t is the number of years past 2010.

(a) Find the function that models the rate of change of $E(t)$. Report this function as $E'(t)$ with 3 significant digits.

(b) Find and interpret $E'(15)$.

63. *Modeling Severe obesity* Obesity (BMI ≥ 30) increases the risk of diabetes, heart disease, and many other ailments, but the severely obese (BMI ≥ 40) are most at risk and are the most expensive to treat. The table gives the percent of the Americans who are severely obese for the years from 1990 and projected to 2030.

(a) Find an exponential function that models the data, with x equal to the number of years after 1980 and y equal to the percent. Report the model with 3 significant digits.

(b) Use the reported model to find the instantaneous rate of change of severe obesity.

(c) At what rate is severe obesity projected to increase in 2020?

Year	1990	2000	2010	2015	2020	2025	2030
Severely Obese %	0.8	2.2	4.9	6.4	7.9	9.5	11.1

Source: American Journal of Preventive Medicine 42 (June 2012)

64. *Modeling Centenarians* The following table gives the projected population, in thousands, of Americans over 100 years of age.

(a) Create an exponential function that models the projected population y, in thousands, as a function of the number of years past 2010. Report the model with three significant digits.

(b) Use the reported model to find a function that gives the rate of change in the projected number of centenarians.

(c) What is the projected rate of change in the number of centenarians in 2040?

Year	Centenarians (thousands)	Year	Centenarians (thousands)
2015	78	2040	230
2020	106	2045	310
2025	143	2050	442
2030	168	2055	564
2035	188	2060	690

Source: U.S. Census Bureau

65. *Disposable income per capita* Using U.S. Energy Information Administration data for selected years from 2010 and projected to 2040, the U.S. real disposable income per capita (in thousands of dollars) can be modeled by

$$I(t) = 32.11(1.014)^t$$

where t is the number of years after 2010.
(a) Write the function that models the rate of change of U.S. per capita real disposable income. Use 4 significant digits.
(b) Predict the rate of change of U.S. per capita real disposable income in 2025.

66. *Energy use* U.S. energy use per dollar of GDP indexed to 1980 means that energy use for any year is viewed as a percent of the use per dollar of GDP in 1980. Using U.S. Department of Energy data for selected years from 1985 and projected to 2035, energy use per dollar of GDP can be modeled by the function

$$E(t) = 96e^{-0.019t}$$

where t is the number of years past 1980.
(a) Find the function that describes how rapidly the energy use per dollar of GDP is changing.
(b) Find and interpret $E(50)$ and $E'(50)$.

67. Modeling *Annual wages* The table gives the average annual wage, in thousands of dollars, for selected years from 2012 and projected to 2050.
(a) Find an exponential function that models the data, with x equal to the number of years after 2010 and y equal to the average annual wage in thousands of dollars. Report the model with three significant digits.
(b) Use the reported model to find a function that gives the instantaneous rate of change of the average annual wage. Report this function with 3 significant digits.
(c) Use the result in part (b) to predict the rate of growth of the average annual wage in 2040.

Year	Annual Wage ($ thousands)	Year	Annual Wage ($ thousands)
2012	44.6	2030	93.2
2014	48.6	2035	113.2
2016	53.3	2040	137.6
2018	58.7	2045	167.1
2020	63.7	2050	202.5
2025	76.8		

Source: Social Security Administration

Implicit Differentiation

OBJECTIVES

* To find derivatives using implicit differentiation
* To find slopes of tangents using implicit differentiation

APPLICATION PREVIEW

In the retail electronics industry, suppose the monthly demand for Precision, Inc., headphones is given by

$$p = \frac{10{,}000}{(x + 1)^2}$$

where p is the price in dollars per set of headphones and x is demand in hundreds of sets of headphones. If we want to find the rate of change of the quantity demanded with respect to the price, then we need to find dx/dp. (See Example 8.) Although we can solve this equation for x so that dx/dp can be found, the resulting equation does not define x as a function of p. In this case, and in other cases where we cannot solve equations for the variables we need, we can find derivatives with a technique called implicit differentiation.

Up to this point, functions involving x and y have been written in the form $y = f(x)$, defining y as an *explicit function* of x. However, not all equations involving x and y can be written in the form $y = f(x)$, and we need a new technique for taking their derivatives. For example, solving $y^2 = x$ for y gives $y = \pm\sqrt{x}$ so that y is not a function of x. We can write $y = \sqrt{x}$ and $y = -\sqrt{x}$, but then finding the derivative $\dfrac{dy}{dx}$ at a point on the graph of $y^2 = x$ would require determining which of these functions applies before taking the derivative. Alternatively, we can *imply* that y is a function of x and use a technique called **implicit differentiation.** When y is an implied function of x, we find $\dfrac{dy}{dx}$ by differentiating both sides of the equation with respect to x and then algebraically solving for $\dfrac{dy}{dx}$.

EXAMPLE 1   **Implicit Differentiation**

(a) Use implicit differentiation to find $\dfrac{dy}{dx}$ for $y^2 = x$.

(b) Find the slopes of the tangents to the graph of $y^2 = x$ at the points $(4, 2)$ and $(4, -2)$.

Solution

(a) First take the derivative of both sides of the equation with respect to x.

$$\frac{d}{dx}(y^2) = \frac{d}{dx}(x)$$

Because y is an implied, or implicit, function of x, we can think of $y^2 = x$ as meaning $[u(x)]^2 = x$ for some function u. We use the Chain Rule to take the derivative of y^2 in the same way we would for $[u(x)]^2$. Thus

$$\frac{d}{dx}(y^2) = \frac{d}{dx}(x) \quad \text{gives} \quad 2y\frac{dy}{dx} = 1$$

Solving for $\dfrac{dy}{dx}$ gives $\dfrac{dy}{dx} = \dfrac{1}{2y}$.

(b) To find the slopes of the tangents at the points $(4, 2)$ and $(4, -2)$, we use the coordinates of the points to evaluate $\dfrac{dy}{dx}$ at those points.

$$\frac{dy}{dx}\bigg|_{(4, 2)} = \frac{1}{2(2)} = \frac{1}{4} \quad \text{and} \quad \frac{dy}{dx}\bigg|_{(4, -2)} = \frac{1}{2(-2)} = \frac{-1}{4}$$

Figure 11.8 shows the graph of $y^2 = x$ with tangent lines drawn at $(4, 2)$ and $(4, -2)$. ▪

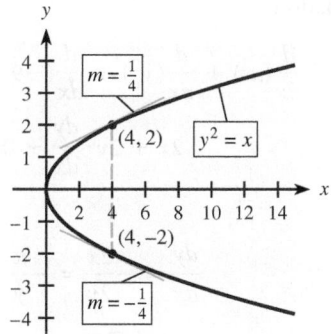

Figure 11.8

As noted previously, solving $y^2 = x$ for y gives the two functions $y = \sqrt{x} = x^{1/2}$ and $y = -\sqrt{x} = -x^{1/2}$; see Figures 11.9(a) and (b).

Figure 11.9   (a)   (b)

We now compare the results obtained in Example 1 with the results from the derivatives of the two functions $y = \sqrt{x}$ and $y = -\sqrt{x}$. The derivatives of these two functions are as follows:

$$\text{For } y = x^{1/2}, \text{ then } \frac{dy}{dx} = \frac{1}{2}x^{-1/2} = \frac{1}{2\sqrt{x}}$$

$$\text{For } y = -x^{1/2}, \text{ then } \frac{dy}{dx} = -\frac{1}{2}x^{-1/2} = \frac{-1}{2\sqrt{x}}$$

We cannot find the slope of a tangent line at $x = 4$ unless we also know the y-coordinate and hence which function and which derivative to use.

$$\text{At } (4, 2) \text{ use } y = \sqrt{x}, \quad \text{so} \quad \left.\frac{dy}{dx}\right|_{(4,\, 2)} = \frac{1}{2\sqrt{4}} = \frac{1}{4}$$

$$\text{At } (4, -2) \text{ use } y = -\sqrt{x}, \quad \text{so} \quad \left.\frac{dy}{dx}\right|_{(4,\, -2)} = \frac{-1}{2\sqrt{4}} = \frac{-1}{4}$$

These are the same results that we obtained directly after implicit differentiation. In this example, we could easily solve for y in terms of x and work the problem two different ways. However, implicit differentiation is used so that explicit solution is not required to find a derivative.

EXAMPLE 2   Slope of a Tangent

Find the slope of the tangent to the graph of $x^2 + y^2 - 9 = 0$ at $(\sqrt{5}, 2)$.

Solution
We find the derivative dy/dx from $x^2 + y^2 - 9 = 0$ by taking the derivative term by term on both sides of the equation.

$$\frac{d}{dx}(x^2) + \frac{d}{dx}(y^2) + \frac{d}{dx}(-9) = \frac{d}{dx}(0)$$

$$2x + 2y \cdot \frac{dy}{dx} + 0 = 0$$

Solving for dy/dx gives

$$\frac{dy}{dx} = -\frac{2x}{2y} = -\frac{x}{y}$$

The slope of the tangent to the curve at $(\sqrt{5}, 2)$ is the value of the derivative at this point. Evaluating $dy/dx = -x/y$ at $(\sqrt{5}, 2)$ gives the slope of the tangent as $-\sqrt{5}/2$. ▪

As we have seen in Examples 1 and 2, the Chain Rule yields

$$\frac{d}{dx}(y^n) = ny^{n-1}\frac{dy}{dx}$$

Just as we needed this result to find derivatives of powers of y, we need to use the product rule to find the derivatives of terms containing both x and y. The next example shows how to use implicit differentiation in an equation involving xy.

EXAMPLE 3   Equation of a Tangent Line

Write the equation of the tangent to the graph of $x^3 + xy + 4 = 0$ at the point $(2, -6)$.

Solution

Note that the second term is the *product* of x and y. Because we are assuming that y is a function of x, and because x is a function of x, we must use the Product Rule to find $\dfrac{d}{dx}(xy)$.

$$\frac{d}{dx}(xy) = x \cdot 1\frac{dy}{dx} + y \cdot 1 = x\frac{dy}{dx} + y$$

Thus we have

$$\frac{d}{dx}(x^3) + \frac{d}{dx}(xy) + \frac{d}{dx}(4) = \frac{d}{dx}(0)$$

$$3x^2 + \left(x\frac{dy}{dx} + y\right) + 0 = 0$$

We solve for $\dfrac{dy}{dx}$ as follows:

$$3x^2 + x\frac{dy}{dx} + y = 0 \Rightarrow x\frac{dy}{dx} = -3x^2 - y$$

$$\Rightarrow \frac{dy}{dx} = \frac{-3x^2 - y}{x}$$

The slope of the tangent to the curve at $x = 2$, $y = -6$ is

$$m = \frac{-3(2)^2 - (-6)}{2} = -3$$

The equation of the tangent line is

$$y - (-6) = -3[x - (2)], \quad \text{or} \quad y = -3x$$

Technology Note   A graphing utility can be used to graph the function of Example 3 and the line that is tangent to the curve at $(2, -6)$. To graph the equation, we solve the equation for y, getting

$$y = \frac{-x^3 - 4}{x}$$

The graph of the equation and the line that is tangent to the curve at $(2, -6)$ are shown in Figure 11.10.

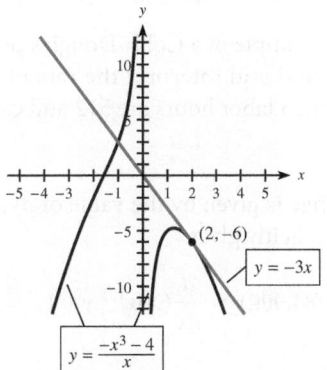

Figure 11.10

In each of the previous examples, we could have explicitly solved for y in terms of x before finding the derivative. But for many functions, solving for y is difficult or impossible and implicit differentiation is necessary.

EXAMPLE 4   Implicit Differentiation

Find dy/dx if $x^4 + 5xy^4 = 2y^2 + x - 1$.

Solution

By viewing $5xy^4$ as the product $(5x)(y^4)$ and differentiating implicitly, we get

$$\frac{d}{dx}(x^4) + \frac{d}{dx}(5xy^4) = \frac{d}{dx}(2y^2) + \frac{d}{dx}(x) - \frac{d}{dx}(1)$$

$$4x^3 + 5x\left(4y^3\frac{dy}{dx}\right) + y^4(5) = 4y\frac{dy}{dx} + 1$$

To solve for $\dfrac{dy}{dx}$, we first rewrite the equation with terms containing $\dfrac{dy}{dx}$ on one side and the other terms on the other side.

$$20xy^3\frac{dy}{dx} - 4y\frac{dy}{dx} = 1 - 4x^3 - 5y^4$$

Now $\dfrac{dy}{dx}$ is a factor of one side. To complete the solution, we factor out $\dfrac{dy}{dx}$ and divide both sides by its coefficient.

$$(20xy^3 - 4y)\frac{dy}{dx} = 1 - 4x^3 - 5y^4$$

$$\frac{dy}{dx} = \frac{1 - 4x^3 - 5y^4}{20xy^3 - 4y}$$

CHECKPOINT

1. Find the following:

   (a) $\dfrac{d}{dx}(x^3)$ (b) $\dfrac{d}{dx}(y^4)$ (c) $\dfrac{d}{dx}(x^2y^5)$

2. Find $\dfrac{dy}{dx}$ for $x^3 + y^4 = x^2y^5$.

EXAMPLE 5   Production

Suppose that a company's weekly production output is $384,000 and that this output is related to hours of labor x and dollars of capital investment y by

$$384{,}000 = 30x^{1/3}\,y^{2/3}$$

(This relationship is an example of a Cobb-Douglas production function, studied in more detail in Chapter 14.) Find and interpret the rate of change of capital investment with respect to labor hours when labor hours are 512 and capital investment is $64,000.

Solution

The desired rate of change is given by the value of dy/dx when $x = 512$ and $y = 64{,}000$. Taking the derivative implicitly gives

$$\frac{d}{dx}(384{,}000) = \frac{d}{dx}(30x^{1/3}\,y^{2/3})$$

$$0 = 30x^{1/3}\left(\frac{2}{3}y^{-1/3}\frac{dy}{dx}\right) + y^{2/3}(10x^{-2/3})$$

$$0 = \frac{20x^{1/3}}{y^{1/3}} \cdot \frac{dy}{dx} + \frac{10y^{2/3}}{x^{2/3}}$$

$$\frac{-20x^{1/3}}{y^{1/3}} \cdot \frac{dy}{dx} = \frac{10y^{2/3}}{x^{2/3}}$$

Multiplying both sides by $\dfrac{-y^{1/3}}{20x^{1/3}}$ gives

$$\frac{dy}{dx} = \left(\frac{10y^{2/3}}{x^{2/3}}\right)\left(\frac{-y^{1/3}}{20x^{1/3}}\right) = \frac{-y}{2x}$$

When $x = 512$ and $y = 64{,}000$, we obtain

$$\frac{dy}{dx} = \frac{-64{,}000}{2(512)} = -62.5$$

This means that when labor hours are 512 and capital investment is \$64,000, changing labor hours by 1 hour results in a decrease of about \$62.50 in capital investment. ◼

EXAMPLE 6   Horizontal and Vertical Tangents

(a) At what point(s) does $x^2 + 4y^2 - 2x + 4y - 2 = 0$ have a horizontal tangent?
(b) At what point(s) does it have a vertical tangent?

Solution

(a) First, we find the derivative implicitly, with y' representing $\dfrac{dy}{dx}$.

$$2x + 8y \cdot y' - 2 + 4y' - 0 = 0$$

We isolate the y' terms, factor out y', and solve for y'.

$$8yy' + 4y' = 2 - 2x$$
$$(8y + 4)y' = 2 - 2x$$
$$y' = \frac{2 - 2x}{8y + 4} = \frac{1 - x}{4y + 2}$$

Horizontal tangents will occur where $y' = 0$; that is, where $1 - x = 0$, or $x = 1$. We can now find the corresponding y-value(s) by substituting 1 for x in the original equation and solving.

$$1 + 4y^2 - 2 + 4y - 2 = 0$$
$$4y^2 + 4y - 3 = 0$$
$$(2y - 1)(2y + 3) = 0$$
$$y = \frac{1}{2} \quad \text{or} \quad y = -\frac{3}{2}$$

Thus horizontal tangents occur at $\left(1, \frac{1}{2}\right)$ and $\left(1, -\frac{3}{2}\right)$; see Figure 11.11.

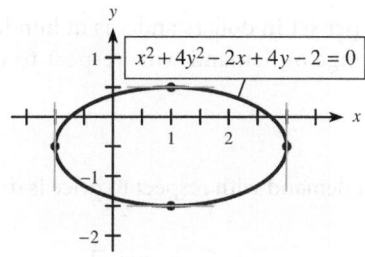

Figure 11.11

(b) Vertical tangents will occur where the derivative is undefined—that is, where $4y + 2 = 0$, or $y = -\frac{1}{2}$. To find the corresponding x-value(s), we substitute $-\frac{1}{2}$ in the equation for y and solve for x.

$$x^2 + 4\left(-\frac{1}{2}\right)^2 - 2x + 4\left(-\frac{1}{2}\right) - 2 = 0$$

$$x^2 - 2x - 3 = 0$$
$$(x - 3)(x + 1) = 0$$
$$x = 3 \quad \text{or} \quad x = -1$$

Thus vertical tangents occur at $\left(3, -\frac{1}{2}\right)$ and $\left(-1, -\frac{1}{2}\right)$. See Figure 11.11.

EXAMPLE 7   Implicit Derivatives with Logarithms and Exponentials

Find dy/dx for each of the following.
(a) $\ln xy = 6$ (b) $4x^2 + e^{xy} = 6y$

Solution
(a) Using the properties of logarithms, we have

$$\ln x + \ln y = 6$$

which leads to the implicit derivative

$$\frac{1}{x} + \frac{1}{y}\frac{dy}{dx} = 0$$

Solving gives $\dfrac{1}{y}\dfrac{dy}{dx} = -\dfrac{1}{x}$ so $\dfrac{dy}{dx} = -\dfrac{y}{x}$

(b) We take the derivative of both sides of $4x^2 + e^{xy} = 6y$ and obtain

$$8x + e^{xy}\left(x\frac{dy}{dx} + y\right) = 6\frac{dy}{dx}$$

$$8x + xe^{xy}\frac{dy}{dx} + ye^{xy} = 6\frac{dy}{dx}$$

$$8x + ye^{xy} = 6\frac{dy}{dx} - xe^{xy}\frac{dy}{dx}$$

$$8x + ye^{xy} = (6 - xe^{xy})\frac{dy}{dx}$$ so $\dfrac{8x + ye^{xy}}{6 - xe^{xy}} = \dfrac{dy}{dx}$

EXAMPLE 8   Demand | APPLICATION PREVIEW |

Suppose the demand for Precision, Inc. headphones is given by

$$p = \frac{10,000}{(x + 1)^2}$$

where p is the price per set in dollars and x is in hundreds of headphone sets demanded. Find the rate of change of demand with respect to price when 19 (hundred) sets are demanded.

Solution
The rate of change of demand with respect to price is dx/dp. Using implicit differentiation, we get

$$\frac{d}{dp}(p) = \frac{d}{dp}\left[\frac{10,000}{(x + 1)^2}\right] = \frac{d}{dp}[10,000(x + 1)^{-2}]$$

$$1 = 10,000\left[-2(x+1)^{-3}\frac{dx}{dp}\right]$$

$$1 = \frac{-20,000}{(x+1)^3} \cdot \frac{dx}{dp}$$

$$\frac{(x+1)^3}{-20,000} = \frac{dx}{dp}$$

When 19 (hundred) headphone sets are demanded, we use $x = 19$, and the rate of change of demand with respect to price is

$$\frac{dx}{dp}\bigg|_{x=19} = \frac{(19+1)^3}{-20,000} = \frac{8000}{-20,000} = -0.4$$

This result means that when 19 (hundred) headphone sets are demanded, if the price per set is increased by \$1, then the expected change in demand is a decrease of about 0.4 hundred, or 40, headphone sets. ◼

Calculator Note   To graph a function using a graphing calculator, we need to write y as an *explicit* function of x (such as $y = \sqrt{4 - x^2}$). If an equation defines y as an *implicit* function of x, we must solve for y in terms of x before we can use the graphing calculator. Sometimes we cannot solve for y, and other times, such as for

$$x^{2/3} + y^{2/3} = 8^{2/3}$$

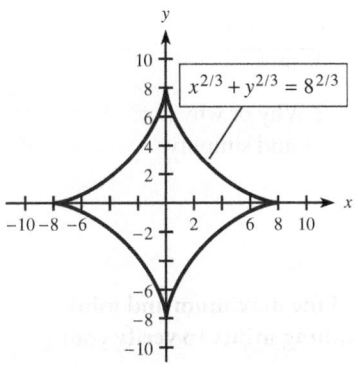

y cannot be written as a single function of x. If this equation is solved for y as a single function and a graphing calculator is used to graph that function, the resulting graph usually shows only the portion of the graph that lies in Quadrants I and II. To graph $x^{2/3} + y^{2/3} = 8^{2/3}$, we solve for y.

$$y^{2/3} = 8^{2/3} - x^{2/3} \Rightarrow y^2 = (8^{2/3} - x^{2/3})^3 \Rightarrow y = \pm\sqrt{(8^{2/3} - x^{2/3})^3}$$

Graphing $Y_1 = \sqrt{(8^{2/3} - x^{2/3})^3}$ and $Y_2 = -\sqrt{(8^{2/3} - x^{2/3})^3}$ on a window such as 5:ZSquare gives a complete graph like the one shown in Figure 11.12. In general, for the graph of an implicitly defined function, a graphing calculator must be used carefully (and sometimes cannot be used at all). ◼

Figure 11.12

CHECKPOINT
ANSWERS

1. (a) $\dfrac{d}{dx}(x^3) = 3x^2$ (b) $\dfrac{d}{dx}(y^4) = 4y^3\dfrac{dy}{dx}$

(c) $\dfrac{d}{dx}(x^2y^5) = x^2\left(5y^4\dfrac{dy}{dx}\right) + y^5(2x)$

2. $\dfrac{dy}{dx} = \dfrac{3x^2 - 2xy^5}{5x^2y^4 - 4y^3}$

EXERCISES 11.3

In Problems 1–6, find dy/dx at the given point without first solving for y.

1. $x^2 - 4y - 17 = 0$ at $(1, -4)$
2. $3x^2 - 10y + 400 = 0$ at $(10, 70)$
3. $xy^2 = 8$ at $(2, 2)$
4. $e^y = x$ at $(1, 0)$
5. $x^2 + 3xy - 4 = 0$ at $(1, 1)$
6. $x^2 + 5xy + 4 = 0$ at $(1, -1)$

Find dy/dx for the functions in Problems 7–10.

7. $x^2 + 2y^2 - 4 = 0$
8. $x + y^2 - 4y + 6 = 0$
9. $x^2 + 4x + y^2 - 3y + 1 = 0$
10. $x^2 - 5x + y^3 - 3y - 3 = 0$
11. If $x^2 + y^2 = 4$, find y'.
12. If $p^2 + 4p - q = 4$, find dp/dq.
13. If $xy^2 - y^3 = 1$, find y'.

14. If $p^2 - q = 4$, find dp/dq.
15. If $p^2q = 4p - 2$, find dp/dq.
16. If $x^2 - 3y^4 = 2x^5 + 7y^3 - 5$, find dy/dx.
17. If $3x^5 - 5y^3 = 5x^2 + 3y^5$, find dy/dx.
18. If $x^2 + 3x^2y^4 = y + 8$, find dy/dx.
19. If $x^4 + 2x^3y^2 = x - y^3$, find dy/dx.
20. If $(x + y)^2 = 5x^4y^3$, find dy/dx.
21. Find dy/dx for $x^4 + 3x^3y^2 - 2y^5 = (2x + 3y)^2$.
22. Find y' for $2x + 2y = \sqrt{x^2 + y^2}$.

For Problems 23–26, find the slope of the line tangent to the curve.

23. $x^2 + 4x + y^2 + 2y - 4 = 0$ at $(1, -1)$
24. $2x^2 - 10x + 2y^3 + 14 = 0$ at $(3, -1)$
25. $x^2 + 2xy + 3 = 0$ at $(-1, 2)$
26. $y^2 + 2x^2 + 4xy + 7 = 0$ at $(-2, 3)$

In Problems 27–30, write the equation of the tangent line to each curve at the given point.

27. $x^2 - 2y^2 + 4 = 0$ at $(2, 2)$
28. $x^2 + y^2 + 6x - 3y + 7 = 0$ at $(-1, 2)$
29. $4x^2 - 2y^2 + 3xy - 3x = 26$ at $(-2, -1)$
30. $8xy + y^2 - x^2 + 38x = 217$ at $(3, 4)$
31. If $\ln x = y^2$, find dy/dx.
32. If $\ln (x + y) = y^2$, find dy/dx.
33. If $y^2 \ln x = 4$, find dy/dx.
34. If $\ln (xy - 1) = x + 2$, find dy/dx.
35. If $xe^y = 6$, find dy/dx.
36. If $x + e^{xy} = 10$, find dy/dx.
37. If $xe^{xy} = 4$, find dy/dx.
38. If $x - xe^y = 3$, find dy/dx.
39. If $ye^x - y = 3$, find dy/dx.
40. If $x^2y = e^{x+y}$, find dy/dx.
41. Find the slope of the tangent to the curve $y^2 \ln x + x^2y = 3$ at the point $(1, 3)$.
42. Write the equation of the line tangent to the curve $x \ln y + 2xy = 2$ at the point $(1, 1)$.
43. Find the slope of the line tangent to the graph of $ye^x = y^2 + x - 2$ at $(0, 2)$.
44. Find the slope of the line tangent to the curve $xe^y = 3x^2 + y - 24$ at $(3, 0)$.
45. Write the equation of the line tangent to the curve $xe^y = 2y + 3$ at $(3, 0)$.
46. Write the equation of the line tangent to the curve $ye^x = 2y + 1$ at $(0, -1)$.
47. At what points does the curve defined by $x^2 + 4y^2 - 4x - 4 = 0$ have
    (a) horizontal tangents?
    (b) vertical tangents?
48. At what points does the curve defined by $x^2 + 4y^2 - 4 = 0$ have
    (a) horizontal tangents?
    (b) vertical tangents?
49. In Problem 11, the derivative y' was found to be
$$y' = \frac{-x}{y}$$

when $x^2 + y^2 = 4$.
(a) Take the implicit derivative of the equation for y' to show that
$$y'' = \frac{-y + xy'}{y^2}$$
(b) Substitute $-x/y$ for y' in the expression for y'' in part (a) and simplify to show that
$$y'' = -\frac{(x^2 + y^2)}{y^3}$$
(c) Does $y'' = -4/y^3$? Why or why not?

50. (a) Find y' implicitly for $x^3 - y^3 = 8$.
(b) By taking derivatives implicitly, use part (a) to show that
$$y'' = \frac{2x(y - xy')}{y^3}$$
(c) Substitute x^2/y^2 for y' in the expression for y'' and simplify to show that
$$y'' = \frac{2x(y^3 - x^3)}{y^5}$$
(d) Does $y'' = -16x/y^5$? Why or why not?

51. Find y'' for $\sqrt{x} + \sqrt{y} = 1$ and simplify.

52. Find y'' for $\dfrac{1}{x} - \dfrac{1}{y} = 1$.

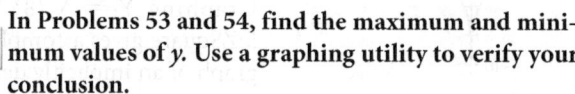

In Problems 53 and 54, find the maximum and minimum values of y. Use a graphing utility to verify your conclusion.

53. $x^2 + y^2 - 9 = 0$ 54. $4x^2 + y^2 - 8x = 0$

APPLICATIONS

55. *Advertising and sales* Suppose that a company's sales volume y (in thousands of units) is related to its advertising expenditures x (in thousands of dollars) according to
$$xy - 20x + 10y = 0$$
Find the rate of change of sales volume with respect to advertising expenditures when $x = 10$ (thousand dollars).

56. *Insect control* Suppose that the number of mosquitoes N (in thousands) in a certain swampy area near a community is related to the number of pounds of insecticide x sprayed on the nesting areas according to
$$Nx - 10x + N = 300$$
Find the rate of change of N with respect to x when 49 pounds of insecticide is used.

57. *Production* Suppose that a company can produce 12,000 units when the number of hours of skilled labor y and unskilled labor x satisfy

$$384 = (x + 1)^{3/4}(y + 2)^{1/3}$$

Find the rate of change of skilled-labor hours with respect to unskilled-labor hours when $x = 255$ and $y = 214$. This can be used to approximate the change in skilled-labor hours required to maintain the same production level when unskilled-labor hours are increased by 1 hour.

58. *Production* Suppose that production of 10,000 units of a certain agricultural crop is related to the number of hours of labor x and the number of acres of the crop y according to

$$300x + 30,000y = 11xy - 0.0002x^2 - 5y$$

Find the rate of change of the number of hours with respect to the number of acres.

59. *Demand* If the demand function for q units of a product at $\$p$ per unit is given by

$$p(q + 1)^2 = 200,000$$

find the rate of change of quantity with respect to price when $p = \$80$. Interpret this result.

60. *Demand* If the demand function for q units of a commodity at $\$p$ per unit is given by

$$p^2(2q + 1) = 100,000$$

find the rate of change of quantity with respect to price when $p = \$50$. Interpret this result.

61. *Radioactive decay* The number of grams of radium, y, that will remain after t years if 100 grams existed originally can be found by using the equation

$$-0.000436t = \ln\left(\frac{y}{100}\right)$$

Use implicit differentiation to find the rate of change of y with respect to t—that is, the rate at which the radium will decay.

62. *Disease control* Suppose the proportion P of people affected by a certain disease is described by

$$\ln\left(\frac{P}{1 - P}\right) = 0.5t$$

where t is the time in months. Find dP/dt, the rate at which P grows.

63. *Summer Simmer Index* In the late 1980s, J. Pepi developed the most recent model for measuring the effects of high temperature and humidity. Pepi's model is called the Summer Simmer Index and is given by

$$S = 1.98T - 1.09(1 - H)(T - 58) - 56.8$$

where T is the air temperature (in degrees Fahrenheit) and H is the relative humidity (as a decimal). If S remains constant, find the rate of change of humidity with respect to temperature when the temperature is 80°F.

SECTION 11.4

Related Rates

OBJECTIVES

• To use implicit differentiation to solve problems that involve related rates

• To solve problems that involve percent rates of change

APPLICATION PREVIEW

According to Poiseuille's law, the flow of blood F is related to the radius r of the vessel according to

$$F = kr^4$$

where k is a constant. When the radius of a blood vessel is reduced, such as by cholesterol deposits, the flow of blood is restricted. Drugs can be administered that increase the radius of the blood vessel and hence the flow of blood. The rate of change of the blood flow and the rate of change of the radius of the blood vessel are time rates of change that are related to each other, so they are called related rates. We can use these related rates to find the percent rate of change in the blood flow that corresponds to the percent rate of change in the radius of the blood vessel caused by the drug. (See Example 2.)

Related Rates   We have seen that the derivative represents the instantaneous rate of change of one variable with respect to another. When the derivative is taken with respect to time, it represents the rate at which that variable is changing with respect to time. For example, if distance x is measured in miles and time t in hours, then dx/dt is measured in miles per hour and indicates how fast x is changing. Similarly, if V represents the volume (in cubic feet) of water in a swimming pool and t is time (in minutes), then dV/dt is measured in cubic feet per minute (ft^3/min) and might measure the rate at which the pool is being filled with water or being emptied.

Sometimes two (or more) quantities that depend on time are also related to each other. For example, the height of a tree h (in feet) is related to the radius r (in inches) of its trunk, and this relationship can be modeled by

$$h = kr^{2/3}$$

where k is a constant.* Of course, both h and r are related to time, so the rates of change dh/dt and dr/dt are related to each other. Thus they are called **related rates.**

The specific relationship between dh/dt and dr/dt can be found by differentiating $h = kr^{2/3}$ implicitly with respect to time t.

EXAMPLE 1   Tree Height and Trunk Radius

Suppose that for a certain type of tree, the height of the tree (in feet) is related to the radius of its trunk (in inches) by

$$h = 15r^{2/3}$$

Suppose that the rate of change of r is $\frac{3}{4}$ inch per year. Find how fast the height is changing when the radius is 8 inches.

Solution

To find how the rates dh/dt and dr/dt are related, we differentiate $h = 15r^{2/3}$ implicitly with respect to time t.

$$\frac{dh}{dt} = 10r^{-1/3}\frac{dr}{dt}$$

Using $r = 8$ inches and $dr/dt = \frac{3}{4}$ inch per year gives

$$\frac{dh}{dt} = 10(8)^{-1/3}\left(\frac{3}{4}\right) = \frac{15}{4} = 3\tfrac{3}{4} \text{ feet per year}$$

Percent Rates of Change   The work in Example 1 shows how to obtain related rates, but the different units (feet per year and inches per year) may be somewhat difficult to interpret. For this reason, many applications in the life sciences deal with **percent rates of change.** The percent rate of change of a quantity is the rate of change of the quantity divided by the quantity.

EXAMPLE 2   Blood Flow | APPLICATION PREVIEW |

Poiseuille's law expresses the flow of blood F as a function of the radius r of the vessel according to

$$F = kr^4$$

where k is a constant. When the radius of a blood vessel is restricted, such as by cholesterol deposits, drugs can be administered that will increase the radius of the blood vessel (and hence the blood flow). Find the percent rate of change of the flow of blood that corresponds to the percent rate of change of the radius of a blood vessel caused by the drug.

Solution

We seek the percent rate of change of flow, $(dF/dt)/F$, that results from a given percent rate of change of the radius $(dr/dt)/r$. We first find the related rates of change by differentiating

$$F = kr^4$$

*T. McMahon, "Size and Shape in Biology," *Science* 179 (1979): 1201.

implicitly with respect to time.

$$\frac{dF}{dt} = k\left(4r^3 \frac{dr}{dt}\right)$$

Then the percent rate of change of flow can be found by dividing both sides of the equation by F.

$$\frac{\frac{dF}{dt}}{F} = \frac{4kr^3 \frac{dr}{dt}}{F}$$

If we replace F on the right side of the equation with kr^4 and reduce, we get

$$\frac{\frac{dF}{dt}}{F} = \frac{4kr^3 \frac{dr}{dt}}{kr^4} = 4\left(\frac{\frac{dr}{dt}}{r}\right)$$

Thus we see that the percent rate of change of the flow of blood is 4 times the corresponding percent rate of change of the radius of the blood vessel. This means that a drug that would cause a 12% increase in the radius of a blood vessel at a certain time would produce a corresponding 48% increase in blood flow through that vessel at that time.

Solving Related-Rates Problems

In the examples above, the equation relating the time-dependent variables has been given. For some problems, the original equation relating the variables must first be developed from the statement of the problem. These problems can be solved with the aid of the following procedure.

SOLVING A RELATED-RATES PROBLEM

Procedure	Example
To solve a related-rates problem:	Sand falls at a rate of 5 ft³/min on a conical pile, with the diameter always equal to the height of the pile. At what rate is the height increasing when the pile is 10 ft high?
1. Use geometric and/or physical conditions to write an equation that relates the time-dependent variables.	1. The conical pile has its volume given by $$V = \frac{1}{3}\pi r^2 h$$
2. Substitute into the equation values or relationships that are true at *all times*.	2. The radius $r = \frac{1}{2}h$ at all times, so $$V = \frac{1}{3}\pi \left(\frac{1}{4}h^2\right)h = \frac{\pi}{12}h^3$$
3. Differentiate both sides of the equation implicitly with respect to time. This equation is valid for all times.	3. $\dfrac{dV}{dt} = \dfrac{\pi}{12}\left(3h^2 \dfrac{dh}{dt}\right) = \dfrac{\pi}{4}h^2 \dfrac{dh}{dt}$
4. Substitute the values that are known at the instant specified and solve the equation.	4. $\dfrac{dV}{dt} = 5$ at all times, so when $h = 10$, $$5 = \frac{\pi}{4}(10^2)\frac{dh}{dt}$$
5. Solve for the specified quantity at the given time.	5. $\dfrac{dh}{dt} = \dfrac{20}{100\pi} = \dfrac{1}{5\pi}$ (feet/minute)

Note that you should *not* substitute numerical values for any quantity that varies with time until after the derivative is taken. If values are substituted before the derivative is taken, that quantity will have the constant value resulting from the substitution and hence will have a derivative equal to zero.

EXAMPLE   3   **Hot Air Balloon**

A hot air balloon has a velocity of 50 feet per minute and is flying at a constant height of 500 feet above an observer on the ground who is watching the balloon approach. How fast is the distance between the balloon and the observer changing when the balloon is 1000 feet from the observer?

Figure 11.13

Solution
If we let r be the distance between the balloon and the observer and let x be the horizontal distance from the balloon to a point directly above the observer, then we see that these quantities are related by the equation

$$x^2 + 500^2 = r^2 \quad \text{(See Figure 11.13.)}$$

Because the distance x is decreasing, we know that dx/dt must be negative. Thus we are given that $dx/dt = -50$ at all times, and we need to find dr/dt when $r = 1000$. Taking the derivative with respect to t of both sides of the equation $x^2 + 500^2 = r^2$ gives

$$2x\frac{dx}{dt} + 0 = 2r\frac{dr}{dt}$$

Using $dx/dt = -50$ and $r = 1000$, we get

$$2x(-50) = 2000\frac{dr}{dt}$$

$$\frac{dr}{dt} = \frac{-100x}{2000} = \frac{-x}{20}$$

Using $r = 1000$ in $x^2 + 500^2 = r^2$ gives $x^2 = 750{,}000$. Thus $x = 500\sqrt{3}$, and

$$\frac{dr}{dt} = \frac{-500\sqrt{3}}{20} = -25\sqrt{3} \approx -43.3$$

The distance between the balloon and the observer is decreasing at 43.3 feet per minute. ▪

CHECKPOINT

1. If V represents volume, write a mathematical symbol that represents "the rate of change of volume with respect to time."
2. (a) Differentiate $x^2 + 64 = y^2$ implicitly with respect to time.
   (b) Suppose we know that y is increasing at 2 units per minute. Use part (a) to find the rate of change of x at the instant when $x = 6$ and $y = 10$.
3. True or false: In solving a related-rates problem, we substitute all numerical values into the equation before we take derivatives.

EXAMPLE   4   **Spread of an Oil Slick**

Suppose that oil is spreading in a circular pattern from a leak at an offshore rig. If the radius of the oil slick is growing at 1 foot per minute, at what rate is the area of the oil slick growing when the radius is 600 feet?

Solution

The area of the circular oil slick is given by

$$A = \pi r^2$$

where r is the radius. The rate at which the area is changing is

$$\frac{dA}{dt} = 2\pi r \frac{dr}{dt}$$

Using $r = 600$ feet and $dr/dt = 1$ foot per minute gives

$$\frac{dA}{dt} = 2\pi (600 \text{ ft})(1 \text{ ft/min}) = 1200\pi \text{ ft}^2/\text{min}$$

Thus when the radius of the oil slick is 600 feet, the area is growing at the rate of 1200π square feet per minute, or approximately 3770 square feet per minute.

CHECKPOINT
ANSWERS

1. dV/dt

2. (a) $x \dfrac{dx}{dt} = y \dfrac{dy}{dt}$ (b) $\dfrac{10}{3}$ units per minute

3. False; the numerical value for any variable that is changing with time should not be substituted until after the derivative is taken.

EXERCISES 11.4

In Problems 1–4, find dy/dt using the given values.
1. $y = x^3 - 3x$ for $x = 2$, $dx/dt = 4$
2. $y = 3x^3 + 5x^2 - x$ for $x = 4$, $dx/dt = 3$
3. $xy = 4$ for $x = 8$, $dx/dt = -2$
4. $xy = x + 3$ for $x = 3$, $dx/dt = -1$

In Problems 5–8, assume that x and y are differentiable functions of t. In each case, find dx/dt given that $x = 5$, $y = 12$, and $dy/dt = 2$.
5. $x^2 + y^2 = 169$
6. $y^2 - x^2 = 119$
7. $y^2 = 2xy + 24$
8. $x^2(y - 6) = 12y + 6$
9. If $x^2 + y^2 = z^2$, find dy/dt when $x = 3$, $y = 4$, $dx/dt = 10$, and $dz/dt = 2$.
10. If $s = 2\pi r(r + h)$, find dr/dt when $r = 2$, $h = 8$, $dh/dt = 3$, and $ds/dt = 10\pi$.
11. A point is moving along the graph of the equation $y = -4x^2$. At what rate is y changing when $x = 5$ and is changing at a rate of 2 units/sec?
12. A point is moving along the graph of the equation $y = 5x^3 - 2x$. At what rate is y changing when $x = 4$ and is changing at a rate of 3 units/sec?
13. The radius of a circle is increasing at a rate of 2 ft/min. At what rate is its area changing when the radius is 3 ft? (Recall that for a circle, $A = \pi r^2$.)
14. The area of a circle is changing at a rate of 1 in²/sec. At what rate is its radius changing when the radius is 2 in.?

15. The volume of a cube is increasing at a rate of 64 in³/sec. At what rate is the length of each edge of the cube changing when the edges are 6 in. long? (Recall that for a cube, $V = x^3$.)
16. The lengths of the edges of a cube are increasing at a rate of 8 ft/min. At what rate is the surface area changing when the edges are 24 ft long? (Recall that for a cube, $S = 6x^2$.)

APPLICATIONS

17. *Profit* Suppose that the daily profit (in dollars) from the production and sale of x units of a product is given by

$$P = 180x - \frac{x^2}{1000} - 2000$$

At what rate per day is the profit changing when the number of units produced and sold is 100 and is increasing at a rate of 10 units per day?

18. *Profit* Suppose that the monthly revenue and cost (in dollars) for x units of a product are

$$R = 400x - \frac{x^2}{20} \quad \text{and} \quad C = 5000 + 70x$$

At what rate per month is the profit changing if the number of units produced and sold is 200 and is increasing at a rate of 5 units per month?

19. *Demand* Suppose that the price p (in dollars) of a product is given by the demand function

$$p = \frac{18{,}000 - 60x}{400 - x}$$

where x represents the quantity demanded and $x < 300$. If the daily demand is *decreasing* at a rate of 20 units per day, at what rate is the price changing when the price per unit is $30?

20. *Supply* The supply function for a product is given by $p = 40 + 100\sqrt{2x + 9}$, where x is the number of units supplied and p is the price in dollars. If the price is increasing at a rate of $1 per month, at what rate is the supply changing when the price per unit is $740?

21. *Capital investment and production* Suppose that for a particular product, the number of units x produced per month depends on the number of thousands of dollars y invested, with $x = 30y + 20y^2$. At what rate will production increase if $10,000 is invested and if the investment capital is increasing at a rate of $1000 per month?

22. *Boyle's law* Boyle's law for enclosed gases states that at a constant temperature, the pressure is related to the volume by the equation

$$P = \frac{k}{V}$$

where k is a constant. If the volume is increasing at a rate of 5 cu in. per hour, at what rate is the pressure changing when the volume is 30 cu in. and $k = 2$ in-lb?

Tumor growth **For Problems 23 and 24, suppose that a tumor in a person's body has a spherical shape and that treatment is causing the radius of the tumor to decrease at a rate of 1 mm per month.**

23. At what rate is the volume decreasing when the radius is 3 mm? (Recall that $V = \frac{4}{3}\pi r^3$.)

24. At what rate is the surface area of the tumor decreasing when the radius is 3 mm? (Recall that for a sphere, $S = 4\pi r^2$.)

25. *Allometric relationships—fish* For many species of fish, the allometric relationship between the weight W and the length L is approximately $W = kL^3$, where k is a constant. Find the percent rate of change of the weight as a corresponding percent rate of change of the length.

26. *Blood flow* The resistance R of a blood vessel to the flow of blood is a function of the radius r of the blood vessel and is given by

$$R = \frac{k}{r^4}$$

where k is a constant. Find the percent rate of change of the resistance of a blood vessel in terms of the percent rate of change in the radius of the blood vessel.

27. *Allometric relationships—crabs* For fiddler crabs, data gathered by Thompson* show that the allometric relationship between the weight C of the claw and the weight W of the body is given by

$$C = 0.11W^{1.54}$$

Find the percent rate of change of the claw weight in terms of the percent rate of change of the body weight for fiddler crabs.

28. *Body weight and surface area* For human beings, the surface area S of the body is related to the body's weight W according to

$$S = kW^{2/3}$$

where k is a constant. Find the percent rate of change of the body's surface area in terms of the percent rate of change of the body's weight.

29. *Cell growth* A bacterial cell has a spherical shape. If the volume of the cell is increasing at a rate of 4 cubic micrometers per day, at what rate is the radius of the cell increasing when it is 2 micrometers? (Recall that for a sphere, $V = \frac{4}{3}\pi r^3$.)

30. *Water purification* Assume that water is being purified by causing it to flow through a conical filter that has a height of 15 in. and a radius of 5 in. If the depth of the water is decreasing at a rate of 1 in. per minute when the depth is 6 in., at what rate is the volume of water flowing out of the filter at this instant?

31. *Volume and radius* Suppose that air is being pumped into a spherical balloon at a rate of 5 in^3/min. At what rate is the radius of the balloon increasing when the radius is 5 in.?

32. *Boat docking* Suppose that a boat is being pulled toward a dock by a winch that is 5 ft above the level of the boat deck, as shown in the figure. If the winch is pulling the cable at a rate of 3 ft/min, at what rate is the boat approaching the dock when it is 12 ft from the dock?

33. *Ladder safety* A 30-ft ladder is leaning against a wall. If the bottom is pulled away from the wall at a rate of 1 ft/sec, at what rate is the top of the ladder sliding down the wall when the bottom is 18 ft from the wall?

34. *Flight* A kite is 30 ft high and is moving horizontally at a rate of 10 ft/min. If the kite string is taut, at what rate is the string being played out when 50 ft of string is out?

*d'Arcy Thompson, *On Growth and Form* (Cambridge, England: Cambridge University Press, 1961).

35. *Flight* A plane is flying at a constant altitude of 1 mile and a speed of 300 mph toward an observer on the ground. How fast is the plane approaching the observer when it is 5 miles from the observer?

36. *Distance* Two boats leave the same port at the same time, with boat A traveling north at 15 knots (nautical miles per hour) and boat B traveling east at 20 knots. How fast is the distance between them changing when boat A is 30 nautical miles from port?

37. *Distance* Two cars are approaching an intersection on roads that are perpendicular to each other. Car A is north of the intersection and traveling south at 40 mph.

Car B is east of the intersection and traveling west at 55 mph. How fast is the distance between the cars changing when car A is 15 miles from the intersection and car B is 8 miles from the intersection?

38. *Water depth* Water is flowing into a barrel in the shape of a right circular cylinder at the rate of 200 in^3/min. If the radius of the barrel is 18 in., at what rate is the depth of the water changing when the water is 30 in. deep?

39. *Water depth* Suppose that water is being pumped into a rectangular swimming pool of uniform depth at 10 ft^3/hr. If the pool is 10 ft wide and 25 ft long, at what rate is the water rising when it is 4 ft deep?

SECTION 11.5 Applications in Business and Economics

OBJECTIVES

- To find the elasticity of demand
- To apply the relationship between elasticity and revenue
- To find the tax per unit that will maximize tax revenue

APPLICATION PREVIEW

Suppose that the demand for a product is given by

$$p = \frac{1000}{(q + 1)^2}$$

We can measure how sensitive the demand for this product is to price changes by finding the elasticity of demand. (See Example 2.) This elasticity can be used to measure the effects that price changes have on total revenue. We also consider taxation in a competitive market, which examines how a tax levied on goods shifts market equilibrium. We will find the tax per unit that, despite changes in market equilibrium, maximizes tax revenue.

Elasticity of Demand

We know from the law of demand that consumers will respond to changes in prices; if prices increase, the quantities demanded will decrease. But the degree of responsiveness of the consumers to price changes will vary widely for different products. For example, a price increase in insulin will not greatly decrease the demand for it by diabetics, but a price increase in clothes may cause consumers to buy less and wear their old clothes longer. When the response to price changes is considerable, we say that the demand is *elastic*. When price changes cause relatively small changes in demand for a product, the demand is said to be *inelastic* for that product. Economists measure the **elasticity of demand** as follows.

Elasticity

If $p = f(q)$ is the demand for q units and price p, then at the point (q_A, p_A), we have

$$\text{elasticity of demand} = \eta = -\frac{p}{q} \cdot \frac{dq}{dp}\bigg|_{(q_A, p_A)}$$

EXAMPLE 1 Elasticity

Find the elasticity of the demand function $p + 5q = 100$ when
(a) the price is \$40. (b) the price is \$60. (c) the price is \$50.

Solution
Solving the demand function for q gives $q = 20 - \frac{1}{5}p$. Then $dq/dp = -\frac{1}{5}$ and

$$\eta = -\frac{p}{q}\left(-\frac{1}{5}\right)$$

(a) When $p = 40, q = 12$ and $\eta = -\dfrac{p}{q}\left(-\dfrac{1}{5}\right)\Big|_{(12,\,40)} = -\dfrac{40}{12}\left(-\dfrac{1}{5}\right) = \dfrac{2}{3}$.

(b) When $p = 60, q = 8$ and $\eta = -\dfrac{p}{q}\left(-\dfrac{1}{5}\right)\Big|_{(8,\,60)} = -\dfrac{60}{8}\left(-\dfrac{1}{5}\right) = \dfrac{3}{2}$.

(c) When $p = 50, q = 10$ and $\eta = -\dfrac{p}{q}\left(-\dfrac{1}{5}\right)\Big|_{(10,\,50)} = -\dfrac{50}{10}\left(-\dfrac{1}{5}\right) = 1$.

Note that in Example 1, the demand equation was $p + 5q = 100$, so the demand "curve" is a straight line, with slope $m = -5$. But the elasticity was $\eta = \frac{2}{3}$ at (12, 40), $\eta = \frac{3}{2}$ at (8, 60), and $\eta - 1$ at (10, 50). This illustrates that the elasticity of demand may be different at different points on the demand curve, even though the slope of the demand "curve" is constant. (See Figure 11.14.)

Figure 11.14

This example shows that the elasticity of demand is more than just the slope of the demand curve, which is the rate at which the demand is changing. Recall that the elasticity measures the consumers' degree of responsiveness to a price change.

Economists use η to measure how responsive demand is to price at different points on the demand curve for a product.

Elasticity of Demand

- If $\eta > 1$, the demand is **elastic,** and the percent decrease in demand is greater than the corresponding percent increase in price.
- If $\eta < 1$, the demand is **inelastic,** and the percent decrease in demand is less than the corresponding percent increase in price.
- If $\eta = 1$, the demand is **unitary elastic,** and the percent decrease in demand is approximately equal to the corresponding percent increase in price.

We can use implicit differentiation to find dq/dp in evaluating the point elasticity of demand.

EXAMPLE 2   Elasticity | APPLICATION PREVIEW |

The demand for a certain product is given by

$$p = \frac{1000}{(q + 1)^2}$$

where p is the price per unit in dollars and q is demand in units of the product. Find the elasticity of demand with respect to price when $q = 19$.

Solution
To find the elasticity, we need to find dq/dp. Using implicit differentiation gives

$$\frac{d}{dp}(p) = \frac{d}{dp}[1000(q + 1)^{-2}]$$

$$1 = 1000\left[-2(q + 1)^{-3}\frac{dq}{dp}\right]$$

$$1 = \frac{-2000}{(q + 1)^3}\frac{dq}{dp}$$

$$\frac{(q + 1)^3}{-2000} = \frac{dq}{dp}$$

When $q = 19$, we have $p = 1000/(19 + 1)^2 = 1000/400 = 5/2$ and

$$\left.\frac{dq}{dp}\right|_{(q = 19)} = \frac{(19 + 1)^3}{-2000} = \frac{8000}{-2000} = -4$$

The elasticity of demand when $q = 19$ is

$$\eta = \frac{-p}{q}\cdot\frac{dq}{dp} = -\frac{(5/2)}{19}\cdot(-4) = \frac{10}{19} < 1$$

Thus the demand for this product is inelastic.

Elasticity and Revenue

Elasticity is related to revenue in a special way. We can see how by computing the derivative with respect to p of the revenue function

$$R = pq$$

$$\frac{dR}{dp} = p\cdot\frac{dq}{dp} + q\cdot 1$$

$$= \frac{q}{q}\cdot p\cdot\frac{dq}{dp} + q = q\cdot\frac{p}{q}\cdot\frac{dq}{dp} + q$$

$$= q(-\eta) + q$$

$$= q(1 - \eta)$$

From this, we can summarize the relationship of elasticity and revenue.

Elasticity and Revenue

The rate of change of revenue R with respect to price p is related to elasticity in the following way.

- Elastic ($\eta > 1$) means $\dfrac{dR}{dp} < 0.$ $\begin{cases}\text{Hence if price increases, revenue decreases,}\\ \text{and if price decreases, revenue increases.}\end{cases}$

- Inelastic ($\eta < 1$) means $\dfrac{dR}{dp} > 0.$ $\begin{cases}\text{Hence if price increases, revenue increases,}\\ \text{and if price decreases, revenue decreases.}\end{cases}$

- Unitary elastic ($\eta = 1$) means $\dfrac{dR}{dp} = 0.$ Hence an increase or decrease in price will not change revenue. Revenue is optimized at this point.

EXAMPLE 3 Elasticity and Revenue

The demand for a product is given by

$$p = 10\sqrt{100 - q}, \qquad 0 \le q \le 100$$

(a) Find the point at which demand is of unitary elasticity and find intervals in which the demand is inelastic and in which it is elastic.

(b) Find q where revenue is increasing, where it is decreasing, and where it is maximized.

(c) Use a graphing utility to show the graph of the revenue function $R = pq$, with $0 \leq q \leq 100$, and confirm the results from part (b).

Solution

The elasticity is

$$\eta = \frac{-p}{q} \cdot \frac{dq}{dp} = -\frac{10\sqrt{100-q}}{q} \cdot \frac{dq}{dp}$$

We find dq/dp by differentiating $p = 10\sqrt{100-q}$ implicitly with respect to p, as follows.

$$1 = 10\left[\frac{1}{2}(100-q)^{-1/2}\left(-\frac{dq}{dp}\right)\right] = \frac{-5}{\sqrt{100-q}} \cdot \frac{dq}{dp}$$

so

$$\frac{dq}{dp} = \frac{-\sqrt{100-q}}{5}$$

Substituting for dq/dp in the formula for η gives

$$\eta = \left(-\frac{10\sqrt{100-q}}{q}\right)\left(\frac{-\sqrt{100-q}}{5}\right) = \frac{200-2q}{q}$$

(a) Unitary elasticity occurs where $\eta = 1$.

$$1 = \frac{200-2q}{q}$$
$$q = 200 - 2q$$
$$3q = 200$$
$$q = 66\tfrac{2}{3}$$

so unitary elasticity occurs when $66\tfrac{2}{3}$ units are sold, at a price of \$57.74. For values of q between 0 and $66\tfrac{2}{3}$, $\eta > 1$ and demand is elastic. For values of q between $66\tfrac{2}{3}$ and 100, $\eta < 1$ and demand is inelastic.

(b) Because $\eta > 1$ and p decreases when q increases over $0 < q < 66\tfrac{2}{3}$, R increases. Similarly, because $\eta < 1$ and p decreases when q increases over $66\tfrac{2}{3} < q < 100$, R decreases. Thus revenue is maximized where $\eta = 1$, at $q = 66\tfrac{2}{3}$ and $p = 57.74$.

(c) The graph of this revenue function,

$$R = 10q\sqrt{100-q}$$

is shown in Figure 11.15. The maximum revenue is \$3849 at $q = 66\tfrac{2}{3}$.

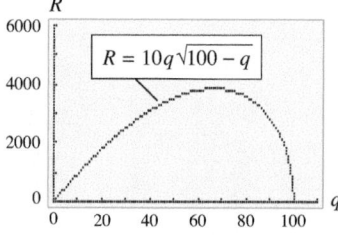

Figure 11.15

---

1. Write the formula for point elasticity, η.
2. (a) If $\eta > 1$, the demand is called _____.
   (b) If $\eta < 1$, the demand is called _____.
   (c) If $\eta = 1$, the demand is called _____.
3. Find the elasticity of demand for $q = \dfrac{100}{p} - 1$ when $p = 10$ and $q = 9$.

Taxation in a Competitive Market

Many taxes imposed by governments are "hidden." That is, the tax is levied on goods produced, and the producers must pay the tax. Of course, the tax becomes a cost to the producers, and they pass that cost on to the consumer in the form of higher prices for goods.

Suppose the government imposes a tax of t dollars on each unit produced and sold by producers. If we are in pure competition in which the consumers' demand depends only on price, the *demand function* will not change. The tax will change the supply function, of course, because at each level of output q, the firm will want to charge a price $p + t$ per unit, where p is the original price per unit and t is the tax per unit.

The graphs of the market demand function, the original market supply function, and the market supply function after taxes are shown in Figure 11.16. Because the tax added to each item is constant, the graph of the new supply function is t units above the original supply function. If $p = f(q)$ defines the original supply function, then $p = f(q) + t$ defines the supply function after taxation.

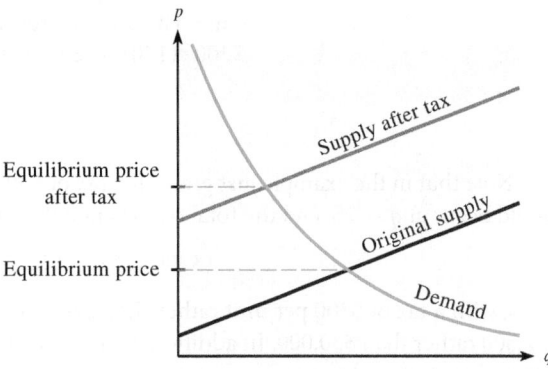

Figure 11.16

Note that after the taxes are imposed, *no* items are supplied at the price that was the equilibrium price before taxation. After the taxes are imposed, the consumers simply must pay more for the product. Because taxation does not change the demand curve, the quantity purchased at market equilibrium will be less than it was before taxation. Thus governments planning taxes should recognize that they will not collect taxes on the original equilibrium quantity. They will collect on the *new* equilibrium quantity, a quantity reduced by their taxation. Thus a large tax on each item may reduce the quantity demanded at the new market equilibrium so much that very little revenue results from the tax!

If the tax revenue is represented by $T = tq$, where t is the tax per unit and q is the equilibrium quantity of the supply and demand functions after taxation, we can use the following procedure for maximizing the total tax revenue in a competitive market.

MAXIMIZING TOTAL TAX REVENUE

Procedure	Example
To find the tax per item (under pure competition) that will maximize total tax revenue:	Suppose the demand and supply functions are given by $p = 600 - q$ and $p = 200 + \frac{1}{3}q$, respectively, where $\$p$ is the price per unit and q is the number of units. Find the tax t that will maximize the total tax revenue T.
1. Write the supply function after taxation.	1. $p = 200 + \frac{1}{3}q + t$
2. Set the demand function and the new supply function equal, and solve for t in terms of q.	2. $600 - q = 200 + \frac{1}{3}q + t$ $400 - \frac{4}{3}q = t$
3. Form the total tax revenue function, $T = tq$, by multiplying the expression for t by q; then take its derivative with respect to q.	3. $T = tq = 400q - \frac{4}{3}q^2$ $T'(q) = \dfrac{dT}{dq} = 400 - \frac{8}{3}q$

(Continued)

4. Set $T' = 0$ and solve for q. This is the q that should maximize T. Use the second-derivative test to verify it.

4. $0 = 400 - \dfrac{8}{3}q$

$q = 150$

$T''(q) = -\dfrac{8}{3}$. Thus T is maximized at $q = 150$.

5. Substitute the value of q in the equation for t (in Step 2). This is the value of t that will maximize T.

5. $t = 400 - \dfrac{4}{3}(150) = 200$

A tax of $200 per item will maximize the total tax revenue. The total tax revenue for the period would be $200 \cdot (150) = \$30,000$.

Note that in the example just given, if a tax of $300 were imposed, market equilibrium would occur at $q = 75$, and the total tax revenue the government would receive would be

$$(\$300)(75) = \$22,500$$

Thus, with a tax of $300 per unit rather than $200, the government's tax revenue would be $22,500 rather than $30,000. In addition, with a $300 tax, suppliers would sell only 75 units rather than 150, and consumers would pay $p = 200 + 25 + 300 = \$525$ per item, which is $75 more than the price with a $200 tax. Thus everyone would suffer if the tax rate were raised to $300.

CHECKPOINT

4. For problems involving taxation in a competitive market, if supply is $p = f(q)$ and demand is $p = g(q)$, is the tax t added to $f(q)$ or to $g(q)$?

EXAMPLE 4 **Maximizing Tax Revenue**

The demand and supply functions for a product are $p = 900 - 20q - \frac{1}{3}q^2$ and $p = 200 + 10q$, respectively, where p is in dollars and q is the number of units. Find the tax per unit that will maximize the tax revenue T.

Solution
After taxation, the supply function is $p = 200 + 10q + t$, where t is the tax per unit. The demand function will meet the new supply function where

$$900 - 20q - \frac{1}{3}q^2 = 200 + 10q + t$$

so

$$t = 700 - 30q - \frac{1}{3}q^2$$

Then the total tax T is $T = tq = 700q - 30q^2 - \frac{1}{3}q^3$, and we maximize T as follows:

$$T'(q) = 700 - 60q - q^2$$
$$0 = -(q + 70)(q - 10)$$
$$q = 10 \quad \text{or} \quad q = -70$$
$$T''(q) = -60 - 2q, \text{ so } T''(q) < 0 \text{ for } q \geq 0$$

Thus the curve is concave down for $q \geq 0$, and $q = 10$ gives an absolute maximum for the tax revenue T. The maximum possible tax revenue is

$$T(10) \approx \$3666.67$$

The tax per unit that maximizes T is

$$t = 700 - 30(10) - \frac{1}{3}(10)^2 \approx \$366.67$$

An infamous example of a tax increase that resulted in decreased tax revenue and economic disaster is the "luxury tax" enacted in 1991. This was a 10% excise tax on the sale of expensive jewelry, furs, airplanes, certain expensive boats, and luxury automobiles. The Congressional Joint Tax Committee had estimated that the luxury tax would raise $6 million from airplanes alone, but it raised only $53,000 while it destroyed the small-airplane market (one company lost $130 million and 480 jobs in a single year). It also capsized the boat market. The luxury tax was repealed at the end of 1993 (except for automobiles).*

CHECKPOINT
ANSWERS

1. $\eta = \dfrac{-p}{q} \cdot \dfrac{dq}{dp}$

2. (a) elastic   (b) inelastic   (c) unitary elastic

3. $\eta = \dfrac{10}{9}$(elastic)

4. Tax t is added to supply: $p = f(q) + t$.

EXERCISES 11.5

ELASTICITY OF DEMAND

In Problems 1–8, p is in dollars and q is the number of units.

1. (a) Find the elasticity of the demand function $p + 4q = 80$ at $(10, 40)$.
   (b) How will a price increase affect total revenue?

2. (a) Find the elasticity of the demand function $2p + 3q = 150$ at the price $p = 15$.
   (b) How will a price increase affect total revenue?

3. (a) Find the elasticity of the demand function $p^2 + 2p + q = 49$ at $p = 6$.
   (b) How will a price increase affect total revenue?

4. (a) Find the elasticity of the demand function $pq = 81$ at $p = 3$.
   (b) How will a price increase affect total revenue?

5. Suppose that the demand for a product is given by $pq + p = 5000$.
   (a) Find the elasticity when $p = \$50$ and $q = 99$.
   (b) Tell what type of elasticity this is: unitary, elastic, or inelastic.
   (c) How would revenue be affected by a price increase?

6. Suppose that the demand for a product is given by $2p^2q = 10{,}000 + 9000p^2$.
   (a) Find the elasticity when $p = \$50$ and $q = 4502$.
   (b) Tell what type of elasticity this is: unitary, elastic, or inelastic.

(c) How would revenue be affected by a price increase?

7. Suppose that the demand for a product is given by $pq + p + 100q = 50{,}000$.
   (a) Find the elasticity when $p = \$401$.
   (b) Tell what type of elasticity this is.
   (c) How would a price increase affect revenue?

8. Suppose that the demand for a product is given by

$$(p + 1)\sqrt{q + 1} = 1000$$

   (a) Find the elasticity when $p = \$39$.
   (b) Tell what type of elasticity this is.
   (c) How would a price increase affect revenue?

9. Suppose the demand function for a product is given by

$$p = \frac{1}{2}\ln\left(\frac{5000 - q}{q + 1}\right)$$

   where p is in hundreds of dollars and q is the number of tons.
   (a) What is the elasticity of demand when the quantity demanded is 2 tons and the price is $371?
   (b) Is the demand elastic or inelastic?

10. Suppose the weekly demand function for a product is

$$q = \frac{5000}{1 + e^{2p}} - 1$$

*Fortune, Sept. 6, 1993; Motor Trend, December 1993.

where p is the price in thousands of dollars and q is the number of units demanded. What is the elasticity of demand when the price is $1000 and the quantity demanded is 595?

In Problems 11 and 12, the demand functions for specialty steel products are given, where p is in dollars and q is the number of units. For both problems

(a) find the elasticity of demand as a function of the quantity demanded, q.

(b) find the point at which the demand is of unitary elasticity and find intervals in which the demand is inelastic and in which it is elastic.

(c) use information about elasticity in part (b) to decide where the revenue is increasing, where it is decreasing, and where it is maximized.

(d) use the graph of the revenue function $R = pq$ to find where revenue is maximized. Is it at the same quantity as that determined in part (c)?

11. $p = 120\sqrt[3]{125 - q}$

12. $p = 30\sqrt{49 - q}$

13. South West Electronics Corporation (SWEC) designs high-tech business and residential security systems. The company's marketing analyst has been assigned to analyze market demand for SWEC's top-selling system, The Terminator. Monthly demand for The Terminator has been estimated as follows:

$$q = 445 - 8p + 25A + 4.5C + 6Y$$

where q = Expected number of system sales per month
  p = Selling price for The Terminator (in dollars)
  A = Advertising (in thousands of dollars)
  C = SWEC's only competitor's average price (in dollars)
  Y = Disposable annual per capita income (in thousands of dollars)

A recent survey of the potential customer market indicates that monthly advertising is $25,000, per capita disposable income is $80,000 per year, and the average price of the only competitor is $100.

(a) Based on this information, what is the monthly demand function $p = f(q)$ for The Terminator?

(b) Find the elasticity of demand for The Terminator.

(c) If SWEC's current price for The Terminator is $175, is demand elastic, inelastic, or unitary elastic? Is SWEC's revenue for The Terminator maximized at the current price?

(d) Use the elasticity of demand found in part (b) to determine the price for The Terminator that would maximize SWEC's revenue. Find the maximum revenue.

14. The owner and manager of Pleasantville Deli is considering the expansion of current menu offerings to include a new line of take-out sandwiches. The deli serves primarily the Pleasantville business district and students from a nearby college, yet it is unclear exactly what level of demand to anticipate for this new product offering and how to price the product to maximize sales.

Over the past few months, the information shown in the table was collected from existing customers and from mailings to businesses in the area.

Sandwich Price	$12	10	8	6	4	2
Weekly Demand	0	400	800	1200	1600	2000

(a) Develop a function $p = f(q)$ that represents this demand schedule.

(b) Compute the elasticity of demand for the new sandwich.

(c) Find the elasticity at the possible prices of $4 and $10. Classify these prices as elastic, inelastic, or unitary elastic.

(d) Determine the price and quantity that would maximize weekly revenues for the new sandwich. Find the maximum weekly revenue.

TAXATION IN A COMPETITIVE MARKET

In Problems 15–24, p is the price per unit in dollars and q is the number of units.

15. If the weekly demand function is $p = 30 - q$ and the supply function before taxation is $p = 6 + 2q$, what tax per item will maximize the total tax revenue?

16. If the demand function for a fixed period of time is given by $p = 38 - 2q$ and the supply function before taxation is $p = 8 + 3q$, what tax per item will maximize the total tax revenue?

17. If the demand and supply functions for a product are $p = 800 - 2q$ and $p = 100 + 0.5q$, respectively, find the tax per unit t that will maximize the tax revenue T.

18. If the demand and supply functions for a product are $p = 2100 - 3q$ and $p = 300 + 1.5q$, respectively, find the tax per unit t that will maximize the tax revenue T.

19. If the weekly demand function is $p = 200 - 2q^2$ and the supply function before taxation is $p = 20 + 3q$, what tax per item will maximize the total tax revenue?

20. If the monthly demand function is $p = 7230 - 5q^2$ and the supply function before taxation is $p = 30 + 30q^2$, what tax per item will maximize the total revenue?

21. Suppose the weekly demand for a product is given by $p + 2q = 840$ and the weekly supply before taxation is given by $p = 0.02q^2 + 0.55q + 7.4$. Find the tax per item that produces maximum tax revenue. Find the tax revenue.

22. If the daily demand for a product is given by the function $p + q = 1000$ and the daily supply before taxation is $p = q^2/30 + 2.5q + 920$, find the tax per item that maximizes tax revenue. Find the tax revenue.

23. If the demand and supply functions for a product are $p = 2100 - 10q - 0.5q^2$ and $p = 300 + 5q + 0.5q^2$, respectively, find the tax per unit t that will maximize the tax revenue T.

24. If the demand and supply functions for a product are $p = 5000 - 20q - 0.7q^2$ and $p = 500 + 10q + 0.3q^2$, respectively, find the tax per unit t that will maximize the tax revenue T.

11 CHAPTER SUMMARY & REVIEW

KEY TERMS AND FORMULAS

Section 11.1

Logarithmic function (p. 693)
$$y = \log_a x, \text{ defined by } x = a^y$$
Natural logarithm (p. 693)
$$\ln x = \log_e x; y = \ln (x) \text{ means } e^y = x$$
Derivatives of logarithmic functions (p. 694)
$$\frac{d}{dx}(\ln x) = \frac{1}{x}$$
$$\frac{d}{dx}(\ln u) = \frac{1}{u} \cdot \frac{du}{dx}$$

Logarithmic Properties I–V for natural logarithms (p. 695)
$$\ln e^x = x; e^{\ln x} = x$$
$$\ln (MN) = \ln M + \ln N$$
$$\ln (M/N) = \ln M - \ln N$$
$$\ln (M^p) = p (\ln M)$$
Change-of-base formula (p. 697)
$$\log_a x = \frac{\ln x}{\ln a}$$

Section 11.2

Derivatives of exponential functions (p. 702)
$$\frac{d}{dx}(e^x) = e^x$$

$$\frac{d}{dx}e^u = e^u \frac{du}{dx}$$
$$\frac{d}{dx}a^u = a^u \frac{du}{dx} \ln a$$

Section 11.3

Implicit differentiation (p. 708)
$$\frac{d}{dx}(y^n) = ny^{n-1} \frac{dy}{dx}$$

Section 11.4

Related rates (p. 717)
  Differentiate implicitly with respect to time, t

Percent rates of change (p. 718)
Solving related rates problems (p. 719)

Section 11.5

Elasticity of demand (p. 723)
$$\eta = \frac{-p}{q} \cdot \frac{dq}{dp}$$
Elastic
  $\eta > 1$
Inelastic
  $\eta < 1$

Unitary elastic
  $\eta = 1$
Elasticity and revenue (p. 725)
Taxation in competitive market (p. 726)
  Supply function after taxation
  $p = f(q) + t$

REVIEW EXERCISES

Sections 11.1 and 11.2

In Problems 1–12, find the derivative of each function.
1. $y = 10e^{3x^2 - x}$
2. $y = 3 \ln (4x + 11)$
3. $p = \ln \left(\dfrac{q}{q^2 - 1} \right)$
4. $y = xe^{x^2}$

5. $f(x) = 5e^{2x} - 40e^{-0.1x} + 11$
6. $g(x) = (2e^{3x+1} - 5)^3$
7. $s = \dfrac{3}{4} \ln (x^{12} - 2x^4 + 5)$
8. $w = (t^2 + 1) \ln (t^2 + 1) - t^2$

9. $y = 3^{3x-4}$
10. $y = 1 + \log_8(x^{10})$
11. $y = \dfrac{\ln x}{x}$
12. $y = \dfrac{1 + e^{-x}}{1 - e^{-x}}$
13. Write the equation of the line tangent to $y = 4e^{x^3}$ at $x = 1$.
14. At $x = 1$, write the equation of the line tangent to $y = 8 + 3x^2 \ln x$

Section 11.3

In Problems 15–20, find the indicated derivative.
15. If $y \ln x = 5y^2 + 11$, find dy/dx.
16. Find dy/dx for $e^{xy} = y$.
17. Find dy/dx for $y^2 = 4x - 1$.
18. Find dy/dx for $x^2 + 3y^2 + 2x - 3y + 2 = 0$.
19. Find dy/dx for $3x^2 + 2x^3y^2 - y^5 = 7$.
20. Find the second derivative y'' if $x^2 + y^2 = 1$.
21. Find the slope of the tangent to the curve $x^2 + 4x - 3y^2 + 6 = 0$ at $(3, 3)$.
22. Find the points where tangents to the graph of the equation in Problem 21 are horizontal.

Section 11.4

23. Suppose $3x^2 - 2y^3 = 10y$, where x and y are differentiable functions of t. If $dx/dt = 2$, find dy/dt when $x = 10$ and $y = 5$.
24. A right triangle with legs of lengths x and y has its area given by

$$A = \frac{1}{2}xy$$

If the rate of change of x is 2 units per minute and the rate of change of y is 5 units per minute, find the rate of change of the area when $x = 4$ and $y = 1$.

APPLICATIONS

Section 11.1

25. *Demographics* Using U.S. Census Bureau data for selected years from 1980 and projected to 2040, the number of White non-Hispanic individuals in the U.S. civilian non-institutional population age 16 years or older, in millions, can be modeled by the function

$$P(t) = 96.1 + 17.4 \ln t$$

where t is the number of years past 1970.
(a) Find $P'(t)$.
(b) Find and interpret $P(58)$ and $P'(58)$.
26. *Life expectancy at age 65* Using Social Security Administration data for selected years from 1950 and projected to 2050, the additional years of life expectancy at age 65 can be modeled by

$$L(y) = -14.6 + 7.10 \ln y$$

where y equals the number of years past 1950.
(a) Find the function that models the rate of change of the years of life expectancy past age 65.
(b) Find and interpret $L(50)$ and $L(80)$.
(c) Find and interpret $L'(50)$ and $L'(80)$.

Section 11.2

27. *Compound interest* If $1000 is invested for n years at 12% compounded continuously, the future value of the investment is given by

$$S = 1000e^{0.12n}$$

(a) Find the function that gives the rate of change of this investment.
(b) Compare the rate at which the future value is growing after 1 year and after 10 years.
28. *Disposable income* Disposable income is the amount available for spending and saving after taxes have been paid and is one gauge for the state of the economy. Using U.S. Energy Administration data for selected years from 2010 and projected to 2040, the total U.S. disposable income, in billions, can be modeled by

$$D(t) = 10{,}020e^{0.02292t}$$

where t is the number of years past 2010.
(a) Find the function that models the rate of change of disposable income.
(b) Find and interpret $D(20)$ and $D'(20)$.
29. *Radioactive decay* A breeder reactor converts stable uranium-238 into the isotope plutonium-239. The decay of this isotope is given by

$$A(t) = A_0 e^{-0.00002876t}$$

where $A(t)$ is the amount of isotope at time t, in years, and A_0 is the original amount. This isotope has a half-life of 24,101 years (that is, half of it will decay away in 24,101 years).
(a) At what rate is $A(t)$ decaying at $t = 24{,}101$ years?
(b) At what rate is $A(t)$ decaying after 1 year?
(c) Is the rate of decay at its half-life greater or less than after 1 year?
30. *Marginal cost* The average cost of producing x units of a product is $\overline{C} = 600e^{x/600}$ dollars per unit. What is the marginal cost when 600 units are produced?
31. *Inflation* The impact of inflation on a $60,000 pension can be measured by the purchasing power P of $60,000 after t years. For an inflation rate of 5% per year, compounded annually, P is given by

$$P = 60{,}000e^{-0.0488t}$$

At what rate is purchasing power changing when $t = 10$? (*Source: Viewpoints*, VALIC)

Section 11.4

32. *Evaporation* A spherical droplet of water evaporates at a rate of 1 mm³/min. Find the rate of change of the radius when the droplet has a radius of 2.5 mm.

33. *Worker safety* A sign is being lowered over the side of a building at the rate of 2 ft/min. A worker handling a guide line is 7 ft away from a spot directly below the sign. How fast is the worker taking in the guide line at the instant the sign is 25 ft from the worker's hands? See the figure.

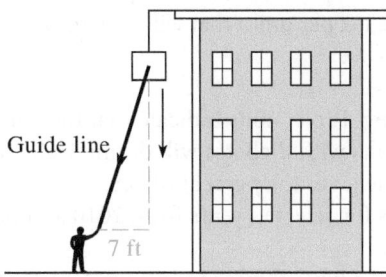

Guide line

7 ft

34. *Environment* Suppose that in a study of water birds, the relationship between the area A of wetlands (in square miles) and the number of different species S of birds found in the area was determined to be

$$S = kA^{1/3}$$

where k is constant. Find the percent rate of change of the number of species in terms of the percent rate of change of the area.

Section 11.5

35. *Elasticity* A demand function is given by

$$pq = 27$$

where p is in dollars and q is the number of units.
(a) Find the elasticity of demand at (9, 3).
(b) How will a price increase affect total revenue?

36. *Elasticity* Suppose the demand for a product is given by

$$p^2(2q + 1) = 10{,}000$$

where p is in dollars and q is the number of units.
(a) Find the elasticity of demand when $p = \$20$.
(b) How will a price increase affect total revenue?

37. *Elasticity* Suppose the weekly demand function for a product is given by

$$p = 100e^{-0.1q}$$

where p is the price in dollars and q is the number of tons demanded.
(a) What is the elasticity of demand when the price is $36.79 and the quantity demanded is 10?
(b) How will a price increase affect total revenue?

38. *Revenue* A product has the demand function

$$p = 100 - 0.5q$$

where p is in dollars and q is the number of units.
(a) Find the elasticity $\eta(q)$ as a function of q and graph the function

$$f(q) = \eta(q)$$

(b) Find where $f(q) = 1$, which gives the quantity for which the product has unitary elasticity.
(c) The revenue function for this product is

$$R(q) = pq = (100 - 0.5q)q$$

Graph $R(q)$ and find the q-value for which the maximum revenue occurs.
(d) What is the relationship between elasticity and maximum revenue?

39. *Taxes* Can increasing the tax per unit sold actually lead to a decrease in tax revenues?

40. *Taxes* Suppose the demand and supply functions for a product are

$$p = 2800 - 8q - \frac{q^2}{3} \quad \text{and} \quad p = 400 + 2q$$

respectively, where p is in dollars and q is the number of units. Find the tax per unit t that will maximize the tax revenue T and find the maximum tax revenue.

41. *Taxes* Suppose the supply and demand functions for a product are

$$p = 40 + 20q \quad \text{and} \quad p = \frac{5000}{q + 1}$$

respectively, where p is in dollars and q is the number of units. Find the tax t that maximizes the tax revenue T and find the maximum tax revenue.

11 CHAPTER TEST

In Problems 1–8, find the derivative of each function.

1. $y = 5e^{x^3} + x^2$

2. $y = 4\ln(x^3 + 1)$

3. $y = \ln(x^4 + 1)^3$

4. $f(x) = 10(3^{2x})$

5. $S = te^{t^4}$

6. $y = \dfrac{e^{x^3+1}}{x}$

7. $y = \dfrac{3\ln x}{x^4}$

8. $g(x) = 2\log_5(4x + 7)$

9. Find y' if $3x^4 + 2y^2 + 10 = 0$.

10. Let $x^2 + y^2 = 100$.

    If $\dfrac{dx}{dt} = 2$, find $\dfrac{dy}{dt}$ when $x = 6$ and $y = 8$.

11. Find y' if $xe^y = 10y$.

12. Suppose the weekly revenue and weekly cost (both in dollars) for a product are given by $R(x) = 300x - 0.001x^2$ and $C(x) = 4000 + 30x$, respectively, where x is the number of units produced and sold. Find the rate at which profit is changing with respect to time when the number of units produced and sold is 50 and is increasing at a rate of 5 units per week.

13. Suppose the demand for a product is $p^2 + 3p + q = 1500$, where p is in dollars and q is the number of units. Find the elasticity of demand at $p = 30$. If the price is raised to $31, does revenue increase or decrease?

14. Suppose the demand function for a product is given by $(p + 1)q^2 = 10{,}000$, where p is the price and q is the quantity. Find the rate of change of quantity with respect to price when $p = \$99$.

15. The sales of a product are given by $S = 80{,}000e^{-0.4t}$, where S is the daily sales and t is the number of days after the end of an advertising campaign. Find the rate of sales decay 10 days after the end of the ad campaign.

16. Using U.S. Centers for Medicare and Medicaid Services data from 2000 and projected to 2024, the total U.S. expenditures (in billions of dollars) for professional health services and retail medical products (including prescription drugs) can be modeled by

    $$y = 617e^{0.0505t}$$

    where t is the number of years after 2000.
    (a) Find the function that models the rate of change.

(b) Find the model's value for the rate of change of U.S. expenditures for professional health services and retail medical products in 2010 and in 2020.

17. Suppose the demand and supply functions for a product are $p = 1100 - 5q$ and $p = 20 + 0.4q$, respectively, where p is in dollars and q is the number of units. Find the tax per unit t that will maximize the tax revenue $T = tq$.

18. *Modeling* Projections indicate that the percent of U.S. adults with diabetes will dramatically increase. The table gives the percent of U.S. adults with diabetes for selected years from 2010 and projected to 2050.
    (a) Find a logarithmic model, $y = f(x)$, for these data. Use x as the number of years after 2000.
    (b) Find the function that models the rate of change of the percent of U.S. adults with diabetes.
    (c) Find and interpret $f(25)$ and $f'(25)$.

Year	Percent	Year	Percent
2010	15.7	2035	29.0
2015	18.9	2040	31.4
2020	21.1	2045	32.1
2025	24.2	2050	34.3
2030	27.2		

Source: Centers for Disease Control and Prevention

19. Prices for goods and services tend to rise over time, and this results in the erosion of purchasing power. With the 2012 dollar as a reference, a purchasing power of 0.921 for a certain year means that in that year, a dollar will purchase 92.1% of the goods and services that could be purchased for $1 in 2012. Using Social Security Administration data for selected years from 2012 and projected to 2050, the purchasing power of a 2012 dollar can be modeled by the function

    $$P(t) = 1.078(0.9732^t)$$

    where t is the number of years past 2010.
    (a) Find the function that models the rate of change of the purchasing power of a 2012 dollar.
    (b) Find and interpret $P(18)$ and $P'(18)$.

11   EXTENDED APPLICATIONS & GROUP PROJECTS

I. Inflation

Hollingsworth Pharmaceuticals specializes in manufacturing generic medicines. Recently it developed an appetite suppressant with outstanding profit potential. The new appetite suppressant's total costs, sales, and sales growth, as well as projected inflation, are described as follows.

> *Total monthly costs, in dollars, to produce x units (1 unit is 100 capsules):*

$$C(x) = \begin{cases} 15{,}000 + 10x & 0 \le x \le 11{,}000 \\ 15{,}000 + 10x + 0.001(x - 11{,}000)^2 & x \ge 11{,}000 \end{cases}$$

> *Sales:* 10,000 units per month and growing at 1.25% per month, compounded continuously
> *Wholesale selling price:* $34 per unit
> *Inflation:* Approximately 0.25% per month, compounded continuously, affecting both total costs and selling price

Company owners are pleased with the sales growth but are concerned about the projected increase in variable costs when production levels exceed 11,000 units per month. The consensus is that improvements eventually can be made that will reduce costs at higher production levels, thus altering the current cost function model. To plan properly for these changes, Hollingsworth Pharmaceuticals would like you to determine when the company's profits will begin to decrease. To help you determine this, answer the following.

1. If inflation is assumed to be compounded continuously, the selling price and total costs must be multiplied by the factor $e^{0.0025t}$. In addition, if sales growth is assumed

to be compounded continuously, then sales must be multiplied by a factor of the form e^{rt}, where r is the monthly sales growth rate (expressed as a decimal) and t is time in months. Use these factors to write each of the following as a function of time t:
   (a) selling price p per unit (including inflation).
   (b) number of units x sold per month (including sales growth).
   (c) total revenue. (Recall that $R = px$.)
2. Determine how many months it will be before monthly sales exceed 11,000 units.
3. If you restrict your attention to total costs when $x \ge 11{,}000$, then after expanding and collecting like terms, $C(x)$ can be written as follows:

   $$C(x) = 136{,}000 - 12x + 0.001x^2 \quad \text{for } x \ge 11{,}000$$

   Use this form for $C(x)$ with your result from Question 1(b) and with the inflationary factor $e^{0.0025t}$ to express these total costs as a function of time.
4. Form the profit function that will be used when monthly sales exceed 11,000 units using the total revenue function from Question 1(c) and the total cost function from Question 3. This profit function should be a function of time t.
5. Find how long it will be before the profit is maximized. You may have to solve $P'(t) = 0$ by using a graphing calculator or computer to find the t-intercept of the graph of $P'(t)$. In addition, because $P'(t)$ has large numerical coefficients, you may want to divide both sides of $P'(t) = 0$ by 1000 before solving or graphing.

II. Renewable Electric Power (Modeling)

In the United States, consumers of electric power include all sectors of society—residential, commercial, industrial, and transportation related. Because of this broad dependency, reliable and uninterruptible sources of electric power (and those with the lowest environmental impact) are important. The United States has many sources of electrical power generation—predominately coal, natural gas, nuclear power, and renewable sources. The focus of this application is renewable sources because these will not be depleted, even though some renewables can be significant polluters (such as energy from combustion of wood or municipal waste).

The following table shows data for billions of kilowatt-hours of U.S. electrical power generation for selected years from 2016 and projected to 2040.

Power Generation (Billions of kilowatt-hours)

Year	Renewable	Total	Year	Renewable	Total
2016	629	4233	2030	748	4815
2018	651	4342	2032	764	4880
2020	667	4402	2034	778	4962
2022	683	4483	2036	800	5044
2024	700	4583	2038	825	5132
2026	716	4663	2040	851	5219
2028	730	4745			

Source: U.S. Department of Energy

1. Find an exponential function that models the billions of kilowatt-hours of renewable electric power generation, with x as the number of years after 2010. Store the unrounded model as $r(x)$ in Y_1 on your calculator, and report the rounded model as $R(x)$, with 3 significant digits and with base e.

2. Find a linear model for the billions of kilowatt-hours of total electric power generation, with x as the number of years after 2010. Store the unrounded model as $t(x)$ in Y_2 on your calculator, and report the rounded model as $T(x)$, with 3 significant digits.

3. Use the results of Questions 1 and 2 to create a function that models the percent of total electrical power generation that is renewable. Use the unrounded models in Y_1 and Y_2 to create the unrounded model as $p(x)$ and stored in Y_3, and use the rounded models $R(x)$ and $T(x)$ to report the rounded model as $P(x)$.

4. (a) Use the given data sets to create a data set that corresponds to $p(x)$.
   (b) Graph the data set and the model in Y_3 on the same set of axes.
   (c) How well does the model fit these data points?

In Questions 5–9, use the rounded models $R(x)$ and $P(x)$.

5. Find the function that models the rate of change of
   (a) $R(x)$ (b) $P(x)$
6. Find and interpret
   (a) $R(6)$ and $R'(6)$ (b) $R(25)$ and $R'(25)$
7. Find and interpret
   (a) $P(6)$ and $P'(6)$ (b) $P(25)$ and $P'(25)$
8. Find and interpret $P''(6)$ and $P''(25)$.
9. What does your analysis indicate about how the percent of total U.S. electrical power generation that is renewable is changing?

Indefinite Integrals

12

When we know the derivative of a function, it is often useful to determine the function itself. For example, accountants can often translate information about marginal cost or marginal revenue into functions that define these relationships, then use the process of antidifferentiation (or integration) as part of finding the (approximate) total cost or total revenue functions. We can also use integration to optimize profit from information about marginal cost and marginal revenue and to find national consumption from information about marginal propensity to consume.

Integration can also be used in the social and life sciences. For example, we can use information about rates of change of populations, the volume of blood, or the decay of radioactive substances to find functions that describe these applications.

The topics and some representative applications discussed in this chapter include the following.

Prerequisite Problem Type	For Section	Answer	Section for Review
Write as a power: (a) $\sqrt{x}$ (b) $\sqrt{x^2 - 9}$	**12.1–12.4**	(a) $x^{1/2}$ (b) $(x^2 - 9)^{1/2}$	0.4 Radicals
Expand $(x^2 + 4)^2$.	**12.2**	$x^4 + 8x^2 + 16$	0.5 Special powers
Divide $x^4 - 2x^3 + 4x^2 - 7x - 1$ by $x^2 - 2x$.	**12.3**	$x^2 + 4 + \dfrac{x - 1}{x^2 - 2x}$	0.5 Division
Find the derivative of (a) $f(x) = 2x^{1/2}$ (b) $u = x^3 - 3x$	**12.1–12.3**	(a) $f'(x) = x^{-1/2}$ (b) $u' = 3x^2 - 3$	9.4 Derivatives
If $y = \dfrac{(x^2 + 4)^6}{6}$, what is y'?	**12.2**	$y' = (x^2 + 4)^5 2x$	9.6 Derivatives
(a) If $y = \ln u$, what is y'? (b) If $y = e^u$, what is y'?	**12.3**	(a) $y' = \dfrac{1}{u} \cdot u'$ (b) $y' = e^u \cdot u'$	11.1, 11.2 Derivatives
Solve for y: $\ln y = kt + C$	**12.5**	$y = e^{kt + C}$	5.2 Logarithmic functions
Solve for k: $0.5 = e^{5730k}$	**12.5**	$k \approx -0.00012097$	5.3 Exponential equations

Indefinite Integrals

OBJECTIVES

- To use the Powers of x Formula to find indefinite integrals
- To apply properties of indefinite integrals
- To find certain indefinite integrals using the Powers of x Formula in combination with additional integration formulas

APPLICATION PREVIEW

In our study of the theory of the firm, we have worked with total cost, total revenue, and profit functions and have found their marginal functions. In practice, it is often easier for a company to measure marginal cost, revenue, and profit and use these data to form marginal functions from which it can find total cost, total revenue, and profit functions. For example, Jarus Technologies manufactures motherboards, and the company's sales records show that the marginal revenue (in dollars per unit) for its motherboards is given by

$$\overline{MR} = 300 - 0.2x$$

where x is the number of units sold. If we want to use this function to find the total revenue function for Jarus Technologies' motherboards, we need to find $R(x)$ from $\overline{MR} = R'(x)$. (See Example 7.) In this situation, we need to be able to reverse the process of differentiation. This reverse process is called antidifferentiation, or integration.

Indefinite Integrals

We have studied procedures for and applications of finding derivatives of a given function. We now turn our attention to reversing this process of differentiation. When we know the derivative of a function, the process of finding the function itself is called **antidifferentiation.** For example, if the derivative of a function is $2x$, we know that the function could be $f(x) = x^2$ because $\dfrac{d}{dx}(x^2) = 2x$. But the function could also be $f(x) = x^2 + 4$ because $\dfrac{d}{dx}(x^2 + 4) = 2x$. It is clear that any function of the form $f(x) = x^2 + C$, where C is an arbitrary constant, will have $f'(x) = 2x$ as its derivative.

Thus we say that the **general antiderivative** of $f'(x) = 2x$ is $f(x) = x^2 + C$, where C is an arbitrary constant.

The process of finding an antiderivative is also called **integration.** The function that results when integration takes place is called an **indefinite integral** or, more simply, an **integral.** We can denote the indefinite integral (that is, the general antiderivative) of a function $f(x)$ by $\int f(x)\,dx$. Thus we can write $\int 2x\,dx$ to indicate the general antiderivative of the function $f(x) = 2x$. The expression is read as "the integral of $2x$ with respect to x." In this case, $2x$ is called the **integrand.** The **integral sign,** $\int$, indicates the process of integration, and the dx indicates that the integral is to be taken with respect to x. Because the antiderivative of $2x$ is $x^2 + C$, we can write

$$\int 2x\,dx = x^2 + C$$

EXAMPLE 1 Antidifferentiation

If $f'(x) = 3x^2$, what is $f(x)$?

Solution

The derivative of the function $f(x) = x^3$ is $f'(x) = 3x^2$. Other functions also have this derivative, but all will be of the form $f(x) = x^3 + C$, where C is a constant. Thus we write

$$\int 3x^2\,dx = x^3 + C$$

EXAMPLE 2   Integration

If $f'(x) = x^3$, what is $f(x)$?

Solution

We know that $\dfrac{d}{dx}(x^4) = 4x^3$, so the derivative of $f(x) = \frac{1}{4}x^4$ is $f'(x) = x^3$. Thus

$$f(x) = \int f'(x)dx = \int x^3 dx = \frac{1}{4}x^4 + C$$

Powers of x Formula   It is easily seen that

$$\int x^4\, dx = \frac{x^5}{5} + C \text{ because } \frac{d}{dx}\left(\frac{x^5}{5} + C\right) = x^4$$

$$\int x^5\, dx = \frac{x^6}{6} + C \text{ because } \frac{d}{dx}\left(\frac{x^6}{6} + C\right) = x^5$$

In general, we have the following.

Powers of x Formula

$$\int x^n\, dx = \frac{x^{n+1}}{n+1} + C \quad (\text{for } n \neq -1)$$

In the Powers of x Formula, we see that $n \neq -1$ is essential because if $n = -1$, then the denominator $n + 1 = 0$. We will discuss the case when $n = -1$ later. (Can you think what function has $1/x$ as its derivative?)

In addition, we can see that this Powers of x Formula applies for any $n \neq -1$ by noting that

$$\frac{d}{dx}\left(\frac{x^{n+1}}{n+1} + C\right) = \frac{d}{dx}\left(\frac{1}{n+1}x^{n+1} + C\right) = \frac{n+1}{n+1}x^n = x^n$$

EXAMPLE 3   Powers of x Formula

Evaluate $\int x^{-1/2} dx$.

Solution

Using the formula, we get

$$\int x^{-1/2}dx = \frac{x^{-1/2+1}}{-1/2+1} + C = \frac{x^{1/2}}{1/2} + C = 2x^{1/2} + C$$

We can check by noting that the derivative of $2x^{1/2} + C$ is $x^{-1/2}$. ✔

Note that the indefinite integral in Example 3 is a function (actually a number of functions, one for each value of C). Graphs of several members of this family of functions are shown in Figure 12.1. Note that at any given x-value, the tangent line to each curve has the same slope, indicating that all family members have the same derivative.

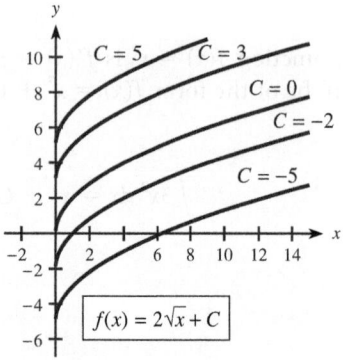

Figure 12.1

EXAMPLE 4   **Powers of x Formula**

Find (a) $\int \sqrt[3]{x}\, dx$ and   (b) $\int \dfrac{1}{x^2}\, dx$.

Solution

(a) $\displaystyle \int \sqrt[3]{x}\, dx = \int x^{1/3}\, dx = \frac{x^{4/3}}{4/3} + C$

$\displaystyle \qquad\qquad = \frac{3}{4} x^{4/3} + C = \frac{3}{4}\sqrt[3]{x^4} + C$

(b) We write the power of x in the numerator so that the integral has the form in the Powers of x Formula.

$$\int \frac{1}{x^2}\, dx = \int x^{-2}\, dx = \frac{x^{-2+1}}{-2+1} + C = \frac{x^{-1}}{-1} + C = \frac{-1}{x} + C$$

Other Formulas and Properties   Other formulas will be useful in evaluating integrals. The following table shows how some new integration formulas result from differentiation formulas.

INTEGRATION FORMULAS

Derivative	Resulting Integral
$\dfrac{d}{dx}(x) = 1$	$\displaystyle \int 1\, dx = \int dx = x + C$
$\dfrac{d}{dx}[c \cdot u(x)] = c \cdot \dfrac{d}{dx} u(x)$	$\displaystyle \int c\,u(x)\, dx = c \int u(x)\, dx$
$\dfrac{d}{dx}[u(x) \pm v(x)] = \dfrac{d}{dx} u(x) \pm \dfrac{d}{dx} v(x)$	$\displaystyle \int [u(x) \pm v(x)]\, dx = \int u(x)\, dx \pm \int v(x)\, dx$

These formulas indicate that we can integrate functions term by term just as we were able to take derivatives term by term.

EXAMPLE 5   **Using Integration Formulas**

Evaluate: (a) $\int 4\, dx$ (b) $\int 8x^5\, dx$ (c) $\int (x^3 + 4x)\, dx$

Solution

(a) $\int 4\, dx = 4 \int dx = 4(x + C_1) = 4x + C$
(Because C_1 is an unknown constant, we can write $4C_1$ as the unknown constant C.)

(b) $\displaystyle \int 8x^5\, dx = 8 \int x^5\, dx = 8\left(\frac{x^6}{6} + C_1 \right) = \frac{4x^6}{3} + C$

(c) $\displaystyle \int (x^3 + 4x)\, dx = \int x^3\, dx + \int 4x\, dx$

$\displaystyle \qquad = \left(\frac{x^4}{4} + C_1 \right) + \left(4 \cdot \frac{x^2}{2} + C_2 \right)$

$\displaystyle \qquad = \frac{x^4}{4} + 2x^2 + C_1 + C_2$

$\displaystyle \qquad = \frac{x^4}{4} + 2x^2 + C$

Note that we need only one constant because the sum of C_1 and C_2 is just a new constant.

EXAMPLE 6 **Integral of a Polynomial**

Evaluate $\int (x^2 - 4)^2 \, dx$.

Solution

We expand $(x^2 - 4)^2$ so that the integrand is in a form that fits the basic integration formulas.

$$\int (x^2 - 4)^2 \, dx = \int (x^4 - 8x^2 + 16) \, dx = \frac{x^5}{5} - \frac{8x^3}{3} + 16x + C$$

CHECKPOINT

1. True or false:

   (a) $\int (4x^3 - 2x) \, dx = \int 4x^3 \, dx - \int 2x \, dx$

   $$= (x^4 + C) - (x^2 + C) = x^4 - x^2$$

   (b) $\int \frac{1}{3x^2} \, dx = \frac{1}{3(x^3/3)} + C = \frac{1}{x^3} + C$

2. Evaluate $\int (2x^3 + x^{-1/2} - 4x^{-5}) \, dx$.

EXAMPLE 7 **Revenue** | APPLICATION PREVIEW |

Sales records at Jarus Technologies show that the rate of change of the revenue (that is, the marginal revenue) in dollars per unit for a motherboard is $\overline{MR} = 300 - 0.2x$, where x represents the quantity sold. Find the total revenue function for the product. Then find the total revenue from the sale of 1000 motherboards.

Solution

We know that the marginal revenue can be found by differentiating the total revenue function. That is,

$$R'(x) = 300 - 0.2x$$

Thus integrating the marginal revenue function gives the total revenue function.

$$R(x) = \int (300 - 0.2x) \, dx = 300x - 0.1x^2 + K^*$$

We can use the fact that there is no revenue when no units are sold to evaluate K. Setting $x = 0$ and $R = 0$ gives $0 = 300(0) - 0.1(0)^2 + K$, so $K = 0$. Thus the total revenue function is

$$R(x) = 300x - 0.1x^2$$

The total revenue from the sale of 1000 motherboards is

$$R(1000) = 300(1000) - 0.1(1000^2) = \$200,000$$

We can check that the $R(x)$ we found in Example 7 is correct by verifying that $R'(x) = 300 - 0.2x$ and $R(0) = 0$. Also, graphs can help us check the reasonableness of our result. Figure 12.2 shows the graphs of $\overline{MR} = 300 - 0.2x$ and of the $R(x)$ we found. Note that $R(x)$ passes through the origin, indicating $R(0) = 0$. Also, reading both graphs from left to right, we see that $R(x)$ increases when $\overline{MR} > 0$, attains its maximum when $\overline{MR} = 0$, and decreases when $\overline{MR} < 0$.

---

*Here we are using K rather than C to represent the constant of integration to avoid confusion between the constant C and the cost function $C = C(x)$.

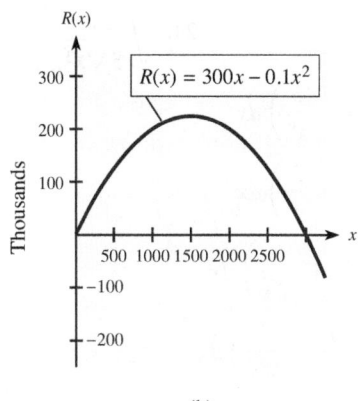

Figure 12.2   (a)   (b)

Calculator Note   We mentioned in Chapter 9, "Derivatives," that graphing calculators have a numerical derivative feature that can be used to check graphically the derivative of a function that has been calculated with a formula. We can also use the numerical integration feature on graphing calculators to check our integration (if we assume temporarily that the constant of integration is 0). We do this by graphing the integral calculated with a formula and the numerical integral from the graphing calculator on the same set of axes. If the graphs lie on top of one another, the integrals agree. Figure 12.3 illustrates this for the function $f(x) = 3x^2 - 2x + 1$. Its integral, with the constant of integration set equal to 0, is shown as $y_1 = x^3 - x^2 + x$ in Figure 12.3(a), and the graphs of the two integrals are shown in Figure 12.3(b). Of course, it is often easier to use the derivative to check integration. See Appendix A, Section 12.1, for details. ■

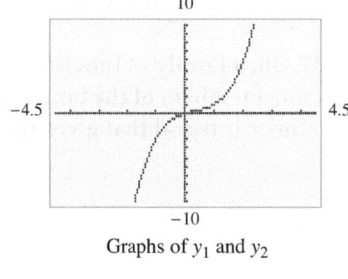

Figure 12.3   (a)   (b)

CHECKPOINT ANSWERS

1. (a) False; $\int (4x^3 - 2x)\, dx = x^4 - x^2 + C$

   (b) False; $\int \dfrac{1}{3x^2}\, dx = \dfrac{-1}{3x} + C$

2. $\int (2x^3 + x^{-1/2} - 4x^{-5})\, dx = \dfrac{x^4}{2} + 2x^{1/2} + x^{-4} + C$

EXERCISES 12.1

1. If $f'(x) = 4x^3$, what is $f(x)$?
2. If $f'(x) = 5x^4$, what is $f(x)$?
3. If $f'(x) = x^6$, what is $f(x)$?
4. If $g'(x) = x^4$, what is $g(x)$?

Evaluate the integrals in Problems 5–28. Check your answers by differentiating.

5. $\int x^7 dx$
6. $\int x^5 dx$
7. $\int 8x^3 dx$
8. $\int 16x^9 dx$

9. $\int (3^3 + x^{13})\, dx$
10. $\int (5^2 + x^{10})\, dx$
11. $\int (3 - x^{3/2})\, dx$
12. $\int (8 + x^{2/3})\, dx$
13. $\int (x^4 - 9x^2 + 3)\, dx$
14. $\int (3x^2 - 4x - 4)\, dx$
15. $\int (13 - 6x + 21x^6)\, dx$
16. $\int (12x^5 + 12x^3 - 7)\, dx$
17. $\int (2 + 2\sqrt{x})\, dx$
18. $\int (17 + \sqrt{x^3})\, dx$
19. $\int 6\sqrt[4]{x}\, dx$
20. $\int 3\sqrt[3]{x^2}\, dx$
21. $\int \dfrac{5}{x^4}\, dx$
22. $\int \dfrac{6}{x^5}\, dx$

23. $\int \dfrac{dx}{2\sqrt[3]{x^2}}$

24. $\int \dfrac{2\,dx}{5\sqrt{x^3}}$

25. $\int \left(x^3 - 4 + \dfrac{5}{x^6}\right) dx$

26. $\int \left(x^3 - 7 - \dfrac{3}{x^4}\right) dx$

27. $\int \left(x^9 - \dfrac{1}{x^3} + \dfrac{2}{\sqrt[3]{x}}\right) dx$

28. $\int \left(3x^8 + \dfrac{4}{x^8} - \dfrac{5}{\sqrt[5]{x}}\right) dx$

In Problems 29–32, use algebra to rewrite the integrands; then integrate and simplify.

29. $\int (4x^2 - 1)^2 x^3\,dx$

30. $\int (x^3 + 1)^2 x\,dx$

31. $\int \dfrac{x+1}{x^3}\,dx$

32. $\int \dfrac{x-3}{\sqrt{x}}\,dx$

In Problems 33 and 34, find the antiderivatives and graph the resulting family members that correspond to $C = 0$, $C = 4$, $C = -4$, $C = 8$, and $C = -8$.

33. $\int (2x + 3)\,dx$

34. $\int (4 - x)\,dx$

35. If $\int f(x)\,dx = 2x^9 - 7x^5 + C$, find $f(x)$.

36. If $\int g(x)\,dx = 11x^{10} - 4x^3 + C$, find $g(x)$.

In each of Problems 37–40, a family of functions is given and graphs of some members of the family are shown. Write the indefinite integral that gives the family.

37. $F(x) = 5x - \dfrac{x^2}{4} + C$

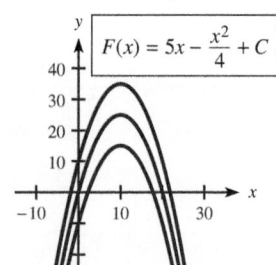

38. $F(x) = \dfrac{x^2}{2} + 3x + C$

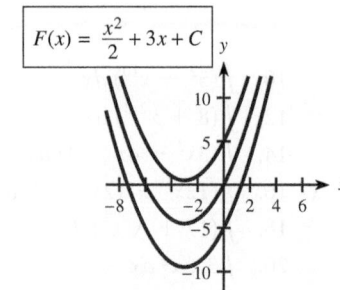

39. $F(x) = x^3 - 3x^2 + C$

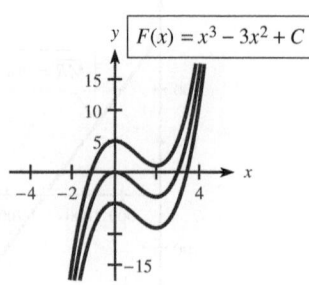

40. $F(x) = 12x - x^3 + C$

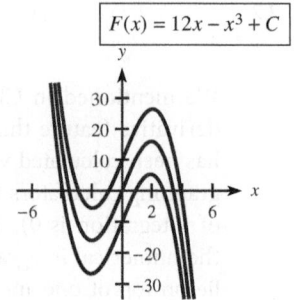

APPLICATIONS

41. *Revenue* If the marginal revenue (in dollars per unit) for a month for a commodity is $\overline{MR} = -0.4x + 30$, find the total revenue function.

42. *Revenue* If the marginal revenue (in dollars per unit) for a month for a commodity is $\overline{MR} = -0.05x + 25$, find the total revenue function.

43. *Revenue* If the marginal revenue (in dollars per unit) for a month is given by $\overline{MR} = -0.3x + 450$, what is the total revenue from the production and sale of 50 units?

44. *Revenue* If the marginal revenue (in dollars per unit) for a month is given by $\overline{MR} = -0.006x + 36$, find the total revenue from the sale of 75 units.

45. *Stimulus-response* Suppose that when a sense organ receives a stimulus at time t, the total number of action potentials is $P(t)$. If the rate at which action potentials are produced is $t^3 + 4t^2 + 6$ and there are 0 action potentials when $t = 0$, find the formula for $P(t)$.

46. *Projectiles* Suppose that a particle has been shot into the air in such a way that the rate at which its height is changing is $v = 320 - 32t$, in feet per second, and suppose that it is 1600 feet high when $t = 10$ seconds. Write the equation that describes the height of the particle at any time t.

47. *Pollution* A factory is dumping pollutants into a river at a rate given by $dx/dt = t^{3/4}/600$ tons per week, where t is the time in weeks since the dumping began and x is the number of tons of pollutants.
    (a) Find the equation for total tons of pollutants dumped.
    (b) How many tons were dumped during the first year?

48. *Population growth* The rate of growth of the population of a city is predicted to be

$$\frac{dp}{dt} = 1000t^{1.08}$$

where p is the population at time t and t is measured in years from the present. Suppose that the current population is 100,000. What is the predicted
(a) rate of growth 5 years from the present?
(b) population 5 years from the present?

49. *Average cost* The DeWitt Company has found that the rate of change of its average cost for a product is

$$\overline{C}'(x) = \frac{1}{4} - \frac{100}{x^2}$$

where x is the number of units and cost is in dollars. The average cost per unit for 20 units is $400.
(a) Find the average cost function for the product.
(b) Find the average cost of 100 units of the product.

50. *Oil leakage* An oil tanker hits a reef and begins to leak. The efforts of the workers repairing the leak cause the rate at which the oil is leaking to decrease. The oil was leaking at a rate of 31 barrels per hour at the end of the first hour after the accident, and the rate is decreasing at a rate of one barrel per hour.
(a) What function describes the rate of loss?
(b) How many barrels of oil will leak in the first 6 hours?
(c) When will the oil leak be stopped? How much will have leaked altogether?

51. *Health expenditures per capita* National health expenditures per capita E (in dollars) have risen dramatically since 2000. By using data from the Centers for Medicare and Medicaid Services from 2002 and projected to 2024, the rate of change of health expenditures per capita can be modeled by

$$\frac{dE}{dt} = 2.73t^2 - 50.6t + 549$$

dollars per year, where t is the number of years past 2000.
(a) Find the function that models the national health expenditures per capita if these expenditures were $8428 in 2010. Use 3 significant digits.
(b) Use the model from part (a) to predict the national health expenditures per capita for 2020.

52. *Total taxable payroll* By using Social Security Administration data for selected years from 2012 and projected to 2050, the rate of change of the total U.S. taxable payroll can be modeled by

$$\frac{dP}{dt} = 27.0t + 112$$

billions of dollars per year, where t is the number of years past 2010.
(a) If total U.S. taxable payroll was $7088 billion in 2016, find the function $P(t)$. Use 3 significant digits.
(b) What does $P(t)$ predict for the total U.S. taxable payroll in 2025?

53. *Wind chill* When the air temperature is 20° F, the rate of change of the wind chill temperature t (°F) is given by

$$\frac{dt}{dw} = -4.352w^{-0.84}$$

where w is wind speed in miles per hour.
(a) Will both the rate of change of wind chill temperature and wind chill temperature decrease as the windspeed increases? Explain.
(b) If the wind chill temperature is 1°F when the wind speed is 31 mph and the air temperature is 20°F, find the function that models the wind chill temperature.

54. *Severe weather ice makers* Hail is produced in severe thunderstorms when an updraft draws moist surface air into subfreezing air above 10,000 feet. The speed of the updraft s, in mph, affects the diameter of hail (in inches). According to National Weather Service data, the rate of change of hail size with respect to updraft speed is

$$\frac{dh}{ds} = 0.001144s^{0.922}$$

inches of diameter per mph of updraft.
(a) When updraft speeds approach 60 mph, hail is golf-ball-sized. Use $h = 1.5$ and $s = 60$ to find a model for $h(s)$.
(b) Use the model to find the hail size for an updraft speed of 100 mph.

55. *U.S. population* With U.S. Census Bureau data (actual and projected) for selected years from 1960 to 2050, the rate of change of U.S. population P can be modeled by

$$\frac{dP}{dt} = -0.0002187t^2 + 0.0276t + 1.98$$

million people per year, where $t = 0$ represents 1960.
(a) In what year does this rate of change reach its maximum?
(b) In 1960, the U.S. population was 181 million. Use this to find a model for $P(t)$.
(c) For 2025, the Census Bureau's predicted U.S. population is 348 million. What does the model predict?

56. *Consumer prices* The consumer price index (CPI) measures how prices have changed for consumers. With 1995 as a reference of 100, a year with CPI = 150 indicates that consumer costs in that year were 1.5 times the 1995 costs. With U.S. Department of Labor data for selected years from 1995 and projected to 2050, the rate of change of the CPI can be modeled by

$$\frac{dC}{dt} = 0.009t^2 - 0.096t + 4.85$$

dollars per year, where $t = 0$ represents 1990.
(a) Find the function that models $C(t)$ if the CPI was 175 in 2010.
(b) What does the model from part (a) predict for the consumer costs in 2030? How does this compare to 2010?

SECTION 12.2　The Power Rule

OBJECTIVES

OBJECTIVES

- To find the differential of a function
- To use the Power Rule to evaluate integrals of the form $\int u^n \cdot u' \, dx = \int u^n du$ if $n \neq -1$
- To identify and evaluate integrals that do not fit the Power Rule

APPLICATION PREVIEW

In the previous section, we saw that total revenue could be found by integrating marginal revenue. That is,

$$R(x) = \int \overline{MR} \, dx$$

For example, if the marginal revenue for a product is given by

$$\overline{MR} = \frac{600}{\sqrt{3x + 1}} + 2$$

then

$$R(x) = \int \left[\frac{600}{\sqrt{3x + 1}} + 2 \right] dx$$

To evaluate this integral, however, we need a more general formula than the Powers of x Formula. (See Example 8.)

In this section, we will extend the Powers of x Formula to a rule for powers of a function of x.

Differentials

Our goal in this section is to extend the Powers of x Formula,

$$\int x^n dx = \frac{x^{n+1}}{n+1} + C, \quad n \neq -1$$

to powers of a function of x. To do this, we must understand the symbol dx.

Recall from Section 9.3, "Rates of Change and Derivatives," that the derivative of $y = f(x)$ with respect to x can be denoted by dy/dx. As we will see, there are advantages to using dy and dx as separate quantities whose ratio dy/dx equals $f'(x)$.

Differentials

If $y = f(x)$ is a differentiable function with derivative $dy/dx = f'(x)$, then the **differential of x** is dx and the **differential of y** is dy, where

$$dy = f'(x) \, dx$$

Although differentials are useful in certain approximation problems, we are interested in the differential notation at this time.

EXAMPLE　1　Differentials

Find (a) dy if $y = x^3 - 4x^2 + 5$ and (b) du if $u = 5x^4 + 11$.

Solution

(a)　$dy = f'(x) \, dx = (3x^2 - 8x) \, dx$

(b)　If the dependent variable in a function is u, then $du = u'(x) \, dx$.

$$du = u'(x) \, dx = 20x^3 \, dx$$

The Power Rule

In terms of our goal of extending the Powers of x Formula, we would suspect that if x is replaced by a function of x, then dx should be replaced by the differential of that function. Let's see whether this is true.

Recall that if $y = [u(x)]^n$, the derivative of y is

$$\frac{dy}{dx} = n[u(x)]^{n-1} \cdot u'(x)$$

Using this formula for derivatives, we can see that

$$\int n[u(x)]^{n-1} \cdot u'(x) \, dx = [u(x)]^n + C$$

It is easy to see that this formula is equivalent to the following formula, which is called the **Power Rule for Integration.**

Power Rule for Integration

$$\int [u(x)]^n \cdot u'(x) \, dx = \frac{[u(x)]^{n+1}}{n+1} + C, \quad n \neq -1$$

Using the fact that

$$du = u'(x) \, dx \quad \text{or} \quad du = u' \, dx$$

we can write the Power Rule in the following alternative form.

Power Rule (Alternative Form)

If $u = u(x)$, then

$$\int u^n \, du = \frac{u^{n+1}}{n+1} + C, \quad n \neq -1$$

Note that this formula has the same form as the formula

$$\int x^n \, dx = \frac{x^{n+1}}{n+1} + C, \quad n \neq -1$$

with the *function u substituted for x and du substituted for dx.*

EXAMPLE 2 **Power Rule**

Evaluate $\int (3x^2 + 4)^5 \cdot 6x \, dx$.

Solution
To use the Power Rule, we must be sure that we have the function $u(x)$, its derivative $u'(x)$, and $n \neq -1$.

$$u = 3x^2 + 4, \quad n = 5$$
$$u' = 6x$$

All required parts are present, so the integral is of the form

$$\int (3x^2 + 4)^5 \, 6x \, dx = \int u^5 \cdot u' \, dx = \int u^5 \, du$$

$$= \frac{u^6}{6} + C = \frac{(3x^2 + 4)^6}{6} + C$$

We can check the integration by noting that the derivative of

$$\frac{(3x^2 + 4)^6}{6} + C \text{ is } (3x^2 + 4)^5 \cdot 6x$$

EXAMPLE 3   Power Rule

Evaluate $\int \sqrt{2x + 3} \cdot 2 \, dx$.

Solution

If we let $u = 2x + 3$, then $u' = 2$, and so we have

$$\int \sqrt{2x + 3} \cdot 2 \, dx = \int \sqrt{u} \, u' dx = \int \sqrt{u} \, du$$

$$= \int u^{1/2} \, du = \frac{u^{3/2}}{3/2} + C$$

Because $u = 2x + 3$, we have

$$\int \sqrt{2x + 3} \cdot 2 \, dx = \frac{2}{3}(2x + 3)^{3/2} + C$$

Check: The derivative of $\frac{2}{3}(2x + 3)^{3/2} + C$ is $(2x + 3)^{1/2} \cdot 2$. ✔

Some members of the family of functions given by

$$\int \sqrt{2x + 3} \cdot 2 \, dx = \frac{2}{3}(2x + 3)^{3/2} + C$$

are shown in Figure 12.4. Note from the graphs that the domain of each function is $x \geq -3/2$. This is because $2x + 3$ must be nonnegative so that $(2x + 3)^{3/2} = (\sqrt{2x + 3})^3$ is a real number.

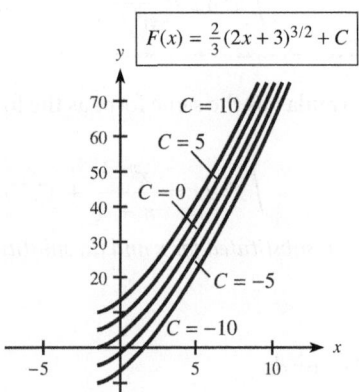

$$F(x) = \frac{2}{3}(2x+3)^{3/2} + C$$

Figure 12.4

EXAMPLE 4   Power Rule

Evaluate $\int x^3(5x^4 + 11)^9 \, dx$.

Solution

If we let $u = 5x^4 + 11$, then $u' = 20x^3$. Thus we do not have an integral of the form $\int u^n \cdot u' dx$, as we had in Example 2 and Example 3; the factor 20 is not in the integrand. To get the integrand in the correct form, we can multiply by 20 and divide it out as follows:

$$\int x^3(5x^4 + 11)^9 \, dx = \int (5x^4 + 11)^9 \cdot x^3 \, dx = \int (5x^4 + 11)^9 \left(\frac{1}{20}\right)(20x^3) \, dx$$

Because $\frac{1}{20}$ is a constant factor, we can factor it outside the integral sign, getting

$$\int (5x^4 + 11)^9 \cdot x^3 \, dx = \frac{1}{20} \int (5x^4 + 11)^9 (20x^3) \, dx$$

$$= \frac{1}{20} \int u^9 \cdot u' dx = \frac{1}{20} \cdot \frac{u^{10}}{10} + C$$

$$= \frac{1}{200}(5x^4 + 11)^{10} + C$$

EXAMPLE 5   **Power Rule**

Evaluate $\int 5x^2\sqrt{x^3 - 4}\,dx$.

Solution

If we let $u = x^3 - 4$, then $u' = 3x^2$. Thus we need the factor 3, rather than 5, in the integrand. If we first reorder the factors and then multiply by the constant factor 3 (and divide it out), we have

$$\int \sqrt{x^3 - 4} \cdot 5x^2\,dx = \int \sqrt{x^3 - 4} \cdot \frac{5}{3}(3x^2)\,dx$$

$$= \frac{5}{3}\int (x^3 - 4)^{1/2} \cdot 3x^2\,dx$$

This integral is of the form $\frac{5}{3}\int u^{1/2} \cdot u'\,dx$, resulting in

$$\frac{5}{3} \cdot \frac{u^{3/2}}{3/2} + C = \frac{5}{3} \cdot \frac{(x^3 - 4)^{3/2}}{3/2} + C = \frac{10}{9}(x^3 - 4)^{3/2} + C \qquad \blacksquare$$

Note that we can factor a constant outside the integral sign to obtain the integrand in the form we seek. But if a variable must be factored outside the integral to obtain the form $u^n \cdot u'\,dx$, we *cannot* use this form and must try something else.

EXAMPLE 6   **Power Rule Fails**

Evaluate $\int (x^2 + 4)^2\,dx$.

Solution

If we let $u = x^2 + 4$, then $u' = 2x$. Because we would have to introduce a variable to get u' in the integral, we cannot solve this problem by using the Power Rule. We must find another method. We can evaluate this integral by squaring and then integrating term by term.

$$\int (x^2 + 4)^2\,dx = \int (x^4 + 8x^2 + 16)\,dx$$

$$= \frac{x^5}{5} + \frac{8x^3}{3} + 16x + C \qquad \blacksquare$$

Note that if we tried to introduce the factor $2x$ into the integral in Example 6, we would get

$$\int (x^2 + 4)^2\,dx = \int (x^2 + 4)^2 \cdot \frac{1}{2x}(2x)\,dx$$

Although it is tempting to factor $1/2x$ outside the integral and use the Power Rule, this leads to an "answer" that does not check. That is, the derivative of the "answer" is not the integrand. (Try it and see.) To emphasize again, we can introduce only *a constant factor* to get an integral in the proper form.

EXAMPLE 7   **Power Rule**

Evaluate:

(a) $\int (2x^2 - 4x)^7(x - 1)\,dx$ (b) $\int \frac{x^2 - 1}{(x^3 - 3x)^3}\,dx$

Solution

(a) To treat this as an integral of the form $\int u^n\,u'\,dx$, let $u = 2x^2 - 4x$, with $n = 7$. Then $u' = 4x - 4 = 4(x - 1)$. Multiplying and dividing by 4 will give us the correct form.

$$\int (2x^2 - 4x)^7 (x - 1)\, dx = \int (2x^2 - 4x)^7 \cdot \frac{1}{4} \cdot 4(x - 1)\, dx$$

$$= \frac{1}{4} \int (2x^2 - 4x)^7 (4x - 4)\, dx$$

$$= \frac{1}{4} \int u^7 u'\, dx = \frac{1}{4} \cdot \frac{u^8}{8} + C$$

$$= \frac{1}{4} \frac{(2x^2 - 4x)^8}{8} + C$$

$$= \frac{1}{32}(2x^2 - 4x)^8 + C$$

(b) This integral can be treated as $\int u^{-3} u'\, dx$ if we let $u = x^3 - 3x$.

$$\int \frac{x^2 - 1}{(x^3 - 3x)^3}\, dx = \int (x^3 - 3x)^{-3}(x^2 - 1)\, dx$$

Then $u' = 3x^2 - 3 = 3(x^2 - 1)$ and we can multiply and divide by 3 to get the form we need.

$$= \int (x^3 - 3x)^{-3} \cdot \frac{1}{3} \cdot 3(x^2 - 1)\, dx$$

$$= \frac{1}{3} \int (x^3 - 3x)^{-3}(3x^2 - 3)\, dx$$

$$= \frac{1}{3} \left[\frac{(x^3 - 3x)^{-2}}{-2} \right] + C$$

$$= \frac{-1}{6(x^3 - 3x)^2} + C$$

CHECKPOINT

1. Which of the following can be evaluated with the Power Rule?
   (a) $\int (4x^2 + 1)^{10}(8x\, dx)$
   (b) $\int (4x^2 + 1)^{10}(x\, dx)$
   (c) $\int (4x^2 + 1)^{10}(8\, dx)$
   (d) $\int (4x^2 + 1)^{10}\, dx$

2. Which of the following is equal to $\int (2x^3 + 5)^{-2}(6x^2\, dx)$?
   (a) $\dfrac{[(2x^4)/4 + 5x]^{-1}}{-1} \cdot \dfrac{6x^3}{3} + C$

   (b) $\dfrac{(2x^3 + 5)^{-1}}{-1} \cdot \dfrac{6x^3}{3} + C$

   (c) $\dfrac{(2x^3 + 5)^{-1}}{-1} + C$

3. True or false: Constants can be factored outside the integral sign.

4. Evaluate the following.
   (a) $\int (x^3 + 9)^5(3x^2\, dx)$
   (b) $\int (x^3 + 9)^{15}(x^2\, dx)$
   (c) $\int (x^3 + 9)^2(x\, dx)$

EXAMPLE 8   **Revenue** | APPLICATION PREVIEW |

Suppose that the marginal revenue for a product is given by

$$\overline{MR} = \frac{600}{\sqrt{3x + 1}} + 2$$

Find the total revenue function.

Solution

$$R(x) = \int \overline{MR}\, dx = \int \left[\frac{600}{(3x+1)^{1/2}} + 2 \right] dx$$

$$= \int 600(3x+1)^{-1/2}\, dx + \int 2\, dx$$

$$= 600 \left(\frac{1}{3} \right) \int (3x+1)^{-1/2}(3\, dx) + 2 \int dx$$

$$= 200 \frac{(3x+1)^{1/2}}{1/2} + 2x + K$$

$$= 400\sqrt{3x+1} + 2x + K$$

We know that $R(0) = 0$, so we have

$$0 = 400\sqrt{1} + 0 + K \quad \text{or} \quad K = -400$$

Thus the total revenue function is

$$R(x) = 400\sqrt{3x+1} + 2x - 400$$

Note in Example 8 that even though $R(0) = 0$, the constant of integration K was *not* 0.

The formulas we have stated and used in this and the previous section are all the result of "reversing" derivative formulas. We summarize in the following box.

Integration Formula		Derivative Formula
$\int dx = x + C$	because	$\dfrac{d}{dx}(x + C) = 1$
$\int x^n\, dx = \dfrac{x^{n+1}}{n+1} + C \ (n \neq -1)$	because	$\dfrac{d}{dx}\left(\dfrac{x^{n+1}}{n+1} + C \right) = x^n$
$\int [u(x) + v(x)]\, dx = \int u(x)\, dx + \int v(x)\, dx$	because	$\dfrac{d}{dx}[u(x) + v(x)] = \dfrac{du}{dx} + \dfrac{dv}{dx}$
$\int [u(x) - v(x)]\, dx = \int u(x)\, dx - \int v(x)\, dx$	because	$\dfrac{d}{dx}[u(x) - v(x)] = \dfrac{du}{dx} - \dfrac{dv}{dx}$
$\int cf(x)\, dx = c \int f(x)\, dx$	because	$\dfrac{d}{dx}[cf(x)] = c\left(\dfrac{df}{dx} \right)$
$\int u^n\, u'\, dx = \dfrac{u^{n+1}}{n+1} + C \ (n \neq -1)$	because	$\dfrac{d}{dx}\left(\dfrac{u^{n+1}}{n+1} + C \right) = u^n \cdot u'$

Note that there are no integration formulas that correspond to "reversing" the derivative formulas for a product or for a quotient. This means that functions that may be easy to differentiate can be quite difficult (or even impossible) to integrate. Hence, in general, integration is a more difficult process than differentiation. In fact, some functions whose derivatives can be readily found cannot be integrated, such as

$$f(x) = \sqrt{x^3 + 1} \quad \text{and} \quad g(x) = \frac{2x^2}{x^4 + 1}$$

In the next section, we will add to this list of basic integration formulas by "reversing" the derivative formulas for exponential and logarithmic functions.

1. Expressions (a) and (b) can be evaluated with the Power Rule. Expressions (c) and (d) do not fit the format of the Power Rule.

2. (c) $\int (2x^3 + 5)^{-2}(6x^2)\, dx = -(2x^3 + 5)^{-1} + C$

3. True

4. (a) $\int (x^3 + 9)^5(3x^2\, dx) = \dfrac{(x^3 + 9)^6}{6} + C$

(b) $\int (x^3 + 9)^{15}(x^2\, dx) = \dfrac{(x^3 + 9)^{16}}{48} + C$

(c) $\int (x^3 + 9)^2(x\, dx) = \int (x^6 + 18x^3 + 81)x\, dx = \dfrac{x^8}{8} + \dfrac{18x^5}{5} + \dfrac{81x^2}{2} + C$

EXERCISES 12.2

In Problems 1–4, find the differential of each function.

1. $u = 2x^5 + 9$ 2. $u = 3x^4 - 4x^3$

3. $p = 7q - 4q^{3/2}$ 4. $z = 4t - 4/t^2$

In each of Problems 5 and 6, one of parts (a) and (b) can be integrated with the Power Rule and the other cannot. Integrate the part that can be done with the Power Rule, and explain why the Power Rule cannot be used to evaluate the other.

5. (a) $\int (3x^4 - 7)^{12} (12x\, dx)$ (b) $\int (5x^3 + 11)^7 (15x^2\, dx)$

6. (a) $\int 5(6 + 5x)^{10}\, dx$ (b) $\int 14x^2(2x^7 + 9)^6\, dx$

Evaluate the integrals in Problems 7–36. Check your results by differentiation.

7. $\int (x^2 + 3)^3\, 2x\, dx$ 8. $\int (3x^3 + 1)^4\, 9x^2\, dx$

9. $\int (5x^3 + 11)^4\, 15x^2\, dx$ 10. $\int (8x^4 + 5)^3\, (32x^3)\, dx$

11. $\int (3x - x^3)^2\, (3 - 3x^2)\, dx$

12. $\int (4x^2 - 3x)^4\, (8x - 3)\, dx$

13. $\int 4x^3(7x^4 + 12)^3\, dx$ 14. $\int 9x^5(3x^6 - 4)^6\, dx$

15. $\int 7(4x - 1)^6\, dx$ 16. $\int 3(5 - x)^{-3}\, dx$

17. $\int 8x^5(4x^6 + 15)^{-3}\, dx$ 18. $\int 5x^3(3x^4 + 7)^{-4}\, dx$

19. $\int (x - 1)(x^2 - 2x + 5)^4\, dx$

20. $\int (2x^3 - x)(x^4 - x^2)^6\, dx$

21. $\int 2(x^3 - 1)(x^4 - 4x + 3)^{-5}\, dx$

22. $\int 3(x^5 - 2x)(x^6 - 6x^2 + 7)^{-2}\, dx$

23. $\int 7x^3\sqrt{x^4 + 6}\, dx$ 24. $\int 3x\sqrt{5 - x^2}\, dx$

25. $\int (x^3 + 1)^2\, (3x\, dx)$ 26. $\int (x^2 - 5)^2\, (2x^2\, dx)$

27. $\int (3x^4 - 1)^2\, 12x\, dx$ 28. $\int (2x^4 + 3)^2\, (8x\, dx)$

29. $\int \sqrt{x^3 - 3x}\, (x^2 - 1)\, dx$ 30. $\int \sqrt[3]{x^2 + 2x}\, (x + 1)\, dx$

31. $\int \dfrac{3x^4\, dx}{(2x^5 - 5)^4}$ 32. $\int \dfrac{5x^3\, dx}{(x^4 - 8)^3}$

33. $\int \dfrac{x^3 - 1}{(x^4 - 4x)^3}\, dx$ 34. $\int \dfrac{3x^5 - 2x^3}{(x^6 - x^4)^5}\, dx$

35. $\int \dfrac{x^2 - 4x}{\sqrt{x^3 - 6x^2 + 2}}\, dx$ 36. $\int \dfrac{x^2 + 1}{\sqrt{x^3 + 3x + 10}}\, dx$

37. If $\int f(x)\, dx = (7x - 13)^{10} + C$, find $f(x)$.

38. If $\int g(x)\, dx = (5x^2 + 2)^6 + C$, find $g(x)$.

In Problems 39 and 40, (a) evaluate each integral and (b) graph the members of the solution family for $C = -5$, $C = 0$, and $C = 5$.

39. $\int x(x^2 - 1)^3\, dx$ 40. $\int (3x - 11)^{1/3}\, dx$

Each of Problems 41 and 42 has the form $\int f(x)\, dx$.
(a) Evaluate each integral to obtain a family of functions.
(b) Find and graph the family member that passes through the point $(0, 2)$. Call that function $F(x)$.
(c) Find any x-values where $f(x)$ is not defined but $F(x)$ is.
(d) At the x-values found in part (c), what kind of tangent line does $F(x)$ have?

41. $\int \dfrac{3\, dx}{(2x - 1)^{3/5}}$ 42. $\int \dfrac{x^2\, dx}{(x^3 - 1)^{1/3}}$

In each of Problems 43 and 44, a family of functions is given, together with the graphs of some functions in the family. Write the indefinite integral that gives the family.

43. $F(x) = (x^2 - 1)^{4/3} + C$

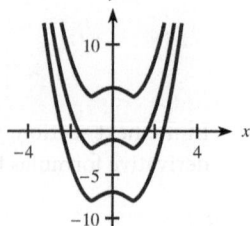

44. $F(x) = 54(4x^2 + 9)^{-1} + C$

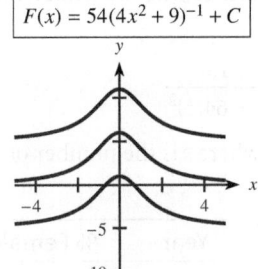

In parts (a)–(c) of Problems 45 and 46, three integrals are given. Integrate those that can be done by the methods studied so far. Additionally, as part (d), give your own example of an integral that looks as though it might use the Power Rule but that cannot be integrated by using methods studied so far.

45. (a) $\displaystyle\int \frac{7x^3\,dx}{(x^3 + 4)^2}$ (b) $\displaystyle\int \frac{7x^2\,dx}{(x^3 + 4)^2}$

(c) $\displaystyle\int \frac{\sqrt{x^2 + 4}}{x}\,dx$

46. (a) $\displaystyle\int \frac{(2x^5 + 1)^{7/2}}{3x^4}\,dx$ (b) $\displaystyle\int 10x(2x^5 + 1)^{7/2}\,dx$

(c) $\displaystyle\int \frac{5x^3}{(2x^4 + 1)^{7/2}}\,dx$

APPLICATIONS

47. *Revenue* Suppose that the marginal revenue for a product is given by

$$\overline{MR} = \frac{-30}{(2x + 1)^2} + 30$$

where x is the number of units and revenue is in dollars. Find the total revenue.

48. *Revenue* The marginal revenue for a new calculator is given by

$$\overline{MR} = 60{,}000 - \frac{40{,}000}{(10 + x)^2}$$

where x represents hundreds of calculators and revenue is in dollars. Find the total revenue function for these calculators.

49. *Physical productivity* The total physical output of a number of machines or workers is called *physical productivity* and is a function of the number of machines or workers. If $P = f(x)$ is the productivity, dP/dx is the marginal physical productivity. If the marginal physical productivity for bricklayers is $dP/dx = 90(x + 1)^2$, where P is the number of bricks laid per day and x is the number of bricklayers, find the physical productivity of 4 bricklayers. (*Note: P = 0 when x = 0.*)

50. *Production* The rate of production of a new line of products is given by

$$\frac{dx}{dt} = 200\left[1 + \frac{400}{(t + 40)^2}\right]$$

where x is the number of items and t is the number of weeks the product has been in production.
   (a) Assuming that $x = 0$ when $t = 0$, find the total number of items produced as a function of time t.
   (b) How many items were produced in the fifth week?

51. *Data entry speed* The rate of change in data entry speed of the average student is $ds/dx = 5(x + 1)^{-1/2}$, where x is the number of lessons the student has had and s is in entries per minute.
   (a) Find the data entry speed as a function of the number of lessons if the average student can complete 10 entries per minute with no lessons ($x = 0$).
   (b) How many entries per minute can the average student complete after 24 lessons?

52. *Productivity* Because a new employee must learn an assigned task, production will increase with time. Suppose that for the average new employee, the rate of performance is given by

$$\frac{dN}{dt} = \frac{1}{2\sqrt{t + 1}}$$

where N is the number of units completed t hours after beginning a new task. If 2 units are completed after 3 hours, how many units are completed after 8 hours?

53. *Film attendance* An excellent film with a very small advertising budget must depend largely on word-of-mouth advertising. In this case, the rate at which weekly attendance might grow can be given by

$$\frac{dA}{dt} = \frac{-100}{(t + 10)^2} + \frac{2000}{(t + 10)^3}$$

where t is the time in weeks since release and A is attendance in millions.
   (a) Find the function that describes weekly attendance at this film.
   (b) Find the attendance at this film in the 10th week.

54. *Product quality and advertising* An inferior product with a large advertising budget does well when it is introduced, but sales decline as people discontinue use of the product. Suppose that the rate of weekly sales revenue is given by

$$S'(t) = \frac{400}{(t + 1)^3} - \frac{200}{(t + 1)^2}$$

where S is sales in thousands of dollars and t is time in weeks.
   (a) Find the function that describes the weekly sales.
   (b) Find the sales for the first week and the ninth week.

55. *Demographics* Because of job outsourcing, a Pennsylvania town predicts that its public school population will decrease at the rate

$$\frac{dN}{dx} = \frac{-300}{\sqrt{x + 9}}$$

where x is the number of years and N is the total school population. If the present population ($x = 0$) is 8000, what population size is expected in 7 years?

56. *Franchise growth* A new fast-food firm predicts that the number of franchises for its products will grow at the rate

$$\frac{dn}{dt} = 9\sqrt{t + 1}$$

where t is the number of years, $0 \le t \le 10$. If there is one franchise ($n = 1$) at present ($t = 0$), how many franchises are predicted 8 years from now?

57. *Obesity* Using data for selected years from 1990 and projected to 2030, the rate of change of the percent of obese Americans who are severely obese can be modeled by the function

$$f'(x) = \frac{375}{(0.743x + 6.97)^2}$$

percentage points per year, where x is the number of years after 1980 (*Source: American Journal of Preventive Medicine*).

(a) If 8.3% of obese Americans were severely obese in 1995, find the function $f(x)$ that gives the percent of obese Americans who are severely obese. Use 3 significant digits.

(b) Use the function from part (a) to predict the percent of obese American adults who will be severely obese in 2025.

58. *Social Security beneficiaries* Suppose the rate of change of the number of Social Security beneficiaries (in millions per year) can be modeled by

$$\frac{dB}{dt} = 0.07149(0.1t + 1)^2 - 0.67114(0.1t + 1) + 2.2016$$

where t is the number of years past 1950.

Year	Number of Beneficiaries (millions)	Year	Number of Beneficiaries (millions)
1950	2.9	2000	44.8
1960	14.3	2010	53.3
1970	25.2	2020	68.8
1980	35.1	2030	82.7
1990	39.5		

Source: Social Security Administration

(a) Use integration and the data point for 2000 to find the function $B(t)$ that models the millions of Social Security beneficiaries.

(b) The data in the table give the millions of Social Security beneficiaries for selected years from 1950 and projected to 2030. Graph $B(t)$ from part (a) with the data in the table.

(c) How well does the model fit the data?

59. *Females in the workforce* Suppose the rate of change of the percent p of total U.S. workers who are female can be modeled by

$$\frac{dp}{dt} = \frac{2154.18}{(1.38t + 64.1)^2}$$

percentage points per year, where t is the number of years past 1950.

Year	% Female	Year	% Female
1950	29.6	2010	47.9
1960	33.4	2015	48.3
1970	38.1	2020	48.1
1980	42.5	2030	48.0
1990	45.2	2040	47.9
2000	46.6	2050	47.9

Source: U.S. Census Bureau

(a) Use integration and the data point for 2040 to find the function $p(t)$ that models the percent of the workforce that is female.

(b) For selected years from 1950 and projected to 2050, the data in the table show the percent of total U.S. workers who are female. With t as the number of years past 1950, graph these data with the model found in part (a).

(c) Comment on the model's fit to the data.

60. *Energy use* For selected years from 1985 and projected to 2035, the following table shows the U.S. energy use per dollar of GDP, viewed as a percent of the 1980 usage. Thus, in 2000, U.S. energy use per dollar of GDP was 67% of what it was in 1980. Suppose the rate of change of energy use per dollar of GDP can be modeled by

$$\frac{dE}{dt} = 0.00468(0.4t + 2)^2 - 0.104(0.4t + 2) - 0.56$$

percentage points per year, where t is the number of years past 1980.

Energy Use per Dollar of GDP

Year	Percent	Year	Percent
1985	83	2015	51
1990	79	2020	45
1995	75	2025	41
2000	67	2030	37
2005	60	2035	34
2010	56		

Source: U.S. Department of Energy

(a) Use integration and the data point for 1990 to find the function $E(t)$ that models the energy use per dollar of GDP. Use 2 significant digits.

(b) Graph the model from part (a) with the data in the table.

(c) Find the model's predicted energy use per dollar of GDP in 2025.

SECTION 12.3

Integrals Involving Exponential and Logarithmic Functions

OBJECTIVES

- To evaluate integrals of the form $\int e^u u' \, dx$ or, equivalently, $\int e^u \, du$
- To evaluate integrals of the form $\int \dfrac{u'}{u} \, dx$ or, equivalently, $\int \dfrac{1}{u} \, du$

APPLICATION PREVIEW

Since the real estate market emerged from the crisis that began in 2008, the rate of growth of the market value of an average home has exceeded the rate of inflation. Suppose, for example, that home prices in a selected area are projected to increase at an average annual rate of 8%. Then the rate of change of the value of a house in this area that cost $200,000 can be modeled by

$$\frac{dV}{dt} = 15.4e^{0.077t}$$

where V is the value of the home in thousands of dollars and t is the time in years since the home was purchased. To find the market value of such a home 10 years after it was purchased in 2015, we would first have to integrate dV/dt. That is, we must be able to integrate an exponential. (See Example 3.)

In this section, we consider integration formulas that result in natural logarithms and formulas for integrating exponentials.

Integrals Involving Exponential Functions

We know that

$$\frac{d}{dx}(e^x) = e^x \quad \text{and} \quad \frac{d}{dx}(e^u) = e^u \cdot u'$$

The corresponding integrals are given by the following.

Exponential Formula

If u is a function of x,

$$\int e^u \cdot u' \, dx = \int e^u \, du = e^u + C$$

In particular, $\int e^x \, dx = e^x + C.$

EXAMPLE 1 **Integral of an Exponential**

Evaluate $\int 5e^x \, dx$.

Solution

$\int 5e^x \, dx = 5\int e^x \, dx = 5e^x + C$

EXAMPLE 2 **Integral of $e^u \, du$**

Evaluate: (a) $\int 2xe^{x^2} \, dx$ (b) $\int \dfrac{x^2 \, dx}{e^{x^3}}$

Solution

(a) Letting $u = x^2$ implies that $u' = 2x$, and the integral is of the form $\int e^u \cdot u' \, dx$. Thus

$$\int 2xe^{x^2} \, dx = \int e^{x^2}(2x) \, dx = \int e^u \cdot u' \, dx = e^u + C = e^{x^2} + C$$

(b) To use $\int e^u \cdot u' \, dx$, we write the exponential in the numerator. Thus

$$\int \frac{x^2 \, dx}{e^{x^3}} = \int e^{-x^3}(x^2 \, dx)$$

This is *almost* of the form $\int e^u \cdot u' \, dx$. Letting $u = -x^3$ gives $u' = -3x^2$. Thus

$$\int e^{-x^3}(x^2 \, dx) = -\frac{1}{3}\int e^{-x^3}(-3x^2 \, dx) = -\frac{1}{3}e^{-x^3} + C = \frac{-1}{3e^{x^3}} + C$$

CHECKPOINT

1   True or false:

(a) $\int e^{x^2}(2x \, dx) = e^{x^2} \cdot x^2 + C$ (b) $\int e^{-3x} \, dx = -\frac{1}{3}e^{-3x} + C$

(c) $\int \frac{dx}{e^{3x}} = \frac{1}{3}\left(\frac{1}{e^{3x}}\right) + C$ (d) $\int e^{3x+1}(3 \, dx) = \frac{e^{3x+2}}{3x+2} + C$

EXAMPLE **3**   **Real Estate Inflation** | APPLICATION PREVIEW |

Suppose the rate of change of the value of a house that cost $200,000 in 2015 can be modeled by

$$\frac{dV}{dt} = 15.4e^{0.077t}$$

where V is the market value of the home in thousands of dollars and t is the time in years since 2015.

(a) Find the function that expresses the value V in terms of t.
(b) Find the predicted value in 2025 (after 10 years).

Solution

(a) $V = \int \dfrac{dV}{dt} \, dt = \int 15.4e^{0.077t} \, dt$

$$V = 15.4 \int e^{0.077t}\left(\frac{1}{0.077}\right)(0.077 \, dt)$$

$$V = 15.4\left(\frac{1}{0.077}\right)\int e^{0.077t}(0.077 \, dt)$$

$$V = 200e^{0.077t} + C$$

Using $V = 200$ (thousand) when $t = 0$, we have

$$200 = 200 + C$$
$$0 = C$$

Thus we have the value as a function of time given by

$$V = 200e^{0.077t}$$

(b) The value after 10 years is found by using $t = 10$.

$$V = 200e^{0.077(10)} = 200e^{0.77} \approx 431.95$$

Thus, in 2025, the predicted value of the home is $431,950.

EXAMPLE **4**   **Graphs of Functions and Integrals**

Figure 12.5 shows the graphs of $g(x) = 5e^{-x^2}$ and $h(x) = -10xe^{-x^2}$. One of these functions is $f(x)$ and the other is $\int f(x) \, dx$ with $C = 0$.
(a) Decide which of $g(x)$ and $h(x)$ is $f(x)$ and which is $\int f(x) \, dx$.
(b) How can the graph of $f(x)$ be used to locate and classify the extrema of $\int f(x) \, dx$?

(c) What feature of the graph of $f(x)$ occurs at the same x-values as the inflection points of the graph of $\int f(x)\,dx$?

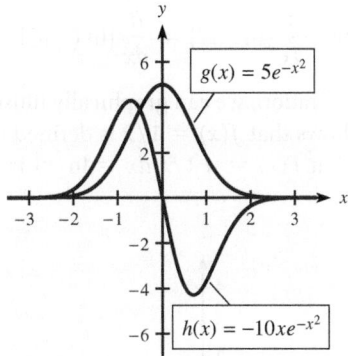

Figure 12.5

Solution

(a) The graph of $h(x)$ looks like the graph of $g'(x)$ because $h(x) > 0$ where $g(x)$ is increasing, $h(x) < 0$ where $g(x)$ is decreasing, and $h(x) = 0$ where $g(x)$ has its maximum. However, if $h(x) = g'(x)$, then, equivalently,

$$\int h(x)\,dx = \int g'(x)\,dx$$
$$= g(x) + C$$

so $h(x) = f(x)$ and $g(x) = \int f(x)\,dx$. We can verify this by noting that

$$\int -10xe^{-x^2}\,dx = 5\int e^{-x^2}(-2x\,dx)$$
$$= 5e^{-x^2} + C$$

(b) We know that $f(x)$ is the derivative of $\int f(x)\,dx$, so, as we saw in part (a), the x-intercepts of $f(x)$ locate the critical values and extrema of $\int f(x)\,dx$.

(c) The first derivative of $\int f(x)\,dx$ is $f(x)$, and its second derivative is $f'(x)$. Hence the inflection points of $\int f(x)\,dx$ occur where $f'(x) = 0$. But $f(x)$ has its extrema where $f'(x) = 0$. Thus the extrema of $f(x)$ occur at the same x-values as the inflection points of $\int f(x)\,dx$. ■

Integrals Involving Logarithmic Functions

Recall that the Power Rule for integrals applies only if $n \neq -1$. That is,

$$\int u^n u'\,dx = \frac{u^{n+1}}{n+1} + C \quad \text{if } n \neq -1$$

The following formula applies when $n = -1$.

Logarithmic Formula

If u is a function of x, then

$$\int u^{-1} u'\,dx = \int \frac{u'}{u}\,dx = \int \frac{1}{u}\,du = \ln|u| + C$$

In particular, $\displaystyle\int \frac{1}{x}\,dx = \ln|x| + C.$

We use the absolute value of u in the integral because the logarithm is defined only when the quantity is positive. This logarithmic formula is a direct result of the fact that

$$\frac{d}{dx}(\ln|u|) = \frac{1}{u}\cdot u'$$

We can see this result by considering the following.

$$\text{For } u > 0: \quad \frac{d}{dx}(\ln|u|) = \frac{d}{dx}(\ln u) = \frac{1}{u} \cdot u'$$

$$\text{For } u < 0: \quad \frac{d}{dx}(\ln|u|) = \frac{d}{dx}[\ln(-u)] = \frac{1}{(-u)} \cdot (-u') = \frac{1}{u} \cdot u'$$

In addition to this verification, we can graphically illustrate the need for the absolute value sign. Figure 12.6(a) shows that $f(x) = 1/x$ is defined for $x \neq 0$, and from Figures 12.6(b) and 12.6(c), we see that $F(x) = \int 1/x\, dx = \ln|x|$ is defined for $x \neq 0$, but $y = \ln x$ is defined only for $x > 0$.

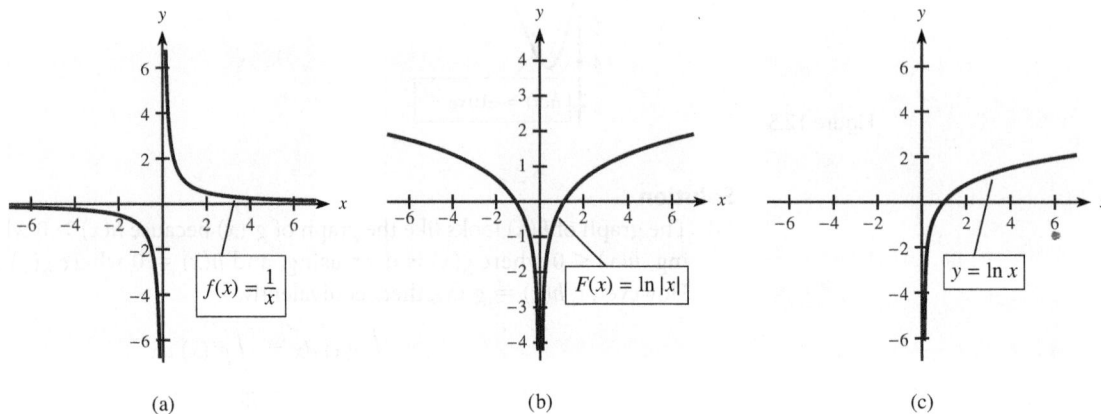

Figure 12.6   (a)   (b)   (c)

EXAMPLE 5   Integral Resulting in a Logarithmic Function

Evaluate $\displaystyle\int \frac{4}{4x + 8}\, dx$.

Solution

This integral is of the form

$$\int \frac{u'}{u}\, dx = \ln|u| + C$$

with $u = 4x + 8$ and $u' = 4$. Thus

$$\int \frac{4}{4x + 8}\, dx = \ln|4x + 8| + C$$

Figure 12.7 shows several members of the family

$$F(x) = \int \frac{4\, dx}{4x + 8} = \ln|4x + 8| + C$$

We can choose different values for C and use a graphing utility to graph families of curves such as those in Figure 12.7.

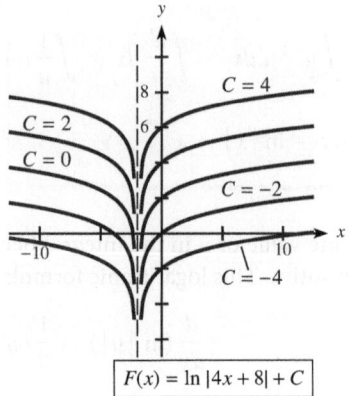

$$F(x) = \ln|4x + 8| + C$$

Figure 12.7

EXAMPLE 6   **Integral of $u'\,dx/u$**

Evaluate $\displaystyle\int \frac{x-3}{x^2-6x+1}\,dx.$

Solution

This integral is of the form $\int (u'/u)\,dx$, *almost.* If we let $u = x^2 - 6x + 1$, then $u = 2x - 6$. If we multiply (and divide) the numerator by 2, we get

$$\int \frac{x-3}{x^2-6x+1}\,dx = \frac{1}{2}\int \frac{2(x-3)}{x^2-6x+1}\,dx$$

$$= \frac{1}{2}\int \frac{2x-6}{x^2-6x+1}\,dx$$

$$= \frac{1}{2}\int \frac{u'}{u}\,dx = \frac{1}{2}\ln |u| + C$$

$$= \frac{1}{2}\ln |x^2 - 6x + 1| + C$$

EXAMPLE 7   **Population Growth**

Because the world contains only about 10 billion acres of arable land, world population is limited. Suppose that world population is limited to 40 billion people and that the rate of population growth per year is given by

$$\frac{dP}{dt} = k(40 - P)$$

where P is the population in billions at time t and k is a positive constant. Then the relationship between the year and the population during that year is equivalent to

$$t = \frac{1}{k}\int \frac{1}{40 - P}\,dP$$

where $40 - P > 0$ because 40 billion is the population's upper limit.

(a) Evaluate this integral to find the relationship.
(b) Use properties of logarithms and exponential functions to write P as a function of t.

Solution

(a) $t = \dfrac{1}{k}\displaystyle\int \dfrac{1}{40 - P}\,dP = -\dfrac{1}{k}\displaystyle\int \dfrac{-dP}{40 - P} = -\dfrac{1}{k}\ln |40 - P| + C_1$

(b) $t = -\dfrac{1}{k}\ln (40 - P) + C_1$ because $40 - P > 0$ means $|40 - P| = 40 - P.$

Solving this equation for P requires converting to exponential form.

$$-k(t - C_1) = \ln (40 - P)$$
$$e^{C_1 k - kt} = 40 - P$$
$$e^{C_1 k} \cdot e^{-kt} = 40 - P$$

Because $e^{C_1 k}$ is an unknown constant, we replace it with C and solve for P.

$$P = 40 - Ce^{-kt}$$

If an integral contains a fraction in which the degree of the numerator is equal to or greater than that of the denominator, we should divide the denominator into the numerator as a first step.

EXAMPLE 8   **Integral Requiring Division**

Evaluate $\int \dfrac{x^4 - 2x^3 + 4x^2 - 7x - 1}{x^2 - 2x}\, dx$.

Solution

Because the numerator is of higher degree than the denominator, we begin by dividing $x^2 - 2x$ into the numerator.

$$
\begin{array}{r}
x^2 \qquad\quad + 4 \\
x^2 - 2x \overline{)\,x^4 - 2x^3 + 4x^2 - 7x - 1\,} \\
\underline{x^4 - 2x^3 \qquad\qquad\qquad} \\
4x^2 - 7x - 1 \\
\underline{4x^2 - 8x \qquad} \\
x - 1
\end{array}
$$

Thus

$$
\int \frac{x^4 - 2x^3 + 4x^2 - 7x - 1}{x^2 - 2x}\, dx = \int \left(x^2 + 4 + \frac{x - 1}{x^2 - 2x} \right) dx
$$

$$
= \int (x^2 + 4)\, dx + \frac{1}{2} \int \frac{2(x - 1)\, dx}{x^2 - 2x}
$$

$$
= \frac{x^3}{3} + 4x + \frac{1}{2} \ln |x^2 - 2x| + C
$$

CHECKPOINT

2. True or false:

(a) $\displaystyle \int \frac{3x^2\, dx}{x^3 + 4} = \ln |x^3 + 4| + C$

(b) $\displaystyle \int \frac{2x\, dx}{\sqrt{x^2 + 1}} = \ln \left| \sqrt{x^2 + 1} \right| + C$

(c) $\displaystyle \int \frac{2}{x}\, dx = 2 \ln |x| + C$

(d) $\displaystyle \int \frac{x}{x + 1}\, dx = x \int \frac{1}{x + 1}\, dx = x \ln |x + 1| + C$

(e) To evaluate $\displaystyle \int \frac{4x}{4x + 1}\, dx$, our first step is to divide $4x + 1$ into $4x$.

3. (a) Divide $4x + 1$ into $4x$.   (b) Evaluate $\displaystyle \int \frac{4x}{4x + 1}\, dx$.

CHECKPOINT
ANSWERS

1. (a) False. The correct solution is $e^{x^2} + C$. (See Example 2a.)
   (b) True
   (c) False; $\displaystyle \int \frac{dx}{e^{3x}} = \frac{-1}{3e^{3x}} + C$
   (d) False; $\displaystyle \int e^{3x + 1}(3\, dx) = e^{3x + 1} + C$

2. (a) True
   (b) False; $\displaystyle \int \frac{2x\, dx}{\sqrt{x^2 + 1}} = 2(x^2 + 1)^{1/2} + C$
   (c) True
   (d) False. We cannot factor the variable x outside the integral sign.
   (e) True

3. (a) $\dfrac{4x}{4x + 1} = 1 - \dfrac{1}{4x + 1}$

   (b) $\displaystyle \int \frac{4x\, dx}{4x + 1} = \int \left(1 - \frac{1}{4x + 1} \right) dx = x - \frac{1}{4} \ln |4x + 1| + C$

EXERCISES 12.3

Evaluate the integrals in Problems 1–32.

1. $\int 3e^{3x}\,dx$

2. $\int 4e^{4x}\,dx$

3. $\int e^{-x}\,dx$

4. $\int e^{2x}\,dx$

5. $\int 1000e^{0.1x}\,dx$

6. $\int 1600e^{0.4x}\,dx$

7. $\int 840e^{-0.7x}\,dx$

8. $\int 250e^{-0.5x}\,dx$

9. $\int x^3 e^{3x^4}\,dx$

10. $\int xe^{2x^2}\,dx$

11. $\int \dfrac{3}{e^{2x}}\,dx$

12. $\int \dfrac{4}{e^{1-2x}}\,dx$

13. $\int \dfrac{x^5}{e^{2-3x^6}}\,dx$

14. $\int \dfrac{x^3}{e^{4x^4}}\,dx$

15. $\int \left(e^{4x} - \dfrac{3}{e^{x/2}}\right)dx$

16. $\int \left(xe^{3x^2} - \dfrac{5}{e^{x/3}}\right)dx$

17. $\int \dfrac{3x^2}{x^3 + 4}\,dx$

18. $\int \dfrac{8x^7}{x^8 - 1}\,dx$

19. $\int \dfrac{dz}{4z + 1}$

20. $\int \dfrac{y}{y^2 + 1}\,dy$

21. $\int \dfrac{6x^3}{2x^4 + 1}\,dx$

22. $\int \dfrac{7x^2}{4x^3 - 9}\,dx$

23. $\int \dfrac{4x}{5x^2 - 4}\,dx$

24. $\int \dfrac{5x^2}{3x^3 - 8}\,dx$

25. $\int \dfrac{3x^2 - 2}{x^3 - 2x}\,dx$

26. $\int \dfrac{4x^3 + 2x}{x^4 + x^2}\,dx$

27. $\int \dfrac{z^2 + 1}{z^3 + 3z + 17}\,dz$

28. $\int \dfrac{(x + 2)\,dx}{x^2 + 4x - 9}$

29. $\int \dfrac{x^3 - x^2 + 1}{x - 1}\,dx$

30. $\int \dfrac{2x^3 + x^2 + 2x + 3}{2x + 1}\,dx$

31. $\int \dfrac{x^2 + x + 3}{x^2 + 3}\,dx$

32. $\int \dfrac{x^4 - 2x^2 + x}{x^2 - 2}\,dx$

In Problems 33 and 34, graphs of two functions labeled $g(x)$ and $h(x)$ are given. Decide which is the graph of $f(x)$ and which is one member of the family $\int f(x)\,dx$. Check your conclusions by evaluating the integral.

33.

$g(x) = 2e^{-(1/2)x}$

$h(x) = -e^{-(1/2)x}$

34.

$g(x) = e^{-2x}$

$h(x) = -2e^{-2x}$

In Problems 35 and 36, a function $f(x)$ and its graph are given. Find the family $F(x) = \int f(x)\,dx$ and graph the member that satisfies $F(0) = 0$.

35.

$f(x) = \dfrac{1}{3 - x}$

36.

$f(x) = \dfrac{1}{x + 2}$

In Problems 37–40, a family of functions is given and graphs of some members are shown. Find the function $f(x)$ such that the family is given by $\int f(x)\,dx$.

37. $F(x) = x + \ln|x| + C$ 38. $F(x) = -\ln(x^2 + 4) + C$

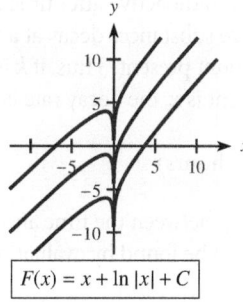

$F(x) = x + \ln|x| + C$

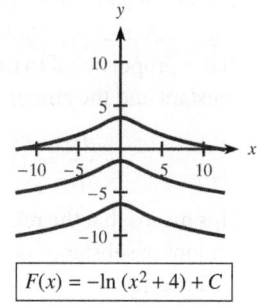

$F(x) = -\ln(x^2 + 4) + C$

39. $F(x) = 5xe^{-x} + C$ 40. $F(x) = e^{0.4x} + e^{-0.4x} + C$

$F(x) = 5xe^{-x} + C$

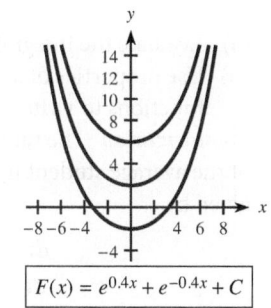

$F(x) = e^{0.4x} + e^{-0.4x} + C$

In parts (a)–(d) of Problems 41 and 42, integrate those that can be done by the methods studied so far.

41. (a) $\int xe^{x^3}\,dx$

(b) $\int \dfrac{x + 2}{x^2 + 2x + 7}\,dx$

(c) $\int \dfrac{x^2 + 2x}{x^3 + 3x^2 + 7}\,dx$ (d) $\int 5x^3 e^{2x^4}\,dx$

42. (a) $\int \dfrac{3x - 1}{x^3 - x + 2}\,dx$

(b) $\int \dfrac{3x - 1}{6x^2 - 4x + 9}\,dx$

(c) $\int 5\sqrt{x}\,e^{\sqrt{x}}\,dx$ (d) $\int 6xe^{-x^2/8}\,dx$

APPLICATIONS

43. *Revenue* Suppose that the marginal revenue from the sale of x units of a product is $\overline{MR} = R'(x) = 6e^{0.01x}$. What is the revenue in dollars from the sale of 100 units of the product?

44. *Concentration of a drug* Suppose that the rate at which the concentration of a drug in the blood changes with respect to time t is given by

$$C'(t) = \frac{c}{b-a}(be^{-bt} - ae^{-at}), \quad t \geq 0$$

where a, b, and c are constants depending on the drug administered, with $b > a$. Assuming that $C(t) = 0$ when $t = 0$, find the formula for the concentration of the drug in the blood at any time t.

45. *Radioactive decay* The rate of disintegration of a radioactive substance can be described by

$$\frac{dn}{dt} = n_0(-K)e^{-Kt}$$

where n_0 is the number of radioactive atoms present when time t is 0, and K is a positive constant that depends on the substance involved. Using the fact that the constant of integration is 0, integrate dn/dt to find the number of atoms n that are still radioactive after time t.

46. *Radioactive decay* Radioactive substances decay at a rate that is proportional to the amount present. Thus, if k is a constant and the amount present is x, the decay rate is

$$\frac{dx}{dt} = kx \quad (t \text{ in hours})$$

This means that the relationship between the time and the amount of substance present can be found by evaluating the integral

$$t = \int \frac{dx}{kx}$$

(a) Evaluate the integral to find the relationship.
(b) Use properties of logarithms and exponential functions to write x as a function of t.

47. *Memorization* The rate of vocabulary memorization of the average student in a foreign language course is given by

$$\frac{dv}{dt} = \frac{40}{t+1}$$

where t is the number of continuous hours of study, $0 < t \leq 4$, and v is the number of words. How many words would the average student memorize in 3 hours?

48. *Population growth* The rate of growth of world population can be modeled by

$$\frac{dN}{dt} = N_0 re^{rt}, \quad r < 1$$

where t is the time in years from the present and N_0 and r are constants. What function describes world population if the present population is N_0?

49. *Compound interest* If $\$P$ is invested for n years at 10% compounded continuously, the rate at which the future value is growing is

$$\frac{dS}{dn} = 0.1Pe^{0.1n}$$

(a) What function describes the future value at the end of n years?
(b) In how many years will the future value double?

50. *Temperature changes* When an object is moved from one environment to another, its temperature T changes at a rate given by

$$\frac{dT}{dt} = kCe^{kt}$$

where t is the time in the new environment (in hours), C is the temperature difference (old − new) between the two environments, and k is a constant. If the temperature of the object (and the old environment) is 70°F and $C = -10$°F, what function describes the temperature T of the object t hours after it is moved?

51. *Blood pressure in the aorta* The rate at which blood pressure decreases in the aorta of a normal adult after a heartbeat is

$$\frac{dp}{dt} = -46.645e^{-0.491t}$$

where t is time in seconds.
(a) What function describes the blood pressure in the aorta if $p = 95$ when $t = 0$?
(b) What is the blood pressure 0.1 second after a heartbeat?

52. *Sales and advertising* A store finds that its sales decline after the end of an advertising campaign, with its daily sales for the period declining at the rate $S'(t) = -1477.8e^{-0.2t}$, $0 \leq t \leq 35$, where t is the number of days since the end of the campaign. Suppose that $S = 7389$ units when $t = 0$.
(a) Find the function that describes the number of daily sales t days after the end of the campaign.
(b) Find the total number of sales 10 days after the end of the advertising campaign.

53. *Life expectancy* Suppose the rate of change of the expected life span l at birth of people born in the United States can be modeled by

$$\frac{dl}{dt} = \frac{14.9}{t+20}$$

where t is the number of years past 1920.

Year	Life Span (years)	Year	Life Span (years)
1920	54.1	2000	76.8
1930	59.7	2010	78.7
1940	62.9	2020	80.2
1950	68.2	2030	81.7
1960	69.7	2040	83.0
1970	70.8	2050	84.4
1980	73.7		
1990	75.4		

Source: National Center for Health Statistics

(a) Use integration and the data point for 2010 to find the function that models the life span. Report the model with 3 significant digit coefficients.

(b) The data in the table give the expected life spans for people born in various years. How well does the model from part (a) fit the data?

(c) Use the reported model from part (a) to predict the life span for someone born in 2025.

 54. *Non-farm employment* The following table shows the number of U.S. non-farm employees N (in millions) for selected years from 2010 and projected to 2040. Suppose the rate of change of the number of these employees can be modeled by

$$\frac{dN}{dt} = \frac{28.2}{t + 5}$$

where t is the number of years after 2005.

(a) Use integration and the data point for 2010 to find the function $N(t)$ that models the number of U.S. non-farm employees. Report your model with 3 significant digit coefficients.

(b) How well does the model from part (a) fit the data in the table?

(c) Use the reported model from part (a) to predict the number of U.S. non-farm employees in 2020.

Year	Millions	Year	Millions
2010	131	2026	157
2014	138	2030	161
2018	148	2035	165
2022	152	2040	170

Source: U.S. Energy Information Administration

55. *Consumer price index* The Social Security Administration makes projections about the consumer price index (CPI) to understand the effects of inflation on Social Security benefits and to plan for cost-of-living increases. Suppose the rate of change of the CPI can be modeled with the function

$$\frac{dC}{dt} = 3.087e^{0.0384t}$$

dollars per year, where C is the consumer price index and t is the number of years past 1990.

(a) Does the model for the rate reflect the fact that the Social Security Administration's data (actual and projected for selected years from 1995 to 2070) in the table show that the CPI is increasing? Explain.

(b) Use integration and the table's data point for 2005 to find the function that models the Social Security Administration's CPI figures.

(c) Find and interpret $C(35)$ and $C'(35)$.

Year	CPI	Year	CPI
1995	100.00	2035	465.98
2000	118.21	2040	566.94
2005	143.67	2045	689.77
2010	174.80	2050	839.21
2015	212.67	2055	1021.02
2020	258.74	2060	1242.23
2025	314.80	2065	1511.36
2030	383.00	2070	1838.81

Source: Social Security Administration

56. *Average annual wage* The following table shows the U.S. average annual wage in thousands of dollars for selected years from 2012 and projected to 2050. Suppose the rate of change of the U.S. average annual wage can be modeled by

$$\frac{dW}{dt} = 1.66e^{0.0395t}$$

thousand dollars per year, where t is the number of years past 2010.

(a) Use the data to find the average rates of change of the U.S. average annual wage from 2014 to 2016 and from 2016 to 2018. Which of these average rates better approximates the instantaneous rate in 2016?

(b) Use the data point from 2016 to find the function that models $W(t)$. Use 3 significant digits.

Year	Average Annual Wage ($ thousands)	Year	Average Annual Wage ($ thousands)
2012	44.6	2030	93.2
2014	48.6	2035	113.2
2016	53.3	2040	137.6
2018	58.7	2045	167.1
2020	63.7	2050	202.5
2025	76.8		

Source: Social Security Administration

SECTION 12.4 Applications of the Indefinite Integral in Business and Economics

APPLICATION PREVIEW

Marginal propensity to consume is the rate of change (the derivative) of the national consumption function, and it is related to the marginal propensity to save. Thus if we know that the consumption of a nation is $9 billion when disposable income is $0 and the marginal propensity to save is 0.25, we can find the national consumption function by first finding the marginal propensity to consume and then using integration. (See Example 6.)

In this section, we also use integration to derive total cost and profit functions from the marginal cost and marginal revenue functions. One of the reasons for the marginal approach in economics is that firms can observe marginal changes in real life. If they know the marginal cost and the total cost when a given quantity is sold, they can develop their total cost function.

Total Cost and Profit   We know that the marginal cost for a commodity is the derivative of the total cost function—that is, $\overline{MC} = C'(x)$, where $C(x)$ is the total cost function. Thus if we have the marginal cost function, we can integrate (or "reverse" the process of differentiation) to find the total cost. That is, $C(x) = \int \overline{MC}\,dx$.

If, for example, the marginal cost is $\overline{MC} = 4x + 3$, the total cost is given by

$$C(x) = \int \overline{MC}\,dx$$

$$= \int (4x + 3)\,dx$$

$$= 2x^2 + 3x + K$$

where K represents the constant of integration. We know that the total revenue is 0 if no items are produced, but the total cost may not be 0 if nothing is produced. The fixed costs accrue whether goods are produced or not. Thus the value of the constant of integration depends on the fixed costs FC of production, and we cannot determine the total cost function from the marginal cost unless additional information is available to help us determine the fixed costs.

EXAMPLE 1   Total Cost

Suppose the marginal cost function for a month for a certain product is $\overline{MC} = 3x + 50$, where x is the number of units and cost is in dollars. If the fixed costs related to the product amount to $10,000 per month, find the total cost function for the month.

Solution
The total cost function is

$$C(x) = \int (3x + 50)\,dx$$

$$= \frac{3x^2}{2} + 50x + K$$

The constant of integration K is found by using the fact that $C(0) = FC = 10,000$. Thus

$$3(0)^2 + 50(0) + K = 10,000, \text{ so } K = 10,000$$

and the total cost for the month is given by

$$C(x) = \frac{3x^2}{2} + 50x + 10,000$$

| EXAMPLE 2 | **Cost** |

Suppose monthly records show that the rate of change of the cost (that is, the marginal cost) for a product is $\overline{MC} = 3(2x + 25)^{1/2}$, where x is the number of units and cost is in dollars. If the fixed costs for the month are \$11,125, what would be the total cost of producing 300 items per month?

Solution

We can integrate the marginal cost to find the total cost function.

$$C(x) = \int \overline{MC}\, dx = \int 3(2x + 25)^{1/2}\, dx$$

$$= 3 \cdot \left(\frac{1}{2}\right) \int (2x + 25)^{1/2}\,(2\, dx)$$

$$= \left(\frac{3}{2}\right) \frac{(2x + 25)^{3/2}}{3/2} + K$$

$$= (2x + 25)^{3/2} + K$$

We can find K by using the fact that fixed costs are \$11,125.

$$C(0) = 11{,}125 = (25)^{3/2} + K$$
$$11{,}125 = 125 + K, \text{ or } K = 11{,}000$$

Thus the total cost function is

$$C(x) = (2x + 25)^{3/2} + 11{,}000$$

and the cost of producing 300 items per month is

$$C(300) = (625)^{3/2} + 11{,}000$$
$$= 26{,}625 \text{ (dollars)}$$

We now turn our attention to determining the profit function from marginal profit. It can be shown that the profit is usually maximized when $\overline{MR} = \overline{MC}$. To see that this does not always give us a maximum *positive* profit, consider the following facts concerning the manufacture of one particular product over the period of a month.

1. The marginal revenue is $\overline{MR} = 400 - 30x$.
2. The marginal cost is $\overline{MC} = 20x + 50$.
3. When 5 units are produced and sold, the total cost is \$1750. The profit *should* be maximized when $\overline{MR} = \overline{MC}$, or when $400 - 30x = 20x + 50$. Solving for x gives $x = 7$. To see whether our profit is maximized when 7 units are produced and sold, let us examine the profit function.

The profit function is given by $P(x) = R(x) - C(x)$, where

$$R(x) = \int \overline{MR}\, dx \text{ and } C(x) = \int \overline{MC}\, dx$$

Integrating, we get

$$R(x) = \int (400 - 30x)\, dx = 400x - 15x^2 + K$$

but $R(0) = 0$ gives $K = 0$ for this total revenue function, so

$$R(x) = 400x - 15x^2$$

The total cost function is

$$C(x) = \int (20x + 50)\, dx = 10x^2 + 50x + K$$

The value of fixed cost can be determined by using the fact that 5 units cost \$1750. This tells us that $C(5) = 1750 = 250 + 250 + K$, so $K = 1250$.

Thus the total cost is $C(x) = 10x^2 + 50x + 1250$, so the profit is

$$P(x) = R(x) - C(x) = (400x - 15x^2) - (10x^2 + 50x + 1250)$$

Simplifying gives

$$P(x) = 350x - 25x^2 - 1250$$

We have found that $\overline{MR} = \overline{MC}$ if $x = 7$, and the graph of $P(x)$ is a parabola that opens downward, so profit is maximized at $x = 7$. But if $x = 7$, profit is

$$P(7) = 2450 - 1225 - 1250 = -25$$

That is, the production and sale of 7 items result in a loss of $25.

The preceding discussion indicates that even though setting $\overline{MR} = \overline{MC}$ may optimize profit, it does not indicate the level of profit or loss, as forming the profit function does.

If this firm is in a competitive market and its optimal level of production results in a loss, it has two options. It can continue to produce at the optimal level in the short run until it can lower or eliminate its fixed costs, even though it is losing money, or it can take a larger loss (its fixed cost) by stopping production. Producing 7 units causes a loss of $25 per month, and ceasing production results in a loss of $1250 (the fixed cost) per month. If this firm and many others like it cease production, the supply will be reduced, causing an eventual increase in price. The firm can resume production when the price increase indicates that it can make a profit.

EXAMPLE 3 Maximum Profit

Suppose that each day a company has a product with $\overline{MR} = 200 - 4x$, $\overline{MC} = 50 + 2x$, and the total cost of producing 10 units is $700. At what level should this company hold its daily production to maximize profits?

Solution

Setting $\overline{MR} = \overline{MC}$, we can solve for the production level that maximizes profit.

$$200 - 4x = 50 + 2x$$
$$150 = 6x$$
$$25 = x$$

The level of production that should optimize profit is 25 units. To see whether 25 units maximizes profits or minimizes the losses (in the short run), we must find the total revenue and total cost functions.

$$R(x) = \int (200 - 4x)\, dx = 200x - 2x^2 + K$$
$$= 200x - 2x^2 \quad \text{because } K = 0$$
$$C(x) = \int (50 + 2x)\, dx = 50x + x^2 + K$$

We find K by noting that $C(x) = 700$ when $x = 10$.

$$700 = 50(10) + (10)^2 + K$$

so $K = 100$. Thus the cost is given by $C = C(x) = 50x + x^2 + 100$.

Thus the profit function is $P(x) = R(x) - C(x) = -3x^2 + 150x - 100$, whose graph is concave down, and the profit function is maximized at $x = 25$. The maximum daily profit is $P(25) = \$1775$. ■

Calculator Note   If it is difficult to solve $\overline{MC} = \overline{MR}$ analytically, we can use a graphing calculator to solve this equation by finding the point of intersection of the graphs of $\overline{MC}$ and $\overline{MR}$. We may also be able to integrate $\overline{MC}$ and $\overline{MR}$ to find the functions $C(x)$ and $R(x)$ and then use a graphing calculator to graph them. From the graphs of $C(x)$ and $R(x)$, we can learn about these functions—and hence about profit. ■

EXAMPLE 4

Cost, Revenue, and Profit

Suppose that $\overline{MC} = 1.01(x + 190)^{0.01}$ and $\overline{MR} = (1/\sqrt{2x + 1}) + 2$, where x is the number of thousands of units and both revenue and cost are in thousands of dollars. Suppose further that fixed costs are \$100,236 and that production is limited to at most 180 thousand units.

(a) Determine $C(x)$ and $R(x)$ and graph them to determine whether a profit can be made.

(b) Estimate the level of production that yields maximum profit and find the maximum profit.

Solution

(a) $C(x) = \displaystyle\int \overline{MC}\, dx = \int 1.01(x + 190)^{0.01}\, dx$

$$= 1.01\frac{(x + 190)^{1.01}}{1.01} + K$$

When we say that fixed costs equal \$100,236, we mean that $C(0) = 100.236$.

$$100.236 = C(0) = (190)^{1.01} + K$$
$$100.236 \approx 200.236 + K$$
$$-100 \approx K$$

Thus we use $C(x) = (x + 190)^{1.01} - 100$.

$$R(x) = \int \overline{MR}\, dx = \int [(2x + 1)^{-1/2} + 2]dx$$

$$= \frac{1}{2}\int (2x + 1)^{-1/2}(2\, dx) + \int 2\, dx$$

$$= \frac{1}{2}\left[\frac{(2x + 1)^{1/2}}{1/2}\right] + 2x + K$$

$R(0) = 0$ means

$$0 = R(0) = (1)^{1/2} + 0 + K, \quad \text{or} \quad K = -1$$

Thus $R(x) = (2x + 1)^{1/2} + 2x - 1$.

The graphs of $C(x)$ and $R(x)$ are shown in Figure 12.8. [The x-range is chosen to include the production range from 0 to 180 (thousand) units. The y-range is chosen to extend beyond fixed costs of about 100 thousand dollars.]

From the figure, we see that a profit can be made as long as the number of units sold exceeds about 95 (thousand). We could locate this break-even value more precisely by using INTERSECT.

(b) From the graph, we also see that $R(x) - C(x) = P(x)$ is at its maximum at the right edge of the graph. Because production is limited to at most 180 thousand units, profit will be maximized when $x = 180$ and the maximum profit is

$$P(180) = R(180) - C(180)$$
$$= [(361)^{1/2} + 360 - 1] - [(370)^{1.01} - 100]$$
$$\approx 85.46 \ (\text{thousand dollars})$$

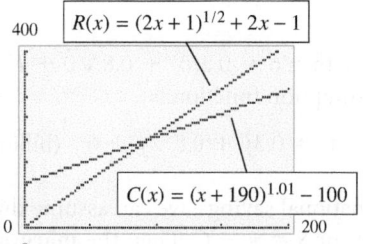

Figure 12.8

1. True or false:
   (a) If $C(x) = \int \overline{MC}\, dx$, then the constant of integration equals the fixed costs.
   (b) If $R(x) = \int \overline{MR}\, dx$, then the constant of integration equals 0.
2. Find $C(x)$ if $\overline{MC} = \dfrac{100}{\sqrt{x+1}}$ and fixed costs are $8000.

National Consumption and Savings

The consumption function is one of the basic ingredients in a larger discussion of how an economy can have persistent high unemployment or persistent high inflation. This study is often called **Keynesian analysis,** after its founder John Maynard Keynes (pronounced "canes").

If C represents national consumption (in billions of dollars), then a **national consumption function** has the form $C = f(y)$, where y is national disposable income (also in billions of dollars). The **marginal propensity to consume** is the derivative of the national consumption function with respect to y, or $dC/dy = f'(y)$. For example, suppose that

$$C = f(y) = 0.8y + 6$$

is a national consumption function; then the marginal propensity to consume is $f'(y) = 0.8$.

If we know the marginal propensity to consume, we can integrate with respect to y to find national consumption:

$$C = \int f'(y)\, dy = f(y) + K$$

We can find the unique national consumption function if we have additional information to help us determine the value of K, the constant of integration.

EXAMPLE 5   National Consumption

If national consumption C is $6 billion when national disposable income y is $0 and the marginal propensity to consume is $dC/dy = 0.3 + 0.4/\sqrt{y}$, find the national consumption function.

Solution
If

$$\frac{dC}{dy} = 0.3 + \frac{0.4}{\sqrt{y}}$$

then

$$
\begin{aligned}
C &= \int \left(0.3 + \frac{0.4}{\sqrt{y}} \right) dy \\
&= \int (0.3 + 0.4y^{-1/2})\, dy \\
&= 0.3y + 0.4\,\frac{y^{1/2}}{1/2} + K = 0.3y + 0.8y^{1/2} + K
\end{aligned}
$$

If $C = 6$ when $y = 0$, then $6 = 0.3(0) + 0.8\sqrt{0} + K$. Thus the constant of integration is $K = 6$, and the consumption function is

$$C = 0.3y + 0.8\sqrt{y} + 6 \quad \text{(billions of dollars)}$$

If S represents national savings, we can assume that the national disposable income is given by $y = C + S$, or $S = y - C$. Then the **marginal propensity to save** is $dS/dy = 1 - dC/dy$.

EXAMPLE 6 **Consumption and Savings** | APPLICATION PREVIEW |

If the national consumption is \$9 billion when national disposable income is \$0 and the marginal propensity to save is 0.25, find the consumption function.

Solution
If $dS/dy = 0.25$, then $0.25 = 1 - dC/dy$, or $dC/dy = 0.75$. Thus

$$C = \int 0.75 \, dy = 0.75y + K$$

If $C = 9$ when $y = 0$, then $9 = 0.75(0) + K$, or $K = 9$. Then the consumption function is $C = 0.75y + 9$ (billions of dollars).

CHECKPOINT

3. If the marginal propensity to save is

$$\frac{dS}{dy} = 0.7 - \frac{0.4}{\sqrt{y}}$$

find the marginal propensity to consume.
4. Find the national consumption function if the marginal propensity to consume is

$$\frac{dC}{dy} = \frac{1}{\sqrt{y + 4}} + 0.2$$

and national consumption is \$6.8 billion when disposable income is \$0.

CHECKPOINT ANSWERS

1. (a) False. $C(0)$ equals the fixed costs. It may or may not be the constant of integration.
   (b) False. We use $R(0) = 0$ to determine the constant of integration, but it may be nonzero.
2. $C(x) = 200\sqrt{x + 1} + 7800$
3. $\dfrac{dC}{dy} = 1 - \dfrac{dS}{dy} = 0.3 + \dfrac{0.4}{\sqrt{y}}$
4. $C(y) = 2\sqrt{y + 4} + 0.2y + 2.8$.

EXERCISES 12.4

TOTAL COST AND PROFIT

In Problems 1–12, cost, revenue, and profit are in dollars and x is the number of units.

1. If the daily marginal cost for a product is $\overline{MC} = 2x + 100$, with fixed costs amounting to \$200, find the total cost function for each day.
2. If the monthly marginal cost for a product is $\overline{MC} = x + 30$ and the related fixed costs are \$5000, find the total cost function for the month.
3. If the marginal cost for a product is $\overline{MC} = 4x + 2$ and the production of 10 units results in a total cost of \$300, find the total cost function.
4. If the marginal cost for a product is $\overline{MC} = 4x + 40$ and the total cost of producing 25 units is \$3000, find the cost of producing 30 units.

5. If the marginal cost for a product is $\overline{MC} = 140 + 0.15\sqrt{x}$ and the total cost of producing 100 units is \$25,000, find the total cost function and fixed costs.
6. If the marginal cost for producing a product is $\overline{MC} = 88 - 2e^{-0.01x}$, with a fixed cost of \$6200, find the total cost function and the cost of producing 20 units (to the nearest dollar).
7. A firm knows that its marginal cost for a product is $\overline{MC} = 3x + 20$, that its marginal revenue is $\overline{MR} = 44 - 5x$, and that the cost of production of 80 units is \$11,400.
   (a) Find the optimal level of production.
   (b) Find the profit function.
   (c) Find the profit or loss at the optimal level.

8. A certain firm's marginal cost for a product is $\overline{MC} = 6x + 60$, its marginal revenue is $\overline{MR} = 180 - 2x$, and its total cost of production of 10 items is $1000.
   (a) Find the optimal level of production.
   (b) Find the profit function.
   (c) Find the profit or loss at the optimal level of production.
   (d) Should production be continued for the short run?
   (e) Should production be continued for the long run?

9. Suppose that the marginal revenue for a product is $\overline{MR} = 900$ and the marginal cost is $MC = 30\sqrt{x + 4}$, with a fixed cost of $1000.
   (a) Find the profit or loss from the production and sale of 5 units.
   (b) How many units will result in a maximum profit?

10. Suppose that the marginal cost for a product is $\overline{MC} = 60\sqrt{x + 1}$ and its fixed cost is $340. If the marginal revenue for the product is $\overline{MR} = 80x$, find the profit or loss from production and sale of
    (a) 3 units.   (b) 8 units.

11. The average cost of a product changes at the rate
$$\overline{C}'(x) = -6x^{-2} + 1/6$$
    and the average cost of 6 units is $10.
    (a) Find the average cost function.
    (b) Find the average cost of 12 units.

12. The average cost of a product changes at the rate
$$\overline{C}'(x) = \frac{-10}{x^2} + \frac{1}{10}$$
    and the average cost of 10 units is $20.
    (a) Find the average cost function.
    (b) Find the average cost of 20 units.

13. Suppose that marginal cost for a certain product is given by $\overline{MC} = 1.05(x + 180)^{0.05}$ and marginal revenue is given by $\overline{MR} = (1/\sqrt{0.5x + 4}) + 2.8$, where x is in thousands of units and both revenue and cost are in thousands of dollars. Fixed costs are $200,000, and production is limited to at most 200 thousand units.
    (a) Find $C(x)$ and $R(x)$.
    (b) Graph $C(x)$ and $R(x)$ to determine whether a profit can be made.
    (c) Determine the level of production that yields maximum profit and find the maximum profit (or minimum loss).

14. Suppose that the marginal cost for a certain product is given by $\overline{MC} = 1.02(x + 200)^{0.02}$ and marginal revenue is given by $\overline{MR} = (2/\sqrt{4x + 1}) + 1.75$, where x is in thousands of units and revenue and cost are in thousands of dollars. Suppose further that fixed costs are $150,000 and production is limited to at most 200 thousand units.
    (a) Find $C(x)$ and $R(x)$.
    (b) Graph $C(x)$ and $R(x)$ to determine whether a profit can be made.
    (c) Determine what level of production yields maximum profit and find the maximum profit (or minimum loss).

NATIONAL CONSUMPTION AND SAVINGS

15. If national consumption is $7 billion when disposable income is $0 and if the marginal propensity to consume is 0.80, find the national consumption function (in billions of dollars).

16. If national consumption is $9 billion when disposable income is $0 and if the marginal propensity to consume is 0.30, what is consumption when disposable income is $20 billion?

17. If consumption is $8.7 billion when disposable income is $1 billion and if the marginal propensity to consume is
$$\frac{dC}{dy} = 0.3 + \frac{0.2}{\sqrt{y}}$$
    find the national consumption function.

18. If consumption is $6 billion when disposable income is $1 billion and if the marginal propensity to consume is
$$\frac{dC}{dy} = 0.4 + \frac{0.3}{\sqrt{y}}$$
    find the national consumption function.

19. If consumption is $6 billion when disposable income is $0 and if the marginal propensity to consume is
$$\frac{dC}{dy} = \frac{1}{\sqrt{y + 1}} + 0.4$$
    find the national consumption function.

20. If consumption is $5.8 billion when disposable income is $0 and if the marginal propensity to consume is
$$\frac{dC}{dy} = \frac{1}{\sqrt{2y + 9}} + 0.8$$
    find the national consumption function.

21. Suppose that the marginal propensity to consume is
$$\frac{dC}{dy} = 0.7 - e^{-2y}$$
    and that consumption is $5.65 billion when disposable income is $0. Find the national consumption function.

22. Suppose that the marginal propensity to consume is
$$\frac{dC}{dy} = 0.6 - e^{-0.5y}$$
    and that consumption is $9.5 billion when disposable income is $0. Find the national consumption function.

23. Suppose that the marginal propensity to save is
$$\frac{dS}{dy} = 0.15$$
    and that consumption is $5.15 billion when disposable income is $0. Find the national consumption function.

24. Suppose that the marginal propensity to save is
$$\frac{dS}{dy} = 0.22$$
    and that consumption is $8.6 billion when disposable income is $0. Find the national consumption function.

25. Suppose that the marginal propensity to save is

$$\frac{dS}{dy} = 0.2 - \frac{1}{y + 1}$$

and that consumption is $12 billion when disposable income is $0. Find the national consumption function.

26. If consumption is $3 billion when disposable income is $0 and if the marginal propensity to save is

$$\frac{dS}{dy} = 0.2 + e^{-1.5y}$$

find the national consumption function.

27. Suppose that the marginal propensity to save is

$$\frac{dS}{dy} = 0.2 - \frac{1}{\sqrt{3y + 7}}$$

and that consumption is $6 billion when disposable income is $0. Find the national consumption function.

28. Suppose that the marginal propensity to save is

$$\frac{dS}{dy} = 0.96 - \frac{\ln(y + 1)}{y + 1}$$

and that consumption is $6.04 billion when disposable income is $0. Find the national consumption function.

29. **Modeling *U.S. national consumption*** The following table gives the U.S. national consumption and disposable income (both in billions of dollars) for selected years from 2012 and projected to 2040. Suppose the marginal propensity to consume can be modeled by

$$\frac{dC}{dy} = 0.0169y + 0.617$$

where y equals the disposable income.
(a) Use the data point for 2012 to find the U.S. national consumption function.
(b) Use the data to develop a model of the same function type as found in part (a). Report your model with 3 significant digit coefficients.
(c) Compare your answers to parts (a) and (b). Name one other function type that would be a good model for these data.

Year	Income	Consumption	Year	Income	Consumption
2012	10.2	9.6	2028	17.1	15.4
2014	11.8	10.9	2030	17.8	16.1
2016	12.6	11.6	2032	18.5	16.8
2018	13.5	12.3	2034	19.3	17.5
2020	14.2	12.9	2036	20.1	18.3
2022	14.8	13.4	2038	20.9	19.1
2024	15.5	14.0	2040	21.9	19.9
2026	16.3	14.7			

Source: U.S. Energy Information Administration

SECTION 12.5   Differential Equations

OBJECTIVES

- To show that a function is the solution to a differential equation
- To use integration to find the general solution to a differential equation
- To find particular solutions to differential equations using given conditions
- To solve separable differential equations
- To solve applied problems involving separable differential equations

APPLICATION PREVIEW

Carbon-14 dating, used to determine the age of fossils, is based on three facts. First, the half-life of carbon-14 is 5730 years. Second, the amount of carbon-14 in any living organism is essentially constant. Third, when an organism dies, the rate of change of carbon-14 in the organism is proportional to the amount present. If y represents the amount of carbon-14 present in the organism, then we can express the rate of change of carbon-14 by the differential equation

$$\frac{dy}{dt} = ky$$

where k is a constant and t is time in years. In this section, we study methods that allow us to find a function y that satisfies this differential equation, and then we use that function to date a fossil. (See Example 6.)

Recall that we introduced the derivative as an instantaneous rate of change and denoted the instantaneous rate of change of y with respect to time as dy/dt. For many growth or decay processes, such as carbon-14 decay, the rate of change of the amount of a substance with respect to time is proportional to the amount present. As we noted above, this can be represented by the equation

$$\frac{dy}{dt} = ky \quad (k = \text{constant})$$

An equation of this type, where y is an unknown function of x or t, is called a **differential equation** because it contains derivatives (or differentials). In this section, we restrict ourselves to differential equations where the highest derivative present in the equation is the first derivative. These differential equations are called **first-order differential equations.** Examples are

$$f'(x) = \frac{1}{x+1}, \quad \frac{dy}{dt} = 2t, \text{ and } x\,dy = (y+1)\,dx$$

Solution of Differential Equations

The solution to a differential equation is a function that, when used in the differential equation, results in an identity.

EXAMPLE 1 Differential Equation

Show that $y = 4e^{-5t}$ is a solution to $dy/dt + 5y = 0$.

Solution

We must show that substituting $y = 4e^{-5t}$ into the equation $dy/dt + 5y = 0$ results in an identity:

$$\frac{d}{dt}(4e^{-5t}) + 5(4e^{-5t}) = 0$$
$$-20e^{-5t} + 20e^{-5t} = 0$$
$$0 = 0$$

Thus $y = 4e^{-5t}$ is a solution.

Now that we know what it means for a function to be a solution to a differential equation, we consider how to find solutions.

The most elementary differential equations are of the form

$$\frac{dy}{dx} = f(x)$$

where $f(x)$ is a continuous function. Solutions of these equations are found by integration:

$$y = \int f(x)\,dx$$

EXAMPLE 2 Solving a Differential Equation

Find the solution of

$$f'(x) = \frac{1}{x+1}$$

Solution

The solution is

$$f(x) = \int f'(x)\,dx = \int \frac{1}{x+1}\,dx = \ln|x+1| + C$$

The solution in Example 2, $f(x) = \ln|x+1| + C$, is called the **general solution** because every solution to the equation has this form, and different values of C give different **particular solutions.** Figure 12.9 shows the graphs of several members of the family of solutions to this differential equation. (We cannot, of course, show all of them.)

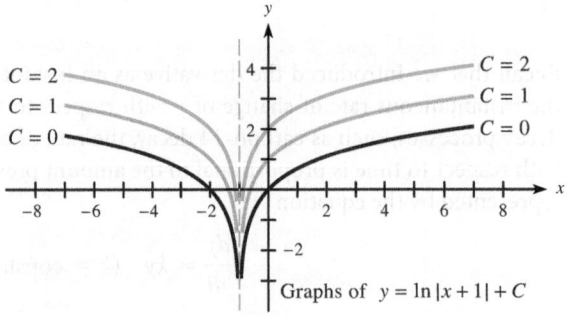

Figure 12.9

Graphs of $y = \ln|x+1| + C$

We can find a particular solution to a differential equation when we know that the solution must satisfy additional conditions, such as **initial conditions** or **boundary conditions**. For instance, to find the particular solution to

$$f'(x) = \frac{1}{x + 1} \quad \text{with the condition that} \quad f(-2) = 2$$

we use $f(-2) = 2$ in the general solution, $f(x) = \ln|x + 1| + C.$

$$2 = f(-2) = \ln|-2 + 1| + C$$
$$2 = \ln|-1| + C \text{ so } C = 2$$

Thus the particular solution is

$$f(x) = \ln|x + 1| + 2$$

and is shown in Figure 12.9 with $C = 2$.

We frequently denote the value of the solution function $y = f(t)$ at the initial time $t = 0$ as $y(0)$ instead of $f(0)$.

CHECKPOINT

1. Given $f'(x) = 2x - [1/(x + 1)]$, $f(0) = 4$,
   (a) find the general solution to the differential equation.
   (b) find the particular solution that satisfies $f(0) = 4$.

Just as we can find the differential of both sides of an equation, we can find the solution to a differential equation of the form

$$g(y)\, dy = f(x)\, dx$$

by integrating both sides.

EXAMPLE 3

Differential Equation with a Boundary Condition

Solve $3y^2\, dy = 2x\, dx$, if $y(1) = 2$.

Solution

We find the general solution by integrating both sides.

$$\int 3y^2\, dy = \int 2x\, dx$$
$$y^3 + C_1 = x^2 + C_2$$
$$y^3 = x^2 + C, \qquad \text{where } C = C_2 - C_1$$

By using $y(1) = 2$, we can find C.

$$2^3 = 1^2 + C$$
$$7 = C$$

Thus the particular solution is given implicitly by

$$y^3 = x^2 + 7$$

Calculator Note We can use a graphing calculator to help solve a differential equation of the form $\dfrac{dy}{dx} = f(x)$, with boundary conditions. After integrating to get $y = F(x) + C$, we can use SOLVER with the known x-value and corresponding y-value to find C. The general solution to $\dfrac{dy}{dx} = 2x - 4$ is $y = x^2 - 4x + C$. The value of C that satisfies the boundary condition $y = 8$ when $x = -1$ is found to be 3, as shown in Figure 12.10; thus the particular solution is $y = x^2 - 4x + 3$. Details can be found in Appendix A, Section 12.5.

Figure 12.10

Separable Differential Equations

It is frequently necessary to change the form of a differential equation before it can be solved by integrating both sides.

For example, the equation

$$\frac{dy}{dx} = y^2$$

cannot be solved by simply integrating both sides of the equation with respect to x because we cannot evaluate $\int y^2\, dx$.

However, we can multiply both sides of $dy/dx = y^2$ by dx/y^2 to obtain an equation that has all terms containing y on one side of the equation and all terms containing x on the other side. That is, we obtain

$$\frac{dy}{y^2} = dx$$

Separable Differential Equations

When a differential equation can be equivalently expressed in the form

$$g(y)\, dy = f(x)\, dx$$

we say that the equation is **separable.**

The solution of a separable differential equation is obtained by integrating both sides of the equation after the variables have been separated.

EXAMPLE 4 | Separable Differential Equation

Solve the differential equation

$$(x^2 y + x^2)\, dy = x^3\, dx$$

Solution

To write the equation in separable form, we first factor x^2 from the left side and divide both sides by it.

$$x^2(y + 1)\, dy = x^3\, dx$$

$$(y + 1)\, dy = \frac{x^3}{x^2}\, dx$$

The equation is now separated, so we integrate both sides.

$$\int (y + 1)\, dy = \int x\, dx$$

$$\frac{y^2}{2} + y + C_1 = \frac{x^2}{2} + C_2$$

This equation, as well as the equation

$$y^2 + 2y - x^2 = C, \quad \text{where} \quad C = 2(C_2 - C_1)$$

gives the solution implicitly.

Note that we need not write both C_1 and C_2 when we integrate because it is always possible to combine the two constants into one.

EXAMPLE 5   **Separable Differential Equation**

Solve the differential equation

$$\frac{dy}{dt} = ky \quad (k = \text{constant})$$

Solution

To solve the equation, we write it in separated form and integrate both sides:

$$\frac{dy}{y} = k\,dt \ \Rightarrow \ \int \frac{dy}{y} = \int k\,dt \ \Rightarrow \ \ln |y| = kt + C_1$$

Assuming that $y > 0$ and writing this equation in exponential form give

$$y = e^{kt + C_1}$$

$$y = e^{kt} \cdot e^{C_1} = Ce^{kt}, \quad \text{where } C = e^{C_1}$$

This solution,

$$y = Ce^{kt}$$

is the general solution to the differential equation $dy/dt = ky$ because all solutions have this form, with different values of C giving different particular solutions. The case of $y < 0$ is covered by values of $C < 0$. ▪

CHECKPOINT

2. True or false:
    (a) The general solution to $dy = (x/y)\,dx$ can be found from
    $$\int y\,dy = \int x\,dx$$
    (b) The first step in solving $dy/dx = -2xy^2$ is to separate it.
    (c) The equation $dy/dx = -2xy^2$ separates as $y^2\,dy = -2x\,dx$.
3. Suppose that $(xy + x)(dy/dx) = x^2y + y$.
    (a) Separate this equation. (b) Find the general solution.

Applications of Differential Equations   We now consider two applications that can be modeled by differential equations. These are radioactive decay and one-container mixture problems (as a model for drugs in an organ). In these applications, as in many applied problems that can be modeled with differential equations, conditions are given that allow us to find a particular solution.

EXAMPLE 6   **Carbon-14 Dating** | APPLICATION PREVIEW |

When an organism dies, the rate of change of the amount of carbon-14 present is proportional to the amount present and is represented by the differential equation

$$\frac{dy}{dt} = ky$$

where y is the amount present, k is a constant, and t is time in years. Suppose that anthropologists discover a fossil that contains 1% of the initial amount of carbon-14. Find the age of the fossil. (The half-life of carbon-14 is 5730 years.)

Solution

If we denote the initial amount of carbon-14 in an organism as y_0, then $y = y_0$ represents the amount present at time $t = 0$ (when the organism dies). We must find a particular solution to

$$\frac{dy}{dt} = ky$$

subject to the fact that when $t = 0$, $y = y_0$, and we must determine the value of k on the basis of the half-life of carbon-14 ($t = 5730$ years, $y = \frac{1}{2}y_0$ units). From Example 5, we know that the general solution to the differential equation $dy/dt = ky$ is $y = Ce^{kt}$. Using $y = y_0$ when $t = 0$, we obtain $y_0 = C$, so the equation becomes $y = y_0 e^{kt}$. Then using $t = 5730$ and $y = \frac{1}{2}y_0$ in this equation gives

$$\frac{1}{2}y_0 = y_0 e^{5730k} \quad \text{or} \quad 0.5 = e^{5730k}$$

Rewriting this equation in logarithmic form and then solving for k, we get

$$\ln{(0.5)} = 5730k$$
$$\frac{\ln{(0.5)}}{5730} = k$$
$$-0.00012097 \approx k$$

Thus the equation we seek is

$$y = y_0 e^{-0.00012097t}$$

Using the fact that $y = 0.01y_0$ when the fossil was discovered, we can find its age t by solving

$$0.01y_0 = y_0 e^{-0.00012097t} \quad \text{or} \quad 0.01 = e^{-0.00012097t}$$

Rewriting this in logarithmic form and then solving give

$$\ln{(0.01)} = -0.00012097t$$
$$\frac{\ln{(0.01)}}{-0.00012097} = t$$
$$38{,}069 \approx t$$

Thus the fossil is approximately 38,069 years old.

The differential equation $dy/dt = ky$, which describes the decay of radioactive substances in Example 6, also models the rate of growth of an investment that is compounded continuously and the rate of decay of purchasing power due to inflation.

Another application of differential equations comes from a group of applications called *one-container mixture problems*. In problems of this type, there is a substance whose amount in a container is changing with time, and the goal is to determine the amount of the substance at any time t. The differential equations that model these problems are of the following form:

$$\begin{bmatrix} \text{Rate of change} \\ \text{of the amount} \\ \text{of the substance} \end{bmatrix} = \begin{bmatrix} \text{Rate at which} \\ \text{the substance} \\ \text{enters the container} \end{bmatrix} - \begin{bmatrix} \text{Rate at which} \\ \text{the substance} \\ \text{leaves the container} \end{bmatrix}$$

We consider this application as it applies to the amount of a drug in an organ.

EXAMPLE 7 Drug in an Organ

A liquid carries a drug into an organ of volume 300 cubic centimeters at a rate of 5 cubic centimeters per second, where the liquid becomes well mixed and then leaves the organ at the same rate. If the concentration of the drug in the entering liquid is 0.1 gram per cubic centimeter and x represents the amount of drug in the organ at any time t, then using the fact that the rate of change of the amount of the drug in the organ, dx/dt, equals the rate at which the drug enters minus the rate at which it leaves, we have

$$\frac{dx}{dt} = \left(\frac{5 \text{ cc}}{\text{s}}\right)\left(\frac{0.1 \text{ g}}{\text{cc}}\right) - \left(\frac{5 \text{ cc}}{\text{s}}\right)\left(\frac{x \text{ g}}{300 \text{ cc}}\right)$$

or

$$\frac{dx}{dt} = 0.5 - \frac{x}{60} = \frac{30}{60} - \frac{x}{60} = \frac{30 - x}{60}, \text{ in grams per second}$$

Find the amount of the drug in the organ as a function of time t.

Solution

Multiplying both sides of the equation $\dfrac{dx}{dt} = \dfrac{30 - x}{60}$ by $\dfrac{dt}{(30 - x)}$ gives

$$\frac{dx}{30 - x} = \frac{1}{60}\, dt$$

The equation is now separated, so we can integrate both sides.

$$\int \frac{dx}{30 - x} = \int \frac{1}{60}\, dt$$

$$-\ln(30 - x) = \frac{1}{60}t + C_1 \quad (30 - x > 0)$$

$$\ln(30 - x) = -\frac{1}{60}t - C_1$$

Rewriting this in exponential form gives

$$30 - x = e^{-t/60 - C_1} = e^{-t/60} \cdot e^{-C_1}$$

Letting $C = e^{-C_1}$ yields

$$30 - x = Ce^{-t/60}$$

so

$$x = 30 - Ce^{-t/60}$$

and we have the desired function.

CHECKPOINT
ANSWERS

1. (a) $f(x) = \int \left(2x - \dfrac{1}{x + 1}\right) dx = x^2 - \ln|x + 1| + C$
   (b) $f(x) = x^2 - \ln|x + 1| + 4$
2. (a) True
   (b) True
   (c) False. It separates as $dy/y^2 = -2x\, dx$.
3. (a) $\dfrac{y + 1}{y}\, dy = \dfrac{x^2 + 1}{x}\, dx$ (b) $y + \ln|y| = \dfrac{x^2}{2} + \ln|x| + C$

EXERCISES 12.5

In Problems 1–4, show that the given function is a solution to the differential equation.

1. $y = x^2$; $4y - 2xy' = 0$
2. $y = x^3$; $3y - xy' = 0$
3. $y = 3x^2 + 1$; $2y\, dx - x\, dy = 2\, dx$
4. $y = 4x^3 + 2$; $3y\, dx - x\, dy = 6\, dx$

In Problems 5–10, use integration to find the general solution to each differential equation.

5. $dy = xe^{x^2 + 1}\, dx$
6. $dy = x^2 e^{x^3 - 1}\, dx$
7. $2y\, dy = 4x\, dx$
8. $4y\, dy = 4x^3\, dx$
9. $3y^2\, dy = (2x - 1)\, dx$
10. $4y^3\, dy = (3x^2 + 2x)\, dx$

In Problems 11–14, find the particular solution.

11. $y' = e^{x-3}$ $y(0) = 2$
12. $y' = e^{2x+1}$ $y(0) = e$
13. $dy = \left(\dfrac{1}{x} - x\right) dx$ $y(1) = 0$
14. $dy = \left(x^2 - \dfrac{1}{x + 1}\right) dx$ $y(0) = \dfrac{1}{3}$

In Problems 15–28, find the general solution to the given differential equation.

15. $\dfrac{dy}{dx} = \dfrac{x^2}{y}$
16. $y^3\, dx = \dfrac{dy}{x^3}$
17. $dx = x^3 y\, dy$
18. $dy = x^2 y^3\, dx$
19. $dx = (x^2 y^2 + x^2)dy$
20. $dy = (x^2 y^3 + xy^3)\, dx$
21. $y^2\, dx = x\, dy$
22. $y\, dx = x\, dy$
23. $\dfrac{dy}{dx} = \dfrac{x}{y}$
24. $\dfrac{dy}{dx} = \dfrac{x^2 + x}{y + 1}$

25. $(x + 1)\dfrac{dy}{dx} = y$

26. $x^2y\dfrac{dy}{dx} = y^2 + 1$

27. $(x^2 + 2)e^{y^2} dx = xy\,dy$

28. $e^{4x}(y + 1)\,dx + e^{2x}y\,dy = 0$

In Problems 29–36, find the particular solution to each differential equation.

29. $\dfrac{dy}{dx} = \dfrac{x^2}{y^3}$ when $x = 1, y = 1$

30. $\dfrac{dy}{dx} = \dfrac{x + 1}{xy}$ when $x = 1, y = 3$

31. $2y^2\,dx = 3x^2\,dy$ when $x = 2, y = -1$

32. $(x + 1)\,dy = y^2\,dx$ when $x = 0, y = 2$

33. $x^2e^{2y}\,dy = (x^3 + 1)\,dx$ when $x = 1, y = 0$

34. $y' = \dfrac{1}{xy}$ when $x = 1, y = 3$

35. $2xy\dfrac{dy}{dx} = y^2 + 1$ when $x = 1, y = 2$

36. $xe^y\,dx = (x + 1)\,dy$ when $x = 0, y = 0$

APPLICATIONS

37. *Allometric growth* If x and y are measurements of certain parts of an organism, then the rate of change of y with respect to x is proportional to the ratio of y to x. That is, if k is a constant, then these measurements satisfy
$$\frac{dy}{dx} = k\frac{y}{x}$$
which is referred to as an allometric law of growth. Solve this differential equation.

38. *Bimolecular chemical reactions* A bimolecular chemical reaction is one in which two chemicals react to form another substance. Suppose that one molecule of each of the two chemicals reacts to form two molecules of a new substance. If x represents the number of molecules of the new substance at time t, then the rate of change of x is proportional to the product of the numbers of molecules of the original chemicals available to be converted. That is, if each of the chemicals initially contained A molecules, then
$$\frac{dx}{dt} = k(A - x)^2$$
where k is a constant. If 40% of the initial amount A is converted after 1 hour, how long will it be before 90% is converted?

Compound interest **In Problems 39 and 40, use the following information.**

When interest is compounded continuously, the rate of change of the amount x of the investment is proportional to the amount present. In this case, the proportionality constant is the annual interest rate r (as a decimal); that is,
$$\frac{dx}{dt} = rx$$

39. (a) If \$10,000 is invested at 6% compounded continuously, find an equation for the future value of the investment as a function of time t in years.
    (b) What is the future value of the investment after 1 year? After 5 years?
    (c) How long will it take for the investment to double?

40. (a) If \$2000 is invested at 8% compounded continuously, find an equation for the future value of the investment as a function of time t, in years.
    (b) How long will it take for the investment to double?
    (c) What will be the future value of this investment after 35 years?

41. *Investing* When the interest on an investment is compounded continuously, the investment grows at a rate that is proportional to the amount in the account. That is, if the amount present is P, then
$$\frac{dP}{dt} = kP$$
where P is in dollars, t is in years, and k is a constant. If \$100,000 is invested (when $t = 0$) and the amount in the account after 15 years is \$211,700, find the function that gives the value of the investment as a function of t. What is the interest rate on this investment?

42. *Investing* When the interest on an investment is compounded continuously, the investment grows at a rate that is proportional to the amount in the account. If \$20,000 is invested (when $t = 0$) and the amount in the account after 22 years is \$280,264, find the function that gives the value of the investment as a function of t. What is the interest rate on this investment?

43. *Bacterial growth* Suppose that the growth of a certain population of bacteria satisfies
$$\frac{dy}{dt} = ky$$
where y is the number of organisms, t is the number of hours, and k is a constant. If initially there are 10,000 organisms and the number triples after 2 hours, how long will it be before the population reaches 100 times the original population?

44. *Bacterial growth* Suppose that for a certain population of bacteria, growth occurs according to
$$\frac{dy}{dt} = ky \quad (t \text{ in hours, } k \text{ constant})$$
If the doubling rate depends on temperature, find how long it takes for the number of bacteria to reach 50 times the original number at each given temperature in parts (a) and (b).
    (a) At 90°F, the number doubles after 30 minutes ($\frac{1}{2}$ hour).
    (b) At 40°F, the number doubles after 3 hours.

45. *Sales and pricing* Suppose that in a certain company, the relationship between the price per unit p of its

product and the weekly sales volume y in thousands of dollars is given by

$$\frac{dy}{dp} = -\frac{2}{5}\left(\frac{y}{p+8}\right)$$

Solve this differential equation if $y = 8$ when $p = \$24$.

46. *Sales and pricing* Suppose that a chain of auto service stations, Quick-Oil, Inc., has found that the relationship between its price p for an oil change and its monthly sales volume y in thousands of dollars is

$$\frac{dy}{dp} = -\frac{1}{2}\left(\frac{y}{p+4}\right)$$

Solve this differential equation if $y = 18$ when $p = \$60$.

47. *Half-life* A breeder reactor converts uranium-238 into an isotope of plutonium-239 at a rate proportional to the amount present at any time. After 10 years, 0.03% of the radioactivity has dissipated (that is, 0.9997 of the initial amount remains). Suppose that initially there is 100 pounds of this substance. Find the half-life.

48. *Radioactive decay* A certain radioactive substance has a half-life of 50 hours. Find how long it will take for 90% of the radioactivity to be dissipated if the amount of material x satisfies

$$\frac{dx}{dt} = kx \quad (t \text{ in hours, } k \text{ constant})$$

49. *Drug in an organ* Suppose that a liquid carries a drug into a 100-cc organ at a rate of $5\,\text{cc/s}$ and leaves the organ at the same rate. Suppose that the concentration of the drug entering is $0.06\,\text{g/cc}$. If initially there is no drug in the organ, find the amount of drug in the organ as a function of time t.

50. *Drug in an organ* Suppose that a liquid carries a drug into a 250-cc organ at a rate of $10\,\text{cc/s}$ and leaves the organ at the same rate. Suppose that the concentration of the drug entering is $0.15\,\text{g/cc}$. Find the amount of drug in the organ as a function of time t if initially there is none in the organ.

51. *Drug in an organ* Suppose that a liquid carries a drug with concentration $0.1\,\text{g/cc}$ into a 200-cc organ at a rate of $5\,\text{cc/s}$ and leaves the organ at the same rate. If initially there is 10 g of the drug in the organ, find the amount of drug in the organ as a function of time t.

52. *Drug in an organ* Suppose that a liquid carries a drug with concentration $0.05\,\text{g/cc}$ into a 150-cc organ at a rate of $6\,\text{cc/s}$ and leaves at the same rate. If initially there is 1.5 g of drug in the organ, find the amount of drug in the organ as a function of time t.

53. *Tumor volume* Let V denote the volume of a tumor and suppose that the growth rate of the tumor satisfies

$$\frac{dV}{dt} = 0.2Ve^{-0.1t}$$

If the initial volume of the tumor is 1.86 units, find an equation for V as a function of t.

54. *Gompertz curves* The differential equation

$$\frac{dx}{dt} = x(a - b \ln x)$$

where x represents the number of objects at time t and a and b are constants is the model for Gompertz curves. Recall from Section 5.3, "Equations and Applications with Exponential and Logarithmic Functions," that Gompertz curves can be used to study growth or decline of populations, organizations, and revenue from sales of a product, as well as forecast equipment maintenance costs. Solve the differential equation to obtain the Gompertz curve formula

$$x = e^{a/b}e^{-ce^{-bt}}$$

55. *Cell growth* If V is the volume of a spherical cell, then in certain cell growth and fetal growth models, the rate of change of V is given by

$$\frac{dV}{dt} = kV^{2/3}$$

where k is a constant depending on the organism. If $V = 0$ when $t = 0$, find V as a function of t.

56. *Atmospheric pressure* The rate of change of atmospheric pressure P with respect to the altitude above sea level h is proportional to the pressure. That is,

$$\frac{dP}{dh} = kP \quad (k \text{ constant})$$

Suppose that the pressure at sea level is denoted by P_0 and at 18,000 ft the pressure is half what it is at sea level. Find the pressure, as a percent of P_0, at 25,000 ft.

57. *Newton's law of cooling* Newton's law of cooling (and warming) states that the rate of change of temperature $u = u(t)$ of an object is proportional to the temperature difference between the object and its surroundings, where T is the constant temperature of the surroundings. That is,

$$\frac{du}{dt} = k(u - T) \quad (k \text{ constant})$$

Suppose an object at 0°C is placed in a room where the temperature is 20°C. If the temperature of the object is 8°C after 1 hour, how long will it take the object to reach 18°C?

58. *Newton's law of cooling* Newton's law of cooling can be used to estimate time of death. (Actually the estimate may be quite rough because cooling does not begin until metabolic processes have ceased.) Suppose a corpse is discovered at noon in a 70°F room and at that time the body temperature is 96.1°F. If at 1 P.M. the body temperature is 94.6°F, use Newton's law of cooling to estimate the time of death.

59. *Fossil-fuel emissions* Carbon in the atmosphere is due to carbon dioxide (CO_2) emissions from fossil-fuel burning and is considered to be a primary contributor

to climate change. Using data from the Organization for Economic Cooperation and Development (OECD) for selected years from 1980 and projected to 2050, global CO_2 emissions can be modeled by the differential equation

$$\frac{dE}{dt} = 0.0164E$$

where t is the number of years past 1980 and E is global CO_2 emissions (in gigatons).

(a) Solve this differential equation and find a particular solution that satisfies $E(0) = 18.5$.

(b) Graph your solution and compare it with the following graph that shows OECD's data and projections.

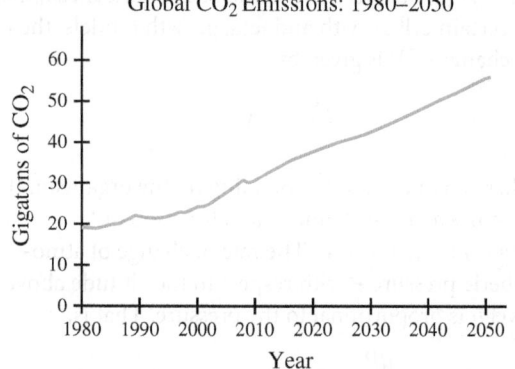

Global CO_2 Emissions: 1980–2050

Source: OECD Environmental Outlook Baseline

60. *Gross domestic product* With Social Security Administration data from 1995 and projected to 2070, the billions of dollars G of gross domestic product (GDP) can be modeled by

$$\frac{dG}{dt} = 0.05317G, \quad G(15) = 12,145$$

where t is the number of years past 1990 [and thus $G(15)$ is the GDP in 2005].

(a) Find the particular solution to this differential equation.

(b) The Social Security Administration's forecast for the 2020 GDP is $27,683 billion. What does the model predict for the 2020 GDP?

61. *Impact of inflation* The impact of a 5% inflation rate on an $80,000-per-year pension can be severe. If P represents the purchasing power (in dollars) of an $80,000 pension, then the effect of a 5% inflation rate can be modeled by the differential equation

$$\frac{dP}{dt} = -0.05P, \quad P(0) = 80,000$$

where t is in years.

(a) Find the particular solution to this differential equation.

(b) Find the purchasing power after 15 years.

62. *Alzheimer's disease* The rate of change of the number of Americans over age 65 with Alzheimer's disease (in millions per year) for years from 2000 and projected to 2050 can be modeled by the differential equation

$$\frac{dA}{dt} = 0.0228A$$

where t is the number of years after 2000 (*Source:* Alzheimer's Association).

(a) Given that in 2010 Alzheimer's disease affected 5.15 million Americans over age 65, find the particular solution to the differential equation. This solution models the number of Americans over age 65 with Alzheimer's disease.

(b) Use the model found in part (a) to project the number of Americans over age 65 with Alzheimer's disease in 2035.

12 CHAPTER SUMMARY & REVIEW

KEY TERMS AND FORMULAS

Section 12.1

General antiderivative of $f'(x)$ (p. 739)

  $f(x) + C$

Indefinite integral (p. 739)

  $\int f(x)\, dx$

Powers of x Formula (p. 740)

$$\int x^n\, dx = \frac{x^{n+1}}{n+1} + C \ (n \neq -1)$$

Integration Formulas (p. 741)

$$\int dx = x + C$$

$$\int cu(x)\, dx = c \int u(x)\, dx \quad (c = \text{a constant})$$

$$\int [u(x) \pm v(x)]\, dx = \int u(x)\, dx \pm \int v(x)\, dx$$

Section 12.2

Differentials (p. 746)

Power Rule (p. 747)

$$\int [u(x)]^n\, u'(x)\, dx = \frac{[u(x)]^{n+1}}{n+1} + C \ (n \neq -1)$$

Section 12.3

Exponential Formula (p. 755)

$$\int e^u u' \, dx = \int e^u \, du = e^u + C$$

Logarithmic Formula (p. 757)

$$\int \frac{u'}{u} \, dx = \int \frac{1}{u} \, du = \ln |u| + C$$

Section 12.4

Total cost (p. 764)
$$C(x) = \int \overline{MC} \, dx$$
Total revenue (p. 765)
$$R(x) = \int \overline{MR} \, dx$$
Profit (p. 766)
National consumption (p. 768)

$$C = \int f'(y) \, dy = \int \frac{dC}{dy} \, dy$$

Marginal propensity to consume (p. 768)

$$\frac{dC}{dy}$$

Marginal propensity to save (p. 768)

$$\frac{dS}{dy} = 1 - \frac{dC}{dy}$$

Section 12.5

Differential equations (p. 771)
   General solution
   Particular solution
First order (p. 772)

$$\frac{dy}{dx} = f(x) \Rightarrow y = \int f(x) \, dx$$

Initial and boundary conditions (p. 773)
Separable (p. 774)

$$g(y) \, dy = f(x) \, dx \Rightarrow \int g(y) \, dy = \int f(x) \, dx$$

Radioactive decay (p. 775)

$$\frac{dy}{dt} = ky$$

Drug in an organ (p. 776)
   Rate = (rate in) − (rate out)

REVIEW EXERCISES

Sections 12.1–12.3

Evaluate the integrals in Problems 1–26.

1. $\int x^6 \, dx$

2. $\int x^{1/2} \, dx$

3. $\int (12x^3 - 3x^2 + 4x + 5) \, dx$

4. $\int 7(x^2 - 1)^2 \, dx$

5. $\int 7x(x^2 - 1)^2 \, dx$

6. $\int (x^3 - 3x^2)^5 (x^2 - 2x) \, dx$

7. $\int (x^3 + 4)^2 3x \, dx$

8. $\int 5x^2(3x^3 + 7)^6 \, dx$

9. $\int \frac{x^2}{x^3 + 1} \, dx$

10. $\int \frac{x^2}{(x^3 + 1)^2} \, dx$

11. $\int \frac{x^2 \, dx}{\sqrt[3]{x^3 - 4}}$

12. $\int \frac{x^2 \, dx}{x^3 - 4}$

13. $\int \frac{x^3 + 1}{x^2} \, dx$

14. $\int \frac{x^3 - 3x + 1}{x - 1} \, dx$

15. $\int y^2 e^{y^3} \, dy$

16. $\int (3x - 1)^{12} \, dx$

17. $\int \frac{3x^2}{2x^3 - 7} \, dx$

18. $\int \frac{5 \, dx}{e^{4x}}$

19. $\int (x^3 - e^{3x}) \, dx$

20. $\int xe^{1 + x^2} \, dx$

21. $\int \frac{6x^7}{(5x^8 + 7)^3} \, dx$

22. $\int \frac{7x^3}{\sqrt{1 - x^4}} \, dx$

23. $\int \left(\frac{e^{2x}}{2} + \frac{2}{e^{2x}} \right) dx$

24. $\int \left[x - \frac{1}{(x + 1)^2} \right] dx$

25. (a) $\int (x^2 - 1)^4 x \, dx$ (b) $\int (x^2 - 1)^{10} x \, dx$
    (c) $\int (x^2 - 1)^7 3x \, dx$ (d) $\int (x^2 - 1)^{-2/3} x \, dx$

26. (a) $\int \frac{2x \, dx}{x^2 - 1}$ (b) $\int \frac{2x \, dx}{(x^2 - 1)^2}$
    (c) $\int \frac{3x \, dx}{\sqrt{x^2 - 1}}$ (d) $\int \frac{3x \, dx}{x^2 - 1}$

Section 12.5

In Problems 27–32, find the general solution to each differential equation.

27. $\frac{dy}{dt} = 4.6e^{-0.05t}$

28. $dy = (64 + 76x - 36x^2) \, dx$

29. $\frac{dy}{dx} = \frac{4x}{y - 3}$

30. $t \, dy = \frac{dt}{y + 1}$

31. $\frac{dy}{dx} = \frac{x}{e^y}$

32. $\frac{dy}{dt} = \frac{4y}{t}$

In Problems 33 and 34, find the particular solution to each differential equation.

33. $y' = \frac{x^2}{y + 1}$, $y(0) = 4$

34. $y' = \frac{2x}{1 + 2y}$, $y(2) = 0$

APPLICATIONS

Section 12.1

35. *Revenue* If the marginal revenue for a month for a product is $\overline{MR} = 0.06x + 12$ dollars per unit, find the total revenue from the sale of $x = 800$ units of the product.

36. *Productivity* Suppose that the rate of change of production of the average worker at a factory is given by

$$\frac{dp}{dt} = 27 + 24t - 3t^2, \quad 0 \le t \le 8$$

where p is the number of units the worker produces in t hours. How many units will the average worker produce in an 8-hour shift? (Assume that $p = 0$ when $t = 0$.)

Section 12.2

37. *Oxygen levels in water* The rate of change of the oxygen level (in mmol/l) per month in a body of water after an oil spill is given by

$$P'(t) = 400\left[\frac{5}{(t + 5)^2} - \frac{50}{(t + 5)^3}\right]$$

where t is the number of months after the spill. What function gives the oxygen level P at any time t if $P = 400$ mmol/l when $t = 0$?

38. *Bacterial growth* A population of bacteria grows at the rate

$$\frac{dp}{dt} = \frac{100,000}{(t + 100)^2}$$

where p is the population and t is time. If the population is 1000 when $t = 1$, write the equation that gives the size of the population at any time t.

Section 12.3

39. *Market share* The rate of change of the market share (as a percent) a firm expects for a new product is

$$\frac{dy}{dt} = 2.4e^{-0.04t}$$

where t is the number of months after the product is introduced.
   (a) Write the equation that gives the expected market share y at any time t. (Note that $y = 0$ when $t = 0$.)
   (b) What market share does the firm expect after 1 year?

40. *Revenue* If the marginal revenue for a product is

$$\overline{MR} = \frac{800}{x + 2},$$ find the total revenue function.

Section 12.4

41. *Cost* The marginal cost for a product is $\overline{MC} = 6x + 4$ dollars per unit, and the cost of producing 100 items is $31,400.
   (a) Find the fixed costs.
   (b) Find the total cost function.

42. *Profit* Suppose a product has a daily marginal revenue $\overline{MR} = 46$ and a daily marginal cost $\overline{MC} = 30 + \frac{1}{5}x$, both in dollars per unit. If the daily fixed cost is $200, how many units will give maximum profit and what is the maximum profit?

43. *National consumption* If national consumption is $8.5 billion when disposable income is $0 and if the marginal propensity to consume is

$$\frac{dC}{dy} = \frac{1}{\sqrt{2y + 16}} + 0.6$$

find the national consumption function.

44. *National consumption* Suppose that the marginal propensity to save is

$$\frac{dS}{dy} = 0.2 - 0.1e^{-2y}$$

and consumption is $7.8 billion when disposable income is $0. Find the national consumption function.

Section 12.5

45. *Allometric growth* For many species of fish, the length L and weight W of a fish are related by

$$\frac{dW}{dL} = \frac{3W}{L}$$

The general solution to this differential equation expresses the allometric relationship between the length and weight of a fish. Find the general solution.

46. *Investment* When the interest on an investment is compounded continuously, the investment grows at a rate that is proportional to the amount in the account so that if the amount present is P, then

$$\frac{dP}{dt} = kP \quad (k \text{ constant})$$

where P is in dollars, t is in years, and k is a constant.
   (a) Solve this differential equation to find the relationship.
   (b) Use properties of logarithms and exponential functions to write P as a function of t.
   (c) If $50,000 is invested (when $t = 0$) and the amount in the account after 10 years is $135,914, find the function that gives the value of the investment as a function of t.
   (d) In part (c), what does the value of k represent?

47. *Fossil dating* Radioactive beryllium is sometimes used to date fossils found in deep-sea sediment. The amount of radioactive material x satisfies

$$\frac{dx}{dt} = kx$$

Suppose that 10 units of beryllium are present in a living organism and that the half-life of beryllium is 4.6 million years. Find the age of a fossil if 20% of the original radioactivity is present when the fossil is discovered.

48. *Drug in an organ* Suppose that a liquid carries a drug into a 120-cc organ at a rate of 4 cc/s and leaves the

organ at the same rate. If initially there is no drug in the organ and if the concentration of drug in the liquid is 3 g/cc, find the amount of drug in the organ as a function of time.

49. *Chemical mixture* A 300-gal tank initially contains a solution with 100 lb of a chemical. A mixture containing 2 lb/gal of the chemical enters the tank at 3 gal/min, and the well-stirred mixture leaves at the same rate. Find an equation that gives the amount of the chemical in the tank as a function of time. How long will it be before there is 500 lb of chemical in the tank?

12 CHAPTER TEST

Evaluate the integrals in Problems 1–11.

1. $\displaystyle\int (6x^2 + 8x - 7)\, dx$

2. $\displaystyle\int (11 - 2x^3)\, dx$

3. $\displaystyle\int 5(x^2 - 1)\, dx$

4. $\displaystyle\int \left(4 + \sqrt{x} - \frac{1}{x^2}\right) dx$

5. $\displaystyle\int 6x^2(7 + 2x^3)^9\, dx$

6. $\displaystyle\int 5x^2(4x^3 - 7)^9\, dx$

7. $\displaystyle\int (3x^2 - 6x + 1)^{-3}(2x - 2)\, dx$

8. $\displaystyle\int \left(e^x + \frac{5}{x} - 1\right) dx$

9. $\displaystyle\int \frac{s^3}{2s^4 - 5}\, ds$

10. $\displaystyle\int 100e^{-0.01x}\, dx$

11. $\displaystyle\int 5y^3 e^{2y^4 - 1}\, dy$

12. Evaluate $\displaystyle\int \frac{4x^2}{2x + 1}\, dx$. Use long division.

13. If $\displaystyle\int f(x)\, dx = 2x^3 - x + 5e^x + C$, find $f(x)$.

14. Find the general solution to $f'(x) = \dfrac{x^2}{3} - \dfrac{5}{8}$.

In Problems 15 and 16, find the particular solution to each differential equation.

15. $y' = 4x^3 + 3x^2$, if $y(0) = 4$

16. $\dfrac{dy}{dx} = e^{4x}$, if $y(0) = 2$

17. Find the general solution of the separable differential equation $\dfrac{dy}{dx} = x^3 y^2$.

18. Suppose the rate of growth of the population of a city is predicted to be

$$\frac{dp}{dt} = 2000t^{1.04}$$

where p is the population and t is the number of years past 2018. If the population in the year 2018 is 50,000, what is the predicted population in the year 2028?

19. Suppose that the marginal cost for x units of a product is $\overline{MC} = 4x + 50$, the marginal revenue is $\overline{MR} = 500$, and the cost of the production and sale of 10 units is \$1000. What is the profit function for this product?

20. Suppose the marginal propensity to save is given by

$$\frac{dS}{dy} = 0.22 - \frac{0.25}{\sqrt{0.5y + 1}}$$

and national consumption is \$6.6 billion when disposable income is \$0. Find the national consumption function.

21. A certain radioactive material has a half-life of 100 days and the amount of material present, x, satisfies

$$\frac{dx}{dt} = kx$$

where t is in days and k is constant.
 (a) If there are initially 100 g of this material, find $x = f(t)$. Give your answer with 3 significant digit coefficients.
 (b) Use your answer from part(a) to find how long (to the nearest day) it takes for 90% of the radioactivity to dissipate.

22. Suppose that a liquid carries a drug with concentration 0.1 g/cc into a 160-cc organ at the rate of 4 cc/sec and leaves at the same rate. Find the amount of drug in the organ as a function of time t if initially there is none in the organ.

12 EXTENDED APPLICATIONS & GROUP PROJECTS

I. Employee Production Rate

The manager of a plant has been instructed to hire and train a sufficient number of new employees so that within 30 days, they will be producing 2500 units of the product each day.

Suppose that research on similar projects indicates that production increases with training, so that for the average employee, the rate of production per day is given by

$$\frac{dN}{dt} = be^{-at}$$

where N is the number of units produced per day after t days of training and a and b are constants that depend on the project. Because of experience with a similar project, the manager expects the rate for this project to be

$$\frac{dN}{dt} = 2.5e^{-0.05t}$$

The manager tested her training program with 5 employees and learned that the average employee could produce

11 units per day after 5 days of training. On the basis of this information, she must decide how many employees to hire and begin to train so that a month from now they will be producing 2500 units of the product per day. She estimates that it will take her 10 days to hire the employees, and thus she will have 15 days remaining to train them. She also expects a 10% attrition rate during this period.

How many employees should the plant manager hire? Check your advice by answering the following questions.

1. Use the expected rate of production and the results of the manager's test to find the function relating N and t—that is, $N = N(t)$.
2. Find the number of units the average employee can produce after 15 days of training. How many such employees would be needed to maintain a production rate of 2500 units per day?
3. Explain how you would revise this last result to account for the expected 10% attrition rate. How many new employees should the manager hire?

II. Supply and Demand

If p is the price in dollars of a given commodity at time t, then we can think of price as a function of time. Similarly at any time, the number of units demanded by consumers q_d and the number of units supplied by producers q_s may be considered as functions of time as well as functions of price.

Both the quantity demanded and the quantity supplied depend not only on the price at the time, but also on the direction and rate of change that consumers and producers ascribe to prices. For example, even when prices are high, if consumers believe that prices are rising, the demand may rise.

If we assume that prices are determined in the marketplace by supply and demand, then the equilibrium price is the one we seek.

Suppose the supply and demand functions for a certain commodity in a competitive market are given in hundreds of units by

$$q_s = 30 + p + 5\frac{dp}{dt}$$

$$q_d = 51 - 2p + 4\frac{dp}{dt}$$

where dp/dt denotes the rate of change of the price with respect to time. If the market equilibrium price is $12 at

$t = 0$, we can express the market equilibrium price as a function of time. Our goals are as follows.

A. To express the market equilibrium price as a function of time.
B. To determine whether there is price stability in the marketplace for this item (that is, to determine whether the equilibrium price approaches a constant over time).

To achieve these goals, do the following.

1. Set the expressions for q_s and q_d equal to each other.
2. Solve this equation for $\frac{dp}{dt}$.
3. Solve the differential equation from Question 2.
4. Solve the resulting equation for p in terms of t.
5. Use the fact that $p = 12$ when $t = 0$ to find C, the constant of integration, and write the market equilibrium price p as a function of time t.
6. Find $\lim\limits_{t \to \infty} p$, which gives the price we can expect this product to approach. If this limit is finite, then for this item, there is price stability in the marketplace. If $p \to \infty$ as $t \to \infty$, then price will continue to increase until economic conditions change.

Definite Integrals: Techniques of Integration

13

We saw some applications of the indefinite integral in Chapter 12. In this chapter, we define the definite integral and discuss a theorem and techniques that are useful in evaluating or approximating it. We will see how it can be used in many interesting applications, such as consumer's and producer's surplus and total value, present value, and future value of continuous income streams. Improper integrals can be used to find the capital value of a continuous income stream.

The topics and some representative applications discussed in this chapter include the following.

Prerequisite Problem Type	For Section	Answer	Section for Review
Simplify: $\dfrac{1}{n^3}\left[\dfrac{n(n+1)(2n+1)}{6} - \dfrac{2n(n+1)}{2} + n\right]$	**13.1**	$\dfrac{2n^2 - 3n + 1}{6n^2}$	0.7 Fractions
(a) If $F(x) = \dfrac{x^4}{4} + 4x + C$, what is $\qquad F(4) - F(2)$? (b) If $F(x) = -\dfrac{1}{9}\ln\left(\dfrac{9 + \sqrt{81 - 9x^2}}{3x}\right)$ $\qquad$ what is $F(3) - F(2)$?	**13.2** **13.5**	(a) 68 (b) $\dfrac{1}{9}\ln\left(\dfrac{3 + \sqrt{5}}{2}\right)$	1.2 Function notation
Find the limit: (a) $\displaystyle\lim_{n\to\infty} \dfrac{n^2 + n}{2n^2}$ (b) $\displaystyle\lim_{n\to\infty} \dfrac{2n^2 - 3n + 1}{6n^2}$ (c) $\displaystyle\lim_{b\to\infty}\left(1 - \dfrac{1}{b}\right)$ (d) $\displaystyle\lim_{b\to\infty}\left(\dfrac{-100{,}000}{e^{0.10b}} + 100{,}000\right)$	**13.1** **13.7**	(a) $\frac{1}{2}$ (b) $\frac{1}{3}$ (c) 1 (d) 100,000	9.2 Limits at infinity
Find the derivative of $y = \ln x$.	**13.6**	$\dfrac{1}{x}$	11.1 Derivatives of logarithmic functions
Integrate: (a) $\displaystyle\int (x^3 + 4)\,dx$ (b) $\displaystyle\int x\sqrt{x^2 - 9}\,dx$ (c) $\displaystyle\int e^{2x}\,dx$	**13.2–13.7**	(a) $\dfrac{x^4}{4} + 4x + C$ (b) $\frac{1}{3}(x^2 - 9)^{3/2} + C$ (c) $\frac{1}{2}e^{2x} + C$	12.1, 12.2, 12.3 Integration

Area Under a Curve

OBJECTIVES

- To use the sum of areas of rectangles to approximate the area under a curve
- To use Σ notation to denote sums
- To find the exact area under a curve

APPLICATION PREVIEW

One way to find the accumulated production (such as the production of ore from a mine) over a period of time is to graph the rate of production as a function of time and find the area under the resulting curve over a specified time interval. For example, if a coal mine produced at a rate of 30 tons per day, the production over 10 days ($30 \cdot 10 = 300$) could be represented by the area under the line $y = 30$ between $x = 0$ and $x = 10$. (See Figure 13.1.)

Using area to determine the accumulated production is very useful when the rate-of-production function varies at different points in time. For example, if the rate of production (in tons per day) is represented by

$$y = 100e^{-0.1x}$$

where x represents the number of days, then the area under the curve (and above the x-axis) from $x = 0$ to $x = 10$ represents the total production over the 10-day period. [See Figure 13.2(a) and Example 1.] To determine the accumulated production and to solve other types of problems, we need a method for finding areas under curves. That is the goal of this section.

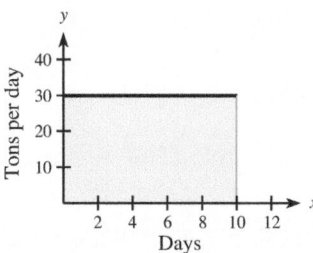

Figure 13.1

Area Under a Curve   To estimate the accumulated production for the example above, with rate $y = 100e^{-0.1x}$, we approximate the area under the graph of the production rate function. We can find a rough approximation of the area under this curve by fitting two rectangles to the curve as shown in Figure 13.2(b). The area of the first rectangle is $5 \cdot 100 = 500$ square units, and the area of the second rectangle is $(10 - 5)[100e^{-0.1(5)}] \approx 303.27$ square units, so this rough approximation is 803.27 square units or 803.27 tons of ore. This approximation is clearly larger than the exact area under the curve. Why?

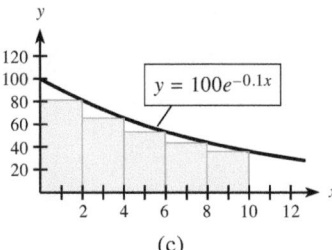

Figure 13.2   (a)   (b)   (c)

EXAMPLE **1**   **Ore Production** | APPLICATION PREVIEW |

Find another, more accurate approximation of the tons of ore produced by approximating the area under the curve in Figure 13.2(a). Fit five rectangles with equal bases inside the area under the curve $y = 100e^{-0.1x}$ and use them to approximate the area under the curve from $x = 0$ to $x = 10$. [See Figure 13.2(c).]

Solution

Each of the five rectangles has base 2, and the height of each rectangle is the value of the function at the right-hand endpoint of the interval forming its base. Thus the areas of the rectangles are as follows.

Rectangle	Base	Height	Area = Base × Height
1	2	$100e^{-0.1(2)} \approx 81.87$	$2(81.87) = 163.74$
2	2	$100e^{-0.1(4)} \approx 67.03$	$2(67.03) = 134.06$
3	2	$100e^{-0.1(6)} \approx 54.88$	$2(54.88) = 109.76$
4	2	$100e^{-0.1(8)} \approx 44.93$	$2(44.93) = 89.86$
5	2	$100e^{-0.1(10)} \approx 36.79$	$2(36.79) = 73.58$

The area under the curve is approximately equal to

$$163.74 + 134.06 + 109.76 + 89.86 + 73.58 = 571$$

so approximately 571 tons of ore are produced in the 10-day period. The area is actually 632.12, to 2 decimal places (or 632.12 tons of ore), so the approximation 571 is smaller than the actual area but is much better than the one we obtained with just two rectangles. In general, if we use bases of equal width, the approximation of the area under a curve improves when more rectangles are used.

Suppose that we want to find the area between the curve $y = 2x$ and the x-axis from $x = 0$ to $x = 1$. (See Figure 13.3.) As we saw in Example 1, one way to approximate this area is to use the areas of rectangles whose bases are on the x-axis and whose heights are the vertical distances from points on their bases to the curve. We can divide the interval $[0, 1]$ into n equal subintervals and use them as the bases of n rectangles whose heights are determined by the curve. (See Figure 13.4.) The width of each of these rectangles is $1/n$. Using the function value at the right-hand endpoint of each subinterval as the height of the rectangle, we get n rectangles as shown in Figure 13.4. Because part of each rectangle lies above the curve, the sum of the areas of the rectangles will overestimate the area.

Figure 13.3

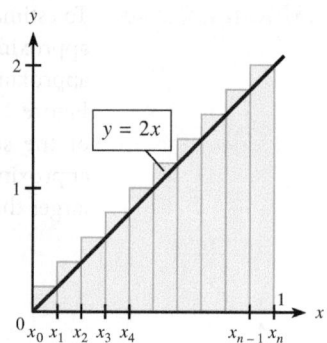

Figure 13.4

With $y = f(x) = 2x$ and subinterval width $1/n$, the areas of the rectangles are as shown in the following table.

Rectangle	Base	Right Endpoint	Height	Area = Base × Height
1	$\dfrac{1}{n}$	$x_1 = \dfrac{1}{n}$	$f(x_1) = 2\left(\dfrac{1}{n}\right)$	$\dfrac{1}{n} \cdot \dfrac{2}{n} = \dfrac{2}{n^2}$
2	$\dfrac{1}{n}$	$x_2 = \dfrac{2}{n}$	$f(x_2) = 2\left(\dfrac{2}{n}\right)$	$\dfrac{1}{n} \cdot \dfrac{4}{n} = \dfrac{4}{n^2}$
3	$\dfrac{1}{n}$	$x_3 = \dfrac{3}{n}$	$f(x_3) = 2\left(\dfrac{3}{n}\right)$	$\dfrac{1}{n} \cdot \dfrac{6}{n} = \dfrac{6}{n^2}$
$\vdots$				
i	$\dfrac{1}{n}$	$x_i = \dfrac{i}{n}$	$f(x_i) = 2\left(\dfrac{i}{n}\right)$	$\dfrac{1}{n} \cdot \dfrac{2i}{n} = \dfrac{2i}{n^2}$
$\vdots$				
n	$\dfrac{1}{n}$	$x_n = \dfrac{n}{n}$	$f(x_n) = 2\left(\dfrac{n}{n}\right)$	$\dfrac{1}{n} \cdot \dfrac{2n}{n} = \dfrac{2n}{n^2}$

Note that $2i/n^2$ gives the area of the ith rectangle for *any* value of i. Thus for any value of n, this area can be approximated by the sum

$$A \approx \frac{2}{n^2} + \frac{4}{n^2} + \frac{6}{n^2} + \cdots + \frac{2i}{n^2} + \cdots + \frac{2n}{n^2}$$

In particular, we have the following approximations of this area for specific values of n (the number of rectangles).

$$n = 5: \quad A \approx \frac{2}{25} + \frac{4}{25} + \frac{6}{25} + \frac{8}{25} + \frac{10}{25} = \frac{30}{25} = 1.20$$

$$n = 10: \quad A \approx \frac{2}{100} + \frac{4}{100} + \frac{6}{100} + \cdots + \frac{20}{100} = \frac{110}{100} = 1.10$$

$$n = 100: \quad A \approx \frac{2}{10,000} + \frac{4}{10,000} + \frac{6}{10,000} + \cdots + \frac{200}{10,000}$$
$$= \frac{10,100}{10,000} = 1.01$$

Figure 13.5 shows the rectangles associated with each of these approximations ($n = 5$, 10, and 100) to the area under $y = 2x$ from $x = 0$ to $x = 1$. For larger n, the rectangles closely approximate the area under the curve.

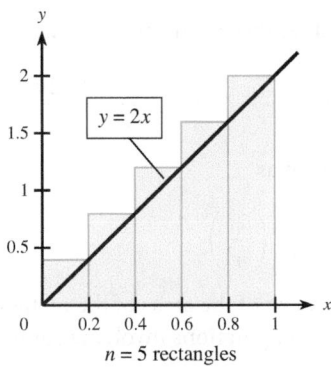
$n = 5$ rectangles
(a)

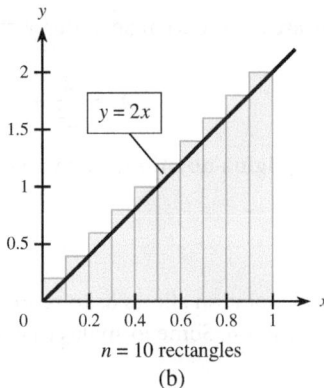
$n = 10$ rectangles
(b)

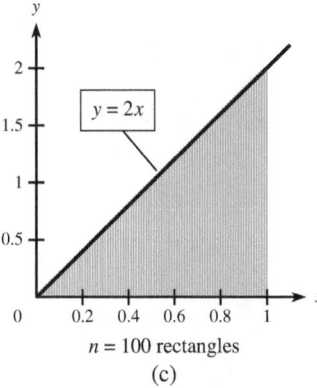
$n = 100$ rectangles
(c)

Figure 13.5

We can find this sum for any n more easily if we observe that the common denominator is n^2 and that the numerator is twice the sum of the first n terms of an arithmetic sequence with first term 1 and last term n. As you may recall from Section 6.1, "Simple Interest; Sequences," the first n terms of this arithmetic sequence add to $n(n + 1)/2$. Thus the area is approximated by

$$A \approx \frac{2(1 + 2 + 3 + \cdots + n)}{n^2} = \frac{2[n(n + 1)/2]}{n^2} = \frac{n + 1}{n}$$

Using this formula, we see the following.

$$n = 5: \quad A \approx \frac{5 + 1}{5} = \frac{6}{5} = 1.20$$

$$n = 10: \quad A \approx \frac{10 + 1}{10} = \frac{11}{10} = 1.10$$

$$n = 100: \quad A \approx \frac{100 + 1}{100} = \frac{101}{100} = 1.01$$

As Figure 13.5 indicated, as n gets larger, the number of rectangles increases, the area of each rectangle decreases, and the approximation becomes more accurate. If we let n increase without bound, the approximation approaches the exact area.

$$A = \lim_{n \to \infty} \frac{n + 1}{n} = \lim_{n \to \infty} \left(1 + \frac{1}{n}\right) = 1$$

We can see that this area is correct, for we are computing the area of a triangle with base 1 and height 2. The formula for the area of a triangle gives

$$A = \frac{1}{2}bh = \frac{1}{2} \cdot 1 \cdot 2 = 1$$

Summation Notation   A special notation exists that uses the Greek letter Σ (capital sigma) to express the sum of numbers or expressions. (We used sigma notation informally in Chapter 8, "Further Topics in Probability; Data Description.") We may indicate the sum of the n numbers $a_1, a_2, a_3, a_4, \ldots, a_n$ by

$$\sum_{i=1}^{n} a_i = a_1 + a_2 + a_3 + \cdots + a_n$$

This may be read as "The sum of a_i as i goes from 1 to n." The subscript i in a_i is replaced first by 1, then by 2, then by 3, ... , until it reaches the value above the sigma. The i is called the **index of summation,** and it starts with the lower limit, 1, and ends with the upper limit, n. For example, if $x_1 = 2$, $x_2 = 3$, $x_3 = -1$, and $x_4 = -2$, then

$$\sum_{i=1}^{4} x_i = x_1 + x_2 + x_3 + x_4 = 2 + 3 + (-1) + (-2) = 2$$

The area of the triangle under $y = 2x$ that we discussed above was approximated by

$$A \approx \frac{2}{n^2} + \frac{4}{n^2} + \frac{6}{n^2} + \cdots + \frac{2i}{n^2} + \cdots + \frac{2n}{n^2}$$

Using **sigma notation,** we can write this sum as

$$A \approx \sum_{i=1}^{n} \left(\frac{2i}{n^2} \right)$$

Sigma notation allows us to represent the sums of the areas of the rectangles in an abbreviated fashion. Some formulas that simplify computations involving sums follow.

Sum Formulas

I. $\displaystyle\sum_{i=1}^{n} 1 = n$

IV. $\displaystyle\sum_{i=1}^{n} i = \frac{n(n+1)}{2}$

II. $\displaystyle\sum_{i=1}^{n} cx_i = c \sum_{i=1}^{n} x_i \quad (c = \text{constant})$

V. $\displaystyle\sum_{i=1}^{n} i^2 = \frac{n(n+1)(2n+1)}{6}$

III. $\displaystyle\sum_{i=1}^{n} (x_i + y_i) = \sum_{i=1}^{n} x_i + \sum_{i=1}^{n} y_i$

We found that the area of the triangle discussed above was approximated by

$$A \approx \sum_{i=1}^{n} \frac{2i}{n^2}$$

We can use formulas II and IV to simplify this sum as follows.

$$\sum_{i=1}^{n} \frac{2i}{n^2} = \frac{2}{n^2} \sum_{i=1}^{n} i = \frac{2}{n^2} \left[\frac{n(n+1)}{2} \right] = \frac{n+1}{n}$$

Note that this is the same formula we obtained previously using other methods.

We can use these sum formulas to evaluate a particular sum. For example,

$$\sum_{i=1}^{100}(2i^2 - 3) = \sum_{i=1}^{100}2i^2 - \sum_{i=1}^{100}3(1) \qquad \text{formula III}$$

$$= 2\sum_{i=1}^{100}i^2 - 3\sum_{i=1}^{100}1 \qquad \text{formula II}$$

$$= 2\left[\frac{100(101)(201)}{6}\right] - 3(100) \qquad \text{formulas I and V with } n = 100$$

$$= 676,400$$

Areas and Summation Notation

The following example shows that we can find the area by evaluating the function at the left-hand endpoints of the subintervals.

EXAMPLE 2 Area Under a Curve

Use rectangles to find the area under $y = x^2$ (and above the x-axis) from $x = 0$ to $x = 1$.

Solution

We again divide the interval $[0, 1]$ into n equal subintervals of length $1/n$. If we evaluate the function at the left-hand endpoints of these subintervals to determine the heights of the rectangles, the sum of the areas of the rectangles will underestimate the area. (See Figure 13.6.) Thus we have the information shown in the following table.

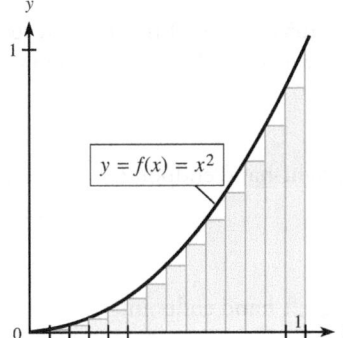

Figure 13.6

Rectangle	Base	Left Endpoint	Height	Area = Base × Height
1	$\frac{1}{n}$	$x_0 = 0$	$f(x_0) = 0$	$\frac{1}{n}\cdot 0 = 0$
2	$\frac{1}{n}$	$x_1 = \frac{1}{n}$	$f(x_1) = \frac{1}{n^2}$	$\frac{1}{n}\cdot\frac{1}{n^2} = \frac{1}{n^3}$
3	$\frac{1}{n}$	$x_2 = \frac{2}{n}$	$f(x_2) = \frac{4}{n^2}$	$\frac{1}{n}\cdot\frac{4}{n^2} = \frac{4}{n^3}$
4	$\frac{1}{n}$	$x_3 = \frac{3}{n}$	$f(x_3) = \frac{9}{n^2}$	$\frac{1}{n}\cdot\frac{9}{n^2} = \frac{9}{n^3}$
$\vdots$				
i	$\frac{1}{n}$	$x_{i-1} = \frac{i-1}{n}$	$\frac{(i-1)^2}{n^2}$	$\frac{(i-1)^2}{n^3}$
$\vdots$				
n	$\frac{1}{n}$	$x_{n-1} = \frac{n-1}{n}$	$\frac{(n-1)^2}{n^2}$	$\frac{(n-1)^2}{n^3}$

Thus: Area $= A \approx 0 + \dfrac{1}{n^3} + \dfrac{4}{n^3} + \dfrac{9}{n^3} + \cdots + \dfrac{(i-1)^2}{n^3} + \cdots + \dfrac{(n-1)^2}{n^3}$.

Note that $(i - 1)^2/n^3 = (i^2 - 2i + 1)/n^3$ gives the area of the ith rectangle for *any* value of i. The sum of these areas may be written as

$$S = \sum_{i=1}^{n}\frac{i^2 - 2i + 1}{n^3} = \frac{1}{n^3}\left(\sum_{i=1}^{n}i^2 - 2\sum_{i=1}^{n}i + \sum_{i=1}^{n}1\right) \qquad \text{formulas II and III}$$

$$= \frac{1}{n^3}\left[\frac{n(n+1)(2n+1)}{6} - \frac{2n(n+1)}{2} + n\right] \qquad \text{formulas V, IV, and I}$$

$$= \frac{2n^3 + 3n^2 + n}{6n^3} - \frac{n^2 + n}{n^3} + \frac{n}{n^3} = \frac{2n^2 - 3n + 1}{6n^2}$$

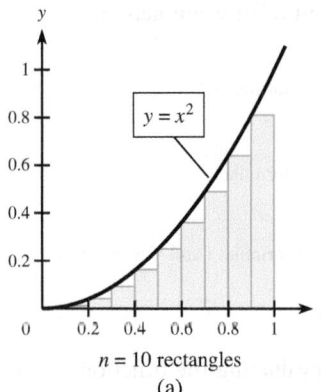

$n = 10$ rectangles
(a)

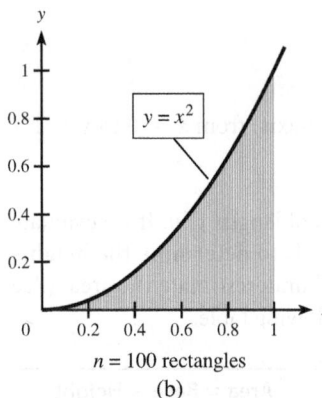

$n = 100$ rectangles
(b)

Figure 13.7

We can use this formula to find the approximate area (value of S) for different values of n.

$$\text{If } n = 10: \quad \text{Area} \approx S(10) = \frac{200 - 30 + 1}{600} = 0.285$$

$$\text{If } n = 100: \quad \text{Area} \approx S(100) = \frac{20{,}000 - 300 + 1}{60{,}000} = 0.328$$

Figure 13.7 shows the rectangles associated with each of these approximations.

As Figure 13.7 shows, the larger the value of n, the better the value of the sum approximates the exact area under the curve. If we let n increase without bound, we find the exact area.

$$A = \lim_{n \to \infty} \left(\frac{2n^2 - 3n + 1}{6n^2} \right) = \lim_{n \to \infty} \left(\frac{2 - \frac{3}{n} + \frac{1}{n^2}}{6} \right) = \frac{1}{3}$$

Note that the approximations with $n = 10$ and $n = 100$ are less than $\frac{1}{3}$. This is because all the rectangles are *under* the curve. (See Figure 13.7.)

Thus we see that we can determine the area under a curve $y = f(x)$ from $x = a$ to $x = b$ by dividing the interval $[a, b]$ into n equal subintervals of width $(b - a)/n$ and evaluating

$$A = \lim_{n \to \infty} S_R = \lim_{n \to \infty} \sum_{i=1}^{n} f(x_i) \left(\frac{b - a}{n} \right) \qquad \text{(using right-hand endpoints)}$$

or

$$A = \lim_{n \to \infty} S_L = \lim_{n \to \infty} \sum_{i=1}^{n} f(x_{i-1}) \left(\frac{b - a}{n} \right) \qquad \text{(using left-hand endpoints)}$$

CHECKPOINT

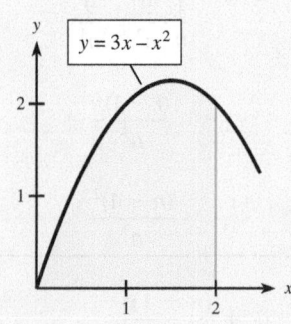

1. For the interval $[0, 2]$, determine whether the following statements are true or false.

    (a) For 4 subintervals, each subinterval has width $\dfrac{1}{2}$.

    (b) For 200 subintervals, each subinterval has width $\dfrac{1}{200}$.

    (c) For n subintervals, each subinterval has width $\dfrac{2}{n}$.

    (d) For n subintervals, $x_0 = 0$, $x_1 = \dfrac{2}{n}$, $x_2 = 2\left(\dfrac{2}{n}\right)$, $\dots$, $x_i = i\left(\dfrac{2}{n}\right)$, $\dots$, $x_n = 2$.

2. Find the area under $y = f(x) = 3x - x^2$ from $x = 0$ to $x = 2$ using right-hand endpoints. (See the figure.) To accomplish this, use $\dfrac{b - a}{n} = \dfrac{2}{n}$, $x_i = \dfrac{2i}{n}$, and $f(x) = 3x - x^2$; find and simplify the following.

    (a) $f(x_i)$

    (b) $f(x_i)\left(\dfrac{b - a}{n}\right)$

    (c) $S_R = \displaystyle\sum_{i=1}^{n} f(x_i)\left(\dfrac{b - a}{n}\right)$

    (d) $A = \displaystyle\lim_{n \to \infty} S_R = \lim_{n \to \infty} \sum_{i=1}^{n} f(x_i)\left(\dfrac{b - a}{n}\right)$

Technology Note

Graphing calculators and Excel can be used to approximate the area under a curve. These technologies are especially useful when summations approximating the area do not simplify easily. Example 3 shows steps for using both a graphing calculator and Excel to approximate an area. See Appendices A and B, Section 13.1, for additional details.

EXAMPLE 3

Estimating an Area with Technology

Approximate the area under the graph of $f(x) = \sqrt{x}$ on the interval $[0, 4]$ by using $n = 8$ rectangles with:

(a) a graphing calculator and both left-hand and right-hand endpoints.
(b) Excel and left-hand endpoints.

Solution

Figure 13.8(a) shows the graph of $y = \sqrt{x}$ with 8 rectangles whose heights are determined by evaluating the function at the left-hand endpoint of each interval. (The first of these rectangles has height 0.) Figure 13.8(b) shows the same graph with 8 rectangles whose heights are determined at the right-hand endpoints.

(a) To approximate the area with a graphing calculator, first enter the function as $Y_1 = \sqrt{x}$. With $n = 8$, each rectangle has base width $(4 - 0)/8 = 0.5$. The subdivision values are $x_0 = 0$, $x_1 = 0.5$, $x_2 = 1, \ldots x_7 = 3.5$, $x_8 = 4$.
Because $Y_1(x_i)$ on a graphing calculator gives $\sqrt{x_i}$, the height of a rectangle at x_i, the left approximation of the area is

$$S_L = \sum_{i=1}^{8} f(x_{i-1})\Delta x \text{ which is found with } \left[Y_1(x_0) + Y_1(x_1) + \cdots + Y_1(x_{8-1})\right]\Delta x$$

$$= [Y_1(0) + Y_1(0.5) + Y_1(1) + Y_1(1.5) + Y_1(2) + Y_1(2.5) + Y_1(3) + Y_1(3.5)](0.5)$$

$$\approx 4.765$$

Figure 13.8(c) shows the right approximation of the area to be $S_R \approx 5.765$.

(b) To find the approximate area with Excel using the left-hand endpoints of rectangles with base width 0.5, we proceed as follows.

1. Enter "x" and the eight x-values of the left-hand endpoints of each rectangle in Column B, starting with 0.
2. Enter the formula for the function, $=$SQRT(B2), in C2 and fill down column C to get the function values that are the heights of the rectangles.
3. Enter the rectangle width, 0.5, in each cell of Column D.
4. Enter the formula for the area of each rectangle, $=$C2*D2, in E2 and fill down to get the area of each rectangle.
5. Enter "Total" in A10 and the formula $=$SUM(E2:E9) in E10 to get the approximate area, $S_L \approx 4.765$.

The following Excel output shows this S_L calculation. Note that S_R can be found by removing Row 2, adding a new row with $x = 4$, and proceeding as above.

(a)

(b)

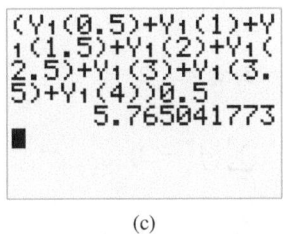

(c)

Figure 13.8

	A	B	C	D	E
1	Rectangle	x	y	Width	Area
2	1	0	0	0.5	0
3	2	0.5	0.707107	0.5	0.353553
4	3	1	1	0.5	0.5
5	4	1.5	1.224745	0.5	0.612372
6	5	2	1.414214	0.5	0.707107
7	6	2.5	1.581139	0.5	0.790569
8	7	3	1.732051	0.5	0.866025
9	8	3.5	1.870829	0.5	0.935414
10	Total				4.765042

CHECKPOINT
ANSWERS

1. (a), (c), and (d) are true. (b) False: $\dfrac{(b-a)}{n} = \dfrac{1}{100}$

2. (a) $f(x_i) = \dfrac{6i}{n} - \dfrac{4i^2}{n^2}$

    (b) $f(x_i)\dfrac{b-a}{n} = \dfrac{12i}{n^2} - \dfrac{8i^2}{n^3}$

    (c) $S_R = \dfrac{12}{n^2}\left[\dfrac{n(n+1)}{2}\right] - \dfrac{8}{n^3}\left[\dfrac{n(n+1)(2n+1)}{6}\right]$

    $= \dfrac{6(n+1)}{n} - \dfrac{4(n+1)(2n+1)}{3n^2}$

    (d) $A = \lim\limits_{n\to\infty}\sum\limits_{i=1}^{n} f(x_i)\dfrac{b-a}{n} = 6 - \dfrac{8}{3} = \dfrac{10}{3}$

EXERCISES 13.1

In Problems 1–4, approximate the area under each curve over the specified interval by using the indicated number of subintervals (or rectangles) and evaluating the function at the *right-hand* endpoints of the subintervals. (See Example 1.)

1. $f(x) = 4x - x^2$ from $x = 0$ to $x = 2$; 2 subintervals
2. $f(x) = x^3$ from $x = 0$ to $x = 3$; 3 subintervals
3. $f(x) = 9 - x^2$ from $x = 1$ to $x = 3$; 4 subintervals
4. $f(x) = x^2 + x + 1$ from $x = -1$ to $x = 1$;
    4 subintervals

In Problems 5–8, approximate the area under each curve by evaluating the function at the *left-hand* endpoints of the subintervals.

5. $f(x) = 4x - x^2$ from $x = 0$ to $x = 2$; 2 subintervals
6. $f(x) = x^3$ from $x = 0$ to $x = 3$; 3 subintervals
7. $f(x) = 9 - x^2$ from $x = 1$ to $x = 3$; 4 subintervals
8. $f(x) = x^2 + x + 1$ from $x = -1$ to $x = 1$;
    4 subintervals

When the area under $f(x) = x^2 + x$ from $x = 0$ to $x = 2$ is approximated, the formulas for the sum of n rectangles using *left-hand* endpoints and *right-hand* endpoints are

Left-hand endpoints: $S_L = \dfrac{14}{3} - \dfrac{6}{n} + \dfrac{4}{3n^2}$

Right-hand endpoints: $S_R = \dfrac{14n^2 + 18n + 4}{3n^2}$

Use these formulas to answer Problems 9–13.
9. Find $S_L(10)$ and $S_R(10)$.
10. Find $S_L(100)$ and $S_R(100)$.
11. Find $\lim\limits_{n\to\infty} S_L$ and $\lim\limits_{n\to\infty} S_R$.
12. Compare the right-hand and left-hand values by finding $S_R - S_L$ for $n = 10$, for $n = 100$, and as $n \to \infty$. (Use Problems 9–11.)
13. Because $f(x) = x^2 + x$ is increasing over the interval from $x = 0$ to $x = 2$, function values at the right-hand endpoints are maximum values for each subinterval

and function values at the left-hand endpoints are minimum values for each subinterval. How would the approximate area using $n = 10$ and *any* other point within each subinterval compare with $S_L(10)$ and $S_R(10)$? What would happen to the area result as $n \to \infty$ if any other point in each subinterval were used?

In Problems 14–19, find the value of each sum.

14. $\sum\limits_{k=1}^{3} x_k$, if $x_1 = 1, x_2 = 3, x_3 = -1, x_4 = 5$

15. $\sum\limits_{i=1}^{4} x_i$, if $x_1 = 3, x_2 = -1, x_3 = 3, x_4 = -2$

16. $\sum\limits_{i=3}^{5} (i^2 + 1)$ 17. $\sum\limits_{j=2}^{5} (j^2 - 3)$

18. $\sum\limits_{i=4}^{7} \left(\dfrac{i-3}{i^2}\right)$ 19. $\sum\limits_{j=0}^{4} (j^2 - 4j + 1)$

In Problems 20–25, use the sum formulas I–V to express each of the following without the summation symbol. In Problems 20–23, find the numerical value.

20. $\sum\limits_{k=1}^{50} 1$ 21. $\sum\limits_{j=1}^{60} 3$

22. $\sum\limits_{k=1}^{50} (6k^2 + 5)$ 23. $\sum\limits_{k=1}^{30} (k^2 + 4k)$

24. $\sum\limits_{i=1}^{n} \left(1 - \dfrac{i^2}{n^2}\right)\left(\dfrac{2}{n}\right)$ 25. $\sum\limits_{i=1}^{n} \left(1 - \dfrac{2i}{n} + \dfrac{i^2}{n^2}\right)\left(\dfrac{3}{n}\right)$

Use the function $y = 2x$ from $x = 0$ to $x = 1$ and n equal subintervals with the function evaluated at the *left-hand* endpoint of each subinterval for Problems 26 and 27.
26. What is the area of the
    (a) first rectangle?
    (b) second rectangle?
    (c) ith rectangle?

27. (a) Find a formula for the sum of the areas of the n rectangles. (Call this S.) Then find
    (b) $S(10)$.   (c) $S(100)$.
    (d) $S(1000)$.   (e) $\lim_{n \to \infty} S$.

28. How do your answers to Problems 27(a)–(e) compare with the corresponding calculations in the discussion (after Example 1) of the area under $y = 2x$ using *right-hand* endpoints?

29. For parts (a)–(e), use the function $y = x^2$ from $x = 0$ to $x = 1$ with n equal subintervals and the function evaluated at the *right-hand* endpoints.
    (a) Find a formula for the sum of the areas of the n rectangles. (Call this S.) Then find
    (b) $S(10)$.   (c) $S(100)$.
    (d) $S(1000)$.   (e) $\lim_{n \to \infty} S$.

30. How do your answers to Problems 29(a)–(e) compare with the corresponding calculations in Example 2?

31. Use rectangles to find the area between $y = x^2 - 6x + 8$ and the x-axis from $x = 0$ to $x = 2$. Divide the interval $[0, 2]$ into n equal subintervals so that each subinterval has length $2/n$.

32. Use rectangles to find the area between $y = 4x - x^2$ and the x-axis from $x = 0$ to $x = 4$. Divide the interval $[0, 4]$ into n equal subintervals so that each subinterval has length $4/n$.

APPLICATIONS

33. *Per capita health care expenses* The annual per capita out-of-pocket expenses (to the nearest dollar) for U.S. health care for selected years from 2013 and projected to 2021 are shown in the table and figure.
    (a) Use $n = 4$ equal subdivisions and left-hand endpoints to estimate the area under the graph from 2013 to 2021.
    (b) What does this area represent in terms of per capita out-of-pocket expenses for U.S. health care?

Year	Dollars
2013	1020
2015	1022
2017	1097
2019	1209
2021	1325

Source: U.S. Centers for Medicare and Medicaid Services

34. *Oil imports* Crude oil and petroleum products are imported continuously by the United States. The following table and figure show the net expenditures for U.S. oil imports for selected years (in billions of dollars per year) (*Source:* Energy Information Administration).
    (a) Use $n = 5$ equal subdivisions and left-hand endpoints to estimate the area under the graph from 2014 to 2024.
    (b) What does this area represent in terms of U.S. oil imports?

Year	Billions of Dollars
2014	219.5
2016	192.0
2018	191.0
2020	198.9
2022	214.5
2024	228.4

35. *Speed trials* The figure gives the time it takes a Porsche 911 to reach speeds from 0 mph to 100 mph, in increments of 10 mph, with a curve connecting them. The area under this curve from $t = 0$ seconds to $t = 14$ seconds represents the total amount of distance traveled over the 14-second period. Count the squares under the curve to estimate this distance. This car will travel 1/4 mile in 14 seconds, to a speed of 100.2 mph. Is your estimate close to this result? (Be careful with time units.)

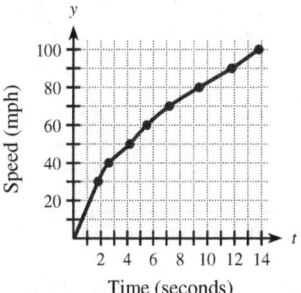

Source: Motor Trend

36. *Speed trials* The figure gives the time it takes a Mitsubishi Eclipse GSX to reach speeds from 0 mph to 100 mph, in increments of 10 mph, with a curve connecting them. The area under this curve from $t = 0$ seconds to $t = 21.1$ seconds represents the total amount of distance traveled over the 21.1-second period. Count the squares under the curve to estimate this distance. This car will travel 1/4 mile in 15.4 seconds, to a speed of 89.0 mph, so your estimate should be more than 1/4 mile. Is it? (Be careful with time units.)

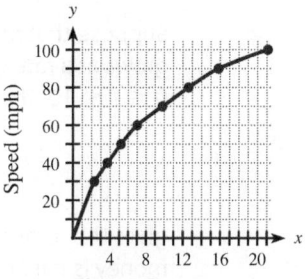

Source: Road & Track

37. *Pollution monitoring* Suppose the presence of phosphates in certain waste products dumped into a lake promotes the growth of algae. Rampant growth of algae affects the oxygen supply in the water, so an environmental group wants to estimate the area of algae growth. The group measures the length across the algae growth (see the figure) and obtains the data (in feet) in the table.

x	Length	x	Length
0	0	50	27
10	15	60	24
20	18	70	23
30	18	80	0
40	30		

Use 8 rectangles with bases of 10 feet and lengths measured at the left-hand endpoints to approximate the area of the algae growth.

38. *Drug levels in the blood* The manufacturer of a medicine wants to test how a new 300-mg capsule is released into the bloodstream. After a volunteer is given a capsule, blood samples are drawn every half hour, and the number of milligrams of the drug in the bloodstream is calculated. The results obtained are shown in the table.

Time t (hr)	$N(t)$ (mg)	Time t (hr)	$N(t)$ (mg)
0	0	2.0	178.3
0.5	247.3	2.5	113.9
1.0	270.0	3.0	56.2
1.5	236.4	3.5	19.3

Use 7 rectangles, each with height $N(t)$ at the left endpoint and with width 0.5 hr, to estimate the area under the graph representing these data. Divide this area by 3.5 hr to estimate the average drug level over this time period.

39. *Emissions* With U.S. Department of Energy data for selected years from 2000 and projected to 2030, sulphur dioxide emissions from electricity generation (in millions of short tons per year) can be modeled by

$$E(x) = 0.0112x^2 + 0.612x + 11.9$$

where x is the number of years past 2000. Use $n = 10$ equal subdivisions and right-hand endpoints to approximate (to the nearest unit) the area under the graph of $E(x)$ between $x = 15$ and $x = 25$. What does this area represent?

40. *Per capita income* The per capita disposable income (in dollars per year) in the United States for selected years from 2014 and projected to 2040 can be modeled by

$$I(t) = 0.5532t^2 + 738.5t + 34,430$$

where t is the number of years past 2010 (*Source*: U.S. Energy Information Administration). Use $n = 10$ equal subdivisions with right-hand endpoints to approximate (to the nearest 10 units) the area under the graph of $I(t)$ between $t = 8$ and $t = 13$. What does this area represent?

SECTION 13.2

The Definite Integral: The Fundamental Theorem of Calculus

OBJECTIVES

- To evaluate definite integrals using the Fundamental Theorem of Calculus
- To use definite integrals to find the area under a curve

APPLICATION PREVIEW

Suppose that money flows continuously into a slot machine at a casino and grows at a rate given by $A'(t) = 100e^{0.1t}$, where t is the time in hours and $0 \le t \le 10$. Then the definite integral

$$\int_0^{10} 100e^{0.1t}\, dt$$

gives the total amount of money that accumulates over the 10-hour period if no money is paid out. (See Example 6.)

(continued)

In the previous section, we used the sums of areas of rectangles to approximate the areas under curves. In this section, we will see how such sums are related to the definite integral and how to evaluate definite integrals. In addition, we will see how definite integrals can be used to solve several types of applied problems.

Riemann Sums and the Definite Integral

In the previous section, we saw that we could determine the area under a curve $y = f(x)$ over a closed interval $[a, b]$ by using equal subintervals and the function values at either the left-hand endpoints or the right-hand endpoints of the subintervals. In fact, we can use subintervals that are not of equal length, and we can use any point within each subinterval, denoted by x_i^*, to determine the height of each rectangle. For the ith rectangle (for any i), if we denote the width as Δx_i, then the height is $f(x_i^*)$ and the area is $f(x_i^*)\Delta x_i$. If $[a, b]$ is divided into n subintervals, the sum of the areas of the n rectangles is

$$S = \sum_{i=1}^{n} f(x_i^*)\Delta x_i$$

Such a sum is called a **Riemann sum** of f on $[a, b]$. Increasing the number of subintervals and making sure that every interval becomes smaller will in the long run improve the estimation. Thus for any subdivision of $[a, b]$ and any x_i^*, the exact area is given by

$$A = \lim_{\substack{\max \Delta x_i \to 0 \\ (n \to \infty)}} \sum_{i=1}^{n} f(x_i^*)\Delta x_i \quad \text{provided that this limit exists}$$

In addition to giving the exact area, this limit of the Riemann sum has other important applications and is called the **definite integral** of $f(x)$ over interval $[a, b]$.

Definite Integral

If f is a function on the interval $[a, b]$, then for any subdivision of $[a, b]$ and any choice of x_i^* in the ith subinterval, the **definite integral** of f from a to b is

$$\int_a^b f(x)dx = \lim_{\substack{\max \Delta x_i \to 0 \\ (n \to \infty)}} \sum_{i=1}^{n} f(x_i^*)\Delta x_i$$

If f is a continuous function and $\Delta x_i \to 0$ as $n \to \infty$, then the limit exists and we say that f is integrable on $[a, b]$.

Note that for some intervals, values of f may be negative. In this case, the product $f(x_i^*)\Delta x_i$ will be negative and can be thought of geometrically as a "signed area." (Remember that area is a positive number.) Thus a definite integral can be thought of geometrically as the sum of signed areas, just as a derivative can be thought of geometrically as the slope of a tangent line. In the case where $f(x)$ is positive for all x from a to b, the definite integral equals the area between the graph of $y = f(x)$ and the x-axis.

Fundamental Theorem of Calculus

The obvious question is how this definite integral is related to the indefinite integral (the antiderivative) discussed in Chapter 12. The connection between these two concepts is the most important result in calculus because it connects derivatives, indefinite integrals, and definite integrals.

To help see the connection, consider the marginal revenue function

$$R'(x) = 300 - 0.2x$$

and the revenue function which is the indefinite integral of the marginal function:

$$R(x) = \int (300 - 0.2x)\, dx = 300x - 0.1x^2$$

Figure 13.9 (a) on the next page shows the graph of $R(x)$.

Using this revenue function, we can find the revenue from the sale of 1000 units to be

$$R(1000) = 300(1000) - 0.1(1000)^2 = 200,000 \text{ dollars}$$

and the revenue from the sale of 500 units to be

$$R(500) = 300(500) - 0.1(500)^2 = 125,000 \text{ dollars}$$

Thus the additional revenue received from the sale of 500 units to 1000 units is

$$200,000 - 125,000 = 75,000 \text{ dollars}$$

If we used the definition of the definite integral (or geometry) to find the area under the graph of the marginal revenue function from $x = 500$ to $x = 1000$, we would find that the area is 75,000. [See Figure 13.9(b).] Note in Figure 13.9(b) that the shaded area is given by

$$\text{Area} = \text{Area from 500 to 1500} - \text{Area from 1000 to 1500}$$

Each of these regions is a triangle, and the area of a triangle is $\frac{1}{2}$(base)(height) so we have

$$\text{Area} = \tfrac{1}{2}(1000)(200) - \tfrac{1}{2}(500)(100) = 75,000$$

Because the area under $R'(x)$ is given by the definite integral, we can find this additional revenue when sales are increased from 500 to 1000 by evaluating

$$\int_{500}^{1000} (300 - 0.2x)\, dx$$

(a)

(b)

Figure 13.9

In general, the definite integral

$$\int_a^b f(x)\, dx$$

can be used to find the change in the function $F(x)$ when x changes from a to b, where $f(x)$ is the derivative of $F(x)$. This result is the **Fundamental Theorem of Calculus.**

Fundamental Theorem of Calculus

Let f be a continuous function on the closed interval $[a, b]$; then the definite integral of f exists on this interval, and

$$\int_a^b f(x)\, dx = F(b) - F(a)$$

where F is any function such that $F'(x) = f(x)$ for all x in $[a, b]$.

Stated differently, this theorem says that if the function F is an indefinite integral of a function f that is continuous on the interval $[a, b]$, then

$$\int_a^b f(x)\, dx = F(b) - F(a)$$

Thus we apply the Fundamental Theorem of Calculus by using the following two steps.

1. Integration of $f(x)$: $\displaystyle\int_a^b f(x)\, dx = F(x)\, \Big|_a^b$

2. Evaluation of $F(x)$: $\displaystyle F(x)\, \Big|_a^b = F(b) - F(a)$

EXAMPLE 1   **Definite Integral**

Evaluate $\displaystyle\int_2^4 (x^3 + 4)\, dx$.

Solution

1. $\displaystyle\int_2^4 (x^3 + 4)\, dx = \frac{x^4}{4} + 4x + C\, \Big|_2^4$

2. $\displaystyle\qquad\qquad = \left[\frac{(4)^4}{4} + 4(4) + C \right] - \left[\frac{(2)^4}{4} + 4(2) + C \right]$

$\qquad\qquad = (64 + 16 + C) - (4 + 8 + C) = 68$

Notice that the Cs subtract out because C represents the same constant in each expression. ■

Note that the Fundamental Theorem states that F can be *any* indefinite integral of f, so we need not add the constant of integration to the integral.

EXAMPLE 2   **Fundamental Theorem**

Evaluate $\displaystyle\int_1^3 (3x^2 + 6x)\, dx$.

Solution

$$\int_1^3 (3x^2 + 6x)\, dx = x^3 + 3x^2\, \Big|_1^3$$
$$= (3^3 + 3 \cdot 3^2) - (1^3 + 3 \cdot 1^2)$$
$$= 54 - 4 = 50$$

■

Properties   The properties of definite integrals given next follow from properties of summations.

1. $\displaystyle\int_a^b [f(x) \pm g(x)]\, dx = \int_a^b f(x)\, dx \pm \int_a^b g(x)\, dx$

2. $\displaystyle\int_a^b kf(x)\, dx = k \int_a^b f(x)\, dx$,   where k is a constant

The following example uses both of these properties.

EXAMPLE 3   **Definite Integral**

Evaluate $\displaystyle\int_3^5 (\sqrt{x^2 - 9} + 2)x\, dx$.

Solution

$$\int_3^5 (\sqrt{x^2 - 9} + 2)x\, dx = \int_3^5 \sqrt{x^2 - 9}(x\, dx) + \int_3^5 2x\, dx$$
$$= \frac{1}{2}\int_3^5 (x^2 - 9)^{1/2}(2x\, dx) + \int_3^5 2x\, dx$$
$$= \frac{1}{2}\left[\frac{2}{3}(x^2 - 9)^{3/2} \right]_3^5 + x^2\, \Big|_3^5$$

$$= \frac{1}{3}[(16)^{3/2} - (0)^{3/2}] + (25 - 9)$$

$$= \frac{64}{3} + 16 = \frac{64}{3} + \frac{48}{3} = \frac{112}{3}$$

In the integral $\int_a^b f(x)\, dx$, we call a the *lower limit* and b the *upper limit* of integration. Although we developed the definite integral with the assumption that the lower limit was less than the upper limit, the following properties permit us to evaluate the definite integral even when that is not the case.

3. $\displaystyle\int_a^a f(x)\, dx = 0$

4. If f is integrable on $[a, b]$, then

$$\int_b^a f(x)\, dx = -\int_a^b f(x)\, dx$$

The following examples illustrate these properties.

EXAMPLE 4 Properties of Definite Integrals

(a) Evaluate $\displaystyle\int_4^4 x^2\, dx$. (b) Compare $\displaystyle\int_2^4 3x^2\, dx$ and $\displaystyle\int_4^2 3x^2\, dx$.

Solution

(a) $\displaystyle\int_4^4 x^2\, dx = \left.\frac{x^3}{3}\right|_4^4 = \frac{4^3}{3} - \frac{4^3}{3} = 0$

This illustrates Property 3.

(b) $\displaystyle\int_2^4 3x^2\, dx = \left. x^3 \right|_2^4 = 4^3 - 2^3 = 56$ and $\displaystyle\int_4^2 3x^2\, dx = \left. x^3 \right|_4^2 = 2^3 - 4^3 = -56$

This illustrates Property 4.

Another property of definite integrals is called the additive property.

5. If f is continuous on some interval containing a, b, and c,* then

$$\int_a^c f(x)\, dx + \int_c^b f(x)\, dx = \int_a^b f(x)\, dx$$

EXAMPLE 5 Properties of Definite Integrals

Show that $\displaystyle\int_2^3 4x\, dx + \int_3^5 4x\, dx = \int_2^5 4x\, dx$.

Solution

$$\int_2^3 4x\, dx = \left. 2x^2 \right|_2^3 = 18 - 8 = 10 \quad\text{and}\quad \int_3^5 4x\, dx = \left. 2x^2 \right|_3^5 = 50 - 18 = 32$$

Thus $\displaystyle\int_2^5 4x\, dx = \left. 2x^2 \right|_2^5 = 50 - 8 = 42 = \int_2^3 4x\, dx + \int_3^5 4x\, dx$

The Definite Integral and Areas We now return to area problems to see the relationship between the definite integral and the area under a curve. By applying the formula for the area of a triangle or by using rectangles and the limit definition of area, the area under the curve (line) $y = x$ from $x = 0$

---

*Note that c need not be between a and b.

to $x = 1$ can be shown to be $\frac{1}{2}$. [See Figure 13.10(a).] Using the definite integral to find the area gives

$$A = \int_0^1 x \, dx = \left.\frac{x^2}{2}\right|_0^1 = \frac{1}{2} - 0 = \frac{1}{2}$$

In the previous section, we used rectangles to find that the area under $y = x^2$ from $x = 0$ to $x = 1$ was $\frac{1}{3}$. [See Figure 13.10(b).] Using the definite integral, we get

$$A = \int_0^1 x^2 \, dx = \left.\frac{x^3}{3}\right|_0^1 = \frac{1}{3} - 0 = \frac{1}{3}$$

which agrees with the answer obtained previously.

However, not every definite integral represents the area between the curve and the x-axis over an interval. For example,

$$\int_0^2 (x - 2) \, dx = \left.\frac{x^2}{2} - 2x\right|_0^2 = (2 - 4) - (0) = -2$$

This would indicate that the area between the curve and the x-axis is negative, but area must be positive. A look at the graph of $y = x - 2$ [see Figure 13.10(c)] shows us what is happening.

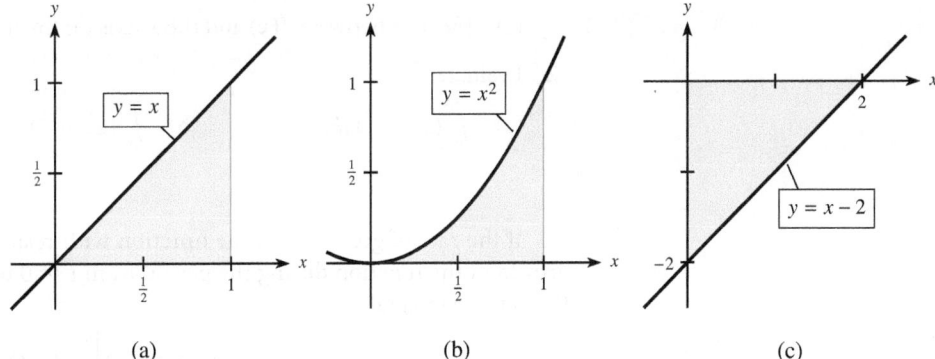

(a)	(b)	(c)

Figure 13.10

The region bounded by $y = x - 2$ and the x-axis between $x = 0$ and $x = 2$ is a triangle whose base is 2 and whose height is 2, so its area is $\frac{1}{2}bh = \frac{1}{2}(2)(2) = 2$. The integral has value -2 because $y = x - 2$ lies below the x-axis from $x = 0$ to $x = 2$, and the function values over the interval $[0, 2]$ are negative. Thus the value of the definite integral over *this* interval does not represent the area between the curve and the x-axis but, rather, represents the "signed" area as we mentioned previously.

In general, the definite integral will give the **area under the curve** and above the x-axis only when $f(x) \geq 0$ for all x in $[a, b]$.

Area Under a Curve

If f is a continuous function on $[a, b]$ and $f(x) \geq 0$ on $[a, b]$, then the exact area between $y = f(x)$ and the x-axis from $x = a$ to $x = b$ is given by

$$\text{Area (shaded)} = \int_a^b f(x) \, dx$$

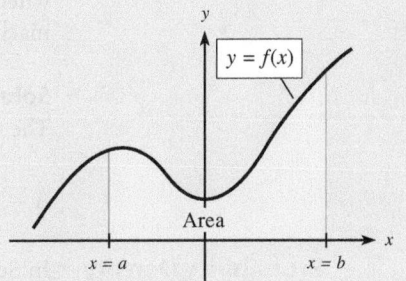

Note also that if $f(x) \leq 0$ for all x in $[a, b]$, then

$$\int_a^b f(x) \, dx = -\text{Area (between } f(x) \text{ and the } x\text{-axis)}$$

Calculator Note The approximate area under the graph of $y = f(x)$ and above the x-axis can be found with a graphing calculator. After we enter the function in the Y= menu and graph it, we choose 7: $\int f(x)dx$ under the CALC menu, press ENTER, and select the lower and upper x-values for the interval on which we seek the area. Figure 13.11 shows the steps in finding the area under the graph of $f(x) = x^2 + 1$ from $x = 0$ to $x = 3$ after the function is graphed. See Appendix A, Section 13.2, for details. ∎

Figure 13.11

CHECKPOINT

1. True or false:
   (a) For any integral, we can omit the constant of integration (the $+C$).

   (b) $-\int_{-1}^{3} f(x)\,dx = \int_{3}^{-1} f(x)\,dx$, if f is integrable on $[-1, 3]$.

   (c) The area between $f(x)$ and the x-axis on the interval $[a, b]$ is given by $\int_{a}^{b} f(x)\,dx$.

2. Evaluate:
   (a) $\int_{0}^{3} (x^2 + 1)\,dx$ (b) $\int_{0}^{3} (x^2 + 1)^4 x\,dx$

If the rate of growth of some function with respect to time t is $f'(t)$, then the total growth of the function during the period from $t = 0$ to $t = k$ can be found by evaluating the definite integral

$$\int_{0}^{k} f'(t)\,dt = f(t)\Big|_{0}^{k} = f(k) - f(0)$$

For nonnegative rates of growth, this definite integral (and thus growth) is the same as the area under the graph of $f'(t)$ from $t = 0$ to $t = k$.

EXAMPLE 6   **Income Stream** | APPLICATION PREVIEW |

Suppose that money flows continuously into a slot machine at a casino and grows at a rate given by

$$A'(t) = 100e^{0.1t}$$

where t is time in hours and $0 \le t \le 10$. Find the total amount that accumulates in the machine during the 10-hour period if no money is paid out.

Solution
The total dollar amount is given by

$$A = \int_{0}^{10} 100e^{0.1t}\,dt = \frac{100}{0.1}\int_{0}^{10} e^{0.1t}(0.1)\,dt = 1000e^{0.1t}\Big|_{0}^{10} = 1000e - 1000 \approx 1718.28 \; \blacksquare$$

Probability Density Functions   In Section 8.4, "Normal Probability Distribution," we stated that the total area under the normal curve is 1 and that the area under the curve from value x_1 to value x_2 represents the probability that a score chosen at random will lie between x_1 and x_2.

The normal distribution is an example of a **continuous probability distribution** because the values of the random variable are considered over intervals rather than at discrete values. The statements above relating probability and area under the graph apply to other continuous probability distributions determined by **probability density functions (pdf)**. In Section 13.7, we will formally define probability density functions for continuous random variables (and verify that the function in the next example is a pdf). For now, we note that if x is a continuous random variable with probability density function $f(x)$, then the probability that x is between a and b is

$$\Pr(a \leq x \leq b) = \int_a^b f(x)\, dx$$

EXAMPLE 7 Product Life

Suppose the probability density function for the life of a computer component is $f(x) = 0.10e^{-0.10x}$, where $x \geq 0$ is the number of years the component is in use.
(a) Find the probability that the component will last between 3 and 5 years.
(b) Find the conditional probability that the component lasts at least 3 years given that it lasts no more than 5 years.

Solution

(a) The probability that the component will last between 3 and 5 years is the area under the graph of the function between $x = 3$ and $x = 5$. The probability is given by

$$\Pr(3 \leq x \leq 5) = \int_3^5 0.10e^{-0.10x}\, dx = -e^{-0.10x}\Big|_3^5 = -e^{-0.5} + e^{-0.3}$$

$$\approx -0.6065 + 0.7408 = 0.1343$$

(b) In Section 7.3, we defined the conditional probability of an event A, given event B, denoted $\Pr(A\,|\,B)$, as follows:

$$\Pr(A\,|\,B) = \frac{\Pr(A \text{ and } B)}{\Pr(B)}$$

Thus we seek

$$\Pr(x \geq 3\,|\,x \leq 5) = \frac{\Pr(x \geq 3 \text{ and } x \leq 5)}{\Pr(x \leq 5)} = \frac{\Pr(3 \leq x \leq 5)}{\Pr(0 \leq x \leq 5)}$$

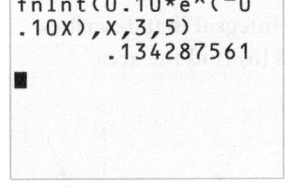

```
fnInt(0.10*e^(-0
.10X),X,3,5)
          .134287561
■
```

Figure 13.12

In part (a), we found the value of the numerator to be 0.1343. The value of the denominator is

$$\Pr(0 \leq x \leq 5) = \int_0^5 0.10e^{-0.10x}\, dx = -e^{-0.10x}\Big|_0^5 = -e^{-0.5} + 1 \approx 0.3935$$

Hence $\Pr(x \geq 3\,|\,x \leq 5) = \dfrac{0.1343}{0.3935} \approx 0.3413$.

Calculator Note

Using fnInt($f(x)$, x, a, b) under MATH on a graphing calculator gives the definite integral of the function $y = f(x)$ from $x = a$ to $x = b$. This feature can be used to evaluate definite integrals directly or to check those done with the Fundamental Theorem of Calculus. Figure 13.12 shows the numerical integration feature applied to the integral in Example 7(a). Note that when this answer is rounded to 4 decimal places, the results agree. See Appendix A, Section 13.2, for details. ■

CHECKPOINT ANSWERS

1. (a) False; this is true *only* for definite integrals.
   (b) True   (c) False; this is true only if $f(x) \geq 0$ on $[a, b]$

2. (a) $\displaystyle\int_0^3 (x^2 + 1)\, dx = \frac{x^3}{3} + x\Big|_0^3 = 12$

   (b) $\displaystyle\int_0^3 (x^2 + 1)^4 x\, dx = \frac{1}{2} \cdot \frac{(x^2 + 1)^5}{5}\Big|_0^3 = \frac{1}{10}(10^5 - 1) = 9999.9$

EXERCISES 13.2

Evaluate the definite integrals in Problems 1–32.

1. $\displaystyle\int_0^3 4x \, dx$

2. $\displaystyle\int_0^1 8x \, dx$

3. $\displaystyle\int_2^4 dx$

4. $\displaystyle\int_1^5 2 \, dy$

5. $\displaystyle\int_2^4 x^3 \, dx$

6. $\displaystyle\int_0^5 x^2 \, dx$

7. $\displaystyle\int_1^3 36z^{-3} \, dz$

8. $\displaystyle\int_{-2}^{-1} 24w^{-2} \, dw$

9. $\displaystyle\int_1^4 (10 - 4x) \, dx$

10. $\displaystyle\int_{-1}^4 (6x - 9) \, dx$

11. $\displaystyle\int_2^4 (4x^3 - 6x^2 - 5x) \, dx$

12. $\displaystyle\int_0^2 (x^4 - 5x^3 + 2x) \, dx$

13. $\displaystyle\int_0^5 4\sqrt[3]{x^2} \, dx$

14. $\displaystyle\int_2^4 3\sqrt{x} \, dx$

15. $\displaystyle\int_1^3 \frac{3}{y^2} \, dy$

16. $\displaystyle\int_1^2 \frac{5}{z^3} \, dz$

17. $\displaystyle\int_3^4 (x - 4)^9 \, dx$

18. $\displaystyle\int_{-1}^0 (x + 2)^{13} \, dx$

19. $\displaystyle\int_2^4 (x^2 + 2)^3 x \, dx$

20. $\displaystyle\int_0^1 5x^2 (4x^3 - 2)^4 \, dx$

21. $\displaystyle\int_{-1}^2 (x^3 - 3x^2)^3 (x^2 - 2x) \, dx$

22. $\displaystyle\int_0^3 (2x - x^2)^4 (1 - x) \, dx$

23. $\displaystyle\int_{-2}^2 15x^3 (x^4 - 6)^6 \, dx$

24. $\displaystyle\int_0^4 (3x^2 - 2)^4 x \, dx$

25. $\displaystyle\int_0^4 \sqrt{4x + 9} \, dx$

26. $\displaystyle\int_0^2 \sqrt[3]{2x^3 - 8} \, x^2 \, dx$

27. $\displaystyle\int_0^1 e^{3x} \, dx$

28. $\displaystyle\int_0^2 e^{4x-3} \, dx$

29. $\displaystyle\int_1^e \frac{4}{z} \, dz$

30. $\displaystyle\int_1^{5e} 3y^{-1} \, dy$

31. $\displaystyle\int_0^2 8x^2 e^{-x^3} \, dx$

32. $\displaystyle\int_0^1 \frac{3x^3 \, dx}{4x^4 + 9}$

In Problems 33–36, evaluate each integral (a) with the Fundamental Theorem of Calculus and (b) with a graphing calculator (as a check).

33. $\displaystyle\int_3^6 \frac{x}{3x^2 + 4} \, dx$

34. $\displaystyle\int_0^2 \frac{x}{x^2 + 4} \, dx$

35. $\displaystyle\int_1^2 \frac{x^2 + 3}{x} \, dx$

36. $\displaystyle\int_1^4 \frac{4\sqrt{x} + 5}{\sqrt{x}} \, dx$

37. In the figures, which of the shaded regions (A, B, C, or D) has the area given by

  (a) $\displaystyle\int_a^b f(x) \, dx$?   (b) $-\displaystyle\int_a^b f(x) \, dx$?

A

B

C

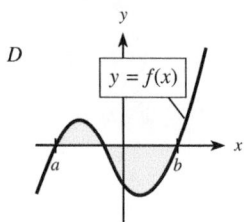

D

38. For which of the following functions $f(x)$ does

$$\int_0^2 f(x) \, dx$$

give the area between the graph of $f(x)$ and the x-axis from $x = 0$ to $x = 2$?

  (a) $f(x) = x^2 + 1$ (b) $f(x) = -x^2$

  (c) $f(x) = x - 1$

In Problems 39–42, (a) write the integral that describes the area of the shaded region and (b) find the area.

39.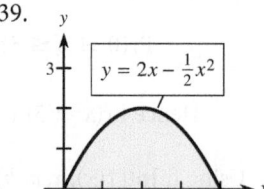

$y = 2x - \frac{1}{2}x^2$

40.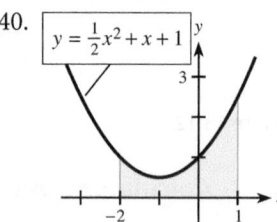

$y = \frac{1}{2}x^2 + x + 1$

41.

$y = x^3 + 1$

42.

$y = x^2 - x^3$

43. Find the area between the curve $y = -x^2 + 3x - 2$ and the x-axis from $x = 1$ to $x = 2$.

44. Find the area between the curve $y = x^2 + 3x + 2$ and the x-axis from $x = -1$ to $x = 3$.
45. Find the area between the curve $y = xe^{x^2}$ and the x-axis from $x = 1$ to $x = 3$.
46. Find the area between the curve $y = e^{-x}$ and the x-axis from $x = -1$ to $x = 1$.

In Problems 47 and 48, use the figures to decide which of $\int_0^a f(x)\, dx$ or $\int_0^a g(x)\, dx$ is larger or if they are equal. Explain your choices.

47.

48.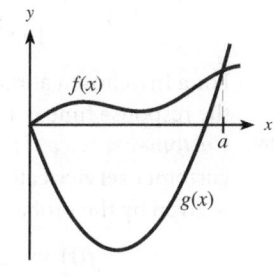

In Problems 49–54, use properties of definite integrals.

49. How does $\int_{-1}^{-3} x\sqrt{x^2 + 1}\, dx$ compare with

$$\int_{-3}^{-1} x\sqrt{x^2 + 1}\, dx?$$

50. If $\int_{-1}^{0} x^3\, dx = -\frac{1}{4}$ and $\int_{0}^{1} x^3\, dx = \frac{1}{4}$, what does $\int_{-1}^{1} x^3\, dx$ equal?

51. If $\int_{1}^{2}(2x - x^2)\, dx = \frac{2}{3}$ and $\int_{2}^{4}(2x - x^2)\, dx = -\frac{20}{3}$,

what does $\int_{1}^{4}(x^2 - 2x)\, dx$ equal?

52. If $\int_{1}^{2}(2x - x^2)\, dx = \frac{2}{3}$, what does $\int_{1}^{2} 6(2x - x^2)\, dx$ equal?

53. Evaluate $\int_{4}^{4}\sqrt{x^2 - 2}\, dx$.

54. Evaluate $\int_{2}^{2}(x^3 + 4x)^{-6}\, dx$.

APPLICATIONS

55. *Depreciation* The rate of depreciation of a building is given by $D'(t) = 3000(20 - t)$ dollars per year, $0 \le t \le 20$; see the following figure.
    (a) Use the graph to find the total depreciation of the building over the first 10 years ($t = 0$ to $t = 10$).
    (b) Use a definite integral to find the total depreciation over the first 10 years.

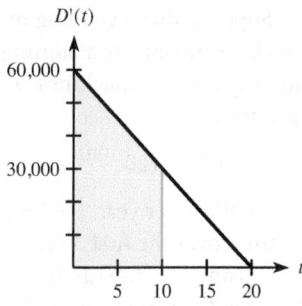

56. *Depreciation* The rate of depreciation of a building is given by $D'(t) = 3000(20 - t)$ dollars per year, $0 \le t \le 20$; see the figure in Problem 55.
    (a) Use the graph to find the total depreciation of the building over the first 20 years.
    (b) Use a definite integral to find the total depreciation over the first 20 years.
    (c) Use the graph to find the total depreciation between 10 years and 20 years and check it with a definite integral.

57. *Sales and advertising* A store finds that its sales revenue changes at a rate given by

$$S'(t) = -30t^2 + 360t \quad \text{dollars per day}$$

where t is the number of days after an advertising campaign ends and $0 \le t \le 30$.
    (a) Find the total sales for the first week after the campaign ends ($t = 0$ to $t = 7$).
    (b) Find the total sales for the second week after the campaign ends ($t = 7$ to $t = 14$).

58. *Health care costs* The U.S. total annual health care costs (actual and projected, in billions of dollars) for selected years are given in the table. These costs can be modeled by

$$C(t) = 0.32t^3 - 7.7t^2 + 170t + 1300$$

where $C(t)$ is in billions of dollars per year and t is the number of years past 2000. Use a definite integral and this model to find the total U.S. health care costs over the period 2010–2020.

Year	Cost	Year	Cost
2003	1778	2015	3244
2006	2167	2018	3785
2009	2506	2021	4543
2012	2817	2024	5425

Source: U.S. Department of Health and Human Services

59. *Total income* The income from an oil change service chain can be considered as flowing continuously at an annual rate given by

$$f(t) = 10,000e^{0.02t} \quad \text{(dollars/year)}$$

Find the total income for this chain over the first 2 years (from $t = 0$ to $t = 2$).

60. *Total income* Suppose that a vending machine service company models its income by assuming that money flows continuously into the machines, with the annual rate of flow given by

$$f(t) = 120e^{0.01t}$$

in thousands of dollars per year. Find the total income from the machines over the first 3 years.

61. *CO_2 emissions* Using U.S. Energy Information Administration data from 2010 and projected to 2030, the carbon dioxide emissions from biomass energy combustion (in millions of metric tons per year) can be modeled by

$$C(t) = 19.12t + 319.0$$

where t is the number of years past 2010. Evaluate $\int_0^{10} C(t)\, dt$ and tell what it represents.

62. *Per capita heath expenses* The annual per capita share of U.S. total expenditures for heath care (in dollars per year) for selected years from 2002 and projected to 2024 can be modeled by

$$H(t) = 5330\,e^{0.0442t}$$

where t is the number of years after 2000 (*Source:* U.S. Centers for Medicare and Medicaid Services). Assuming that the model remains valid, evaluate

$\int_{15}^{25} H(t)\, dt$ and tell what it represents.

Velocity of blood **In Problems 63 and 64, the velocity of blood through a vessel is given by $v = K(R^2 - r^2)$, where K is a constant, R is the (constant) radius of the vessel, and r is the distance of the particular corpuscle from the center of the vessel. The rate of flow can be found by measuring the volume of blood that flows past a point in a given time period. This volume, V, is given by**

$$V = \int_0^R v(2\pi r\, dr)$$

63. If $R = 0.30$ cm and $v = (0.30 - 3.33r^2)$ cm/s, find the volume.

64. Develop a general formula for V by evaluating

$$V = \int_0^R v(2\pi r\, dr)$$

using $v = K(R^2 - r^2)$.

Production **In Problems 65 and 66, the rate of production of a new line of products is given by**

$$\frac{dx}{dt} = 200\left[1 + \frac{400}{(t + 40)^2}\right]$$

where x is the number of items produced and t is the number of weeks the products have been in production.

65. How many units were produced in the first 5 weeks?

66. How many units were produced in the sixth week?

67. *Testing* The time t (in minutes) needed to read an article appearing on a foreign-language placement test is given by the probability density function

$$f(t) = 0.012t^2 - 0.0012t^3, \qquad 0 \le t \le 10$$

For a test taker chosen at random, find the probability that this person takes 8 minutes or more to read the article.

68. *Response time* In a small city, the response time t (in minutes) of the fire company is given by the probability density function

$$f(t) = \frac{60t^2 - 4t^3}{16,875}, \qquad 0 \le t \le 15$$

For a fire chosen at random, find the probability that the response time is 10 minutes or less.

69. *Customer service* The duration t (in minutes) of customer service calls received by a certain company is given by the probability density function

$$f(t) = 0.3e^{-0.3t}, \qquad t \ge 0$$

Find the probability that a call selected at random lasts
(a) 3 minutes or less.   (b) between 5 and 10 minutes.
(c) 3 minutes or less given that it lasts 5 minutes or less.

70. *Product life* The useful life of a car battery t (in years) is given by the probability density function

$$f(t) = 0.2e^{-0.2t}, \qquad t \ge 0$$

Find the probability that a battery chosen at random lasts
(a) 2 years or less.   (b) between 4 and 6 years.
(c) more than 4 years given that it lasts less than 6 years.

71. *Testing* The length of time for students to complete a 1-hour timed standardized mathematics test has probability density function

$$f(t) = 1.5t^2 + t, \qquad 0 \le t \le 1$$

where t is the time in hours. Find the probability that the time it takes a randomly selected student to complete the test is
(a) more than 45 minutes.
(b) more than 30 minutes given that it is less than 45 minutes.

72. *Psychology* In a study of intelligence, the time (in seconds) for a laboratory animal to reach a reward in a maze was found to have probability density function

$$f(t) = \frac{10}{t^2}, \qquad t \ge 10$$

where 10 seconds is the minimum time to traverse the maze. Find the probability that an animal chosen at random takes
(a) between 15 and 30 seconds.
(b) more than 15 seconds given that it took less than 30 seconds.

73. *Modeling Gasoline usage* In the United States, gasoline for motor vehicles is used continuously, and that usage,

in billions of gallons per year, is shown in the table for selected years from 2014 and projected to 2024.

(a) Find a quadratic function that models these data, with t as the number of years past 2014. Report the model as $G(t)$ with 3 significant digits.

(b) Evaluate $\int_0^{10} G(t)\,dt$ and tell what it represents.

Gasoline usage (billions of gallons)

Year	2014	2016	2018	2020	2022	2024
Usage	132.8	133.5	130.4	126.1	121.2	116.3

Source: U.S. Department of Energy

74. **Modeling *SRT Viper acceleration*** Table 13.1(a) shows the time in seconds an SRT Viper requires to reach various speeds up to 100 mph. Table 13.1(b) shows the same data, but with speeds in miles per second.

(a) Fit a power model to the data in Table 13.1(b). Report the model with 3 significant digits.

(b) Use a definite integral from 0 to 9.2 of the function you found in part (a) to find the distance traveled by the Viper as it went from 0 mph to 100 mph in 9.2 seconds.

TABLE 13.1

(a)		(b)	
Time (seconds)	**Speed (mph)**	**Time (seconds)**	**Speed (mi/s)**
1.7	30	1.7	0.00833
2.4	40	2.4	0.01111
3.2	50	3.2	0.01389
4.1	60	4.1	0.01667
5.8	70	5.8	0.01944
6.2	80	6.2	0.02222
7.8	90	7.8	0.02500
9.2	100	9.2	0.02778

Source: Motor Trend

SECTION 13.3 Area Between Two Curves

OBJECTIVES

- To find the area between two curves
- To find the average value of a function

APPLICATION PREVIEW

In economics, the **Lorenz curve** is used to represent the inequality of income distribution among different groups in the population of a country. The curve is constructed by plotting the cumulative percent of families at or below a given income level and the cumulative percent of total personal income received by these families. For example, the following table shows the coordinates of some points on the Lorenz curve $y = L(x)$ that divide the income (for the United States in 2015) into 5 equal income levels (quintiles). The point (0.40, 0.113) is on the Lorenz curve because the families with incomes in the bottom 40% of the country received 11.3% of the total income in 2015. The graph of the Lorenz curve $y = L(x)$ is shown in Figure 13.13.

Figure 13.13

U.S. Income Distribution for 2015 (Points on the Lorenz Curve)

x, Cumulative Proportion of Families below Income Level	$y = L(x)$, Cumulative Proportion of Total Income
0	0
0.20	0.031
0.40	0.113
0.60	0.256
0.80	0.488
1	1

Source: U.S. Bureau of the Census

(continued)

Equality of income would result if each family received an equal proportion of the total income, so that the bottom 20% would receive 20% of the total income, the bottom 40% would receive 40%, and so on. The Lorenz curve representing this would have the equation $y = x$.

The inequality of income distribution is measured by the Gini coefficient of income, which measures how far the Lorenz curve falls below $y = x$. It is defined as

$$\frac{\text{Area between } y = x \text{ and } y = L(x)}{\text{Area below } y = x}$$

Because the area of the triangle below $y = x$ and above the x-axis from $x = 0$ to $x = 1$ is $1/2$, the Gini coefficient of income is

$$\frac{\text{Area between } y = x \text{ and } y = L(x)}{1/2} = 2 \cdot [\text{area between } y = x \text{ and } y = L(x)]$$

In this section, we will use the definite integral to find the area between two curves. We will use the area between two curves to find the Gini coefficient of income (see Example 4) and to find average cost, average revenue, average profit, and average inventory.

Area Between Two Curves

We have used the definite integral to find the area of the region between a curve and the x-axis over an interval where the curve lies above the x-axis. We can easily extend this technique to finding the area between two curves over an interval.

Suppose that the graphs of both $y = f(x)$ and $y = g(x)$ lie above the x-axis and that the graph of $y = f(x)$ lies above $y = g(x)$ throughout the interval from $x = a$ to $x = b$; that is, $f(x) \geq g(x)$ on $[a, b]$. (See Figure 13.14.)

Then Figures 13.15(a) and 13.15(b) show the areas under $y = f(x)$ and $y = g(x)$. Figure 13.15(c) shows how the difference of these two areas can be used to find the area of the region between the graphs of $y = f(x)$ and $y = g(x)$. That is,

Figure 13.14

$$\text{Area between the curves} = \int_a^b f(x)\, dx - \int_a^b g(x)\, dx$$

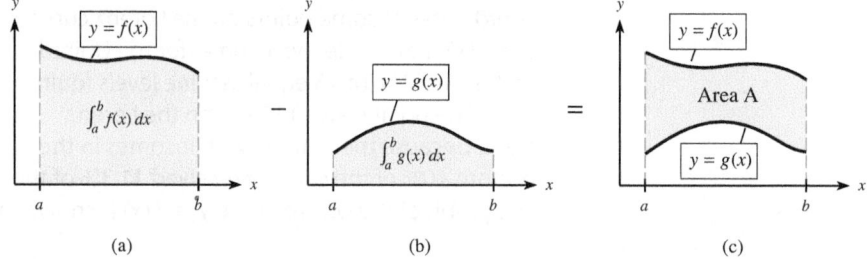

Figure 13.15   (a)   (b)   (c)

Although Figure 13.15(c) shows the graphs of both $y = f(x)$ and $y = g(x)$ lying above the x-axis, this difference of their integrals will always give the area between their graphs if both functions are continuous and if $f(x) \geq g(x)$ on the interval $[a, b]$. Using the fact that

$$\int_a^b f(x)\, dx - \int_a^b g(x)\, dx = \int_a^b [f(x) - g(x)]\, dx$$

we have the following result for the **area between two curves.**

Area Between Two Curves

If f and g are continuous functions on $[a, b]$ and if $f(x) \geq g(x)$ on $[a, b]$, then the area of the region bounded by $y = f(x)$, $y = g(x)$, $x = a$, and $x = b$ is

$$A = \int_a^b [f(x) - g(x)]\, dx$$

EXAMPLE 1   Area Between Two Curves

Find the area of the region bounded by $y = x^2 + 4$, $y = x$, $x = 0$, and $x = 3$.

Solution

We first sketch the graphs of the functions on the same set of axes. The graph of the region is shown in Figure 13.16. Because $y = x^2 + 4$ lies above $y = x$ in the interval from $x = 0$ to $x = 3$, the area is

$$A = \int_0^3 (\text{top curve} - \text{bottom curve})\, dx$$

$$A = \int_0^3 [(x^2 + 4) - x]\, dx = \frac{x^3}{3} + 4x - \frac{x^2}{2}\Big|_0^3$$

$$= \left(9 + 12 - \frac{9}{2}\right) - (0 + 0 - 0) = 16\tfrac{1}{2} \text{ square units}$$

Figure 13.16

We are sometimes asked to find the area enclosed by two curves. In this case, we find the points of intersection of the curves to determine a and b.

EXAMPLE 2   Area Enclosed by Two Curves

Find the area enclosed by $y = x^2$ and $y = 2x + 3$.

Solution

We first find a and b by finding the x-coordinates of the points of intersection of the graphs. Setting the y-values equal gives

$$x^2 = 2x + 3$$
$$x^2 - 2x - 3 = 0$$
$$(x - 3)(x + 1) = 0$$
$$x = 3, \quad x = -1$$

Figure 13.17

Thus with $a = -1$ and $b = 3$, we sketch the graphs of these functions on the same set of axes. Because the graphs do not intersect on the interval $(-1, 3)$, we can determine which function is larger on this interval by evaluating $2x + 3$ and x^2 at any value c where $-1 < c < 3$. Figure 13.17 shows the region between the graphs, with $2x + 3 \geq x^2$ from $x = -1$ to $x = 3$. The area of the enclosed region is

$$A = \int_{-1}^3 [(2x + 3) - x^2]\, dx = x^2 + 3x - \frac{x^3}{3}\Big|_{-1}^3$$

$$= (9 + 9 - 9) - \left(1 - 3 + \frac{1}{3}\right) = 10\tfrac{2}{3} \text{ square units}$$

Some graphs enclose two or more regions because they have more than two points of intersection.

EXAMPLE 3   A Region with Two Sections

Find the area of the region enclosed by the graphs of

$$y = f(x) = x^3 - x^2 \quad \text{and} \quad y = g(x) = 2x.$$

Solution

To find the points of intersection of the graphs, we solve $f(x) = g(x)$, or $x^3 - x^2 = 2x$.

$$x^3 - x^2 - 2x = 0$$
$$x(x - 2)(x + 1) = 0$$
$$x = 0, x = 2, x = -1$$

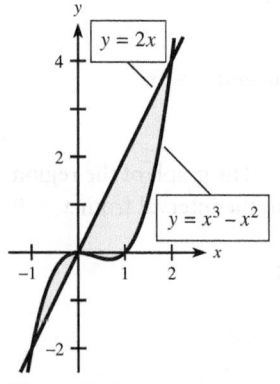

Figure 13.18

Figure 13.18 shows the graphs of these functions between $x = -1$ and $x = 2$. We see that for any x-value in the interval $(-1, 0)$, $f(x) \geq g(x)$, so $f(x) \geq g(x)$ for the region enclosed by the curves from $x = -1$ to $x = 0$. But evaluating the functions for any x-value in the interval $(0, 2)$ shows that $f(x) \leq g(x)$ for the region enclosed by the curves from $x = 0$ to $x = 2$.

Thus we need one integral to find the area of the region from $x = -1$ to $x = 0$ and a second integral to find the area from $x = 0$ to $x = 2$. The area is found by summing these two integrals.

$$A = \int_{-1}^{0} [(x^3 - x^2) - (2x)]\, dx + \int_{0}^{2} [(2x) - (x^3 - x^2)]\, dx$$

$$= \int_{-1}^{0} (x^3 - x^2 - 2x)\, dx + \int_{0}^{2} (2x - x^3 + x^2)\, dx$$

$$= \left(\frac{x^4}{4} - \frac{x^3}{3} - x^2 \right)\Bigg|_{-1}^{0} + \left(x^2 - \frac{x^4}{4} + \frac{x^3}{3} \right)\Bigg|_{0}^{2}$$

$$= \left[(0) - \left(\frac{1}{4} - \frac{-1}{3} - 1 \right) \right] + \left[\left(4 - \frac{16}{4} + \frac{8}{3} \right) - (0) \right] = \frac{37}{12}$$

The area between the curves is $\frac{37}{12}$ square units.

Calculator Note

We've seen how to perform numerical integration with a graphing calculator. We can use 9:fnInt with the difference of two functions over the appropriate interval(s) to find the area between the curves. Figure 13.19 shows that the area between $y = x^2$ and $y = 2x + 3$ is $10\frac{2}{3}$, as we found in Example 2. Appendix A, Section 13.3, shows two methods of approximating the area between two curves with a graphing calculator.

Figure 13.19

CHECKPOINT

1. True or false:
   (a) Over the interval $[a, b]$, the area between the continuous functions $f(x)$ and $g(x)$ is

$$\int_{a}^{b} [f(x) - g(x)]\, dx$$

   (b) If $f(x) \geq g(x)$ and the area between $f(x)$ and $g(x)$ is given by

$$\int_{a}^{b} [f(x) - g(x)]\, dx$$

   then $x = a$ and $x = b$ represent the left and right boundaries, respectively, of the region.
   (c) To find points of intersection of $f(x)$ and $g(x)$, solve $f(x) = g(x)$.

2. Consider the functions $f(x) = x^2 + 3x - 9$ and $g(x) = \frac{1}{4}x^2$.
   (a) Find the points of intersection of $f(x)$ and $g(x)$.
   (b) Determine which function is greater than the other between the points found in part (a).
   (c) Set up the integral used to find the area between the curves in the interval between the points found in part (a).
   (d) Find the area.

EXAMPLE **4**   **Income Distribution** | APPLICATION PREVIEW |

The inequality of income distribution is measured by the **Gini coefficient** of income, which is defined as

$$\frac{\text{Area between } y = x \text{ and } y = L(x)}{\text{Area below } y = x} = \frac{\int_0^1 [x - L(x)] \, dx}{1/2}$$

$$= 2 \int_0^1 [x - L(x)] \, dx$$

The function $y = L(x) = 2.36x^4 - 3.29x^3 + 2.10x^2 - 0.170x$ models the 2015 income distribution data in the Application Preview.

(a) Use this $L(x)$ to find the Gini coefficient of income for 2015.
(b) If the Census Bureau Gini coefficient of income for 1991 is 0.428, during which year was the distribution of income more nearly equal?

Solution
(a) The Gini coefficient of income for 2015 is

$$2 \int_0^1 [x - L(x)] \, dx = 2 \int_0^1 [x - (2.36x^4 - 3.29x^3 + 2.10x^2 - 0.170x)] \, dx$$

$$= 2[-0.472x^5 + 0.8225x^4 - 0.700x^3 + 0.585x^2]_0^1 \approx 0.471$$

(b) Absolute equality of income would occur if the Gini coefficient of income were 0, and smaller coefficients indicate more nearly equal incomes. Thus the distribution of income was more nearly equal in 1991 than in 2015. ▪

Average Value   If the graph of $y = f(x)$ lies on or above the x-axis from $x = a$ to $x = b$, then the area between the graph and the x-axis is

$$A = \int_a^b f(x) \, dx \quad [\text{See Figure 13.20(a).}]$$

The area A is also the area of a rectangle with base equal to $b - a$ and height equal to the **average value** (or average height) of the function $y = f(x)$. [See Figure 13.20(b).]

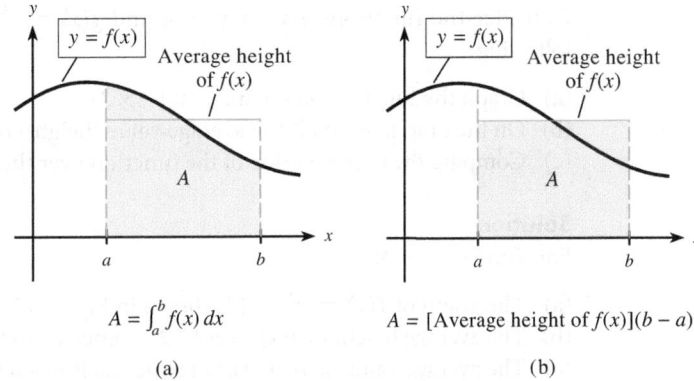

$$A = \int_a^b f(x)\,dx \qquad\qquad A = [\text{Average height of } f(x)](b - a)$$

Figure 13.20   (a)   (b)

Thus the average value of the function in Figure 13.20 is

$$\frac{A}{b - a} = \frac{1}{b - a} \int_a^b f(x) \, dx$$

Even if $f(x) \leq 0$ on all or part of the interval $[a, b]$, we can find the average value by using the integral. Thus we have the following.

Average Value	The **average value** of a continuous function $y = f(x)$ over the interval $[a, b]$ is

$$\text{Average value} = \frac{1}{b - a} \int_a^b f(x)\, dx$$

EXAMPLE 5 Average Cost

Suppose that the cost in dollars for x table lamps is given by $C(x) = 400 + x + 0.3x^2$.

(a) What is the average value of $C(x)$ for 10 to 20 lamps?
(b) Find the average cost per unit if 40 lamps are produced.

Solution

(a) The average value of $C(x)$ from $x = 10$ to $x = 20$ is

$$\frac{1}{20 - 10} \int_{10}^{20} (400 + x + 0.3x^2)\, dx = \frac{1}{10} \left(400x + \frac{x^2}{2} + 0.1x^3 \right)\Big|_{10}^{20}$$

$$= \frac{1}{10}[(8000 + 200 + 800) - (4000 + 50 + 100)]$$

$$= 485 \quad \text{(dollars)}$$

(b) The average cost per unit if 40 units are produced is the average cost function evaluated at $x = 40$. The average cost function is

$$\overline{C}(x) = \frac{C(x)}{x} = \frac{400}{x} + 1 + 0.3x$$

Thus the *average cost per unit* if 40 units are produced is

$$\overline{C}(40) = \frac{400}{40} + 1 + 0.3(40) = 23 \quad \text{[dollars per unit (i.e., lamp)]}$$

CHECKPOINT

3. Find the average value of $f(x) = x^2 - 4$ over $[-1, 3]$.

EXAMPLE 6 Average Value of a Function

Consider the functions $f(x) = x^2 - 4$ and $g(x) = x^3 - 4x$. For each function, do the following.

(a) Graph the function on the interval $[-3, 3]$.
(b) On the graph, "eyeball" the average value (height) of each function on $[-2, 2]$.
(c) Compute the average value of the function over the interval $[-2, 2]$.

Solution

For $f(x) = x^2 - 4$:

(a) The graph of $f(x) = x^2 - 4$ is shown in Figure 13.21(a) on the next page.
(b) The average height of $f(x)$ over $[-2, 2]$ appears to be near -2.
(c) The average value of $f(x)$ over the interval is given by

$$\frac{1}{2 - (-2)} \int_{-2}^{2} (x^2 - 4)\, dx = \frac{1}{4} \left(\frac{x^3}{3} - 4x \right)\Big|_{-2}^{2}$$

$$= \left(\frac{8}{12} - 2 \right) - \left(-\frac{8}{12} + 2 \right) = \frac{4}{3} - 4 = -\frac{8}{3} = -2\frac{2}{3}$$

For $g(x) = x^3 - 4x$:

(a) The graph of $g(x) = x^3 - 4x$ is shown in Figure 13.21(b).

(b) The average height of $g(x)$ over $[-2, 2]$ appears to be approximately 0.

(c) The average value of $g(x)$ is given by

$$\frac{1}{2 - (-2)} \int_{-2}^{2} (x^3 - 4x)\, dx = \frac{1}{4} \left(\frac{x^4}{4} - \frac{4x^2}{2} \right) \Bigg|_{-2}^{2}$$

$$= \left(\frac{16}{16} - \frac{16}{8} \right) - \left(\frac{16}{16} - \frac{16}{8} \right) = 0$$

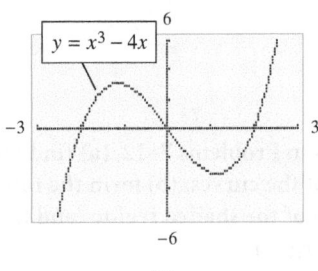

Figure 13.21

(a)   (b)

**CHECKPOINT
ANSWERS**

1. (a) False. This is true only if $f(x) \geq g(x)$ over $[a, b]$.

(b) True   (c) True

2. (a) Solve $f(x) = g(x)$, or $x^2 + 3x - 9 = \frac{1}{4}x^2$. The solutions are
$x = -6$ and $x = 2$. The points of intersection are $(-6, 9)$ and $(2, 1)$.

(b) $g(x) \geq f(x)$ on the interval $[-6, 2]$.

(c) $A = \int_{-6}^{2} \left[\frac{1}{4}x^2 - (x^2 + 3x - 9) \right] dx$

(d) $A = \frac{x^3}{12} - \frac{x^3}{3} - \frac{3x^2}{2} + 9x \Bigg|_{-6}^{2} = 64$ square units

3. $\frac{1}{3 - (-1)} \int_{-1}^{3} (x^2 - 4)\, dx = -\frac{5}{3}$

EXERCISES 13.3

**For each shaded region in Problems 1–6, (a) form the
integral that represents the area of the shaded region and
(b) find the area of the region.**

1.

2.

3.

4.

5.

6.

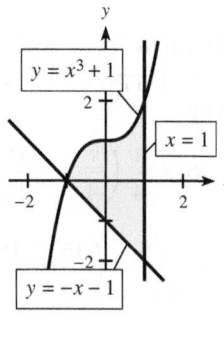

15. $y = x^3 - 1$; $y = x - 1$; to the right of the y-axis
16. $y = x^2 - 2x + 1$; $y = x^2 - 5x + 4$; $x = 2$
17. $y = \frac{1}{2}x^2$; $y = x^2 - 2x$
18. $y = x^2$; $y = 4x - x^2$
19. $h(x) = x^2$; $k(x) = \sqrt{x}$
20. $g(x) = 1 - x^2$; $h(x) = x^2 + x$
21. $f(x) = x^3$; $g(x) = x^2 + 2x$
22. $f(x) = x^3$; $g(x) = 2x - x^2$
23. $f(x) = \dfrac{3}{x}$; $g(x) = 4 - x$
24. $f(x) = \dfrac{6}{x}$; $g(x) = -x - 5$
25. $y = \sqrt{x + 3}$; $x = -3$; $y = 2$
26. $y = \sqrt{4 - x}$; $x = 4$; $y = 3$

For each shaded region in Problems 7–12, (a) find the points of intersection of the curves, (b) form the integral that represents the area of the shaded region, and (c) find the area of the shaded region.

7.

8.

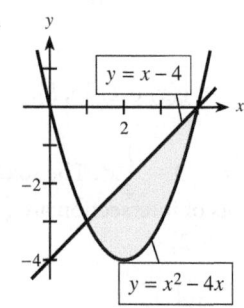

In Problems 27–32, find the average value of each function over the given interval.
27. $f(x) = 9 - x^2$ over $[0, 3]$
28. $f(x) = 2x - x^2$ over $[0, 2]$
29. $f(x) = x^3 - x$ over $[-1, 1]$
30. $f(x) = \frac{1}{2}x^3 + 1$ over $[-2, 0]$
31. $f(x) = \sqrt{x} - 2$ over $[1, 4]$
32. $f(x) = \sqrt[3]{x}$ over $[-8, -1]$
33. Use a graphing calculator to find the area between the curves $y = f(x) = x^3 - 4x$ and $y = g(x) = x^2 - 4$.
34. Use a graphing calculator to find the area between the curves $f(x) = \sqrt[3]{x}$ and $g(x) = x^3 - x$.

9.

10.

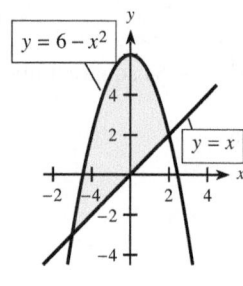

APPLICATIONS

35. *Average profit* For the product whose total cost and total revenue are shown in the figure, represent total revenue by $R(x)$ and total cost by $C(x)$ and write an integral that gives the average profit for the product over the interval from x_0 to x_1.

11.

12.

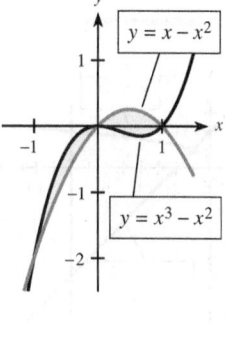

36. *Sales and advertising* The figure shows the sales growth rates under different levels of distribution and advertising from a to b. Set up an integral to determine the extra sales growth if \$4 million is used in advertising rather than \$2 million.

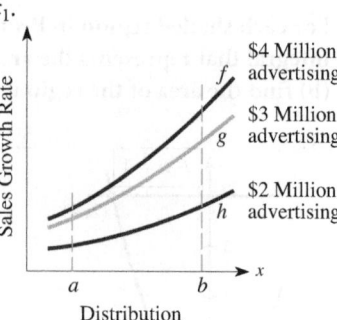

In Problems 13–26, equations are given whose graphs enclose a region. In each problem, find the area of the region.
13. $f(x) = x^2 + 2$; $g(x) = -x^2$; $x = 0$; $x = 2$
14. $f(x) = x^2$; $g(x) = -\frac{1}{10}(10 + x)$; $x = 0$; $x = 3$

37. *Cost* The cost of producing x smart phones is $C(x) = x^2 + 400x + 2000$.

(a) Use $C(x)$ to find the average cost of producing 1000 smart phones.

(b) Find the average value of the cost function $C(x)$ over the interval from 0 to 1000.

38. *Inventory management* The figure shows how an inventory of a product is depleted each quarter of a given year. What is the average inventory per month for the first 3 months for this product? [Assume that the graph is a line joining (0, 1300) and (3, 100).]

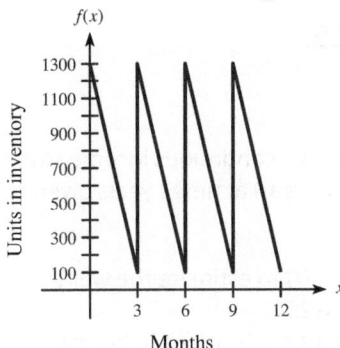

39. *Sales and advertising* The number of daily sales of a product was found to be given by

$$S = 100xe^{-x^2} + 100$$

x days after the start of an advertising campaign for this product.

(a) Find the average daily sales during the first 20 days of the campaign—that is, from $x = 0$ to $x = 20$.

(b) If no new advertising campaign is begun, what is the average number of sales per day for the next 10 days (from $x = 20$ to $x = 30$)?

40. *Demand* The demand function for a certain product is given by

$$p = 500 + \frac{1000}{q + 1}$$

where p is the price and q is the number of units demanded. Find the average price as demand ranges from 49 to 99 units.

41. *Social Security beneficiaries* With data from the Social Security Trustees Report for selected years from 1950 and projected to 2030, the number of Social Security beneficiaries (in millions) can be modeled by

$$B(t) = 0.00024t^3 - 0.026t^2 + 1.6t + 2.2$$

where t is the number of years past 1950. Use the model to find the average number of Social Security beneficiaries per year (actual and predicted) between

(a) 1980 and 2000.   (b) 2010 and 2030.

42. *Total income* Suppose that the income from a slot machine in a casino flows continuously at a rate of

$$f(t) = 100e^{0.1t}$$

where t is the time in hours since the casino opened. Then the total income during the first 10 hours is given by

$$\int_0^{10} 100e^{0.1t}\, dt$$

Find the average income over the first 10 hours.

43. *Drug levels in the blood* A drug manufacturer has developed a time-release capsule with the number of milligrams of the drug in the bloodstream given by

$$S = 30x^{18/7} - 240x^{11/7} + 480x^{4/7}$$

where x is in hours and $0 \leq x \leq 4$. Find the average number of milligrams of the drug in the bloodstream for the first 4 hours after a capsule is taken.

44. *Income distribution* With data from the U.S. Census Bureau, the Lorenz curves for the income distribution for 2012 in the United States for White non-Hispanic households and for Asian households are given below. Find the Gini coefficient of income for both groups and compare the distribution of income for these groups.

White non-Hispanic:
$$y = 2.344x^4 - 3.340x^3 + 2.154x^2 - 0.1588x + 0.0005952$$

Asian:
$$y = 2.240x^4 - 3.222x^3 + 2.169x^2 - 0.1871x + 0.0004762$$

45. *Income distribution* With U.S. Census Bureau data, the Lorenz curves for the income distribution in the United States for Black households and for Hispanic households (of any race) are given below. Find the Gini coefficient of income for both groups and compare the distribution of income for these groups.

Black:
$$y = 2.292x^4 - 3.127x^3 + 2.006x^2 - 0.1710x + 0.0005556$$

Hispanic:
$$y = 1.830x^4 - 2.564x^3 + 1.806x^2 - 0.1137x + 0.0003512$$

46. *Income distribution* In an effort to make the distribution of income more nearly equal, the government of a country passes a tax law that changes the Lorenz curve from $y = 0.99x^{2.1}$ for one year to $y = 0.32x^2 + 0.68x$ for the next year. Find the Gini coefficient of income for both years and compare the distributions of income before and after the tax law was passed. Interpret the result.

47. *Income distribution* The Lorenz curves for the income distribution in the United States for all races for 2015 and for 1980 are given below (*Source*: U.S. Census Bureau). Find the Gini coefficient of income for both years and compare their distributions of income.

2015: $y = x^{2.661}$ 1980: $y = x^{2.241}$

48. *Income distribution* Suppose the Gini coefficient of income for a certain country is $2/5$. Find the value of p if the Lorenz curve for this country is

$$L(x) = \frac{1}{3}x + \frac{2}{3}x^p.$$

49. *Gini coefficient* If the Lorenz curve for the income distribution for a given year is $L(x) = x^p$, use integration to find a simple formula for the corresponding Gini coefficient.

50. *Lorenz curve* If the Lorenz curve for the income distribution for a given year has the form $L(x) = x^p$ and the Gini coefficient is G, find a formula for p.

Applications of Definite Integrals in Business and Economics

OBJECTIVES

- To use definite integrals to find total income, present value, and future value of continuous income streams
- To use definite integrals to find the consumer's surplus
- To use definite integrals to find the producer's surplus

APPLICATION PREVIEW

Suppose the oil pumped from a well is considered as a continuous income stream with annual rate of flow (in thousands of dollars per year) at time t years given by

$$f(t) = 600e^{-0.2(t+5)}$$

The company can use a definite integral involving $f(t)$ to estimate the well's present value over the next 10 years. (See Example 2.)

The definite integral can be used in a number of applications in business and economics. In addition to finding the present value of a continuous income stream, the definite integral can be used to find the total income and future value of the stream.

Definite integrals also can be used to determine the savings realized in the marketplace by some consumers (called consumer's surplus) and some producers (called producer's surplus).

Continuous Income Streams

An oil company's profits depend on the amount of oil that can be pumped from a well. Thus we can consider a pump at an oil field as producing a **continuous stream of income** for the owner. Because both the pump and the oil field "wear out" with time, the continuous stream of income is a function of time. Suppose $f(t)$ is the (annual) *rate* of flow of income from this pump; then we can find the total income from the rate of income by using integration. In particular, the total income for k years is given by

$$\text{Total income} = \int_0^k f(t)\, dt$$

EXAMPLE 1   Oil Revenue

© Wade H. Massie/Sutterstock.com

Now ──────────▶ 10 Years From Now
$2,594,000 – Total Income

A small oil company considers the continuous pumping of oil from a well as a continuous income stream with its annual rate of flow at time t in years given by

$$f(t) = 600e^{-0.2t}$$

in thousands of dollars per year. Find an estimate of the total income from this well over the next 10 years.

Solution

$$\text{Total income} = \int_0^{10} f(t)\, dt = \int_0^{10} 600e^{-0.2t}\, dt$$

$$= \frac{600}{-0.2}e^{-0.2t}\Big|_0^{10} \approx 2594 \quad \text{(to the nearest integer)}$$

Thus the total income is approximately $2,594,000.

In addition to the total income from a continuous income stream, the **present value** of the stream is also important. The present value is the value today of a continuous income stream that will be providing income in the future. The present value is useful in deciding when to replace machinery or what new equipment to select.

To find the present value of a continuous stream of income with rate of flow $f(t)$, we first graph the function $f(t)$ and divide the time interval from 0 to k into n subintervals of width Δt_i, $i = 1$ to n.

The total amount of income is the area under this curve between $t = 0$ and $t = k$. We can approximate the amount of income in each subinterval by finding the area of the rectangle in that subinterval. (See Figure 13.22.)

Figure 13.22

We have shown that the future value S that accrues if $\$P$ is invested for t years at an annual rate r compounded continuously is $S = Pe^{rt}$. Thus the present value of the investment that yields the single payment of $\$S$ after t years is

$$P = \frac{S}{e^{rt}} = Se^{-rt}$$

The contribution to S in the ith subinterval is $S_i = f(t_i)\,\Delta t_i$, and the present value of this amount is $P_i = f(t_i)\,\Delta t_i e^{-rt_i}$. Thus the total present value of S can be approximated by

$$\sum_{i=1}^{n} f(t_i)\,\Delta t_i e^{-rt_i}$$

This approximation improves as $\Delta t_i \to 0$ with the present value given by

$$\lim_{\Delta t_i \to 0} \sum_{i=1}^{n} f(t_i)\,\Delta t_i e^{-rt_i}$$

This limit gives the **present value** as a definite integral.

Present Value of a Continuous Income Stream	If $f(t)$ is the rate of continuous income flow earning interest at rate r compounded continuously, then the **present value of the continuous income stream** is $$\text{Present value} = \int_0^k f(t)e^{-rt}\,dt$$ where $t = 0$ to $t = k$ is the time interval.

EXAMPLE 2   **Present Value** | APPLICATION PREVIEW |

Suppose that the oil company in Example 1 is planning to sell one of its wells because of its remote location. Suppose further that the company wants to use the present value of this well over the next 10 years to help establish its selling price. If the company determines that the annual rate of flow is

$$f(t) = 600e^{-0.2(t + 5)}$$

in thousands of dollars per year and if money is worth 10% compounded continuously, find this present value.

Solution

$$\text{Present value} = \int_0^{10} f(t)e^{-rt}\, dt$$

$$= \int_0^{10} 600e^{-0.2(t+5)}e^{-0.1t}\, dt = \int_0^{10} 600e^{-0.3t-1}\, dt$$

If $u = -0.3t - 1$, then $u' = -0.3$, and we get

$$\frac{1}{-0.3}\int_0^{10} 600e^{-0.3t-1}(-0.3\, dt) = \frac{600}{-0.3}e^{-0.3t-1}\Big|_0^{10}$$

$$= -2000\,(e^{-4} - e^{-1}) \approx 699 \quad \text{(to the nearest integer)}$$

Thus the present value is \$699,000.

Recall that the future value of a continuously compounded investment at rate r after k years is Pe^{rk}, where P is the amount invested (or the present value). Thus for a continuous income stream, the **future value** is found as follows.

Future Value of a Continuous Income Stream	If $f(t)$ is the rate of continuous income flow for k years earning interest at rate r compounded continuously, then the **future value of the continuous income stream** is $$FV = e^{rk}\int_0^k f(t)e^{-rt}\, dt$$

EXAMPLE 3   **Future Value**

If the rate of flow of income from an asset is $1000e^{0.02t}$ millions of dollars per year and the income is invested at 6% compounded continuously, find the future value of the asset 4 years from now.

Solution
The future value is given by

$$FV = e^{rk}\int_0^k f(t)e^{-rt}\, dt$$

$$= e^{(0.06)4}\int_0^4 1000e^{0.02t}e^{-0.06t}\, dt = e^{0.24}\int_0^4 1000e^{-0.04t}\, dt$$

$$= e^{0.24}(-25,000e^{-0.04t})\Big|_0^4 = -25,000e^{0.24}(e^{-0.16} - 1)$$

$$\approx 4699.05 \quad \text{(millions of dollar)}$$

CHECKPOINT

1. Suppose that a continuous income stream has an annual rate of flow given by $f(t) = 5000e^{-0.01t}$ and money is worth 7% compounded continuously. Create the integral used to find

    (a) the total income for the next 5 years.
    (b) the present value for the next 5 years.
    (c) the future value 5 years from now.

Consumer's Surplus   Suppose that the demand for a product is given by $p = f(x)$ and that the supply of the product is described by $p = g(x)$. The price p_1 where the graphs of these functions intersect is the **equilibrium price**. [See Figure 13.23(a) on the next page.] As the demand curve shows, some consumers (but not all) would be willing to pay more than $\$p_1$ for the product.

For example, some consumers would be willing to buy x_3 units if the price were $\$p_3$. Those consumers willing to pay more than $\$p_1$ are benefiting from the lower price. The total gain for all those consumers willing to pay more than $\$p_1$ is called the **consumer's surplus,** and under proper assumptions, the area of the shaded region in Figure 13.23(a) represents this consumer's surplus.

Looking at Figure 13.23(b), we see that if the demand curve has equation $p = f(x)$, the consumer's surplus is given by the area between $f(x)$ and the x-axis from 0 to x_1, *minus* the area of the rectangle denoted TR:

$$\text{Consumer's Surplus} = CS = \int_0^{x_1} f(x)\, dx - p_1 x_1$$

Note that with equilibrium price p_1 and equilibrium quantity x_1, the product $p_1 x_1$ is the area of the rectangle that represents the total dollars spent by consumers and received as revenue by producers. [See Figure 13.23(b).]

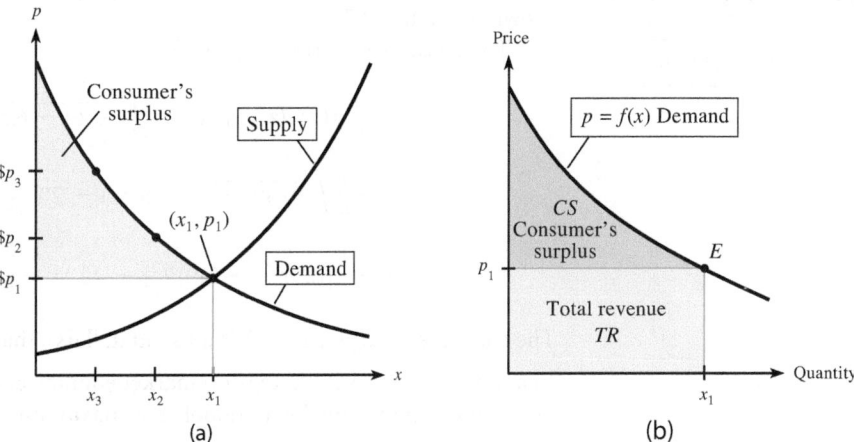

Figure 13.23   (a)   (b)

EXAMPLE 4   Consumer's Surplus

The demand function for x units of a product is $p = f(x) = 1020/(x + 1)$ dollars. If the equilibrium price is $20, what is the consumer's surplus?

Solution
We must first find the quantity that will be purchased at this price. Letting $p = 20$ and solving for x, we get

$$20 = \frac{1020}{x + 1} \quad \text{so} \quad 20(x + 1) = 1020$$

Thus $20x + 20 = 1020$ or $20x = 1000$ so $x = 50$
Thus the equilibrium point is $(x_1, p_1) = (50, 20)$. The consumer's surplus is given by

$$CS = \int_0^{x_1} f(x)\, dx - p_1 x_1 = \int_0^{50} \frac{1020}{x + 1}\, dx - 20 \cdot 50$$

$$= 1020 \ln |x + 1| \Big|_0^{50} - 1000$$

$$= 1020(\ln 51 - \ln 1) - 1000$$

$$\approx 4010.46 - 1000 = 3010.46$$

The consumer's surplus is $3010.46.

EXAMPLE 5   **Consumer's Surplus**

A product's demand function is $p = f(x) = \sqrt{49 - 6x}$ and its supply function is $p = g(x) = x + 1$, where p is the price per unit in dollars and x is thousands of units. Find the equilibrium point and the consumer's surplus there.

Solution

We can determine the equilibrium point by solving the two equations simultaneously.

$$\sqrt{49 - 6x} = x + 1$$
$$49 - 6x = (x + 1)^2$$
$$0 = x^2 + 8x - 48$$
$$0 = (x + 12)(x - 4)$$
$$x = 4 \quad \text{or} \quad x = -12$$

Thus the equilibrium quantity is $x_1 = 4$ (thousand units) and the equilibrium price is $p_1 = \$5$ ($x = -12$ is not a solution). The graphs of the supply and demand functions are shown in Figure 13.24.

The consumer's surplus is given by

$$CS = \int_0^4 f(x)\, dx - p_1 x_1 = \int_0^4 \sqrt{49 - 6x}\, dx - 5 \cdot 4$$

$$= -\frac{1}{6}\int_0^4 \sqrt{49 - 6x}\,(-6\, dx) - 20 = -\frac{1}{9}(49 - 6x)^{3/2}\Big|_0^4 - 20$$

$$= -\frac{1}{9}[(25)^{3/2} - (49)^{3/2}] - 20 = -\frac{1}{9}(125 - 343) - 20 \approx 4.22$$

The consumer's surplus is 4.22 (thousand dollars); that is, $4220.

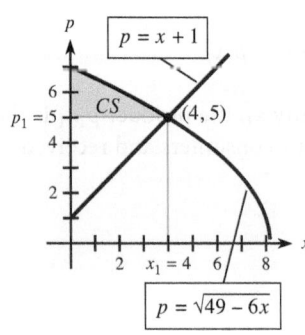

Figure 13.24

In a monopoly market, there is no market equilibrium point, and we find consumer's surplus at the point where the monopoly has maximum profit.

EXAMPLE 6   **Monopoly Market**

Suppose a monopoly has its total cost (in dollars) for a certain product given by $C(x) = 6000 + 0.2x^3$. Suppose also that demand is given by $p = f(x) = 300 - 0.1x$, where p is in dollars and x is the number of units. Find the consumer's surplus at the point where the monopoly has maximum profit.

Solution

We must first find the point where the profit function is maximized. Because the demand for x units is $p = 300 - 0.1x$, the total revenue is

$$R(x) = (300 - 0.1x)x = 300x - 0.1x^2$$

Thus the profit function is

$$P(x) = R(x) - C(x)$$
$$P(x) = 300x - 0.1x^2 - (6000 + 0.2x^2)$$
$$P(x) = 300x - 6000 - 0.3x^2$$

Then $P'(x) = 300 - 0.6x$, so $0 = 300 - 0.6x$ has the solution $x = 500$.

Because $P''(500) = -0.6 < 0$, the profit for the monopoly is maximized when $x = 500$ units are sold at price $p = 300 - 0.1(500) = 250$ dollars per unit.

The consumer's surplus at $x_1 = 500$, $p_1 = 250$ is given by

$$CS = \int_0^{500} f(x)\, dx - 500 \cdot 250 = \int_0^{500} (300 - 0.1x)\, dx - 125,000$$

$$= 300x - \frac{0.1x^2}{2}\Big|_0^{500} - 125,000 = (150,000 - 12,500) - 125,000 = 12,500$$

The consumer's surplus is $12,500.

MONEY ON THE TABLE

Another way to understand consumer surplus is through the popular concept of "money on the table." Imagine you have $500 to spend on an iPad. When you get to the Apple store, the model you want costs only $450. You're delighted to spend only $450, but you **would** have spent all your money if the iPad had been priced at $500. In this example, Apple left money—$50 to be exact—on the table (or in your pocket). That's a consumer's surplus.

GRAVY

Now think of the iPad example in another way. Suppose Apple meets all its profit targets at a price of $400 per iPad. The fact that you pay $450 means that there is a producer surplus. Apple would sell that iPad at the $400 price point, but because you were willing to part with $450, the company receives an extra $50—or gravy—for its bottom line. That is, a producer's surplus.

Producer's Surplus

Figure 13.25

When a product is sold at the equilibrium price, p_1, some producers will benefit because they would have sold the product at a lower price. The area between the line $p = p_1$ and the supply curve (from $x = 0$ to $x = x_1$) gives the producer's surplus. (See Figure 13.25.)

If the supply function is $p = g(x)$, the **producer's surplus** is given by the area between the graph of $p = g(x)$ and the x-axis from 0 to x_1 *subtracted from* p_1x_1, the area of the rectangle shown in Figure 13.25.

$$\text{Producer's Surplus} = PS = p_1x_1 - \int_0^{x_1} g(x)\, dx$$

Note that p_1x_1 represents the total revenue at the equilibrium point.

EXAMPLE **7** **Producer's Surplus**

Suppose that the supply function for x million units of a product is $p = x^2 + x$ dollars per unit. If the equilibrium price is $20 per unit, what is the producer's surplus?

Solution

Because $p = 20$, we can find the equilibrium quantity x as follows:

$$20 = x^2 + x$$
$$0 = x^2 + x - 20$$
$$0 = (x + 5)(x - 4)$$
$$x = -5, \quad x = 4$$

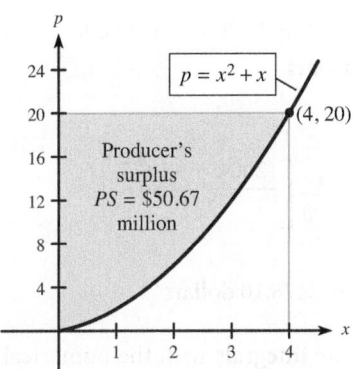

Figure 13.26

The equilibrium point is $x_1 = 4$ million units, $p_1 = \$20$. The producer's surplus is given by

$$PS = 20 \cdot 4 - \int_0^4 (x^2 + x)\, dx$$

$$= 80 - \left(\frac{x^3}{3} + \frac{x^2}{2}\right)\Bigg|_0^4$$

$$= 80 - \left(\frac{64}{3} + 8\right)$$

$$\approx 50.67$$

The producer's surplus is $50.67 million. See Figure 13.26.

EXAMPLE 8   Producer's Surplus

The demand function for a product is $p = \sqrt{49 - 6x}$ and the supply function is $p = x + 1$, where p is price per unit (in dollars) and x is thousands of units. Find the producer's surplus.

Solution

We found the equilibrium point for these functions to be $(4, 5)$ in Example 5. (See Figure 13.24 earlier in this section.) The producer's surplus is

$$PS = 5 \cdot 4 - \int_0^4 (x + 1)\, dx = 20 - \left(\frac{x^2}{2} + x \right)\Big|_0^4$$

$$= 20 - (8 + 4) = 8$$

The producer's surplus is $8000.

CHECKPOINT

2. Suppose that for a certain product, the supply function is $p = f(x)$, the demand function is $p = g(x)$, and the equilibrium point is (x_1, p_1). Decide whether the following are true or false.

(a) $CS = \int_0^{x_1} f(x)\, dx - p_1 x_1$ (b) $PS = \int_0^{x_1} f(x)\, dx - p_1 x_1$

3. If demand is $p = \dfrac{100}{x + 1}$, supply is $p = x + 1$, and the market equilibrium is $(9, 10)$, create the integral used to find the

(a) consumer's surplus.   (b) producer's surplus.

EXAMPLE 9   Consumer's Surplus and Producer's Surplus

Suppose that for x units of a certain product, the demand function is $p = 200e^{-0.01x}$ dollars and the supply function is $p = \sqrt{200x + 49}$ dollars.

(a) Use a graphing calculator to find the market equilibrium point.
(b) Find the consumer's surplus.
(c) Find the producer's surplus.

(a)

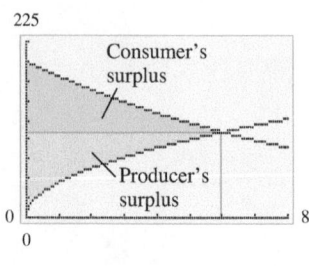

(b)

Figure 13.27

Solution

(a) Solving $200e^{-0.01x} = \sqrt{200x + 49}$ is very difficult using algebraic techniques. Using SOLVER or INTERSECT on a graphing calculator gives $x = 60$, to the nearest unit, with a price of $109.76. [See Figure 13.27(a).]

(b) The consumer's surplus, shown in Figure 13.27(b), is

$$\int_0^{60} 200e^{-0.01x}\, dx - 109.76(60) = (-20,000e^{-0.01x})\Big|_0^{60} - 6585.60$$

$$= -20,000e^{-0.6} + 20,000 - 6585.60$$

$$\approx 2438.17 \text{ dollars}$$

(c) The producer's surplus, shown in Figure 13.27(b), is

$$60(109.76) - \int_0^{60} \sqrt{200x + 49}\, dx = 6585.60 - \frac{1}{200}\left[\frac{(200x + 49)^{3/2}}{3/2} \right]_0^{60}$$

$$= 6585.60 - \frac{1}{300}[(12,049^{3/2} - 49^{3/2})] \approx 2178.10 \text{ dollars}$$

Note that we also could have evaluated these definite integrals with the numerical integration feature of a graphing calculator, and we would have obtained the same results.

**CHECKPOINT
ANSWERS**

1. (a) $\int_0^5 5000e^{-0.01t}\, dt$

   (b) $\int_0^5 (5000e^{-0.01t})(e^{-0.07t})\, dt = \int_0^5 5000e^{-0.08t}\, dt$

   (c) $e^{(0.07)(5)} \int_0^5 (5000e^{-0.01t})(e^{-0.07t})\, dt = e^{0.35} \int_0^5 5000e^{-0.08t}\, dt$

2. (a) False. Consumer's surplus uses the demand function, so

   $$CS = \int_0^{x_1} g(x)\, dx - p_1 x_1$$

   (b) False. Producer's surplus uses the supply function, but the formula is

   $$PS = p_1 x_1 - \int_0^{x_1} f(x)\, dx$$

3. (a) $CS = \int_0^9 \dfrac{100}{x+1}\, dx - 90$ (b) $PS = 90 - \int_0^9 (x+1)\, dx$

EXERCISES 13.4

CONTINUOUS INCOME STREAMS

1. Find the total income over the next 10 years from a continuous income stream that has an annual rate of flow at time t given by $f(t) = 12{,}000e^{0.01t}$ (dollars per year).

2. Find the total income over the next 8 years from a continuous income stream with an annual rate of flow at time t given by $f(t) = 8500e^{-0.2t}$ (dollars per year).

3. Suppose that a steel company views the production of its continuous caster as a continuous income stream with a monthly rate of flow at time t given by

   $f(t) = 24{,}000e^{0.03t}$ (dollars per month)

   Find the total income from this caster in the first year.

4. Suppose that the Quick-Fix Car Service franchise finds that the income generated by its stores can be modeled by assuming that the income is a continuous stream with a monthly rate of flow at time t given by

   $f(t) = 10{,}000e^{0.02t}$ (dollars per month)

   Find the total income from a Quick-Fix store for the first 2 years of operation.

5. A small brewery considers the output of its bottling machine as a continuous income stream with an annual rate of flow at time t given by

   $f(t) = 80e^{-0.1t}$

   in thousands of dollars per year. Find the income from this stream for the next 10 years.

6. A company that services a number of vending machines considers its income as a continuous stream with an annual rate of flow at time t given by

   $f(t) = 120e^{-0.4t}$

   in thousands of dollars per year. Find the income from this stream over the next 5 years.

7. A franchise models the profit from its store as a continuous income stream with a monthly rate of flow at time t given by

   $f(t) = 3000e^{0.004t}$ (dollars per month)

   When a new store opens, its manager is judged against the model, with special emphasis on the second half of the first year. Find the total profit for the second 6-month period ($t = 6$ to $t = 12$).

8. The Medi Spa franchise has a continuous income stream with a monthly rate of flow modeled by $f(t) = 20{,}000e^{0.03t}$ (dollars per month). Find the total income for years 2 through 5.

9. A continuous income stream has an annual rate of flow at time t given by

   $f(t) = 12{,}000e^{0.04t}$ (dollars per year)

   If money is worth 8% compounded continuously, find the present value of this stream for the next 8 years.

10. A continuous income stream has an annual rate of flow at time t given by

    $f(t) = 9000e^{0.12t}$ (dollars per year)

    Find the present value of this income stream for the next 10 years if money is worth 6% compounded continuously.

11. The income from an established chain of laundromats is a continuous stream with its annual rate of flow at time t given by $f(t) = 630{,}000$ (dollars per year). If money is worth 7% compounded continuously, find the present value and future value of this chain over the next 5 years.

12. The profit from an insurance agency can be considered as a continuous income stream with an annual rate of flow at time t given by $f(t) = 840{,}000$ (dollars per year). Find the present value and future value of this agency

over the next 12 years if money is worth 8% compounded continuously.

13. Suppose that a printing firm considers its production as a continuous income stream. If the annual rate of flow at time t is given by

$$f(t) = 97.5e^{-0.2(t+3)}$$

in thousands of dollars per year and money is worth 6% compounded continuously, find the present value and future value of the presses over the next 10 years.

14. Suppose that a vending machine company is considering selling some of its machines. Suppose further that the income from these particular machines is a continuous stream with an annual rate of flow at time t given by

$$f(t) = 12e^{-0.4(t+3)}$$

in thousands of dollars per year. Find the present value and future value of the machines over the next 5 years if money is worth 10% compounded continuously.

15. A 58-year-old couple are considering opening a business of their own. They will either purchase an established Gift and Card Shoppe or open a new Wine Boutique. The Gift Shoppe has a continuous income stream with an annual rate of flow at time t given by

$$G(t) = 30,000 \quad \text{(dollars per year)}$$

and the Wine Boutique has a continuous income stream with a projected annual rate of flow at time t given by

$$W(t) = 21,600e^{0.08t} \quad \text{(dollars per year)}$$

The initial investment is the same for both businesses, and money is worth 10% compounded continuously. Find the present value of each business over the next 7 years (until the couple reach age 65) to see which is the better buy.

16. If the couple in Problem 15 plan to keep the business until age 70 (for the next 12 years), find each present value to see which business is the better buy in this case.

CONSUMER'S SURPLUS

In Problems 17–26, p and C are in dollars and x is the number of units.

17. The demand function for a product is $p = 34 - x^2$. If the equilibrium price is $9 per unit, what is the consumer's surplus?

18. The demand function for a product is $p = 100 - 4x$. If the equilibrium price is $40 per unit, what is the consumer's surplus?

19. The demand function for a product is $p = 200/(x + 2)$. If the equilibrium quantity is 8 units, what is the consumer's surplus?

20. The demand function for a certain product is $p = 100/(1 + 2x)$. If the equilibrium quantity is 12 units, what is the consumer's surplus?

21. The demand function for a certain product is $p = 81 - x^2$, and the supply function is $p = x^2 + 4x + 11$. Find the equilibrium point and the consumer's surplus there.

22. The demand function for a product is $p = 49 - x^2$, and the supply function is $p = 4x + 4$. Find the equilibrium point and the consumer's surplus there.

23. If the demand function for a product is $p = 12/(x + 1)$ and the supply function is $p = 1 + 0.2x$, find the consumer's surplus under pure competition.

24. If the demand function for a good is $p = 110 - x^2$ and the supply function for it is $p = 2 - 1.2x + 0.2x^2$, find the consumer's surplus under pure competition.

25. A monopoly has a total cost function $C = 1000 + 120x + 6x^2$ for its product, which has demand function $p = 360 - 3x - 2x^2$. Find the consumer's surplus at the point where the monopoly has maximum profit.

26. A monopoly has a total cost function $C = 500 + 2x^2 + 10x$ for its product, which has demand function $p = -\frac{1}{3}x^2 - 2x + 30$. Find the consumer's surplus at the point where the monopoly has maximum profit.

PRODUCER'S SURPLUS

In Problems 27–36, p is in dollars and x is the number of units.

27. Suppose that the supply function for a good is $p = 4x^2 + 2x + 2$. If the equilibrium price is $422 per unit, what is the producer's surplus there?

28. Suppose that the supply function for a good is $p = 0.1x^2 + 3x + 20$. If the equilibrium price is $36 per unit, what is the producer's surplus there?

29. If the supply function for a commodity is $p = 10e^{x/3}$, what is the producer's surplus when 15 units are sold?

30. If the supply function for a commodity is $p = 40 + 100(x + 1)^2$, what is the producer's surplus at $x = 20$?

31. Find the producer's surplus at market equilibrium for a product if its demand function is $p = 81 - x^2$ and its supply function is $p = x^2 + 4x + 11$.

32. Find the producer's surplus at market equilibrium for a product if its demand function is $p = 49 - x^2$ and its supply function is $p = 4x + 4$.

33. Find the producer's surplus at market equilibrium for a product with demand function $p = 12/(x + 1)$ and supply function $p = 1 + 0.2x$.

34. Find the producer's surplus at market equilibrium for a product with demand function $p = 110 - x^2$ and supply function $p = 2 - \frac{6}{5}x + \frac{1}{5}x^2$.

35. The demand function for a certain product is $p = 144 - 2x^2$ and the supply function is $p = x^2 + 33x + 48$. Find the producer's surplus at the equilibrium point.

36. The demand function for a product is $p = 280 - 4x - x^2$ and the supply function for it is $p = 160 + 4x + x^2$. Find the producer's surplus at the equilibrium point.

Using Tables of Integrals

OBJECTIVE

- To use tables of integrals to evaluate certain integrals

APPLICATION PREVIEW

The rate of change of the total value of real U.S. exports (in billions of dollars per year) for selected years from 2014 and projected to 2040 is given by

$$\frac{dE}{dt} = 74.62(1.044)^t$$

where t is the number of years after 2010 and E was \$2086 billion in 2014 (*Source*: U.S. Energy Information Administration). Finding the function $E(t)$ that models the value of real U.S. exports requires evaluating the integral

$$E(t) = \int \frac{dE}{dt}dt = \int 74.62(1.044)^t dt$$

Evaluating this integral is made easier by using a formula such as those given in Table 13.2. (See Example 4.) The examples in this section illustrate how some of these formulas are used.

The formulas in Table 13.2 (and others listed in other resources) extend the number of integrals that can be evaluated. Using the formulas is not quite as easy as it may sound because finding the correct formula and using it properly may present problems.

TABLE 13.2

INTEGRATION FORMULAS

1. $\int u^n\, du = \dfrac{u^{n+1}}{n+1} + C, \text{ for } n \neq -1$

2. $\int \dfrac{du}{u} = \int u^{-1}\, du = \ln|u| + C$

3. $\int a^u\, du = a^u \log_a e + C = \dfrac{a^u}{\ln a} + C$

4. $\int e^u\, du = e^u + C$

5. $\int \dfrac{du}{a^2 - u^2} = \dfrac{1}{2a} \ln\left|\dfrac{a+u}{a-u}\right| + C$

6. $\int \sqrt{u^2 + a^2}\, du = \dfrac{1}{2}(u\sqrt{u^2 + a^2} + a^2 \ln|u + \sqrt{u^2 + a^2}|) + C$

7. $\int \sqrt{u^2 - a^2}\, du = \dfrac{1}{2}(u\sqrt{u^2 - a^2} - a^2 \ln|u + \sqrt{u^2 - a^2}|) + C$

8. $\int \dfrac{du}{\sqrt{u^2 + a^2}} = \ln|u + \sqrt{u^2 + a^2}| + C$

9. $\int \dfrac{du}{u\sqrt{a^2 - u^2}} = -\dfrac{1}{a} \ln\left|\dfrac{a + \sqrt{a^2 - u^2}}{u}\right| + C$

10. $\int \dfrac{du}{\sqrt{u^2 - a^2}} = \ln|u + \sqrt{u^2 - a^2}| + C$

11. $\int \dfrac{du}{u\sqrt{a^2 + u^2}} = -\dfrac{1}{a} \ln\left|\dfrac{a + \sqrt{a^2 + u^2}}{u}\right| + C$

12. $\int \dfrac{u\, du}{au + b} = \dfrac{u}{a} - \dfrac{b}{a^2} \ln|au + b| + C$

(Continued)

TABLE 13.2

INTEGRATION FORMULAS (*continued*)

13. $\displaystyle\int \frac{du}{u(au + b)} = \frac{1}{b} \ln \left| \frac{u}{au + b} \right| + C$

14. $\displaystyle\int \ln u\, du = u(\ln u - 1) + C$

15. $\displaystyle\int \frac{u\, du}{(au + b)^2} = \frac{1}{a^2} \left(\ln |au + b| + \frac{b}{au + b} \right) + C$

16. $\displaystyle\int u\sqrt{au + b}\, du = \frac{2(3au - 2b)(au + b)^{3/2}}{15a^2} + C$

EXAMPLE 1   Using an Integration Formula

Evaluate $\displaystyle\int \frac{dx}{\sqrt{x^2 + 4}}$.

Solution

We must find a formula in Table 13.2 that is of the same form as this integral. We see that formula 8 has the desired form *if* we let $u = x$ and $a = 2$. Thus

$$\int \frac{dx}{\sqrt{x^2 + 4}} = \ln \left| x + \sqrt{x^2 + 4} \right| + C$$

EXAMPLE 2   Fitting Integration Formulas

Evaluate (a) $\displaystyle\int_1^2 \frac{dx}{x^2 + 2x}$ and   (b) $\displaystyle\int \ln (2x + 1)\, dx$.

Solution

(a) There does not appear to be any formula that has the exact form as this integral. But if we rewrite the integral as

$$\int_1^2 \frac{dx}{x(x + 2)}$$

we see that formula 13 will work. Letting $u = x$, $a = 1$, and $b = 2$, we get

$$\int_1^2 \frac{dx}{x(x + 2)} = \frac{1}{2} \ln \left| \frac{x}{x + 2} \right| \Big|_1^2 = \frac{1}{2} \ln \left| \frac{2}{4} \right| - \frac{1}{2} \ln \left| \frac{1}{3} \right|$$

$$= \frac{1}{2} \left(\ln \frac{1}{2} - \ln \frac{1}{3} \right)$$

$$= \frac{1}{2} \ln \frac{3}{2} \approx 0.2027$$

(b) This integral has the form of formula 14, with $u = 2x + 1$. But if $u = 2x + 1$, du must be represented by the differential of $2x + 1$ (that is, $2\, dx$). Thus

$$\int \ln (2x + 1)\, dx = \frac{1}{2} \int \ln (2x + 1)(2\, dx)$$

$$= \frac{1}{2} \int \ln (u)\, du = \frac{1}{2} u[\ln (u) - 1] + C$$

$$= \frac{1}{2}(2x + 1)[\ln (2x + 1) - 1] + C$$

CHECKPOINT

1. Can both $\displaystyle\int \frac{dx}{\sqrt{x^2 - 4}}$ and $\displaystyle -\int \frac{dx}{\sqrt{4 - x^2}}$ be evaluated with formula 10 in Table 13.2?

2. Determine the formula used to evaluate $\displaystyle\int \frac{3x}{4x - 5}\, dx$ and show how the formula would be applied.

3. True or false: For us to use a formula, the given integral must correspond exactly to the formula, including du.

4. True or false: $\displaystyle\int \frac{dx}{x^2(3x^2 - 7)}$ can be evaluated with formula 13.

5. True or false: $\displaystyle\int \frac{dx}{(6x + 1)^2}$ can be evaluated with either formula 1 or formula 15.

6. True or false: $\displaystyle\int \sqrt{x^2 + 4}\; dx$ can be evaluated with formula 1, formula 6, or formula 16.

EXAMPLE 3   Fitting an Integration Formula

Evaluate $\displaystyle\int_1^2 \frac{dx}{x\sqrt{81 - 9x^2}}$.

Solution
This integral is similar to that of formula 9 in Table 13.2. Letting $a = 9$, letting $u = 3x$, and multiplying the numerator and denominator by 3 give the proper form.

$$\int_1^2 \frac{dx}{x\sqrt{81 - 9x^2}} = \int_1^2 \frac{3\, dx}{3x\sqrt{81 - 9x^2}}$$

$$= -\frac{1}{9}\ln\left|\frac{9 + \sqrt{81 - 9x^2}}{3x}\right| \Bigg|_1^2$$

$$= \left[-\frac{1}{9}\ln\left(\frac{9 + \sqrt{45}}{6}\right)\right] - \left[-\frac{1}{9}\ln\left(\frac{9 + \sqrt{72}}{3}\right)\right]$$

$$\approx 0.088924836$$

Remember that the formulas given in Table 13.2 represent only a very small sample of all possible integration formulas. Additional formulas may be found in books of mathematical tables or online.

EXAMPLE 4   U.S. Exports | APPLICATION PREVIEW |

The rate of change of the total value of real U.S. exports (in billions of dollars per year) for selected years from 2014 and projected to 2040 is given by

$$\frac{dE}{dt} = 74.62(1.044)^t$$

where t is the number of years after 2010 and E was \$2086 billion in 2014 (*Source:* U.S. Energy Information Administration).
(a) Find the function $E(t)$ that models the total value of real U.S. exports.
(b) Find the predicted value of real U.S. exports in 2030.

Solution
(a) To find $E(t)$, we integrate $\dfrac{dE}{dt}$ by using formula 3 with $a = 1.044$ and $u = t$.

$$E(t) = \int 74.62(1.044)^t\, dt = 74.62 \int (1.044)^t\, dt$$

$$= 74.62\, \frac{(1.044)^t}{\ln(1.044)} + C \approx 1733(1.044)^t + C$$

We use $E = \$2086$ billion in 2014 (when $t = 4$) to find the value of C.
$$2086 = 1733(1.044)^4 + C \quad \Rightarrow \quad 2086 \approx 2059 + C$$
$$\Rightarrow \quad C \approx 27$$

Thus $E(t) = 1733(1.044)^t + 27$.

(b) The predicted value of U.S. exports in 2030 (when $t = 20$) is
$$E(20) = 1733(1.044)^{20} + 27 \approx \$4127 \text{ billion}$$

Calculator Note   Numerical integration with a graphing calculator is especially useful in evaluating definite integrals when the formulas for the integrals are difficult to use or are not available. For example, evaluating the definite integral in Example 3 with the numerical integration feature of a graphing calculator gives 0.08892484. The decimal approximation of the answer found in Example 3 is 0.088924836, so the numerical approximation of the answer agrees for the first 8 decimal places.

CHECKPOINT
ANSWERS

1. No. $\sqrt{4 - x^2}$ cannot be written in the form $\sqrt{u^2 - a^2}$.
2. Use formula 12: $\dfrac{3x}{4} + \dfrac{15}{16} \ln |4x - 5| + C$
3. True.
4. False. With $u = x^2$, we must have $du = 2x\, dx$.
5. False. The integral can be evaluated with formula 1, but not with formula 15.
6. False. The integral can be evaluated only with formula 6.

EXERCISES 13.5

Evaluate the integrals in Problems 1–32. Identify the formula used.

1. $\displaystyle\int \dfrac{dx}{16 - x^2}$

2. $\displaystyle\int \dfrac{dx}{x(3x + 5)}$

3. $\displaystyle\int_1^4 \dfrac{dx}{x\sqrt{9 + x^2}}$

4. $\displaystyle\int \dfrac{dx}{x\sqrt{9 - x^2}}$

5. $\displaystyle\int \ln w\, dw$

6. $\displaystyle\int 4(3^x)\, dx$

7. $\displaystyle\int_0^2 \dfrac{q\, dq}{6q + 9}$

8. $\displaystyle\int_1^5 \dfrac{dq}{q\sqrt{25 + q^2}}$

9. $\displaystyle\int \dfrac{dv}{v(3v + 8)}$

10. $\displaystyle\int_0^3 \sqrt{x^2 + 16}\, dx$

11. $\displaystyle\int_5^7 \sqrt{x^2 - 25}\, dx$

12. $\displaystyle\int \dfrac{x\, dx}{(3x + 2)^2}$

13. $\displaystyle\int w\sqrt{4w + 5}\, dw$

14. $\displaystyle\int \dfrac{dy}{\sqrt{9 + y^2}}$

15. $\displaystyle\int x\, 5^{x^2}\, dx$

16. $\displaystyle\int \sqrt{9x^2 + 4}\, dx$

17. $\displaystyle\int_0^3 x\sqrt{x^2 + 4}\, dx$

18. $\displaystyle\int x\sqrt{x^4 - 36}\, dx$

19. $\displaystyle\int \dfrac{5\, dx}{x\sqrt{4 - 9x^2}}$

20. $\displaystyle\int x\, e^{x^2}\, dx$

21. $\displaystyle\int \dfrac{dx}{\sqrt{9x^2 - 4}}$

22. $\displaystyle\int \dfrac{dx}{25 - 4x^2}$

23. $\displaystyle\int \dfrac{3x\, dx}{(2x - 5)^2}$

24. $\displaystyle\int_0^1 \dfrac{x\, dx}{6 - 5x}$

25. $\displaystyle\int \dfrac{dx}{\sqrt{(3x + 1)^2 + 1}}$

26. $\displaystyle\int \dfrac{dx}{9 - (2x + 3)^2}$

27. $\displaystyle\int_0^3 x\sqrt{(x^2 + 1)^2 + 9}\, dx$

28. $\displaystyle\int_1^e x \ln x^2\, dx$

29. $\displaystyle\int \dfrac{x\, dx}{7 - 3x^2}$

30. $\displaystyle\int_0^1 \dfrac{e^x}{1 + e^x}\, dx$

31. $\displaystyle\int \dfrac{dx}{\sqrt{4x^2 + 7}}$

32. $\displaystyle\int e^{2x}\sqrt{3e^x + 1}\, dx$

Use formulas or numerical integration with a graphing calculator to evaluate the definite integrals in Problems 33–36.

33. $\displaystyle\int_2^3 \dfrac{e^{\sqrt{x-1}}}{\sqrt{x - 1}}\, dx$

34. $\displaystyle\int_2^4 \dfrac{3x}{\sqrt{x^4 - 9}}\, dx$

35. $\displaystyle\int_0^1 \dfrac{x^3\, dx}{(4x^2 + 5)^2}$

36. $\displaystyle\int_0^1 (e^x + 1)^3 e^x\, dx$

APPLICATIONS

37. **Producer's surplus** If the supply function for x units of a commodity is $p = 40 + 100 \ln (x + 1)^2$ dollars, what is the producer's surplus at $x = 20$?

38. **Consumer's surplus** If the demand function for wheat is $p = \dfrac{1500}{\sqrt{x^2 + 1}} + 4$ dollars, where x is the number of hundreds of bushels of wheat, what is the consumer's surplus at $x = 7, p = 216.13$?

39. **Cost** Suppose that the marginal cost for x units of a good is $\overline{MC} = \sqrt{x^2 + 9}$ (dollars per unit) and the fixed cost is $300.
    (a) What is the total cost function of the good?
    (b) What is the total cost of producing 4 units of this good?

40. *Consumer's surplus* Suppose that the demand function for an appliance is

$$p = \frac{400q + 400}{(q + 2)^2}$$

where q is the number of units and p is in dollars. What is the consumer's surplus if the equilibrium price is $19 and the equilibrium quantity is 18?

41. *Income streams* Suppose that when a new oil well is opened, its production is viewed as a continuous income stream with monthly rate of flow

$$f(t) = 10 \ln (t + 1) - 0.1t$$

where t is time in months and $f(t)$ is in thousands of dollars per month. Find the total income over the next 10 years (120 months).

42. *Spread of disease* An isolated community of 1000 people susceptible to a certain disease is exposed when one member returns carrying the disease. If x represents the number infected with the disease at time t (in days), then the rate of change of x is proportional to the product of the number infected, x, and the number still susceptible, $1000 - x$. That is,

$$\frac{dx}{dt} = kx(1000 - x) \quad \text{or} \quad \frac{dx}{x(1000 - x)} = k\, dt$$

(a) If $k = 0.001$, integrate both sides to solve this differential equation.
(b) Find how long it will be before half the population of the community is affected.
(c) Find the rate of new cases, dx/dt, every other day for the first 13 days.

Integration by Parts

OBJECTIVE

- To evaluate integrals using the method of integration by parts

APPLICATION PREVIEW

If the value of oil produced by a piece of oil extraction equipment is considered a continuous income stream with an annual rate of flow (in dollars per year) at time t in years given by

$$f(t) = 300{,}000 - 2500t, \quad 0 \le t \le 10$$

and if money can be invested at 8% compounded continuously, then the present value of the piece of equipment is

$$\int_0^{10}(300{,}000 - 2500t)e^{-0.08t}\, dt$$

$$= 300{,}000 \int_0^{10} e^{-0.08t}\, dt - 2500 \int_0^{10} te^{-0.08t}\, dt$$

The first integral can be evaluated with the formula $\int e^u\, du = e^u + C$.

Evaluating the second integral can be done using integration by parts, which is a special technique that is used when the integrand contains a product and involves rewriting an integral in a form that can be evaluated. (See Example 6.)

Integration by parts is an integration technique that uses a formula that follows from the Product Rule for derivatives (actually differentials) as follows:

$$\frac{d}{dx}(uv) = u\frac{dv}{dx} + v\frac{du}{dx} \quad \text{so} \quad d(uv) = u\, dv + v\, du$$

Rearranging the differential form and integrating both sides give the following.

$$u\, dv = d(uv) - v\, du$$
$$\int u\, dv = \int d(uv) - \int v\, du$$
$$\int u\, dv = uv - \int v\, du$$

Integration by Parts Formula	$$\int u\, dv = uv - \int v\, du$$

Integration by parts is very useful if the integral we seek to evaluate can be treated as the product of one function, u, and the differential dv of a second function so that the two integrals $\int dv$ and $\int v\, du$ can be found. Note that we do not add a constant of integration to the results of $\int dv$ and $\int v\, du$, but only to the final result. We consider an example using this method.

| EXAMPLE | 1 | **Integration by Parts** |

Evaluate $\int xe^x \, dx$.

Solution

We cannot evaluate this integral using methods we have learned. But we can "split" the integrand into two parts, setting one part equal to u and the other part equal to dv. This "split" must be done in such a way that $\int dv$ and $\int v \, du$ can be evaluated. Letting $u = x$ and letting $dv = e^x \, dx$ are possible choices. If we make these choices, we have

$$u = x \quad dv = e^x \, dx$$

$$du = 1 \, dx \quad v = \int e^x \, dx = e^x$$

Then

$$\int xe^x \, dx = uv - \int v \, du$$

$$= xe^x - \int e^x \, dx = xe^x - e^x + C$$

We see that choosing $u = x$ and $dv = e^x dx$ worked in evaluating $\int xe^x \, dx$ in Example 1. If we had chosen $u = e^x$ and $dv = x \, dx$, the results would not have been so successful.

How can we select u and dv to make integration by parts work? As a general guideline, we do the following.

First identify the types of functions occurring in the problem in the order

Logarithm,   Polynomial (or Power of x),   Radical,   Exponential*

Thus, in Example 1, we had x and e^x, a polynomial and an exponential, respectively.

Second, choose u to equal the function whose type occurs first on the list; hence in Example 1, we chose $u = x$. Then dv equals the rest of the integrand (and always includes dx) so that $u \, dv$ equals the original integrand. A helpful way to remember the order of the function types that help us choose u is the sentence

"Lazy People Rarely Excel."

in which the first letters, LPRE, coordinate with the order and types of functions. Consider the following examples.

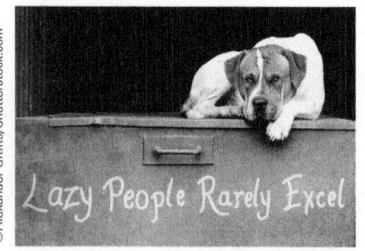

| EXAMPLE | 2 | **Integration by Parts** |

Evaluate $\int x \ln x \, dx$.

Solution

The integral contains a logarithm ($\ln x$) and a polynomial (x). Thus choose $u = \ln x$ and $dv = x \, dx$. Then

$$du = \frac{1}{x} \, dx \quad \text{and} \quad v = \frac{x^2}{2}$$

so $\quad \int x \ln x \, dx = u \cdot v - \int v \, du = (\ln x) \frac{x^2}{2} - \int \frac{x^2}{2} \cdot \frac{1}{x} \, dx$

$$= \frac{x^2}{2} \ln x - \int \frac{x}{2} \, dx = \frac{x^2}{2} \ln x - \frac{x^2}{4} + C$$

Note in Example 2 that letting $dv = \ln x \, dx$ is contrary to our guidelines and would lead to great difficulty in evaluating $\int dv$ and $\int v \, du$.

---

*This order is related to the ease with which the function types can be integrated.

EXAMPLE   3   **Integration by Parts**

Evaluate $\int \ln x^2 \, dx$.

Solution

The only function in this problem is a logarithm, the first function type on our list for choosing u. Thus

Choose: $u = \ln x^2$ $dv = dx$

Calculate: $du = \dfrac{2x}{x^2} \, dx = \dfrac{2}{x} \, dx$ $v = x$

Then

$$\int \ln x^2 \, dx = x \ln x^2 - \int x \cdot \frac{2}{x} \, dx = x \ln x^2 - 2x + C$$

Note that if we write $\ln x^2$ as $2 \ln x$, we can evaluate this integral using formula 14 in Table 13.2 in the previous section, so integration by parts would not be needed. ▪

CHECKPOINT

1. True or false: In evaluating $\int u \, dv$ by parts,
   (a) the parts u and dv are selected and the parts du and v are calculated.
   (b) the differential (often dx) is always chosen as part of dv.
   (c) the parts du and v are found from u and dv as follows:

   $$du = u' \, dx \quad \text{and} \quad v = \int dv$$

   (d) For $\int \dfrac{3x}{e^{2x}} \, dx$, we could choose $u = 3x$ and $dv = e^{2x} \, dx$.

2. For $\int \dfrac{\ln x}{x^4} \, dx$,

   (a) identify u and dv.
   (b) find du and v.
   (c) complete the evaluation of the integral.

Sometimes it is necessary to repeat integration by parts to complete the evaluation. When this occurs, at each use of integration by parts, it is important to choose u and dv consistently according to our guidelines.

EXAMPLE   4   **Repeated Integration by Parts**

Evaluate $\int x^2 e^{2x} \, dx$.

Solution

Choose $u = x^2$ and $dv = e^{2x} \, dx$. Then we calculate $du = 2x \, dx$ and $v = \frac{1}{2} e^{2x}$. Thus

$$\int x^2 e^{2x} \, dx = \frac{1}{2} x^2 e^{2x} - \int x e^{2x} \, dx$$

We cannot evaluate $\int x e^{2x} \, dx$ directly, but this new integral is simpler than the original, and a second integration by parts will be successful. Choosing $u = x$ and $dv = e^{2x} \, dx$, we calculate $du = dx$ and $v = \frac{1}{2} e^{2x}$. Thus

$$\int x^2 e^{2x} \, dx = \frac{1}{2} x^2 e^{2x} - \left(\frac{1}{2} x e^{2x} - \int \frac{1}{2} e^{2x} \, dx \right)$$

$$= \frac{1}{2} x^2 e^{2x} - \frac{1}{2} x e^{2x} + \frac{1}{4} e^{2x} + C$$

$$= \frac{1}{4} e^{2x} (2x^2 - 2x + 1) + C$$ ▪

The most obvious choices for u and dv are not always the correct ones, as the following example shows. Integration by parts may still involve some trial and error.

EXAMPLE 5 | A Tricky Integration by Parts

Evaluate $\int x^3 \sqrt{x^2 + 1}\, dx$.

Solution

Here we have a polynomial (x^3) and a radical. However, if we choose $u = x^3$, then the resulting $dv = \sqrt{x^2 + 1}\, dx$ cannot be integrated easily. But we can use $\sqrt{x^2 + 1}$ as part of dv and evaluate $\int dv$, if we let $dv = x\sqrt{x^2 + 1}\, dx$. Then

$$u = x^2 \qquad dv = (x^2 + 1)^{1/2} x\, dx$$

$$du = 2x\, dx \qquad v = \int (x^2 + 1)^{1/2}(x\, dx) = \frac{1}{2}\int (x^2 + 1)^{1/2}(2x\, dx)$$

$$v = \frac{1}{2}\frac{(x^2 + 1)^{3/2}}{3/2} = \frac{1}{3}(x^2 + 1)^{3/2}$$

Then
$$\int x^3 \sqrt{x^2 + 1}\, dx = \frac{x^2}{3}(x^2 + 1)^{3/2} - \int \frac{1}{3}(x^2 + 1)^{3/2}(2x\, dx)$$

$$= \frac{x^2}{3}(x^2 + 1)^{3/2} - \frac{1}{3}\frac{(x^2 + 1)^{5/2}}{5/2} + C$$

$$= \frac{x^2}{3}(x^2 + 1)^{3/2} - \frac{2}{15}(x^2 + 1)^{5/2} + C$$

EXAMPLE 6 | Equipment Present Value | APPLICATION PREVIEW |

Suppose that the value of oil produced by a piece of oil extraction equipment is considered a continuous income stream with an annual rate of flow (in dollars per year) at time t in years given by

$$f(t) = 300{,}000 - 2500t, \quad 0 \le t \le 10$$

and that money is worth 8% compounded continuously. Find the present value of the piece of equipment.

Solution

The present value of the piece of equipment is given by

$$\int_0^{10} (300{,}000 - 2500t)e^{-0.08t}\, dt = 300{,}000 \int_0^{10} e^{-0.08t}\, dt - 2500 \int_0^{10} te^{-0.08t}\, dt$$

$$= \frac{300{,}000}{-0.08} e^{-0.08t} \Big|_0^{10} - 2500 \int_0^{10} te^{-0.08t}\, dt$$

The value of the first integral is

$$\frac{300{,}000}{-0.08} e^{-0.08t} \Big|_0^{10} = \frac{300{,}000}{-0.08} e^{-0.8} - \frac{300{,}000}{-0.08}$$

$$\approx 2{,}065{,}016.385$$

The second of these integrals can be evaluated using integration by parts, with $u = t$ and $dv = e^{-0.08t}\, dt$. Then $du = 1\, dt$ and $v = \dfrac{e^{-0.08t}}{-0.08}$, and this integral is

$$-2500 \int_0^{10} te^{-0.08t}\, dt = -2500\frac{te^{-0.08t}}{-0.08} \Big|_0^{10} + 2500 \int_0^{10} \frac{e^{-0.08t}}{-0.08}\, dt$$

$$= \frac{2500}{0.08} te^{-0.08t} \Big|_0^{10} + \frac{2500}{0.0064} e^{-0.08t} \Big|_0^{10}$$

$$= \frac{2500}{0.08} 10e^{-0.8} + \frac{2500}{0.0064} e^{-0.8} - \frac{2500}{0.0064} \approx -74{,}690.572$$

Thus the sum of the integrals is

$$2{,}065{,}016.385 + (-74{,}690.572) = 1{,}990{,}325.813$$

so the present value of this piece of equipment is $1,990,325.81.

Calculator Note Using the numerical integration feature of a graphing calculator to evaluate the integral in Example 6 gives the present value of $1,990,325.81, so this answer is the same as that found in Example 6.

One further note about integration by parts: It can be very useful on certain types of problems, but not on all types. Don't attempt to use integration by parts when easier methods are available.

CHECKPOINT
ANSWERS

1. (a) True   (b) True   (c) True
   (d) False. The *product* of u and dv must equal the original integrand.
2. (a) $u = \ln x$ and $dv = x^{-4}\, dx$
   (b) $du = \dfrac{1}{x}\, dx$ and $v = \displaystyle\int x^{-4}\, dx = \dfrac{x^{-3}}{-3}$
   (c) $-\dfrac{\ln x}{3x^3} - \dfrac{1}{9x^3} + C$

EXERCISES 13.6

In Problems 1–16, use integration by parts to evaluate the integral.

1. $\displaystyle\int xe^{3x}\, dx$

2. $\displaystyle\int xe^{-x}\, dx$

3. $\displaystyle\int x^2 \ln x\, dx$

4. $\displaystyle\int x^3 \ln x\, dx$

5. $\displaystyle\int_4^6 q\sqrt{q-4}\, dq$

6. $\displaystyle\int_0^1 y(1-y)^{3/2}\, dy$

7. $\displaystyle\int \frac{\ln x}{x^2}\, dx$

8. $\displaystyle\int \frac{\ln(x-1)}{\sqrt{x-1}}\, dx$

9. $\displaystyle\int_1^e \ln x\, dx$

10. $\displaystyle\int \frac{x}{\sqrt{x-3}}\, dx$

11. $\displaystyle\int x \ln(2x-3)\, dx$

12. $\displaystyle\int x \ln(4x)\, dx$

13. $\displaystyle\int q^3 \sqrt{q^2-3}\, dq$

14. $\displaystyle\int \frac{x^3}{\sqrt{9-x^2}}\, dx$

15. $\displaystyle\int_0^4 x^3 \sqrt{x^2+9}\, dx$

16. $\displaystyle\int \sqrt{x}\, \ln x\, dx$

In Problems 17–24, use integration by parts to evaluate the integral. Note that evaluation may require integration by parts more than once.

17. $\displaystyle\int x^2 e^{-x}\, dx$

18. $\displaystyle\int_0^1 4x^2 e^x\, dx$

19. $\displaystyle\int_0^2 3x^3 e^{x^2}\, dx$

20. $\displaystyle\int x^3 e^x\, dx$

21. $\displaystyle\int x^3 \ln^2 x\, dx$

22. $\displaystyle\int \frac{x^2}{\sqrt{x-3}}\, dx$

23. $\displaystyle\int e^{2x} \sqrt{e^x+1}\, dx$

24. $\displaystyle\int_1^2 (\ln x)^2\, dx$

In Problems 25–30, select the formula or method (I–IV) that should be used to evaluate each integral. Then evaluate the integral.

I. Integration by parts

II. $\displaystyle\int e^u\, du$

III. $\displaystyle\int \frac{du}{u}$

IV. $\displaystyle\int u^n\, du$

25. $\displaystyle\int xe^{x^2}\, dx$

26. $\displaystyle\int \frac{x}{9-4x^2}\, dx$

27. $\displaystyle\int e^x \sqrt{e^x+1}\, dx$

28. $\displaystyle\int 4x^2 e^{x^3}\, dx$

29. $\displaystyle\int_0^4 \frac{t}{e^t}\, dt$

30. $\displaystyle\int x^2 \sqrt{x-1}\, dx$

APPLICATIONS

31. *Producer's surplus* If the supply function for x units of a commodity is $p = 30 + 100 \ln(2x+1)$ dollars, what is the producer's surplus at $x = 30$?

32. *Cost* If the marginal cost function for x units of a product is $\overline{MC} = 1 + 3 \ln(x+1)$ dollars per unit and if the fixed cost is $100, find the total cost function.

33. *Present value* Suppose that a machine's production can be considered as a continuous income stream with annual rate of flow at time t given by

$$f(t) = 10{,}000 - 500t \quad \text{(dollars per year)}$$

If money is worth 10% compounded continuously, find the present value of the machine over the next 5 years.

34. *Present value* Suppose that the production of a machine used to mine coal is considered as a

continuous income stream with annual rate of flow at time t given by

$$f(t) = 280{,}000 - 14{,}000t \quad \text{(dollars per year)}$$

If money is worth 7% compounded continuously, find the present value of this machine over the next 8 years.

35. *Income distribution* Suppose the Lorenz curve for the distribution of income of a certain country is given by

$$y = xe^{x-1}$$

Find the Gini coefficient of income.

36. *Income streams* Suppose the income from an Internet access business is a continuous income stream with annual rate of flow given by

$$f(t) = 100te^{-0.1t}$$

in thousands of dollars per year. Find the total income over the next 10 years.

37. *Demographics* The number of millions of White non-Hispanic individuals in the U.S. civilian non-institutional population age 16 or older for selected years from 1980 and projected to 2050 can be modeled by

$$P(x) = 96.1 + 17.4 \ln x$$

with x equal to the number of years past 1970 (*Source:* U.S. Census Bureau). Find the projected average population over the years 2020 through 2030.

38. *Natural gas* The percent of natural gas in the United States extracted from shale rock from 2012 and projected to 2040 is given by the function $y = -0.843 + 13.8 \ln x$, where x is the is the number of years after 2010 (*Source:* Energy Information Administration). What does this model project the average percent to be for the years 2015 through 2030?

SECTION 13.7 Improper Integrals and Their Applications

OBJECTIVES

- To evaluate improper integrals
- To apply improper integrals to continuous income streams and to probability density functions

APPLICATION PREVIEW

We saw in Section 13.4, "Applications of Definite Integrals in Business and Economics," that the present value of a continuous income stream over a fixed number of years can be found by using a definite integral. When this notion is extended to an infinite time interval, the result is called the capital value of the income stream and is given by

$$\text{Capital value} = \int_0^\infty f(t)e^{-rt}\, dt$$

where $f(t)$ is the annual rate of flow at time t and r is the annual interest rate compounded continuously. This is called an improper integral. For example, the capital value of a trust that provides $f(t) = \$10{,}000$ per year indefinitely (when interest is 10% compounded continuously) is found by evaluating an improper integral. (See Example 2.)

Improper Integral   Some applications of calculus to statistics or business (such as capital value) involve definite integrals over intervals of infinite length (**improper integrals**). The area of a region that extends infinitely to the left or right along the x-axis (see Figure 13.28) could be described by an improper integral.

Figure 13.28

To see how to find such an area and hence evaluate an improper integral, we consider how to find the area between the curve $y = 1/x^2$ and the x-axis to the right of $x = 1$. To find the area under this curve from $x = 1$ to $x = b$, where b is any number greater than 1 (see Figure 13.29), we evaluate

Figure 13.29

$$A = \int_1^b \frac{1}{x^2}\, dx = \frac{-1}{x}\bigg|_1^b = \frac{-1}{b} - \left(\frac{-1}{1}\right) = 1 - \frac{1}{b}$$

Note that the larger b is, the closer the area is to 1. If $b = 100$, $A = 0.99$; if $b = 1000$, $A = 0.999$; and if $b = 1{,}000{,}000$, $A = 0.999999$.

We can represent the area of the region under $1/x^2$ to the right of 1 using the notation

$$\lim_{b \to \infty} \int_1^b \frac{1}{x^2}\, dx = \lim_{b \to \infty}\left(1 - \frac{1}{b}\right)$$

where $\lim\limits_{b \to \infty}$ represents the limit as b gets larger without bound. Note that $\dfrac{1}{b} \to 0$ as $b \to \infty$, so

$$\lim_{b \to \infty}\left(1 - \frac{1}{b}\right) = 1 - 0 = 1$$

Thus the area under the curve $y = 1/x^2$ to the right of $x = 1$ is 1.

In general, we define the area under a curve $y = f(x)$ to the right of $x = a$, with $f(x) \geq 0$, to be

$$\text{Area} = \lim_{b \to \infty}(\text{area from } a \text{ to } b) = \lim_{b \to \infty} \int_a^b f(x)\, dx$$

This motivates the definition that follows.

Improper Integral

$$\int_a^\infty f(x)\, dx = \lim_{b \to \infty} \int_a^b f(x)\, dx$$

If the limit defining the **improper integral** is a unique finite number, we say that the integral *converges;* otherwise, we say that the integral *diverges.*

EXAMPLE 1   Improper Integrals

Evaluate the following improper integrals, if they converge.

(a) $\displaystyle\int_1^\infty \frac{1}{x^3}\, dx$ (b) $\displaystyle\int_1^\infty \frac{1}{x}\, dx$

Solution

(a) $\displaystyle\int_1^\infty \frac{1}{x^3}\, dx = \lim_{b \to \infty} \int_1^b x^{-3}\, dx = \lim_{b \to \infty}\left(\frac{x^{-2}}{-2}\right)\bigg|_1^b$

$$= \lim_{b \to \infty}\left[\frac{-1}{2b^2} - \left(\frac{-1}{2(1)^2}\right)\right] = \lim_{b \to \infty}\left(\frac{-1}{2b^2} + \frac{1}{2}\right)$$

Notice that $1/(2b^2) \to 0$ as $b \to \infty$, so the limit converges to $0 + \frac{1}{2} = \frac{1}{2}$. That is,

$$\int_1^\infty \frac{1}{x^3}\, dx = \frac{1}{2}$$

(b) $\displaystyle\int_1^\infty \frac{1}{x}\, dx = \lim_{b \to \infty} \int_1^b \frac{1}{x}\, dx = \lim_{b \to \infty}\left(\ln |x|\right)\bigg|_1^b = \lim_{b \to \infty}(\ln b - \ln 1)$

Because $\ln b$ increases without bound as $b \to \infty$, the limit diverges and we write

$$\int_1^\infty \frac{1}{x}\, dx = \infty$$

From Example 1, we can conclude that the area under the curve $y = 1/x^3$ to the right of $x = 1$ is $1/2$, whereas the corresponding area under the curve $y = 1/x$ is infinite. (We have already seen that the corresponding area under $y = 1/x^2$ is 1.)

As Figure 13.30 shows, the graphs of $y = 1/x^2$ and $y = 1/x$ look similar, but the graph of $y = 1/x^2$ gets "close" to the x-axis much more rapidly than does the graph of $y = 1/x$. The area under $y = 1/x$ does not converge to a finite number because as $x \to \infty$, the graph of $1/x$ does not approach the x-axis rapidly enough.

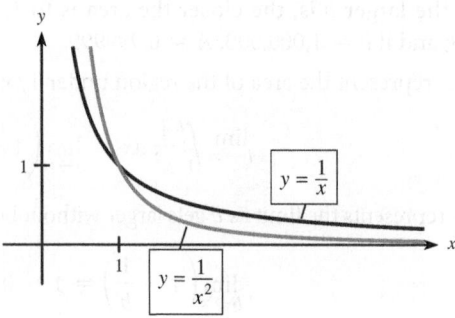

Figure 13.30

EXAMPLE 2   Capital Value | APPLICATION PREVIEW |

Suppose that an organization wants to establish a trust fund that will provide a continuous income stream with an annual rate of flow at time t given by $f(t) = 10{,}000$ dollars per year. If the interest rate remains at 10% compounded continuously, find the capital value of the fund.

Solution
The capital value of the fund uses the formula

$$\text{Capital value} = \int_0^\infty f(t)e^{-rt}\, dt$$

where $f(t)$ is the annual rate of flow at time t and r is the annual interest rate compounded continuously.

$$\int_0^\infty 10{,}000e^{-0.10t}\, dt = \lim_{b \to \infty} \int_0^b 10{,}000e^{-0.10t}\, dt = \lim_{b \to \infty} \left(-100{,}000e^{-0.10t} \right)\Big|_0^b$$

$$= \lim_{b \to \infty} \left(\frac{-100{,}000}{e^{0.10b}} + 100{,}000 \right) = 100{,}000$$

Thus the capital value of the fund is $100,000.

Another term for a fund such as the one in Example 2 is a **perpetuity.** Usually the rate of flow of a perpetuity is a constant. If the rate of flow is a constant A, it can be shown that the capital value is given by A/r. (See Example 2 and Problem 37 in the 13.7 Exercises.)

CHECKPOINT

1. True or false:

   (a) $\displaystyle \lim_{b \to \infty} \frac{1}{b^p} = 0$ if $p > 0$ (b) If $p > 0$, $b^p \to \infty$ as $b \to \infty$

   (c) $\displaystyle \lim_{b \to \infty} e^{-pb} = 0$ if $p > 0$

2. Evaluate the following (if they exist).

   (a) $\displaystyle \int_1^\infty \frac{1}{x^{4/3}}\, dx = \lim_{b \to \infty} \int_1^b x^{-4/3}\, dx$ (b) $\displaystyle \int_0^\infty \frac{dx}{\sqrt{x+1}}$

Two **additional improper integrals** involving infinite limits are defined as follows:

Additional Improper Integrals

$$\int_{-\infty}^{b} f(x)\, dx = \lim_{a \to \infty} \int_{-a}^{b} f(x)\, dx$$

The integral converges if the limit is finite. Otherwise, it diverges.

$$\int_{-\infty}^{\infty} f(x)\, dx = \lim_{a \to \infty} \int_{-a}^{c} f(x)\, dx + \lim_{b \to \infty} \int_{c}^{b} f(x)\, dx$$

for any finite constant c. (Often, c is chosen to be 0.) If both limits are finite, the improper integral converges; otherwise, it diverges.

EXAMPLE 3   **Improper Integrals**

Evaluate the following integrals.

(a) $\displaystyle\int_{-\infty}^{4} e^{3x}\, dx$ (b) $\displaystyle\int_{-\infty}^{\infty} \frac{x^3}{(x^4 + 3)^2}\, dx$

Solution

(a) $\displaystyle\int_{-\infty}^{4} e^{3x}\, dx = \lim_{a \to \infty} \int_{-a}^{4} e^{3x}\, dx = \lim_{a \to \infty} \left[\left(\frac{1}{3} \right) e^{3x} \right]_{-a}^{4}$

$= \lim_{a \to \infty} \left[\left(\frac{1}{3} \right) e^{12} - \left(\frac{1}{3} \right) e^{-3a} \right] = \lim_{a \to \infty} \left[\left(\frac{1}{3} \right) e^{12} - \left(\frac{1}{3} \right)\left(\frac{1}{e^{3a}} \right) \right]$

$= \dfrac{1}{3} e^{12}$ (because $1/e^{3a} \to 0$ as $a \to \infty$)

(b) $\displaystyle\int_{-\infty}^{\infty} \frac{x^3}{(x^4 + 3)^2}\, dx = \lim_{a \to \infty} \int_{-a}^{0} \frac{x^3}{(x^4 + 3)^2}\, dx + \lim_{b \to \infty} \int_{0}^{b} \frac{x^3}{(x^4 + 3)^2}\, dx$

$= \lim_{a \to \infty} \left[\frac{1}{4} \frac{(x^4 + 3)^{-1}}{-1} \right]_{-a}^{0} + \lim_{b \to \infty} \left[\frac{1}{4} \frac{(x^4 + 3)^{-1}}{-1} \right]_{0}^{b}$

$= \lim_{a \to \infty} \left[-\frac{1}{4}\left(\frac{1}{3} - \frac{1}{a^4 + 3} \right) \right] + \lim_{b \to \infty} \left[-\frac{1}{4}\left(\frac{1}{b^4 + 3} - \frac{1}{3} \right) \right]$

$= -\dfrac{1}{12} + 0 + 0 + \dfrac{1}{12} = 0 \left(\text{since } \lim_{a \to \infty} \frac{1}{a^4 + 3} = 0 \text{ and } \lim_{b \to \infty} \frac{1}{b^4 + 3} = 0 \right)$ ■

Probability   We noted in Chapter 8, "Further Topics in Probability; Data Description," that the sum of the probabilities for a probability distribution (a **probability density function**) equals 1. In particular, we stated that the area under the normal probability curve is 1. The normal distribution is an example of a continuous probability distribution because the values of the random variable are considered over intervals rather than at discrete values. There are many important continuous probability distributions besides the normal distribution, but all such distributions satisfy the following definition.

Probability Density Function

If $f(x) \geq 0$ for all x, then f is a **probability density function** for a continuous random variable x if and only if

$$\int_{-\infty}^{\infty} f(x)\, dx = 1$$

We have noted previously that when $f(x)$ is a continuous probability density function, then

$$Pr(a \leq x \leq b) = \int_{a}^{b} f(x)\, dx$$

In the next example, we revisit a probability density function application from Example 7 of Section 13.2.

EXAMPLE 4 | **Product Life**

Suppose the probability density function for the life span of a computer component is given by

$$f(x) = \begin{cases} 0.10e^{-0.10x} & \text{if } x \geq 0 \\ 0 & \text{if } x < 0 \end{cases}$$

(a) Verify that $f(x)$ is a probability density function.
(b) Find the probability that such a component lasts more than 3 years.

Solution

(a) To verify that $f(x)$ is a probability density function, we show $\int_{-\infty}^{\infty} f(x)\, dx = 1$:

$$\int_{-\infty}^{\infty} f(x)\, dx = \int_{-\infty}^{0} f(x)\, dx + \int_{0}^{\infty} f(x)\, dx = \int_{-\infty}^{0} 0\, dx + \int_{0}^{\infty} 0.10e^{-0.10x}\, dx$$

$$= 0 + \lim_{b \to \infty} \int_{0}^{b} 0.10e^{-0.10x}\, dx$$

$$= \lim_{b \to \infty} (-e^{-0.10x})\Big|_0^b = \lim_{b \to \infty} (-e^{-0.10b} + 1) = 1$$

(b) The probability that the component lasts more than 3 years is given by

$$\Pr(x \geq 3) = \int_{3}^{\infty} 0.10e^{-0.10x}\, dx$$

$$= \lim_{b \to \infty} \int_{3}^{b} 0.10e^{-0.10x}\, dx = \lim_{b \to \infty} (-e^{-0.10x})\Big|_3^b$$

$$= \lim_{b \to \infty} (-e^{-0.10b} + e^{-0.3}) = e^{-0.3} \approx 0.7408$$

In Section 8.3, "Discrete Probability Distributions; The Binomial Distribution," we found the expected value (mean) of a discrete probability distribution using the formula

$$E(x) = \sum x \Pr(x)$$

For continuous probability distributions such as the normal probability distribution, the **expected value**, or **mean**, can be found as follows.

Mean (Expected Value)	If x is a continuous random variable with probability density function f, then the **mean (expected value)** of the probability distribution is $$\mu = \int_{-\infty}^{\infty} x f(x)\, dx$$

The normal distribution density function, in standard form, is

$$f(x) = \frac{1}{\sqrt{2\pi}} e^{-x^2/2}$$

so the mean of the normal probability distribution is given by

$$\mu = \int_{-\infty}^{\infty} x \left(\frac{1}{\sqrt{2\pi}} e^{-x^2/2} \right) dx$$

$$= \lim_{a \to \infty} \int_{-a}^{0} \frac{1}{\sqrt{2\pi}} x e^{-x^2/2}\, dx + \lim_{b \to \infty} \int_{0}^{b} \frac{1}{\sqrt{2\pi}} x e^{-x^2/2}\, dx$$

$$= \lim_{a \to \infty} \frac{1}{\sqrt{2\pi}} \left(-e^{-x^2/2} \right)\Big|_{-a}^{0} + \lim_{b \to \infty} \frac{1}{\sqrt{2\pi}} \left(-e^{-x^2/2} \right)\Big|_{0}^{b}$$

$$= \frac{1}{\sqrt{2\pi}} (-1 + 0) + \frac{1}{\sqrt{2\pi}} (0 + 1) = 0$$

This verifies the statement in Chapter 8 that the mean of the standard normal distribution is 0.

EXERCISES 13.7

**In Problems 1–20, evaluate the improper integrals that
converge.**

1. $\displaystyle\int_1^\infty \frac{dx}{x^6}$

2. $\displaystyle\int_1^\infty \frac{1}{x^4}\, dx$

3. $\displaystyle\int_1^\infty \frac{dt}{t^{3/2}}$

4. $\displaystyle\int_5^\infty \frac{dx}{(x-1)^3}$

5. $\displaystyle\int_1^\infty e^{-x}\, dx$

6. $\displaystyle\int_0^\infty x^2 e^{-x^3}\, dx$

7. $\displaystyle\int_1^\infty \frac{dt}{t^{1/3}}$

8. $\displaystyle\int_1^\infty \frac{1}{\sqrt{x}}\, dx$

9. $\displaystyle\int_0^\infty e^{3x}\, dx$

10. $\displaystyle\int_1^\infty x e^{x^2}\, dx$

11. $\displaystyle\int_{-\infty}^{-1} \frac{10}{x^2}\, dx$

12. $\displaystyle\int_{-\infty}^{-2} \frac{x}{\sqrt{(x^2-1)^3}}\, dx$

13. $\displaystyle\int_{-\infty}^0 x^2 e^{-x^3}\, dx$

14. $\displaystyle\int_{-\infty}^0 \frac{x}{(x^2+1)^2}\, dx$

15. $\displaystyle\int_{-\infty}^{-1} \frac{6}{x}\, dx$

16. $\displaystyle\int_{-\infty}^{-2} \frac{5}{3x+5}\, dx$

17. $\displaystyle\int_{-\infty}^\infty \frac{2x}{(x^2+1)^2}\, dx$

18. $\displaystyle\int_{-\infty}^\infty \frac{9x^5}{(3x^6+7)^2}\, dx$

19. $\displaystyle\int_{-\infty}^\infty x^3 e^{-x^4}\, dx$

20. $\displaystyle\int_{-\infty}^\infty x^4 e^{-x^5}\, dx$

21. For what value of c does $\displaystyle\int_0^\infty \frac{c}{e^{0.5t}}\, dt = 1$?

22. For what value of c does $\displaystyle\int_{10}^\infty \frac{c}{x^3}\, dx = 1$?

**In Problems 23–26, find the area, if it exists, of the region
under the graph of $y = f(x)$ and to the right of $x = 1$.**

23. $f(x) = \dfrac{x}{e^{x^2}}$

24. $f(x) = \dfrac{1}{\sqrt[5]{x^3}}$

25. $f(x) = \dfrac{1}{\sqrt[3]{x^5}}$

26. $f(x) = \dfrac{1}{x\sqrt{x}}$

27. Show that the function
$$f(x) = \begin{cases} \dfrac{200}{x^3} & \text{if } x \ge 10 \\ 0 & \text{otherwise} \end{cases}$$
is a probability density function.

28. Show that
$$f(t) = \begin{cases} 3e^{-3t} & \text{if } t \ge 0 \\ 0 & \text{if } t < 0 \end{cases}$$
is a probability density function.

29. For what value of c is the function
$$f(x) = \begin{cases} c/x^2 & \text{if } x \ge 1 \\ 0 & \text{otherwise} \end{cases}$$
a probability density function?

30. For what value of c is the function
$$f(x) = \begin{cases} c/x^3 & \text{if } x \ge 100 \\ 0 & \text{otherwise} \end{cases}$$
a probability density function?

31. Find the value of c so that
$$f(x) = \begin{cases} ce^{-x/4} & x \ge 0 \\ 0 & x < 0 \end{cases}$$
is a probability density function.

32. Find the value of c (in terms of k) so that
$$f(x) = \begin{cases} ce^{-kx} & \text{if } x \ge 0 \\ 0 & \text{if } x < 0 \end{cases}$$
is a probability density function.

33. Find the mean of the probability distribution if the
probability density function is
$$f(x) = \begin{cases} \dfrac{200}{x^3} & \text{if } x \ge 10 \\ 0 & \text{otherwise} \end{cases}$$

34. Find the mean of the probability distribution if the
probability density function is
$$f(x) = \begin{cases} c/x^4 & \text{if } x \ge 10 \\ 0 & \text{otherwise} \end{cases}$$

35. Find the area below the graph of $y = f(x)$ and above
the x-axis for $f(x) = 24xe^{-3x}$. Use the graph of
$y = f(x)$ to find the interval for which $f(x) \ge 0$ and
the graph of the integral of $f(x)$ over this interval to
find the area.

36. Find the area below the graph of $y = f(x)$ and above the x-axis for $f(x) = x^2e^{-x}$ and $x \geq 0$. Use the graph of the integral of $f(x)$ over this interval to find the area.

APPLICATIONS

37. *Capital value* Suppose that a continuous income stream has an annual rate of flow at time t given by $f(t) = A$, where A is a constant. If the interest rate is r (as a decimal, $r > 0$) compounded continuously, show that the capital value of the stream is A/r.

38. *Capital value* Suppose that a donor wants to provide a cash gift to a hospital that will generate a continuous income stream with an annual rate of flow at time t given by $f(t) = \$20,000$ per year. If the annual interest rate is 12% compounded continuously, find the capital value of this perpetuity.

39. *Capital value* Suppose that a business provides a continuous income stream with an annual rate of flow at time t given by $f(t) = 120e^{0.04t}$ in thousands of dollars per year. If the interest rate is 9% compounded continuously, find the capital value of the business.

40. *Capital value* Suppose that the output of the machinery in a factory can be considered as a continuous income stream with annual rate of flow at time t given by $f(t) = 450e^{-0.09t}$ (in thousands of dollars per year). If the annual interest rate is 6% compounded continuously, find the capital value of the machinery.

41. *Capital value* A business has a continuous income stream with an annual rate of flow at time t given by $f(t) = 56,000e^{0.02t}$ (dollars per year). If the interest rate is 10% compounded continuously, find the capital value of the business.

42. *Capital value* Suppose that a business provides a continuous income stream with an annual rate of flow at time t given by $f(t) = 10,800e^{0.06t}$ (dollars per year). If money is worth 12% compounded continuously, find the capital value of the business.

43. *Repair time* In a manufacturing process involving several machines, the average down time t (in hours) for a machine that needs repair has the probability density function
$$f(t) = 0.5e^{-0.5t} \quad t \geq 0$$
Find the probability that a failed machine's down time is
(a) 2 hours or more.   (b) 8 hours or more.

44. *Customer service* The duration t (in minutes) of customer service calls received by a certain company is given by the probability density function
$$f(t) = 0.4e^{-0.4t} \quad t \geq 0$$
Find the probability that a call selected at random lasts
(a) 4 minutes or more.
(b) 10 minutes or more.

45. *Quality control* The probability density function for the life span of an electronics part is $f(t) = 0.08e^{-0.08t}$, where t is the number of months in service. Find the probability that a randomly selected part of this type lasts

(a) longer than 24 months.
(b) longer than 24 months given that it lasts longer than 12 months.

46. *Warranties* A manufacturer of electrical components has determined that the length of time t (in hundreds of hours) before a certain one of its components fails has probability density function
$$f(t) = 2te^{-t^2}$$
Find the probability that a randomly selected one of these components lasts
(a) more than 150 hours.
(b) more than 150 hours given that it lasts more than 100 hours.

47. *Learning experiments* In a psychology experiment, laboratory rats are timed through a maze to reach a food reward. The minutes m required to reach the reward have probability density function
$$f(m) = \frac{1.5}{m^2} \quad (m > 1.5)$$
Find the probability that the time for a randomly selected lab rat to complete the maze is more than
(a) 2 minutes.   (b) 4 minutes.
(c) 4 minutes given that it is more than 2 minutes.

48. *Earthquakes* Suppose the recorded Richter scale magnitude M of earthquakes in a certain region of South America has probability density function
$$f(M) = 0.4e^{-0.4M}$$
Find the probability that an earthquake in this region has magnitude greater than
(a) 2.5.   (b) 4.5.
(c) 4.5 given it was greater than 2.5.

49. *Radioactive waste* Suppose that the rate at which a nuclear power plant produces radioactive waste is proportional to the number of years it has been operating, according to $f(t) = 500t$ (in pounds per year). Suppose also that the waste decays exponentially at a rate of 3% per year. Then the amount of radioactive waste that will accumulate in b years is given by
$$\int_0^b 500te^{-0.03(b-t)} \, dt$$
(a) Evaluate this integral.
(b) How much waste will accumulate in the long run? Take the limit as $b \to \infty$ in part (a).

50. *Inventory management* A company uses wood chips in the manufacture of processed wood pieces of various sizes. Suppose the tons of wood chips T used per day has probability density function
$$f(T) = 0.125e^{-0.125T}$$
(a) Find the probability of using more than 8 tons of wood chips in a day.
(b) Find the number of tons T (to the nearest ton) so that the probability of using more than T tons in a day is 0.05.

Numerical Integration Methods: The Trapezoidal Rule and Simpson's Rule

OBJECTIVES

- To approximate definite integrals using the Trapezoidal Rule
- To approximate definite integrals using Simpson's Rule

APPLICATION PREVIEW

A pharmaceutical company tests the body's assimilation of a new drug by administering a 200-milligram dose and collecting the following data from blood samples, where t is time in hours and $R(t)$ gives the assimilation of the drug in milligrams per hour.

t	0	0.5	1.0	1.5	2.0	2.5	3.0
$R(t)$	0.0	15.3	32.3	51.0	74.8	102.0	130.9

The company would like to find the amount of drug assimilated in 3 hours, which is given by

$$\int_0^3 R(t)\, dt$$

In this section, we develop straightforward and accurate methods for approximating integrals such as this, even when, as with $R(t)$, only function data, rather than a formula, are given. (See Example 4.)

We have studied several techniques for integration and have even used tables to evaluate some integrals. Yet some functions that arise in practical problems cannot be integrated by using any formula. For any function $f(x) \geq 0$ on an interval $[a, b]$, however, we have seen that a definite integral can be viewed as an area and that we can usually approximate the area and hence the integral. (See Figure 13.31.) One such approximation method uses rectangles, as we saw when we defined the definite integral. In this section, we consider two other **numerical integration methods** to approximate a definite integral: the **Trapezoidal Rule** and **Simpson's Rule.**

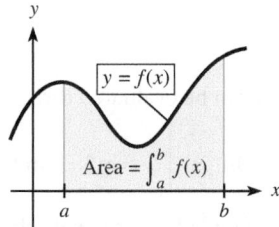

Figure 13.31

Trapezoidal Rule

To develop the Trapezoidal Rule formula, we assume that $f(x) \geq 0$ on $[a, b]$ and subdivide the interval $[a, b]$ into n equal pieces, each of length $(b - a)/n = h$. Within each subdivision, we can approximate the area using a trapezoid. See Figure 13.32. We can use the formula for the area of a trapezoid to approximate the area of the first subdivision.

Figure 13.32

Continuing in this way for each trapezoid, we have

$$\int_a^b f(x)\, dx \approx A_1 + A_2 + A_3 + \cdots + A_{n-1} + A_n$$

$$= \left[\frac{f(x_0) + f(x_1)}{2}\right] h + \left[\frac{f(x_1) + f(x_2)}{2}\right] h +$$

$$\left[\frac{f(x_2) + f(x_3)}{2}\right] h + \cdots + \left[\frac{f(x_{n-1}) + f(x_n)}{2}\right] h$$

$$= \frac{h}{2}\left[f(x_0) + f(x_1) + f(x_1) + f(x_2) + f(x_2) + \cdots + f(x_{n-1}) + f(x_{n-1}) + f(x_n)\right]$$

This can be simplified to obtain the **Trapezoidal Rule**.

Trapezoidal Rule

If f is continuous on $[a, b]$, then

$$\int_a^b f(x)\, dx \approx \frac{h}{2}\left[f(x_0) + 2f(x_1) + 2f(x_2) + \cdots + 2f(x_{n-1}) + f(x_n)\right]$$

where $h = \dfrac{b - a}{n}$ and n is the number of equal subdivisions of $[a, b]$.

Despite the fact that we used areas to develop the Trapezoidal Rule, we can use this rule to evaluate definite integrals even if $f(x) < 0$ on all or part of $[a, b]$.

EXAMPLE 1   **Trapezoidal Rule**

Use the Trapezoidal Rule to approximate $\displaystyle\int_1^3 \frac{1}{x}\, dx$ with

(a) $n = 4$.
(b) $n = 8$.

Solution
First, we note that this integral can be evaluated directly:

$$\int_1^3 \frac{1}{x}\, dx = \ln |x| \,\Big|_1^3 = \ln 3 - \ln 1 = \ln 3 \approx 1.099$$

(a) The interval $[1, 3]$ must be divided into 4 equal subintervals of width $h = \frac{3-1}{4} = \frac{2}{4} = \frac{1}{2}$ as follows:

$$
\begin{array}{ccccc}
1 & 1.5 & 2 & 2.5 & 3 \\
\mid & \mid & \mid & \mid & \mid \\
x_0 & x_1 & x_2 & x_3 & x_4
\end{array}
$$

Thus from the Trapezoidal Rule, we have

$$\int_1^3 \frac{1}{x}\, dx \approx \frac{h}{2}\left[f(x_0) + 2f(x_1) + 2f(x_2) + 2f(x_3) + f(x_4)\right]$$

$$= \frac{1/2}{2}\left[f(1) + 2f(1.5) + 2f(2) + 2f(2.5) + f(3)\right]$$

$$= \frac{1}{4}\left[1 + 2\left(\frac{1}{1.5}\right) + 2\left(\frac{1}{2}\right) + 2\left(\frac{1}{2.5}\right) + \frac{1}{3}\right] \approx 1.117$$

(b) In this case, the interval $[1, 3]$ is divided into 8 equal subintervals of width $h = \frac{3-1}{8} = \frac{2}{8} = \frac{1}{4}$ as follows.

$$
\begin{array}{ccccccccc}
1 & 1.25 & 1.5 & 1.75 & 2 & 2.25 & 2.5 & 2.75 & 3 \\
\mid & \mid & \mid & \mid & \mid & \mid & \mid & \mid & \mid \\
x_0 & x_1 & x_2 & x_3 & x_4 & x_5 & x_6 & x_7 & x_8
\end{array}
$$

Thus, from the Trapezoidal Rule, we have

$$\int_1^3 \frac{1}{x}\,dx \approx \frac{h}{2}[f(x_0) + 2f(x_1) + 2f(x_2) + 2f(x_3) + 2f(x_4) + 2f(x_5)$$

$$+\; 2f(x_6) + 2f(x_7) + f(x_8)]$$

$$= \frac{1/4}{2}\left[\frac{1}{1} + 2\left(\frac{1}{1.25}\right) + 2\left(\frac{1}{1.5}\right) + 2\left(\frac{1}{1.75}\right) + 2\left(\frac{1}{2}\right) + 2\left(\frac{1}{2.25}\right)\right.$$

$$\left.+\; 2\left(\frac{1}{2.5}\right) + 2\left(\frac{1}{2.75}\right) + \frac{1}{3}\right]$$

$$\approx 1.103$$

In Example 1, because we know that the value of the integral is $\ln 3 \approx 1.099$, we can measure the accuracy of each approximation. We can see that a larger value of n (namely, $n = 8$) produced a more accurate approximation to $\ln 3$. In general, larger values of n produce more accurate approximations, but they also make computations more difficult.

Calculator Note

The TABLE feature of a graphing calculator can be used to find the values of $f(x_0), f(x_1), f(x_2)$, etc., needed for the Trapezoidal Rule. Figure 13.33(a) shows the TABLE set up for Example 1(b), and Figures 13.33(b) and 13.33(c) show the TABLE values.

TABLE SETUP
TblStart=1
▲Tbl=.25
Indpnt: **Auto** Ask
Depend: **Auto** Ask

X	Y₁
1	1
1.25	.8
1.5	.66667
1.75	.57143
2	.5
2.25	.44444
2.5	.4
X=1	

X	Y₁
1.5	.66667
1.75	.57143
2	.5
2.25	.44444
2.5	.4
2.75	.36364
3	.33333
Y₁=.5	

Figure 13.33   (a)   (b)   (c)

Thus for the Trapezoidal Rule, we get

$$\int_1^3 \frac{1}{x}\,dx \approx \frac{0.25}{2}\left[\begin{array}{l}1(1) + 2(0.8) + 2(0.66667) + 2(0.57143) + 2(0.5) \\ +\; 2(0.44444) + 2(0.4) + 2(0.36364) + 1(0.33333)\end{array}\right] \approx 1.103$$

just as we did in Example 1(b).

Spreadsheet Note

The following spreadsheet shows the Trapezoidal Rule approximation of the definite integral $\int_1^3 \frac{1}{x}\,dx$ with $n = 8$ trapezoids, found in Example 1(b).

	A	B	C	D	E
1	x	f(x)	Weight	(b−a)/(2n)	Terms
2	1	1	1	0.125	0.125
3	1.25	0.8	2	0.125	0.2
4	1.5	0.666667	2	0.125	0.166667
5	1.75	0.571429	2	0.125	0.142857
6	2	0.5	2	0.125	0.125
7	2.25	0.444444	2	0.125	0.111111
8	2.5	0.4	2	0.125	0.1
9	2.75	0.363636	2	0.125	0.090909
10	3	0.333333	1	0.125	0.041667
11	$\int_1^3 \frac{1}{x}\,dx$				1.103211

Cells A2 through A10 contain the x-values at the endpoints of the subintervals, and cells B2 through B10 contain the functional values at the endpoints of the subintervals. The coefficients (weights) given in the Trapezoidal Rule formula and the value $h/2 = (b - a)/(2n) = 2/16$, half the width of each subinterval, are contained in columns C and D, respectively. The formula =B2*C2*D2 in E2 and filled down through E10 gives the terms appearing in the Trapezoidal Rule formula, and the formula =SUM(E2:E10) in E11 approximates the value of $\int_1^3 \frac{1}{x}\, dx$. Note that this value agrees with the value found in Example 1(b). See Appendix B, Section 13.8, or the Online Excel Guide for more details. ∎

Because the exact value of an integral is rarely available when an approximation is used, it is important to have some way to judge the accuracy of an answer. The following formula, which we state without proof, can be used to bound the error that results from using the Trapezoidal Rule.

Trapezoidal Rule Error

The error E in using the Trapezoidal Rule to approximate $\int_a^b f(x)\, dx$ satisfies

$$|E| \le \frac{(b-a)^3}{12n^2}\left[\max_{a \le x \le b}|f''(x)|\right]$$

where n is the number of equal subdivisions of $[a, b]$.

For a numerical method to be worthwhile, there must be some way of assessing its accuracy. Hence, this formula is important. We leave its application, however, to more advanced courses.

Simpson's Rule

The Trapezoidal Rule was developed by using a line segment to approximate the function over each subinterval and then using the areas under the line segments to approximate the area under the curve. Another numerical method, **Simpson's Rule,** uses a parabola to approximate the function over each pair of subintervals (see Figure 13.34) and then uses the areas under the parabolas to approximate the area under the curve. Because Simpson's Rule is based on pairs of subintervals, n must be even.

Simpson's Rule (n Even)

If $f(x)$ is continuous on $[a, b]$ and $[a, b]$ is divided into an *even* number n of equal subdivisions, then

$$\int_a^b f(x)\, dx \approx \frac{h}{3}[f(x_0) + 4f(x_1) + 2f(x_2) + 4f(x_3) + \cdots + 2f(x_{n-2})$$

$$+ 4f(x_{n-1}) + f(x_n)]$$

where $h = \dfrac{b - a}{n}$.

We leave the derivation of Simpson's Rule to more advanced courses.

Figure 13.34

EXAMPLE 2 **Simpson's Rule**

Use Simpson's Rule with $n = 4$ to approximate $\int_1^3 \dfrac{1}{x}\, dx$.

Solution

Because $n = 4$ is even, Simpson's Rule can be used, and the interval is divided into four subintervals of length $h = \dfrac{3-1}{4} = \dfrac{1}{2}$ as follows:

$$
\begin{array}{cccccc}
1 & 1.5 & 2 & 2.5 & 3 \\
\hline
x_0 & x_1 & x_2 & x_3 & x_4
\end{array}
$$

$$\int_1^3 \frac{1}{x}\, dx \approx \frac{1/2}{3}\left[f(1) + 4f(1.5) + 2f(2) + 4f(2.5) + f(3) \right]$$

$$= \frac{1}{6}\left[\frac{1}{1} + 4\left(\frac{1}{1.5}\right) + 2\left(\frac{1}{2}\right) + 4\left(\frac{1}{2.5}\right) + \frac{1}{3} \right]$$

$$\approx 1.100$$

Note that the result of Example 2 is better than both the $n = 4$ and the $n = 8$ Trapezoidal Rule approximations done in Example 1. In general, Simpson's Rule is more accurate than the Trapezoidal Rule for a given number of subdivisions. We can determine the accuracy of Simpson's Rule approximations by using the following formula.

Simpson's Rule Error Formula

The error E in using Simpson's Rule to approximate $\int_a^b f(x)\, dx$ satisfies

$$|E| \le \frac{(b-a)^5}{180n^4}\left[\max_{a \le x \le b} \left| f^{(4)}(x) \right| \right]$$

where n is the number of equal subdivisions of $[a, b]$ and $f^{(4)}(x)$ is the fourth derivative of $f(x)$.

The presence of the factor $180n^4$ in the denominator indicates that the error will often be quite small for even a modest value of n. Although Simpson's Rule often leads to more accurate results than the Trapezoidal Rule for a fixed choice of n, the Trapezoidal Rule is sometimes used because its error is more easily determined than that of Simpson's Rule or, more important, because the number of subdivisions is odd.

CHECKPOINT

1. Suppose [1, 4] is divided into 6 equal subintervals.
   (a) Find the width h of each subinterval.
   (b) Find the subdivision points.
2. True or false:
   (a) When the Trapezoidal Rule is used, the number of subdivisions, n, must be even.
   (b) When Simpson's Rule is used, the number of subdivisions, n, must be even.
3. We can show that $\int_0^2 4x^3\, dx = 16$. Use $n = 4$ subdivisions to find
   (a) the Trapezoidal Rule approximation of this integral.
   (b) the Simpson's Rule approximation of this integral.

Technology Note The TABLE feature of a graphing calculator can be used in exactly the same way with Simpson's Rule as it was with the Trapezoidal Rule. An Excel spreadsheet can also be used in the same way with Simpson's Rule as with the Trapezoidal Rule.

EXAMPLE 3   Simpson's Rule

Use Simpson's Rule with $n = 10$ subdivisions to approximate

$$\int_1^6 [\ln(x)]^2 \, dx$$

Solution

With $Y_1 = [\ln(x)]^2$ and $h = \dfrac{b-a}{n} = \dfrac{6-1}{10} = 0.5$, we can use a graphing calculator with ΔTbl $= 0.5$ to find the following table of values.

X	Y_1	X	Y_1
1	0	4	1.9218
1.5	0.1644	4.5	2.2622
2	0.48045	5	2.5903
2.5	0.83959	5.5	2.9062
3	1.2069	6	3.2104
3.5	1.5694		

Thus Simpson's Rule yields

$$\int_1^6 [\ln(x)]^2 \, dx$$

$$\approx \frac{0.5}{3}\left[\begin{array}{l} 1(0) + 4(0.1644) + 2(0.48045) + 4(0.83959) + 2(1.2069) + 4(1.5694) \\ \quad + 2(1.9218) + 4(2.2622) + 2(2.5903) + 4(2.9062) + 1(3.2104) \end{array} \right]$$

$$\approx 7.7627$$

One advantage that both the Trapezoidal Rule and Simpson's Rule offer is that they may be used when only function values at the subdivision points are known and the function formula itself is not known. This can be especially useful in applied problems.

EXAMPLE 4   Pharmaceutical Testing | APPLICATION PREVIEW |

A pharmaceutical company tests the body's ability to assimilate a drug. The test is done by administering a 200-milligram dose and then, every half hour, monitoring the rate of assimilation. The following table gives the data; t is time in hours, and $R(t)$ is the rate of assimilation in milligrams per hour.

t	0	0.5	1.0	1.5	2.0	2.5	3.0
$R(t)$	0.0	15.3	32.3	51.0	74.8	102.0	130.9

To find the total amount of the drug (in milligrams) that is assimilated in the first 3 hours, the company must find

$$\int_0^3 R(t) \, dt$$

Use Simpson's Rule to approximate this definite integral.

Solution

The values of t correspond to the endpoints of the subintervals, and the values of $R(t)$ correspond to function values at those endpoints. From the table, we see that $h = \frac{1}{2}$ and $n = 6$ (even); thus Simpson's Rule is applied as follows:

$$\int_0^3 R(t) \, dt \approx \frac{h}{3}[R(t_0) + 4R(t_1) + 2R(t_2) + 4R(t_3) + 2R(t_4) + 4R(t_5) + R(t_6)]$$

$$= \frac{\frac{1}{2}}{3}[0 + 4(15.3) + 2(32.3) + 4(51.0) + 2(74.8) + 4(102.0) + 130.9]$$

$$\approx 169.7 \text{ mg}$$

Thus at the end of 3 hours, the body has assimilated approximately 169.7 milligrams of the 200-milligram dose.

Note in Example 4 that the Trapezoidal Rule could be used because it relies only on the values of $R(t)$ at the subdivision endpoints.

In practice, these kinds of approximations are usually done with a computer, where the computations can be done quickly, even for large values of n. In addition, numerical methods (and hence computer programs) exist that approximate the errors, even in cases such as Example 4 where the function is not known. We leave any further discussion of error approximation formulas and additional numerical techniques for a more advanced course.

CHECKPOINT ANSWERS

1. (a) $h = \dfrac{1}{2} = 0.5$
   (b) $x_0 = 1, x_1 = 1.5, x_2 = 2, x_3 = 2.5, x_4 = 3, x_5 = 3.5, x_6 = 4$
2. (a) False. With the Trapezoidal Rule, n can be even or odd.
   (b) True
3. (a) 17
   (b) 16

EXERCISES 13.8

For each interval $[a, b]$ and value of n given in Problems 1–6, find h and the values of $x_0, x_1, \ldots x_n$.
1. $[0, 2]$ $n = 4$
2. $[0, 4]$ $n = 8$
3. $[1, 4]$ $n = 6$
4. $[2, 5]$ $n = 9$
5. $[-1, 4]$ $n = 5$
6. $[-1, 2]$ $n = 6$

For each integral in Problems 7–12, do the following.
(a) Approximate its value using the Trapezoidal Rule.
(b) Approximate its value using Simpson's Rule.
(c) Find its exact value by integration.
(d) State which approximation is more accurate.
   (Round each result to 2 decimal places.)

7. $\displaystyle\int_0^3 x^2\, dx;\quad n = 6$

8. $\displaystyle\int_0^1 x^3\, dx;\quad n = 4$

9. $\displaystyle\int_1^2 \frac{1}{x^2}\, dx;\quad n = 4$

10. $\displaystyle\int_1^4 \frac{1}{x}\, dx;\quad n = 6$

11. $\displaystyle\int_0^4 x^{1/2}\, dx;\quad n = 8$

12. $\displaystyle\int_0^2 x^{3/2}\, dx;\quad n = 8$

In Problems 13–18, approximate each integral by
(a) the Trapezoidal Rule.
(b) Simpson's Rule.
Use $n = 4$ and round answers to three decimal places.

13. $\displaystyle\int_0^2 \sqrt{x^3 + 1}\, dx$

14. $\displaystyle\int_0^2 \frac{dx}{\sqrt{4x^3 + 1}}$

15. $\displaystyle\int_0^1 e^{-x^2}\, dx$

16. $\displaystyle\int_0^1 e^{x^2}\, dx$

17. $\displaystyle\int_1^5 \ln(x^2 - x + 1)\, dx$

18. $\displaystyle\int_1^5 \ln(x^2 + x + 2)\, dx$

Use the table of values given in each of Problems 19–22 to approximate $\displaystyle\int_a^b f(x)\, dx$. Use Simpson's Rule whenever n is even; otherwise, use the Trapezoidal Rule. Round answers to 1 decimal place.

19. Find $\displaystyle\int_1^4 f(x)\, dx$.

x	$f(x)$
1	1
1.6	2.2
2.2	1.8
2.8	2.9
3.4	4.6
4.0	2.1

20. Find $\displaystyle\int_1^2 f(x)\, dx$.

x	$f(x)$
1	1
1.2	0.5
1.4	0.3
1.6	0.1
1.8	0.8
2.0	0.1

21. Find $\displaystyle\int_{1.2}^{3.6} f(x)\, dx$.

x	$f(x)$
1.2	6.1
1.6	4.8
2.0	3.1
2.4	2.0
2.8	2.8
3.2	5.6
3.6	9.7

22. Find $\displaystyle\int_0^{1.8} f(x)\, dx$.

x	$f(x)$
0	8.8
0.3	4.6
0.6	1.5
0.9	0
1.2	0.7
1.5	2.8
1.8	7.6

APPLICATIONS

In Problems 23–30, round all calculations to 2 decimal places.

23. *Total income* Suppose that the production from an assembly line can be considered as a continuous income stream with annual rate of flow given by

$$f(t) = 100\frac{e^{0.1t}}{t + 1} \quad \text{(in thousands of dollars per year)}.$$

Use Simpson's Rule with $n = 4$ to approximate the total income over the first 2 years, given by

$$\text{Total income} = \int_0^2 \frac{100e^{0.1t}}{t + 1}\, dt$$

24. *Present value* Suppose that the rate of flow of a continuous income stream is given by $f(t) = 500t$ (in thousands of dollars per year). If money is worth 7% compounded continuously, then the present value of this stream over the next 5 years is given by

$$\text{Present value} = \int_0^5 500t\, e^{-0.07t}\, dt$$

Use the Trapezoidal Rule with $n = 5$ to approximate this present value.

25. *Cost* Suppose that a company's total cost (in dollars) of producing x items is given by $C(x) = (x^2 + 1)^{3/2} + 1000$. Use the Trapezoidal Rule with $n = 3$ to approximate the average total cost for the production of $x = 30$ to $x = 33$ items.

26. *Demand* Suppose that the demand for q units of a certain product at $\$p$ per unit is given by

$$p = 850 + \frac{100}{q^2 + 1}$$

Use Simpson's Rule with $n = 6$ to approximate the average price as demand ranges from 3 to 9 items.

Supply and demand **Use the supply and demand schedules in Problems 27 and 28, with p in dollars and x as the number of units.**

Supply Schedule		Demand Schedule	
x	p	x	p
0	120	0	2400
10	260	10	1500
20	380	20	1200
30	450	30	950
40	540	40	800
50	630	50	730
60	680	60	680
70	720	70	640

27. Use Simpson's Rule to approximate the producer's surplus at market equilibrium. Note that market equilibrium can be found from the tables.

28. Use Simpson's Rule to approximate the consumer's surplus at market equilibrium.

29. *Production* Suppose that the rate of production of a product (in units per week) is measured at the end of each of the first 5 weeks after start-up and the data in the table are obtained.

Weeks t	Rate $R(t)$	Weeks t	Rate $R(t)$
0	250.0	3	243.3
1	247.6	4	241.3
2	245.4	5	239.5

Approximate the total number of units produced in the first 5 weeks.

30. *Drug levels in the blood* The manufacturer of a medicine wants to test how a new 300-milligram capsule is released into the bloodstream. After a volunteer is given a capsule, blood samples are drawn every half-hour, and the number of milligrams of the drug in the bloodstream is calculated. The results obtained are as follows.

Time t (hr)	$N(t)$ (mg)	Time t (hr)	$N(t)$ (mg)
0	0	2.0	178.3
0.5	247.3	2.5	113.9
1.0	270	3.0	56.2
1.5	236.4	3.5	19.3

Approximate the *average* number of milligrams in the bloodstream during the first $3\frac{1}{2}$ hours.

Income distribution **If the Lorenz curves for years a and b are given by $L_a(x)$ and $L_b(x)$, respectively, then from year a to year b, the change in the Gini coefficient $(G_b - G_a)$ is given by**

$$2\int_0^1 [L_a(x) - L_b(x)]\, dx$$

In Problems 31 and 32, complete the following.
(a) Use the data in the table and make a new table for x and the corresponding values of $[L_a(x) - L_b(x)]$ for the given years, where year b is 2015.
(b) Use the table from part (a) in the Trapezoidal Rule to approximate

$$2\int_0^1 [L_a(x) - L_b(x)]\, dx$$

which gives $G_b - G_a$, the difference of the Gini coefficients for the two years.
(c) Is the value of the integral positive or negative? In which year was the income more equally distributed?

x	0.0	0.2	0.4	0.6	0.8	1.0
			$L(x)$ for Blacks			
2015	0.0	0.026	0.102	0.239	0.469	1.0
1990	0.0	0.031	0.111	0.260	0.511	1.0

x	0.0	0.2	0.4	0.6	0.8	1.0
			$L(x)$ for Asians			
2015	0.0	0.027	0.112	0.259	0.495	1.0
2009	0.0	0.027	0.109	0.253	0.483	1.0

Source: U.S. Bureau of the Census

31. Complete parts (a)–(c) above for Blacks in 1990 and 2015.

32. Complete parts (a)–(c) above for Asians in 2009 and 2015.

33. *Pollution monitoring* Suppose that the presence of phosphates in certain waste products dumped into a lake promotes the growth of algae. Rampant growth of algae affects the oxygen supply in the water, so an environmental group wants to estimate the area of algae growth. Group members measure across the algae growth (see Figure 13.35) and obtain the data (in feet) in the table.

x	Width w	x	Width w
0	0	50	27
10	15	60	24
20	18	70	23
30	18	80	0
40	30		

(a) Can either the Trapezoidal Rule or Simpson's Rule be used to calculate the area of the algae growth?

(b) When either the Trapezoidal Rule or Simpson's Rule can be used, which is usually more accurate?

(c) Use Simpson's Rule to approximate the area of the algae growth.

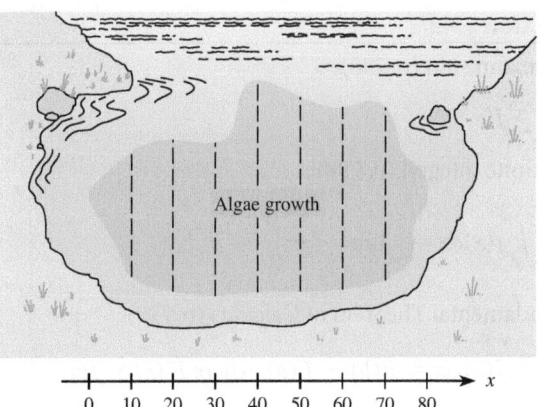

Figure 13.35

34. *Development costs* A land developer is planning to dig a small lake and build a group of homes around it. To estimate the cost of the project, the area of the lake must be calculated from the proposed measurements (in feet) given in Figure 13.36 and in the data in the table. Use Simpson's Rule to approximate the area of the lake.

x	Width $w(x)$
0	0
100	300
200	200
300	400
400	0

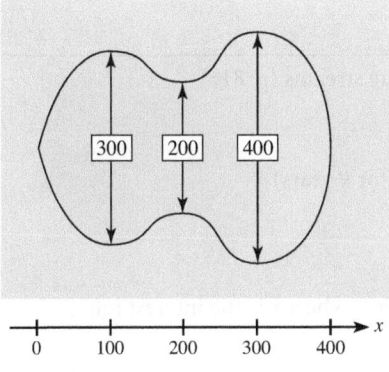

Figure 13.36

13 CHAPTER SUMMARY & REVIEW

KEY TERMS AND FORMULAS

Section 13.1

Sigma (summation) notation (p. 791)

$$\sum_{i=1}^{n} a_i = a_1 + a_2 + \cdots + a_n$$

Formulas (p. 791)

$$\sum_{i=1}^{n} 1 = n; \quad \sum_{i=1}^{n} i = \frac{n(n+1)}{2}$$

$$\sum_{i=1}^{n} i^2 = \frac{n(n+1)(2n+1)}{6}$$

Area (p. 792)

Right-hand endpoints

$$\lim_{n \to \infty} \sum_{i=1}^{n} f(x_i) \frac{b-a}{n}; \quad x_i = a + i\left(\frac{b-a}{n}\right)$$

Left-hand endpoints

$$\lim_{n \to \infty} \sum_{i=1}^{n} f(x_{i-1}) \frac{b-a}{n}; \quad x_{i-1} = a + (i-1)\left(\frac{b-a}{n}\right)$$

Section 13.2

Riemann sum (p. 798)

$$\sum_{i=1}^{n} f(x_i^*) \Delta x_i$$

Definite integral (p. 798)

$$\int_a^b f(x)dx = \lim_{\substack{max\,\Delta x_i \to 0 \\ n \to \infty}} \sum_{i=1}^{n} f(x_i^*) \Delta x_i$$

Fundamental Theorem of Calculus (p. 799)

$$\int_a^b f(x)\, dx = F(b) - F(a), \text{ where } F'(x) = f(x)$$

Definite integral properties (pp. 800–801)

$$\int_a^a f(x)\, dx = 0$$

$$\int_b^a f(x)\, dx = -\int_a^b f(x)\, dx$$

$$\int_a^b [f(x) \pm g(x)]\, dx = \int_a^b f(x)\, dx \pm \int_a^b g(x)\, dx$$

$$\int_a^b kf(x)\, dx = k \int_a^b f(x)\, dx$$

$$\int_a^c f(x)\, dx + \int_c^b f(x)\, dx = \int_a^b f(x)\, dx$$

Area under $f(x)$, where $f(x) \geq 0$ (p. 802)

$$A = \int_a^b f(x)\, dx$$

$f(x)$ is a probability density function (p. 803)

$$\Pr(a \leq x \leq b) = \int_a^b f(x)\, dx$$

Section 13.3

Lorenz curve, $L(x)$ (p. 807)
Area between $f(x)$ and $g(x)$, where $f(x) \geq g(x)$ (p. 808)

$$A = \int_a^b [f(x) - g(x)]dx$$

Gini coefficient (p. 811)

$$2 \int_0^1 [x - L(x)]\, dx$$

Average value of f over $[a, b]$ (p. 811)

$$\frac{1}{b - a} \int_a^b f(x)\, dx$$

Section 13.4

Continuous income streams (p. 816)
   Total income

$$\int_0^k f(t)\, dt \quad \text{(for } k \text{ years)}$$

   Present value

$$\int_0^k f(t)e^{-rt}\, dt, \quad \text{where } r \text{ is the interest rate}$$

Future value

$$e^{rk} \int_0^k f(t)e^{-rt}\, dt$$

Consumer's surplus [demand is $f(x)$] (p. 818)

$$CS = \int_0^{x_1} f(x)\, dx - p_1 x_1$$

Producer's surplus [supply is $g(x)$] (p. 821)

$$PS = p_1 x_1 - \int_0^{x_1} g(x)\, dx$$

Section 13.5

Integration by formulas (p. 825)

See Table 13.2.

Section 13.6

Integration by parts (p. 829)

$$\int u\, dv = uv - \int v\, du$$

Section 13.7

Improper integrals (p. 834)

$$\int_a^\infty f(x)\, dx = \lim_{b \to \infty} \int_a^b f(x)\, dx$$

$$\int_{-\infty}^b f(x)\, dx = \lim_{a \to \infty} \int_{-a}^b f(x)\, dx$$

$$\int_{-\infty}^\infty f(x)\, dx = \int_{-\infty}^c f(x)\, dx + \int_c^\infty f(x)\, dx$$

Capital value of a continuous income stream (p. 836)

$$\int_0^\infty f(t)e^{-rt}\, dt$$

Probability density function, $f(x)$ (p. 837)

$$f(x) \geq 0 \text{ and } \int_{-\infty}^\infty f(x)\, dx = 1$$
Mean

$$u = \int_{-\infty}^\infty x f(x)\, dx$$

Section 13.8

Trapezoidal Rule (p. 841)

$$\int_a^b f(x)dx \approx \frac{h}{2}[f(x_0) + 2f(x_1) + \cdots + 2f(x_{n-1}) + f(x_n)]$$

where $h = \dfrac{b-a}{n}$

Error formula

$$|E| \le \frac{(b-a)^3}{12n^2}\left[\max_{a \le x \le b}|f''(x)|\right]$$

Simpson's Rule (p. 843)

$$\int_a^b f(x)\,dx \approx \frac{h}{3}[f(x_0) + 4f(x_1) + 2f(x_2) + 4f(x_3)$$
$$+ \cdots + 2f(x_{n-2}) + 4f(x_{n-1}) + f(x_n)],$$

where n is even and $h = \dfrac{b-a}{n}$

Error formula

$$|E| \le \frac{(b-a)^5}{180n^4}\left[\max_{a \le x \le b}|f^{(4)}(x)|\right]$$

REVIEW EXERCISES

Section 13.1

1. Calculate $\displaystyle\sum_{k=1}^{8}(k^2 + 1)$.

2. Use formulas to simplify

$$\sum_{i=1}^{n}\frac{3i}{n^3}$$

3. Use 6 subintervals of the same size to approximate the area under the graph of $y = 3x^2$ from $x = 0$ to $x = 1$. Use the right-hand endpoints of the subintervals to find the heights of the rectangles.

4. Use rectangles to find the exact area under the graph of $y = 3x^2$ from $x = 0$ to $x = 1$. Use n equal subintervals.

Section 13.2

5. Use a definite integral to find the area under the graph of $y = 3x^2$ from $x = 0$ to $x = 1$.

6. Find the area between the graph of $y = x^3 - 4x + 5$ and the x-axis from $x = 1$ to $x = 3$.

Evaluate the integrals in Problems 7–18.

7. $\displaystyle\int_1^4 4\sqrt{x^3}\,dx$

8. $\displaystyle\int_{-3}^2 (x^3 - 3x^2 + 4x + 2)\,dx$

9. $\displaystyle\int_0^5 (x^3 + 4x)\,dx$

10. $\displaystyle\int_{-1}^3 (3x + 4)^{-2}\,dx$

11. $\displaystyle\int_{-3}^{-1}(x + 1)\,dx$

12. $\displaystyle\int_2^3 \frac{x^2}{2x^3 - 7}\,dx$

13. $\displaystyle\int_{-1}^2 (x^2 + x)\,dx$

14. $\displaystyle\int_1^4 \left(\frac{1}{x} + \sqrt{x}\right)dx$

15. $\displaystyle\int_0^2 5x^2(6x^3 + 1)^{1/2}\,dx$

16. $\displaystyle\int_0^1 \frac{x}{x^2 + 1}\,dx$

17. $\displaystyle\int_0^1 e^{-2x}\,dx$

18. $\displaystyle\int_0^1 xe^{x^2}\,dx$

Section 13.3

Find the area between the curves in Problems 19–22.

19. $y = x^2 - 3x + 2$ and $y = x^2 + 4$ from $x = 0$ to $x = 5$

20. $y = x^2$ and $y = 4x + 5$

21. $y = x^3$ and $y = x$ from $x = -1$ to $x = 0$

22. $y = x^3 - 1$ and $y = x - 1$

Section 13.5

Evaluate the integrals in Problems 23–26, using the formulas in Table 13.2.

23. $\displaystyle\int \sqrt{x^2 - 4}\,dx$

24. $\displaystyle\int_0^1 3^x\,dx$

25. $\displaystyle\int x \ln x^2\,dx$

26. $\displaystyle\int \frac{dx}{x(3x + 2)}$

Section 13.6

In Problems 27–30, use integration by parts to evaluate.

27. $\displaystyle\int x^5 \ln x\,dx$

28. $\displaystyle\int x^2 e^{-2x}\,dx$

29. $\displaystyle\int \frac{x\,dx}{\sqrt{x + 5}}$

30. $\displaystyle\int_{0.5}^{e/2} 6 \ln (2x)\,dx$

Section 13.7

Evaluate the improper integrals in Problems 31–34.

31. $\displaystyle\int_1^{\infty} \frac{1}{x + 1}\,dx$

32. $\displaystyle\int_{-\infty}^{-1} \frac{200}{x^3}\,dx$

33. $\displaystyle\int_0^{\infty} 5e^{-3x}\,dx$

34. $\displaystyle\int_{-\infty}^0 \frac{x}{(x^2 + 1)^2}\,dx$

35. Find c so that $f(x) = \dfrac{c}{x^3}$ for $x \ge 5$ is a probability density function.

Section 13.8

36. Evaluate $\displaystyle\int_1^3 \frac{2}{x^3}\, dx$

    (a) exactly.
    (b) using the Trapezoidal Rule with $n = 4$ (to 3 decimal places).
    (c) using Simpson's Rule with $n = 4$ (to 3 decimal places).

37. Use the Trapezoidal Rule with $n = 5$ to approximate

    $$\int_0^1 \frac{4\, dx}{x^2 + 1}$$

    Round your answer to 3 decimal places.

38. Use the table that follows to approximate

    $$\int_1^{2.2} f(x)\, dx$$

    using Simpson's Rule. Round your answer to 1 decimal place.

x	$f(x)$
1	0
1.3	2.8
1.6	5.1
1.9	4.2
2.2	0.6

39. Suppose that a definite integral is to be approximated and it is found that to achieve a specified accuracy, n must satisfy $n \geq 4.8$. What is the smallest n that can be used, if
    (a) the Trapezoidal Rule is used?
    (b) Simpson's Rule is used?

APPLICATIONS

Section 13.2

40. *Maintenance* Maintenance costs for buildings increase as the buildings age. If the rate of increase in maintenance costs for a building is

    $$M'(t) = \frac{14{,}000}{\sqrt{t + 16}}$$

    where M is in dollars and t is time in years, $0 \leq t \leq 15$, find the total maintenance cost for the first 9 years ($t = 0$ to $t = 9$).

41. *Quality control* Suppose the probability density function for the life expectancy of a battery is

    $$f(x) = \begin{cases} 1.4e^{-1.4x} & x \geq 0 \\ 0 & x < 0 \end{cases}$$

    Find the probability that a randomly selected battery lasts
    (a) 2 years or less.
    (b) at most half a year given that it lasts a year or less.

Section 13.3

42. *Savings* The future value of $1000 invested in a savings account at 10% compounded continuously is $S = 1000e^{0.1t}$, where t is in years. Find the average amount in the savings account during the first 5 years.

43. *Income streams* Suppose the total income in dollars from a machine is given by

    $$I = 50e^{0.2t}, \quad 0 \leq t \leq 4, t \text{ in hours}$$

    Find the average income over this 4-hour period.

44. *Income distribution* In 1969, after the "Great Society" initiatives of the Johnson administration, the Lorenz curve for the U.S. income distribution was $L(x) = x^{2.1936}$. In 2000, after the stock market's historic 10-year growth, the Lorenz curve for the U.S. income distribution was $L(x) = x^{2.4870}$. Find the Gini coefficient of income for both years and determine in which year income was more equally distributed.

Section 13.4

45. *Income streams* Find the total income over the next 10 years from a continuous income stream that has an annual flow rate at time t given by $f(t) = 125e^{0.05t}$ in thousands of dollars per year.

46. *Income streams* Suppose that a machine's production is considered a continuous income stream with an annual rate of flow at time t given by $f(t) = 150e^{-0.2t}$ in thousands of dollars per year. Money is worth 8% compounded continuously.
    (a) Find the present value of the machine's production over the next 5 years.
    (b) Find the future value of the production 5 years from now.

    Consumer's and producer's surplus **The demand function for a product under pure competition is $p = \sqrt{64 - 4x}$, and the supply function is $p = x - 1$, where x is the number of units and p is in dollars. Use these functions in Problems 47 and 48.**

47. (a) Find the market equilibrium.
    (b) Find the consumer's surplus at market equilibrium.

48. Find the producer's surplus at market equilibrium.

Section 13.5

49. *Average cost* Suppose the cost function for x units of a product is given by $C(x) = \sqrt{40{,}000 + x^2}$ dollars. Find the average cost over the first 150 units.

50. *Producer's surplus* Suppose the supply function for x units of a certain lamp is given by

    $$p = 0.02x + 50.01 - \frac{10}{\sqrt{x^2 + 1}}$$

    where p is in dollars. Find the producer's surplus if the equilibrium price is $70 and the equilibrium quantity is 1000.

Section 13.6

51. *Income streams* Suppose the present value of a continuous income stream over the next 5 years is given by

$$P = 9000 \int_0^5 te^{-0.08t}\, dt$$

with P in dollars and t in years. Find the present value.

52. *Cost* If the marginal cost for x units of a product is $\overline{MC} = 3 + 60(x + 1) \ln (x + 1)$ dollars per unit and if the fixed cost is $2000, find the total cost function.

Section 13.7

53. *Quality control* The length of time (in years) until a copier feed mechanism needs to be replaced has probability density function given by

$$f(t) = 0.6e^{-0.6t} \qquad t \geq 0$$

If one of these copiers is selected at random, find the probability that this mechanism lasts
   (a) more than 3 years.
   (b) more than 3 years given that it lasts more than 1 year.

54. *Capital value* Find the capital value of a business if its income is considered a continuous income stream with annual rate of flow given by

$$f(t) = 120e^{0.03t}$$

in thousands of dollars per year and the current interest rate is 6% compounded continuously.

Section 13.8

55. *Total income* Suppose that a continuous income stream has an annual rate of flow $f(t) = 100e^{-0.01t^2}$ (in thousands of dollars per year). Use Simpson's Rule with $n = 4$ to approximate the total income from this stream over the next 2 years.

56. *Revenue* A company has the data shown in the table from the sale of its product.

x	MR
0	0
2	480
4	720
6	720
8	480
10	0

If x represents hundreds of units and revenue R is in hundreds of dollars, approximate the total revenue from the sale of 1000 units by approximating

$$\int_0^{10} \overline{MR}\, dx$$

with the Trapezoidal Rule.

13 CHAPTER TEST

1. Use left-hand endpoints and $n = 4$ subdivisions to approximate the area under $f(x) = \sqrt{4 - x^2}$ on the interval $[0, 2]$.

2. Consider $f(x) = 5 - 2x$ from $x = 0$ to $x = 1$ with n equal subdivisions.
   (a) If $f(x)$ is evaluated at right-hand endpoints, find a formula for the sum, S, of the areas of the n rectangles.
   (b) Find $\lim\limits_{n\to\infty} S$.

3. Express the area in Quadrant I under $y = 12 + 4x - x^2$ (shaded in the figure) as an integral. Then evaluate the integral to find the area.

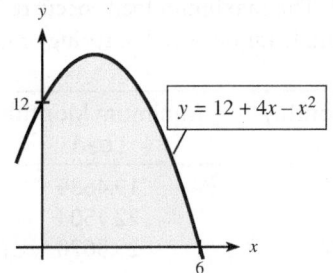

4. Evaluate the following definite integrals. (Do not approximate with technology.)

   (a) $\displaystyle\int_0^4 (9 - 4x)\, dx$ \qquad (b) $\displaystyle\int_0^3 x(8x^2 + 9)^{-1/2}\, dx$

   (c) $\displaystyle\int_1^4 \frac{5}{4x - 1}\, dx$ \qquad (d) $\displaystyle\int_1^\infty \frac{7}{x^2}\, dx$

   (e) $\displaystyle\int_4^4 \sqrt{x^3 + 10}\, dx$ \qquad (f) $\displaystyle\int_0^1 5x^2 e^{2x^3}\, dx$

5. Use integration by parts to evaluate the following.
   (a) $\displaystyle\int 3xe^x\, dx$ \qquad (b) $\displaystyle\int x \ln (2x)\, dx$

6. If $\displaystyle\int_1^4 f(x)\, dx = 3$ and $\displaystyle\int_3^4 f(x)\, dx = 7$, find $\displaystyle\int_1^3 2f(x)\, dx$.

7. Use Table 13.2 in Section 13.5 to evaluate each of the following.
   (a) $\displaystyle\int \ln (2x)\, dx$ \qquad (b) $\displaystyle\int x\sqrt{3x - 7}\, dx$

8. Use the numerical integration feature of a graphing calculator to approximate $\int_1^4 \sqrt{x^3 + 10}\, dx$.

9. Suppose the supply function for a product is $p = 40 + 0.001x^2$ and the demand function is $p = 120 - 0.2x$, where x is the number of units and p is the price in dollars. If the market equilibrium price is $80, find (a) the consumer's surplus and (b) the producer's surplus.

10. Suppose a continuous income stream has an annual rate of flow $f(t) = 85e^{-0.01t}$, in thousands of dollars per year, and the current interest rate is 7% compounded continuously.
    (a) Find the total income over the next 12 years.
    (b) Find the present value over the next 12 years.
    (c) Find the capital value of the stream.

11. Find the area between $y = 2x + 4$ and $y = x^2 - x$.

12. The figure shows typical supply and demand curves. On the figure, sketch and shade the region whose area represents the consumer's surplus.

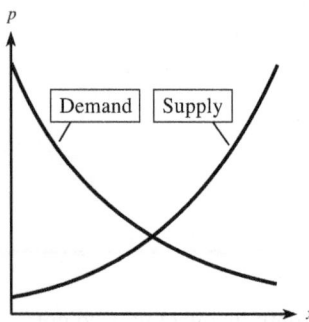

13. In an effort to make the distribution of income more nearly equal, the government of a country passes a tax

law that changes the Lorenz curve from $y = 0.998x^{2.6}$ for one year to $y = 0.57x^2 + 0.43x$ for the next year. Find the Gini coefficient of income for each year and determine whether the distribution of income is more or less equitable after the tax law is passed. Interpret the result.

14. With data from the U.S. Department of Energy, the number of billions of barrels of U.S. crude oil produced per year from 2010 and projected to 2030 can be modeled by the function

$$f(t) = -0.001t^2 + 0.037t + 1.94$$

where t is the number of years past 2010.
    (a) Find the total number of barrels of oil produced from 2010 to 2020.
    (b) Find the average number of barrels produced per year from 2010 to 2018.

15. Use the Trapezoidal Rule to approximate

$$\int_1^3 (x \ln x)\, dx$$

with $n = 4$ subintervals.

16. The environmental effects of a chemical spill in the Clarion River can be estimated from the river's flow volume. To measure this flow volume, it is necessary to find the cross-sectional area of the river at a point downriver from the spill. The distance across the river is 240 feet, and the table gives depth measurements, $D(x)$, in feet, of the river at various distances x from one bank of the river. Use these measurements with Simpson's Rule to estimate the cross-sectional area.

x	0	40	80	120	160	200	240
$D(x)$	0	22	35	48	32	24	0

13   EXTENDED APPLICATIONS & GROUP PROJECTS

I. Purchasing Electrical Power (Modeling)

To plan its purchases of electrical power from suppliers over the next 5 years, the PAC Electric Company needs to model its load data (demand for power by its customers) and use this model to predict future loads. The company pays for the electrical power each month on the basis of the peak load (demand) at any point during the month. The table gives, for the years 2002–2020, the load in megawatts (that is, in

millions of watts) for the month when the maximum load occurred and the load in megawatts for the month when the minimum load occurred. The maximum loads occurred in summer, and the minimum loads occurred in spring or fall.

Year	Maximum Monthly Load	Minimum Monthly Load
2002	40.9367	19.4689
2003	45.7127	22.1504
2004	48.0460	25.3670

Year	Maximum Monthly Load	Minimum Monthly Load
2005	56.1712	28.7254
2006	55.5793	31.0460
2007	62.4285	31.3838
2008	76.6536	34.8426
2009	73.8214	38.4544
2010	74.8844	40.6080
2011	83.0590	47.3621
2012	88.3914	45.8393
2013	88.7704	48.7956
2014	94.2620	48.3313
2015	105.1596	52.7710
2016	95.8301	54.4757
2017	97.8854	55.2210
2018	102.8912	55.1360
2019	109.5541	57.2162
2020	111.2516	58.3216

The company wants to predict the average monthly load over the next 5 years so that it can plan its future monthly purchases. To assist the company, proceed as follows.

1. (a) Using the years and the maximum monthly load given for each year, graph the data, with x representing the number of years past 2002 and y representing the maximum load in megawatts.

(b) Find the equation that best fits the data, using both a quadratic model and a cubic model. Report the model with 4 significant digits.

(c) Graph the data and both of these models from 2002 to 2022 (that is, from $x = 0$ to $x = 20$).

2. Do the two models appear to fit the data equally well in the interval 2002–2022? Which model appears to be a better predictor for the next decade after 2022?

3. Use the quadratic model to predict the maximum monthly load in the year 2025. How can this value be used by the company? Should this number be used to plan monthly power purchases for each month in 2025?

4. To create a "typical" monthly load function:
   (a) Create a table with the year as the independent variable and the average of the maximum and minimum monthly loads as the dependent variable.
   (b) Find the quadratic model that best fits these data points, using x as the number of years after 2002. Report the model with 4 significant digits.

5. Use a definite integral with the reported model for the typical monthly load function to predict the average monthly load over the years 2022–2027.

6. What factors in addition to the average monthly load should be considered when the company plans future purchases of power?

II. Retirement Planning

A 52-year-old client asks an accountant how to plan for his future retirement at age 62. He expects income from Social Security in the amount of $21,600 per year and a retirement pension of $40,500 per year from his employer. He wants to make monthly contributions to an investment plan that pays 8% compounded monthly for 10 years so that he will have a total income of $83,700 per year for 30 years. What must the size of the monthly contributions be to accomplish this goal, if it is assumed that money will be worth 8% compounded continuously throughout the period after he is 62?

To help you answer this question, complete the following.

1. How much money must the client withdraw annually from his investment plan during his retirement so that his total income goal is met?

2. How much money S must the client's account contain when he is 62 so that it will generate this annual amount for 30 years? (*Hint: S* can be considered the present value over 30 years of a continuous income stream with the amount you found in Question 1 as its annual rate of flow.)

3. The monthly contribution R that would, after 10 years, amount to the present value S found in Question 2 can be obtained from the formula

$$R = S\left[\frac{i}{(1 + i)^n - 1}\right]$$

where i represents the monthly interest rate and n the number of months. Find the client's monthly contribution, R.

14

Functions of Two or More Variables

In this chapter, we will extend our study of functions to functions of two or more variables. We will use these concepts to solve problems in the management, life, and social sciences. In particular, we will discuss joint cost functions, utility functions that describe the customer satisfaction derived from the consumption of two products, Cobb-Douglas production functions, and wind chill temperatures as a function of air temperature and wind speed.

We will use derivatives with respect to one of two variables (called partial derivatives) to find marginal cost, marginal productivity, marginal utility, marginal demand, and other rates of change. We will use partial derivatives to find maxima and minima of functions of two variables, and we will use Lagrange multipliers to optimize functions of two variables subject to a condition that constrains these variables. These skills are used to maximize profit, production, and utility and to minimize cost subject to constraints.

The topics and some representative applications discussed in this chapter include the following.

Prerequisite Problem Type	For Section	Answer	Section for Review
If $y = f(x)$, x is the independent variable and y is the _____ variable.	14.1	Dependent	1.2 Functions
What is the domain of $f(x) = \dfrac{3x}{x-1}$?	14.1	All reals except $x = 1$	1.2 Domains
If $C(x) = 5 + 5x$, what is $C(0.20)$?	14.1	6	1.2 Function notation
(a) Solve for x and y: $\begin{cases} 0 = 50 - 2x - 2y \\ 0 = 60 - 2x - 4y \end{cases}$ (b) Solve for x and y: $\begin{cases} x = 2y \\ x + y - 9 = 0 \end{cases}$	14.4 14.5	(a) $x = 20$, $y = 5$ (b) $x = 6$, $y = 3$	1.5 Systems of equations
If $z = 4x^2 + 5x^3 - 7$, what is $\dfrac{dz}{dx}$?	14.2–14.5	$\dfrac{dz}{dx} = 8x + 15x^2$	9.4 Derivatives
If $f(x) = (x^2 - 1)^2$, what is $f'(x)$?	14.2	$f'(x) = 4x(x^2 - 1)$	9.6 Derivatives
If $z = 10y - \ln y$, what is $\dfrac{dz}{dy}$?	14.2	$\dfrac{dz}{dy} = 10 - \dfrac{1}{y}$	11.1 Derivatives of logarithmic functions
If $z = 5x^2 + e^x$, what is $\dfrac{dz}{dx}$?	14.2	$\dfrac{dz}{dx} = 10x + e^x$	11.2 Derivatives of exponential functions
Find the slope of the tangent to $y = 4x^3 - 4e^x$ at $(0, -4)$.	14.2	-4	9.3, 9.4, 11.2 Derivatives

SECTION 14.1

Functions of Two or More Variables

OBJECTIVES

- To find the domain of a function of two or more variables
- To evaluate a function of two or more variables given values for the independent variables

APPLICATION PREVIEW

The relations we have studied up to this point have been limited to two variables, usually with one of the variables assumed to be a function of the other. But there are many instances where one variable may depend on two or more other variables. For example, a company's quantity of output or production Q (measured in units or dollars) can be modeled according to the equation

$$Q = AK^{\alpha}L^{1-\alpha}$$

where A is a constant, K is the company's capital investment, L is the size of the labor force (in work-hours), and α is a constant with $0 < \alpha < 1$. Functions of this type are called **Cobb-Douglas production functions,** and they are frequently used in economics. For example, suppose the Cobb-Douglas production function for a company is given by

$$Q = 4K^{0.4}L^{0.6}$$

where Q is thousands of dollars of production value, K is hundreds of dollars of capital investment, and L is hours of labor. We could use this function to determine the production value for a given amount of capital investment and available work-hours of labor. We could also find how production is affected by changes in capital investment or available work-hours. (See Example 5.)

In addition, the demand function for a commodity frequently depends on the price of the commodity, available income, and prices of competing goods. Other examples from economics will be presented later in this chapter.

We write $z = f(x, y)$ to state that z is a function of both x and y. The variables x and y are called the **independent variables** and z is called the **dependent variable.** Thus the function f associates with each pair of possible values for the independent variables (x and y) exactly one value of the dependent variable (z).

The equation $z = x^2 - xy$ defines z as a function of x and y. We can denote this by writing $z = f(x, y) = x^2 - xy$. The domain of the function is the set of all ordered pairs (of real numbers), and the range is the set of all real numbers.

EXAMPLE 1   Domain

Give the domain of the function

$$g(x, y) = \frac{x^2 - 3y}{x - y}$$

Solution

The domain of the function is the set of ordered pairs that do not give a 0 denominator. That is, the domain is the set of all ordered pairs where the first and second elements are not equal (that is, where $x \neq y$). ∎

CHECKPOINT

1. Find the domain of the function

$$f(x, y) = \frac{2}{\sqrt{x^2 - y^2}}$$

We graph the function $z = f(x, y)$ by using three dimensions. We can construct a three-dimensional coordinate space by drawing three mutually perpendicular axes, as in

Figure 14.1. By setting up scales of measurement along the three axes from the origin of each axis, we can determine the three coordinates (x, y, z) for any point P. The point shown in Figure 14.1 is $+2$ units in the x-direction, $+3$ units in the y-direction, and $+4$ units in the z-direction, so the coordinates of the point are $(2, 3, 4)$.

The pairs of axes determine the three **coordinate planes;** the xy-plane, the yz-plane, and the xz-plane. The planes divide the space into eight **octants.** The point $P(2, 3, 4)$ is in the first octant.

If we are given a function $z = f(x, y)$, we can find the z-value corresponding to $x = a$ and $y = b$ by evaluating $f(a, b)$.

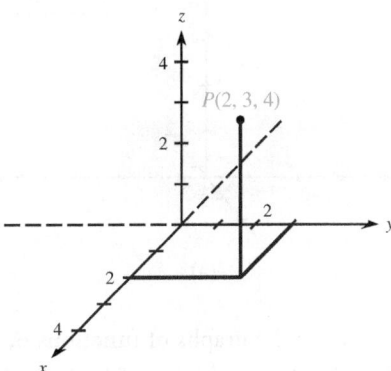

Figure 14.1

EXAMPLE 2   **Function Values**

If $z = f(x, y) = x^2 - 4xy + xy^3$, find the following.

(a) $f(1, 2)$ (b) $f(2, 5)$ (c) $f(-1, 3)$

Solution

(a) $f(1, 2) = 1^2 - 4(1)(2) + (1)(2)^3 = 1$

(b) $f(2, 5) = 2^2 - 4(2)(5) + (2)(5)^3 = 214$

(c) $f(-1, 3) = (-1)^2 - 4(-1)(3) + (-1)(3)^3 = -14$

CHECKPOINT

2. (a) If $f(x, y) = 5x^2 - y^x$, find $f(3, 2)$.

   (b) If $f(x, y, z) = x^2 + 2y - z$, find $f(2, 3, 4)$.

EXAMPLE 3   **Cost**

A small furniture company's cost (in dollars) to manufacture 1 unit of several different all-wood items is given by

$$C(x, y) = 5 + 5x + 22y$$

where x represents the number of board-feet of material used and y represents the number of work-hours of labor required for assembly and finishing. A certain bookcase uses 20 board-feet of material and requires 2.5 work-hours for assembly and finishing. Find the cost of manufacturing this bookcase.

Solution

The cost is

$$C(20, 2.5) = 5 + 5(20) + 22(2.5) = 160 \quad \text{dollars}$$

For a given function $z = f(x, y)$, we can construct a table of values by assigning values to x and y and finding the corresponding values of z. To each pair of values for x and y there corresponds a unique value of z and thus a unique point in a three-dimensional coordinate system. From a table of values such as this, a finite number of points can be plotted.

TABLE 14.1

x	y	z
−2	0	0
0	−2	0
−1	0	3
0	−1	3
−1	−1	2
0	0	4
1	0	3
0	1	3
1	1	2
2	0	0
0	2	0

All points that satisfy the equation form a "surface" in space. Because z is a function of x and y, lines parallel to the z-axis will intersect such a surface in at most one point. The graph of the equation $z = 4 - x^2 - y^2$ is the surface shown in Figure 14.2(a). The portion of the surface above the xy-plane resembles a bullet and is called a **paraboloid.** Some points on the surface are given in Table 14.1.

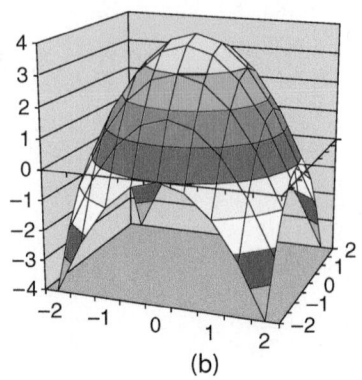

Figure 14.2   (a)   (b)

Spreadsheet Note

We can create the graphs of functions of two variables with Excel in a manner similar to that used to graph functions of one variable. Figure 14.2(b) shows the Excel graph of $z = 4 - x^2 - y^2$. Appendix B, Section 14.1, shows the steps used in graphing functions of two variables. See also the Online Excel Guide.

     In practical applications of functions of two variables, we will have little need to construct the graphs of the surfaces. For this reason, we will not discuss methods of sketching the graphs. Although you will not be asked to sketch graphs of these surfaces, the fact that the graphs do *exist* will be used in studying relative maxima and minima of functions of two variables.

     The properties of functions of one variable can be extended to functions of two variables. The precise definition of continuity for functions of two variables is technical and may be found in more advanced books. We may think of continuous functions as functions whose graphs consist of surfaces without "holes" or "breaks" in them.

Utility Functions   Let the function $U = f(x, y)$ represent the **utility** (that is, satisfaction) derived by a consumer from the consumption of two goods, X and Y, where x and y represent the amounts of X and Y, respectively. Because we will assume that the utility function is continuous, a given level of utility can be derived from an infinite number of combinations of x and y. The graph of all points (x, y) that give the same utility is called an **indifference curve.** A set of indifference curves corresponding to different levels of utility is called an **indifference map.** (See Figure 14.3.)

EXAMPLE **4**   **Utility**

Suppose that the utility function for two goods, X and Y, is $U = x^2y^2$ and a consumer purchases 10 units of X and 2 units of Y.

(a) What is the level of utility U for these two products?
(b) If the consumer purchases 5 units of X, how many units of Y must be purchased to retain the same level of utility?
(c) Graph the indifference curve for this level of utility.
(d) Graph the indifference curves for this utility function if $U = 100$ and if $U = 36$.

Figure 14.3

Solution

(a) If $x = 10$ and $y = 2$ satisfy the utility function, then the level of utility is $U = 10^2 \cdot 2^2 = 400$.
(b) If x is 5, y must satisfy $400 = 5^2y^2$; so $y = \pm 4$, and 4 units of Y must be purchased.

(c) The indifference curve for $U = 400$ is $400 = x^2y^2$. The graph for positive x and y is shown in Figure 14.3.

(d) The indifference map in Figure 14.3 contains these indifference curves.

Technology Note   A graphing calculator or Excel can be used to graph each indifference curve in the indifference map shown in Figure 14.3. To graph the indifference curve for a given value of U, we must recognize that y will be positive and solve for y to express it as a function of x. Try it for $U = 100$. Does your graph agree with the one shown in Figure 14.3?

Sometimes functions of two variables are studied by fixing a value for one variable and graphing the resulting function of a single variable. We'll do this in Section 14.3 with production functions.

EXAMPLE 5   **Production** | APPLICATION PREVIEW |

Suppose a company has the Cobb-Douglas production function

$$Q = 4K^{0.4}L^{0.6}$$

where Q is thousands of dollars of production value, K is hundreds of dollars of capital investment per week, and L is work-hours of labor per week.

(a) If current capital investment is \$72,900 per week and work-hours are 3072 per week, find the current weekly production value.

(b) If weekly capital investment is increased to \$97,200 and new employees are hired so that there are 4096 total weekly work-hours, find the percent increase in the production value.

Solution

(a) Capital investment of \$72,900 means that $K = 729$. We use this value and $L = 3072$ in the production function.

$$Q = 4(729)^{0.4}(3072)^{0.6} = 6912$$

Thus the weekly production value is \$6,912,000.

(b) In this case, we use $K = 972$ and $L = 4096$.

$$Q = 4(972)^{0.4}(4096)^{0.6} = 9216$$

This is an increase in production value of $9216 - 6912 = 2304$, which is equivalent to a weekly increase of

$$\frac{2304}{6912} = 0.33\tfrac{1}{3} = 33\tfrac{1}{3}\%$$

CHECKPOINT ANSWERS

1. $x^2 > y^2$; that is, where $|x| > |y|$.
2. (a) $f(3, 2) = 37$ (b) $f(2, 3, 4) = 6$

EXERCISES 14.1

Give the domain of each function in Problems 1–8.

1. $z = x^2 + y^2$

2. $z = 4x - 3y$

3. $z = \dfrac{4x - 3}{y}$

4. $z = \dfrac{x + y^2}{\sqrt{x}}$

5. $z = \dfrac{4x^3y - x}{2x - y}$

6. $z = \sqrt{x - y}$

7. $q = \sqrt{p_1} + 3p_2$

8. $q = 5p_1 - \sqrt{p_1 - p_2}$

In Problems 9–14, evaluate the functions at the given values of the independent variables.

9. $z = x^3 + 4xy + y^2$; $x = 1, y = -1$

10. $z = 4x^2 - 3xy^3$; $x = 2, y = 2$

11. $z = \dfrac{x - y}{x + y}$; $x = 4, y = -1$

12. $z = \dfrac{x^2 + xy}{x - y}$; $x = 3, y = 2$

13. $C(x_1, x_2) = 600 + 4x_1 + 6x_2$; $x_1 = 400, x_2 = 50$

14. $C(x_1, x_2) = 500 + 5x_1 + 7x_2$; $x_1 = 200, x_2 = 300$

In Problems 15–22, evaluate each function as indicated.

15. $q_1(p_1, p_2) = \dfrac{p_1 + 4p_2}{p_1 - p_2}$;   find $q_1(40, 35)$.

16. $q_1(p_1, p_2) = \dfrac{5p_1 - p_2}{p_1 + 3p_2}$;   find $q_1(50, 10)$.

17. $z(x, y) = xe^{x+y}$;   find $z(3, -3)$.

18. $f(x, y) = ye^{2x} + y^2$;   find $f(0, 7)$.

19. $f(x, y) = \dfrac{\ln(xy)}{x^2 + y^2}$;   find $f(-3, -4)$.

20. $z(x, y) = x \ln y - y \ln x$;   find $z(1, 1)$.

21. $w(x, y, z) = \dfrac{x^2 + 4yz}{xyz}$;   find $w(1, 3, 1)$.

22. $f(w, x, y, z) = \dfrac{wx - yz^2}{xy - wz}$;   find $f(2, 3, 1, -1)$.

APPLICATIONS

23. *Investment* The future value S of an investment earning 6% compounded continuously is a function of the principal P and the length of time t the principal has been invested. It is given by

$$S = f(P, t) = Pe^{0.06t}$$

Find $f(2000, 20)$ and interpret your answer.

24. *Amortization* If $100,000 is borrowed to purchase a home, then the monthly payment R is a function of the interest rate i (expressed as a percent) and the number of years n before the mortgage is paid. It is given by

$$R = f(i, n) = 100,000 \left[\frac{0.01(i/12)}{1 - (1 + 0.01(i/12))^{-12n}} \right]$$

Find $f(7.25, 30)$ and interpret your answer.

25. *Curve speeds* One method traffic planners use to calculate recommended curve speeds for trucks is with the formula

$$S = \sqrt{\frac{15R(112 - 0.66\,V + 0.091\,V^2 + 10B)}{1000 + 1.36R}}$$

where S is the recommended curve speed in mph, R is the radius of the curve (in feet), V is the average truck speed on the straight approaching the curve (in mph), and B is the banking of the curve (as a percent). Find the recommended curve speed if the radius is 195 feet, the average approach speed is 60 mph, and the curve banking is 10% (*Source: Car and Driver, June 2016*).

Shah Rohani/Shutterstock.com

26. *Wilson's lot size formula* In economics, the most economical quantity Q of goods (TVs, dresses, gallons of paint, etc.) for a store to order is given by Wilson's lot size formula

$$Q = f(K, M, h) = \sqrt{2KM/h}$$

where K is the cost of placing the order, M is the number of items sold per week, and h is the weekly holding cost for each item (the cost of storage space, utilities, taxes, security, etc.). Find $f(200, 625, 1)$ and interpret your answer.

Temperature-humidity models **The "feels like" temperature often reported in summer weather forecasts measures the combined effects of humidity and high temperatures. Two of the most common models used to determine this effect are the Summer Simmer Index (S) developed by John W. Pepi and the Apparent Temperature (A) developed by Robert Steadman. These models are given by**

$$S = 1.98T - 1.09(1 - H)(T - 58) - 56.9$$

$$A = -42.38 + 2.049T + 1014H - 22.48TH - 0.006838T^2$$
$$- 548.2H^2 + 0.1229T^2H + 8.528TH^2 - 0.0199T^2H^2$$

where T is the air temperature (in degrees Fahrenheit) and H is the relative humidity (expressed as a decimal). Use these models in Problems 27 and 28.

27. In Dallas, Texas, the following represent the average daily temperatures and humidities for July.

> Maximum: 97.8°F with 44% humidity
> Minimum: 74.7°F with 80% humidity

Calculate the Summer Simmer Index S and the Apparent Temperature A for both the average daily maximum and the average daily minimum temperature.

28. In Orlando, Florida, the following represent the average daily temperatures and humidities for August.

> Maximum: 91.6°F with 60% humidity
> Minimum: 73.4°F with 92% humidity

Calculate the Summer Simmer Index S and the Apparent Temperature A for both the average daily maximum and the average daily minimum temperature.

29. *Mortgage* The following tables show that a monthly mortgage payment, R, is a function of the amount financed, A, in thousands of dollars; the duration of the loan, n, in years; and the annual interest rate, r, as a percent. If $R = f(A, n, r)$, use the tables to find the following and then write a sentence of explanation for each.

(a) $f(90, 20, 8)$ (b) $f(160, 15, 9)$

8% Annual Percent Rate
Monthly Payments (Principal and Interest)

Amount Financed	10 Years	15 Years	20 Years	25 Years	30 Years
$50,000	$606.64	$477.83	$418.22	$385.91	$366.88
60,000	727.97	573.39	501.86	463.09	440.26
70,000	849.29	668.96	585.51	540.27	513.64
80,000	970.62	764.52	669.15	617.45	587.01
90,000	1091.95	860.09	752.80	694.63	660.39
100,000	1213.28	955.65	836.44	771.82	733.76
120,000	1455.94	1146.78	1003.72	926.18	880.52
140,000	1698.58	1337.92	1171.02	1080.54	1027.28
160,000	1941.24	1529.04	1338.30	1234.90	1174.02
180,000	2183.90	1720.18	1505.60	1389.26	1320.78
200,000	2426.56	1911.30	1672.88	1543.64	1467.52

9% Annual Percent Rate
Monthly Payments (Principal and Interest)

Amount Financed	10 Years	15 Years	20 Years	25 Years	30 Years
$50,000	$633.38	$507.13	$449.86	$419.60	$402.31
60,000	760.05	608.56	539.84	503.52	482.77
70,000	886.73	709.99	629.81	587.44	563.24
80,000	1013.41	811.41	719.78	671.36	643.70
90,000	1140.08	912.84	809.75	755.28	724.16
100,000	1266.76	1014.27	899.73	839.20	804.62
120,000	1520.10	1217.12	1079.68	1007.04	965.54
140,000	1773.46	1419.96	1259.62	1174.88	1126.48
160,000	2026.82	1622.82	1439.56	1342.72	1287.40
180,000	2280.16	1825.68	1619.50	1510.56	1448.32
200,000	2533.52	2028.54	1799.46	1678.40	1609.24

Source: The Mortgage Money Guide, Federal Trade Commission

30. *Wind chill* Wind and cold temperatures combine to make the air temperature feel colder than it actually is. This combination is reported as *wind chill*. The table shows the latest wind chill calculations from the National Weather Service and indicates that wind chill temperatures, WC, are a function of wind speed, s, and air temperature, t. If $WC = f(s, t)$, use the table to find and interpret each of the following.

(a) $f(25, 5)$ (b) $f(15, -15)$

Wind Speed (mph)	Air Temperature (°F)						
	35	25	15	5	−5	−15	−25
5	31	19	7	−5	−16	−28	−40
15	25	13	0	−13	−26	−39	−51
25	23	9	−4	−17	−31	−44	−58
35	21	7	−7	−21	−34	−48	−62
45	19	5	−9	−23	−37	−51	−65

Source: National Weather Service

31. *Utility* Suppose that the utility function for two goods X and Y is given by $U = xy^2$ and a consumer purchases 9 units of X and 6 units of Y.
   (a) If the consumer purchases 9 units of Y, how many units of X must be purchased to retain the same level of utility?
   (b) If the consumer purchases 81 units of X, how many units of Y must be purchased to retain the same level of utility?
   (c) Graph the indifference curve for the utility level found in parts (a) and (b). Use the graph to confirm your answers to parts (a) and (b).

32. *Utility* Suppose that an indifference curve for two goods, X and Y, has the equation $xy = 400$.
   (a) If 25 units of X are purchased, how many units of Y must be purchased to remain on this indifference curve?
   (b) Graph this indifference curve and confirm your results in part (a).

33. *Production* Suppose that a company's production for Q units of its product is given by the Cobb-Douglas production function

$$Q = 30K^{1/4}L^{3/4}$$

   where K is dollars of capital investment and L is labor hours.
   (a) Find Q if $K = \$10,000$ and $L = 625$ hours.
   (b) Show that if *both* K and L are doubled, then the output is doubled.
   (c) If capital investment is held at $10,000, graph Q as a function of L.

34. *Production* Suppose that a company's production for Q units of its product is given by the Cobb-Douglas production function

$$Q = 70K^{2/3}L^{1/3}$$

   where K is dollars of capital investment and L is labor hours.
   (a) Find Q if $K = \$64,000$ and $L = 512$ hours.
   (b) Show that if both K and L are halved, then Q is also halved.
   (c) If capital investment is held at $64,000, graph Q as a function of L.

35. *Production* Suppose that the number of units of a good produced, z, is given by $z = 20xy$, where x is the number of machines working properly and y is the average number of work-hours per machine. Find the production for a week in which
   (a) 12 machines are working properly and the average number of work-hours per machine is 30.
   (b) 10 machines are working properly and the average number of work-hours per machine is 25.

36. *Profit* The Kirk Kelly Kandy Company makes two kinds of candy, Kisses and Kreams. The profit in dollars for the company is given by

$$P(x, y) = 10x + 6.4y - 0.001x^2 - 0.025y^2$$

where x is the number of pounds of Kisses sold per week and y is the number of pounds of Kreams. What is the company's profit if it sells
  (a) 20 pounds of Kisses and 10 pounds of Kreams?
  (b) 100 pounds of Kisses and 16 pounds of Kreams?
  (c) 10,000 pounds of Kisses and 256 pounds of Kreams?

37. *Epidemic* The cost per day to society of an epidemic is
$$C(x, y) = 20x + 200y$$
where C is in dollars, x is the number of people infected on a given day, and y is the number of people who

die on a given day. If 14,000 people are infected and 20 people die on a given day, what is the cost to society?

38. *Pesticide* An area of land is to be sprayed with two brands of pesticide: x liters of brand 1 and y liters of brand 2. If the number of thousands of insects killed is given by
$$f(x, y) = 10,000 - 6500e^{-0.01x} - 3500e^{-0.02y}$$
how many insects would be killed if 80 liters of brand 1 and 120 liters of brand 2 were used?

SECTION 14.2 Partial Differentiation

OBJECTIVES

- To find partial derivatives of functions of two or more variables
- To evaluate partial derivatives of functions at given points
- To use partial derivatives to find slopes of tangents to surfaces
- To find and evaluate second- and higher-order partial derivatives

APPLICATION PREVIEW

Suppose that a company's sales are related to its television advertising by
$$s = 20,000 + 10nt + 20n^2$$
where n is the number of commercials per day and t is the length of the commercials in seconds. To find the instantaneous rate of change of sales with respect to the number of commercials per day if the company is running ten 30-second commercials, we find the partial derivative of s with respect to n. (See Example 7.)

In this section, we find partial derivatives of functions of two or more variables and use these derivatives to find rates of change and slopes of tangents to surfaces. We will also find second- and higher-order partial derivatives of functions of two variables.

First-Order Partial Derivatives

If $z = f(x, y)$, we find the **partial derivative** of z with respect to x (denoted $\partial z/\partial x$) by treating the variable y as a constant and taking the derivative of $z = f(x, y)$ with respect to x. We can also take the partial derivative of z with respect to y by holding the variable x constant and taking the derivative of $z = f(x, y)$ with respect to y. We denote this derivative as $\partial z/\partial y$. Note that dz/dx represents the derivative of a function of one variable, x, and that $\partial z/\partial x$ represents the partial derivative of a function of two or more variables. Notations used to represent the partial derivative of $z = f(x, y)$ with respect to x are
$$\frac{\partial z}{\partial x}, \quad \frac{\partial f}{\partial x}, \quad \frac{\partial}{\partial x}f(x, y), \quad f_x(x, y), \quad f_x, \quad \text{and} \quad z_x$$

and notations used to represent the partial derivative of $z = f(x, y)$ with respect to y are
$$\frac{\partial z}{\partial y}, \quad \frac{\partial f}{\partial y}, \quad \frac{\partial}{\partial y}f(x, y), \quad f_y(x, y), \quad f_y, \quad \text{and} \quad z_y$$

EXAMPLE 1 Partial Derivatives

If $z = 4x^2 + 5x^2y^2 + 6y^3 - 7$, find $\partial z/\partial x$ and $\partial z/\partial y$.

Solution
To find $\partial z/\partial x$ we hold y constant so that the term $6y^3$ is constant, and its derivative is 0; the term $5x^2y^2$ is viewed as the constant $(5y^2)$ times (x^2), so its derivative is $(5y^2)(2x) = 10xy^2$. Thus
$$\frac{\partial z}{\partial x} = 8x + 10xy^2$$

Similarly for $\partial z/\partial y$, the term $4x^2$ is constant and the partial derivative of $5x^2y^2$ is the constant $5x^2$ times the derivative of y^2, so its derivative is $(5x^2)(2y) = 10x^2y$. Thus

$$\frac{\partial z}{\partial y} = 10x^2y + 18y^2$$

EXAMPLE 2 Marginal Cost

Suppose that the total cost of manufacturing a product is given by

$$C(x, y) = 5 + 5x + 2y$$

where x represents the cost of 1 ounce of materials and y represents the labor cost in dollars per hour.

(a) Find the rate at which the total cost changes with respect to the material cost x. This is the marginal cost of the product with respect to the material cost.
(b) Find the rate at which the total cost changes with respect to the labor cost y. This is the marginal cost of the product with respect to the labor cost.

Solution

(a) The rate at which the total cost changes with respect to the material cost x is the partial derivative found by treating the y-variable as a constant and taking the derivative of both sides of $C(x, y) = 5 + 5x + 2y$ with respect to x.

$$\frac{\partial C}{\partial x} = 0 + 5 + 0, \text{ or } \frac{\partial C}{\partial x} = 5$$

The partial derivative $\partial C/\partial x = 5$ tells us that a change of $1 in the cost of materials will cause an increase of $5 in total costs, *if* labor costs remain constant.

(b) The rate at which the total cost changes with respect to the labor cost y is the partial derivative found by treating the x-variable as a constant and taking the derivative of both sides of $C(x, y) = 5 + 5x + 2y$ with respect to y.

$$\frac{\partial C}{\partial y} = 0 + 0 + 2, \text{ or } \frac{\partial C}{\partial y} = 2$$

The partial derivative $\partial C/\partial y = 2$ tells us that a change of $1 in the cost of labor will cause an increase of $2 in total costs, *if* material costs remain constant.

EXAMPLE 3 Partial Derivatives

If $z = x^2y + e^x - \ln y$, find z_x and z_y.

Solution

$$z_x = \frac{\partial z}{\partial x} = 2xy + e^x$$

$$z_y = \frac{\partial z}{\partial y} = x^2 - \frac{1}{y}$$

EXAMPLE 4 Power Rule

If $f(x, y) = (x^2 - y^2)^2$, find the following.
(a) f_x
(b) f_y

Solution

(a) $f_x = 2(x^2 - y^2)2x = 4x^3 - 4xy^2$
(b) $f_y = 2(x^2 - y^2)(-2y) = -4x^2y + 4y^3$

1. If $z = 100x + 10xy - y^2$, find the following.

   (a) z_x

   (b) $\dfrac{\partial z}{\partial y}$

EXAMPLE 5   Quotient Rule

If $q = \dfrac{p_1 p_2 + 2p_1}{p_1 p_2 - 2p_2}$, find $\partial q / \partial p_1$.

Solution

$$
\begin{aligned}
\frac{\partial q}{\partial p_1} &= \frac{(p_1 p_2 - 2p_2)(p_2 + 2) - (p_1 p_2 + 2p_1)p_2}{(p_1 p_2 - 2p_2)^2} \\[2mm]
&= \frac{p_1 p_2^2 + 2p_1 p_2 - 2p_2^2 - 4p_2 - p_1 p_2^2 - 2p_1 p_2}{(p_1 p_2 - 2p_2)^2} \\[2mm]
&= \frac{-2p_2^2 - 4p_2}{p_2^2(p_1 - 2)^2} = \frac{-2p_2(p_2 + 2)}{p_2^2(p_1 - 2)^2} \\[2mm]
&= \frac{-2(p_2 + 2)}{p_2(p_1 - 2)^2}
\end{aligned}
$$

We may evaluate partial derivatives by substituting values for x and y in the same way we did with derivatives of functions of one variable. For example, if $\partial z / \partial x = 2x - xy$, the value of the partial derivative with respect to x at $x = 2$, $y = 3$ is

$$
\frac{\partial z}{\partial x}\bigg|_{(2, 3)} = 2(2) - 2(3) = -2
$$

Other notations used to denote evaluation of partial derivatives with respect to x at (a, b) are

$$
z_x(a, b), \qquad \frac{\partial}{\partial x} f(a, b), \qquad \text{and} \qquad f_x(a, b)
$$

We denote the evaluation of partial derivatives with respect to y at (a, b) by

$$
z_y(a, b), \qquad \frac{\partial z}{\partial y}\bigg|_{(a, b)}, \qquad \frac{\partial}{\partial y} f(a, b), \qquad \text{or} \qquad f_y(a, b)
$$

EXAMPLE 6   Partial Derivative at a Point

Find the partial derivative of $f(x, y) = x^2 + 3xy + 4$ with respect to x at the point $(1, 2, 11)$.

Solution

$$
\begin{aligned}
f_x(x, y) &= 2x + 3y \\
f_x(1, 2) &= 2(1) + 3(2) = 8
\end{aligned}
$$

2. If $g(x, y) = 4x^2 - 3xy + 10y^2$, find the following.

   (a) $\dfrac{\partial g}{\partial x}(1, 3)$ (b) $g_y(4, 2)$

EXAMPLE 7 **Marginal Sales** | APPLICATION PREVIEW |

Suppose that a company's sales are related to its television advertising by

$$s = 20{,}000 + 10nt + 20n^2$$

where n is the number of commercials per day and t is the length of the commercials in seconds. Find the partial derivative of s with respect to n and use the result to find the instantaneous rate of change of sales with respect to the number of commercials per day, if the company is currently running ten 30-second commercials per day.

Solution

The partial derivative of s with respect to n is $\partial s/\partial n = 10t + 40n$. At $n = 10$ and $t = 30$, the rate of change in sales is

$$\left. \frac{\partial s}{\partial n} \right|_{\substack{n=10 \\ t=30}} = 10(30) + 40(10) = 700$$

Thus, increasing the number of 30-second commercials by 1 would result in approximately 700 additional sales. This is the marginal sales with respect to the number of commercials per day at $n = 10, t = 30$.

We have seen that the partial derivative $\partial z/\partial x$ is found by holding y constant and taking the derivative of z with respect to x and that the partial derivative $\partial z/\partial y$ is found by holding x constant and taking the derivative of z with respect to y. We now give formal definitions of these **partial derivatives.**

Partial Derivatives

The **partial derivative** of $z = f(x, y)$ with respect to x at the point (x, y) is

$$\frac{\partial z}{\partial x} = \frac{\partial}{\partial x} f(x, y) = \lim_{h \to 0} \frac{f(x + h, y) - f(x, y)}{h}$$

provided this limit exists.
The **partial derivative** of $z = f(x, y)$ with respect to y at the point (x, y) is

$$\frac{\partial z}{\partial y} = \frac{\partial}{\partial y} f(x, y) = \lim_{h \to 0} \frac{f(x, y + h) - f(x, y)}{h}$$

provided this limit exists.

We have already stated that the graph of $z = f(x, y)$ is a surface in three dimensions. The partial derivative with respect to x of such a function may be thought of as the slope of the tangent to the surface at a point (x, y, z) on the surface in the *positive direction of the x-axis*. That is, if a plane parallel to the xz-plane cuts the surface, passing through the point (x_0, y_0, z_0), the line in the plane that is tangent to the surface will have a slope equal to $\partial z/\partial x$ evaluated at the point. Thus

$$\left. \frac{\partial z}{\partial x} \right|_{(x_0, y_0)}$$

represents the slope of the tangent to the surface at (x_0, y_0, z_0), in the positive direction of the x-axis. (See Figure 14.4 on the next page.)

Similarly,

$$\left. \frac{\partial z}{\partial y} \right|_{(x_0, y_0)} = \frac{\partial}{\partial y} f(x_0, y_0)$$

represents the slope of the tangent to the surface at (x_0, y_0, z_0) in the positive direction of the y-axis. (See Figure 14.5 on the next page.)

Figure 14.4

Figure 14.5

EXAMPLE 8 Slopes of Tangents

Let $z = 4x^3 - 4e^x + 4y^2$ and let P be the point $(0, 2, 12)$. Find the slope of the tangent to z at the point P in the positive direction of (a) the x-axis and (b) the y-axis.

Solution

(a) The slope of z at P in the positive x-direction is given by $\dfrac{\partial z}{\partial x}$, evaluated at P.

$$\frac{\partial z}{\partial x} = 12x^2 - 4e^x \text{ and } \frac{\partial z}{\partial x}\bigg|_{(0,\,2)} = 12(0)^2 - 4e^0 = -4$$

This tells us that z *decreases* approximately 4 units for an increase of 1 unit in x at this point.

(b) The slope of z at P in the positive y-direction is given by $\dfrac{\partial z}{\partial y}$, evaluated at P.

$$\frac{\partial z}{\partial y} = 8y \text{ and } \frac{\partial z}{\partial y}\bigg|_{(0,\,2)} = 8(2) = 16$$

Thus at the point P $(0, 2, 12)$, the function *increases* approximately 16 units in the z-value for a unit increase in y.

Up to this point, we have considered derivatives of functions of two variables. We can extend the concept to functions of three or more variables. We can find the partial derivative with respect to any one independent variable by taking the derivative of the function with respect to that variable while holding all other independent variables constant.

EXAMPLE 9 Functions of Four Variables

If $u = f(w, x, y, z) = 3x^2y + w^3 - 4xyz$, find the following.

(a) $\dfrac{\partial u}{\partial w}$ (b) $\dfrac{\partial u}{\partial x}$ (c) $\dfrac{\partial u}{\partial y}$ (d) $\dfrac{\partial u}{\partial z}$

Solution

(a) $\dfrac{\partial u}{\partial w} = 3w^2$ (b) $\dfrac{\partial u}{\partial x} = 6xy - 4yz$

(c) $\dfrac{\partial u}{\partial y} = 3x^2 - 4xz$ (d) $\dfrac{\partial u}{\partial z} = -4xy$

EXAMPLE 10   **Functions of Three Variables**

If $C = 4x_1 + 2x_1^2 + 3x_2 - x_1x_2 + x_3^2$, find the following.

(a) $\dfrac{\partial C}{\partial x_1}$ (b) $\dfrac{\partial C}{\partial x_2}$ (c) $\dfrac{\partial C}{\partial x_3}$

Solution

(a) $\dfrac{\partial C}{\partial x_1} = 4 + 4x_1 - x_2$ (b) $\dfrac{\partial C}{\partial x_2} = 3 - x_1$ (c) $\dfrac{\partial C}{\partial x_3} = 2x_3$

CHECKPOINT

3. If $f(w, x, y, z) = 8xy^2 + 4yz - xw^2$, find

(a) $\dfrac{\partial f}{\partial x}$ (b) $\dfrac{\partial f}{\partial w}$ (c) $\dfrac{\partial f}{\partial y}(1, 2, 1, 3)$ (d) $\dfrac{\partial f}{\partial z}(0, 2, 1, 3)$

High-Order Partial Derivatives

Just as we have taken derivatives of derivatives to obtain higher-order derivatives of functions of one variable, we may take partial derivatives of partial derivatives to obtain higher-order partial derivatives of a function of more than one variable. If $z = f(x, y)$, then the partial derivative functions z_x and z_y are called *first partials*. Partial derivatives of z_x and z_y are called *second partials*, so $z = f(x, y)$ has *four* **second partial derivatives.** The notations for these second partial derivatives follow.

Second Partial Derivatives

$z_{xx} = \dfrac{\partial^2 z}{\partial x^2} = \dfrac{\partial}{\partial x}\left(\dfrac{\partial z}{\partial x}\right):$ both derivatives taken with respect to x

$z_{yy} = \dfrac{\partial^2 z}{\partial y^2} = \dfrac{\partial}{\partial y}\left(\dfrac{\partial z}{\partial y}\right):$ both derivatives taken with respect to y

$z_{xy} = \dfrac{\partial^2 z}{\partial y\, \partial x} = \dfrac{\partial}{\partial y}\left(\dfrac{\partial z}{\partial x}\right):$ first derivative taken with respect to x, second with respect to y

$z_{yx} = \dfrac{\partial^2 z}{\partial x\, \partial y} = \dfrac{\partial}{\partial x}\left(\dfrac{\partial z}{\partial y}\right):$ first derivative taken with respect to y, second with respect to x

EXAMPLE 11   **Second Partial Derivatives**

If $z = x^3y - 3xy^2 + 4$, find each of the second partial derivatives of the function.

Solution

Because $z_x = 3x^2y - 3y^2$ and $z_y = x^3 - 6xy$,

$$z_{xx} = \frac{\partial}{\partial x}(3x^2y - 3y^2) = 6xy$$

$$z_{xy} = \frac{\partial}{\partial y}(3x^2y - 3y^2) = 3x^2 - 6y$$

$$z_{yy} = \frac{\partial}{\partial y}(x^3 - 6xy) = -6x$$

$$z_{yx} = \frac{\partial}{\partial x}(x^3 - 6xy) = 3x^2 - 6y$$

Note that z_{xy} and z_{yx} are equal for the function in Example 11. This will always occur if the derivatives of the function are continuous.

$z_{xy} = z_{yx}$	If the second partial derivatives z_{xy} and z_{yx} of a function $z = f(x, y)$ are continuous at a point, they are equal there.

EXAMPLE 12   **Second Partial Derivatives**

Find each of the second partial derivatives of $z = x^2y + e^{xy}$.

Solution

Because $z_x = 2xy + e^{xy} \cdot y = 2xy + ye^{xy}$,

$$z_{xx} = 2y + e^{xy} \cdot y^2 = 2y + y^2e^{xy}$$

Notice that when we calculate z_{xy} from z_x the term ye^{xy} requires the Product Rule.

$$z_{xy} = 2x + (e^{xy} \cdot 1 + ye^{xy} \cdot x)$$
$$= 2x + e^{xy} + xye^{xy}$$

Because $z_y = x^2 + e^{xy} \cdot x = x^2 + xe^{xy}$,

$$z_{yy} = 0 + xe^{xy} \cdot x = x^2e^{xy}$$

We need the Product Rule to find z_{yx}.

$$z_{yx} = 2x + (e^{xy} \cdot 1 + xe^{xy} \cdot y)$$
$$= 2x + e^{xy} + xye^{xy}$$ ∎

CHECKPOINT

4. If $z = 4x^3y^4 + 4xy$, find the following.
   (a) z_{xx} (b) z_{yy} (c) z_{xy} (d) z_{yx}

5. If $z = x^2 + 4e^{xy}$, find z_{xy}.

We can find partial derivatives of orders higher than the second. For example, we can find the third-order partial derivatives z_{xyx} and z_{xyy} for the function in Example 11 from the second derivative $z_{xy} = 3x^2 - 6y$.

$$z_{xyx} = 6x$$
$$z_{xyy} = -6$$

EXAMPLE 13   **Third Partial Derivatives**

If $y = 4y \ln x + e^{xy}$, find z_{xyy}.

Solution

$$z_x = 4y \cdot \frac{1}{x} + e^{xy} \cdot y$$

$$z_{xy} = 4 \cdot \frac{1}{x} \cdot 1 + e^{xy} \cdot 1 + y \cdot e^{xy} \cdot x = \frac{4}{x} + e^{xy} + xye^{xy}$$

$$z_{xyy} = 0 + e^{xy} \cdot x + xy \cdot e^{xy} \cdot x + e^{xy} \cdot x = x^2ye^{xy} + 2xe^{xy}$$ ∎

CHECKPOINT ANSWERS

1. (a) $z_x = 100 + 10y$

   (b) $\dfrac{\partial z}{\partial y} = 10x - 2y$

2. (a) $\dfrac{\partial g}{\partial x} = 8x - 3y$ and $\dfrac{\partial g}{\partial x}(1, 3) = -1$

   (b) $g_y = -3x + 20y$ and $g_y(4, 2) = 28$

3. (a) $\dfrac{\partial f}{\partial x} = 8y^2 - w^2$ (b) $\dfrac{\partial f}{\partial w} = -2xw$

(c) $\dfrac{\partial f}{\partial y} = 16xy + 4z$ and $\dfrac{\partial f}{\partial y}(1, 2, 1, 3) = 44$

(d) $\dfrac{\partial f}{\partial z} = 4y$ and $\dfrac{\partial f}{\partial z}(0, 2, 1, 3) = 4$

4. $z_x = 12x^2y^4 + 4y$ and $z_y = 16x^3y^3 + 4x$

(a) $z_{xx} = 24xy^4$ (b) $z_{yy} = 48x^3y^2$

(c) $z_{xy} = 48x^2y^3 + 4$ (d) $z_{yx} = 48x^2y^3 + 4$

5. $z_x = 2x + 4e^{xy}(y) = 2x + 4ye^{xy}$

$z_{xy} = 4xye^{xy} + 4e^{xy}$

EXERCISES 14.2

1. If $z = x^4 - 5x^2 + 6x + 3y^3 - 5y + 7$, find $\dfrac{\partial z}{\partial x}$ and $\dfrac{\partial z}{\partial y}$.

2. If $z = x^5 - 6x + 4y^4 - y^2$, find $\dfrac{\partial z}{\partial x}$ and $\dfrac{\partial z}{\partial y}$.

3. If $z = x^3 + 4x^2y + 6y^2$, find z_x and z_y.

4. If $z = 3xy + y^2$, find z_x and z_y.

5. If $f(x, y) = (x^3 + 2y^2)^3$, find $\dfrac{\partial f}{\partial x}$ and $\dfrac{\partial f}{\partial y}$.

6. If $f(x, y) = (xy^3 + y)^2$, find $\dfrac{\partial f}{\partial x}$ and $\dfrac{\partial f}{\partial y}$.

7. If $f(x, y) = \sqrt{2x^2 - 5y^2}$, find f_x and f_y.

8. If $g(x, y) = \sqrt{xy - x}$, find g_x and g_y.

9. If $C(x, y) = 600 - 4xy + 10x^2y$, find $\dfrac{\partial C}{\partial x}$ and $\dfrac{\partial C}{\partial y}$.

10. If $C(x, y) = 1000 - 4x + xy^2$, find $\dfrac{\partial C}{\partial x}$ and $\dfrac{\partial C}{\partial y}$.

11. If $Q(s, t) = \dfrac{2s - 3t}{s^2 + t^2}$, find $\dfrac{\partial Q}{\partial s}$ and $\dfrac{\partial Q}{\partial t}$.

12. If $q = \dfrac{5p_1 + 4p_2}{p_1 + p_2}$, find $\dfrac{\partial q}{\partial p_1}$ and $\dfrac{\partial q}{\partial p_2}$.

13. If $z = e^{2x} + y \ln x$, find z_x and z_y.

14. If $z = \ln(1 + x^2y) - ye^{-x}$, find z_x and z_y.

15. If $f(x, y) = \ln(xy + 1)$, find $\dfrac{\partial f}{\partial x}$ and $\dfrac{\partial f}{\partial y}$.

16. If $f(x, y) = 100e^{xy}$, find $\dfrac{\partial f}{\partial x}$ and $\dfrac{\partial f}{\partial y}$.

17. Find the partial derivative of

$$f(x, y) = 4x^3 - 5xy + y^2$$

with respect to x at the point $(1, 2, -2)$.

18. Find the partial derivative of

$$f(x, y) = 3x^2 + 4x + 6xy$$

with respect to y at $x = 2$, $y = -1$.

19. Find the slope of the tangent in the positive x-direction to the surface $z = 5x^3 - 4xy$ at the point $(1, 2, -3)$.

20. Find the slope of the tangent in the positive y-direction to the surface $z = x^3 - 5xy$ at $(2, 1, -2)$.

21. Find the slope of the tangent in the positive y-direction to the surface $z = 3x + 2y - 7e^{xy}$ at $(3, 0, 2)$.

22. Find the slope of the tangent in the positive x-direction to the surface $z = 2xy + \ln(4x + 3y)$ at $(1, -1, -2)$.

23. If $u = f(w, x, y, z) = y^2 - x^2z + 4x$, find the following.

(a) $\dfrac{\partial u}{\partial w}$ (b) $\dfrac{\partial u}{\partial x}$ (c) $\dfrac{\partial u}{\partial y}$ (d) $\dfrac{\partial u}{\partial z}$

24. If $u = x^2 + 3xy + xz$, find the following.

(a) u_x (b) u_y (c) u_z

25. If $C(x_1, x_2, x_3) = 4x_1^2 + 5x_1x_2 + 6x_2^2 + x_3$, find the following.

(a) $\dfrac{\partial C}{\partial x_1}$ (b) $\dfrac{\partial C}{\partial x_2}$ (c) $\dfrac{\partial C}{\partial x_3}$

26. If $f(x, y, z) = 2x\sqrt{yz - 1} + x^2z^3$, find the following.

(a) $\dfrac{\partial f}{\partial x}$ (b) $\dfrac{\partial f}{\partial y}$ (c) $\dfrac{\partial f}{\partial z}$

27. If $z = x^2 + 4x - 5y^3$, find the following.

(a) z_{xx} (b) z_{xy} (c) z_{yx} (d) z_{yy}

28. If $z = x^3 - 5y^2 + 4y + 1$, find the following.

(a) z_{xx} (b) z_{xy} (c) z_{yx} (d) z_{yy}

29. If $z = x^2y - 4xy^2$, find the following.

(a) z_{xx} (b) z_{xy} (c) z_{yx} (d) z_{yy}

30. If $z = xy^2 + 4xy - 5$, find the following.

(a) z_{xx} (b) z_{xy} (c) z_{yx} (d) z_{yy}

31. If $f(x, y) = x^2 + e^{xy}$, find the following.

(a) $\dfrac{\partial^2 f}{\partial x^2}$ (b) $\dfrac{\partial^2 f}{\partial y \partial x}$ (c) $\dfrac{\partial^2 f}{\partial x \partial y}$ (d) $\dfrac{\partial^2 f}{\partial y^2}$

32. If $z = xe^{xy}$, find the following.

(a) z_{xx} (b) z_{yy} (c) z_{xy} (d) z_{yx}

33. If $f(x, y) = y^2 - \ln xy$, find the following.

(a) $\dfrac{\partial^2 f}{\partial x^2}$ (b) $\dfrac{\partial^2 f}{\partial y\, \partial x}$ (c) $\dfrac{\partial^2 f}{\partial x\, \partial y}$ (d) $\dfrac{\partial^2 f}{\partial y^2}$

34. If $f(x, y) = x^3 + \ln(xy - 1)$, find the following.

(a) $\dfrac{\partial^2 f}{\partial x^2}$ (b) $\dfrac{\partial^2 f}{\partial y^2}$ (c) $\dfrac{\partial^2 f}{\partial x\, \partial y}$ (d) $\dfrac{\partial^2 f}{\partial y\, \partial x}$

35. If $f(x, y) = x^3 y + 4xy^4$, find $\dfrac{\partial^2}{\partial x^2} f(x, y)\Big|_{(1, -1)}$.

36. If $f(x, y) = x^4 y^2 + 4xy$, find $\dfrac{\partial^2}{\partial y^2} f(x, y)\Big|_{(1, 2)}$.

37. If $f(x, y) = \dfrac{2x}{x^2 + y^2}$, find the following.

(a) $\dfrac{\partial^2 f}{\partial x^2}\Big|_{(-1, 4)}$ (b) $\dfrac{\partial^2 f}{\partial y^2}\Big|_{(-1, 4)}$

38. If $f(x, y) = \dfrac{2y^2}{3xy + 4}$, find the following.

(a) $\dfrac{\partial^2 f}{\partial x^2}\Big|_{(1, -2)}$ (b) $\dfrac{\partial^2 f}{\partial y^2}\Big|_{(1, -2)}$

39. If $z = x^2 y + ye^{x^2}$, find $z_{yx}\big|_{(1, 2)}$.

40. If $z = xy^3 + x \ln y^2$, find $z_{xy}\big|_{(1, 2)}$.

41. If $z = x^2 - xy + 4y^3$, find z_{xyx}.

42. If $z = x^3 - 4x^2 y + 5y^3$, find z_{yyx}.

43. If $w = 4x^3 y + y^2 z + z^3$, find the following.

(a) w_{xxy} (b) w_{xyx} (c) w_{xyz}

44. If $w = 4xyz + x^3 y^2 z + x^3$, find the following.

(a) w_{xyz} (b) w_{xzz} (c) w_{yyz}

APPLICATIONS

45. *Mortgage* When a homeowner has a 25-year variable-rate mortgage loan, the monthly payment R is a function of the amount of the loan A and the current interest rate i (as a percent); that is, $R = f(A, i)$. Interpret each of the following.

(a) $f(100,000, 8) = 771.82$

(b) $\dfrac{\partial f}{\partial i}(100,000, 8) = 66.25$

46. *Mass transportation ridership* Suppose that in a certain city, the number of people N using the mass transportation system is a function of the fare f and the daily cost of downtown parking p, so that $N = N(f, p)$. Interpret each of the following.

(a) $N(5, 20) = 65,000$ (b) $\dfrac{\partial N}{\partial f}(5, 20) = -4000$

(c) $\dfrac{\partial N}{\partial p}(5, 20) = 2500$

47. *Wilson's lot size formula* In economics, the most economical quantity Q of goods (TVs, dresses, gallons of paint, etc.) for a store to order is given by Wilson's lot size formula

$$Q = \sqrt{2KM/h}$$

where K is the cost of placing the order, M is the number of items sold per week, and h is the weekly holding costs for each item (the cost of storage space, utilities, taxes, security, etc.).

(a) Explain why $\dfrac{\partial Q}{\partial M}$ will be positive.

(b) Explain why $\dfrac{\partial Q}{\partial h}$ will be negative.

48. *Cost* Suppose that the total cost (in dollars) of producing a product is $C(x, y) = 25 + 2x^2 + 3y^2$, where x is the cost per pound for material and y is the cost per hour for labor.

(a) If material costs are held constant, at what rate will the total cost increase for each $1-per-hour increase in labor?

(b) If the labor costs are held constant, at what rate will the total cost increase for each increase of $1 in material cost?

49. *Pesticide* Suppose that the number of thousands of insects killed by two brands of pesticide is given by

$$f(x, y) = 10,000 - 6500e^{-0.01x} - 3500e^{-0.02y}$$

where x is the number of liters of brand 1 and y is the number of liters of brand 2. What is the rate of change of insect deaths with respect to the number of liters of brand 1 if 100 liters of each brand are currently being used? What does this mean?

50. *Profit* Suppose that the profit (in dollars) from the sale of Kisses and Kreams is given by

$$P(x, y) = 10x + 6.4y - 0.001x^2 - 0.025y^2$$

where x is the number of pounds of Kisses and y is the number of pounds of Kreams. Find $\partial P/\partial y$ and give the approximate rate of change of profit with respect to the number of pounds of Kreams that are sold, if 100 pounds of Kisses and 16 pounds of Kreams are currently being sold. What does this mean?

51. *Utility* If $U = f(x, y)$ is the utility function for goods X and Y, the *marginal utility* of X is $\partial U/\partial x$ and the *marginal utility* of Y is $\partial U/\partial y$. If $U = x^2 y^2$, find the marginal utility of

(a) X. (b) Y.

52. *Utility* If the utility function for goods X and Y is $U = xy + y^2$, find the marginal utility of

(a) X. (b) Y.

53. *Production* Suppose that the output Q (in units) of a certain company is $Q = 75K^{1/3} L^{2/3}$, where K is the capital expenditures in thousands of dollars and L is the number of labor hours. Find $\partial Q/\partial K$ and $\partial Q/\partial L$ when capital expenditures are $729,000 and the labor hours total 5832. Interpret each answer.

54. *Production* Suppose that the production Q (in gallons of paint) of a paint manufacturer can be modeled by $Q = 140K^{1/2} L^{1/2}$, where K is the company's capital expenditures in thousands of dollars and L is the size of the labor force (in hours worked). Find $\partial Q/\partial K$ and $\partial Q/\partial L$ when capital expenditures are $250,000 and the labor hours are 1225. Interpret each answer.

Wind chill **Dr. Paul Siple conducted studies testing the effect of wind on the formation of ice at various temperatures and developed the concept of *wind chill,* which we hear reported during winter weather reports. In 2001, the National Weather Service introduced the new wind chill index given in the table. This new index is more accurate at measuring how cold it feels when it is windy. For example, the table shows that an air temperature of 15°F together with a wind speed of 35 mph feels the same as an air temperature of −7°F when there is no wind.**

Wind Speed (mph)	Air Temperature (°F)						
	35	25	15	5	−5	−15	−25
5	31	19	7	−5	−16	−28	−40
15	25	13	0	−13	−26	−39	−51
25	23	9	−4	−17	−31	−44	−58
35	21	7	−7	−21	−34	−48	−62
45	19	5	−9	−23	−37	−51	−65

Source: National Weather Service

The wind chill *WC* has been modeled by

$$WC = 35.74 + 0.6215t - 35.75s^{0.16} + 0.4275ts^{0.16}$$

where *s* is the wind speed and *t* actual air temperature. Use this model to answer Problems 55 and 56

55 (a) To see how the wind chill temperature changes with wind speed, find $\partial WC/\partial s$.

(b) Find $\partial WC/\partial s$ when the temperature is 10°F and the wind speed is 25 mph. What does this mean?

56. (a) To see how wind chill temperature changes with temperature, find $\partial WC/\partial t$.

(b) Find $\partial WC/\partial t$ when the temperature is 10°F and the wind speed is 25 mph. What does this mean?

SECTION 14.3

Applications of Functions of Two Variables in Business and Economics

OBJECTIVES

- To evaluate cost functions at given levels of production
- To find marginal costs from total cost and joint cost functions
- To find marginal productivity for given production functions
- To find marginal demand functions from demand functions for a pair of related products

APPLICATION PREVIEW

Suppose that the joint cost function for two commodities is

$$C = 50 + x^2 + 8xy + y^3$$

where *x* and *y* represent the quantities of each commodity and *C* is the total cost for the two commodities. We can take the partial derivative of *C* with respect to *x* to find the marginal cost of the first product, and we can take the partial derivative of *C* with respect to *y* to find the marginal cost of the second product. (See Example 1.) This is one of three types of applications that we will consider in this section. In the second case, we consider production functions and revisit Cobb-Douglas production functions. Marginal productivity is introduced, and its meaning is explained. Finally, we consider demand functions for two products in a competitive market. Partial derivatives are used to define marginal demands, and these marginals are used to classify the products as competitive or complementary.

Joint Cost and Marginal Cost

Suppose that a firm produces two products using the same inputs in different proportions. In such a case, the **joint cost function** is of the form $C = Q(x, y)$, where *x* represents the quantity of product *X* and *y* represents the quantity of product *Y*. Then $\partial C/\partial x$ is the **marginal cost** of the first product and $\partial C/\partial y$ is the marginal cost of the second product.

EXAMPLE 1 Joint Cost | APPLICATION PREVIEW |

If the joint cost function for two products is

$$C = Q(x, y) = 50 + x^2 + 8xy + y^3$$

where *x* represents the quantity of product *X* and *y* represents the quantity of product *Y*, find the marginal cost with respect to the number of units of:

(a) Product *X*   (b) Product *Y*   (c) Product *X* at (5, 3)   (d) Product *Y* at (5, 3)

Solution

(a) The marginal cost with respect to the number of units of product X is $\dfrac{\partial C}{\partial x} = 2x + 8y$.

(b) The marginal cost with respect to the number of units of product Y is $\dfrac{\partial C}{\partial y} = 8x + 3y^2$.

(c) $\left.\dfrac{\partial C}{\partial x}\right|_{(5,\,3)} = 2(5) + 8(3) = 34$

Thus if 5 units of product X and 3 units of product Y are produced, the total cost will increase by approximately \$34 for a unit increase in product X if y is held constant.

(d) $\left.\dfrac{\partial C}{\partial y}\right|_{(5,\,3)} = 8(5) + 3(3)^2 = 67$

Thus if 5 units of product X and 3 units of product Y are produced, the total cost will increase by approximately \$67 for a unit increase in product Y if x is held constant. ■

CHECKPOINT

1. If the joint cost in dollars for two products is given by

$$C = 100 + 3x + 10xy + y^2$$

find the marginal cost with respect to (a) the number of units of Product X and (b) the number of units of Product Y at (7, 3).

Production Functions

An important problem in economics concerns how the factors necessary for production determine the output of a product. For example, the output of a product depends on available labor, land, capital, material, and machines. If the amount of output z of a product depends on the amounts of two inputs x and y, then the quantity z is given by the **production function** $z = f(x, y)$.

EXAMPLE 2 Crop Harvesting

Suppose that it is known that z bushels of a crop can be harvested according to the function

$$z = \frac{21(6xy + 4x^2 - 3y)}{2x + 0.01y}$$

when 100x work-hours of labor are employed on y acres of land. What would be the output (in bushels) if 200 work-hours were used on 300 acres?

Solution
Because $z = f(x, y)$,

$$f(2, 300) = \frac{(21)[6(2)(300) + 4(2)^2 - 3(300)]}{2(2) + 0.01(300)} = 8148 \quad \text{(bushels)} \qquad ▨$$

If $z = f(x, y)$ is a production function, $\partial z/\partial x$ represents the rate of change in the output z with respect to input x while input y remains constant. This partial derivative is called the **marginal productivity of x**. The partial derivative $\partial z/\partial y$ is the **marginal productivity of y** and measures the rate of change of z with respect to input y.

Marginal productivity (for either input) will be positive over a wide range of inputs, but it increases at a decreasing rate, and it may eventually reach a point where it no longer increases and begins to decrease.

EXAMPLE 3 Production

If a production function is given by $z = 5x^{1/2}y^{1/4}$, find the marginal productivity of

(a) x.   (b) y.

Solution

(a) $\dfrac{\partial z}{\partial x} = \dfrac{5}{2}x^{-1/2}y^{1/4}$ (b) $\dfrac{\partial z}{\partial y} = \dfrac{5}{4}x^{1/2}y^{-3/4}$

Note that the marginal productivity of x is positive for all values of x but that it decreases as x gets larger (because of the negative exponent). The same is true for the marginal productivity of y. ▪

CHECKPOINT

2. If the production function for a product is

$$P = 10x^{1/4}y^{1/2}$$

find the marginal productivity of x.

Calculator Note   If we have a production function and fix a value for one variable, then we can use a graphing calculator to analyze the marginal productivity with respect to the other variable. Example 4 illustrates the use of a graphing calculator to analyze the marginal productivity of x and of y. ▪

  EXAMPLE 4   **Production**

Suppose the Cobb-Douglas production function for a company is given by

$$z = 100x^{1/4}y^{3/4}$$

where x is the company's capital investment (in dollars) and y is the size of the labor force (in work-hours).

(a) Find the marginal productivity of x.
(b) If the current available labor is 625 work-hours, substitute $y = 625$ in your answer to part (a) and graph the result.
(c) From the graph in part (b), what can be said about the effect on production of additional capital investment when the work-hours remain at 625?
(d) Find the marginal productivity of y.
(e) If current capital investment is $10,000, substitute $x = 10,000$ in your answer to part (d) and graph the result.
(f) From the graph in part (e), what can be said about the effect on production of additional work-hours when capital investment remains at $10,000?

Solution

(a) $z_x = 25x^{-3/4}y^{3/4}$

(b) If $y = 625$, then z_x becomes

$$z_x = 25x^{-3/4}(625)^{3/4} = 25\left(\frac{1}{x^{3/4}}\right)(125) = \frac{3125}{x^{3/4}}$$

The graph of z_x can be limited to Quadrant I because the capital investment is $x > 0$, and hence $z_x > 0$. Knowledge of asymptotes can help us determine range values for x and z_x that give an accurate graph. (See Figure 14.6.)

(c) Figure 14.6 shows that $z_x > 0$ for $x > 0$. This means that any increases in capital investment will result in increases in productivity. However, Figure 14.6 also shows that z_x is decreasing for $x > 0$, which means that as capital investment increases, productivity increases, but at a slower rate.

(d) $z_y = 75x^{1/4}y^{-1/4}$

(e) If $x = 10,000$, then z_y becomes

$$z_y = 75(10,000)^{1/4}\left(\frac{1}{y^{1/4}}\right) = \frac{750}{y^{1/4}}$$

The graph is shown in Figure 14.7(a) on the next page.

500

0   500
0

$z_x = \dfrac{3125}{x^{3/4}}$

Figure 14.6

(f) Figure 14.7(a) also shows that $z_y > 0$ when $y > 0$, so increasing work-hours increases productivity. Note that z_y is decreasing for $y > 0$, but Figure 14.7(b) shows that it does so more slowly than z_x. This indicates that increases in work-hours have a diminishing impact on productivity, but still a more significant one than increases in capital expenditures.

Figure 14.7

(a)

(b)

Demand Functions   Suppose that two products are sold at prices p_1 and p_2 (both in dollars) in a competitive market consisting of a fixed number of consumers with given tastes and incomes. Then the amount of each *one* of the products demanded by the consumers is dependent on the prices of *both* products on the market. If q_1 represents the demand for the number of units of the first product, then $q_1 = f(p_1, p_2)$ is the **demand function** for that product. The graph of such a function is called a **demand surface**. An example of a demand function in two variables is $q_1 = 400 - 2p_1 - 4p_2$. Here q_1 is a function of two variables p_1 and p_2. If $p_1 = \$10$ and $p_2 = \$20$, the demand would equal $400 - 2(10) - 4(20) = 300$ units.

EXAMPLE 5 Demand

The demand functions for two products are

$$q_1 = 50 - 5p_1 - 2p_2$$
$$q_2 = 100 - 3p_1 - 8p_2$$

where q_1 and q_2 are the numbers of units and p_1 and p_2 are in dollars.

(a) What is the demand for each of the products if the price of the first is $p_1 = \$5$ and the price of the second is $p_2 = \$8$?

(b) Find a pair of prices p_1 and p_2 such that the demands for product 1 and product 2 are equal.

Solution

(a)
$$q_1 = 50 - 5(5) - 2(8) = 9$$
$$q_2 = 100 - 3(5) - 8(8) = 21$$

Thus if these are the prices, the demand for product 2 is higher than the demand for product 1.

(b) We want q_1 to equal q_2. Setting $q_1 = q_2$, we see that

$$50 - 5p_1 - 2p_2 = 100 - 3p_1 - 8p_2$$
$$6p_2 - 50 = 2p_1$$
$$p_1 = 3p_2 - 25$$

Any pair of positive values that satisfies this equation will make the demands equal. Letting $p_2 = 10$, we see that $p_1 = 5$ will satisfy the equation. Thus the prices $p_1 = 5$ and $p_2 = 10$ will make the demands equal. The prices $p_1 = 2$ and $p_2 = 9$ also make the demands equal. Many pairs of values (that is, all those satisfying $p_1 = 3p_2 - 25$) will equalize the demands.

If the demand functions for a pair of related products, product 1 and product 2, are $q_1 = f(p_1, p_2)$ and $q_2 = g(p_1, p_2)$, respectively, then the partial derivatives of q_1 and q_2 are called **marginal demand functions.**

$$\frac{\partial q_1}{\partial p_1}$$ is the marginal demand of q_1 with respect to p_1.

$$\frac{\partial q_1}{\partial p_2}$$ is the marginal demand of q_1 with respect to p_2.

$$\frac{\partial q_2}{\partial p_1}$$ is the marginal demand of q_2 with respect to p_1.

$$\frac{\partial q_2}{\partial p_2}$$ is the marginal demand of q_2 with respect to p_2.

For typical demand functions, if the price of product 2 is fixed, the demand for product 1 will decrease as its price p_1 increases. In this case, the marginal demand of q_1 with respect to p_1 will be negative; that is, $\partial q_1/\partial p_1 < 0$. Similarly, $\partial q_2/\partial p_2 < 0$.

But what about $\partial q_2/\partial p_1$ and $\partial q_1/\partial p_2$? If $\partial q_2/\partial p_1$ and $\partial q_1/\partial p_2$ are both positive, the two products are **competitive** because an increase in price p_1 will result in an increase in demand for product 2 (q_2) if the price p_2 is held constant and an increase in price p_2 will increase the demand for product 1 (q_1) if p_1 is held constant. Stated more simply, an increase in the price of one of the two products will result in an increased demand for the other, so the products are in competition. For example, an increase in the price of a Japanese automobile will result in an increase in demand for an American automobile if the price of the American automobile is held constant.

If $\partial q_2/\partial p_1$ and $\partial q_1/\partial p_2$ are both negative, the products are **complementary** because an increase in the price of one product will cause a decrease in demand for the other product if the price of the second product doesn't change. Under these conditions, a *decrease* in the price of product 1 will result in an *increase* in the demand for product 2, and a decrease in the price of product 2 will result in an increase in the demand for product 1. For example, a decrease in the price of gasoline will result in an increase in the demand for large automobiles.

If the signs of $\partial q_2/\partial p_1$ and $\partial q_1/\partial p_2$ are different, the products are neither competitive nor complementary. This situation rarely occurs but is possible.

EXAMPLE 6   **Demand**

The demand functions for two related products, product 1 and product 2, are given by

$$q_1 = 400 - 5p_1 + 6p_2 \quad \text{and} \quad q_2 = 250 + 4p_1 - 5p_2$$

(a) Determine the four marginal demands.
(b) Are product 1 and product 2 complementary or competitive?

Solution

(a) $\dfrac{\partial q_1}{\partial p_1} = -5; \quad \dfrac{\partial q_2}{\partial p_2} = -5; \quad \dfrac{\partial q_1}{\partial p_2} = 6; \quad \dfrac{\partial q_2}{\partial p_1} = 4$

(b) Because $\partial q_1/\partial p_2$ and $\partial q_2/\partial p_1$ are positive, products 1 and 2 are competitive.

CHECKPOINT

3. If the demand functions for two products are
$$q_1 = 200 - 3p_1 - 4p_2 \quad \text{and} \quad q_2 = 50 - 6p_1 - 5p_2$$
find the marginal demand of
(a) q_1 with respect to p_1.   (b) q_2 with respect to p_2.

EXERCISES 14.3

JOINT COST AND MARGINAL COST

1. The cost (in dollars) of manufacturing one item is given by

$$C(x, y) = 30 + 3x + 5y$$

where x is the cost of 1 hour of labor and y is the cost of 1 pound of material.
   (a) If the hourly cost of labor is $20 and the material costs $3 per pound, what is the cost of manufacturing one of these items?
   (b) Find and interpret the partial derivative of C with respect to x.

2. The manufacture of 1 unit of a product has a cost (in dollars) given by

$$C(x, y, z) = 10 + 8x + 3y + z$$

where x is the cost of 1 pound of one raw material, y is the cost of 1 pound of a second raw material, and z is the cost of 1 work-hour of labor.
   (a) If the cost of the first raw material is $16 per pound, the cost of the second raw material is $8 per pound, and labor costs $18 per work-hour, what will it cost to produce 1 unit of the product?
   (b) Find and interpret the partial derivative of C with respect to x.

3. The total cost of producing 1 unit of a product is

$$C(x, y) = 30 + 2x + 4y + \frac{xy}{50} \quad \text{dollars}$$

where x is the cost per pound of raw materials and y is the cost per hour of labor.
   (a) If labor costs are held constant, find the function that describes the rate at which total cost increases for each increase of $1 per pound in material cost.
   (b) If material costs are held constant, find the function that describes the rate at which total cost increases for each $1 per hour increase in labor costs.

4. The total cost of producing an item is

$$C(x, y) = 40 + 4x + 6y + \frac{x^2 y}{100} \quad \text{dollars}$$

where x is the cost per pound of raw materials and y is the cost per hour for labor. Find the function that can be used to determine how an increase of
   (a) $1 per pound of raw materials affects the total cost.
   (b) $1 per hour in labor costs affects the total cost.

5. The total cost of producing 1 unit of a product is given by

$$C(x, y) = 20x + 70y + \frac{x^2}{1000} + \frac{xy^2}{100} \quad \text{dollars}$$

where x represents the cost per pound of raw materials and y represents the hourly rate for labor. The present cost for raw materials is $10 per pound and the present hourly rate for labor is $24. How will an increase of
   (a) $1 per pound for raw materials affect the total cost?
   (b) $1 per hour in labor costs affect the total cost?

6. The total cost of producing 1 unit of a product is given by

$$C(x, y) = 30 + 0.5x^2 + 30y - xy \quad \text{dollars}$$

where x is the hourly labor rate and y is the cost per pound of raw materials. The current hourly rate is $25, and the raw materials cost $6 per pound. How will an increase of
   (a) $1 per pound for the raw materials affect the total cost?
   (b) $1 in the hourly labor rate affect the total cost?

7. The joint cost (in dollars) for two products is given by

$$C(x, y) = 30 + x^2 + 3y + 2xy$$

where x represents the quantity of product X produced and y represents the quantity of product Y produced.
   (a) Find and interpret the marginal cost with respect to x if 8 units of product X and 10 units of product Y are produced.
   (b) Find and interpret the marginal cost with respect to y if 8 units of product X and 10 units of product Y are produced.

8. The joint cost (in dollars) for products X and Y is given by

$$C(x, y) = 40 + 3x^2 + y^2 + xy$$

where x represents the quantity of X and y represents the quantity of Y.

(a) Find and interpret the marginal cost with respect to x if 20 units of product X and 15 units of product Y are produced.

(b) Find and interpret the marginal cost with respect to y if 20 units of X and 15 units of Y are produced.

9. If the joint cost function for two products is

$$C(x, y) = x\sqrt{y^2 + 1} \quad \text{dollars}$$

(a) find the marginal cost (function) with respect to x.
(b) find the marginal cost with respect to y.

10. Suppose the joint cost function for x units of product X and y units of product Y is given by

$$C(x, y) = 2500\sqrt{xy + 1} \quad \text{dollars}$$

Find the marginal cost with respect to
(a) x. (b) y.

11. Suppose that the joint cost function for two products is

$$C(x, y) = 1200 \ln(xy + 1) + 10{,}000 \quad \text{dollars}$$

Find the marginal cost with respect to
(a) x. (b) y.

12. Suppose that the joint cost function for two products is

$$C(x, y) = y \ln(x + 1) \quad \text{dollars}$$

Find the marginal cost with respect to
(a) x. (b) y.

PRODUCTION FUNCTIONS

13. Suppose that the production function for a product is $z = \sqrt{4xy}$, where x represents the number of work-hours per month and y is the number of available machines. Determine the marginal productivity of
(a) x. (b) y.

14. Suppose the production function for a product is

$$z = 60x^{2/5}y^{3/5}$$

where x is the capital expenditures and y is the number of work-hours. Find the marginal productivity of
(a) x. (b) y.

15. Suppose that the production function for a product is $z = \sqrt{x} \ln(y + 1)$, where x represents the number of work-hours and y represents the available capital (per week). Find the marginal productivity of
(a) x. (b) y.

16. Suppose that a company's production function for a certain product is

$$z = (x + 1)^{1/2} \ln(y^2 + 1)$$

where x is the number of work-hours of unskilled labor and y is the number of work-hours of skilled labor. Find the marginal productivity of
(a) x. (b) y.

For Problems 17–19, suppose that the number of crates of an agricultural product is given by

$$z = \frac{11xy - 0.0002x^2 - 5y}{0.03x + 3y}$$

where x is the number of hours of labor and y is the number of acres of the crop.

17. Find the output when $x = 300$ and $y = 500$.

18. Find and interpret the marginal productivity of the number of acres of the crop (y) when $x = 300$ and $y = 500$.

19. Find and interpret the marginal productivity of the number of hours of labor (x) when $x = 300$ and $y = 500$.

20. If a production function is given by $z = 12x^{3/4}y^{1/3}$, find the marginal productivity of
(a) x. (b) y.

21. Suppose the Cobb-Douglas production function for a company is given by
$$z = 400x^{3/5}y^{2/5}$$
where x is the company's capital investment and y is the size of the labor force (in work-hours).

(a) Find the marginal productivity of x.
(b) If the current labor force is 1024 work-hours, substitute $y = 1024$ in your answer to part (a) and graph the result.
(c) Find the marginal productivity of y.
(d) If the current capital investment is \$59,049, substitute $x = 59{,}049$ in your answer to part (c) and graph the result.
(e) Interpret the graphs in parts (b) and (d) with regard to what they say about the effects on productivity of an increased capital investment [part (b)] and of an increased labor force [part (d)].

22. Suppose the Cobb-Douglas production function for a company is given by
$$z = 300x^{2/3}y^{1/3}$$
where x is the company's capital investment and y is the size of the labor force (in work-hours).

(a) Find the marginal productivity of x.
(b) If the current labor force is 729 work-hours, substitute $y = 729$ in your answer to part (a) and graph the result.
(c) Find the marginal productivity of y.
(d) If the current capital investment is \$27,000, substitute $x = 27{,}000$ in your answer to part (c) and graph the result.
(e) Interpret the graphs in parts (b) and (d) with regard to what they say about the effects on productivity of an increased capital investment [part (b)] and of an increased labor force [part (d)].

DEMAND FUNCTIONS

In Problems 23–26, prices p_1 and p_2 are in dollars and q_1 and q_2 are numbers of units.

23. The demand functions for two products are given by
$$q_1 = 300 - 8p_1 - 4p_2$$
$$q_2 = 400 - 5p_1 - 10p_2$$
Find the demand for each of the products if the price of the first is $p_1 = \$10$ and the price of the second is $p_2 = \$8$.

24. The demand functions for two products are given by
$$q_1 = 900 - 9p_1 + 2p_2$$
$$q_2 = 1200 + 6p_1 - 10p_2$$
Find the demands q_1 and q_2 if $p_1 = \$10$ and $p_2 = \$12$.

25. Find a pair of prices p_1 and p_2 such that the demands for the two products in Problem 23 will be equal.

26. Find a pair of prices p_1 and p_2 such that the demands for the two products in Problem 24 will be equal.

In Problems 27–30, the demand functions for q_A and q_B units of two related products, A and B, are given. Complete parts (a)–(e) for each problem. Assume that p_A and p_B are in dollars.
(a) Find the marginal demand of q_A with respect to p_A.
(b) Find the marginal demand of q_A with respect to p_B.
(c) Find the marginal demand of q_B with respect to p_B.
(d) Find the marginal demand of q_B with respect to p_A.
(e) Are the two goods competitive or complementary?

27. $\begin{cases} q_A = 400 - 3p_A - 2p_B \\ q_B = 250 - 5p_A - 6p_B \end{cases}$

28. $\begin{cases} q_A = 600 - 4p_A + 6p_B \\ q_B = 1200 + 8p_A - 4p_B \end{cases}$

29. $\begin{cases} q_A = 5000 - 50p_A - \dfrac{600}{p_B + 1} \\ q_B = 10{,}000 - \dfrac{400}{p_A + 4} + \dfrac{400}{p_B + 4} \end{cases}$

30. $\begin{cases} q_A = 2500 + \dfrac{600}{p_A + 2} - 40p_B \\ q_B = 3000 - 100p_A + \dfrac{400}{p_B + 5} \end{cases}$

31. The markets for new cars and for used cars are related. As new car sales increase, the available supply of used cars (trade-ins) increases. This tends to decrease the price of used cars. As the prices of used cars decline, typically the demand for new cars also declines.
(a) Does this analysis suggest that new cars and used cars are complementary or competitive products? Explain.
(b) Suppose a large automobile dealership has the following monthly market demand and supply functions for its new and used cars.

Demand for New Cars:
$$p_{\text{NEW}} = 78{,}000 - 30q_{\text{NEW}} + 2p_{\text{USED}}$$

Supply of New Cars:
$$p_{\text{NEW}} = 20{,}000 + 10q_{\text{NEW}}$$

Demand for Used Cars:
$$p_{\text{USED}} = 3000 - 4q_{\text{USED}} + 0.05p_{\text{NEW}}$$

Supply of Used Cars:
$$p_{\text{USED}} = 2000 + q_{\text{USED}}$$

(i) Solve each demand equation for the quantity in terms of the prices for new cars and used cars.
(ii) Calculate the necessary partial derivatives to confirm or refute your answer in part (a).

SECTION 14.4 Maxima and Minima

OBJECTIVES

- To find relative maxima, minima, and saddle points of functions of two variables
- To apply linear regression formulas

APPLICATION PREVIEW

Adele Lighting manufactures 20-inch lamps and 31-inch lamps. Suppose that x is the number of thousands of 20-inch lamps and that the demand for these is given by $p_1 = 50 - x$, where p_1 is in dollars. Similarly, suppose that y is the number of thousands of 31-inch lamps and that the demand for these is given by $p_2 = 60 - 2y$, where p_2 is also in dollars. Adele Lighting's joint cost function for these lamps is $C = 2xy$ (in thousands of dollars). Therefore, Adele Lighting's profit (in thousands of dollars) is a function of the two variables x and y. To determine Adele's maximum profit, we need to develop methods for finding maximum values for a function of two variables. (See Example 4.)

In this section, we will find relative maxima and minima of functions of two variables and use them to solve applied optimization problems. We will use minimization of functions of two variables to develop the linear regression formulas. Recall that we first used linear regression in Chapter 2.

Maxima and Minima   In our study of differentiable functions of one variable, we saw that for a relative maximum or minimum to occur at a point, the tangent line to the curve had to be horizontal at that point. The function $z = f(x, y)$ describes a surface in three dimensions. If all partial derivatives of $f(x, y)$ exist, then there must be a horizontal plane tangent to the surface at a point for the surface to have a relative maximum at that point [see Figure 14.8(a)] or a minimum at that point [see Figure 14.8(b)]. But if the plane tangent to the surface at the point is horizontal, then all the tangent lines to the surface at that point must be horizontal, because they lie in the tangent plane. In particular, the tangent line in the direction of the x-axis will be horizontal, so $\partial z/\partial x = 0$ at the point. Also, the tangent line in the direction of the y-axis will be horizontal so $\partial z/\partial y = 0$ at the point. Thus those points where *both* $\partial z/\partial x = 0$ and $\partial z/\partial y = 0$ are called **critical points** for the surface.

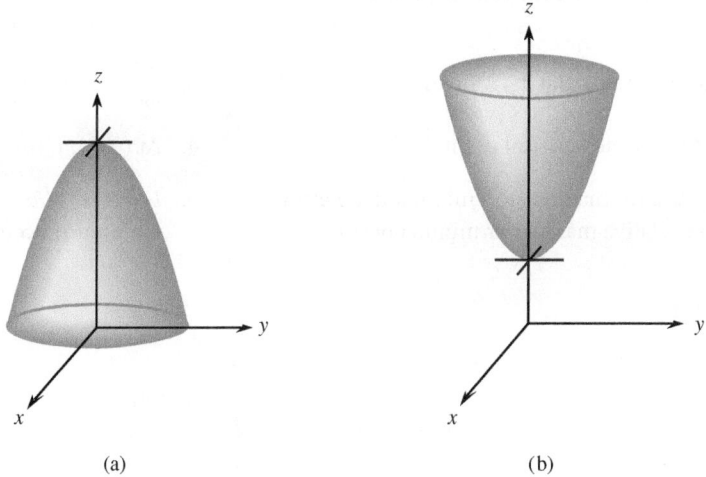

Figure 14.8   (a)   (b)

How can we determine whether a critical point is a relative maximum, a relative minimum, or neither of these? Finding that $\partial^2 z/\partial x^2 < 0$ and $\partial^2 z/\partial y^2 < 0$ is not enough to tell us that we have a relative maximum. The "second-derivative" test we must use involves the values of all of the second partial derivatives at the critical point (a, b).

We state, without proof, the result that determines whether there is a relative maximum, a relative minimum, or neither at the critical point (a, b).

Test for Maxima and Minima

Let $z = f(x, y)$ be a function for which both

$$\frac{\partial z}{\partial x} = 0 \text{ and } \frac{\partial z}{\partial y} = 0 \text{ at a point } (a, b)$$

and suppose that all second partial derivatives are continuous there. Define

$$D = \frac{\partial^2 z}{\partial x^2} \cdot \frac{\partial^2 z}{\partial y^2} - \left(\frac{\partial^2 z}{\partial x \partial y}\right)^2 = (z_{xx})(z_{yy}) - (z_{xy})^2$$

Evaluate D at the critical point (a, b) and conclude the following:

1. If $D(a, b) > 0$:
   (a) $z_{xx}(a, b) > 0 \Rightarrow$ a relative minimum occurs at (a, b). [Note $z_{yy}(a, b) > 0$ also.]
   (b) $z_{xx}(a, b) < 0 \Rightarrow$ a relative maximum occurs at (a, b). [Note $z_{yy}(a, b) < 0$ also.]
2. $D(a, b) < 0$, then neither a relative maximum nor a relative minimum occurs at (a, b).
3. $D(a, b) = 0$, then the test fails; investigate the function near the point.

We can test for relative maxima and minima by using the following procedure.

MAXIMA AND MINIMA OF $z = f(x, y)$

Procedure	Example
To find relative maxima and minima of $z = f(x, y)$:	Test $z = 4 - 4x^2 - y^2$ for relative maxima and minima.
1. Find $\partial z/\partial x$ and $\partial z/\partial y$.	1. $\dfrac{\partial z}{\partial x} = -8x;\quad \dfrac{\partial z}{\partial y} = -2y$
2. Find the point(s) that satisfy *both* $\partial z/\partial x = 0$ and $\partial z/\partial y = 0$. These are the critical points.	2. $\dfrac{\partial z}{\partial x} = 0$ if $x = 0.\quad \dfrac{\partial z}{\partial y} = 0$ if $y = 0$. The critical point is $(0, 0, 4)$.
3. Find all second partial derivatives.	3. $\dfrac{\partial^2 z}{\partial x^2} = -8;\quad \dfrac{\partial^2 z}{\partial y^2} = -2;\quad \dfrac{\partial^2 z}{\partial x\, \partial y} = \dfrac{\partial^2 z}{\partial y\, \partial x} = 0$
4. Evaluate D at each critical point.	4. At $(0, 0)$, $D = (-8)(-2) - 0^2 = 16$.
5. Use the test for maxima and minima to determine whether relative maxima or minima occur.	5. $D > 0, \partial^2 z/\partial x^2 < 0$, and $\partial^2 z/\partial y^2 < 0$. A relative maximum occurs at $(0, 0)$. (See Figure 14.9.)

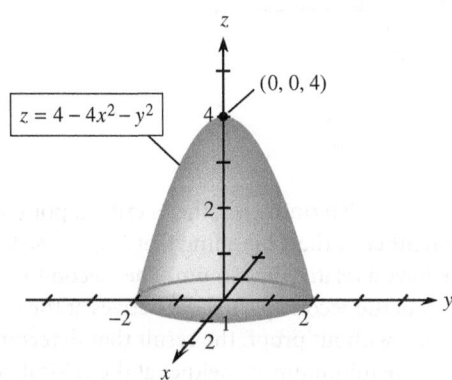

Figure 14.9

$z = 4 - 4x^2 - y^2$ (0, 0, 4)

EXAMPLE 1   Relative Maxima and Minima

Let $z = x^2 + y^2 - 2x + 1$. Find the relative maxima and minima of z, if they exist.

Solution

1. $\dfrac{\partial z}{\partial x} = 2x - 2;\quad \dfrac{\partial z}{\partial y} = 2y$

2. $\dfrac{\partial z}{\partial x} = 0$ if $x = 1.\quad \dfrac{\partial z}{\partial y} = 0$ if $y = 0$.

    Both are 0 if $x = 1$ and $y = 0$, so the critical point is $(1, 0, 0)$.

3. $\dfrac{\partial^2 z}{\partial x^2} = 2;\quad \dfrac{\partial^2 z}{\partial y^2} = 2;\quad \dfrac{\partial^2 z}{\partial x \partial y} = \dfrac{\partial^2 z}{\partial y\, \partial x} = 0$

4. At $(1, 0)$, $D = 2 \cdot 2 - 0^2 = 4$.
5. $D > 0, \partial^2 z/\partial x^2 > 0$, and $\partial^2 z/\partial y^2 > 0$.
    A relative minimum occurs at $(1, 0)$.
    (See Figure 14.10.)

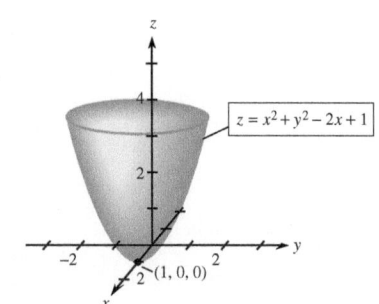

$z = x^2 + y^2 - 2x + 1$

Figure 14.10

EXAMPLE 2   **Saddle Points**

Let $z = y^2 - x^2$. Find the relative maxima and minima of z, if they exist.

Solution

1. $\dfrac{\partial z}{\partial x} = -2x;\quad \dfrac{\partial z}{\partial y} = 2y$

2. $\dfrac{\partial z}{\partial x} = 0$ if $x = 0;\quad \dfrac{\partial z}{\partial y} = 0$ if $y = 0$.

   Thus both equal 0 if $x = 0$, $y = 0$. The critical point is $(0, 0, 0)$.

3. $\dfrac{\partial^2 z}{\partial x^2} = -2;\quad \dfrac{\partial^2 z}{\partial y^2} = 2;\quad \dfrac{\partial^2 z}{\partial x\,\partial y} = \dfrac{\partial^2 z}{\partial y\,\partial x} = 0$

4. $D = (-2)(2) - 0 = -4$

5. $D < 0$, so the critical point is neither a relative maximum nor a relative minimum. As Figure 14.11 shows, the surface formed has the shape of a saddle. For this reason, critical points that are neither relative maxima nor relative minima are called **saddle points**.

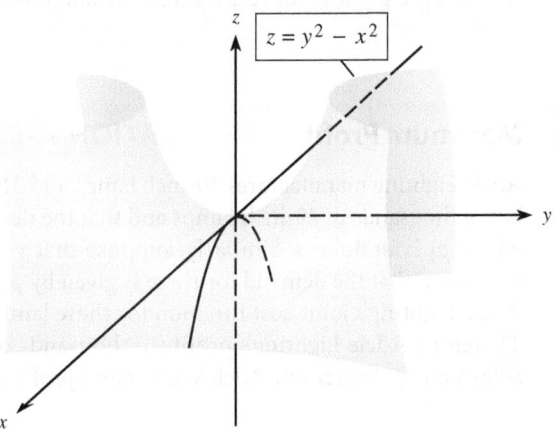

$z = y^2 - x^2$

Figure 14.11

The following example involves a surface with two critical points.

EXAMPLE 3   **Maxima and Minima**

Let $z = x^3 + y^2 + 6xy + 24x$. Find the relative maxima, relative minima, and saddle points for z, if they exist.

Solution

1. $\dfrac{\partial z}{\partial x} = 3x^2 + 6y + 24$ and $\dfrac{\partial z}{\partial y} = 2y + 6x$

2. $\dfrac{\partial z}{\partial x} = 0$ if $0 = 3x^2 + 6y + 24$,   and $\dfrac{\partial z}{\partial y} = 0$ if $0 = 2y + 6x$.

   But $0 = 2y + 6x$ means $y = -3x$. Because *both* partial derivatives must equal zero, we substitute $(-3x)$ for y in $0 = 3x^2 + 6y + 24$ to obtain

   $$0 = 3x^2 + 6(-3x) + 24 = 3x^2 - 18x + 24$$
   $$0 = 3(x^2 - 6x + 8) = 3(x - 2)(x - 4)$$

   Thus the solutions are $x = 2$ and $x = 4$.
   When $x = 2$, $y = -3x = -6$, and $z = 2^3 + (-6)^2 + 6(2)(-6) + 24(2) = 20$, so one critical point is $(2, -6, 20)$.

When $x = 4$, $y = -3x = -12$, and $z = 4^3 + (-12)^2 + 6(4)(-12) + 24(4) = 16$, so another critical point is $(4, -12, 16)$.

3. $\dfrac{\partial^2 z}{\partial x^2} = 6x$; $\dfrac{\partial^2 z}{\partial y^2} = 2$; $\dfrac{\partial^2 z}{\partial x\,\partial y} = \dfrac{\partial^2 z}{\partial y\,\partial x} = 6$

4. $D = (6x)(2) - 6^2$

5. At $(2, -6)$, $\dfrac{\partial^2 z}{\partial x^2} = 6 \cdot 2 = 12 > 0$, $\dfrac{\partial^2 z}{\partial y^2} = 2 > 0$, and $D = (6 \cdot 2)(2) - 6^2 = -12 < 0$,

    so a saddle point occurs at $(2, -6, 20)$.

    At $(4, -12)$, $\dfrac{\partial^2 z}{\partial x^2} = 6 \cdot 4 = 24 > 0$, $\dfrac{\partial^2 z}{\partial y^2} = 2 > 0$, and $D = (6 \cdot 4)(2) - 6^2 = 12 > 0$,

    so a relative minimum occurs at $(4, -12, 16)$.

CHECKPOINT

Suppose that $z = 4 - x^2 - y^2 + 2x - 4y$.
1. Find z_x and z_y.
2. Solve $z_x = 0$ and $z_y = 0$ simultaneously to find the critical point(s) for the graph of this function.
3. Test the point(s) for relative maxima and minima.

EXAMPLE 4   Maximum Profit | APPLICATION PREVIEW |

Adele Lighting manufactures 20-inch lamps and 31-inch lamps. Suppose that x is the number of thousands of 20-inch lamps and that the demand for these is given by $p_1 = 50 - x$, where p_1 is in dollars. Similarly, suppose that y is the number of thousands of 31-inch lamps and that the demand for these is given by $p_2 = 60 - 2y$, where p_2 is also in dollars. Adele Lighting's joint cost function for these lamps is $C = 2xy$ (in thousands of dollars). Therefore, Adele Lighting's profit (in thousands of dollars) is a function of the two variables x and y. Determine Adele's maximum profit.

Solution

The profit function is $P(x, y) = p_1 x + p_2 y - C(x, y)$. Thus

$$P(x, y) = (50 - x)x + (60 - 2y)y - 2xy$$
$$= 50x - x^2 + 60y - 2y^2 - 2xy$$

gives the profit in thousands of dollars. To maximize the profit, we proceed as follows.

$$P_x = 50 - 2x - 2y \quad \text{and} \quad P_y = 60 - 4y - 2x$$

Solving $P_x = 0$ and $P_y = 0$ simultaneously, we have

$$\begin{cases} 0 = 50 - 2x - 2y \\ 0 = 60 - 2x - 4y \end{cases}$$

Subtraction gives $-10 + 2y = 0$, so $y = 5$. With $y = 5$, the equation $0 = 50 - 2x - 2y$ becomes $0 = 40 - 2x$, so $x = 20$. Now

$$P_{xx} = -2, \ P_{yy} = -4, \text{ and } P_{xy} = -2, \text{ and}$$
$$D = (P_{xx})(P_{yy}) - (P_{xy})^2 = (-2)(-4) - (-2)^2 = 4$$

Because $P_{xx} < 0$, $P_{yy} < 0$, and $D > 0$, the values $x = 20$ and $y = 5$ yield maximum profit. Therefore, when $x = 20$ and $y = 5$, $p_1 = 30$, $p_2 = 50$, and the maximum profit is

$$P(20, 5) = 600 + 250 - 200 = 650$$

That is, Adele Lighting's maximum profit is $650,000 when the company sells 20,000 of the 20-inch lamps at $30 each and 5000 of the 31-inch lamps at $50 each.

Linear Regression   We have used different types of functions to model cost, revenue, profit, demand, supply, and other real-world relationships. Sometimes we have used calculus to study the behavior of these functions, finding, for example, marginal cost, marginal revenue, producer's surplus, and so on. We now have the mathematical tools to understand and develop the formulas that graphing calculators and other technology use to find the equations for linear models.

The formulas used to find the equation of the straight line that is the best fit for a set of data are developed using max-min techniques for functions of two variables. This line is called the **regression line.** In Figure 14.12, we define line ℓ to be the best fit for the data points (that is, the regression line) if the sum of the squares of the differences between the actual y-values of the data points and the y-values of the points on the line is a minimum.

In general, to find the equation of the regression line, we assume that the relationship between x and y is approximately linear and that we can find a straight line with equation

$$\hat{y} = a + bx$$

where the values of $\hat{y}$ will approximate the y-values of the points we know. That is, for each given value of x, the point $(x, \hat{y})$ will be on the line. For any given x-value, x_i, we are interested in the deviation between the y-value of the data point (x_i, y_i) and the $\hat{y}$-value from the equation, $\hat{y}_i$, that results when x_i is substituted for x. These deviations are of the form

$$d_i = \hat{y}_i - y_i, \quad \text{for } i = 1, 2, \ldots, n$$

See Figure 14.12 for a general case with the deviations exaggerated.

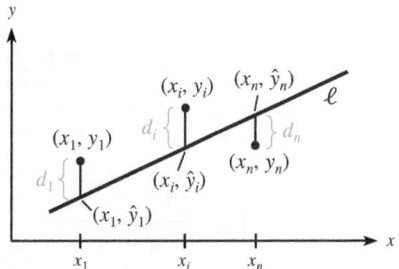

Figure 14.12

To measure the deviations in a way that accounts for the fact that some of the y-values will be above the line and some below, we will say that the line that is the best fit for the data is the one for which the sum of the squares of the deviations is a minimum. That is, we seek the a and b in the equation

$$\hat{y} = a + bx$$

such that the sum of the squares of the deviations,

$$S = \sum_{i=1}^{n} (\hat{y}_i - y_i)^2 = \sum_{i=1}^{n} [(bx_i + a) - y_i]^2$$
$$= (bx_1 + a - y_1)^2 + (bx_2 + a - y_2)^2 + \cdots + (bx_n + a - y_n)^2$$

is a minimum. The procedure for determining a and b is called the **method of least squares.**

We seek the values of b and a that make S a minimum, so we find the values that make

$$\frac{\partial S}{\partial b} = 0 \text{ and } \frac{\partial S}{\partial a} = 0$$

where

$$\frac{\partial S}{\partial b} = 2(bx_1 + a - y_1)x_1 + 2(bx_2 + a - y_2)x_2 + \cdots + 2(bx_n + a - y_n)x_n$$

$$\frac{\partial S}{\partial a} = 2(bx_1 + a - y_1) + 2(bx_2 + a - y_2) + \cdots + 2(bx_n + a - y_n)$$

Setting each equation equal to 0, dividing by 2, and using sigma notation give

$$0 = b\sum_{i=1}^{n} x_i^2 + a\sum_{i=1}^{n} x_i - \sum_{i=1}^{n} x_i y_i \qquad (1)$$

$$0 = b\sum_{i=1}^{n}x_i + a\sum_{i=1}^{n}1 - \sum_{i=1}^{n}y_i \tag{2}$$

We can write equations (1) and (2) as follows:

$$\sum_{i=1}^{n}x_i y_i = a\sum_{i=1}^{n}x_i + b\sum_{i=1}^{n}x_i^2 \tag{3}$$

$$\sum_{i=1}^{n}y_i = an + b\sum_{i=1}^{n}x_i \tag{4}$$

Multiplying equation (3) by n and equation (4) by $\sum_{i=1}^{n}x_i$ permits us to begin to solve for b.

$$n\sum_{i=1}^{n}x_i y_i = na\sum_{i=1}^{n}x_i + nb\sum_{i=1}^{n}x_i^2 \tag{5}$$

$$\sum_{i=1}^{n}x_i \sum_{i=1}^{n}y_i = na\sum_{i=1}^{n}x_i + b\left(\sum_{i=1}^{n}x_i\right)^2 \tag{6}$$

Subtracting equation (5) from equation (6) gives

$$\sum_{i=1}^{n}x_i \sum_{i=1}^{n}y_i - n\sum_{i=1}^{n}x_i y_i = b\left(\sum_{i=1}^{n}x_i\right)^2 - nb\sum_{i=1}^{n}x_i^2$$

$$= b\left[\left(\sum_{i=1}^{n}x_i\right)^2 - n\sum_{i=1}^{n}x_i^2\right]$$

Thus

$$b = \frac{\sum_{i=1}^{n}x_i \sum_{i=1}^{n}y_i - n\sum_{i=1}^{n}x_i y_i}{\left(\sum_{i=1}^{n}x_i\right)^2 - n\sum_{i=1}^{n}x_i^2}$$

and from equation (4),

$$a = \frac{\sum_{i=1}^{n}y_i - b\sum_{i=1}^{n}x_i}{n}$$

It can be shown that these values for b and a give a minimum value for S, so we have the following.

Linear Regression Equation

Given a set of data points (x_1, y_1), (x_2, y_2), ..., (x_n, y_n), the equation of the line that is the best fit for these data is

$$\hat{y} = a + bx$$

where

$$b = \frac{\sum_{i=1}^{n}x_i \sum_{i=1}^{n}y_i - n\sum_{i=1}^{n}x_i y_i}{\left(\sum_{i=1}^{n}x_i\right)^2 - n\sum_{i=1}^{n}x_i^2}, \quad a = \frac{\sum_{i=1}^{n}y_i - b\sum_{i=1}^{n}x_i}{n}$$

EXAMPLE 5 Inventory

The data in the table show the relation between the diameter of a partial roll of blue denim material at MacGregor Mills and the actual number of yards remaining on the roll. Use linear regression to find the linear equation that gives the number of yards as a function of the diameter.

Diameter (inches)	Yards/Roll	Diameter (inches)	Yards/Roll
14.0	120	22.5	325
15.0	145	24.0	360
16.5	170	24.5	380
17.75	200	25.25	405
18.5	220	26.0	435
19.8	255	26.75	460
20.5	270	27.0	470
22.0	305	28.0	500

Solution

Let x be the diameter of the partial roll and y be the number of yards on the roll. Before finding the values for a and b, we evaluate some parts of the formulas.

$$n = 16$$

$$\sum_{i=1}^{n} x_i = 348.05$$

$$\sum_{i=1}^{n} x_i^2 = 7871.48$$

$$\sum_{i=1}^{n} y_i = 5020$$

$$\sum_{i=1}^{n} x_i y_i = 117{,}367.75$$

$$b = \frac{\sum_{i=1}^{n} x_i \sum_{i=1}^{n} y_i - n \sum_{i=1}^{n} x_i y_i}{\left(\sum_{i=1}^{n} x_i\right)^2 - n \sum_{i=1}^{n} x_i^2}$$

$$= \frac{(348.05)(5020) - 16(117{,}367.75)}{(348.05)^2 - 16(7871.48)} \approx 27.1959$$

$$a = \frac{\sum_{i=1}^{n} y_i - b \sum_{i=1}^{n} x_i}{n}$$

$$= \frac{(5020) - (27.1959)(348.05)}{16} \approx -277.8458$$

Thus the linear equation that can be used to estimate the number of yards of denim remaining on a roll is

$$\hat{y} = -277.85 + 27.196x$$

Note that if we use the linear regression capability of a graphing utility, we obtain exactly the same equation.

CHECKPOINT

4. Use linear regression to write the equation of the line that is the best fit for the following points.

x	50	25	10	5
y	2	4	10	20

Finally, we note that formulas for models other than linear ones, such as power models ($y = ax^b$), exponential models ($y = ab^x$), and logarithmic models [$y = a + b \ln(x)$], can be developed with the least-squares method. That is, we apply max-min techniques for functions of two variables to minimize the sum of the squares of the deviations.

EXERCISES 14.4

In Problems 1–16, find each function's relative maxima, relative minima, and saddle points, if they exist.

1. $z = 9 - x^2 - y^2$
2. $z = 16 - 4x^2 - 9y^2$
3. $z = (x + 2)^2 + y^2 + 4$
4. $z = 3x^2 + (y - 11)^2 - 8$
5. $z = x^2 - y^2 + 4x - 6y + 11$
6. $z = 4y^2 - x^2 + 4y + 10x + 12$
7. $z = x^2 + y^2 - 2x + 4y + 5$
8. $z = 4x^2 + y^2 + 4x + 1$
9. $z = x^2 + 6xy + y^2 + 16x$
10. $z = x^2 - 4xy + y^2 - 6y$
11. $z = 24 - x^2 + xy - y^2 + 36y$
12. $z = 46 - x^2 + 2xy - 4y^2$
13. $z = x^2 + xy + y^2 - 4y + 10x$
14. $z = x^2 + 5xy + 10y^2 + 8x - 40y$
15. $z = x^3 + y^3 - 6xy$
16. $z = 6xy - x^3 - y^2$

In Problems 17 and 18, use the points given in the tables to write the equation of the line that is the best fit for the points.

17.
x	3	4	5	6
y	15	22	28	32

18.
x	10	20	30	40
y	2	6	5	6

APPLICATIONS

19. *Profit* Suppose that the quarterly profit from the sale of Kisses and Kreams is given by

$P(x, y) = 10x + 6.4y - 0.001x^2 - 0.025y^2$ dollars

where x is the number of pounds of Kisses and y is the number of pounds of Kreams. Selling how many pounds of Kisses and Kreams will maximize profit? What is the maximum profit?

20. *Profit* The profit from the sales of two products is given by

$P(x, y) = 20x + 70y - x^2 - y^2$ dollars

where x is the number of units of product 1 sold and y is the number of units of product 2. Selling how much

of each product will maximize profit? What is the maximum profit?

21. *Nutrition* A new food is designed to add weight to mature beef cattle. The weight in pounds is given by $W = 13xy(20 - x - 2y)$, where x is the number of units of the first ingredient and y is the number of units of the second ingredient. How many units of each ingredient will maximize the weight? What is the maximum weight?

22. *Profit* The profit for a grain crop is related to fertilizer and labor. The profit per acre is

$P = 100x + 40y - 5x^2 - 2y^2$ dollars

where x is the number of units of fertilizer and y is the number of work-hours. What values of x and y will maximize the profit? What is the maximum profit?

23. *Production* Suppose that

$P = 3.78x^2 + 1.5y^2 - 0.09x^3 - 0.01y^3$ tons

is the production function for a product with x units of one input and y units of a second input. Find the values of x and y that will maximize production. What is the maximum production?

24. *Production* Suppose that x units of one input and y units of a second input result in

$P = 40x + 50y - x^2 - y^2 - xy$

units of a product. Determine the inputs x and y that will maximize P. What is the maximum production?

25. *Profit* Suppose that a manufacturer produces two brands of a product, brand 1 and brand 2. Suppose the demand for brand 1 is $x = 70 - p_1$ thousand units and the demand for brand 2 is $y = 80 - p_2$ thousand units, where p_1 and p_2 are prices in dollars. If the joint cost function is $C = xy$ in thousands of dollars, how many of each brand should be produced to maximize profit? What is the maximum profit?

26. *Profit* Suppose that a firm produces two products, A and B, that sell for $\$a$ and $\$b$, respectively, with the total cost of producing x units of A and y units of B equal to $C(x, y)$. Show that when the profit from these products is maximized,

$$\frac{\partial C}{\partial x}(x, y) = a \text{ and } \frac{\partial C}{\partial y}(x, y) = b$$

27. *Manufacturing* Find the values for each of the dimensions of an open-top box of length x, width y, and height $500,000/(xy)$ (in inches) such that the box requires the least amount of material to make.

28. *Manufacturing* Find the values for each of the dimensions of a closed-top box of length x, width y, and height z (in inches) if the volume equals 27,000 cubic inches and the box requires the least amount of material to make. (*Hint:* First write the height in terms of x and y, as in Problem 27.)

29. *Profit* A company manufactures two products, A and B. If x is the number of thousands of units of A and y is the number of thousands of units of B, then the cost and revenue in thousands of dollars are

$$C(x, y) = 2x^2 - 2xy + y^2 - 7x - 10y + 11$$
$$R(x, y) = 5x + 8y$$

Find the number of each type of product that should be manufactured to maximize profit. What is the maximum profit?

30. *Production* Let x be the number of work-hours required and let y be the amount of capital required to produce z units of a product. Show that the average production per work-hour, z/x, is maximized when

$$\frac{\partial z}{\partial x} = \frac{z}{x}$$

Use $z = f(x, y)$ and assume that a maximum exists.

The manager of the Sea Islands Chicken Shack is interested in finding new ways to improve sales and profitability. Currently, Sea Islands offers both "eat-in" and "take-out" chicken dinners at \$3.25 each, sells 6250 dinners per week, and has short-run weekly costs (in dollars) given by

$$C = 500 + 1.2x$$

where x is the total number of eat-in and take-out chicken dinners.

The Sea Islands manager recently commissioned a local consulting firm to study the eat-in and take-out market demand per week. The study results provided the following weekly demand estimates for each of the two market segments:

$$\text{Eat-in:} \quad x = 6000 - 1000p_x$$
$$\text{Take-out:} \quad y = 10{,}000 - 2000p_y$$

where x is the number of eat-in dinners, with p_x as the price of each, and y is the number of take-out dinners, with p_y as the price of each. Use this information in Problems 31 and 32.

31. (a) If Sea Islands Chicken Shack prices chicken dinners differently for eat-in and take-out customers, how many dinners per week would it expect to sell to each type of customer to maximize weekly profit?

(b) What prices should Sea Islands charge each market segment to maximize the total weekly profit, and what is that profit?

(c) Would it be more profitable for Sea Islands to continue charging \$3.25 per dinner (and sell 6250 dinners per week) or to change the policy and to price differently for each type of customer? Explain.

32. When eat-in and take-out dinners are considered separately, Sea Islands Chicken Shack's short-run weekly cost function becomes

$$C = 500 + 0.60x + 1.60y$$

(a) Use this revised cost function to find the number of eat-in and take-out chicken dinners that would give maximum profit.

(b) What price should be charged for each type of dinner now, and what is the maximum weekly profit?

(c) Based on the results of parts (a) and (b), which is the best pricing strategy? Explain.

33. **Modeling** *U.S. National consumption* The following table gives the U.S. national consumption and disposable income (both in billions of dollars) for presidential election years from 2012 and projected to 2040.

(a) Use linear regression to find the linear equation that is the best fit for these data, with y representing the disposable income and C representing the consumption. Report the model with 3 significant digits.

(b) Graph the data and the linear regression line and discuss the fit.

(c) Use the linear model to predict the U.S. disposable income when the U.S. national consumption is \$19 billion.

(d) Find and interpret the slope of the reported model.

Year	Income	Consumption	Year	Income	Consumption
2012	10.2	9.6	2028	17.1	15.4
2016	12.6	11.6	2032	18.5	16.8
2020	14.2	12.9	2036	20.1	18.3
2024	15.5	14.0	2040	21.9	19.9

Source: U.S. Energy Information Administration

34. **Modeling** *Retirement benefits* The following table gives the approximate benefits for PepsiCo executives who earned an average of \$250,000 per year during the last 5 years of service, based on the number of years of service, from 15 years to 45 years.

(a) Use linear regression to find the linear equation that is the best fit for the data. Report the model with 3 significant digits.

(b) Use the equation to find the expected annual retirement benefits after 38 years of service.

(c) Write a sentence that interprets the slope of the linear regression line.

Years of Service	Annual Retirement
25	$109,280
30	121,130
35	132,990
40	145,490
45	160,790

Source: TRICON Salaried Employees Retirement Plan

35. **Modeling** *World population* The table gives the actual or projected world population in billions for selected years from 2000 to 2050.
   (a) Use linear regression to find the linear equation that is the best fit for the data, with x equal to the number of years past 2000. Report the model with 3 significant digits.
   (b) Use the reported equation to predict the population in 2025.
   (c) Write a sentence that interprets the slope of the linear regression line.

Years	Population (billions)
2000	6.08
2010	6.82
2020	7.54
2030	8.18
2040	8.72
2050	9.19

Source: U.S. Bureau of the Census, International Data Base

36. **Modeling** *Student loans* The following table shows the balance of federal direct student loans (in billions of dollars) for selected years from 2011 and projected to 2023.
   (a) Find the linear regression equation for the federal direct student loan balance as a function of the years past 2010. Report the model with three significant digit coefficients.
   (b) What does the reported model predict for this balance in 2025?
   (c) Write a sentence that interprets the slope of your linear regression equation.

Years	Amount ($ billion)
2011	702
2013	940
2015	1220
2017	1500
2019	1775
2021	2000
2023	2250

Source: U.S. Office of Management and Budget

Maxima and Minima of Functions Subject to Constraints: Lagrange Multipliers

OBJECTIVES

- To find the maximum or minimum value of a function of two or more variables subject to a condition that constrains the variables

APPLICATION PREVIEW

Many practical problems require that a function of two or more variables be maximized or minimized subject to certain conditions, or constraints, that limit the variables involved. For example, a firm will want to maximize its profits within the limits (constraints) imposed by its production capacity. Similarly, a city planner may want to locate a new building to maximize access to public transportation yet may be constrained by the availability and cost of building sites.

Specifically, suppose that the utility function for commodities X and Y is given by $U = x^2y^2$, where x and y are the numbers of units (in thousands) of X and Y, respectively. If P_1 and P_2 represent the prices in dollars of X and Y, respectively, and I represents the consumer's income available to purchase these two commodities, the equation $p_1x + p_2y = I$ is called the *budget constraint*. If the price of X is $2, the price of Y is $4, and the income available is $40 thousand, then the budget constraint is $2x + 4y = 40$. Thus we seek to maximize the consumer's utility $U = x^2y^2$ subject to the budget constraint $2x + 4y = 40$. (See Example 4.) In this section, we develop methods to solve this type of constrained maximum or minimum.

We can obtain maxima and minima for a function $z = f(x, y)$ subject to the constraint $g(x, y) = 0$ by using the method of **Lagrange multipliers,** named for the famous eighteenth-century mathematician Joseph Louis Lagrange. Lagrange multipliers can be used with functions of two or more variables when the constraints are given by an equation.

To find the critical values of a function $f(x, y)$ subject to the constraint $g(x, y) = 0$, we will use the new variable λ to form the **objective function**

$$F(x, y, \lambda) = f(x, y) + \lambda g(x, y)$$

It can be shown that the critical values of $F(x, y, \lambda)$ will satisfy the constraint $g(x, y) = 0$ and will be critical points of $f(x, y)$. Thus we need only find the critical points of $F(x, y, \lambda)$ to find the required critical points.

To find the critical points of $F(x, y, \lambda)$, we must find the points that make all the partial derivatives equal to 0. That is, the points must satisfy

$$\partial F/\partial x = 0, \quad \partial F/\partial y = 0, \quad \text{and} \quad \partial F/\partial \lambda = 0$$

Because $F(x, y, \lambda) = f(x, y) + \lambda g(x, y)$, these equations may be written as

$$\frac{\partial f}{\partial x} + \lambda \frac{\partial g}{\partial x} = 0$$

$$\frac{\partial f}{\partial y} + \lambda \frac{\partial g}{\partial y} = 0$$

$$g(x, y) = 0$$

Finding the values of x and y that satisfy these three equations simultaneously gives the critical values.

This method will not tell us whether the critical points correspond to maxima or minima, but this can be determined either from the physical setting for the problem or by testing according to a procedure similar to that used for unconstrained maxima and minima. The following examples illustrate the use of Lagrange multipliers.

EXAMPLE 1   Maxima Subject to Constraints

Find the maximum value of $z = x^2 y$ subject to $x + y = 9$, $x \geq 0$, $y \geq 0$.

Solution

The function to be maximized is $f(x, y) = x^2 y$. The constraint is $g(x, y) = 0$, where $g(x, y) = x + y - 9$. The objective function is

$$F(x, y, \lambda) = f(x, y) + \lambda g(x, y) = x^2 y + \lambda(x + y - 9)$$

Thus

$$\frac{\partial F}{\partial x} = 2xy + \lambda(1) = 0, \text{ or } 2xy + \lambda = 0$$

$$\frac{\partial F}{\partial y} = x^2 + \lambda(1) = 0, \text{ or } x^2 + \lambda = 0$$

$$\frac{\partial F}{\partial \lambda} = 0 + 1(x + y - 9) = 0, \text{ or } x + y - 9 = 0$$

Solving the first two equations for λ and substituting give

$$\lambda = -2xy$$
$$\lambda = -x^2$$
$$2xy = x^2$$
$$2xy - x^2 = 0$$
$$x(2y - x) = 0$$
$$x = 0 \quad \text{or} \quad x = 2y$$

Because $x = 0$ could not make $z = x^2y$ a maximum, we substitute $x = 2y$ into $x + y - 9 = 0$.

$$2y + y = 9 \quad \Rightarrow \quad y = 3$$
$$\text{and} \quad x = 2y \quad \Rightarrow \quad x = 6$$

Thus the function $z = x^2y$ is maximized at 108 when $x = 6$, $y = 3$ if the constraint is $x + y = 9$. Testing values near $x = 6$, $y = 3$ and satisfying the constraint shows that the function is maximized there. (Try $x = 5.5$, $y = 3.5$; $x = 7$, $y = 2$; and so on.)

EXAMPLE 2 Minima Subject to Constraints

Find the minimum value of the function $z = x^3 + y^3 + xy$ subject to the constraint $x + y - 4 = 0$.

Solution

The function to be minimized is $f(x, y) = x^3 + y^3 + xy$. The constraint function is $g(x, y) = x + y - 4$. The objective function is

$$F(x, y, \lambda) = f(x, y) + \lambda g(x, y) = x^3 + y^3 + xy + \lambda(x + y - 4)$$

Then

$$\frac{\partial F}{\partial x} = 3x^2 + y + \lambda = 0$$

$$\frac{\partial F}{\partial y} = 3y^2 + x + \lambda = 0$$

$$\frac{\partial F}{\partial \lambda} = x + y - 4 = 0$$

Solving the first two equations for λ and substituting, we get

$$\lambda = -(3x^2 + y)$$
$$\lambda = -(3y^2 + x)$$
$$3x^2 + y = 3y^2 + x$$

Solving $x + y - 4 = 0$ for y gives $y = 4 - x$. Substituting for y in the equation above, we get

$$3x^2 + (4 - x) = 3(4 - x)^2 + x$$
$$3x^2 + 4 - x = 48 - 24x + 3x^2 + x$$
$$22x = 44 \text{ or } x = 2$$

Thus when $x + y - 4 = 0$, $x = 2$ and $y = 2$ give the minimum value $z = 20$ because other values that satisfy the constraint give larger z-values.

CHECKPOINT

Find the minimum value of $f(x, y) = x^2 + y^2 - 4xy$, subject to the constraint $x + y = 10$, by
1. forming the objective function $F(x, y, \lambda)$,
2. finding $\dfrac{\partial F}{\partial x}, \dfrac{\partial F}{\partial y}$, and $\dfrac{\partial F}{\partial \lambda}$,
3. setting the three partial derivatives (from Question 2) equal to 0 and solving the equations simultaneously for x and y,
4. finding the value of $f(x, y)$ at the critical values of x and y.

We can also use Lagrange multipliers to find the maxima and minima of functions of three (or more) variables, subject to two (or more) constraints. The method involves using two multipliers, one for each constraint, to form an objective function $F = f + \lambda g_1 + \mu g_2$. We leave further discussion for more advanced courses.

We can easily extend the method to functions of three or more variables, as the following example shows.

EXAMPLE 3   Minima of Function of Three Variables

Find the minimum value of the function $w = x + y^2 + z^2$, subject to the constraint $x + y + z = 1$.

Solution

The function to be minimized is $f(x, y, z) = x + y^2 + z^2$. The constraint is $g(x, y, z) = 0$, where $g(x, y, z) = x + y + z - 1$. The objective function is

$$F(x, y, z, \lambda) = f(x, y, z) + \lambda g(x, y, z) = x + y^2 + z^2 + \lambda(x + y + z - 1)$$

Then

$$\frac{\partial F}{\partial x} = 1 + \lambda = 0$$

$$\frac{\partial F}{\partial y} = 2y + \lambda = 0$$

$$\frac{\partial F}{\partial z} = 2z + \lambda = 0$$

$$\frac{\partial F}{\partial \lambda} = x + y + z - 1 = 0$$

Solving the first three equations simultaneously gives

$$\lambda = -1, \quad y = \frac{1}{2}, \quad z = \frac{1}{2}$$

Substituting these values in the fourth equation (which is the constraint), we get $x + \frac{1}{2} + \frac{1}{2} - 1 = 0$, so $x = 0, y = \frac{1}{2}, z = \frac{1}{2}$. Thus $w = \frac{1}{2}$ is the minimum value because other values of x, y, and z that satisfy $x + y + z = 1$ give larger values of w.   ■

EXAMPLE 4   Utility | APPLICATION PREVIEW |

Find x and y that maximize the utility function $U = x^2 y^2$ subject to the budget constraint $2x + 4y = 40$.

Solution

First, we rewrite the constraint as $2x + 4y - 40 = 0$. Then the objective function is

$$F(x, y, \lambda) = x^2 y^2 + \lambda(2x + 4y - 40)$$

$$\frac{\partial F}{\partial x} = 2xy^2 + 2\lambda, \quad \frac{\partial F}{\partial y} = 2x^2 y + 4\lambda, \quad \frac{\partial F}{\partial \lambda} = 2x + 4y - 40$$

Setting these partial derivatives equal to 0 and solving give

$$-\lambda = xy^2 = x^2 y/2, \quad \text{or} \quad xy^2 - x^2 y/2 = 0$$

so

$$xy(y - x/2) = 0$$

yields $x = 0$, $y = 0$, or $x = 2y$. Neither $x = 0$ nor $y = 0$ maximizes utility. If $x = 2y$, then $0 = 2x + 4y - 40$ becomes

$$0 = 4y + 4y - 40 \quad \text{or} \quad 40 = 8y$$

Thus $y = 5$ and $x = 10$.

Testing values near $x = 10$, $y = 5$ shows that these values maximize utility at $U = 2500$.   ■

Figure 14.13

Figure 14.13 shows the budget constraint $2x + 4y = 40$ from Example 4 graphed with the indifference curves for $U = x^2 y^2$ that correspond to $U = 500$, $U = 2500$, and $U = 5000$.

Whenever an indifference curve intersects the budget constraint, that utility level is attainable within the budget. Note that the highest attainable utility (such as $U = 2500$

found in Example 4) corresponds to the indifference curve that touches the budget constraint at exactly one point—that is, the curve that has the budget constraint as a tangent line. Note also that utility levels greater than $U = 2500$ are not attainable within the budget because the indifference curve "misses" the budget constraint line (as for $U = 5000$).

EXAMPLE 5   Production

Suppose that the Cobb-Douglas production function for a certain manufacturer gives the number of units of production z according to

$$z = f(x, y) = 100x^{4/5}y^{1/5}$$

where x is the number of units of labor and y is the number of units of capital. Suppose further that labor costs \$160 per unit, capital costs \$200 per unit, and the total cost for capital and labor is limited to \$100,000, so that production is constrained by

$$160x + 200y = 100,000$$

Find the number of units of labor and the number of units of capital that maximize production.

Solution

The objective function is

$$F(x, y, \lambda) = 100x^{4/5}y^{1/5} + \lambda(160x + 200y - 100,000)$$

$$\frac{\partial F}{\partial x} = 80x^{-1/5}y^{1/5} + 160\lambda, \qquad \frac{\partial F}{\partial y} = 20x^{4/5}y^{-4/5} + 200\lambda$$

$$\frac{\partial F}{\partial \lambda} = 160x + 200y - 100,000$$

Setting these partial derivatives equal to 0 and solving give

$$\lambda = \frac{-80x^{-1/5}y^{1/5}}{160} = \frac{-20x^{4/5}y^{-4/5}}{200} \quad \text{or} \quad \frac{y^{1/5}}{2x^{1/5}} = \frac{x^{4/5}}{10y^{4/5}}$$

This means $5y = x$. Using this in $\dfrac{\partial F}{\partial \lambda} = 0$ gives

$$160(5y) + 200y - 100,000 = 0$$
$$1000y = 100,000$$
$$y = 100$$
$$x = 5y = 500$$

Thus production is maximized at $z = 100(500)^{4/5}(100)^{1/5} \approx 36,239$ when $x = 500$ (units of labor) and $y = 100$ (units of capital). (See Figure 14.14.)

In problems of this type, economists call the value of $-\lambda$ the **marginal productivity of money.** In this case,

$$-\lambda = \frac{y^{1/5}}{2x^{1/5}} = \frac{(100)^{0.2}}{2(500)^{0.2}} \approx 0.362$$

Figure 14.14

This means that each additional dollar spent on production results in approximately 0.362 additional unit produced.

Finally, Figure 14.14 shows the graph of the constraint, together with some production function curves that correspond to different production levels.

 Spreadsheet Note   The Excel tool called Solver can be used to find maxima and minima of functions subject to constraints. For details of this solution method, see Appendix B, Section 14.5, or the Online Excel Guide. In Example 5, the numbers of units of labor and capital that maximize production if the production is given by the Cobb-Douglas function

$$P(x, y) = 100x^{4/5}y^{1/5}$$

and if capital and labor are constrained by

$$160x + 200y = 100,000$$

were found to be 500 and 100, respectively. The following Excel screen shows the entries for beginning the solution of this problem.

	A	B	C
1	**Variables**		
2			
3	units labor (x)	0	
4	units capital (y)	0	
5			
6	**Objective**		
7			
8	Maximize production	= 100*B3^(4/5)*B4^(1/5)	
9			
10	**Constraint**		
11		Amount used	Available
12	Cost	= 160*B3 + 200*B4	100000
13			

The solution, found with Solver, is shown below.

	A	B	C
1	**Variables**		
2			
3	units labor (x)	500	
4	units capital (y)	100	
5			
6	**Objective**		
7			
8	Maximize production	36238.98	
9			
10	**Constraint**		
11		Amount used	Available
12	Cost	100000	100000
13			

EXERCISES 14.5

1. Find the minimum value of $z = x^2 + y^2$ subject to the condition $x + y = 6$.
2. Find the minimum value of $z = 4x^2 + y^2$ subject to the constraint $x + y = 5$.
3. Find the minimum value of $z = 3x^2 + 5y^2 - 2xy$ subject to the constraint $x + y = 5$.
4. Find the maximum value of $z = 2xy - 3x^2 - 5y^2$ subject to the constraint $x + y = 5$.
5. Find the maximum value of $z = x^2y$ subject to $x + y = 6, x \geq 0, y \geq 0$.
6. Find the maximum value of the function $z = x^3y^2$ subject to $x + y = 10, x \geq 0, y \geq 0$.
7. Find the maximum value of the function $z = 2xy - 2x^2 - 4y^2$ subject to the condition $x + 2y = 8$.
8. Find the minimum value of $z = 2x^2 + y^2 - xy$ subject to the constraint $2x + y = 8$.
9. Find the maximum value of $z = xy$ subject to $9x^2 + 25y^2 = 450; x \geq 0, y \geq 0$.
10. Find the maximum value of $z = xy^2$ subject to $2x^2 + y^2 = 600; x \geq 0, y \geq 0$.
11. Find the minimum value of $w = x^2 + y^2 + z^2$ subject to the constraint $x + y + z = 3$.
12. Find the minimum value of $w = x^2 + y^2 + z^2$ subject to the condition $2x - 4y + z = 21$.
13. Find the maximum value of $w = xz + y$ subject to the constraint $x^2 + y^2 + z^2 = 1$.
14. Find the maximum value of $w = x^2yz$ subject to the constraint $4x + y + z = 4, x \geq 0, y \geq 0$, and $z \geq 0$.

APPLICATIONS

15. *Utility* Suppose that the utility function for two commodities is given by $U = xy^2$ and that the budget constraint is $3x + 6y = 18$. What values of x and y will maximize utility?
16. *Utility* Suppose that the budget constraint in Problem 15 is $5x + 20y = 90$. What values of x and y will maximize $U = xy^2$?
17. *Utility* Suppose that the utility function for two products is given by $U = x^2y$, and the budget constraint is $2x + 3y = 120$. Find the values of x and y that

maximize utility. Check by graphing the budget constraint with the indifference curve for maximum utility and with two other indifference curves.

18. *Utility* Suppose that the utility function for two commodities is given by $U = x^2y^3$, and the budget constraint is $10x + 15y = 250$. Find the values of x and y that maximize utility. Check by graphing the budget constraint with the indifference curve for maximum utility and with two other indifference curves.

19. *Production* A company has the Cobb-Douglas production function

$$z = 400x^{0.6}y^{0.4}$$

where x is the number of units of labor, y is the number of units of capital, and z is the units of production. Suppose labor costs $150 per unit, capital costs $100 per unit, and the total cost of labor and capital is limited to $100,000.
  (a) Find the number of units of labor and the number of units of capital that maximize production.
  (b) Find the marginal productivity of money and interpret it.
  (c) Graph the constraint with the optimal value for production and with two other z-values (one smaller than the optimal value and one larger).

20. *Production* Suppose a company has the Cobb-Douglas production function

$$z = 100^{0.75}y^{0.25}$$

where x is the number of units of labor, y is the number of units of capital, and z is the units of production. Suppose further that labor costs $90 per unit, capital costs $150 per unit, and the total costs of labor and capital are limited to $90,000.
  (a) Find the number of units of labor and the number of units of capital that maximize production.
  (b) Find the marginal productivity of money and interpret it.
  (c) Graph the constraint with the optimal value for production and with two other z-values (one smaller than the optimal value and one larger).

21. *Cost* A firm has two plants, X and Y. Suppose that the cost of producing x units at plant X is $x^2 + 1200$ dollars and the cost of producing y units of the same product at plant Y is given by $3y^2 + 800$ dollars. If the firm has an order for 1200 units, how many should it produce at each plant to fill this order and minimize the cost of production?

22. *Cost* Suppose that the cost of producing x units at plant X is $(3x + 4)x$ dollars and that the cost of producing y units of the same product at plant Y is $(2y + 8)y$ dollars. If the firm that owns the plants has an order for 149 units, how many should it produce at each plant to fill this order and minimize its cost of production?

23. *Revenue* On the basis of past experience, a company has determined that its monthly sales revenue (in dollars) is related to its advertising according to the formula $s = 20x + y^2 + 4xy$, where x is the amount spent on print advertising and y is the amount spent on cable advertising. If the company plans to spend $30,000 per month on these two means of advertising, how much should it spend on each method to maximize its monthly sales revenue?

24. *Manufacturing* Find the dimensions x, y, and z (in inches) of the rectangular box with the largest volume that satisfies

$$3x + 4y + 12z = 12$$

25. *Manufacturing* Find the dimensions (in centimeters) of the box with square base, open top, and volume $500{,}000 \text{ cc}^3$ that requires the least materials.

26. *Manufacturing* Show that a box with a square base, an open top, and a fixed volume requires the least material to build if it has a height equal to one-half the length of one side of the base.

14 CHAPTER SUMMARY & REVIEW

KEY TERMS AND FORMULAS

Section 14.1

Cobb-Douglas production function (p. 858)
$$Q = AK^{\alpha}L^{1-\alpha}$$
Function of two variables (p. 858)
$$z = f(x, y)$$
Independent variables: x and y
Dependent variable: z
Domain

Coordinate planes (p. 859)
Utility (p. 860)
Indifference curve
Indifference map

Section 14.2

First-order partial derivative (p. 864)
With respect to x
$$z_x = \frac{\partial z}{\partial x}$$

With respect to y
$$z_y = \frac{\partial z}{\partial y}$$
Higher-order partial derivatives (p. 869)
Second partial derivatives
z_{xx}, z_{yy}, z_{xy}, and z_{yx}

Section 14.3

Joint cost function (p. 873)
$$C = Q(x, y)$$
Marginal cost (p. 873)
Marginal productivity (p. 874)

Demand function (p. 876)
Marginal demand functions (p. 877)
Competitive products (p. 877)
Complementary products (p. 877)

Section 14.4

Critical values for maxima, minima, and saddle points (p. 881)
Solve simultaneously $\begin{cases} z_x = 0 \\ z_y = 0 \end{cases}$.

Test for critical values (p. 881)
Use $D(x, y) = (z_{xx})(z_{yy}) - (z_{xy})^2$
Saddle points (p. 883)

Linear regression (p. 885)
$$\hat{y} = a + bx$$
$$b = \frac{\Sigma x \cdot \Sigma y - n\Sigma xy}{(\Sigma x)^2 - n\Sigma x^2}$$

$$a = \frac{\Sigma y - b\Sigma x}{n}$$

Section 14.5

Lagrange multipliers (p. 891)
Objective function (p. 891)
$$F(x, y, \lambda) = f(x, y) + \lambda g(x, y)$$

Maxima and minima subject to constraints (p. 891)
Marginal productivity of money (p. 894)

REVIEW EXERCISES

Section 14.1

1. What is the domain of $z = \dfrac{3}{2x - y}$?

2. What is the domain of $z = \dfrac{3x + 2\sqrt{y}}{x^2 + y^2}$?

3. If $w(x, y, z) = x^2 - 3yz$, find $w(2, 3, 1)$.

4. If $Q(K, L) = 70K^{2/3}L^{1/3}$, find $Q(64{,}000, 512)$.

Section 14.2

5. Find $\dfrac{\partial z}{\partial x}$ if $z = 5x^3 + 6xy + y^2$.

6. Find $\dfrac{\partial z}{\partial y}$ if $z = 12x^5 - 14x^3y^3 + 6y^4 - 1$.

In Problems 7–12, find z_x and z_y.

7. $z = 4x^2y^3 + \dfrac{x}{y}$

8. $z = \sqrt{x^2 + 2y^2}$

9. $z = (xy + 1)^{-2}$

10. $z = e^{x^2y^3}$

11. $z = e^{xy} + y \ln x$

12. $z = e^{\ln xy}$

13. Find the partial derivative of $f(x, y) = 4x^3 - 5xy^2 + y^3$ with respect to x at the point $(1, 2, -8)$.

14. Find the slope of the tangent in the x-direction to the surface $z = 5x^4 - 3xy^2 + y^2$ at $(1, 2, -3)$.

In Problems 15–18, find the second partials.
(a) z_{xx} **(b)** z_{yy} **(c)** z_{xy} **(d)** z_{yx}

15. $z = x^2y - 3xy$

16. $z = 3x^3y^4 - \dfrac{x^2}{y^2}$

17. $z = x^2e^{y^2}$

18. $z = \ln(xy + 1)$

Section 14.4

In Problems 19 and 20, find each function's relative maxima, relative minima, and saddle points, if they exist.

19. $z = 16 - x^2 - xy - y^2 + 24y$

20. $z = x^3 + y^3 - 12x - 27y$

Section 14.5

21. Find the minimum value of $z = 4x^2 + y^2$ subject to the constraint $x + y = 10$.

22. Find the maximum value of $z = x^4y^2$ subject to the constraint $x + y = 9$, $x \geq 0$, $y \geq 0$.

APPLICATIONS

Sections 14.1–14.2

23. *Utility* Suppose that the utility function for two goods X and Y is given by $U = x^2y$.
    (a) Write the equation of the indifference curve for a consumer who purchases 6 units of X and 15 units of Y.
    (b) If the consumer purchases 60 units of Y, how many units of X must be purchased to retain the same level of utility?

24. *Savings plans* The accumulated value A of a monthly savings plan over a 20-year period is a function of the monthly contribution R and the interest rate $r\%$ compounded monthly, according to

$$A = f(R, r) = \frac{1200R\left[\left(1 + \dfrac{r}{1200}\right)^{240} - 1\right]}{r}$$

   (a) Find the accumulated value of a plan that contributes \$100 per month with interest rate 6%.
   (b) Interpret $f(250, 7.8) \approx 143{,}648$.
   (c) Interpret $\dfrac{\partial A}{\partial r}(250, 7.8) \approx 17{,}770$.
   (d) Find $\dfrac{\partial A}{\partial R}(250, 7.8)$ and interpret the result.

25. *Retirement benefits* The monthly benefit B (in thousands of dollars) from a retirement account that is invested at 9% compounded monthly is a function of the account value V (also in thousands of dollars) and the number of years t that benefits are paid, and it can be approximated by

$$B = f(V, t) = \frac{3V}{400 - 400e^{-0.0897t}}$$

   (a) Find the benefit if the account value is \$1,000,000 and the monthly benefits last 20 years.
   (b) Find and interpret $\dfrac{\partial B}{\partial V}(1000, 20)$.
   (c) Find and interpret $\dfrac{\partial B}{\partial t}(1000, 20)$.

26. *Advertising and sales* The number of units of sales of a product, S, is a function of the dollars spent for

advertising, A, and the product's price, p. Suppose $S = f(A,p)$ is the function relating these quantities.

(a) Explain why $\dfrac{\partial S}{\partial A} > 0$.

(b) Do you think $\dfrac{\partial S}{\partial p}$ is positive or negative? Explain.

Section 14.3

27. *Cost* The joint cost, in dollars, for two products is given by $C(x, y) = x^2\sqrt{y^2} + 13$. Find the marginal cost with respect to
    (a) x if 20 units of x and 6 units of y are produced.
    (b) y if 20 units of x and 6 units of y are produced.
28. *Production* Suppose that the production function for a company is given by

    $$Q = 80K^{1/4}L^{3/4}$$

    where Q is the output (in hundreds of units), K is the capital expenditures (in thousands of dollars), and L is the work-hours. Find $\partial Q/\partial K$ and $\partial Q/\partial L$ when expenditures are \$625,000 and total work-hours are 4096. Interpret the results.
29. *Marginal demand* The demand functions for two related products, product A and product B, are given by

    $$q_A = 400 - 2p_A - 3p_B$$
    $$q_B = 300 - 5p_A - 6p_B$$

    where p_A and p_B are the respective prices in dollars.
    (a) Find the marginal demand of q_A with respect to p_A.
    (b) Find the marginal demand of q_B with respect to p_B.
    (c) Are the products complementary or competitive?
30. *Marginal demand* Suppose that the demand functions for two related products, A and B, are given by

    $$q_A = 800 - 40p_A - \frac{2}{p_B + 1}$$
    $$q_B = 1000 - \frac{10}{p_A + 4} - 30p_B$$

    where p_A and p_B are the respective prices in dollars. Determine whether the products are competitive or complementary.

Section 14.4

31. *Profit* The weekly profit (in dollars) from the sale of two products is given by

    $$P(x, y) = 40x + 80y - x^2 - y^2$$

    where x is the number of units of product 1 and y is the number of units of product 2. Selling how much of each product will maximize profit? Find the maximum weekly profit.
32. *Cost* Suppose a company has two separate plants that manufacture the same item. Suppose x is the amount

produced at plant I and y is the amount produced at plant II. If the total cost function for the two plants is

$$C(x, y) = 22{,}500 - 12x - 30y + 0.03x^2 + 0.01y^2$$

find the production allocation that minimizes the company's total cost.

Section 14.5

33. *Utility* If the utility function for two commodities is $U = x^2y$ and the budget constraint is $4x + 5y = 60$, find the values of x and y that maximize utility.
34. *Production* Suppose a company has the Cobb-Douglas production function

    $$z = 300x^{2/3}y^{1/3}$$

    where x is the number of units of labor, y is the number of units of capital, and z is the units of production. Suppose labor costs are \$50 per unit, capital costs are \$50 per unit, and total costs are limited to \$75,000.
    (a) Find the number of units of labor and the number of units of capital that maximize production.
    (b) Find the marginal productivity of money and interpret your result.
    (c) Graph the constraint with the production function when $z = 180{,}000$, $z = 300{,}000$, and when the z-value is optimal.

Section 14.4

35. *Modeling U.S. average wage* The table gives the average annual U.S. wage from 2011 and projected through 2021.
    (a) Use linear regression to find the best linear model for the wage as a function of the number of years after 2010. Report the model with 4 significant digits.
    (b) Use the reported model to predict the average annual wage in 2025.

Year	Wage (\$)	Year	Wage (\$)
2011	43,009	2017	55,989
2012	44,644	2018	58,698
2013	46,496	2019	61,179
2014	48,595	2020	63,676
2015	50,893	2021	66,161
2016	53,317		

Source: Social Security Administration

36. *Modeling Civilian workforce* The following table gives the number of women and the number of men (both in millions) in the U.S. civilian labor force for selected years from 1950 and projected to 2050.
    (a) Let x represent the millions of women and y represent the millions of men and find the linear regression model for $y = f(x)$. Report the model to 3 significant digits.
    (b) Find and interpret the slope of the reported model.

U.S. Civilian Workforce (in millions): 1950–2050

Women	Men	Women	Men	Women	Men	Women	Men
18.4	43.8	45.5	61.5	75.5	82.2	81.6	88.5
23.2	46.4	56.8	69.0	78.6	84.2	86.5	94.0
31.5	51.2	65.7	75.2	79.3	85.4	91.5	100.3

Source: U.S. Bureau of Labor Statistics

14 CHAPTER TEST

1. Consider the function $f(x, y) = \dfrac{2x + 3y}{\sqrt{x^2 - y}}$.

   (a) Find the domain of $f(x, y)$.
   (b) Evaluate $f(-4, 12)$.

2. Find all first and second partial derivatives of
$$z = f(x, y) = 5x - 9y^2 + 2(xy + 1)^5$$

3. Let $z = 6x^2 + x^2y + y^2 - 4y + 9$. Find the pairs (x, y) that are critical points for z and then classify each as a relative maximum, a relative minimum, or a saddle point.

4. Suppose a company's monthly production value Q in thousands of dollars is given by the Cobb-Douglas production function
$$Q = 10K^{0.45}L^{0.55}$$
   where K is thousands of dollars of capital investment per month and L is the total hours of labor per month. Capital investment is currently \$10,000 per month, and monthly work-hours of labor total 1590.
   (a) Find the monthly production value (to the nearest thousand dollars).
   (b) Find the marginal productivity with respect to capital investment and interpret your result.
   (c) Find the marginal productivity with respect to total hours of labor and interpret your result.

5. The monthly payment R on a loan is a function of the amount borrowed, A, in thousands of dollars; the length of the loan, n, in years; and the annual interest rate, r, as a percent. Thus $R = f(A, n, r)$. In parts (a) and (b), write a sentence that explains the practical meaning of each mathematical statement.

   (a) $f(94.5, 25, 7) = \$667.91$

   (b) $\dfrac{\partial f}{\partial r}(94.5, 25, 7) = \$60.28$

   (c) Would $\dfrac{\partial f}{\partial n}(94.5, 25, 7)$ be positive, negative, or zero? Explain.

6. Let $f(x, y) = 2e^{x^2y^2}$. Find $\dfrac{\partial^2 f}{\partial x\, \partial y}$.

7. Suppose the demand functions for two products are
$$q_1 = 300 - 2p_1 - 5p_2 \text{ and } q_2 = 150 - 4p_1 - 7p_2$$

where q_1 and q_2 represent quantities demanded and p_1 and p_2 represent prices. What calculations enable us to decide whether the products are competitive or complementary? Are these products competitive or complementary?

8. Suppose a store sells two brands of disposable razors and the profit for these is a function of their two selling prices. The type 1 razor sells for \$x, the type 2 sells for \$y, and profit is given by
$$P = 915x - 30x^2 - 45xy + 975y - 30y^2 - 3500$$

Find the selling prices that maximize profit. Find the maximum profit.

9. Find x and y that maximize the utility function $U = x^3y$ subject to the budget constraint $30x + 20y = 8000$.

10. **Modeling** In the last half of the twentieth century, the U.S. population grew more diverse both racially and ethnically, with persons of Hispanic origin representing one of the fastest-growing segments. The table gives the percent of the U.S. civilian non-institutional population of Hispanic origin for selected years from 1980 and projected to 2050.
    (a) Find the linear regression line for these data. Use x as the number of years after 1980 and report the model with 3 significant digits.
    (b) How well does the regression line fit the data?
    (c) Using the reported linear regression equation, predict the percent of the U.S. civilian non-institutional population of Hispanic origin in 2025.

Year	Percent
1980	5.7
1990	8.4
2000	10.7
2010	13.0
2015	14.1
2020	15.3
2030	17.8
2040	20.3
2050	22.8

Source: U.S. Bureau of the Census

14   EXTENDED APPLICATIONS & GROUP PROJECTS

I. Advertising

To model sales of its tires, the manufacturer of GRIPPER tires used the quadratic equation $S = a_0 + a_1x + a_2x^2 + b_1y$, where S is regional sales in millions of dollars, x is TV advertising expenditures in millions of dollars, and y is other promotional expenditures in millions of dollars. (See the Extended Application/Group Project "Marginal Return to Sales," in Chapter 9.)

Although this model represents the relationship between advertising and sales dollars for small changes in advertising expenditures, it is clear to the vice president of advertising that it does not apply to large expenditures for TV advertising on a national level. He knows from experience that increased expenditures for TV advertising result in more sales, but at a decreasing rate of return for the product.

The vice president is aware that some advertising agencies model the relationship between advertising and sales by the function

$$S = b_0 + b_1(1 - e^{-ax}) + c_1y$$

where $a > 0$, S is sales in millions of dollars, x is TV advertising expenditures in millions of dollars, and y is other promotional expenditures in millions of dollars.* The equation

$$S_n = 24.58 + 325.18(1 - e^{-x/14}) + b_1y$$

has the form mentioned previously as being used by some advertising agencies. For TV advertising expenditures up to $20 million, this equation closely approximates

$$S_1 = 30 + 20x - 0.4x^2 + b_1y$$

which, in the Extended Application/Group Project in Chapter 9, was used with fixed promotional expenses to describe advertising and sales in Region 1.

To help the vice president decide whether this is a better model for large expenditures, answer the following questions.

1. What is $\partial S_1/\partial x$? Does this indicate that sales might actually decline after some amount is spent on TV advertising? If so, what is this amount?
2. Does the quadratic model $S_1(x, y)$ indicate that sales will become negative after some amount is spent on TV advertising? Does this model cease to be useful in predicting sales after a certain point?
3. What is $\partial S_n/\partial x$? Does this indicate that sales will continue to rise if additional money is devoted to TV advertising? Is S_n growing at a rate that is increasing or decreasing when promotional sales are held constant? Is S_n a better model for large expenditures?
4. If the S_n model describes the relationship between advertising and sales and if promotional expenditures are held constant at y_0, is there an upper limit to the sales even if an unlimited amount of money is spent on TV advertising? If so, what is it?

II. Competitive Pricing

Retailers often sell different brands of competing products. Depending on the joint demand for the products, the retailer may be able to set prices that regulate demand and, therefore, influence profits.

Suppose HOME-ALL, Inc., a national chain of home improvement retailers, sells two competing brands of motion sensor outdoor light sets, Dark-B-Gone 100 and Croyle & James, which the chain purchases for $8 per set and $10 per set, respectively. HOME-ALL's research department has determined the following two monthly demand equations for these light sets:

$$D = 120 - 40d + 30c \quad \text{and} \quad C = 680 + 30d - 40c$$

where D is hundreds of Dark-B-Gone 100 light sets demanded at $$d$ per set and C is hundreds of Croyle & James

light sets demanded at $$c$ per set. For what prices should HOME-ALL sell these light sets to maximize its monthly profit on these items?

To answer this question, complete the following.

1. Recall that revenue is a product's selling price per item times the number of items sold. With this in mind, formulate HOME-ALL's total revenue function for the two light set brands as a function of their prices.
2. Form HOME-ALL's profit function for the two light set brands (in terms of their selling prices).
3. Determine the price of each type of light set that will maximize HOME-ALL's profit.
4. Write a brief report to management that details your pricing recommendations and justifies them.

* Edwin Mansfield, *Managerial Economics* (New York: Norton, 1990).

Appendix A:
Graphing Calculator Guide

Operating the TI-83 and TI-84 Plus Calculators

Turning the Calculator On and Off

ON	Turns the calculator on.
2nd ON	Turns the calculator off.

Adjusting the Display Contrast

2nd ▲	Increases the contrast (darkens the screen).
2nd ▼	Decreases the contrast (lightens the screen).

Note: If the display begins to dim (especially during calculations) and you must adjust the contrast to 8 or 9 to see the screen, then batteries are low and you should replace them soon.

The TI-83 and TI-84 Plus keyboards are divided into four zones: graphing keys, editing keys, advanced function keys, and scientific calculator keys (Figure 1).

Home screen

Graphing keys

Editing keys (Allow you to edit expressions and variables)

Advanced function keys (Display menus that access advanced functions)

Scientific calculator keys

Courtesy of Texas Instruments

Figure 1

Chapter 1

Section 1.4 Graphing Equations

Entering Equations for Graphing

To graph an equation in the variables x and y, first solve the equation for y in terms of x. If the equation has variables other than x and y, solve for the dependent variable and replace the independent variable with x. Press the $Y =$ key to access the function entry screen and enter the equation.

To erase an equation, press CLEAR. To return to the homescreen, select QUIT (2nd MODE).

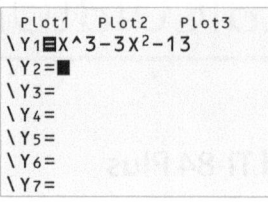

Setting Windows

The window defines the highest and lowest values of x and y on the graph of the function that will be shown on the screen.

The values that define the viewing window can be set by using ZOOM keys. The standard window (ZOOM 6) is often appropriate. The standard window gives x- and y-values between -10 and 10.

To set the window manually, press the WINDOW key and enter the values you want.

The Xscl (x scale) is the distance between tic marks on the x-axis, going in both directions from the origin, and the Yscl (y scale) is the distance between tic marks on the y-axis, going in both directions from the origin. The scales can be set individually and are useful in visually determining x- and y-intercepts of graphs.

Graphing Equations

Determine an appropriate viewing window. The window should be set so that the important parts of the graph are shown and the unseen parts are suggested. Such a graph is called **complete**. Using the displayed coordinates from TRACE helps to determine an appropriate window.

Pressing GRAPH or a ZOOM key will activate the graph.

Graph of $y = x^3 - 3x^2 - 13$

With standard window   Using $[-5, 10]$ by $[-25, 10]$

Section 1.4 Finding Function Values

Using TRACE on the Graph

Enter the function to be evaluated in Y_1. Choose a window so that it contains the x-value whose y-value you seek.

Press TRACE and then enter the selected x-value followed by ENTER. The cursor will move to the selected value and give the resulting y-value if the selected x-value is in the window. If the selected x-value is not in the window, Err: INVALID occurs. If the x-value is in the window, the y-value will occur even if it is not visible in the window.

To evaluate $y = -x^2 + 8x + 9$ when $x = -5$ and when $x = 3$, graph the function using the window $[-10, 10]$ by $[-10, 30]$.

Using the TABLE ASK Feature

Enter the function with the $Y =$ key. (Note: The $=$ sign must be highlighted.) Select TBLSET (2nd WINDOW), move the cursor to Ask opposite Indpnt:, and press ENTER. This allows you to input specific values for x. Then select TABLE and enter the specific values. Pressing DEL clears an entry. The table on the right evaluates $y = -x^2 + 8x + 9$ at -5 and at 3.

Making a Table of Values

If the Indpnt variable is on Auto, enter an initial x-value for the table in TblStart, and enter the desired change in the x-value as ΔTbl.

Enter TABLE to get a list of x-values and the corresponding y-values. The value of the function at the given value of x can be read from the table. Use the up or down arrow to find the x-values where the function is to be evaluated. The table on the right evaluates $y = -x^2 + 8x + 9$ for integer x-values from -3 to 3.

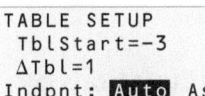

Section 1.4 Solving Linear Equations by the x-Intercept Method

To find the solution to $f(x) = 0$ (the x-value where the graph crosses the x-axis):

1. Set one side of the equation to 0 and enter the other side as Y_1 in the $Y =$ menu.
2. Set the window so that the x-intercept to be located can be seen.
3. Access the CALC menu and select 2:zero.
4. Answer the question "*Left Bound?*" with ENTER after moving the cursor close to and to the left of an x-intercept.
5. Answer the question "*Right Bound?*" with ENTER after moving the cursor close to and to the right of this x-intercept.
6. To the question "*Guess?*" press ENTER. The coordinates of the x-intercept are displayed. The x-value is a solution.

The solution to $5x - 9 = 0$ is found to be $x = 1.8$.

Section 1.5 Solving Systems of Equations in Two Variables

To solve a system with intersect of linear equations in two variables graphically:

1. Solve both equations for y.
2. Graph the first equation as Y_1 and the second as Y_2.
3. To find the point of intersection of the graphs:
    (a) Access the CALC menu and select 5:intersect.
    (b) Answer the question "*First curve?*" by pressing ENTER and "*Second curve?*" by pressing ENTER.
    (c) To the question "*Guess?*" press ENTER. The solution is shown on the right.

If the two lines intersect at one point, the coordinates give the x- and y-values of the solution.

The solution of the system at the right is $x = 2$, $y = 1$.

To solve $\begin{cases} 4x + 3y = 11 \\ 2x - 5y = -1 \end{cases}$ graphically, graph

$y_1 = -\dfrac{4}{3}x + \dfrac{11}{3}$ and $y_2 = \dfrac{2}{5}x + \dfrac{1}{5}$, then use Intersect.

Chapter 2

Section 2.1 Solving Nonlinear Equations by the x-Intercept Method

To find the solutions to $f(x) = 0$ (the x-values where the graph crosses the x-axis):

1. Set one side of the equation to 0 and enter the other side as Y_1 in the $Y =$ menu.
2. Set the window so that the x-intercepts to be located can be seen.
3. Access the CALC menu and select 2:zero.
4. Answer the question "*Left Bound?*" with ENTER after moving the cursor close to and to the left of an x-intercept.
5. Answer the question "*Right Bound?*" with ENTER after moving the cursor close to and to the right of this x-intercept.
6. To the question "*Guess?*" press ENTER. The coordinates of the x-intercept are displayed. The x-value is a solution.
7. Repeat to get all x-intercepts. The graph of a linear equation will cross the x-axis at most 1 time and the graph of quadratic equation will cross the x-axis at most 2 times, etc.

The solutions to $0 = -x^2 + 8x + 9$ are found to be 9 and -1.

Section 2.1 Solving Nonlinear Equations by the Intersection Method

To solve nonlinear equations by the intersection method:

1. Graph the left side of the equation as Y_1 and the right side as Y_2.
2. Find a point of intersection of the graphs as shown in Section 1.5.
3. To find another point of intersection, repeat while keeping the cursor near the second point.

The solutions to $7x^2 = 16x - 4$ are found at the right.

Section 2.2 Graphing Quadratic Functions

To graph a quadratic function:

1. Solve for y in terms of x and enter it in the $Y =$ menu.
2. Find the coordinates of its vertex, with $x = -b/(2a)$.
3. Set the window so that the x-coordinate of its vertex is near its center and the y-coordinate is visible.
4. Press Graph.

To graph $P(x) = -0.1x^2 + 300x - 1200$, enter $y_1 = -0.1x^2 + 300x - 1200$ on a window with its center near $x = (-300)/[2(-0.1)] = 1500$ and with $y = P(1500) = 223,800$ visible.

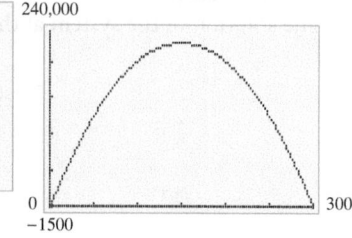

Section 2.4 Graphing Polynomial Functions

To graph a polynomial function:

1. See Table 2.1 in Section 2.4 to determine possible shapes for the graph.
   (The graph of the function $y = x^3 - 16x$ has one of four shapes in the table.)
2. Graph the function in a window large enough to see the shape of the complete graph. This graph is like the graph of Degree 3(b) in the table in Section 2.4.
3. If necessary, adjust the window for a better view of the graph.

$[-40, 40]$ by $[-100,100]$ $[-6, 6]$ by $[-30, 30]$

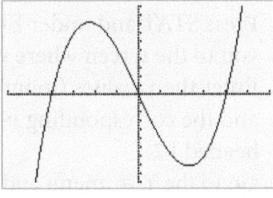

$y = x^3 - 16x$ $y = x^3 - 16x$

(Better view)

Section 2.4 Graphing Rational Functions

To graph a rational function:

1. Determine the vertical and horizontal asymptotes.
2. Set the window so that the x range is centered near the x-value of the vertical asymptote.
3. Set the window so that the horizontal asymptote is near the center of the y range.
4. Graph the function in a window large enough to see the shape of the complete graph.
5. If necessary, adjust the window for a better view of the graph.

To graph $y = \dfrac{12x + 8}{3x - 9}$, set the center of the window near the vertical asymptote $x = 3$ and near the horizontal asymptote $y = 4$.

Section 2.4 Graphing Piecewise Defined Functions

A piecewise defined function is defined differently over two or more intervals.

To graph a piecewise defined function $y = \begin{cases} f(x) \text{ if } x \le a \\ g(x) \text{ if } x > a \end{cases}$

1. Go to the Y = key and enter

   $Y_1 = f(x)/(x \le a)$ and $Y_2 = g(x)/(x > a)$

   (The inequality symbols are found under the TEST menu.)
2. Graph the function using an appropriate window.
3. Evaluating a piecewise defined function at a given value of x requires that the correct equation ("piece") be selected.

To graph $y = \begin{cases} x + 7 \text{ if } x \le -5 \\ -x + 2 \text{ if } x > -5 \end{cases}$

Section 2.5 Modeling

A. To Create a Scatter Plot

1. Press STAT and under EDIT press 1:Edit. This brings you to the screen where you enter data into lists.
2. Enter the *x*-values (input) in the column headed L1 and the corresponding *y*-values (output) in the column headed L2.
3. Go to the Y = menu and use the CLEAR key to remove any functions entered there. To turn off a function, move the cursor over the = sign and press ENTER.
4. Select STAT PLOT, 1:Plot 1. Highlight ON; then highlight the first graph type (Scatter Plot), Enter Xlist:L1, Ylist:L2, and pick the point plot mark you want.
5. Choose an appropriate WINDOW for the graph and press GRAPH or press ZOOM, 9:ZoomStat to plot the data points.

B. To Find an Equation That Models a Set of Data Points

1. Observe the scatter plot to determine what type function would best model the data. Press STAT, move to CALC, and select the function type to be used to model the data.
2. Press the VARS key, move to Y-VARS, and select 1:Function and 1: Y_1. Press ENTER.
    The coefficients of the equation will appear on the screen and the regression equation will appear as Y_1 on the Y = screen.

Pressing ZOOM 9 shows how well the model fits the data.

The Model is $y = 0.0626x + 6.19$.

Chapter 3

Section 3.1 Entering Data into Matrices

To enter data into matrices, press the MATRIX key. Move the cursor to EDIT. Enter the name of the matrix into which the data is to be entered. Enter the dimensions of the matrix, and enter the value for each entry of the matrix. Press ENTER after each entry.

For example, we enter the matrix below as [A].

$$\begin{bmatrix} 1 & 2 & 3 \\ 2 & -2 & 1 \\ 3 & 1 & -2 \end{bmatrix}$$

1. Enter 3's to set the dimension and enter the numbers.
2. To perform operations with the matrix or leave the editor, first press 2nd QUIT.
3. To view the matrix, press MATRIX, the number of the matrix, and ENTER.

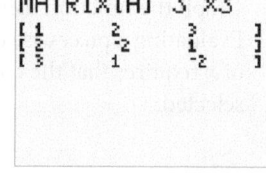

Section 3.1 Operations with Matrices

To find the sum of two matrices, [A] and [D], enter [A] + [D] and press ENTER. For example, the sum

$$\begin{bmatrix} 1 & 2 & 3 \\ 2 & -2 & 1 \\ 3 & 1 & -2 \end{bmatrix} + \begin{bmatrix} 7 & -3 & 2 \\ 4 & -5 & 3 \\ 0 & 2 & 1 \end{bmatrix}$$ is shown at right.

```
[A]+[D]
      [[8  -1 5 ]
       [6  -7 4 ]
       [3  3  -1]]
■
```

```
[A]-[D]
      [[-6 5  1 ]
       [-2 3  -2]
       [3  -1 -3]]
■
```

To find the difference, enter [A] − [D] and press ENTER. We can multiply a matrix [D] by a real number (scalar) k by entering k [D].

```
5[D]
      [[35 -15 10]
       [20 -25 15]
       [0  10  5 ]]
■
```

Section 3.2 Multiplying Two Matrices

To find the product of two matrices, [C] times [A], enter [C][A] and press ENTER. For example, we compute the product

$$\begin{bmatrix} 1 & 2 & 4 \\ -3 & 2 & -1 \end{bmatrix}\begin{bmatrix} 1 & 2 & 3 \\ 2 & -2 & 1 \\ 3 & 1 & -2 \end{bmatrix}$$ at right.

```
[C][A]
      [[17 2   -3]
       [-2 -11 -5]]
```

```
ERR:DIM MISMATCH
1▉Quit
2:Goto
```

Note that entering [A][C] gives an error message. [A][C] cannot be computed because the dimensions do not match in this order.

Section 3.3 Solution of Systems—Reduced Echelon Form

To solve a 3 × 3 system:

1. Enter the coefficients and the constants in an augmented matrix.
2. Under the MATRIX menu, choose MATH and B:rref; then enter the matrix to be reduced followed by ")" and press ENTER.
3. (a) If each row in the coefficient matrix (first 3 columns) contains a 1 with the other elements 0's, the solution is unique and the number in column 4 of a row is the value of the variable corresponding to a 1 in that row.

```
[A]
      [[2 -1 1  6 ]
       [1 2  -3 9 ]
       [3 0  -3 15]]
```

```
NAMES MATH EDIT
6↑randM(
7:augment(
8:Matr▶list(
9:List▶matr(
0:cumSum(
A:ref(
B▉rref(
```

For example, the system $\begin{cases} 2x - y + z = 6 \\ x + 2y - 3z = 9 \\ 3x \quad - 3z = 15 \end{cases}$ is solved at right.

```
rref([A])
      [[1 0 0 4 ]
       [0 1 0 1 ]
       [0 0 1 -1]]
■
```

The solution to the system above is unique: $x = 4$, $y = 1$, and $z = -1$.

(b) If the reduced matrix has all zeros in the third row, the solution is nonunique.

(c) If the reduced matrix has 3 zeros in a row and a nonzero element in the fourth column in that row, there is no solution.

Section 3.4 Finding the Inverse of a Matrix

To find the inverse of a matrix:

1. Enter the elements of the matrix using MATRIX and EDIT. Then select QUIT.
2. Press MATRIX, the name of the matrix, and ENTER; then press the x^{-1} key and ENTER.

For example, the inverse of $E = \begin{bmatrix} 2 & 0 & 2 \\ -1 & 0 & 1 \\ 4 & 2 & 0 \end{bmatrix}$ is shown at right.

3. To see the entries as fractions, press MATH, press 1:Frac, and press ENTER.

Not all matrices have inverses. Matrices that do not have inverses are called singular matrices. See matrix F at the right.

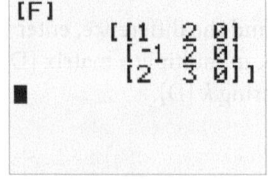

Section 3.4 Solving Systems of Linear Equations with Matrix Inverses

The matrix equation $AX = B$ can be solved by computing $X = A^{-1}B$, if a unique solution exists.

The solution to $\begin{cases} 25x + 20y + 50z = 15{,}000 \\ 25x + 50y + 100z = 27{,}500 \\ 250x + 50y + 500z = 92{,}250 \end{cases}$

is found at the right to be $x = 254$, $y = 385$, $z = 19$.

Chapter 4

Section 4.1 Graphing Solution Regions of Linear Inequalities

To graph the solution of a linear inequality in two variables, first solve the inequality for the dependent variable and enter the other side of the inequality in Y_1, so that $Y_1 = f(x)$. If the inequality has the form $y \leq f(x)$, shade the region below the graphed line, and if the inequality has the form $y \geq f(x)$, shade the region above the line.

In this example, shade the region above the line by moving the cursor to the left of Y_1 and pressing ENTER until a triangle appears in the right upper corner. Then press GRAPH to get the region satisfying the inequality.

To solve $4x - 2y \leq 6$, convert it to $y \geq 2x - 3$ and graph $Y_1 = 2x - 3$.

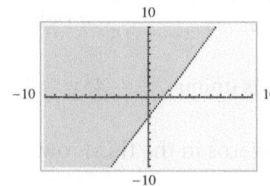

Section 4.1 Graphing Solutions of Systems of Linear Inequalities

To graph the solution region for a system of linear inequalities in two variables, write the inequalities as equations solved for y and graph the equations.

For example, to find the region defined by the inequalities

$$\begin{cases} 5x + 2y \le 54 \\ 2x + 4y \le 60 \\ x \ge 0, y \ge 0 \end{cases}$$

1. Choose a window with x min $= 0$ and y min $= 0$ because the inequalities $x \ge 0, y \ge 0$ limit the graph to Quadrant I.
2. Solve the equations for y, getting $y = 27 - 5x/2$ and $y = 15 - x/2$. Enter these equations as Y_1 and Y_2.
3. Because both inequalities have "$y \le$," move the cursor to the left of Y_1 and press ENTER until a triangle shaded like that in the figure appears and then repeat this with Y_2. Pressing GRAPH then shows the solution to the system as a cross-hatched region.
4. Using INTERSECT with the pair of equations and finding the intercepts give the corners of the solution region, where the borders intersect. These corners of the region are $(0, 0)$ $(0, 15)$, $(6, 12)$, and $(10.8, 0)$.

Section 4.2 Linear Programming

To solve a linear programming problem involving constraints in two variables:

1. Graph the constraint inequalities as equations, solved for y.
2. Test points to determine the feasible region and use INTERSECT to find each of the corners of the region, where the borders intersect.
3. Then evaluate the objective function at each of the corners.

   For example, to maximize $f = 5x + 11y$ subject to the constraints

   $$\begin{cases} 5x + 2y \le 54 \\ 2x + 4y \le 60 \\ x \ge 0, y \ge 0 \end{cases}$$

we graphically find the feasible region (as shown above) and evaluate the objective function at the coordinates of each of the corners of the region. Evaluating $f = 5x + 11y$ at each of the corners determines where this objective function is maximized or minimized.

The corners of the region determined by the inequalities are $(0, 0)$ $(0, 15)$, $(6, 12)$, and $(10.8, 0)$.

At $(0, 0)$, $f = 0$.   At $(0, 15)$, $f = 165$.
At $(6, 12)$, $f = 162$.   At $(10.8, 0)$, $f = 54$.

The maximum value of f is 165 at $x = 0, y = 15$.

Chapter 5

Section 5.1 Graphing Exponential Functions

1. Enter the function as Y_1 in the Y = menu.
2. Set the x-range centered at $x = 0$.
3. Set the y-range to reflect the function's range of $y > 0$.

Note that some graphs (such as the graph of $y = 4^x$ shown here) appear to merge eventually with the negative x-axis. Adjusting the window can show that these graphs never touch the x-axis. For more complicated exponential functions, it may be helpful to use TABLE to find a useful window.

Section 5.1 Modeling with Exponential Functions

1. Create a scatter plot for the data.
2. Choose STAT, then CALC. Scroll down to 0:ExpReg and press ENTER, then VARS, Y-VARS, FUNCTION, Y_1, and ENTER.

    (Recall that this both calculates the requested exponential model and enters its equation as Y_1 in the Y = menu.)

The last screen shows how well the model fits the data.

Find the exponential model for the following data.

x	1	2	3	4	5	6	7	8	9	10
y	43	38	33	29	25	22	19	15	14	12

Section 5.2 Graphing Base e and Base 10 Logarithmic Functions

Enter the function as Y_1 in the Y = menu.

1. For $y = \ln(x)$, use the LN key.
2. For $y = \log(x)$, use the LOG key.
3. Set the window x-range to reflect that the function's domain is $x > 0$.
4. Center the window y-range at $y = 0$.

Section 5.2 Modeling with Logarithmic Functions

1. Create a scatter plot for the data.
2. Choose STAT, then CALC. Scroll down to 9:LnReg and press ENTER, then VARS, Y-VARS, FUNCTION, Y_1, and ENTER.

The last figure on the right shows how well the model fits the data.

Find the logarithmic model for the following data.

x	10	20	30	38
y	2.21	3.79	4.92	5.77

Section 5.2 Graphing Logarithmic Functions with Other Bases

1. Use a change of base formula to rewrite the logarithmic function with base 10 or base e.

$$\log_b x = \frac{\log x}{\log b} \quad \text{or} \quad \log_b x = \frac{\ln x}{\ln b}$$

2. Proceed as described above for graphing base e and base 10 logarithms.

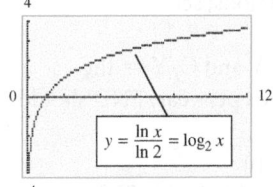

Chapter 6

Section 6.2 Future Value of a Lump Sum

To find the future value of a lump sum investment:

1. Press the APPS key and select Finance; press ENTER.
2. Select TVM Solver; press ENTER.
3. Set N = the total number of periods and set I% = the annual percentage rate.
4. Set the PV = the lump sum preceded by a "−" to indicate that the lump sum is leaving your possession.
5. Set PMT = 0 and set both P/Y and C/Y = the number of compounding periods per year.
6. Put the cursor on FV and press ALPHA ENTER to get the future value.

The future value of $10,000 invested at 9.8% compounded quarterly for 17 years is shown at the right.

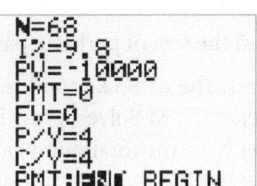

Section 6.3 Future Value of an Annuity

To find the future value of an ordinary annuity:

1. Press the APPS key, select Finance, and press ENTER.
2. Select TVM Solver and press ENTER.
3. Set N = the total number of periods and set I% = the annual percentage rate.
4. Set the PV = 0 and set both P/Y and C/Y = the number of compounding periods per year. END should be highlighted.
5. Set PMT = the periodic payment preceded by a "−" to indicate that the lump sum is leaving your possession.
6. Put the cursor on FV and press ALPHA ENTER to get the future value.
   The future value of an ordinary annuity of $200 deposited at the end of each quarter for $2\frac{1}{4}$ years with interest at 4% compounded quarterly is shown.

For annuities due, all steps are the same except that BEGIN is highlighted.

Ordinary annuity   Annuity due

Section 6.4 Present Value of an Annuity

To find the present value of an ordinary annuity:

1. Press the APPS key and select Finance; press ENTER.
2. Select TVM Solver; press ENTER.
3. Set N = the total number of periods; set I% = the annual percentage rate.
4. Set the FV = 0 and set both P/Y and C/Y = the number of compounding periods per year. END should be highlighted.
5. Set PMT = the periodic payment.
6. Put the cursor on PV and press ALPHA ENTER to get the present value.

The lump sum that needs to be deposited to receive $1000 at the end of each month for 16 years if the annuity pays 9% compounded monthly is shown at the right.
   For annuities due, BEGIN is highlighted.

Ordinary annuity   Annuity due

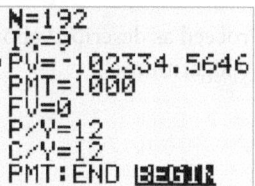

Section 6.5 Finding Payments to Amortize a Loan

To find the size of periodic payments to amortize a loan:

1. Press the APPS key and select Finance; press ENTER.
2. Select TVM Solver; press ENTER.
3. Set N = the total number of periods; set I% = the APR.
4. Set the PV = loan value and set both P/Y and C/Y = the number of periods per year. END should be highlighted.
5. Set FV = 0.
6. Put the cursor on PMT and press ALPHA ENTER to get the periodic payment.

To repay a loan of $10,000 in 5 annual payments with annual interest at 10%, each payment must be $2637.97.

Section 6.5 Finding the Number of Payments to Amortize a Loan

To find the number of payments needed to amortize a loan:

1. Press the APPS key, select Finance, and press ENTER.
2. Select TVM Solver and press ENTER.
3. Set the PV = loan value, set both P/Y and C/Y = the number of periods per year, and set I% = the APR.
4. Set PMT = required payment and set FV = 0.
5. Put the cursor on N and press ALPHA ENTER to get the number of payments.

The number of monthly payments to pay a $2500 credit card loan with $55 payments and 18% interest is 76.9 months, or 6 years, 5 months.

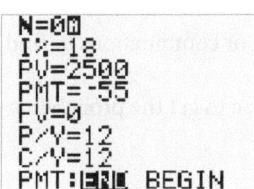

Chapter 7

Section 7.5 Evaluating Factorials

To evaluate factorials:

1. Enter the number whose factorial is to be calculated.
2. Choose MATH, then PRB. Scroll to 4: ! and press ENTER.

Press ENTER again to find the factorial.
7! is shown on the right.

Section 7.5 Evaluating Permutations

To evaluate permutations:

1. For a "permutation of n objects taken r at a time" (such as $_{20}P_4$), first enter the value of n (such as $n = 20$).
2. Choose MATH, then PRB. Scroll to 2: nPr and press ENTER.
3. Enter the value of r (such as $r = 4$) and press ENTER to find the value of nPr.

   $_{20}P_4$ is shown on the right.

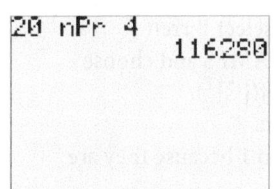

Section 7.5 Evaluating Combinations

To evaluate combinations:

1. For a "combination of n objects taken r at a time" (such as $_{20}C_4$), first enter the value of n (such as $n = 20$).
2. Choose MATH, then PRB. Scroll to 3:nCr and press ENTER.
3. Enter the value of r (such as $r = 4$) and press ENTER to find the value of nCr.

Note that nCr = nC(n − r), as the figure on the right shows for $_{20}C_4$ and $_{20}C_{16}$.

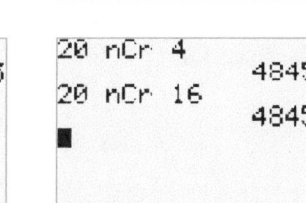

Section 7.6 Finding Probabilities Using Permutations and Combinations

To solve a probability problem that involves permutations or combinations:

1. Determine if permutations or combinations should be used.
2. Enter the ratios of permutations or combinations to find the probability.
3. If desired, use MATH, then 1:Frac to get the probability as a fraction.

If there are 5 defective computer chips in a box of 10, the probability that 2 chips drawn together from the box will both be defective is

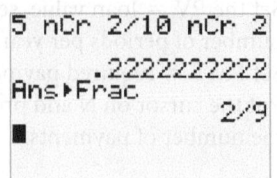

Section 7.7 Evaluating Markov Chains

To evaluate a Markov chain:

1. Enter the initial probability vector as matrix A and the transition matrix as matrix B.
2. To find the probabilities for the nth state, calculate $[A][B]^n$. The 3rd state, $[A][B]^3$, is shown on the right.

```
[A]
        [[.4 .4 .2]]
[B]
        [[.5 .4 .1]
         [.4 .5 .1]
         [.3 .3 .4]]
■
```

```
[A][B]^3
[[.4278 .4278 ...
```

Section 7.7 Finding Steady-State Vectors for Markov Chains

If the transition matrix contains only positive entries, the probabilities will approach a steady-state vector, which is found as follows.

1. Calculate and store $[C] = [B] - [I]$, where $[B]$ is the regular transition matrix and $[I]$ is the appropriately sized identity matrix.
2. Choose MATRIX, MATH and select B:rref(.
3. Enter $[C]$ with the MATRIX, NAMES and choose MATRIX, MATH, 2:$^\text{T}$ to get rref($[C]^\text{T}$).
4. Press ENTER to get the solution.
5. Choose the solutions that add to 1 because they are probabilities.

```
identity(3)→[I]
        [[1 0 0]
         [0 1 0]
         [0 0 1]]
■
```

```
[B]-[I]
        [[-.5  .4   .1 ]
         [ .4  -.5  .1 ]
         [ .3   .3  -.6]]
Ans→[C]■
```

```
rref([C]ᵀ)
        [[1 0 -3]
         [0 1 -3]
         [0 0  0]]
```

Thus $x = 3z$ and $y = 3z$, and $3z + 3z + z = 1$ gives $z = 1/7$; so the probabilities are given in the steady-state vector $\left[\dfrac{3}{7} \ \dfrac{3}{7} \ \dfrac{1}{7}\right]$.

Chapter 8

Section 8.1 Binomial Probabilities

To find binomial probabilities:

1. DISTR, binompdf(n,p,x) computes the probability of x success in n trials of a binomial experiment with probability of success p. Using MATH 1:Frac gives the probabilities as fractions.
   The probability of 3 heads in 6 tosses of a fair coin is found using DISTR, binompdf(6,.5,3).
2. The probabilities can be computed for more than one number in one command, using DISTR, binompdf($n,p,\{x_1,x_2,\ldots\}$).
   The probabilities of 4, 5, or 6 heads in 6 tosses of a fair coin are found using DISTR, binompdf(6,.5,{4,5,6}).
3. The command DISTR, binomcdf(n,p,x) gives the probability of obtaining at most x successes in a binomial experiment with n trials and p equal to the probability of success on each trial. For example, the probability of 4 or fewer heads in 6 tosses of a fair coin is found using DISTR, binomcdf(6,.5,4).

Section 8.2 Histograms

To find a frequency histogram for a set of data:

1. Press STAT, EDIT, 1:edit to enter each number in a column headed by L1 and the corresponding frequency of each number in L2.
2. Select STAT PLOT, 1:Plot 1. Highlight ON and then press ENTER on the histogram icon. Enter L1 in xlist and L2 in Feq.
3. Press ZOOM, 9:ZoomStat or press Graph with an appropriate window.
4. If the data is given in interval form, a histogram can be created using the steps above with the class marks used to represent the intervals.

The frequency histogram for the scores 38, 37, 36, 40, 35, 40, 38, 37, 36, 37, 39, 38 is shown.

Section 8.2 Finding the Mean and Standard Deviation of Sample Data

To find descriptive statistics for a set of data:

1. Enter the data in list L1.
2. To find the mean and standard deviation of the data in L1, press STAT, move to CALC, and press 1:1-Var Stats and then ENTER.

The mean and sample standard deviation of the data 1, 2, 3, 3, 4, 4, 4, 4, 5, 5, 6, 7 are $\bar{x} = 4$ and $s = Sx \approx 1.65$.

Section 8.2 Finding the Mean and Standard Deviation of Grouped Data

To find descriptive statistics for a set of data:

1. Enter the data in list L1 and the frequencies in L2.
2. To find the mean and standard deviation of the data in L1, press STAT, move to CALC, and press 1:1-Var Stats L1, L2, and ENTER.

The mean $\bar{x}$ and standard deviations for the data in the table are shown on the right.

Salary	Number	Salary	Number
$59,000	1	$31,000	1
30,000	2	75,000	1
26,000	7	35,000	1
34,000	2		

The mean is $34,000, and the sample standard deviation is $14,132.84.

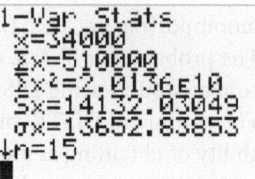

Section 8.4 Standard Normal Probabilites

To calculate standard normal probabilites:

The command DISTR, 2:normalcdf(a,b) gives the probability that a z-score lies between a lower bound a and an upper bound b.

Because $\Pr(z > 10) \approx 0$, the command normalcdf(a, 10) gives the probability that z is greater than a. In addition, $\Pr(z < b)$ is given by the command normalcdf(-10, b).

The probabilities $\Pr(-1 < z < 1.5)$ and $\Pr(z > 2)$ are found below.

Section 8.4 Calculating Normal Probabilites

To calculate normal probabilities:

The command DISTR, 2:normalcdf(lowerbound, upperbound, μ, σ) gives the probability that x lies between the lower bound and the upper bound when the mean is μ and the standard deviation is σ.

The probability that a score lies between 33 and 37 when the mean is 35 and the standard deviation is 2 is found below.

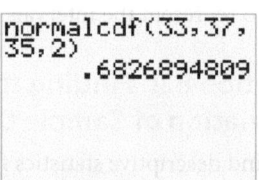

Section 8.4 Graphing Normal Distributions

To graph the normal distribution, press Y = and enter DISTR 1:normalpdf(x, μ, σ) into Y_1.

Then set the window values xmin and xmax so that the mean μ falls between them and press ZOOM, 0:Zoomfit.

Section 8.4 Inverse Normal Probabilites

To find z_0 so that $\Pr(z \leq z_0) = A$:

1. Select DISTR, 3: invNorm.
2. Enter the value A, the area under the standard normal curve to the left of z_0.
3. Press ENTER to find the value of z_0.

Find z_0 so that $\Pr(z \leq z_0) = 0.95$.

Evaluating $z_0 = \text{invNorm}(0.95) \approx 1.645$ indicates that area to the left of $z_0 = 1.645$ is 0.95, so $\Pr(z_0 \leq 1.645) = 0.95$.

```
invNorm(0.95)
            1.644853626
```

To find x_0 so that $\Pr(x \leq x_0) = A$ for a given μ and σ, use invNorm(A, μ, σ).

Find x_0 so that $\Pr(x \leq x_0) = 0.95$ for $\mu = 3.2$ and $\sigma = 0.25$.

Evaluating invNorm$(0.95, 3.2, 0.25) \approx 3.611$ indicates that $\Pr(x < 3.611) = 0.95$ if $\mu = 3.2$ and $\sigma = 0.25$.

```
invNorm(0.95,3.2
,0.25)
            3.611213406
■
```

Chapter 9

Section 9.1 Evaluating Limits

To evaluate $\lim\limits_{x \to c} f(x)$:

1. Enter the function as Y_1 in the Y = menu.
2. Set the x-range so that it contains $x = c$.
3. Evaluate $f(x)$ for several x-values near $x = c$ and on each side by c by using one of the following methods.
   (a) Graphical Evaluation
   TRACE and ZOOM near $x = c$. If the values of y approach the same number L as x approaches c from the left and the right, there is evidence that the limit is L.
   (b) Numerical Evaluation
   Use TBLSET with Indpnt set to *Ask*. Enter values very close to and on both sides of c. The y-values will approach the same limit as above.

Evaluate $\lim\limits_{x \to 3} \dfrac{x^2 - 9}{x - 3}$.

The y-values seem to approach 6.

The limit as x approaches 3 of $f(x)$ appears to be 6.

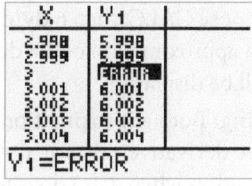

Section 9.1 Limits of Piecewise Functions

Enter the function and then use one of the methods for evaluating limits discussed above.

Find $\lim_{x \to -5} f(x)$ where $f(x) = \begin{cases} x + 7 & \text{if } x \leq -5 \\ -x + 2 & \text{if } x > -5 \end{cases}$

First enter $Y_1 = (x + 7)/(x \leq -5)$ and $Y_2 = (-x + 2)/(x > -5)$.

Both methods indicate that the limit does not exist (DNE).

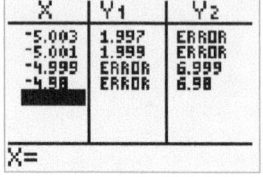

Section 9.2 Limits as $x \to \infty$

Enter the function as Y_1 and then use large values of x with one of the methods for evaluating limits discussed above. Note: Limits as $x \to -\infty$ are done similarly.

Evaluate $\lim_{x \to \infty} \dfrac{3x - 2}{1 - 5x}$.

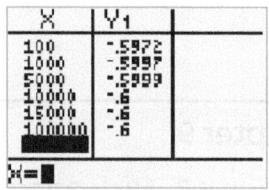

Both methods suggest that the limit is -0.6.

Sections 9.4–9.7 Approximating Derivatives

To find the numerical derivative (approximate derivative) of $f(x)$ at $x = c$, use Method 1 or Method 2.

Method 1
1. Choose MATH, then 8:nDeriv(and press ENTER.
2. Enter the function, x, and the value of c, so the display shows nDeriv($f(x)$, x, c); then press ENTER. The approximate derivative at the specified value will be displayed.

Method 2
1. Enter the function as Y_1 in the Y = menu and graph in a window that contains both c and $f(c)$.
2. Choose CALC, then 6:dy/dx; enter c; and press ENTER. An approximation of the derivative at the specified value will be displayed.

Warning: Both approximation methods above require that the derivative exists at $x = c$ and will give incorrect information when $f'(c)$ does not exist.

Find the numerical derivative of $f(x) = x^3 - 2x^2$ at $x = 2$.

The numerical derivative is approximately 4.

The value of the derivative is approximately 4.

Sections 9.5–9.7 Checking Derivatives

To check the correctness of the derivative function $f(x)$:

1. In the Y = menu, enter as Y_1 the derivative $f'(x)$ that you found and graph it in a convenient window.
2. Enter nDeriv($f(x), x, x$) as Y_2.
3. If the second graph lies on top of the first, the derivative is correct.

Verify the derivative of $f(x) = x^3 - 2x^2$ is $f'(x) = 3x^2 - 4x$.

Section 9.8 Approximating the Second Derivative

To approximate $f''(c)$:

1. Enter $f(x)$ as Y_1 in the Y = menu.
2. Enter nDeriv(Y_1, x, x) as Y_2.
3. Estimate $f''(c)$ by using nDeriv(Y_2, x, c).

Find the second derivative of $f(x) = x^3 - 2x^2$ at $x = 2$.

Thus $f''(2) = 8$.

Chapter 10

Section 10.1 Finding Critical Values

To find or approximate critical values of $f(x)$; that is, x-values that make the derivative equal to 0 or undefined:

I. Find the derivative of $f(x)$.

II. Use Method 1 or Method 2 to find the critical values.

Methods 1 and 2 show how to find the critical values of $f(x) = \frac{1}{3}x^3 - 4x$. Note that the derivative is $f'(x) = x^2 - 4$.

Method 1

1. Enter the derivative in the Y = menu as Y_1 and graph it in a convenient window.
2. Find where $Y_1 = 0$ by one of the following:
   (a) Using TRACE to find the x-intercepts of Y_1.
   (b) Using CALC, then 2:zero.
   (c) Using TABLE to find the values of x that give $Y_1 = 0$.
3. Use the graph of Y_1 (and TRACE or TABLE) to find the values of x that make the derivative undefined.

The only critical values are $x = 2$ and $x = -2$.

Method 2

1. Enter the derivative in the Y = menu as Y_1.
2. Press MATH and select 0:Solver. Press the up arrow, revealing EQUATION SOLVER eqn:0 =, and enter Y_1 (the derivative).
3. Press the down arrow or ENTER and the variable x appears with a value (not the solution). Move the cursor to the line containing the variable whose value is sought.

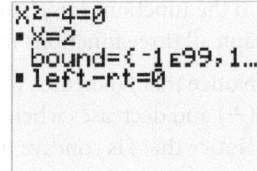

(continued)

4. Press ALPHA SOLVE (ENTER). The value of the variable changes to the solution that is closest to that value originally shown.
5. To find additional solutions (if they exist), change the value of the variable and press ALPHA SOLVE (ENTER). The value of the variable changes to the solution of $Y_1 = 0$ that is closest to that value.
6. If appropriate, use 0:Solver to solve (Denominator of Y_1) $= 0$ to find the critical values for which the derivative is undefined.

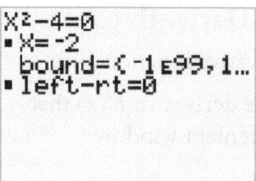

The only critical values are $x = 2$ and $x = -2$.

Section 10.1 Relative Maxima and Minima

To find relative maxima and minima:

1. In the Y $=$ menu, enter the function as Y_1 and the derivative as Y_2.
2. Use TABLE to evaluate the derivative to the left and right of each critical value.
3. Use the signs of the values of the derivative to determine whether f is increasing or decreasing around the critical values, and thus to classify the critical values as relative maxima, relative minima, or horizontal points of inflection.
4. Use Y_1 in the table to find the y-values of the critical points.
5. Graph the function to confirm your conclusions.

Find the relative maxima and minima of $f(x) = \dfrac{1}{3}x^3 - 4x$. Note that the derivative is $f'(x) = x^2 - 4$.

The relative max is at $(-2, 16/3)$, and the relative min is at $(2, -16/3)$.

Section 10.1 Critical Values and Viewing Windows

To use critical values to set a viewing window that shows a complete graph:

1. Once the critical values for a function have been found,
   (a) Enter the function as Y_1 and the derivative as Y_2. Use TABLE to determine where the function is increasing and where it is decreasing.
   (b) Set x-min so that it is smaller than the smallest critical value and set x-max so that it is larger than the largest critical value.
2. Use TABLE to determine the y-coordinates of the critical values. Set y-min and y-max to contain the y-coordinates of the critical points.
3. Graph the function.

Let $f(x) = 0.0001x^3 + 0.003x^2 - 3.6x + 5$. Given that the critical values for $f(x)$ are $x = -120$ and $x = 100$, set a window that shows a complete graph and graph the function.

Section 10.2 Exploring f, f′, and f″ Relationships

To explore relationships among the graphs of a function and its derivatives:

1. Find the functions for f' and f''.
2. Graph all three functions in the same window.

   - Notice that f increases when f' is above the x-axis $(+)$ and decreases when f' is below the x-axis $(-)$.
   - Notice that f is concave up when f'' is above the x-axis $(+)$ and is concave down when f'' is below the x-axis $(-)$.

Let $f(x) = x^3 - 9x^2 + 24x$. Graph $f, f',$ and f'' on the interval $[0, 5]$ to explore the relationships among these functions.

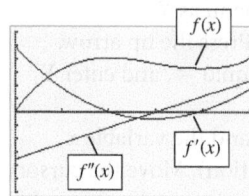

Sections 10.3–10.4 Finding Optimal Values

To find the optimal values of a function when the goal is not to produce a graph:

1. Enter the function as Y_1 in the Y = menu.
2. Select a window that includes the x-values of interest and graph the function.
3. While looking at the graph of the function, choose the CALC menu, scroll to 3:minimum or 4:maximum depending on which one is to be found, and press ENTER. This will result in a "*Left Bound?*" prompt.

    (a) Move the cursor to a point to the left of the point of interest. Press ENTER to select the left bound.
    (b) Move the cursor to the right of the point of interest. Press ENTER to select the right bound.
    (c) Press ENTER at the "*Guess?*" prompt. The resulting point is an approximation of the desired optimum value.

Let $f(x) = 100\sqrt{2304 + x^2} + 50(100 - x)$. Find the minimum value of $f(x)$ on the interval $[0, 100]$ for x.
Note: the following screens use the window x: $[-10, 110]$ and y: $[-2500, 12500]$.
The minimum value is $y \approx 9157$ and occurs when $x \approx 27.7$.

   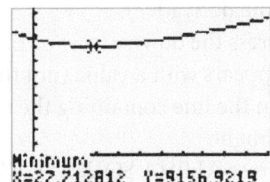

Note: Finding a maximum value works similarly.

Section 10.5 Asymptotes and Window Setting

To use asymptotes and critical values to set a viewing window that shows a complete graph:

1. Once the asymptotes and critical values for a function have been found,
    (a) Determine where the function is increasing and where it is decreasing (by using TABLE and with Y_1 as the function and Y_2 as the derivative).
    (b) Set x-min so that it is smaller than the smallest x-value that is either a vertical asymptote or a critical value and set x-max so that it is larger than the largest of these important x-values.
2. Use TABLE to determine the y-coordinates of the critical values. Set y-min and y-max so that they contain the y-coordinates of all horizontal asymptotes and critical points.
3. Graph the function.

Let $f(x) = \dfrac{x^2}{x - 2}$. This function has the line $x = 2$ as a vertical asymptote, has no horizontal asymptote, and has critical values $x = 0$ and $x = 4$. Set the window and graph $y = f(x)$.
The critical points for $f(x)$ are $(0, 0)$ and $(4, 8)$. The window needs an x-range that contains 0, 2, and 4 and a y-range that contains 0 and 8.

Chapter 11

Section 11.1 Derivatives of Logarithmic Functions

To check that the derivative of $y = \ln(2x^6 - 3x + 2)$

is $Y_1 = \dfrac{12x^5 - 3}{2x^6 - 3x + 2}$, we show that the graph of

$Y_2 = $ nDeriv($\ln(2x^6 - 3x + 2)$, x, x) lies on the graph of

$y_1 = \dfrac{12x^5 - 3}{2x^6 - 3x + 2}$.

Section 11.1 Finding Critical Values

To find the critical values of a function $y = f(x)$:

1. Enter the function as Y_1 in the $Y =$ menu and the derivative as Y_2.
2. Press MATH and select Solver. Press the up arrow, revealing EQUATION SOLVER eqn:0 = , and enter Y_2 (the derivative).
3. Press the down arrow or ENTER, and the variable x appears with a value (not the solution). Place the cursor on the line containing the variable whose value is sought.
4. Press ALPHA SOLVE (ENTER). The value of the variable changes to the solution of the equation that is closest to that value.
5. To find additional solutions (if they exist), change the value of the variable and press ALPHA SOLVE (ENTER). The value of the variable gives the solution of $Y_2 = 0$ that is closest to that value.

To find the critical values of $y = x^2 - 8 \ln x$, we solve
$$0 = 2x - \frac{8}{x}.$$

   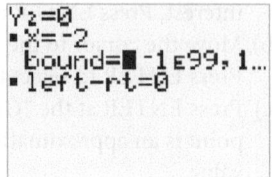

The two critical values are $x = 2$ and $x = -2$.

Section 11.1 Finding Optimal Values

To find the optimal values of a function $y = f(x)$:

1. Find the critical values of a function $y = f(x)$. (Use the steps for finding critical values discussed above.)
2. Graph $y = f(x)$ on a window containing the critical values.
3. The y-values at the critical values (if they exist) are the optimal values of the function.

To find the optimal values of $y = x^2 - 8 \ln x$, we solve
$$0 = 2x - \frac{8}{x}$$ and evaluate $y = x^2 - 8 \ln x$ at the solutions.

   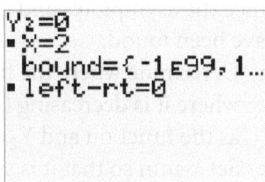

The two critical values are $x = 2$ and $x = -2$.

The minimum of $y = x^2 - 8 \ln x$ is -1.545 at $x = 2$. The function $y = x^2 - 8 \ln x$ is undefined for all negative values because $\ln x$ is undefined for all negative values. Thus, there is no optimum value of the function at $x = -2$.

Section 11.2 Derivatives of Exponential Functions

To check that the derivative of $y = 5^{x^2 + x}$ is $y' = 5^{x^2 + x}(2x + 1) \ln 5$, we show that the graph of $Y_2 = \text{nDeriv}(5^{x^2 + x}, x, x)$ lies on the graph of $Y_1 = 5^{x^2 + x}(2x + 1) \ln 5$.

   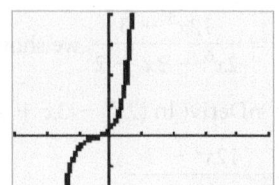

Section 11.2 Finding Critical Values

To find the critical values of a function $y = f(x)$:

1. Enter the function as Y_1 in the Y = menu and the derivative as Y_2.
2. Press MATH and select Solver. Press the up arrow, revealing EQUATION SOLVER eqn:0 =, and enter Y_2 (the derivative).
3. Press the down arrow or ENTER and the variable appears with a value (not the solution). Place the cursor on the variable whose value is sought.
4. Press ALPHA SOLVE (ENTER). The value of the variable changes to the solution of the equation that is closest to that value.
5. To find additional solutions (if they exist), change the value of the variable and press ALPHA SOLVE (ENTER). The value of the variable gives the solution of $Y_2 = 0$ that is closest to that value.

To find the critical values of $y = e^x - 3x^2$, we solve $0 = e^x - 6x$.

A relative maximum of $y = e^x - 3x^2$ occurs at $x \approx 0.204$, and a relative minimum occurs at $x \approx 2.833$.

Chapter 12

Section 12.1 Checking Powers of x Integrals

To check a computed indefinite integral with the command fnInt:

1. Enter the integral of $f(x)$ (without the + C) as Y_1 in Y = menu.
2. Move the cursor to Y_2 and press MATH, 9:fnInt(. Then enter $f(x)$, x, 0, x) to get the equation $Y_2 = $ fnInt $(f(x), x, 0, x)$.
3. Pressing ENTER with the cursor to the left of Y2 changes the thickness of the second graph, making it more evident that the second lies on top of the first.
4. Press GRAPH with an appropriate window. If the second graph lies on top of the first, the graphs agree and the computed integral checks.

Checking that the integral of $f(x) = x^2$ is $\int x^2 \, dx = \dfrac{x^3}{3} + C$:

Sections 12.1–12.2 Families of Functions

To graph some functions in the family of indefinite integrals of $f(x)$:

1. Integrate $f(x)$.
2. Enter equations of the form $\int f(x) \, dx + C$ for different values of C.
3. Press GRAPH with an appropriate window. The graphs will be shifted up or down depending on C.

The graphs of members of the family $y = \int (2x - 4)dx + C$ with $C = 0, 1, -2$, and 3.

Section 12.5 Differential Equations

To solve initial value problems in differential equations:

1. Integrate $f(x)$, getting $y = F(x) + C$. If a value of x and a corresponding value of y in the integral $y = F(x) + C$ are known, this initial value can be used to find one function that satisfies the given conditions.
2. Press MATH and select Solver. Press the up arrow to see EQUATION SOLVER.
3. Set 0 equal the integral minus y, getting $0 = F(x) + C - y$, and press the down arrow.
4. Enter the given values of x and y, place the cursor on C, and press ALPHA, SOLVE. Replace C with this value to find the function satisfying the conditions.

To solve $\dfrac{dy}{dx} = 2x - 4$, we note that the integral of both sides is $y = x^2 - 4x + C$. If $y = 8$ when $x = -1$ in this integral, we can find C, and thus a unique solution, shown below.

The unique solution is $y = x^2 - 4x + 3$.

Chapter 13

Section 13.1 Approximating Areas Under Curves Using Rectangles

To find the area under $y = f(x)$ and above the x-axis over a given interval using rectangles of equal width:

1. Enter $f(x)$ in Y_1 of the Y = menu and calculate the width Δx of the base of each of the n rectangles.
2. Compute the area using left-hand endpoints.

$$S_L = \sum_{i=1}^{n} f(x_{i-1}) \Delta x$$

$$= \left[Y_1(x_0) + Y_1(x_1) + \cdots + Y_1(x_{n-1}) \right] \Delta x$$

3. Use a similar formula to compute the area using right-hand endpoints.

$$S_R = \sum_{i=1}^{n} f(x_i) \Delta x$$

$$= \left[Y_1(x_1) + Y_1(x_2) + \cdots + Y_1(x_n) \right] \Delta x$$

To find the left and right approximations for the area under $f(x) = \sqrt{x}$ from $x = 0$ to $x = 4$ using $n = 8$ equal subdivisions:

1. Each rectangle has base width $(4 - 0)/8 = 0.5$. The subdivision values are
    $x_0 = 0, x_1 = 0.5, x_2 = 1, \cdots x_7 = 3.5, x_8 = 4.$
2. Calculate the left approximation of the area as follows.
    $S_L = 0.5[Y_1(0) + Y_1(0.5) + Y_1(1) + Y_1(1.5) + Y_1(2)$
    $\qquad + Y_1(2.5) + Y_1(3) + Y_1(3.5)] \approx 4.765$
    (See the screen below.)
3. Calculate the right approximation of the area as follows.
    $S_R = [Y_1(0.5) + Y_1(1) + Y_1(1.5) + Y_1(2) + Y_1(2.5)$
    $\qquad + Y_1(3) + Y_1(3.5) + Y_1(4)]0.5 \approx 5.765$

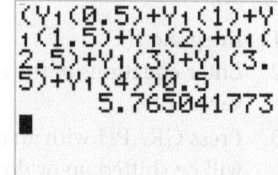

Section 13.2 Approximating Definite Integrals—Areas Under Curves

To approximate the area under the graph of $y = f(x)$ and above the x-axis:

1. Enter $f(x)$ under the Y = menu and graph the function with an appropriate window.

2. Press 2nd CALC and 7: $\int f(x)\, dx$.

3. Press ENTER. Move the cursor to, or enter, the lower limit (the left x-value).

4. Press ENTER. Move the cursor to, or enter, the upper limit (the right x-value).

5. Press ENTER. The area will be displayed.

The approximate area under the graph of $f(x) = x^2 + 1$ from $x = 0$ to $x = 3$ is found below.

 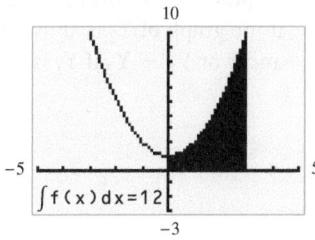

Section 13.2 Approximating Definite Integrals—Alternative Method

To approximate the definite integral of $f(x)$ from $x = a$ to $x = b$:

1. Press MATH, 9: fnInt(. Enter $f(x)$, x, a, b so that the display shows fnInt($f(x)$, x, a, b).

2. Press ENTER to find the approximation of the integral.

3. The approximation may be made closer than that in Step 2 by adding a fifth argument with a number (tolerance) smaller than 0.00001.

The approximation of $\int_{-1}^{3} (4x^2 - 2x)\, dx$ is found as follows.

Section 13.3 Approximating the Area Between Two Curves

To approximate the area between the graphs of two functions:

1. Enter one function as Y_1 and the second as Y_2. Press GRAPH using a window that shows all points of intersection of the graphs.
2. Find the x-coordinates of the points of intersection of the graphs, using CALC, 5:intersect.
3. Determine visually which graph is above the other over the interval between the points of intersection.
4. Press MATH, 9: fnInt(. Enter $f(x)$, x, a, b) so that the display shows fnInt($f(x)$, x, a, b) where $f(x)$ is $Y_2 - Y_1$ if the graph of Y_2 is above the graph of Y_1 between a and b or $Y_1 - Y_2$ if Y_1 is above Y_2.

The area enclosed by the graphs of $y = 4x^2$ and $y = 8x$ is found as follows.

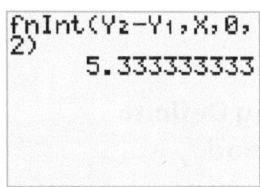

The area between the curves is $16/3$.

Section 13.3 Approximating the Area Between Two Curves—Alternate Method

The area between the graphs can also be found using CALC, $\int f(x)\, dx$.

1. Enter $Y_3 = Y_2 - Y_1$ where Y_2 is above Y_1.
2. Turn off the graphs of Y_1 and Y_2 and graph Y_3 with a window showing where $Y_3 > 0$.
3. Press CALC and select $\int f(x)\, dx$.
4. Press ENTER. Move the cursor to, or enter, the lower limit (the left x-value).
5. Press ENTER. Move the cursor to, or enter, the upper limit (the right x-value).
6. Press ENTER. The area will be displayed.

Appendix B:
Excel Guide Excel 2010 and 2016

Except where noted, the directions given will work in both Excel 2010 and Excel 2016.

Excel Worksheet

When you start Excel by using the instructions for your software and computer, the following screen will appear.

The components of the **spreadsheet** are shown, and the grid shown is called a **worksheet.** You can move to other worksheets by clicking on the tabs at the bottom.

Addresses and Operations

Notice the letters at the top of the columns and the numbers identifying the rows. The cell addresses are given by the column and row; for example, the first cell has address A1. You can move from one cell to another with arrow keys, or you can select a cell by clicking on it. After you type an entry in a cell, press enter to accept it. To edit the contents of a cell, click on the cell and edit the contents in the formula bar at the top. To delete the contents, press the delete key.

The file operations such as "open a new file," "saving a file," and "printing a file" are similar to those in Word. For example, <CTRL>S saves a file. You can format a cell entry by selecting it and using menus similar to those in Word.

Working with Cells

Cell entries, rows containing entries, and columns containing entries can be copied and pasted with the same commands as in Word. For example, a highlighted cell can be copied with <CTRL>C. Sometimes entries exceed the width of the cells containing them, especially if they are text. To widen the cells in a column, place the cursor at the right side of the column heading until you see the symbol ↔; then move the cursor to the right (moving it to the left makes the column narrower). If entering a number results in #####, the number is too long for the cell, and the cell should be widened.

Chapter 1

Section 1.4 Entering Data and Evaluating Functions

The cells are identified by the column and the row. For example, the cell B3 is in the second column and the third row.

1. Put headings on the two columns.
2. Enter the input values in column A.
3. Enter the formula for the function in B2. Use $=1000{*}(1.1)\wedge A2$ to represent $S = 1000(1.1)^t$. Pressing ENTER gives the value when $t = 1$ in B2.
4. Moving the cursor to the lower right corner of B2 until there is a thin " + " sign and dragging the cursor down "fills down" all the required outputs in column B.

The values of $S = 1000(1.1)^t$ for t-inputs 1, 2, and 3 are shown.

	A	B
1	Year	Future Value
2	1	=1000*(1.1)^(A2)
3	2	

	A	B
1	Year	Future Value
2	1	1100
3	2	1210
4	3	1331

Section 1.4 Graphing a Function

1. Put headings on the two columns [x and $f(x)$, for example].
2. Enter the inputs (x-values) in column A.
   For equally-spaced inputs (such as 0, 2, 4, 6, etc.), we can enter the first two values, highlight them, move the cursor to the lower right corner of A3 until there is a thin " + " sign, and drag the cursor down. This "fills down" all the inputs you want to enter.
3. Enter the formula for the function in B2. Use $=6{*}A2{-}3$ to represent $f(x) = 6x - 3$.
4. Pressing ENTER gives the output (y-value) corresponding to the input in A2.
5. Move the cursor to the lower right corner until there is a thin " + " sign.
6. Drag the cursor down to the last cell where the formula is required and press ENTER.
7. Highlight the two columns containing the values of x and $f(x)$.
8. Click the *Insert* tab, click on the *Scatter* icon in the *Charts* group, and select the *smooth curve* option. In the future, we will abbreviate this using *Insert > Scatter > smooth curve*.
9. Once the smooth curve option is selected, the graph will appear within the worksheet.

	A	B
1	x	$f(x) = 6x - 3$
2	−5	−33
3	−2	−15
4	−1	−9
5	0	−3
6	1	3
7	3	15
8	5	27

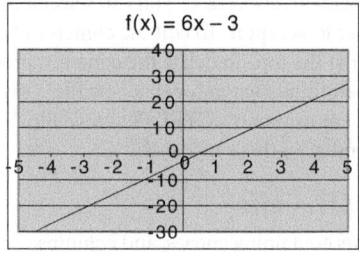

Section 1.4 Solution of Linear Equations

To solve the linear equation $f(x) = 0$:

1. Enter titles x and $f(x)$ in cells A1 and B1.
2. Enter a value of the variable in cell A2 and the formula for the function in cell B2.
3. Click the *Data* tab, select *What-If-Analysis* in the *Data Tools* group, and choose *Goal Seek*.
4. In the *Goal Seek* box:
   a. Click the *Set Cell* box and click on the B2 cell.
   b. Enter 0 in the *To Value* box.
   c. Click the By *Changing Cell* box and click on the A2 cell and the solution appears. (The solution may be approximate.)

The solution to $5x - 8 = 0$ is shown.

	A	B
1	x	$f(x) = 5x - 8$
2	1	=5*A2−8

	A	B
1	x	$f(x) = 5x - 8$
2	1.6	0

Section 1.5 Solving Systems of Two Equations in Two Variables

1. Write the two equations as linear functions in the form $y = mx + b$.
2. Enter a value for the input variable in cell A2 and the formula for each of the two equations in cells B2 and C2, respectively.
3. Enter =B2−C2 in cell D2.
4. Start *Goal Seek* by clicking on the Data tab. Select *What-If Analysis* in the Data Tools group and then *Goal Seek*.
5. In the *Goal Seek* box:
   a. Click the *Set Cell* box and click on the D2 cell.
   b. Enter 0 in the *To Value* box.
   c. Click the *By Changing Cell* box and click on the A2 cell.
6. Click OK in the *Goal Seek* dialog box, getting 0.
7. The *x*-value of the solution is in cell A2, and the *y*-value is in both B2 and C2.

The solution of the system

$$\begin{cases} 3x + 2y = 12 \\ 4x - 3y = -1 \end{cases}$$

is found to be $x = 2$, $y = 3$ using *Goal Seek* as follows.

	A	B	C	D
1	x	=6 − 1.5x	=1/3 + 4x/3	= y1 − y2
2	1	=6−1.5*A2	=1/3+4*A2/3	=B2−C2

	A	B	C	D
1	x	= 6 − 1.5x	= 1/3 + 4x/3	= y1 − y2
2	2	3	3	0

Chapter 2

Section 2.1 Solving Quadratic Equations

To solve a quadratic equation of the form
$$f(x) = ax^2 + bx + c = 0:$$

1. Enter *x*-values centered around the *x*-coordinate $x = \dfrac{-b}{2a}$ in column A and use the function formula to find the values of $f(x)$ in column B.
2. Graph the function, $f(x) = 2x^2 - 9x + 4$ in this case, and observe where the graph crosses the *x*-axis [$f(x)$ near 0]. Insert the graph by selecting *Insert > Scatter > Smooth curve* option.
3. Click the *Data* tab, click on *What-If-Analysis* in the *Data Tools* group, and click on *Goal Seek*. In the future, we will abbreviate this using *Data > What-If-Analysis > Goal Seek*.
4. In the *Goal Seek* box, enter a cell address from column B in *Set cell*, and enter 0 in the *To value* box. Then in the *By Changing cell* box, enter the cell in column A that is in the same row as the cell in *Set cell value*.
5. Click OK to find the *x*-value of the solution in the changing cell. The solution may be approximate. The spreadsheet shows $x = 0.50001$ in A4, which is an approximation of the exact solution $x = 0.5$.
6. After finding the first solution, repeat the process using a second function value at or near 0. The second solution is $x = 4$ in this case.

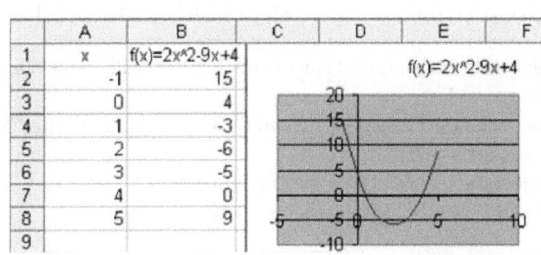

Sections 2.2 and 2.4 Graphing Polynomial Functions

To graph a polynomial function:

1. Use the function to create a table containing values for x and $f(x)$. (See "Graphing a Function" on p. AP-28.)
2. Highlight the two columns containing the values of x and $f(x)$.
3. Find the graph by selecting the *Insert* > *Scatter* > *Smooth curve* option.

	A	B
	x	f(x)
1		
2	−1	13
3	0	0
4	1	−7
5	2	−8
6	3	−3
7	4	8

$f(x) = 3x^2 - 10x$

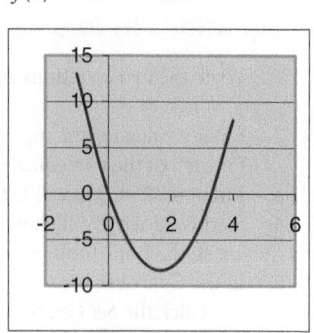

Section 2.4 Graphing Rational Functions

An Excel graph will connect all points corresponding to values in the table, so if the function you are graphing is undefined for some x-value a, enter x-values near this value and leave (or make) the corresponding $f(a)$ cell blank.

To graph $f(x) = \dfrac{1}{x-1}$, which is undefined at $x = 1$:

1. Generate a table for x-values from -1 to 3, with extra values near $x = 1$.
2. Generate the values of $f(x)$, and leave a blank cell for the $f(x)$ value for $x = 1$.
3. Select the table and plot the graph using the *Insert* > *Scatter* > *Smooth curve* option.

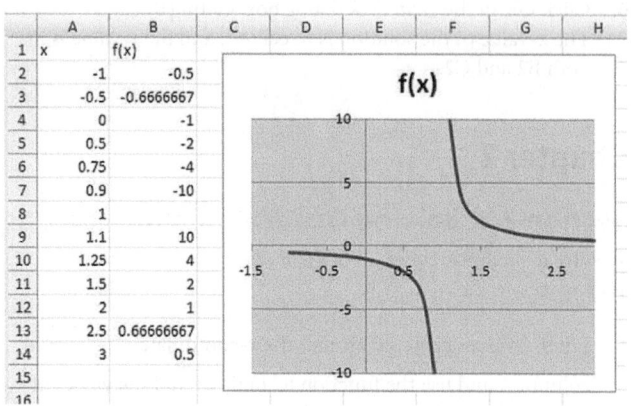

Section 2.5 Modeling

To create a scatter plot of data:

1. Enter the inputs (x-values) in column A and the outputs (y-values) in column B.
2. Highlight the two columns, select *Insert* and click the *Scatter plot* icon (*Insert* > *Scatter*), and choose the points only option to plot the points.
3. To add titles, click on the " + " sign and use *Chart elements* (Excel 2016) or click on the icons in *Charts Layout* (Excel 2010).

To find the equation of a line or curve that best fits a given set of data points:

1. Single-click on the scatter plot of the data in the worksheet.
2. Right-click on one of the data points.
3. Select *Add Trendline*.
4. Select the function type that appears to best fit and check the box that says *Display Equation on chart*. [Note: If *Polynomial* is selected, choose the appropriate Order (degree).]
5. Close the dialog box and you will see the graph of the selected function that is best fit along with its equation.

The power function that models Corvette acceleration follows.

The speed of the Corvette is given by $y = 21.875x^{0.6663}$ where x is the time in seconds.

Chapter 3

Section 3.1 Operations with Matrices

Operations for 3 × 3 matrices can be used for other orders.

1. Type a name A in A1 to identify the first matrix.
2. Enter the matrix elements of matrix A in the cells B1:D3.
3. Type a name B in A5 to identify the second matrix.
4. Enter the matrix elements of matrix B in the cells B5:D7.
5. Type a name A + B in A9 to indicate the matrix sum.
6. Type the formula =B1+B5 in B9 and press ENTER.
7. Use Fill Across to copy this formula across the row to C9 and D9.
8. Use Fill Down to copy the row B9:D9 to B11:D11, which gives the sum.
9. To subtract the matrices, change the formula in B9 to =B1−B5 and proceed as with addition.

	A	B	C	D
1	A	1	2	3
2		4	5	6
3		7	8	9
4				
5	B	−2	−4	3
6		1	4	−5
7		3	6	−1
8				
9	A + B	−1	−2	6
10		5	9	1
11		10	14	8

Section 3.2 Multiplying Two Matrices

Steps for two 3 × 3 matrices:

1. Enter the names and elements of the matrices.
2. Enter the name AxB in A9 to indicate the matrix product.
3. Select a range of cells that is the correct size to contain the product (B9:D11 in this case).
4. Type =mmult(in the formula bar and then select the cells containing the elements of matrix A (B1:D3).
5. Stay in the formula bar, type a comma and select the matrix B elements (B5:D7), and close the parentheses.
6. Hold down the CTRL and SHIFT keys and press ENTER, giving the product.

	A	B	C	D
1	A	1	2	3
2		4	5	6
3		7	8	9
4				
5	B	−2	−4	3
6		1	4	−5
7		3	6	−1
8				
9	AxB	=mmult(B1:D3)		
10		MMULT(**array1**,		
11		**array2**)		

B9	fx	{(= MMULT(B1:D3,B5:D7)}			
	A	B	C	D	E
1	A	1	2	3	
2		4	5	6	
3		7	8	9	
4					
5	B	−2	−4	3	
6		1	4	−5	
7		3	6	−1	
8					
9	AxB	9	22	−10	
10		15	40	−19	
11		21	58	−28	

Section 3.4 Finding the Inverse of a Matrix

Steps for a 3 × 3 matrix:

1. Enter the name A in A1 and the elements of the matrix in B1:D3 as above.
2. Enter the name Inverse(A) in A5 and select a range of cells that is the correct size to contain the inverse [(B5:D7) in this case].
3. Enter =minverse(, select matrix A(B1:D3), and close the parentheses.
4. Hold down the CTRL and SHIFT keys and press ENTER to get the inverse, shown on the next page.

SUM	fx	=minverse(B1:D3)		
	A	B	C	D
1	A	2	1	1
2		1	2	0
3		2	0	1
4				
5	inverse(A)	=minverse(B1:D3)		
6				
7				

Section 3.4 Solving Systems of Linear Equations with Matrix Inverses

A system of linear equations can be solved by multiplying the matrix containing the augment by the inverse of the coefficient matrix. The steps used to solve a 3×3 system follow.

1. Enter the coefficient matrix A in B1:D3.
2. Enter the name inverse(A) in A5 and compute the inverse of A in B5:D7.
3. Enter B in cell A9 and enter the augment matrix in B9:B11.
4. Enter X in A13 and select the cells B13:B15.
5. In the formula bar, type =mmult(; then select matrix inverse(A) in B5:D7, type a comma, select matrix B in B9:B11, and close the parentheses.
6. Hold down the CTRL and SHIFT keys and press ENTER, getting the solution.
7. Matrix X gives the solution.

The system $\begin{cases} 2x + y + z = 8 \\ x + 2y = 6 \\ 2x + z = 5 \end{cases}$ is solved as follows.

B5	fx	{=MINVERSE(B1:D3)}		
	A	**B**	**C**	**D**
1	A	2	1	1
2		1	2	0
3		2	0	1
4				
5	inverse(A)	−2	1	2
6		1	0	−1
7		4	−2	−3

	SUM	fx	=mmult(B5:D7,B9:B11)		
	A	**B**	**C**	**D**	**E**
1	A	2	1	1	
2		1	2	0	
3		2	0	1	
4					
5	inverse(A)	−2	1	2	
6		1	0	−1	
7		4	−2	−3	
8					
9	B	8			
10		6			
11		5			
12					
13	X	=mmult(B5:D7,B9:B11)			
14					
15					

	B13	fx	{(=MMULT(B5:D7,B9:B11)}		
	A	**B**	**C**	**D**	**E**
1	A	2	1	1	
2		1	2	0	
3		2	0	1	
4					
5	inverse(A)	−2	1	2	
6		1	0	−1	
7		4	−2	−3	
8					
9	B	8			
10		6			
11		5			
12					
13	X	0			
14		3			
15		5			

The solution is $x = 0, y = 3, z = 5$.

Chapter 4

Sections 4.3–4.5 Linear Programming

Maximize $f = 12x + 26y + 40z$ subject to the constraints

$$\begin{cases} 5x + 7y + 10z \le 90{,}000 \\ x + 3y + 4z \le 30{,}000 \\ x + y + z \le 9000 \\ x \ge 0, y \ge 0, z \ge 0 \end{cases}$$

1. On a blank spreadsheet, type a heading in cell A1, followed by the variable descriptions in cells A3–A5 and the initial values (zeros) in cells B3–B5.
2. a. Enter the heading Objective in cell A7.
   b. Enter a description of the objective in cell A9 and the formula for the objective function in B9. The formula is =12*B3+26*B4+40*B5.
3. a. Type the heading Constraints in A11 and descriptive labels in A13–A15.
   b. Enter the left side of the constraint inequalities in B13–B15 and the maximums from the right side in C13–C15.
4. Click on the *Data* tab and select *Solver* in the Analysis group. A dialog box will appear.*
5. a. Click the *Set Objective* box (Excel 2016) or the *Set Target Cell* box (Excel 2010) and click on B9 (containing the formula for the objective function).
   b. Check the button *Max* for maximization.
   c. Click the *By Changing Cells* box and select cells B3–B5.
6. a. Click the *Subject to Constraints* entry box. Press the *Add* button to add the first constraint.
   b. Click the left entry box and click cell B13 (containing the formula for the first constraint).
   c. Set the middle entry box to <=.
   d. Click the right entry box and C13 to enter the constraint.
   e. Click Add and repeat the Steps 6b–6d for the remaining constraints.
   f. Click the left entry box for the constraints and select the variables in B3–B5. Set the middle entry to > = and type 0 in the right entry box.
7. Select the Simplex LP option. Click Solve in the *Solver* dialog box. A dialog box states that *Solver* found a solution. To see the *Solver* results, click *Keep Solver Solution* and select *Answer*.
8. Go back to the spreadsheet. The new values in B3–B5 are the values of the variables that give the maximum, and the value in B9 is the maximum value of the objective function.

In *Solver*, *minimization* of an objective function is handled exactly the same as maximization except *min* is checked and the inequality signs are ≥.

When *mixed constraints* are used, simply enter them with "mixed" inequalities.

	A	B	C
1	**Variables**		
2			
3	# small calculators (x)	0	
4	# medium calculators (y)	0	
5	# large calculators (z)	0	
6			
7	**Objective**		
8			
9	Maximize profit	=12*B3+26*B4+40*B5	
10			
11	**Constraints**		
12		Amount used	Maximum
13	Circuit components	=5*B3+7*B4+10*B5	90000
14	Labor	=B3+3*B4+4*B5	30000
15	Cases	=B3+B4+B5	9000

	A	B	C
1	**Variables**		
2			
3	# small calculators (x)	2000	
4	# medium calculators (y)	0	
5	# large calculators (z)	7000	
6			
7	**Objective**		
8			
9	Maximize profit	304000	
10			
11	**Constraints**		
12		Amount used	Maximum
13	Circuit components	80000	90000
14	Labor	30000	30000
15	Cases	9000	9000

*You may need to use an "Add-In" to access *Solver*.

Chapter 5

Section 5.1 Graphing Exponential Functions

Exponential functions are entered into Excel differently for base e than for bases other than e.

A. To graph $y = a^x$, use the formula $= a^\wedge x$.
B. To graph $y = e^x$, use the formula $=\exp(x)$.

To graph $f(x) = 1.5^x$ and $g(x) = e^x$ on the same axes:

1. Type x in cell A1 and numbers centered at 0 in Column A.
2. Type $f(x)$ in cell B1, enter the formula $=1.5^\wedge A2$ in cell B2, and fill down.
3. Type $g(x)$ in cell C1, enter the formula $=\exp(A2)$ in cell C2, and fill down.
4. Select the entire table (including titles) and graph using *Insert>Scatter >Smooth curve* to graph the functions.

	A	B	C
1	x	f(x)	g(x)
2	−2	0.444444	0.135335
3	−1.5	0.544433	0.22313
4	−1	0.666667	0.367879
5	−0.5	0.816497	0.606531
6	0	1	1
7	0.5	1.224745	1.648721
8	1	1.5	2.718282
9	1.5	1.837117	4.481689
10	2	2.25	7.389056
11	2.5	2.755676	12.18249
12	3	3.375	20.08554

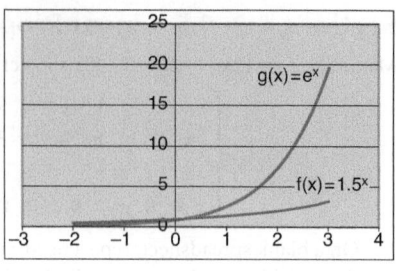

Section 5.1 Modeling with Exponential Functions

To model data with an exponential function:

1. Create a scatter plot for the data using *Insert>Scatter* and the points only option.
2. Single-click on the chart and right-click on one of the data points. Choose *Add Trendline*.
3. Check *Exponential* for the trendline type if that function type appears to be the best fit for the scatter plot, and check the *Display Equation* box to see the equation on the graph.
4. Close the dialog box to see the graph of the function and its equation.

The exponential model for the following data is shown.

x	0	5	10	15	16	17	18
y	170	325	750	1900	2000	2200	2600

Section 5.2 Graphing Base *e* and Base 10 Logarithmic Functions

To graph $y = \ln(x)$:

1. Create a table of *x*-values with $x > 0$ to reflect the function's domain.
2. In cell B2, use the formula =ln(A2) to find the natural logarithm of the number in A2. Then use fill down to complete the table.
3. Select the entire table and graph using *Insert>Scatter >Smooth curve.*

To graph $y = \log(x)$:
Use the steps above with the formula =log10(A2) in cell B2.

	A	B
1	*x*	$f(x) = \ln(x)$
2	0.5	−0.6931472
3	0.9	−0.1053605
4	1	0
5	2	0.6931472
6	3	1.0986123
7	4	1.3862944
8	5	1.6094379
9	6	1.7917595
10	7	1.9459101
11	8	2.0894415
12	9	2.1972246
13	10	2.3025851
14	11	2.3978953

	A	B
1	*x*	$f(x) = \log(x)$
2	0.5	−0.30103
3	0.9	−0.0457575
4	1	0
5	2	0.30103
6	3	0.47712125
7	4	0.60205999
8	5	0.69897
9	6	0.77815125
10	7	0.84509804
11	8	0.90308999
12	9	0.95424251
13	10	1
14	11	1.04139269

f(x)=ln(x)

f(x)=log(x)

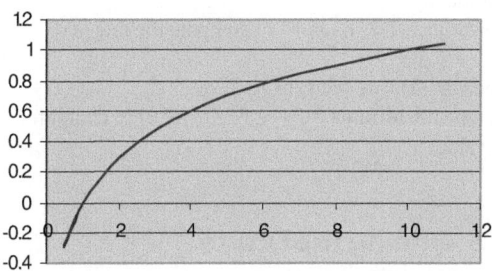

Section 5.2 Modeling Logarithmic Functions

1. Create a scatter plot for the data using *Insert>Scatter* and the points only option.
2. Single-click on the chart and right-click on one of the data points. Choose *Add Trendline* and check *Logarithmic* for *trendline* type.
3. Check the box to display the equation on the graph and close the dialog box by clicking OK.

x	y
10	2.207
20	3.972
30	5.004
40	5.737

Section 5.2 Graphing Logarithmic Functions with Other Bases

To graph $y = \log_b x$ for any base $b > 0$:

1. Create a table of input values for x with $x > 0$ to reflect the function's domain.
2. In cell B2, use the formula $=\log(A2,b)$ to find the logarithm base b of the number in A2. Then use fill down to complete the table.
3. Select the entire table and graph using *Insert>Scatter>Smooth curve.*

	A	B
1	x	$f(x) = \log(x,7)$
2	0.5	−0.356207187
3	0.9	−0.054144594
4	1	0
5	2	0.356207187
6	3	0.564575034
7	4	0.712414374
8	5	0.827087475
9	6	0.920782221
10	7	1
11	8	1.068621561
12	9	1.129150068
13	10	1.183294662
14	11	1.1232274406

The graph of $f(x) = \log_7 x$ is shown below.

Chapter 6

Section 6.2 Finding the Future Value of a Lump Sum

To find the future value of a lump-sum investment:

1. Type the headings in row 1 and enter their values (with the interest rate as a decimal) in row 2. Enter the investment as a negative number.
2. Type the formula $=D2/E2$ in F2 to compute the rate per period.
3. Type the heading Future Value in A4.
4. In cell B4, type the formula $=\text{fv}(F2,B2,C2,A2,0)$ to compute the future value.

This spreadsheet gives the future value of an investment of $10,000 for 17 years at 9.8%, compounded quarterly.

Principal	Number of Periods	Payment	Annual Rate	Periods per Year	Periodic Rate
−10,000	68	0	0.098	4	0.0245
Future Value	$51,857.73				

Section 6.3 Finding the Future Value of an Annuity

To find the future value of an ordinary annuity:

1. Type the headings in row 1 and enter their values (with the interest rate as a decimal) in row 2. Enter the deposit as a negative payment.
2. Type the formula $=D2/E2$ in F2 to compute the rate per period.
3. Type the heading Future Value in A4.
4. In cell B4, type the formula $=\text{fv}(F2,B2,C2,A2,0)$ to compute the future value.

(The 0 indicates that the payments are made at the end of each period.)

For annuities due, use $=\text{fv}(F2,B2,C2,A2,1)$.
The payments are made at the beginning of each period.

This spreadsheet gives the future value of an ordinary annuity of $200 deposited at the end of each quarter for $2\frac{1}{4}$ years with interest at 4% compounded quarterly.

Principal	Number of Periods	Payment	Annual Rate	Periods per Year	Periodic Rate
0	9	−200	0.04	4	0.01
Ordinary annuity					
Future Value	$1,873.71				

Annuities due					
Future Value	$1,892.44				

Section 6.4 Finding the Present Value of an Annuity

To find the present value of an ordinary annuity:

1. Type the headings in row 1 and enter their values (with the interest rate as a decimal) in row 2.
2. Enter the formula =D2/E2 in F2 to compute the rate per period.
3. Type the heading Present Value in A4.
4. In cell B4, type the formula =pv(F2,B2,C2,A2,0) to compute the present value. (The 0 indicates that the payments are made at the end of each period.) The parentheses on the present value in cell B4 mean that it is negative because the money leaves the investor to start the annuity.

   For annuities due, use =pv(F2,B2,C2,A2,1). The payments are made at the beginning of each period.

This spreadsheet gives the lump sum deposit (present value) necessary to receive $1000 per month for 16 years with interest at 9% compounded monthly for both an ordinary annuity and an annuity due.

Future Value	Number of Periods	Payment	Annual Rate	Periods per Year	Peri-odic Rate
0	192	1000	0.09	12	0.0075
Ordinary annuity					
Present Value	($101,572.77)				

Annui-ties due					
Present value	($102,334.56)				

Section 6.5 Finding Payments to Amortize a Loan

To find the periodic payment to pay off a loan:

1. Type the headings in row 1 and their values (with the interest rate as a decimal) in row 2.
2. Enter the formula =D2/E2 in F2 to compute the rate per period.
3. Type the heading Payment in A4.
4. In cell B4, type the formula =Pmt(F2,B2,A2,C2,0) to compute the payment.

This spreadsheet gives the annual payment of a loan of $10,000 over 5 years when interest is 10% per year.

The parentheses indicates a payment out.

Loan Amount	Number of Periods	Future Value	Annual Rate	Periods per Year	Periodic Rate
10000	5	0	0.1	1	0.1
Payment	($2,637.97)				

Chapter 8

Section 8.1 Binomial Probabilities

1. Type headings in cells A1:A3 and their respective values in cells B1:B3.
2. To find exact and cumulative binomial probabilities, use the function =binomdist(B1,B2,B3,cumulative) where

   - B1 is the number of successes.
   - B2 is the number of independent trials.
   - B3 is the probability of success in each trial.
   - True replaces cumulative if a cumulative probability is sought; it is replaced by false otherwise.

   In the example shown, the probability of exactly 3 heads in 6 tosses is found by evaluating =binomdist(B1,B2,B3,false) in B4, and the probability of 3 or fewer heads in 6 tosses is found by evaluating =binomdist(B1,B2,B3,true) in B5.

This spreadsheet gives the probability of 3 heads in 6 tosses of a fair coin and the probability of 3 or fewer heads in 6 tosses.

	A	B
1	Number of successes	3
2	Number of trials	6
3	Probability of success	.5
4	Probability of 3 successes	.3125
5	Probability of 3 or fewer successes	.65625

Section 8.2 Bar Graphs

To construct a bar graph for the given table of test scores:

1. Copy the entries of the table to cells A2:B6.
2. Select the range A2:B6.
3. Click on the *Insert* tab. Then select *Column* > *Clustered Column* (first option), and the graph appears.
4. Single-click on the chart. You can add labels and change the title of the graph by clicking *Layout* under *Chart Tools* and choosing the appropriate options.

	A	B
1	Grade Range	Frequency
2	90–100	2
3	80–89	5
4	70–79	3
5	60–69	3
6	0–59	2

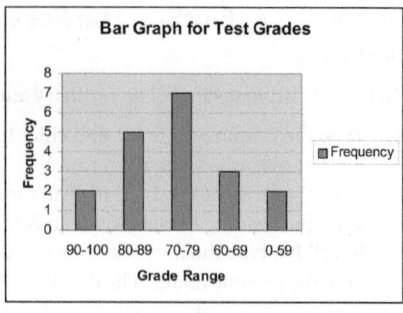

Section 8.2 Finding the Mean, Standard Deviation, and Median of Sample Data

To find the mean, standard deviation, and median of a sample data set:

1. Enter the data in row 1 (cells A1:L1).
2. Type the heading Mean in cell A3.
3. Type the formula =average(A1:L1) in cell B4.
4. Type the heading Standard Deviation in cell A4.
5. In cell B4, type the formula =stdev(A1:L1).
6. In cell A5, type the heading Median.
7. In cell B5, type the formula =median(A1:L1).

The mean, standard deviation, and median for the data 1, 1, 1, 3, 3, 4, 4, 5, 6, 6, 7, 7 are shown below.

	A	B	C	D	E	F	G	H	I	J	K	L
1	1		1	1	3	3	4	4	5	6	6	7	7
2												
3	Mean	4										
4	Standard Deviation	2.2563										
5	Median	4										

Section 8.2 Finding the Mean and Standard Deviation of Grouped Data

To find the mean:

1. Enter the data and headings in the cells A1:C6.
2. In D1, type the heading Class mark*frequency.
3. In D2, type the formula =B2*C2.
4. Copy the formula in D2 to D3:D6.
5. In B7, type the heading Total.
6. In cell C7, type the formula for the total frequencies, =sum(C2:C6).
7. In cell D7, type the formula for the total, = sum(D2:D6).
8. In cell A8, type the heading Mean.
9. In cell A9, type the formula =D7/C7, and the mean appears.

To find the standard deviation:
10. In cell E1, type the heading freq *(Mark − Mean)^2.
11. In cell E2, type the formula =C2*(B2 − A9)^2. (The A9 gives the value in A9; the reference doesn't change as you fill down.)
12. Copy the formula in E2 to E3:E6 by filling down.
13. In cell E7, type the formula =sum(E2:E6).
14. In cell A10, type the heading Standard Deviation.
15. In cell A11, type the formula =sqrt(E7/(C7-1)).

Grade Range	Class Marks	Frequency
90–100	95	3
80–89	84.5	4
70–79	74.5	7
60–69	64.5	0
50–59	54.5	2

	A	B	C	D	E
1	Grade Range	Class Marks	Frequency	Class mark* frequency	freq*(Mark − Mean)^2
2	90-100	95	3	285	832.2919922
3	80-89	84.5	4	338	151.5976563
4	70-79	74.5	7	521.5	103.4208984
5	60-69	64.5	0	0	0
6	50-59	54.5	2	109	1137.048828
7		Total	16	1253.5	2224.359375
8	Mean				
9	78.344				
10	Standard Deviation				
11	12.177				

Section 8.4 Calculating Normal Probabilities

To calculate normal probabilities:

1. Type headings in A1:A4 and their respective values in cells B1:B4.
2. To find the probability that a score X is less than the x1 value in B3, enter the formula =normdist(B3,B1,B2,true) in cell B5.
3. To find the probability that X is less than the x2 value in B4, enter the formula =normdist(B4,B1,B2,true) in cell B6.
4. To find the probability that a score X is more than the value in B3 and less than the x2 value in B4, enter the formula =B6-B5 in cell B7.

Entries in B5, B6, and B7 give the probabilities of a score X being less than 100, less than 115, and between 100 and 115, respectively, when the mean is 100 and the standard deviation is 15.

	A	B
1	Mean	100
2	Standard Deviation	15
3	x1	100
4	x2	115
5	Pr(X < x1)	0.5
6	Pr(X < x2)	0.841345
7	Pr(x1 < X < x2)	0.341345

Chapter 9

Sections 9.1–9.2 Evaluating Limits

To evaluate $\lim\limits_{x \to c} f(x)$:

1. Make a table of values for x and $f(x)$ near $x = c$. Include values on both sides of $x = c$.
2. Use the table of values to predict the limit (or that the limit does not exist).
3. To evaluate the limit in the example on the right, enter the formula =(A2^2−4)/(A2−2) in B2 and fill down.

Note: All limit evaluations with Excel use appropriate tables of values of x and $f(x)$. This is especially useful when $f(x)$ is piecewise-defined and for limits as $\to \infty$.

Find $\lim\limits_{x \to 2} \dfrac{x^2 - 4}{x - 2}$.

	A	B	C	D
1	**x**	**f(x)**	**x**	**f(x)**
2	2.1	4.1	1.9	3.9
3	2.05	4.05	1.95	3.95
4	2.01	4.01	1.99	3.99
5	2.001	4.001	1.999	3.999

The tables suggest that $\lim\limits_{x \to 2} \dfrac{x^2 - 4}{x - 2} = 4$.

Sections 9.3–9.7 Approximating Numerical Derivatives

To approximate $f'(c)$:

1. Numerically investigate the limit in the definition of derivative:

$$f'(c) = \lim_{h \to 0} \frac{f(c + h) - f(c)}{h}$$

2. Use the given $f(x)$ at $x = c$ and create a table of values for h near 0 (and on both sides of $h = 0$). Enter the input values in column A.
3. To investigate $f'(1)$ for $f(x) = x^3$, evaluate $\dfrac{f(1 + h) - f(1)}{h}$ for values of h close to 0, enter the formula =((A2+1)^3−1^3)/A2 in E2, and fill down.

Note that rows 5 and 6 have the values of h closest to 0.

	A	B	C	D	E
	h	**1+h**	**f(1)**	**f(1+h)**	**(f(1+h)-f(1))/h**
1					
2	0.1	1.1	1	1.331	3.31
3	0.01	1.01	1	1.030301	3.0301
4	0.001	1.001	1	1.003003	3.003001
5	0.0001	1.0001	1	1.0003	3.00030001
6	−0.0001	0.9999	1	0.9997	2.99970001
7	−0.001	0.999	1	0.997003	2.997001
8	−0.01	0.99	1	0.970299	2.9701
9	−0.1	0.9	1	0.729	2.71

The table suggests that $f'(1) = 3$, which is the actual value.
Note: Excel has no built-in derivative approximation tool.

Chapter 10
Section 10.1 Relative Maxima and Minima

1. Make a table with columns for *x*-values, the function, and the derivative.
2. Extend the table to include *x*-values to the left and to the right of all critical values.
3. Use the signs of the values of the derivative to determine whether *f* is increasing or decreasing around the critical values, and thus to classify the critical values as relative maxima, relative minima, or horizontal points of inflection. You may want to graph the function to confirm your conclusions.

The spreadsheet shows that the relative maximum of $f(x) = x^3/3 - 4x$ is $(-2, 16/3)$ and the relative is minimum is $(2, -16/3)$. Note that the derivative is $f'(x) = g(x) = x^2 - 4$.

	A	B	C
	x	f(x) = x^3/3 − 4x	g(x) = x^2 − 4
1			
2	−4	−5.33333333	12
3	−3	3	5
4	−2	5.333333333	0
5	−1	3.666666667	−3
6	0	0	−4
7	1	−3.66666667	−3
8	2	−5.33333333	0
9	3	−3	5
10	4	5.333333333	12

Section 10.2 Exploring f, f′, f″ Relationships

To explore relationships among the graphs of a function and its derivatives:

1. Find functions for f' and f''.
2. Graph all three functions on the same plot.
   - Notice that *f* increases when f' is above the *x*-axis (+) and decreases when f' is below the *x*-axis (−).
   - Notice that *f* is concave up when f'' is above the *x*-axis (+) and is concave down when f'' is below the *x*-axis (−).

Let $f(x) = x^3 - 9x^2 + 24x$. Graph *f*, f', and f'' on the interval $[0, 5]$ to explore the relationships among these functions.

	A	B	C	D
1	*x*	*f(x)*	*f′(x)*	*f″(x)*
2	0	0	24	−18
3	0.5	9.875	15.75	−15
4	1	16	9	−12
5	1.5	19.125	3.75	−9
6	2	20	0	−6
7	2.5	19.375	−2.25	−3
8	3	18	−3	0
9	3.5	16.625	−2.25	−3
10	4	16	0	6
11	4.5	16.875	3.75	9
12	5	20	9	12

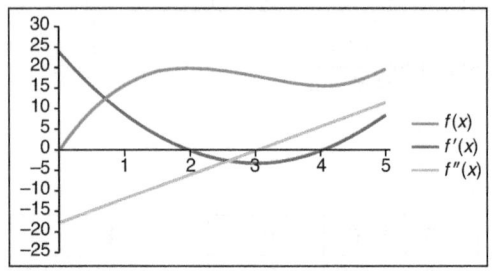

Sections 10.3–10.4 Finding Optimal Values

To find the optimal value of a function without producing a graph:

1. Set up a spreadsheet that identifies the variable and the function whose optimal value is sought.
   Enter an initial value for the variable in B3.
2. Choose *Data > Analysis > Solver*. Then, in the Dialog Box:
   a. Set the *Target Cell* as that of the objective function.
   b. Check *Max* or *Min* according to your goal.
   c. Set the *Changing Cells* to reference the variable.
3. Click on the *Options* box. Make sure "Assume Linear Model" is *not* checked. Then click OK.
4. Click *Solve* in the *Solver* dialog box. You will get a dialog box stating that *Solver* found a solution. Save the solution if desired, and click OK.
5. The cells containing the variable and the function should now contain the optimal values.

Minimize area $A = x^2 + \dfrac{160}{x}$ for $x > 0$.

	A	B
1	**Variable**	
2		
3	x length of base	1
4		
5	**Objective**	
6		
7	Minimize Area	=B3^2+160/B3

	A	B
1	**Variable**	
2		
3	x length of base	4.3089
4		
5	**Objective**	
6		
7	Minimize Area	55.699

The function is minimized for $x = 4.3089$, and the minimum value is $A = 55.699$.

Chapter 13

Section 13.1 Approximating Definite Integrals Using Rectangles

To find the approximate area between $y = f(x)$ and the x-axis over an interval by using the right-hand endpoints of rectangles with equal base width:

1. Enter x and the x- values of the right-hand endpoints of each rectangle in column B. Fill down can be used if the number of rectangles is large.
2. Enter the formula for the function, using cell addresses, in C2 and fill down column C to get the heights of the rectangles.
3. Enter the width of the rectangles in column D.
4. Enter the formula for the area of each rectangle, =C2*D2, in E2 and fill down to get the area of each rectangle.
5. Enter Total in A10 and the formula =SUM(E2:E9) in E10 to get the approximate area.

To find the approximation for the area under $y = \sqrt{x}$ from $x = 0$ to $x = 4$ using $n = 8$ equal subdivisions (with base width 0.5) and right-hand endpoints:

1. Enter x and the eight x-values of the right-hand endpoints (starting with 0.5) in column B.
2. Enter y in C1 and =SQRT(B2) in C2 and fill down column C.
3. Enter width in D1 and 0.5 below in column D.
4. Enter Area in E1, =C2*D2 in E2, and fill down to get the area of each rectangle.
5. Enter Total in A10 and the formula =SUM(E2:E9) in E10 to get the approximate area, $S_R \approx 5.765$.

	A	B	C	D	E
1	Rectangle	x	y	Width	Area
2	1	0.5	0.707107	0.5	0.353553
3	2	1	1	0.5	0.5
4	3	1.5	1.224745	0.5	0.612372
5	4	2	1.414214	0.5	0.707107
6	5	2.5	1.581139	0.5	0.790569
7	6	3	1.732051	0.5	0.866025
8	7	3.5	1.870829	0.5	0.935414
9	8	4	2	0.5	1
10	Total				5.765042

Section 13.8 Trapezoidal Rule

To approximate a definite integral from a to b with the Trapezoidal Rule, using n trapezoids:

1. Enter the x-values of the endpoints of the subintervals in column A and the corresponding functional values in column B, starting with A2 and B2.
2. Put the weight/coefficient (1 or 2) for each term in the formula in column C, starting with C2, and store the value

   $$\frac{h}{2} = \frac{b - a}{2n}$$ in column D.

3. Use the formula =B2*C2*D2 in E2 to get the first term of the formula and use fill down to get the remaining terms.
4. For the example, we use =SUM(E2:E10) in cell E11 to approximate the definite integral. In general, use the formula =SUM(E2:E(n + 2)) in cell E(n + 3), where n is the number of trapezoids.

The spreadsheet approximates the integral of the function $f(x) = 1/x$ from $x = 1$ to $x = 3$, using 8 trapezoids in

$$\frac{b - a}{2n}[f(x_0) + 2f(x_1) + \cdots + 2f(x_{n-1}) + f(x_n)]$$

	A	B	C	D	E
1	x	f(x)	Weight	$(b - a)/(2n)$	Terms
2	1	1	1	0.125	0.125
3	1.25	0.8	2	0.125	0.2
4	1.5	0.666667	2	0.125	0.166667
5	1.75	0.571429	2	0.125	0.142857
6	2	0.5	2	0.125	0.125
7	2.25	0.444444	2	0.125	0.111111
8	2.5	0.4	2	0.125	0.1
9	2.75	0.363636	2	0.125	0.090909
10	3	0.333333	1	0.125	0.041667
11	$\int_1^3 (1/x)dx$				1.103211

Chapter 14

Section 14.1 Graphs of Functions of Two Variables

To create a surface plot for a function of two variables:

1. a. Generate appropriate x-values beginning in B1 and continuing *across*.
    b. Generate appropriate y-values beginning in A2 and continuing *down*.
2. Generate values for the function that correspond to the points (x, y) from Step 1 as follows:
    In cell B2, enter the function formula with B$1 used to represent x and $A2 to represent y. (See the Online Excel Guide for additional information about the role and use of the $ in this step.) Then use fill down and fill across to complete the table.
3. Use *Insert > Scatter > More Scatter Plots > Surface* in Excel 2016, and the graph will appear. In Excel 2010, use *Insert > Other Charts* and choose the first option under *Surface*, and the graph will appear.
4. To rotate the graph, click on the chart and click on *3-D rotation*. You can click on the various options present in the dialog box.

Let $f(x,y) = 10 - x^2 - y^2$. Plot the graph of this function for both x and y in the interval $[-2,2]$.

	A	B	C	D	E	F	G	H	I	J
1		-2	-1.5	-1	-0.5	0	0.5	1	1.5	2
2	-2									
3	-1.5									
4	-1									
5	-0.5									
6	0									
7	0.5									
8	1									
9	1.5									
10	2									

	A	B	C	D	E	F	G	H	I	J
1		-2	-1.5	-1	-0.5	0	0.5	1	1.5	2
2	-2	2	3.75	5	5.75	6	5,75	5	3.75	2
3	-1.5	3.75	5.5	6.75	7.5	7.75	7.5	6.75	5.5	3.75
4	-1	5	6.75	8	8.75	9	8.75	8	6.75	5
5	-0.5	5.75	7.5	8.75	9.5	9.75	9.5	8.75	7.5	5.75
6	0	6	7.75	9	9.75	10	9.75	9	7.75	6
7	0.5	5.75	7.5	8.75	9.5	9.75	9.5	8.75	7.5	5.75
8	1	5	6.75	8	8.75	9	8.75	8	6.75	5
9	1.5	3.75	5.5	6.75	7.5	7.75	7.5	6.75	5.5	3.75
10	2	2	3.75	5	5.75	6	5.75	5	3.75	2

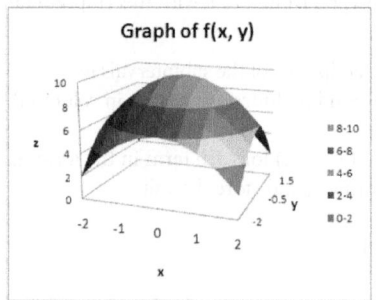

Graph of f(x, y)

Section 14.5 Constrained Optimization and Lagrange Multipliers

To solve a constrained optimization problem:

1. Set up the problem in Excel.
2. Choose *Data > Analysis > Solver* and do the following:
   - Click on the *Set Objective* box (Excel 2016) or the *Target Cell* box (Excel 2010), then click on the cell containing the objective function
   - Check *Max* or *Min* depending on the problem.
   - Choose the cells representing the variables for the *By Changing Cells* box.
   - Click the *Constraints* box and press Add. Then enter the constraint equations.
3. Check the box making the variables nonnegative.
4. Select "GRG Nonlinear" as the solving method.
5. Click *Solve* in the *Solver* dialog box. Then click OK to solve.

Maximize $P = 600l^{2/3}k^{1/3}$ subject to $40l + 100k = 3000$.

	A	B	C
1	**Variables**		
2			
3	units labor (l)	0	
4	units capital (k)	0	
5			
6			
7	**Objective**		
8			
9	Maximize production	=600*B3^(2/3)*B4^(1/3)	
10			
11	**Constraint**		
12		Amount used	Available
13	Cost	=40*B3+100*B4	3000

	A	B	C
1	**Variables**		
2			
3	units labor (l)	50.00000002	
4	units capital (k)	10	
5			
6			
7	**Objective**		
8			
9	Maximize product	17544.10644	
10			
11	**Constraint**		
12		Amount used	Available
13	Cost	3000.000001	3000

Appendix C:
Areas Under the Standard Normal Curve

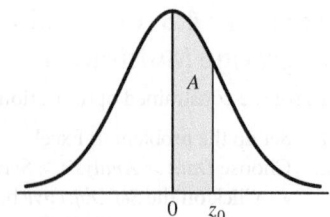

The value of A is the area under the standard normal curve between $z = 0$ and $z = z_0$ for $z_0 \geq 0$. Areas for negative values of z_0 are obtained by symmetry.

z_0	A	z_0	A	z_0	A	z_0	A
0.00	0.0000	0.43	0.1664	0.86	0.3051	1.29	0.4015
0.01	0.0040	0.44	0.1700	0.87	0.3078	1.30	0.4032
0.02	0.0080	0.45	0.1736	0.88	0.3106	1.31	0.4049
0.03	0.0120	0.46	0.1772	0.89	0.3133	1.32	0.4066
0.04	0.0160	0.47	0.1808	0.90	0.3159	1.33	0.4082
0.05	0.0199	0.48	0.1844	0.91	0.3186	1.34	0.4099
0.06	0.0239	0.49	0.1879	0.92	0.3212	1.35	0.4115
0.07	0.0279	0.50	0.1915	0.93	0.3238	1.36	0.4131
0.08	0.0319	0.51	0.1950	0.94	0.3264	1.37	0.4147
0.09	0.0359	0.52	0.1985	0.95	0.3289	1.38	0.4162
0.10	0.0398	0.53	0.2019	0.96	0.3315	1.39	0.4177
0.11	0.0438	0.54	0.2054	0.97	0.3340	1.40	0.4192
0.12	0.0478	0.55	0.2088	0.98	0.3365	1.41	0.4207
0.13	0.0517	0.56	0.2123	0.99	0.3389	1.42	0.4222
0.14	0.0557	0.57	0.2157	1.00	0.3413	1.43	0.4236
0.15	0.0596	0.58	0.2190	1.01	0.3438	1.44	0.4251
0.16	0.0636	0.59	0.2224	1.02	0.3461	1.45	0.4265
0.17	0.0675	0.60	0.2257	1.03	0.3485	1.46	0.4279
0.18	0.0714	0.61	0.2291	1.04	0.3508	1.47	0.4292
0.19	0.0754	0.62	0.2324	1.05	0.3531	1.48	0.4306
0.20	0.0793	0.63	0.2357	1.06	0.3554	1.49	0.4319
0.21	0.0832	0.64	0.2389	1.07	0.3577	1.50	0.4332
0.22	0.0871	0.65	0.2422	1.08	0.3599	1.51	0.4345
0.23	0.0910	0.66	0.2454	1.09	0.3621	1.52	0.4357
0.24	0.0948	0.67	0.2486	1.10	0.3643	1.53	0.4370
0.25	0.0987	0.68	0.2517	1.11	0.3665	1.54	0.4382
0.26	0.1026	0.69	0.2549	1.12	0.3686	1.55	0.4394
0.27	0.1064	0.70	0.2580	1.13	0.3708	1.56	0.4406
0.28	0.1103	0.71	0.2611	1.14	0.3729	1.57	0.4418
0.29	0.1141	0.72	0.2642	1.15	0.3749	1.58	0.4429
0.30	0.1179	0.73	0.2673	1.16	0.3770	1.59	0.4441
0.31	0.1217	0.74	0.2704	1.17	0.3790	1.60	0.4452
0.32	0.1255	0.75	0.2734	1.18	0.3810	1.61	0.4463
0.33	0.1293	0.76	0.2764	1.19	0.3830	1.62	0.4474
0.34	0.1331	0.77	0.2794	1.20	0.3849	1.63	0.4484
0.35	0.1368	0.78	0.2823	1.21	0.3869	1.64	0.4495
0.36	0.1406	0.79	0.2852	1.22	0.3888	1.65	0.4505
0.37	0.1443	0.80	0.2881	1.23	0.3907	1.66	0.4515
0.38	0.1480	0.81	0.2910	1.24	0.3925	1.67	0.4525
0.39	0.1517	0.82	0.2939	1.25	0.3944	1.68	0.4535
0.40	0.1554	0.83	0.2967	1.26	0.3962	1.69	0.4545
0.41	0.1591	0.84	0.2995	1.27	0.3980	1.70	0.4554
0.42	0.1628	0.85	0.3023	1.28	0.3997	1.71	0.4564

(continued)

z_0	A	z_0	A	z_0	A	z_0	A
1.72	0.4573	2.26	0.4881	2.80	0.4974	3.34	0.4996
1.73	0.4582	2.27	0.4884	2.81	0.4975	3.35	0.4996
1.74	0.4591	2.28	0.4887	2.82	0.4976	3.36	0.4996
1.75	0.4599	2.29	0.4890	2.83	0.4977	3.37	0.4996
1.76	0.4608	2.30	0.4893	2.84	0.4977	3.38	0.4996
1.77	0.4616	2.31	0.4896	2.85	0.4978	3.39	0.4997
1.78	0.4625	2.32	0.4898	2.86	0.4979	3.40	0.4997
1.79	0.4633	2.33	0.4901	2.87	0.4979	3.41	0.4997
1.80	0.4641	2.34	0.4904	2.88	0.4980	3.42	0.4997
1.81	0.4649	2.35	0.4906	2.89	0.4981	3.43	0.4997
1.82	0.4656	2.36	0.4909	2.90	0.4981	3.44	0.4997
1.83	0.4664	2.37	0.4911	2.91	0.4982	3.45	0.4997
1.84	0.4671	2.38	0.4913	2.92	0.4982	3.46	0.4997
1.85	0.4678	2.39	0.4916	2.93	0.4983	3.47	0.4997
1.86	0.4686	2.40	0.4918	2.94	0.4984	3.48	0.4997
1.87	0.4693	2.41	0.4920	2.95	0.4984	3.49	0.4998
1.88	0.4699	2.42	0.4922	2.96	0.4985	3.50	0.4998
1.89	0.4706	2.43	0.4925	2.97	0.4985	3.51	0.4998
1.90	0.4713	2.44	0.4927	2.98	0.4986	3.52	0.4998
1.91	0.4719	2.45	0.4929	2.99	0.4986	3.53	0.4998
1.92	0.4726	2.46	0.4931	3.00	0.4987	3.54	0.4998
1.93	0.4732	2.47	0.4932	3.01	0.4987	3.55	0.4998
1.94	0.4738	2.48	0.4934	3.02	0.4987	3.56	0.4998
1.95	0.4744	2.49	0.4936	3.03	0.4988	3.57	0.4998
1.96	0.4750	2.50	0.4938	3.04	0.4988	3.58	0.4998
1.97	0.4756	2.51	0.4940	3.05	0.4989	3.59	0.4998
1.98	0.4761	2.52	0.4941	3.06	0.4989	3.60	0.4998
1.99	0.4767	2.53	0.4943	3.07	0.4989	3.61	0.4998
2.00	0.4772	2.54	0.4945	3.08	0.4990	3.62	0.4999
2.01	0.4778	2.55	0.4946	3.09	0.4990	3.63	0.4999
2.02	0.4783	2.56	0.4948	3.10	0.4990	3.64	0.4999
2.03	0.4788	2.57	0.4949	3.11	0.4991	3.65	0.4999
2.04	0.4793	2.58	0.4951	3.12	0.4991	3.66	0.4999
2.05	0.4798	2.59	0.4952	3.13	0.4991	3.67	0.4999
2.06	0.4803	2.60	0.4953	3.14	0.4992	3.68	0.4999
2.07	0.4808	2.61	0.4955	3.15	0.4992	3.69	0.4999
2.08	0.4812	2.62	0.4956	3.16	0.4992	3.70	0.4999
2.09	0.4817	2.63	0.4957	3.17	0.4992	3.71	0.4999
2.10	0.4821	2.64	0.4959	3.18	0.4993	3.72	0.4999
2.11	0.4826	2.65	0.4960	3.19	0.4993	3.73	0.4999
2.12	0.4830	2.66	0.4961	3.20	0.4993	3.74	0.4999
2.13	0.4834	2.67	0.4962	3.21	0.4993	3.75	0.4999
2.14	0.4838	2.68	0.4963	3.22	0.4994	3.76	0.4999
2.15	0.4842	2.69	0.4964	3.23	0.4994	3.77	0.4999
2.16	0.4846	2.70	0.4965	3.24	0.4994	3.78	0.4999
2.17	0.4850	2.71	0.4966	3.25	0.4994	3.79	0.4999
2.18	0.4854	2.72	0.4967	3.26	0.4994	3.80	0.4999
2.19	0.4857	2.73	0.4968	3.27	0.4995	3.81	0.4999
2.20	0.4861	2.74	0.4969	3.28	0.4995	3.82	0.4999
2.21	0.4864	2.75	0.4970	3.29	0.4995	3.83	0.4999
2.22	0.4868	2.76	0.4971	3.30	0.4995	3.84	0.4999
2.23	0.4871	2.77	0.4972	3.31	0.4995	3.85	0.4999
2.24	0.4875	2.78	0.4973	3.32	0.4995	3.86	0.4999
2.25	0.4878	2.79	0.4974	3.33	0.4996		

Answers

Below are the answers to odd-numbered Section Exercises and all the Chapter Review and Chapter Test problems.

0.1 EXERCISES

1. $\in$ **3.** $\notin$ **5.** $\{1, 2, 3, 4, 5, 6, 7\}$

7. $\{x : x$ is a natural number greater than 2 and less than 8$\}$

9. $\varnothing, A, B$ **11.** no   **13.** $D \subseteq C$

15. $A \subseteq B$ or $B \subseteq A$ **17.** yes   **19.** no

21. A and B, B and D, C and D

23. $A \cap B = \{4, 6\}$ **25.** $A \cap B = \varnothing$

27. $A \cup B = \{1, 2, 3, 4, 5\}$

29. $A \cup B = \{1, 2, 3, 4\} = B$

31. $A' = \{4, 6, 9, 10\}$

33. $A \cap B' = \{1, 2, 5, 7\}$

35. $(A \cup B)' = \{6, 9\}$

37. $A' \cup B' = \{1, 2, 4, 5, 6, 7, 9, 10\}$

39. $(A \cap B') \cup C' = \{1, 2, 3, 5, 7, 9\}$

41. $(A \cap B')' \cap C = \{4, 6, 8, 10\}$

43. $A - B = \{1, 7\}$

45. $A - B = \varnothing$ or $\{ \}$

47. (a) $B = \{2005, 2006, 2007, 2009, 2010, 2011, 2012\}$
   $E = \{2006, 2007, 2011, 2012, 2013, 2014, 2015, 2016\}$
   $P = \{2005, 2007, 2008, 2011, 2015\}$
   (b) no
   (c) P' is the set of years in which the Dow Jones annual percent change was 7% or more.
   (d) $B' \cap P' = \{2013, 2014, 2016\}$; this describes the set of years in which the Dow Jones beginning value was 13,000 or more and the annual percent change was 7% or more.
   (e) $E' \cap P = \{2005, 2008\}$; this describes the set of years in which the Dow Jones ending value was 12,000 or less and the annual percent change was less than 7%.

49. (a) 130   (b) 840   (c) 520

51. (a)

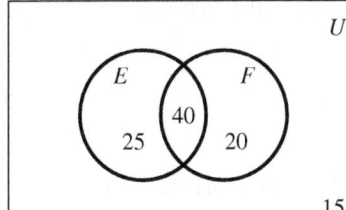

   (b) 40
   (c) 85
   (d) 25

53.

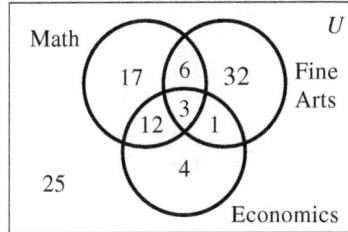

   (a) 25
   (b) 43
   (c) 53

55. (a) and (b)

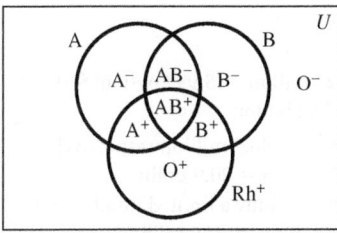

   (c) A^+: 34%; B^+: 9%; O^+: 38%; AB^+: 3%; O^-: 7%; A^-: 6%; B^-: 2%; AB^-: 1%

0.2 EXERCISES

1. (a) irrational   (b) rational, integer
   (c) rational, integer, natural   (d) meaningless

3. (a) Commutative   (b) Distributive

5. (a) Associative   (b) Additive identity

7. $<$ **9.** $<$ **11.** $<$ **13.** $>$ **15.** 11

17. 4   **19.** 2   **21.** $\frac{-4}{3}$ **23.** 3   **25.** $\frac{17}{11}$

27. entire line

29. $(1, 3]$; half open

31. $(2, 10)$; open

33. $-3 \le x < 5$

35. $x > 4$

37. $(-3, 4)$

39. $(4, \infty)$

41. $[-1, \infty)$

43. $(-\infty, 0) \cup (7, \infty)$

45. -0.000038585

47. 9122.387471   **49.** 3240.184509

51. (a) \$1088.91   (b) \$258.62   (c) \$627.20

53. (a) Eq. (2)
   (b) Eq. (1) = 64.3%
   Eq. (2) = 64.7%

55. (a) $190{,}151 \le I \le 413{,}350$; $413{,}351 \le I \le 415{,}050$; $I > 415{,}050$
   (b) \$5183.75; \$18,558.75   (c) $[5183.75, 18{,}558.75]$

0.3 EXERCISES

1. (a) 256   (b). -64 **3.** (a) $\frac{1}{9}$ (b). $-\frac{9}{4}$

5. 2.0736   **7.** 0.1316872428   **9.** 6^8 **11.** $\frac{1}{10}$

13. $9^0 = 1$ **15.** 3^9 **17.** $\left(\frac{3}{2}\right)^2 = \frac{9}{4}$

19. $-1/x^3$ **21.** x/y^2 **23.** x^7

25. $x^{-2} = 1/x^2$ **27.** x^4 **29.** y^{12} **31.** x^{12}

33. $x^2 y^2$ **35.** $16/x^{20}$ **37.** $x^8/(16y^4)$

39. $-16a^2/b^2$ **41.** $2/(xy^2)$ **43.** $1/(x^9 y^6)$

45. $(a^{18}c^{12})/b^6$

47. (a) $1/(2x^4)$ (b) $1/(16x^4)$ (c) $1/x^4$ (d) 8

49. x^{-1} **51.** $8x^3$ **53.** $\frac{1}{4}x^{-2}$ **55.** $-\frac{1}{8}x^3$

57. $S = \$2114.81; I = \$914.81$

59. $S = \$9607.70; I = \$4607.70$

61. $7806.24

63. (a) $40, 54, 64$
  (b) 6625 billion; $15,999$ billion; $30,032$ billion
  (c) $20,582$ billion

65. (a) $31.8, 39.8, 48.7$ million respectively
  (b) $58.2 - 37.3 = 20.9$ million
  (c) There are only a limited number of U.S. adults.
   Upper limit $= 120$ million

67. (a) 10 (b) 1385.5 billion
  (c) 2600.8 billion   (d) 4304.3 billion

0.4 EXERCISES

1. (a) $\frac{16}{3} \approx 5.33$ (b) 1.2 (c) 8 (d) not real

3. (a) $\frac{9}{4}$ (b) 16 (c) $1/16$

5. $(6.12)^{4/9} \approx 2.237$

7. $m^{3/2}$ **9.** $(m^2n^5)^{1/4}$ **11.** $2\sqrt{x}$

13. $\sqrt[6]{x^7}$ **15.** $-1/\!\left(4\sqrt[4]{x^5}\right)$ **17.** $y^{3/4}$

19. $z^{19/4}$ **21.** $1/y^{5/2}$ **23.** x

25. $1/y^{21/10}$ **27.** $x^{1/2}$ **29.** $1/x$

31. $8x^2$ **33.** $8x^2y^2\sqrt{2y}$ **35.** $2x^2y\sqrt[3]{5x^2y^2}$

37. $6x^2y\sqrt{x}$ **39.** $42x^3y^2\sqrt{x}$ **41.** $2xy^5/3$

43. $2b\sqrt[3]{b}/(3a^2)$ **45.** $1/9$ **47.** 7

49. $\sqrt{6}/3$ **51.** $\sqrt{mx}/x$ **53.** $\sqrt[3]{mx^2}/x^2$

55. $-\frac{2}{3}x^{-2/3}$ **57.** $3x^{3/2}$ **59.** $(3\sqrt{x})/2$

61. $1/(2\sqrt{x})$

63. (a) $10^{8.5} = 10^{17/2} = \sqrt{10^{17}}$
  (b) $10^{9.0} = 1,000,000,000$ (c) $10^{2.1} \approx 125.9$

65. (a) $S = 1000\sqrt{\left(1 + \dfrac{r}{100}\right)^5}$
  (b) $1173.26 (nearest cent)

67. (a) $P = 0.924\sqrt[100]{t^{13}}$
  (b) 2005 to 2010; 0.1074 billion vs. 0.0209 billion. By 2045 and 2050, the population will be much larger than earlier in the 21st century and there is a limited number of people that any land can support—in terms of both space and food.

69. 74 kg   **71.** $39,491$

73. (a) 10 (b) 259

0.5 EXERCISES

1. (a) 2 (b) -1 (c) 10 (d) one

3. (a) 5 (b) -14 (c) 0 (d) several

5. (a) 5 (b) 0 (c) 2 (d) -5

7. -12 **9.** -296 **11.** $\frac{-7}{31}$

13. 87.4654 **15.** $21pq - 2p^2$ **17.** $m^2 - 7n^2 - 3$

19. $3q + 12$ **21.** $x^2 - 1$ **23.** $35x^5$

25. $3rs$ **27.** $2ax^4 + a^2x^3 + a^2bx^2$

29. $6y^2 - y - 12$ **31.** $12 - 30x^2 + 12x^4$

33. $16x^2 + 24x + 9$ **35.** $0.01 - 16x^2$

37. $36x^2 - 9$

39. $x^4 - x^2 + \frac{1}{4}$

41. $0.1x^2 - 1.995x - 0.1$

43. $x^3 - 8$ **45.** $x^8 + 3x^6 - 10x^4 + 5x^3 + 25x$

47. $3 + m + 2m^2n$ **49.** $8x^3y^2/3 + 5/(3y) - 2x^2/(3y)$

51. $x^3 + 3x^2 + 3x + 1$

53. $8x^3 - 36x^2 + 54x - 27$

55. $x^2 - 2x + 5 - 11/(x + 2)$

57. $x^2 + 3x - 1 + (-4x + 2)/(x^2 + 1)$

59. (a) $9x^2 - 21x + 13$ (b) 5

61. $x + 2x^2$ **63.** $x - x^{1/2} - 2$ **65.** $x - 9$

67. $4x^2 + 4x$ **69.** $55x$

71. (a) $49.95 + 0.49x$ (b) $114.63

73. (a) $4000 - x$ (b) $0.10x$
  (c) $0.08(4000 - x)$ (d) $0.10x + 0.08(4000 - x)$

75. $(15 - 2x)(10 - 2x)x$

0.6 EXERCISES

1. (a) $3b(3a - 4a^2 + 6b)$ (b) $2x(2x + 4y^2 + y^3)$

3. $(7x^2 + 2)(x - 2)$ **5.** $(6 + y)(x - m)$

7. $(x + 2)(x + 6)$ **9.** $(x - 16)(x + 1)$

11. $(7x + 4)(x - 2)$ **13.** $(x - 5)^2$

15. $(7a + 12b)(7a - 12b)$

17. (a) $(3x - 1)(3x + 8)$ (b) $(9x + 4)(x + 2)$

19. $x(4x - 1)$ **21.** $(x^2 - 5)(x + 4)$

23. $(x - 3)(x + 2)$ **25.** $2(x - 7)(x + 3)$

27. $2x(x - 2)^2$ **29.** $(2x - 3)(x + 2)$

31. $3(x + 4)(x - 3)$ **33.** $2x(x + 2)(x - 2)$

35. $(5x + 2)(2x + 3)$ **37.** $(5x - 1)(2x - 9)$

39. $(y^2 + 4x^2)(y + 2x)(y - 2x)$

41. $(x + 2)^2(x - 2)^2$

43. $(2x + 1)(2x - 1)(x + 1)(x - 1)$

45. $x + 1$ **47.** $1 + x$ **49.** $(x + 1)^3$

51. $(x - 4)^3$ **53.** $(x - 4)(x^2 + 4x + 16)$

55. $(3 + 2x)(9 - 6x + 4x^2)$

57. $P(1 + rt)$ **59.** $m(c - m)$

61. (a) $p(10,000 - 100p); x = 10,000 - 100p$ (b) 6200

63. (a) $R = x(300 - x)$ (b) $300 - x$

0.7 EXERCISES

1. $2y^3/z$ **3.** $\frac{1}{3}$ **5.** $(x - 1)/(x - 3)$

7. $20x/y$ **9.** $\frac{32}{3}$ **11.** $3x + 9$

13. $\dfrac{-(x + 1)(x + 3)}{(x - 1)(x - 3)}$ **15.** $15bc^2/2$ **17.** $5y/(y - 3)$

19. $\dfrac{-x(x - 3)(x + 2)}{x + 3}$ **21.** $\dfrac{1}{x + 1}$

23. $\dfrac{4a - 4}{a(a - 2)}$ **25.** $\dfrac{-x^2 + x + 1}{x + 1}$

27. $\dfrac{16a + 15a^2}{12(x + 2)}$ **29.** $\dfrac{79x + 9}{30(x - 2)}$

31. $\dfrac{9x + 4}{(x - 2)(x + 2)(x + 1)}$ **33.** $(7x - 3x^3)/\sqrt{3 - x^2}$

35. $\frac{1}{6}$ **37.** xy

39. $\dfrac{x + 1}{x^2}$ **41.** $\dfrac{1}{\sqrt{a}} = \dfrac{\sqrt{a}}{a}$

43. (a) -12 (b) $\frac{25}{36}$

45. $2b^2 - a$

47. $(1 - 2\sqrt{x} + x)/(1 - x)$

49. $(x - 5)(\sqrt{x} + 5)/(x - 25)$

51. $1/(\sqrt{x + h} + \sqrt{x})$

53. $(bc + ac + ab)/abc$

55. (a) $\dfrac{0.1x^2 + 55x + 4000}{x}$ (b) $0.1x^2 + 55x + 4000$

57. $\dfrac{t^2 + 9t}{(t + 3)^2}$

CHAPTER 0 REVIEW EXERCISES

1. yes   **2.** no   **3.** no

4. $\{1, 2, 3, 4, 9\}$ **5.** $\{5, 6, 7, 8, 10\}$ **6.** $\{1, 2, 3, 4, 9\}$

7. yes, $(A' \cup B')' = \{1, 3\} = A \cap B$

8. (a) Commutative Property of Addition
   (b) Associative Property of Multiplication
   (c) Distributive Law

9. (a) irrational   (b) rational, integer
   (c) undefined

10. (a) $>$ (b) $<$ (c) $>$

11. 6   **12.** 142   **13.** 10

14. 5/4   **15.** 9   **16.** -29

17. 13/4   **18.** -10.62857888

19. (a) $[0, 5]$, closed

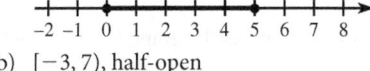

   (b) $[-3, 7)$, half-open

   (c) $(-4, 0)$, open

20. (a) $-1 < x < 16$ (b) $-12 \le x \le 8$
   (c) $x < -1$

21. (a) 1   (b) $2^{-2} = 1/4$ (c) 4^6 (d) 7

22. (a) $1/x^2$ (b) x^{10} (c) x^9 (d) $1/y^8$
   (e) y^6

23. $-x^2y^2/36$ **24.** $9y^8/(4x^4)$ **25.** $y^2/(4x^4)$

26. $-x^8z^4/y^4$ **27.** $3x/(y^7z)$ **28.** $x^5/(2y^3)$

29. (a) 4   (b) 2/7   (c) 1.1

30. (a) $x^{1/2}$ (b) $x^{2/3}$ (c) $x^{-1/4}$

31. (a) $\sqrt[5]{x^3}$ (b) $1/\sqrt{x} = \sqrt{x}/x$ (c) $-x\sqrt{x}$

32. (a) $5y\sqrt{2x}/2$ (b) $\sqrt[3]{x^2y}/x^2$

33. $x^{5/6}$ **34.** y **35.** $x^{17/4}$

36. $x^{11/3}$ **37.** $x^{2/5}$ **38.** x^2y^8

39. $2xy^2\sqrt{3xy}$ **40.** $25x^3y^4\sqrt{2y}$

41. $6x^2y^4\sqrt[3]{5x^2y^2}$ **42.** $8a^2b^4\sqrt{2a}$

43. $2xy$ **44.** $4x\sqrt{3xy}/(3y^4)$

45. $-x - 2$ **46.** $-x^2 - x$

47. $4x^3 + xy + 4y - 4$ **48.** $24x^5y^5$

49. $3x^2 - 7x + 4$ **50.** $3x^2 + 5x - 2$

51. $4x^2 - 7x - 2$ **52.** $6x^2 - 11x - 7$

53. $4x^2 - 12x + 9$ **54.** $16x^2 - 9$

55. $2x^4 + 2x^3 - 5x^2 + x - 3$ **56.** $8x^3 - 12x^2 + 6x - 1$

57. $x^3 - y^3$ **58.** $(2/y) - (3xy/2) - 3x^2$

59. $3x^2 + 2x - 3 + (-3x + 7)/(x^2 + 1)$

60. $x^3 - x^2 + 2x + 7 + 21/(x - 3)$

61. $x^2 - x$ **62.** $2x - a$

63. $x^3(2x - 1)$

64. $2(x^2 + 1)^2(1 + x)(1 - x)$

65. $(2x - 1)^2$

66. $(4 + 3x)(4 - 3x)$

67. $2x^2(x + 2)(x - 2)$ **68.** $(x - 7)(x + 3)$

69. $(3x + 2)(x - 1)$ **70.** $(x - 3)(x - 2)$

71. $(x - 12)(x + 2)$ **72.** $(4x + 3)(3x - 8)$

73. $(2x + 3)^2(2x - 3)^2$ **74.** $x^{2/3} + 1$

75. (a) $\dfrac{x}{x + 2}$ (b) $\dfrac{2xy(2 - 3xy)}{2x - 3y}$

76. $\dfrac{x^2 - 4}{x(x + 4)}$ **77.** $\dfrac{x + 3}{x - 3}$

78. $\dfrac{x^2(3x - 2)}{(x - 1)(x + 2)}$ **79.** $(6x^2 + 9x - 1)/(6x^2)$

80. $\dfrac{4x - x^2}{4(x - 2)}$ **81.** $-\dfrac{x^2 + 2x + 2}{x(x - 1)^2}$

82. $\dfrac{x(x - 4)}{(x - 2)(x + 1)(x - 3)}$ **83.** $\dfrac{(x - 1)^3}{x^2}$

84. $\dfrac{1 - x}{1 + x}$ **85.** $3(\sqrt{x} + 1)$

86. $2/(\sqrt{x} + \sqrt{x - 4})$

87. (a)

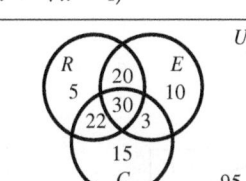

   R: recognized
   E: exercise
   C: community involvement

   (b) 10   (c) 100

88. 87.1 million   **89.** 16

90. (a) $4115.27   (b) $66,788.69

91. (a) 16   (b) $820.40   (c) $3281.60

92. (a) 1.1 inch, about quarter-sized
   (b) 104 mph

93. (a) $10,000\left[\dfrac{(0.0065)(1.0065)^n}{(1.0065)^n - 1}\right]$ (b) $243.19 (for both)

94. (a) $S = k\sqrt[3]{A}$ (b) $\sqrt[3]{2.25} \approx 1.31$

95. $26x - 300 - 0.001x^2$

96. $1,450,000 - 3625x$

97. $(50 + x)(12 - 0.5x)$

98. (a) $\dfrac{12,000p}{100 - p}$

(b) $0. It costs nothing if no effort is made to remove pollution.

(c) $588,000

(d) Undefined. Removing 100% would be impossible, and the cost of getting close would be enormous.

99. $\dfrac{56x^2 + 1200x + 8000}{x}$

CHAPTER 0 TEST

1. (a) $\{3, 4, 6, 8\}$ (b) $\{3, 4\}, \{3, 6\}$, or $\{4, 6\}$

(c) $\{6\}$ or $\{8\}$

2. 21

3. (a) 8   (b) 1   (c) $\frac{1}{2}$ (d) -10

(e) 30   (f) $\frac{5}{6}$ (g) $\frac{2}{3}$ (h) -3

4. (a) $\sqrt[5]{x}$ (b) $1/\sqrt[4]{x^3}$

5. (a) $1/x^5$ (b) x^{21}/y^6

6. (a) $\dfrac{\sqrt{5x}}{5}$ (b) $2a^2b^2\sqrt{6ab}$ (c) $\dfrac{1 - 2\sqrt{x} + x}{1 - x}$

7. (a) 5   (b) -8 (c) -5 (d) -7

8. $(-2, 3]$ (number line from -4 to 6)

9. (a) $2x^2(4x - 1)$ (b) $(x - 4)(x - 6)$

(c) $(3x - 2)(2x - 3)$ (d) $2x^3(1 + 4x)(1 - 4x)$

10. (c); -2

11. $2x + 1 + \dfrac{2x - 6}{x^2 - 1}$

12. (a) $19y - 45$ (b) $-6t^6 + 9t^9$

(c) $4x^3 - 21x^2 + 13x - 2$ (d) $-18x^2 + 15x - 2$

(e) $4m^2 - 28m + 49$ (f) $\dfrac{x^4}{3x + 9}$

(g) $\dfrac{x^7}{81}$ (h) $\dfrac{6 - x}{x - 8}$

(i) $\dfrac{x^2 - 4x - 3}{x(x - 3)(x + 1)}$

13. $\dfrac{y - x}{y + xy^2}$

14. (a)

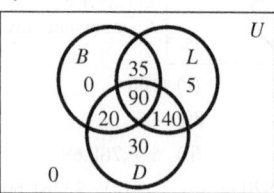

(b) 0

(c) 175

15. $4875.44 (nearest cent)

1.1 EXERCISES

1. $x = -9/4$ **3.** $x = 0$ **5.** $x = -32$

7. $x = 49/18$ **9.** $x = -29/2$ **11.** $x = -5$

13. $x = 17/13$ **15.** $x = -1/3$ **17.** $x = 3$

19. $x = 5/4$ **21.** no solution   **23.** $x \approx -0.279$

25. $x \approx -1147.362$ **27.** $y = \frac{3}{4}x - \frac{15}{4}$

29. $y = -6x + \frac{22}{3}$ **31.** $t = \dfrac{S - P}{Pr}$

33. $x < 2$ **35.** $x < -4$ **37.** $x \le -1$

39. $x < -3$ (number line from -6 to 0)

41. $x < -6$ (number line from -8 to 0)

43. $x < 2$ (number line from 0 to 4)

45. 145 months

47. $3356.50   **49.** 440 thumb drives

51. $29,600

53. (a) 69.0 million   (b) 2020

55. 96

57. $90,000 at 9%; $30,000 at 13%

59. $2160/month; 8% increase

61. $x > 80$ (number line from 0 to 80)

63. $695 + 5.75x \le 900$; 35 or fewer

65. (a) $t = 38$ (b) $t \approx 47.6$ (c) 2028

67. (a) $0.479 \le h \le 1; h = 1$ means 100% humidity

(b) $0 \le h \le 0.237$

1.2 EXERCISES

1. (a) To each x-value there corresponds exactly one y-value.

(b) domain: $\{-7, -1, 0, 3, 4.2, 9, 11, 14, 18, 22\}$

range: $\{0, 1, 5, 9, 11, 22, 35, 60\}$

(c) $f(0) = 1, f(11) = 35$

3. yes; to each x-value there corresponds exactly one y-value; domain $= \{1, 2, 3, 8, 9\}$, range $= \{-4, 5, 16\}$

5. (a) The vertical-line test shows that the graph represents a function of x.

(b) The vertical line test shows the graph is not a function of x.

7. (a) yes   (b) no

9. (a) -10 (b) 6   (c) -34 (d) 2.8

11. (a) -3 (b) 1   (c) 13   (d) 6

13. (a) -251 (b) -128 (c) 22   (d) -4.25

15. (a) $63/8$ (b) 6   (c) -6

17. (a) no, $f(2 + 1) = f(3) = 13$ but $f(2) + f(1) = 10$

(b) $1 + x + h + x^2 + 2xh + h^2$

(c) no, $f(x) + f(h) = 2 + x + h + x^2 + h^2$

(d) no, $f(x) + h = 1 + x + x^2 + h$

(e) $1 + 2x + h$

19. (a) $-2x^2 - 4xh - 2h^2 + x + h$

(b) $-4x - 2h + 1$

21. (a) 10   (b) 6

23. (a) $(1, -3)$, yes   (b) $(3, -3)$, yes

(c) $b = a^2 - 4a$ (d) $x = 0, x = 4$, yes

25. domain: all reals; range: reals $y \ge 4$

27. domain: reals $x \ge -4$; range: reals $y \ge 0$

29. $x \ge 1, x \ne 2$ **31.** $-7 \le x \le 7$

33. (a) $3x + x^3$ (b) $3x - x^3$ (c) $3x^4$ (d) $\dfrac{3}{x^2}$

35. (a) $\sqrt{2x} + x^2$ (b) $\sqrt{2x} - x^2$

    (c) $x^2\sqrt{2x}$ (d) $\dfrac{\sqrt{2x}}{x^2}$

37. (a) $-8x^3$ (b) $1 - 2(x - 1)^3$

    (c) $[(x - 1)^3 - 1]^3$ (d) $(x - 1)^6$

39. (a) $2\sqrt{x^4 + 5}$ (b) $16x^2 + 5$

    (c) $2\sqrt{2}\sqrt{x}$ (d) $4x$

41. (a) $f(20) = 199{,}000$ means that if $199{,}000 is borrowed, it can be repaid in 20 years (of $1600-per-month payments).

    (b) no; $f(5 + 5) = f(10) = 135{,}000$, but $f(5) + f(5) = 80{,}000 + 80{,}000 = 160{,}000$

    (c) 15 years; $f(15) = 173{,}000$

43. (a) $866; $1080

    (b) $1160; starting benefits at age 68 provides $1160 per month.

    (c) $250; starting benefits at age 66 gives $250 more per month than starting at age 62.

45. (a) $W(100) \approx 155$ million; $O(140) \approx 120$ million

    (b) 166.3; in 2020 there are expected to be 166.3 million White, non-Hispanics in the civilian non-institutional labor force (CN-ILF).

    (c) 42.6; in 1990 there were 42.6 million non-Whites or Hispanics in the CN-ILF.

    (d) 79.5; in 2020 there are expected to be 79.5 million more White non-Hispanics in the CN-ILF than others.

    (e) 312.4; in 2050 the total size of the CN-ILF is expected to be 312.4 million.

    (f) $(W - O)(100)$ is greater; the graphs are further apart at $t = 100$ than at $t = 140$.

47. (a) yes

    (b) all reals for F

    (c) domain: $32 < F < 212$

    range: $0 < C < 100$

    (d) $C = \left(\dfrac{40}{9}\right)^\circ$

49. (a) $C(10) = 4210

    (b) $C(100) = $32{,}200$

    (c) The total cost of producing 100 items is $32,200.

51. (a) $0 \le p < 100$

    (b) $5972.73; to remove 45% of the particulate pollution would cost $5972.73.

    (c) $65,700; to remove 90% of the particulate pollution would cost $65,700.

    (d) $722,700; to remove 99% of the particulate pollution would cost $722,700.

    (e) $1,817,700; to remove 99.6% of the particulate pollution would cost $1,817,700.

53. (a) $(P \circ q)(t) = 180(1000 + 10t)$
$$-\dfrac{(1000 + 10t)^2}{100} - 200$$

    (b) $x = 1150, P = $193{,}575$

55. (a) yes; the output of g (customers) is the input for f.

    (b) no; the output of f is revenue, and this is not the input for g.

    (c) $f \circ g$: input (independent variable) is advertising dollars. output (dependent variable) is revenue dollars.

    $f \circ g$ shows how advertising dollars result in revenue dollars.

57. $L = 2x + 3200/x$

59. $R = (30 + x)(100 - 2x)$

1.3 EXERCISES

1. x-intercept 4
y-intercept 3

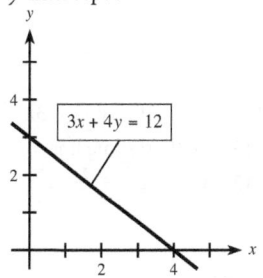

3. x-intercept 12
y-intercept -7.5

5. $m = 4$ **7.** $m = -1/2$ **9.** $m = 0$ **11.** 0

13. 0   **15.** (a) negative   (b) undefined

17. $m = 7/3, b = -1/4$ **19.** $m = 0, b = 3$

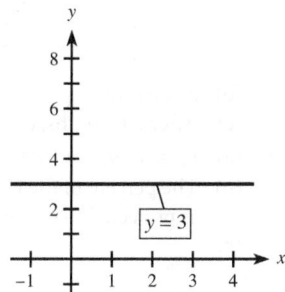

21. undefined slope, no y-intercept   **23.** $m = -2/3, b = 2$

25.

27.

29.

31.

33.

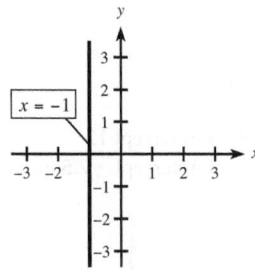

35. $y = 2x - 4$ **37.** $-x + 13y = 32$ **39.** $y = -3x - 12$

41. perpendicular   **43.** neither; same line

45. $y = -\frac{3}{5}x - \frac{41}{5}$ **47.** $y = -\frac{6}{5}x + \frac{23}{5}$

49. (a)

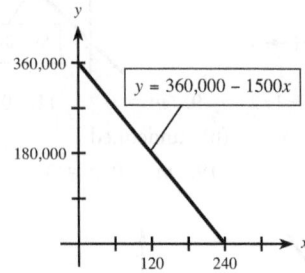

(b) 240 months

(c) After 60 months, the value of the building is $270,000.

51. (a) $m = 1.19; p = 58.0$

(b) The percent of the U.S. population that uses the Internet is projected to rise by 1.19 percentage points per year.

(c)

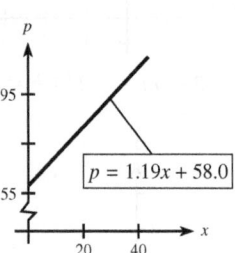

53. (a) $m = -0.650$ (b) 13 beats per minute

(c)

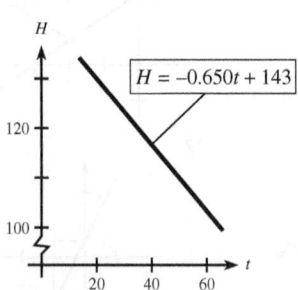

55. (a) $m = 0.150$

(b) This population is projected to increase by 0.150 million, or 150,000 per year.

(c) 40.4 million

57. $y = 0.0838x + 16.37$

59. (a) $y = 1.296x - 2465$

(b) The U.S. civilian workforce changes at the rate of 1.296 million workers per year.

61. (a) $y = 5.183x - 10,349.10$

(b) The CPI is changing at the rate of about $5.18/year.

63. $p = 85,000 - 1700x$ **65.** $R = 3.2t - 0.2$

67. $y = 0.48x - 71$

1.4 EXERCISES

1.

3.

5.

7.

9.

11. $y = (3x + 7)/(x^2 + 4)$

13. (a) $y = 0.01x^3 + 0.3x^2 - 72x + 150$

(b) standard window

15. (a) $y = \dfrac{x + 15}{x^2 + 400}$

(b) standard window

17. (a) x-intercept 30, y-intercept -0.03

(b)

19.

21.

23.

Linear

25.

Not linear

27.

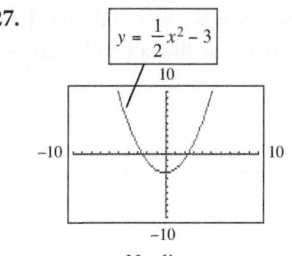

Not linear

29. $f(-2) = -18; f\left(\frac{3}{4}\right) = 0.734375$

31.

33.

35. $x = 3.5$

37. either $x = 5$ or $x = -2$

39. (a) $-1.1098, 8.1098$ (b) $-1.1098, 8.1098$

41. (a)

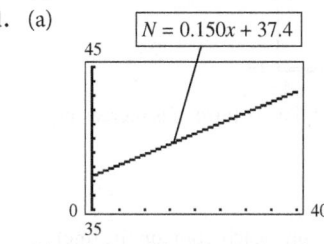

(b) The model projects that the number of U.S. females under the age of 18 will be 40.4 million in 2040.

(c) 38.9 million

43. (a)

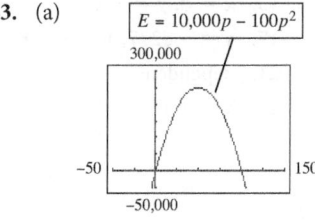

(b) $E \geq 0$ when $0 \leq p \leq 100$

45. (a)

(b) decreasing; as more people become aware of the product, there are fewer to learn about it, so the rate will decrease.

47. (a) x-min $= 0, x$-max $= 130$

(b) y-max $= 65$

(c)
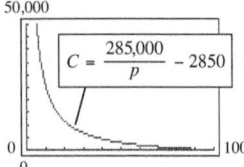

$P = 0.000078x^3 - 0.0107x^2 - 0.182x + 64.68$

(d) The percent decreases from 57.4% in 1920 to 17.5% in 2000, and then it increases to 31.6% in 2030.

49. (a)
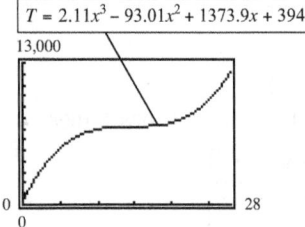

$C = \dfrac{285{,}000}{p} - 2850$

(b) Near $p = 0$, cost grows without bound.

(c) The coordinates of the point mean that obtaining stream water with 1% of the current pollution levels would cost $282,150.

(d) The p-intercept means that stream water with 100% of the current pollution levels would cost $0.

51. (a)

$T = 2.11x^3 - 93.01x^2 + 1373.9x + 394$

13,000

0 ⌐   ⌐ 28
0

(b) increasing; the per capita tax burden is increasing

1.5 EXERCISES

1. (a) one solution; $(-1, -2)$

(b) infinitely many solutions (each point on the line)

3. $x = 2, y = 2$ **5.** no solution

7. $x = 10/3, y = 2$ **9.** $x = 14/11, y = 6/11$

11. $x = 4, y = -1$ **13.** $x = 3, y = -2$

15. $x = 2, y = 1$ **17.** $x = -52/7, y = -128/7$

19. $x = 1, y = 1$ **21.** dependent

23. $x = 4, y = 2$ **25.** $x = -1, y = 1$

27. $x = -17, y = 7, z = 5$

29. $x = 4, y = 12, z = -1$

31. $x = 44, y = -9, z = -1/2$

33. (a) $C = 10, F = 50$

(b) The tourist formula overestimates the F temperature—it adds 2°F to the estimate for each 1°C, but actual change is 1.8°C.

35. (a) $x + y = 1800$ (b) $20x$ (c) $30y$

(d) $20x + 30y = 42{,}000$

(e) 1200 tickets at $20; 600 tickets at $30

37. $68,000 at 18%; $77,600 at 10%

39. 116 of product 1; 380 of product 2

41. 4 oz of A, $6\frac{2}{3}$ oz of B

43. 4550 of species A, 1500 of species B

45. 7 cc of 20%; 3 cc of 5%

47. 10,000 at $40; 6000 at $60

49. 80 cc   **51.** 5 oz of A, 1 oz of B, 5 oz of C

53. 200 type A, 100 type B, 200 type C

1.6 EXERCISES

1. (a) $P(x) = 34x - 6800$ (b) $95,200

3. (a) $P(x) = 37x - 1850$

(b) -740, loss of $740   (c) 50

5. (a) $m = 5, C = 250$

(b) $\overline{MC} = 5$ means that each additional unit produced costs $5.

(c) Fixed costs $= 250

(d) slope $=$ marginal cost; C-intercept $=$ fixed costs

(e) 5, 5

7. (a) 27

(b) $\overline{MR} = 27$ means that each additional unit sold brings in $27.

(c) 27, 27

9. (a) $P(x) = 22x - 250$ (b) 22   (c) $\overline{MP} = 22$

(d) Each unit sold adds $22 to profits at all levels of production, so sell as many units as possible.

11. $P = 58x - 8500, \overline{MP} = 58$

13. (a) $C(x) = 35x + 6600$ (b) $R(x) = 60x$

(c) $P(x) = 25x - 6600$

(d) $C(200) = 13{,}600$ dollars is the cost of producing 200 helmets.

$R(200) = 12{,}000$ dollars is the revenue from selling 200 helmets.

$P(200) = -1600$ dollars; will lose $1600 from production and sale of 200 helmets.

(e) $C(300) = 17{,}100$ dollars is the cost of producing 300 helmets.

$R(300) = 18{,}000$ dollars is the revenue from selling 300 helmets.

$P(300) = 900$ dollars; will profit $900 from production and sale of 300 helmets.

(f) $\overline{MP} = 25$ dollars per unit; each additional unit produced and sold increases profit by $25.

15. (a) Revenue passes through the origin.

(b) $2000   (c) 400 units

(d) $\overline{MC} = 2.5$; $\overline{MR} = 7.5$

17. 33

19. (a) $R(x) = 12x; C(x) = 8x + 1600$

(b) 400 units

21. (a) $P(x) = 4x - 1600$

(b) $x = 400$ units to break even

23. (a) $C(x) = 4.5x + 1045$

(b) $R(x) = 10x$

(c) $P(x) = 5.5x - 1045$

(d) 190 surge protectors

25. (a) $R(x) = 54.90x$ (b) $C(x) = 14.90x + 20{,}200$

(c) 505

27. (a) *R* starts at origin and is the steeper line.
 FC is a horizontal line.
 VC starts at origin and is not as steep as *R*. (See figure.)

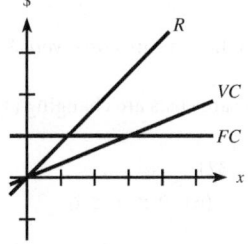

(b) *C* starts where *FC* meets the $-axis and is parallel to *VC*.
 Where *C* meets *R* is the break-even point (*BE*). *P* starts
 on the $-axis at the negative of *FC* and crosses the *x*-axis
 at *BE*. (See figure.)

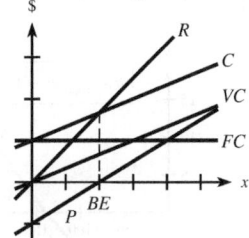

29. Demand decreases.

31. (a) 600   (b) 300   (c) shortage

33. 16 demanded, 25 supplied; surplus

35. $p = -2q/3 + 1060$

37. $p = 0.001q + 5$

39. (a) demand falls; supply rises   (b) (30, $25)

41. (a) $q = 20$ (b) $q = 40$
 (c) shortage, 20 units short

43. shortage   **45.** $q = 20, p = \$18$

47. $q = 10, p = \$180$ **49.** $q = 100, p = \$325$

51. (a) $15   (b) $q = 100, p = \$100$
 (c) $q = 50, p = \$110$ (d) yes

53. $q = 8; p = \$188$

55. $q = 500; p = \$40$

57. $q = 1200; p = \$15$

CHAPTER 1 REVIEW EXERCISES

1. $x = \frac{31}{3}$ **2.** $x = -13$ **3.** $x = -\frac{29}{8}$

4. $x = -\frac{1}{9}$ **5.** $x = 8$

6. no solution   **7.** $y = -\frac{2}{3}x - \frac{4}{3}$

8. $x \le 3$

9. $x \ge -20/3$

10. $x \ge -15/13$

11. yes   **12.** no   **13.** yes

14. domain: reals $x \le 9$; range: reals $y \ge 0$

15. (a) 2   (b) 37   (c) 29/4

16. (a) 0   (b) 9/4   (c) 10.01

17. $9 - 2x - h$ **18.** yes   **19.** no

20. 4   **21.** $x = 0, x = 4$

22. (a) domain: $\{-2, -1, 0, 1, 3, 4\}$
 range: $\{-3, 2, 4, 7, 8\}$
 (b) 7   (c) $x = -1, x = 3$
 (d)

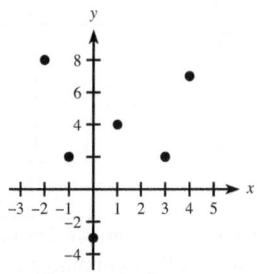

(e) no; for $y = 2$, there are two different *x*-values, -1 and 3.

23. (a) $x^2 + 3x + 5$ (b) $(3x + 5)/x^2$
 (c) $3x^2 + 5$ (d) $9x + 20$

24. $x = 2, y = 5$ **25.** $x = 3/2, y = 9/5$

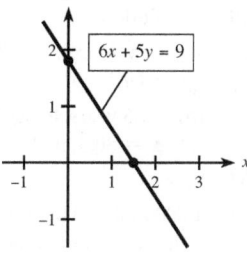

26. $x = -2, y$: none

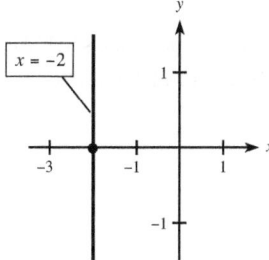

27. $m = 1$ **28.** undefined   **29.** $m = -\frac{2}{5}, b = 2$

30. $m = -\frac{4}{3}, b = 2$ **31.** $y = 4x + 2$ **32.** $y = -\frac{1}{2}x + 3$

33. $y = \frac{2}{5}x + \frac{9}{5}$ **34.** $y = -\frac{11}{8}x + \frac{17}{4}$ **35.** $x = -1$

36. $y = 4x + 2$ **37.** $y = \frac{4}{3}x + \frac{10}{3}$ **38.** $y = \frac{1}{3}x - 2$

39.

40.

41. (a)

(b) Standard window view

(c)   The graph in (a) shows a complete graph. The graph in (b) shows a piece that rises toward the high point and a piece between the high and low points.

42. (a)   (b)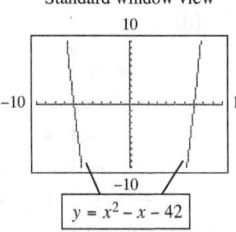

(c)   The graph in (a) shows a complete graph. The one in (b) shows pieces that fall toward the minimum point and rise from it.

43.   reals $x \geq -3$ with $x \neq 0$

44. $0.2857 \approx 2/7$

45. $x = 2, y = 1$

46. $x = 10, y = -1$

47. $x = 3, y = -2$

48.   no solution

49. $x = 10, y = -71$

50. $x = 1, y = -1, z = 2$

51. $x = 11, y = 10, z = 9$

52. (a)   2020
(b)   21.5 years, to age 86.5
(c) $x = 80.5$; in 2031

53.   95%

54.   40,000 miles. He probably would drive more than 40,000 miles in 7 years, so he should buy a diesel.

55. (a)   yes   (b)   no   (c)   4

56. (a) $989.49   (b)   180
(c)   The monthly payment on a $160,000 loan is $1130.85.

57. (a) $(P \circ q)(t) = 330(100 + 10t) - 0.05(100 + 10t)^2 - 5000$
(b) $x = 250, P = \$74{,}375$

58. $(W \circ L)(t) = 0.03[65 - 0.1(t - 25)^2]^3$

59. (a)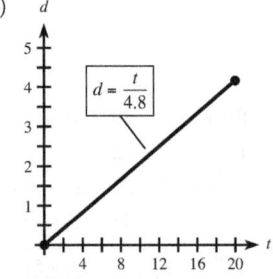

(b)   When the time between seeing lightning and hearing thunder is 9.6 seconds, the storm is 2 miles away.

60.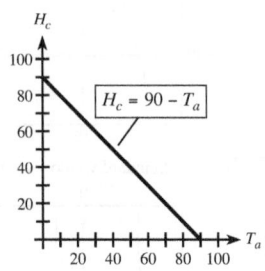

61. (a) $P = 58x - 8500$
(b)   The profit increases by $58 for each unit sold.

62. (a)   yes
(b) $m = 476, b = 5830$
(c)   In 2005, average annual health care costs were $5830 per consumer.
(d)   Average annual health care costs are changing at the rate of $476 per year.

63. $F = \frac{9}{5}C + 32$ or $C = \frac{5}{9}(F - 32)$

64. (a)   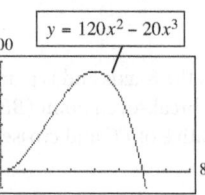   (b) $0 \leq x \leq 6$

65. (a) $v^2 = 1960(h + 10)$
$\dfrac{v^2}{1960} = h + 10$
$h = \dfrac{1}{1960}v^2 - 10$
(b)   12.5 cm

66. $400,000 at 9.5%; $200,000 at 11%

67.   2.8 liters of 20%; 1.2 liters of 70%

68. (a)   12 supplied; 14 demanded   (b)   shortfall
(c)   increase

69.

70. (a)   38.80   (b)   61.30   (c)   22.50   (d)   200

71. (a) $C(x) = 22x + 1500$ (b) $R(x) = 52x$
(c) $P(x) = 30x - 1500$ (d) $\overline{MC} = 22$
(e) $\overline{MR} = 52$ (f) $\overline{MP} = 30$ (g) $x = 50$

72. (a)   S: $p = 4q - 400$
D: $p = -4q + 1520$
(b) $q = 240; p = \$560$

73. $q = 700, p = \$80$

CHAPTER 1 TEST

1. $x = -6$

2. $x = 18/7$

3. $x = -3/7$

4. $x = -38$

5. $5 - 4x - 2h$

6. $x \geq -9$

7. $x = 6; y = -5$ **8.** $x = 3; y = 21/5$

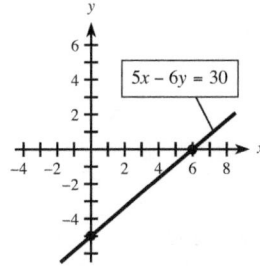

9. (a) domain: $x \geq -4$

range: $f(x) \geq 0$

(b) $2\sqrt{7}$ (c) 6

10. $y = -\frac{3}{2}x + \frac{1}{2}$ **11.** $m = -\frac{5}{4}; b = \frac{15}{4}$

12. (a) $x = -3$ (b) $y = -4x - 13$

13. (a) no; a vertical line intersects the curve twice.

(b) yes; there is exactly one y-value for each x-value.

(c) no; one value of x gives two y-values.

14. (a)

(b)

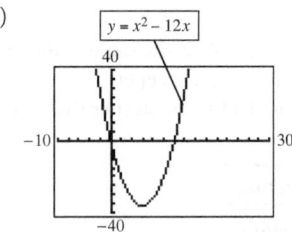

15. $x = -2, y = 2$

16. (a) $5x^3 + 2x^2 - 3x$ (b) $x + 2$

(c) $5x^2 + 7x + 2$

17. (a)

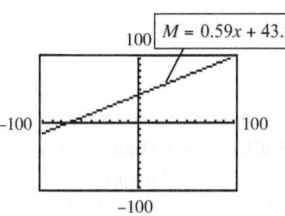

(b) The model predicts that there will be 90.4 million men in the U.S. workforce in 2030.

(c) 102.2 million

18. (a) 30   (b) $P = 8x - 1200$ (c) 150

(d) $\overline{MP} = 8$; the sale of each additional unit gives $8 more profit.

19. (a) $R = 50x$

(b) 19,000; it costs $19,000 to produce 100 units.   (c) 450

20. $q = 200, p = \$2500$

21. (a) 720,000; original value of the building

(b) -2000; building depreciates $2000 per month.

22. 400   **23.** $12,000 at 9%; $8000 at 6%

2.1 EXERCISES

1. $x^2 + 2x - 1 = 0$ **3.** $y^2 + 3y - 2 = 0$

5. $-2, 6$ **7.** $\frac{3}{2}, -\frac{3}{2}$ **9.** $0, 1$ **11.** $\frac{1}{2}$ **13.** $5/6, 1$

15. (a) $2 + 2\sqrt{2}, 2 - 2\sqrt{2}$ (b) $4.83, -0.83$

17. no real solutions

19. $-1 + 2\sqrt{2} \approx 1.828; -1 - 2\sqrt{2} \approx -3.828$

21. $\sqrt{7}, -\sqrt{7}$ **23.** $4, -4$ **25.** $1, -9$ **27.** $-7, 3$

29. $8, -4$ **31.** $-\frac{7}{4}, \frac{3}{4}$ **23.** $-6, 2$

35. $(1 + \sqrt{31})/5, (1 - \sqrt{31})/5$ **37.** $-2, 5$

39. $-300, 100$ **41.** $0.69, -0.06$ **43.** $8, 1$ **45.** $1/2$

47. $-9, -10$ **49.** $x = 20$ or $x = 70$

51. (a) $x = 10$ or $x = 345\frac{5}{9}$

(b) yes; for any $x > 10$ and $x < 345\frac{5}{9}$

53. 6 seconds

55. (a) ± 50

(b) $s = 50$; there is no particulate pollution in the air above the plant.

57. 97.0 mph   **59.** $t \approx 16.2$; in 2017   **61.** $80

63. $x \approx 30$; in 2030

65. (a) 18   (b) ≈ 31

(c) Speed triples, but K changes only by a factor of 1.72.

2.2 EXERCISES

1. (a) $(-1, -\frac{1}{2})$ (b) minimum

(c) -1 (d) $-\frac{1}{2}$

3. (a) $(1, 9)$ (b) maximum   (c) 1   (d) 9

5. (a) $(3, 9)$ (b) maximum   (c) 3   (d) 9

7. maximum, $(2, 1)$; zeros $(0, 0)$, $(4, 0)$;

y-intercept $= 0$

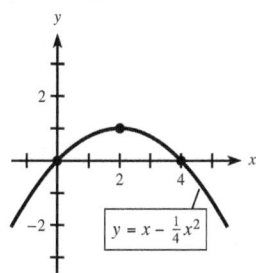

9. minimum, $(-2, 0)$; zero $(-2, 0)$;

y-intercept $= 4$

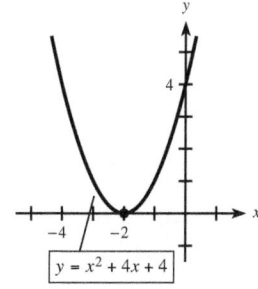

11. minimum, $(-1, -3\frac{1}{2})$; zeros $(-1 + \sqrt{7}, 0)$, $(-1 - \sqrt{7}, 0)$; y-intercept $= -3$

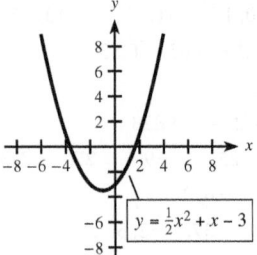

$y = \frac{1}{2}x^2 + x - 3$

13. (a) 3 units to the right and 1 unit up
(b)

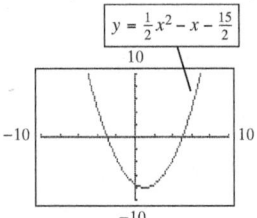

$y = (x - 3)^2 + 1$

15. (a) 2 units to the left and 2 units down
(b)

$y = (x + 2)^2 - 2$

17. vertex $(1, -8)$; zeros $(-3, 0), (5, 0)$

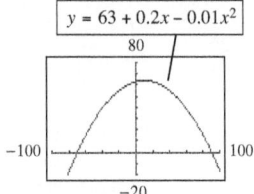

$y = \frac{1}{2}x^2 - x - \frac{15}{2}$

19. vertex $(-6, 3)$;
no real zeros

$y = \frac{1}{4}x^2 + 3x + 12$

21. -5

23. vertex $(10, 64)$; zeros $(90, 0), (-70, 0)$

$y = 63 + 0.2x - 0.01x^2$

25. vertex $(0, -0.01)$; zeros $(10, 0), (-10, 0)$

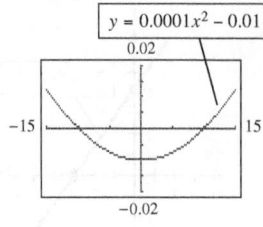

$y = 0.0001x^2 - 0.01$

27. (a) $(1, -24)$ (b) $x \approx -0.732, 2.732$

29. (a) $x = 2$ (b) $x - 2$
(c) $(x - 2)(3x - 2)$ (d) $x = 2, \frac{2}{3}$

31. (a) 800 units (b) $5500

33. 400 trees

35. dosage $= 500$ mg

37. intensity $= 1.5$ lumens

$S = 1000x - x^2$

$R = 270x - 90x^2$

39. equation (a) $(384.62, 202.31)$ (b) $(54, 46)$
Projectile (a) goes higher.

41. (a) From b to c. The average rate is the same as the slope of the segment. Segment b to c is steeper.
(b) $d > b$ to make segment a to d be steeper (have greater slope).

43. (a)

Rent	Revenue
$1800	$90,000
$1860	$91,140
$1920	$92,160

(b) increases
(c) $R = (50 - x)(1800 + 60x)$
(d) $2400

45. (a) quadratic
(b) $a < 0$ because the graph opens downward.
(c) The vertex occurs after 2004 (when $x > 0$). Hence, $-b/2a > 0$ and $a < 0$ means that $b > 0$. The value $c = f(0)$, or the y-value in 2004. Hence, $c > 0$.

47. 2010–2015: $399/year
2015–2020: $605/year

49.

$y = 1.230x^2 - 22.87x + 142.9$

2.3 EXERCISES

1. $x = 40$ units, $x = 50$ units
3. $x = 50$ units, $x = 300$ units
5. $x = 15$ units; reject $x = 100$
7. $43,560 (220 units)   9. $87.50
11. $x = 55$, $P(55) = \$2025$
13. (a)

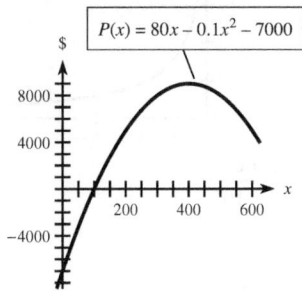

$P(x) = 80x - 0.1x^2 - 7000$

(b) (400, 9000); maximum point   (c) positive
(d) negative   (e) closer to 0 as a gets closer to 400
15. (a) $P(x) = -x^2 + 350x - 15{,}000$; maximum profit is $15,625
(b) no   (c) x-values agree
17. (a) $x = 28$ units, $x = 1000$ units
(b) $651,041.67
(c) $P(x) = -x^2 + 1028x - 28{,}000$; maximum profit is $236,196
(d) $941.60
19. (a) $t \approx 5.1$ in 2016; $R \approx \$60.79$ billion
(b) The data show a smaller revenue, $R = \$60.27$ billion in 2015.
(c)

$R(t) = 0.271t^2 - 2.76t + 67.83$

(d) The model fits the data quite well.
21. (a) $P(t) = -0.019t^2 + 0.284t - 0.546$
(b) 2015
(c)

$P(t) = -0.019t^2 + 0.284t - 0.546$

(d) The model projects decreasing profits, and except for 2019, the data support this.
23. (a)

(b) See E on graph. (c) $q = 4$, $p = \$14$

25. $q = 10$, $p = \$196$
27. $q = 216\frac{2}{3}$, $p = \$27.08$
29. $p = \$40$, $q = 30$
31. $q = 90$, $p = \$50$
33. $q = 70$, $p = \$62$

2.4 EXERCISES

1. b   3. f   5. j   7. k   9. a
11. c   13. (a) cubic   (b) quartic   15. e
17. b   19. d   21. g
23.

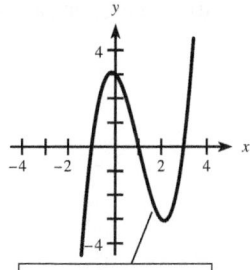

$y = (x + 1)(x - 3)(x - 1)$

25.

$y = \dfrac{1 - 2x}{x}$

27.

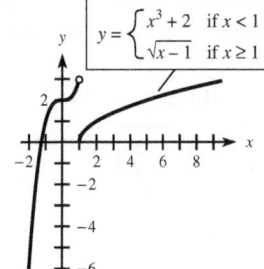

$y = \begin{cases} x^3 + 2 & \text{if } x < 1 \\ \sqrt{x - 1} & \text{if } x \geq 1 \end{cases}$

29. (a) $8/3$ (b) 9.9   (c) -999.999 (d) no
31. (a) 64   (b) 1   (c) 1000   (d) 0.027
33. (a) 2   (b) 4   (c) 0   (d) 2
35. (a)

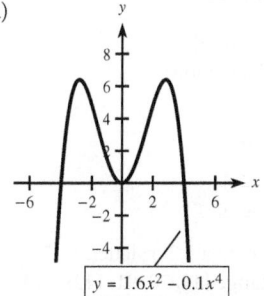

$y = 1.6x^2 - 0.1x^4$

(b) polynomial   (c) no asymptotes
(d) turning points at $x = 0$ and approximately $x = -2.8$ and $x = 2.8$

37. (a)

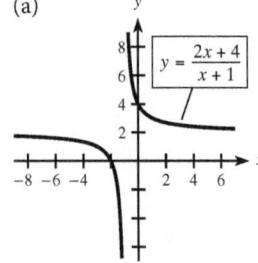

(b) rational
(c) vertical: $x = -1$, horizontal: $y = 2$
(d) no turning points

39. (a)

$$f(x) = \begin{cases} -x & \text{if } x < 0 \\ 5x & \text{if } x \geq 0 \end{cases}$$

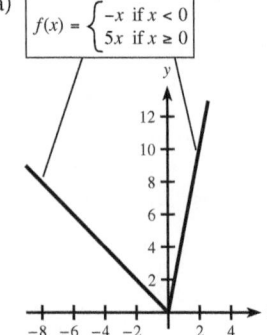

(b) piecewise defined
(c) no asymptotes
(d) turning point at $x = 0$

41. (a) 6800; 11,200   (b) $0 < x < 27$

43. (a) downward   (b)

$y = 200.8x^{0.30}$

(c) 2024

45. (a) yes; $p = 100$ (b) $p \neq 100$ (c) $0 \leq p < 100$
(d) It increases without bound.

47. (a) $A(2) = 96$; $A(30) = 600$ (b) $0 < x < 50$

49. (a)

$$y = \begin{cases} 5.59x^2 - 93.5x + 633 & \text{if } 0 \leq x \leq 55 \\ 6.56x^2 - 519x + 20{,}900 & \text{if } 55 < x \leq 90 \end{cases}$$

(b) \$9933 billion (\$9.933 trillion)
(c) \$18,875 billion (\$18.875 trillion)

51. (a) $P = \begin{cases} 49 & \text{if } 0 < x \leq 1 \\ 70 & \text{if } 1 < x \leq 2 \\ 91 & \text{if } 2 < x \leq 3 \\ 112 & \text{if } 3 < x \leq 4 \end{cases}$

(b) 70; it costs 70 cents to mail a 1.2 oz letter.
(c) Domain $0 < x \leq 4$; Range $\{49, 70, 91, 112\}$
(d) 70 cents and 91 cents

53. (a) $p = \dfrac{200}{2 + 0.1x}$

(b) yes, when $p = \$100$

55. $C(x) = 30(x - 1) + \dfrac{3000}{x + 10}$

(a)

(b) Any turning point would indicate the minimum or the maximum cost. In this case, $x = 0$ gives a minimum.
(c) The y-intercept is the fixed cost of production.

2.5 EXERCISES

1. linear   **3.** quadratic   **5.** quartic

7. quadratic or power

9. $y = 2x - 3$

11. $y = 2x^2 - 1.5x - 4$

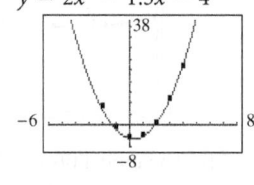

13. $y = x^3 - x^2 - 3x - 4$

15. $y = 2x^{0.5}$

17. (a)

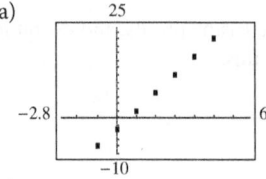

(b) linear
(c) $y = 5x - 3$

19. (a)

(b) quadratic
(c) $y = 0.09595x^2 + 0.4656x + 1.4758$

21. (a)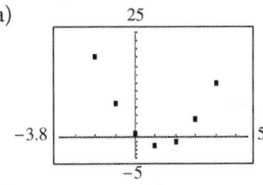

(b) quadratic

(c) $y = 2x^2 - 5x + 1$

23. (a)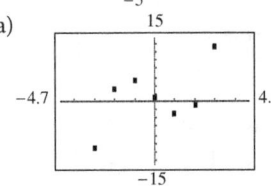

(b) cubic

(c) $y = x^3 - 5x + 1$

25. (a) $y = 154.0x + 35,860$ (b) 40,018,000 (c) 2070

27. (a) A linear function is best; $y = 327.6x + 9591$

(b) $15,160 billion

(c) $m = 327.6$ means that the U.S. disposable income is increasing at the rate of about $327.6 billion per year.

29. (a) $y = 0.0052x^2 - 0.62x + 15$ (b) $x \approx 59.6$

(c) No, the model implies you would feel warmer for winds greater than 60mph. This is impossible.

31. (a)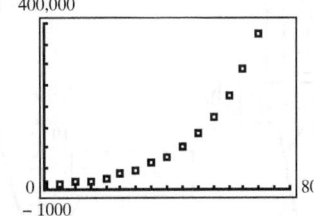

(b) $y = 106x^2 - 2870x + 28,500$

(c) $y = 1.70x^3 - 72.9x^2 + 1970x + 5270$

(d)

Cubic model fits better

33. (a) $y = 0.0157x + 2.01$

(b) $y = -0.00105x^2 + 0.0367x + 1.94$

(c)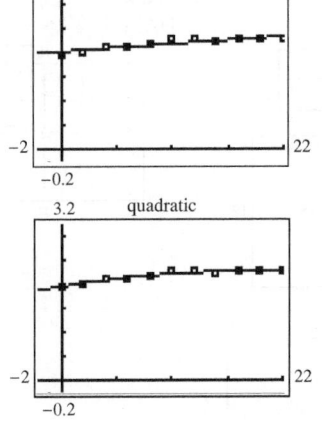

(d) The quadratic model is a slightly better fit.

35. (a) A cubic models fits best because of the two bends.

(b) $y = 0.864x^3 - 128x^2 + 6610x - 62,600$

(c)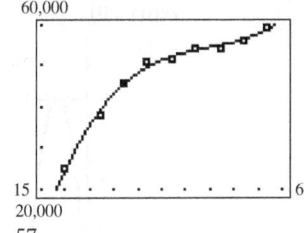

(d) 57

37. (a) $y = 0.0514x^{2.73}$

(b)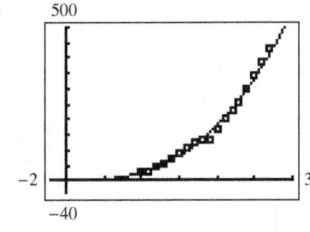

(c) $546 billion

CHAPTER 2 REVIEW EXERCISES

1. $x = 0, x = -\frac{5}{3}$ **2.** $x = 0, x = \frac{4}{3}$

3. $x = -2, x = -3$

4. $x = (-5 + \sqrt{47})/2, x = (-5 - \sqrt{47})/2$

5. no real solutions   **6.** $x = \sqrt{3}/2, x = -\sqrt{3}/2$

7. $\frac{5}{7}, -\frac{4}{5}$ **8.** $(-1 + \sqrt{2})/4, (-1 - \sqrt{2})/4$

9. $7/2, 100$ **10.** $13/5, 90$

11. no real solutions   **12.** $z = -9, z = 3$

13. $x = 8, x = -2$ **14.** $x = 3, x = -1$

15. $x = (-a \pm \sqrt{a^2 - 4b})/2$

16. $r = (2a \pm \sqrt{4a^2 + x^3c})/x$

17. $1.64, -7051.64$ **18.** $0.41, -2.38$

19. vertex $(-2, -2)$;   **20.** vertex $(0, 4)$;
y-intercept: 0;   y-intercept: 4;
zeros $(0, 0), (-4, 0)$ zeros $(4, 0), (-4, 0)$

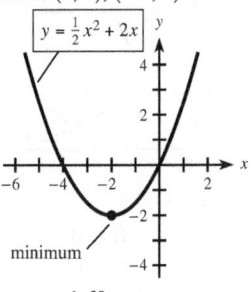

21. vertex $(\frac{1}{2}, \frac{25}{4})$;   **22.** vertex $(2, 1)$;
y-intercept: 6;   y-intercept: 5;
zeros $(-2, 0), (3, 0)$ no real zeros

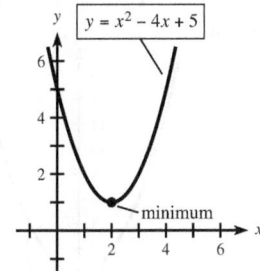

23. vertex $(-3, 0)$;
y-intercept: 9;
zero $(-3, 0)$

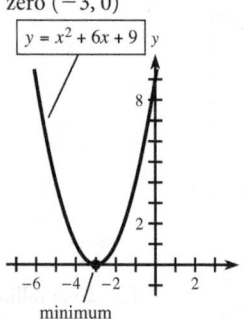

24. vertex $(\frac{3}{2}, 0)$;
y-intercept: -9;
zero $(\frac{3}{2}, 0)$

25. vertex $(0, -3)$;
zeros $(-3, 0), (3, 0)$

26. vertex $(0, 2)$;
no real zeros

27. vertex $(-1, 4)$;
no real zeros

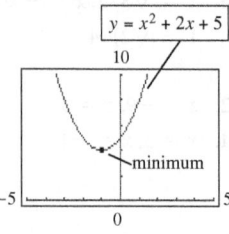

28. vertex $(\frac{7}{2}, \frac{9}{4})$;
zeros $(2, 0), (5, 0)$

29. vertex $(100, 1000)$;
zeros $(0, 0), (200, 0)$

30. vertex $(75, -6.25)$;
zeros $(50, 0), (100, 0)$

31. 20   **32.** 30

33. (a) $(1, -4\frac{1}{2})$ (b) $x = -2, x = 4$ (c) B

34. (a) $(0, 49)$ (b) $x = -7, x = 7$ (c) D

35. (a) $(7, 25)$ approximately, actual is $(7, 24\frac{1}{2})$
(b) $x = 0, x = 14$ (c) A

36. (a) $(-1, 9)$ (b) $x = -4, x = 2$ (c) C

37. (a)

(b)

(c)

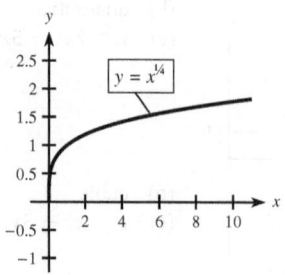

38. (a) 0   (b) 10,000   (c) -25 (d) 0.1

39. (a) -2 (b) 0   (c) 1   (d) 4

40.

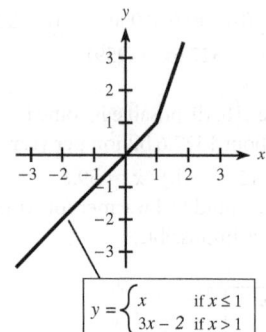

$$y = \begin{cases} x & \text{if } x \le 1 \\ 3x - 2 & \text{if } x > 1 \end{cases}$$

41. (a)

(b)

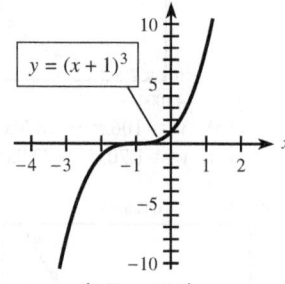

42. turns: $(1, -5), (-3, 27)$

43. turns: $(1.7, -10.4)$,
$(-1.7, 10.4)$

44. VA: $x = 2$;
HA: $y = 0$

45. VA: $x = -3$;
HA: $y = 2$

46. (a)

(b) $y = -2.1786x + 159.8571$

(c) $y = -0.0818x^2 - 0.2143x + 153.3095$

47. (a)

(b) $y = 3.13x + 140$

(c) quadratic: $y = -0.479x^2 + 18.6x + 58.4$

48. (a) $t = -1.65, t = 3.65$ (b) Only $t = 3.65$

(c) at 3.65 seconds

49. $x = 20, x = 800$

50. (a) $t \approx 7.69$, in 2018; $E \approx 12.3$ million

(b) $t \approx 20.2$, in 2031

51. (a) $x = 200$

(b) $A = 30,000$ square feet

52.

53.

54. (a)

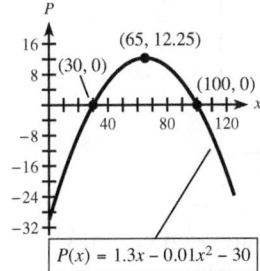

(b) $p = 41, q = 20$

55. $p = 400, q = 10$ **56.** $p = 10, q = 20$

57. $x = 46 + 2\sqrt{89} \approx 64.9, x = 46 - 2\sqrt{89} \approx 27.1$

58. $x = 15, x = 60$

59. max revenue $= \$2500$; max profit $= \$506.25$

60. max profit $= \$12.25$; break-even at $x = 100, x = 30$

61. $x = 50, P(50) = \$640$

62. (a) $C = 15,000 + 140x + 0.04x^2$;
   $R = 300x - 0.06x^2$

(b) $100, 1500$ (c) 2500

(d) $P = 160x - 15,000 - 0.1x^2$; max at 800

(e) at 2500: $P = -\$240,000$; at 800: $P = \$49,000$

63. (a) power   (b) 21.8%

(c) 24.4; in 2025, about 24.4% of U.S. adults are expected to have diabetes.

64. (a)

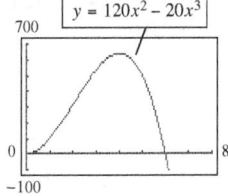

(b) $0 \le x \le 6$

65. (a) rational   (b) $0 \le p < 100$

(c) 0; it costs \$0 to remove no pollution.

(d) $\$475,200$

66. (a) $x = 12; C(12) = \$122.76$

(b) $x = 825; C(825) = \$6939.00$

67. (a) linear, quadratic, cubic, power

(b) and (c)

(d) 55 mph (e) 9.9 seconds

68. (a)

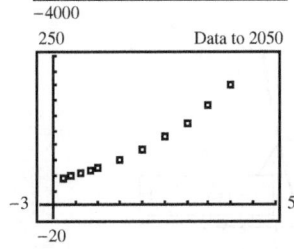

(b) quadratic: $a(x) = 47.70x^2 + 1802x + 40,870$;
   $A(x) = 0.07294x^2 + 0.9815x + 44.45$

(c) 2020 data: \$63,676; $a(10) \approx \$63,664$–closer;
   $A(10) \approx 61.564$ (\$61,564)
   2050 data: 202.5 (\$202,500); $a(40) \approx \$189,292$;
   $A(40) \approx 200.413$ (\$200,413–closer)

(d) $a = 150,000$ when $x \approx 32.5$, in 2043; $A = 150$ thousand when $x \approx 31.9$, in 2042

69. (a) $y = O(x) = 0.743x + 6.97$

(b) $y = S(x) = 0.264x - 2.57$

(c) $F(x) = \dfrac{0.264x - 2.57}{0.743x + 6.97}$. This is called a rational function,

and it measures the fraction of obese adults who are severely obese.

(d) Horizontal asymptote: $y \approx 0.355$ means that if this model remains valid far into the future, then the long-term projection is that about 0.355, or 35.5%, of obese adults will be severely obese.

70. (a) quadratic: $W(x) = -0.00903x^2 + 1.28x + 124$
$O(x) = 0.00645x^2 + 1.02x + 20.0$

(b) $x \approx 91.1$, in 2162

CHAPTER 2 TEST

1. (a)

(b)

(c)

(d)

2. b; a

3.

4. (a)

(b)

5. b; the function is cubic, $f(1) < 0$

6. (a) -10 (b) $-16\frac{1}{2}$ (c) -7

7.

 $g(x) = \begin{cases} x^2 \text{ if } x \le 1 \\ 4 - x \text{ if } x > 1 \end{cases}$

8. y-intercept 21;
vertex $(-2, 25)$;
zeros $-7, 3$

9. $x = 2, x = 1/3$

10. $x = \dfrac{-3 + 3\sqrt{3}}{2}, x = \dfrac{-3 - 3\sqrt{3}}{2}$

11. $x = 2/3$

12. c; $g(x)$ has a vertical asymptote at $x = -2$, as does graph c.

13. HA: $y = 0$; VA: $x = 5$

14. 42

15. (a) quartic   (b) cubic

16. (a)

model:
$y = -0.3577x + 19.9227$
(b) $f(x) = 5.6$
(c) at $x = 55.7$

17. $q = 300, p = \$80$

18. (a) $P(x) = -x^2 + 250x - 15{,}000$

(b) 125 units, \$625   (c) 100 units, 150 units

19. (a) $f(15) = -19.5$ means that when the air temperature is 0°F and the wind speed is 15 mph, the air temperature feels like -19.5°F.

(b) -31.4°F

20. (a)

(b) linear: $y = 13.3x + 182$;
cubic: $y = 0.0463x^3 - 1.40x^2 + 21.9x + 185$
(c) linear: 502, cubic 545; cubic is better.

3.1 EXERCISES

1. 3   **3.** A, F, Z   **5.** $\begin{bmatrix} -1 & -2 & -3 \\ 1 & 0 & -1 \\ -2 & 3 & 4 \end{bmatrix}$

7. A, C, D, F, G, Z

9. 1   **11.** $\begin{bmatrix} 1 & 3 & 4 \\ 0 & 2 & 0 \\ -2 & 1 & 3 \end{bmatrix}$ **13.** $\begin{bmatrix} 0 & 0 & 0 \\ 0 & 0 & 0 \\ 0 & 0 & 0 \end{bmatrix}$

15. $\begin{bmatrix} 9 & 5 \\ 4 & 7 \end{bmatrix}$ **17.** $\begin{bmatrix} 0 & -2 & -5 \\ 4 & 2 & 0 \\ 2 & 3 & 7 \end{bmatrix}$ **19.** $\begin{bmatrix} 2 & 3 & 2 \\ 3 & 4 & 1 \\ 2 & 1 & 6 \end{bmatrix}$

21. impossible   **23.** $\begin{bmatrix} 3 & 3 & 9 & 0 \\ 12 & 6 & 3 & 3 \\ 9 & 6 & 0 & 3 \end{bmatrix}$

25. $\begin{bmatrix} 28 & 16 \\ 10 & 18 \end{bmatrix}$ **27.** impossible

29. $x = 3, y = 2, z = 3, w = 4$

31. $x = 4, y = 1, z = 3, w = 3$

33. $x = 2, y = 2, z = -3$

35. (a) $A = \begin{bmatrix} 74 & 79 & 14 & 20 & 93 \\ 27 & 21 & 23 & 15 & 70 \end{bmatrix}$

$B = \begin{bmatrix} 253 & 214 & 69 & 8 & 19 \\ 20 & 17 & 20 & 1 & 3 \end{bmatrix}$

(b) $A + B = \begin{bmatrix} 327 & 293 & 83 & 28 & 112 \\ 47 & 38 & 43 & 16 & 73 \end{bmatrix}$

(c) $\begin{bmatrix} 179 & 135 & 55 & -12 & -74 \\ -7 & -4 & -3 & -14 & -67 \end{bmatrix}$
more species in the United States

37. (a) $\begin{bmatrix} 11{,}041.7 & 8978.4 & 6461 \\ 8739.8 & 9159.6 & 6877.3 \\ 9798.1 & 9086.7 & 6448.4 \\ 9696.6 & 8926.7 & 6109.5 \end{bmatrix}$

(b) air pollution

39. (a) $\begin{bmatrix} 825 & 580 & 1560 \\ 810 & 650 & 350 \end{bmatrix}$ (b) $\begin{bmatrix} -75 & 20 & -140 \\ 10 & -50 & 50 \end{bmatrix}$

41. (a) $A = \begin{bmatrix} 78.6 & 82.9 \\ 80.2 & 84.1 \\ 81.7 & 85.2 \\ 83.2 & 86.4 \\ 84.5 & 87.4 \end{bmatrix}$; $B = \begin{bmatrix} 74.0 & 79.8 \\ 76.1 & 81.3 \\ 78.0 & 82.8 \\ 79.8 & 84.1 \\ 81.4 & 85.3 \end{bmatrix}$

(b) $A - B = \begin{bmatrix} 4.6 & 3.1 \\ 4.1 & 2.8 \\ 3.7 & 2.4 \\ 3.4 & 2.3 \\ 3.1 & 2.1 \end{bmatrix}$

(c) 2020

43. All answers are in quadrillion BTUs.

(a) $E - M = \begin{bmatrix} 0.41 & -0.18 & -0.33 \\ -1.49 & 0.09 & 1.56 \\ -13.29 & -12.05 & -12.56 \end{bmatrix}$

This represents the U.S. balance of trade for various energy types for selected years.

(b) $\frac{1}{12} C \approx \begin{bmatrix} 3.09 & 3.13 & 3.07 \\ 2.16 & 2.23 & 2.27 \\ 2.90 & 3.06 & 3.18 \end{bmatrix}$

This represents the average monthly U.S. consumption of various energy types for selected years.

(c) $C + E - M = \begin{bmatrix} 37.45 & 37.36 & 36.54 \\ 24.37 & 26.86 & 28.84 \\ 21.53 & 24.68 & 25.63 \end{bmatrix}$

This represents the total U.S production of various energy types for selected years.

45. (a) $\begin{bmatrix} 92.40 & 168 & 420 & 21 \\ 84.00 & 168 & 84 & 0 \\ 117.60 & 294 & 189 & 0 \\ 63.00 & 294 & 84 & 42 \\ 84.00 & 0 & 420 & 21 \end{bmatrix}$

(b) $\begin{bmatrix} 96.80 & 176 & 440 & 22 \\ 88.00 & 176 & 88 & 0 \\ 123.20 & 308 & 198 & 0 \\ 66.00 & 308 & 88 & 44 \\ 88.00 & 0 & 440 & 22 \end{bmatrix}$

47. (a) $A = \begin{bmatrix} 0 & 1 & 1 & 0 \\ 1 & 0 & 1 & 1 \\ 0 & 0 & 0 & 1 \\ 0 & 1 & 1 & 0 \end{bmatrix}$

(b) $B = \begin{bmatrix} 0 & 1 & 1 & 1 \\ 1 & 0 & 1 & 1 \\ 0 & 1 & 0 & 1 \\ 1 & 1 & 1 & 0 \end{bmatrix}$ (c) person 2

49. (a) $\begin{bmatrix} 80 & 75 \\ 58 & 106 \end{bmatrix}$ (b) $\begin{bmatrix} 176 & 127 \\ 139 & 143 \end{bmatrix}$

(c) $\begin{bmatrix} 10 & 4 \\ 7 & 2 \end{bmatrix}$ (d) $\begin{bmatrix} -10 & 19 \\ -7 & 20 \end{bmatrix}$
shortage, taken from inventory.

51. (a) 3, 4, 5, 6   (b) 1

53. Worker 1: 0.9625   Worker 2: 0.9375
Worker 3: 0.9125   Worker 4: 0.8875
Worker 5: 0.85   Worker 6: 0.875
Worker 7: 0.90   Worker 8: 0.925
Worker 9: 0.95
Worker 5 is least efficient; performs best at center 5

3.2 EXERCISES

1. [32]   **3.** [11 17]   **5.** $\begin{bmatrix} 29 & 25 \\ 10 & 12 \end{bmatrix}$

7. $\begin{bmatrix} 14 & 2 & 16 \\ 28 & 5 & 12 \end{bmatrix}$

9. $\begin{bmatrix} 7 & 5 & 3 & 2 \\ 14 & 9 & 11 & 3 \\ 13 & 10 & 12 & 3 \end{bmatrix}$ **11.** impossible

13. $\begin{bmatrix} 13 & 9 & 3 & 4 \\ 9 & 7 & 16 & 1 \end{bmatrix}$ **15.** $\begin{bmatrix} 9 & 7 & 16 \\ 5 & 17 & 20 \end{bmatrix}$

17. $\begin{bmatrix} 9 & 0 & 8 \\ 13 & 4 & 11 \\ 16 & 0 & 17 \end{bmatrix}$ **19.** $\begin{bmatrix} 161 & 126 \\ 42 & 35 \end{bmatrix}$ **21.** no

23. no   **25.** $\begin{bmatrix} -55 & 88 & 0 \\ -42 & 67 & 0 \\ 28 & -44 & 1 \end{bmatrix}$ **27.** $\begin{bmatrix} 0 & 0 & 0 \\ 0 & 0 & 0 \\ 0 & 0 & 0 \end{bmatrix}$

29. $\begin{bmatrix} 0 & 0 & 0 \\ 0 & 0 & 0 \\ 0 & 0 & 0 \end{bmatrix}$ **31.** A **33.** Z

35. no (see Problem 27)

37. (a) $AB = \begin{bmatrix} 1 & 0 \\ 0 & 1 \end{bmatrix}$, $BA = \begin{bmatrix} 1 & 0 \\ 0 & 1 \end{bmatrix}$

(b) $ad - bc \neq 0$

39. $\begin{bmatrix} 2 - 2 + 2 \\ 6 - 4 - 4 \\ 4 + 0 - 2 \end{bmatrix} = \begin{bmatrix} 2 \\ -2 \\ 2 \end{bmatrix}$; solution

41. $\begin{bmatrix} 1 + 2 + 2 \\ 4 + 0 + 1 \\ 2 + 2 + 1 \end{bmatrix} = \begin{bmatrix} 5 \\ 5 \\ 5 \end{bmatrix}$; solution

43. $\begin{bmatrix} 1 & 0 & 0 & 0 & 0 \\ 0 & 1 & 0 & 0 & 0 \\ 0 & 0 & 1 & 0 & 0 \\ 0 & 0 & 0 & 1 & 0 \\ 0 & 0 & 0 & 0 & 1 \end{bmatrix}$ (Some entries may appear as decimal approximations of 0.)

45. $\begin{bmatrix} 31,680 & 36,960 \\ 42,500 & 47,600 \end{bmatrix}$

The entries represent the dealer's cost for each car.

47. (a) $A = \begin{bmatrix} 86.86 & 91.25 & 95.37 \\ 27.57 & 29.82 & 32.05 \\ 6.36 & 6.45 & 6.60 \end{bmatrix}$ and

$B = \begin{bmatrix} 91.1 & 0 & 0 \\ 0 & 86.0 & 0 \\ 0 & 0 & 82.5 \end{bmatrix}$

(b) $AB \approx \begin{bmatrix} 7913 & 7848 & 7868 \\ 2512 & 2565 & 2644 \\ 579.4 & 554.7 & 544.5 \end{bmatrix}$

(c) The 1–1 entry is the trillions of BTUs used in single-family households in 2015. The 2–3 entry is the trillions of BTUs predicted to be used in multifamily households in 2025.

(d) Using AB as stored in a calculator, $[1 \ 1 \ 1] AB \approx [11{,}004.0 \ 10{,}966.7 \ 11{,}056.7]$ Left to right, each entry gives the trillions of BTUs of delivered energy consumed by all households in 2015, 2020, and 2025.

49. (a) $[0.55 \quad 0.45]$ After 5 years, M has 55% and S has 45% of the population.

(b) 10 years: $(PD)D = PD^2$; 15 years: PD^3

(c) 60% in M and 40% in S. Population proportions are stable.

51. 124, 149, 275, 334, 268, 327, 205, 249, 343, 417, 124, 149, 250, 304, 261, 316, 255, 310

53. (a) $B = \begin{bmatrix} \frac{3}{4} & \frac{2}{5} & \frac{1}{4} \\ \frac{1}{4} & \frac{3}{5} & \frac{3}{4} \end{bmatrix}$; $D = \begin{bmatrix} 22 & 30 \\ 12 & 20 \\ 8 & 11 \end{bmatrix}$; $BD = \begin{bmatrix} 23.3 & 33.25 \\ 18.7 & 27.75 \end{bmatrix}$

Houston's need for black crude is 23,300 gal and for gold crude is 18,700 gal. Gulfport needs 33,250 gal of black and 27,750 gal of gold.

(b) $PBD = [56.574 \quad 82.415]$; Houston's cost = $56,574; Gulfport's cost = $82,415

55. (a) $B = \begin{bmatrix} 0.7 & 8.5 & 10.2 & 1.1 & 5.6 & 3.6 \\ 0.5 & 0.2 & 6.1 & 1.3 & 0.2 & 1.0 \\ 2.2 & 0.4 & 8.8 & 1.2 & 1.2 & 4.8 \\ 251.8 & 63.4 & 81.6 & 35.2 & 54.3 & 144.2 \\ 30.0 & 1.0 & 1.0 & 1.0 & 1.0 & 1.0 \\ 788.9 & 0 & 0 & 0 & 0 & 0 \end{bmatrix}$

(b) $A = \begin{bmatrix} 1.11 & 0 & 0 & 0 & 0 & 0 \\ 0 & 0.95 & 0 & 0 & 0 & 0 \\ 0 & 0 & 1.11 & 0 & 0 & 0 \\ 0 & 0 & 0 & 1.11 & 0 & 0 \\ 0 & 0 & 0 & 0 & 0.95 & 0 \\ 0 & 0 & 0 & 0 & 0 & 0.95 \end{bmatrix}$

3.3 EXERCISES

1. $\begin{bmatrix} 1 & -2 & -1 & | & -7 \\ 0 & 7 & 5 & | & 21 \\ 4 & 2 & 2 & | & 1 \end{bmatrix}$

3. $\begin{bmatrix} 1 & -3 & 4 & | & 2 \\ 2 & 0 & 2 & | & 1 \\ 1 & 2 & 1 & | & 1 \end{bmatrix}$ **5.** $x = 2, y = 1/2, z = -5$

7. $x = -5, y = 2, z = 1$

9. $x = 4, y = 1, z = -2$ **11.** $x = 15, y = -13, z = 2$

13. $x = 15, y = 0, z = 2$

15. $x = 1, y = 3, z = 1, w = 0$

17. no solution

19. (a) $x = (11 + 2z)/3, y = (-1 - z)/3,$ $z =$ any real number

(b) many possibilities, including $x = 11/3, y = -\frac{1}{3}, z = 0$ and $x = 13/3, y = -2/3, z = 1$

21. If a row of the matrix has all 0s in the coefficient matrix and a nonzero number in the augment, there is no solution.

23. $x = 0, y = -z, z =$ any real number

25. no solution

27. $x = 1, y = -1, z = 1$

29. $x = 2z - 2, y = 1 + z, z =$ any real number

31. $x = \frac{7}{2} - z, y = -\frac{1}{2}, z =$ any real number

33. $x = \frac{26}{5} - \frac{7}{5}z, y = \frac{4}{5} + \frac{2}{5}z, z =$ any real number

35. $x_1 = 20, x_2 = 60, x_3 = 40$

37. $x_1 = 1, x_2 = 0, x_3 = 1, x_4 = 0$

39. no solution

41. $x_1 = 1 - 2x_4 - 3x_5, x_2 = 4 + 5x_4 + 7x_5,$
$x_3 = -3 - 3x_4 - 5x_5, x_4 =$ any real number,
$x_5 =$ any real number

43. $x = (b_2c_1 - b_1c_2)/(a_1b_2 - a_2b_1)$

45. beef: 2 cups; sirloin: 8 cups

47. (a) $50,000 at 12%, $85,000 at 10%, $100,000 at 8%
   (b) $6000 at 12%, $8500 at 10%, $8000 at 8%

49. AP = 1100, DT = 440, CA = 660

51. AF: 2 oz; FP: 2 oz; NMG: 1 oz

53. 2 of portfolio I, 2 of portfolio II

55. $\frac{3}{8}$ pound of red meat, 6 slices of bread, 4 glasses of milk

57. type I = 3(type IV), type II = 1000 − 2(type IV),
type III = 500 − type IV, type IV = any integer satisfying
$0 \le$ type IV ≤ 500

59. bacteria III = any amount satisfying
$1800 \le$ bacteria III ≤ 2300
bacteria I = 6900 − 3 (bacteria III)
bacteria II = $\frac{1}{2}$(bacteria III) − 900

61. (a) $C = 2800 + 0.6R$
$U = 7000 - R$
$R =$ any integer satisfying $0 \le R \le 7000$
   (b) $R = 1000: C = 3400$
$U = 6000$
$R = 2000: C = 4000$
$U = 5000$
   (c) Min $C = 2800$ when $R = 0$ and $U = 7000$
   (d) Max $C = 7000$ when $R = 7000$ and $U = 0$

63. There are three possibilities:
   (1) 4 of I and 2 of II
   (2) 5 of I, 1 of II, and 1 of III
   (3) 6 of I and 2 of III

3.4 EXERCISES

1. $\begin{bmatrix} 1 & 0 & 0 \\ 0 & 1 & 0 \\ 0 & 0 & 1 \end{bmatrix}$ **3.** yes   **5.** $\begin{bmatrix} 2 & -7 \\ -1 & 4 \end{bmatrix}$

7. no inverse   **9.** $\begin{bmatrix} -\frac{1}{10} & \frac{7}{10} \\ \frac{1}{5} & -\frac{2}{5} \end{bmatrix}$

11. $\begin{bmatrix} \frac{1}{3} & 0 & 0 \\ 0 & \frac{1}{3} & -\frac{2}{3} \\ 0 & 0 & 1 \end{bmatrix}$ **13.** $\begin{bmatrix} -1 & 1 & 0 \\ 1 & 0 & 0 \\ -1 & 0 & 1 \end{bmatrix}$

15. $\begin{bmatrix} \frac{1}{3} & -\frac{1}{3} & \frac{1}{3} \\ -\frac{2}{3} & -\frac{1}{3} & \frac{7}{3} \\ \frac{1}{3} & \frac{2}{3} & -\frac{5}{3} \end{bmatrix}$

17. no inverse   **19.** no inverse

21. $\begin{bmatrix} 1 & 1 & 0 & 0 & -1 \\ -3 & 0 & -3 & 1 & 4 \\ 1 & -2 & 0 & 0 & 1 \\ -3 & 1 & -3 & 1 & 3 \\ -8 & 5 & -8 & 2 & 7 \end{bmatrix}$ **23.** $\begin{bmatrix} 13 \\ 5 \end{bmatrix}$ **25.** $\begin{bmatrix} 9 \\ 6 \\ 3 \end{bmatrix}$

27. $\begin{bmatrix} x \\ y \\ z \end{bmatrix} = \begin{bmatrix} 1 \\ 1 \\ 2 \end{bmatrix}$ **29.** $x = 2, y = 1$

31. $x = 1, y = 2$ **33.** $x = 1, y = 1, z = 1$

35. $x = 1, y = 3, z = 2$

37. $x_1 = 5.6, x_2 = 5.4, x_3 = 3.25, x_4 = 6.1, x_5 = 0.4$

39. (a) -2 (b) inverse exists

41. (a) 0   (b) no inverse

43. (a) -5 (b) inverse exists

45. (a) -19 (b) inverse exists

47. Hang on   **49.** Answers in back

51. $x_0 = 2400, y_0 = 1200$

53. (a) A = 5.5 mg and B = 8.8 mg for patient I
   (b) A = 10 mg and B = 16 mg for patient II

55. $68,000 at 18%, $77,600 at 10%

57. (a) 2 Deluxe, 8 Premium, 32 Ultimate
   (b) 22 Deluxe, 8 Premium, 22 Ultimate
   [New] = [Old] + 8[Col. 1 of A^{-1}]

59. $200,000 at 6%, $300,000 at 8%, $500,000 at 10%

61. (a) $\begin{bmatrix} 0 & 1 & 0 \\ 0 & 0 & 1 \\ 1 & 1 & 1 \end{bmatrix}$ (b) 108

3.5 EXERCISES

1. (a) 15   (b) 4   **3.** 8   **5.** 40

7. most: raw materials; least: fuels

9. raw materials, manufacturing, service

11. farm products = 200; machinery = 40

13. utilities = 200; manufacturing = 400

15. (a) agricultural products = 244; oil products = 732
   (b) agricultural products = 0.4; oil products = 1.2

17. (a) mining = 106; manufacturing = 488
   (b) mining = 1.4; manufacturing = 1.2

19. (a)
$A = \begin{bmatrix} 0.3 & 0.6 \\ 0.2 & 0.2 \end{bmatrix} \begin{matrix} \text{Electronic components} \\ \text{Computers} \end{matrix}$ (EC C)
   (b) electronic components = 1200; computers = 320

21. (a)
$A = \begin{bmatrix} 0.30 & 0.04 \\ 0.35 & 0.10 \end{bmatrix} \begin{matrix} \text{Fishing} \\ \text{Oil} \end{matrix}$ (F O)
   (b) fishing = 100; oil = 1250

23. development = $21,000; promotional = $12,000

25. engineering = $15,000; computer = $13,000

27. fishing = 400; agriculture = 500; mining = 400

29. electronics = 1240; steel = 1260; autos = 720

31. service = 90; manufacturing = 200; agriculture = 100

33. products = $\frac{7}{17}$ households;
machinery = $\frac{1}{17}$ households

35. government = $\frac{10}{19}$ households;
industry = $\frac{11}{19}$ households

37. (a)
$A = \begin{bmatrix} 0.5 & 0.4 & 0.3 \\ 0.4 & 0.5 & 0.3 \\ 0.1 & 0.1 & 0.4 \end{bmatrix} \begin{matrix} \text{Manufacturing} \\ \text{Utilities} \\ \text{Households} \end{matrix}$ (M U H)
   (b) manufacturing = 3 households; utilities = 3 households

39. $\begin{bmatrix} 24 \\ 96 \\ 24 \\ 120 \\ 492 \\ 3456 \end{bmatrix}$ 3456 bolts, 492 braces, 120 panels

41. $\begin{bmatrix} 10 \\ 10 \\ 20 \\ 56 \\ 20 \\ 26 \\ 300 \end{bmatrix}$ 56 2×4s, 20 braces, 26 clamps, 300 nails

CHAPTER 3 REVIEW EXERCISES

1. 4 **2.** 0 **3.** A, B **4.** none **5.** D, F, G, I

6. $\begin{bmatrix} -2 & 5 & 11 & -8 \\ -4 & 0 & 0 & -4 \\ 2 & 2 & -1 & -9 \end{bmatrix}$

7. zero matrix **8.** order

9. $\begin{bmatrix} 6 & -1 & -9 & 3 \\ 10 & 3 & -1 & 4 \\ -2 & -2 & -2 & 14 \end{bmatrix}$ **10.** $\begin{bmatrix} 3 & -3 \\ 4 & -1 \\ 2 & -6 \\ 1 & -2 \end{bmatrix}$

11. $\begin{bmatrix} 2 & 1 \\ 5 & 1 \end{bmatrix}$ **12.** $\begin{bmatrix} 12 & -6 \\ 15 & 0 \\ 18 & 0 \\ 3 & 9 \end{bmatrix}$ **13.** $\begin{bmatrix} 4 & 0 \\ 0 & 4 \end{bmatrix}$

14. $\begin{bmatrix} 2 & -12 \\ -8 & -22 \end{bmatrix}$ **15.** $\begin{bmatrix} 9 & 20 \\ 4 & 5 \end{bmatrix}$ **16.** $\begin{bmatrix} 5 & 16 \\ 6 & 15 \end{bmatrix}$

17. $\begin{bmatrix} 2 & 37 & 61 & -55 \\ -2 & 9 & -3 & -20 \\ 10 & 10 & -14 & -30 \end{bmatrix}$ **18.** $\begin{bmatrix} 43 & -23 \\ 33 & -12 \\ -13 & 15 \end{bmatrix}$

19. $\begin{bmatrix} 10 & 16 \\ 15 & 25 \\ 18 & 30 \\ 6 & 11 \end{bmatrix}$ **20.** $\begin{bmatrix} 17 & 73 \\ 7 & 28 \end{bmatrix}$ **21.** $\begin{bmatrix} 3 & 7 \\ 23 & 42 \end{bmatrix}$

22. F **23.** F **24.** $\begin{bmatrix} -19 & 12 \\ -8 & 5 \end{bmatrix}$ **25.** F

26. (a) infinitely many solutions (bottom row of 0s)
(b) $x = 6 + 2z$
$y = 7 - 3z$
z = any real number
Two specific solutions:
If $z = 0$, then $x = 6, y = 7$.
If $z = 1$, then $x = 8, y = 4$.

27. (a) no solution (last row says $0 = 1$)
(b) no solution

28. (a) unique (coefficient matrix is I_3)
(b) $x = 0, y = -10, z = 14$

29. $(1, 2, 1)$ **30.** $x = 22, y = 9$

31. $x = -3, y = 3, z = 4$

32. $x = -\frac{3}{2}, y = 7, z = -\frac{11}{2}$ **33.** no solution

34. $x = 2 - 2z, y = -1 - 2z, z$ = any real number

35. $x = -2 + 8z$
$y = -2 + 3z$
z = any real number

36. $x_1 = 1, x_2 = 11, x_3 = -4, x_4 = -5$ **37.** yes

38. $\begin{bmatrix} \frac{1}{2} & \frac{1}{4} \\ \frac{5}{2} & \frac{7}{4} \end{bmatrix}$ **39.** $\begin{bmatrix} -1 & -2 & 8 \\ 1 & 2 & -7 \\ 1 & 1 & -4 \end{bmatrix}$

40. $\begin{bmatrix} 2 & 1 & -2 \\ 7 & 5 & -8 \\ -13 & -9 & 15 \end{bmatrix}$

41. $x = -33, y = 30, z = 19$

42. $x = 4, y = 5, z = -13$

43. $A^{-1} = \begin{bmatrix} -41 & 32 & 5 \\ 17 & -13 & -2 \\ -9 & 7 & 1 \end{bmatrix}; x = 4, y = -2, z = 2$

44. no **45.** (a) 16 (b) yes, det $\neq$ 0

46. (a) 0 (b) no, det = 0

47. $\begin{bmatrix} 250 & 140 \\ 480 & 700 \end{bmatrix}$ **48.** $\begin{bmatrix} 1030 & 800 \\ 700 & 1200 \end{bmatrix}$

49. (a) higher in June
(b) higher in July

50. $\begin{matrix} \text{Men} & \text{Women} \\ \begin{bmatrix} 865 & 885 \\ 210 & 270 \end{bmatrix} & \begin{matrix} \text{Robes} \\ \text{Hoods} \end{matrix} \end{matrix}$ **51.** $\begin{bmatrix} 1750 \\ 480 \end{bmatrix} \begin{matrix} \text{Robes} \\ \text{Hoods} \end{matrix}$

52. (a) $\begin{bmatrix} 13,500 & 12,400 \\ 10,500 & 10,600 \end{bmatrix}$
(b) Department A should buy from Kink; Department B should buy from Ace.

53. (a) $[0.20 \quad 0.30 \quad 0.50]$

(b) $\begin{bmatrix} 0.013469 \\ 0.013543 \\ 0.006504 \end{bmatrix}$

(c) $[0.20 \, 0.30 \, 0.50] \begin{bmatrix} 0.013469 \\ 0.013543 \\ 0.006504 \end{bmatrix} = 0.20(0.013469) +$
$0.30(0.013543) + 0.50(0.006504) = 0.0100087$

(d) The historical return of the portfolio, 0.0100087, is the estimated expected monthly return of the portfolio. This is roughly 1% per month.

54. 400 fast food, 700 software, 200 pharmaceutical

55. (a) $A = 2C, B = 2000 - 4C$,
C = any integer satisfying $0 \leq C \leq 500$
(b) yes; $A = 500, B = 1000, C = 250$
(c) max $A = 1000$ when $B = 0, C = 500$

56. (a) 3 passenger, 4 transport, 4 jumbo
(b) 1 passenger, 3 transport, 7 jumbo
(c) column 2

57. (a) shipping = 5680; agriculture = 1960
(b) shipping = 0.4; agriculture = 1.8

58. (a)
$$A = \begin{bmatrix} 0.1 & 0.1 \\ 0.2 & 0.05 \end{bmatrix} \begin{matrix} \text{Shoes} \\ \text{Cattle} \end{matrix}$$
$$\quad\quad\; \begin{matrix} \text{S} & \text{C} \end{matrix}$$
(b) shoes = 1000; cattle = 500

59. mining = 360; manufacturing = 320; fuels = 400

60. government = $\frac{64}{93}$ households; agriculture = $\frac{59}{93}$ households; manufacturing = $\frac{40}{93}$ households

CHAPTER 3 TEST

1. $\begin{bmatrix} 3 & 1 & 5 \\ 1 & 3 & 6 \end{bmatrix}$

2. $\begin{bmatrix} -1 & 2 & 2 \\ 1 & -1 & 6 \end{bmatrix}$

3. $\begin{bmatrix} -12 & -16 & -155 \\ 5 & 12 & 87 \end{bmatrix}$

4. $\begin{bmatrix} 23 & 6 \\ 182 & 45 \\ 21 & 1 \end{bmatrix}$

5. $\begin{bmatrix} 0 & -7 \\ 26 & 1 \end{bmatrix}$

6. $\begin{bmatrix} -43 & -46 & -207 \\ 39 & 30 & -77 \\ 17 & 5 & -216 \end{bmatrix}$

7. $\begin{bmatrix} -2 & 3/2 \\ 1 & -1/2 \end{bmatrix}$

8. $\begin{bmatrix} -3 & 2 & 2 \\ 1 & 0 & -1 \\ 1/2 & -1/2 & 0 \end{bmatrix}$

9. $\begin{bmatrix} 5 \\ 14 \\ 15 \end{bmatrix}$

10. $x = -0.5, y = 0.5, z = 2.5$

11. $x = 4 - 1.8z, y = 0.2z, z = $ any real number

12. no solution

13. $x = 2, y = 2, z = 0, w = -2$

14. $x = 6w - 0.5, y = 0.5 - w, z = 2.5 - 3w, w = $ any real number

15. (a) $B = \$45{,}000, E = \$40{,}000$
(b) $\$0 \le H \le \$25{,}000$ (so $B \ge 0$)
(c) min $E = \$20{,}000$ when $H = \$0$ and $B = \$75{,}000$

16. (a) $\begin{bmatrix} 0.08 & 0.22 & 0.12 \\ 0.10 & 0.08 & 0.19 \\ 0.05 & 0.07 & 0.09 \\ 0.10 & 0.26 & 0.15 \\ 0.12 & 0.04 & 0.24 \end{bmatrix}$
(b) 0.08, 0.22, 0.12 consumed by carnivores 1, 2, 3
(c) plant 5 by 1, plant 4 by 2, plant 5 by 3

17. (a) $[1000 \quad 4000 \quad 2000 \quad 1000]$
(b) $[45{,}000 \quad 55{,}000 \quad 90{,}000 \quad 70{,}000]$
(c) $\begin{bmatrix} 5 \\ 3 \\ 4 \\ 4 \end{bmatrix}$ (d) $[\$1{,}030{,}000]$ (e) $\begin{matrix} A \\ B \\ C \\ D \end{matrix} \begin{bmatrix} 65 \\ 145 \\ 125 \\ 135 \end{bmatrix} \!\!\begin{matrix} \$ \\ \\ \\ \end{matrix}$

18. (a) 121, 46, 247, 95, 261, 99, 287, 111, 179, 69, 169, 64
(b) The die is cast

19. growth, 2000; blue-chip, 400; utility, 400

20. (a) agriculture = 245; minerals = 235
(b) agriculture = 7; minerals = 1
(c) agriculture = 0.5; minerals = 1.5

21. profit = households
nonprofit = $\frac{2}{3}$ households

22. $\begin{bmatrix} 0.2 & 0.1 & 0.1 & 0.1 \\ 0.3 & 0.2 & 0.2 & 0.2 \\ 0.2 & 0.2 & 0.3 & 0.3 \\ 0.1 & 0.4 & 0.2 & 0.2 \end{bmatrix} \begin{matrix} \text{Agriculture} \\ \text{Machinery} \\ \text{Fuel} \\ \text{Steel} \end{matrix}$
$\begin{matrix} \text{Ag} & \text{M} & \text{F} & \text{S} \end{matrix}$

23. agriculture = 5000; machinery = 8000; fuel = 8000; steel = 7000

24. agriculture = $\frac{520}{699}$ households; steel = $\frac{236}{233}$ households; fuel = $\frac{159}{233}$ households

4.1 EXERCISES

1.

3.

5.
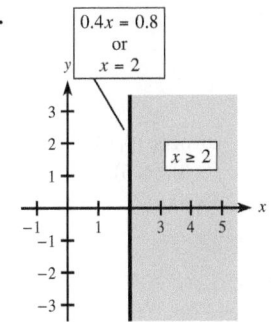

7. $(0, 0), (20, 10), (0, 15), (25, 0)$

9. $(5, 0), (15, 0), (6, 9), (2, 6)$

11. $(0, 5), (1, 2), (3, 1), (6, 0)$

13.

15.

17.

19.

21.

23.

(b)

25.

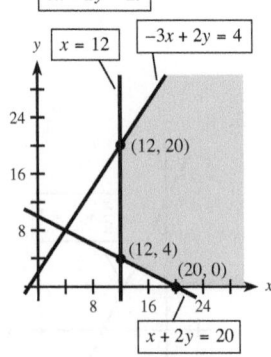

33. (a) Let x = the number of minutes of radio and y = the number of minutes of television.
Constraints are
$$x + y \geq 80$$
$$0.006x + 0.09y \geq 2.16$$
$$x \geq 0, y \geq 0$$

(b)

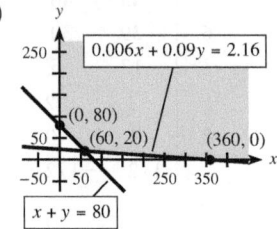

27. (a) Let x = the number of deluxe models and y = the number of economy models.
$$3x + 2y \leq 24$$
$$\tfrac{1}{2}x + y \leq 8$$
$$x \geq 0, y \geq 0$$

(b)

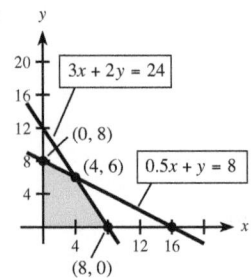

corners: $(0, 0)$,
$(8, 0), (4, 6)$,
$(0, 8)$

35. (a) Let x = the number of pounds of regular hot dogs and y = the number of pounds of all-beef hot dogs.
$$0.18x + 0.75y \leq 1020$$
$$0.2x + 0.2y \geq 500$$
$$0.3x \leq 600$$
$$x \geq 0, y \geq 0$$

(b)

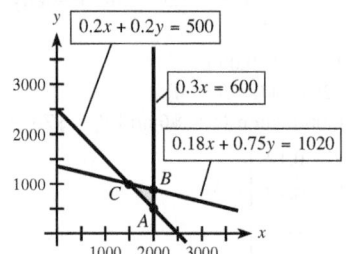

Solution region is triangle ABC, with
$A = (2000, 500)$
$B = (2000, 880)$
$C = (1500, 1000)$

29. (a) Let x = the number of cord-type trimmers and y = the number of cordless trimmers.
Constraints are
$$x + y \leq 300$$
$$2x + 4y \leq 800$$
$$x \geq 0, y \geq 0$$

(b)

4.2 EXERCISES

1. max = 76 at $(4, 4)$; min = 0 at $(0, 0)$

3. no max; min = 11 at $(1, 3)$

5. $(0, 0), (0, 20), (10, 18), (15, 10), (20, 0)$; max = 66 at $(10, 18)$; min = 0 at $(0, 0)$

7. $(0, 60), (10, 30), (20, 20), (70, 0)$; min = 100 at $(20, 20)$; no max

9. max = 1260 at $x = 12, y = 18$

11. min = 66 at $x = 0, y = 3$

13. max = 22 at $(2, 4)$

15. max = 30 on line between $(0, 5)$ and $(3, 4)$

17. min = 32 at $(2, 3)$

19. min = 9 at $(2, 3)$

31. (a) Let x = the number of minutes on finance programs and y = the number of minutes on sports programs.
$$7x + 2y \geq 30$$
$$4x + 12y \geq 28$$
$$x \geq 0, y \geq 0$$

21. max $= 10$ at $(2, 4)$

23. min $= 3100$ at $(40, 60)$

25. If $x =$ the number of deluxe models and $y =$ the number of economy models, then max $= \$792$ at $(4, 6)$.

27. If $x =$ the number of cord-type trimmers and $y =$ the number of cordless trimmers, then max $= \$9000$ at any point with integer coordinates on the segment joining $(0, 200)$ and $(200, 100)$, such as $(20, 190)$.

29. radio $= 60$, $TV = 20$, min $C = \$16,000$

31. inkjet $= 45$, laser $= 25$, max $P = \$3300$

33. 250 fish: 150 bass and 100 trout

35. (a) Max $P = \$1,260,120$ when corn $= 3749.5$ acres and soybeans $= 2251.5$ acres

   (b) Max $P = \$1,260,960$ when corn $= 3746$ acres and soybeans $= 2262$ acres

   (c) $\$120$/acre

37. 30 days for factory 1 and 20 days for factory 2; at minimum cost $= \$700,000$

39. 60 days for location I and 70 days for location II; minimum cost $= \$86,000$

41. reg $= 2000$ lb; all-beef $= 880$ lb; maximum profit $= \$3320$

43. from Pittsburgh: 20 to Blairsville, 40 to Youngstown; from Erie: 15 to Blairsville, 0 to Youngstown; minimum cost $= \$1540$

45. (a) $R = \$366,000$ with 6 satellite and 17 full-service branches

   (b) branches: used 23 of 25 possible; 2 not used (slack) new employees: hired 120 of 120 possible; 0 not hired (slack) Budget: used all $\$11.92$ million; $\$0$ not used (slack)

   (c) Additional new employees and additional budget. These items are completely used in the current optimal solution; more could change and improve the optimal solution.

   (d) Additional branches. The current optimal solution does not use all those allotted; more would just add to the extras.

4.3 EXERCISES

1. $3x + 5y + s_1 = 15$, $3x + 6y + s_2 = 20$

3. $\begin{bmatrix} 2 & 5 & 1 & 0 & 0 & 400 \\ 1 & 2 & 0 & 1 & 0 & 175 \\ \hline -3 & -7 & 0 & 0 & 1 & 0 \end{bmatrix}$

5. $\begin{bmatrix} 2 & 7 & 9 & 1 & 0 & 0 & 0 & 100 \\ 6 & 5 & 1 & 0 & 1 & 0 & 0 & 145 \\ 1 & 2 & 7 & 0 & 0 & 1 & 0 & 90 \\ \hline -2 & -5 & -2 & 0 & 0 & 0 & 1 & 0 \end{bmatrix}$

7. $x = 11$, $y = 9$; $f = 20$

9. $x = 0$, $y = 14$, $z = 11$; $f = 525$

11. (a) $x_1 = 0$, $x_2 = 45$, $s_1 = 14$, $s_2 = 0$, $f = 75$

   (b) not complete

   (c) $\begin{bmatrix} ② & 0 & 1 & -\frac{3}{4} & 0 & 14 \\ 3 & 1 & 0 & \frac{1}{3} & 0 & 45 \\ \hline -6 & 0 & 0 & 3 & 1 & 75 \end{bmatrix}$

   $\frac{1}{2}R_1 \to R_1$, then $-3R_1 + R_2 \to R_2$, $6R_1 + R_3 \to R_3$

13. (a) $x_1 = 0$, $x_2 = 0$, $s_1 = 200$, $s_2 = 400$, $s_3 = 350$, $f = 0$

   (b) not complete

   (c) $\begin{bmatrix} ⑩ & 27 & 1 & 0 & 0 & 0 & 200 \\ 4 & 51 & 0 & 1 & 0 & 0 & 400 \\ 15 & 27 & 0 & 0 & 1 & 0 & 350 \\ \hline -8 & -7 & 0 & 0 & 0 & 1 & 0 \end{bmatrix}$

   $\frac{1}{10}R_1 \to R_1$, then $-4R_1 + R_2 \to R_2$, $-15R_1 + R_3 \to R_3$, $8R_1 + R_4 \to R_4$

15. (a) $x_1 = 24$, $x_2 = 0$, $x_3 = 21$, $s_1 = 16$, $s_2 = 0$, $s_3 = 0$, $f = 780$

   (b) complete (no part (c))

17. (a) $x_1 = 0$, $x_2 = 0$, $x_3 = 12$, $s_1 = 4$, $s_2 = 6$, $s_3 = 0$, $f = 150$

   (b) not complete

   (c) $\begin{bmatrix} 4 & 4 & 1 & 0 & 0 & 2 & 0 & 12 \\ ② & ④ & 0 & 1 & 0 & 1 & 0 & 4 \\ -3 & -11 & 0 & 0 & 1 & -1 & 0 & 6 \\ \hline -3 & -3 & 0 & 0 & 0 & 4 & 1 & 150 \end{bmatrix}$

   Either circled number may act as the next pivot entry, but only one of them. If 4 is used,
   $\frac{1}{4}R_2 \to R_2$, then $-4R_2 + R_1 \to R_1$, $11R_2 + R_3 \to R_3$, $3R_2 + R_4 \to R_4$. If 2 is used,
   $\frac{1}{2}R_2 \to R_2$, then $-4R_2 + R_1 \to R_1$, $3R_2 + R_3 \to R_3$, $3R_2 + R_4 \to R_4$.

19. $x = 0$, $y = 5$; $f = 50$

21. $x = 4$, $y = 3$; $f = 17$

23. $x = 4$, $y = 3$; $f = 11$

25. $x = 0$, $y = 2$, $z = 5$; $f = 40$

27. $x = 4$, $y = 2$, $z = 6$; $f = 16$

29. $x_1 = 36$, $x_2 = 24$; $x_3 = 0$, $x_4 = 8$; $f = 1728$

31. No solution; a new pivot cannot be found in column 2.

33. $x = 50$, $y = 10$; $f = 100$. Multiple solutions are possible; pivot with the 3-5 entry.

35. no solution

37. $x = 0$, $y = 50$ or $x = 40$, $y = 40$; $f = 600$

39. (a) $\begin{bmatrix} 1 & 1 & 1 & 0 & 0 & 60 \\ 1 & 3 & 0 & 1 & 0 & 120 \\ \hline -40 & -60 & 0 & 0 & 1 & 0 \end{bmatrix}$

   (b) Maximum profit is $\$3000$ with 30 of the 500 GB drives and 30 of the 1.5 TB drives.

41. 300 pullover sweatshirts, 450 hooded sweatshirts, maximum $P = \$6900$

43. premium and light $= 175$ each; maximum $P = \$35,000$

45. Aries $= 3$, Belfair $= 5$, Wexford $= 4$; maximum $P = \$305,000$

47. (a) 26 one-bedroom; 40 two-bedroom; 48 three-bedroom

   (b) $\$100,200$ per month

49. 21 newspapers, 13 radio; 230,000 exposures

51. $1650 profit with 46 A, 20 B, 6 C

53. 20-in. LCDs = 40, 42-in. LCDs = 115, 42-in. plasma = 0, 50-in. plasma = 38; max P = $12,540

4.4 EXERCISES

1. (a) $\begin{bmatrix} 5 & 2 & | & 16 \\ 1 & 2 & | & 8 \\ \hline 4 & 5 & | & g \end{bmatrix}$ transpose = $\begin{bmatrix} 5 & 1 & | & 4 \\ 2 & 2 & | & 5 \\ \hline 16 & 8 & | & g \end{bmatrix}$

(b) maximize $f = 16x_1 + 8x_2$ subject to
$5x_1 + x_2 \leq 4, 2x_1 + 2x_2 \leq 5, x_1 \geq 0, x_2 \geq 0$

3. (a) $\begin{bmatrix} 1 & 2 & | & 30 \\ 1 & 4 & | & 50 \\ \hline 7 & 3 & | & g \end{bmatrix}$ transpose = $\begin{bmatrix} 1 & 1 & | & 7 \\ 2 & 4 & | & 3 \\ \hline 30 & 50 & | & g \end{bmatrix}$

(b) maximize $f = 30x_1 + 50x_2$ subject to
$x_1 + x_2 \leq 7, 2x_1 + 4x_2 \leq 3, x_1 \geq 0, x_2 \geq 0$

5. (a) $y_1 = 7, y_2 = 4, y_3 = 0$; min $g = 452$

(b) $x_1 = 15, x_2 = 0, x_3 = 29$; max $f = 452$

7. maximize $f = 11x_1 + 11x_2 + 16x_3$ subject to
$2x_1 + x_2 + x_3 \leq 2$
$x_1 + 3x_2 + 4x_3 \leq 10$
primal: $y_1 = 16, y_2 = 0; g = 32$ (min)
dual: $x_1 = 0, x_2 = 0, x_3 = 2; f = 32$ (max)

9. maximize $f = 11x_1 + 12x_2 + 6x_3$ subject to
$4x_1 + 3x_2 + 3x_3 \leq 3$
$x_1 + 2x_2 + x_3 \leq 1$
primal: $y_1 = 2, y_2 = 3; g = 9$ (min)
dual: $x_1 = 3/5, x_2 = 1/5, x_3 = 0; f = 9$ (max)

11. min = 28 at $x = 2, y = 0, z = 1$

13. $y_1 = 2/5, y_2 = 1/5, y_3 = 1/5; g = 16$ (min)

15. (a) minimize $g = 120y_1 + 50y_2$ subject to
$3y_1 + y_2 \geq 40$
$2y_1 + y_2 \geq 20$

(b) primal: $x_1 = 40, x_2 = 0, f = 1600$ (max)
dual: $y_1 = 40/3, y_2 = 0, g = 1600$ (min)

17. min = 480 at $y_1 = 0, y_2 = 0, y_3 = 16$

19. min = 90 at $y_1 = 0, y_2 = 3, y_3 = 1, y_4 = 0$

21. Atlanta = 150 hr, Fort Worth = 50 hr; min C = $210,000

23. line 1 for 4 hours, line 2 for 1 hour; $1200

25. A = 12 weeks, B = 0 weeks, C = 0 weeks; cost = $12,000

27. factory 1: 50 days, factory 2: 0 days; min cost $500,000

29. 105 minutes on radio, nothing on TV; min cost $10,500

31. (a) Georgia package = 10
Union package = 20
Pacific package = 5

(b) $4630

33. (a) min cost = $4.

(b) Many solutions are possible; two are 16 oz of food I, 0 oz of food II, 0 oz of food III and 11 oz of food I, 1 oz of food II, 0 oz of food III.

35. Mon. = 8, Tues. = 0, Wed. = 5, Thurs. = 4, Fri. = 5, Sat. = 0, Sun. = 3; min = 25

4.5 EXERCISES

1. $-3x + y \leq -5$

3. $-6x - y \leq -40$

5. (a) maximize $f = 2x + 3y$ subject to
$7x + 4y \leq 28$
$3x - y \leq -2$
$x \geq 0, y \geq 0$

(b) $\begin{bmatrix} 7 & 4 & 1 & 0 & 0 & | & 28 \\ 3 & \text{\textcircled{-1}} & 0 & 1 & 0 & | & -2 \\ \hline -2 & -3 & 0 & 0 & 1 & | & 0 \end{bmatrix}$

7. (a) Maximize $-g = -3x - 8y$ subject to
$4x - 5y \leq 50$
$x + y \leq 80$
$x - 2y \leq -4$
$x \geq 0, y \geq 0$

(b) $\begin{bmatrix} 4 & -5 & 1 & 0 & 0 & 0 & | & 50 \\ 1 & 1 & 0 & 1 & 0 & 0 & | & 80 \\ 1 & \text{\textcircled{-2}} & 0 & 0 & 1 & 0 & | & -4 \\ \hline 3 & 8 & 0 & 0 & 0 & 1 & | & 0 \end{bmatrix}$

9. $x = 6, y = 8, z = 12; f = 120$

11. $x = 10, y = 17; f = 57$

13. $x = 5, y = 7; f = 31$

15. $x = 5, y = 15; f = 45$

17. $x = 10, y = 20; f = 120$

19. $x = 20, y = 10, z = 0; f = 40$

21. $x = 5, y = 0, z = 3; f = 22$

23. $x = 70, y = 0, z = 40; f = 2100$

25. $x_1 = 20, x_2 = 10, x_3 = 20, x_4 = 80,$
$x_5 = 10, x_6 = 10; f = 3250$

27. regular = 2000 lb; beef = 880 lb; profit = $3320

29. Produce 200 of each at Monaca; produce 300 commercial components and 550 domestic furnaces at Hamburg; profit = $355,250

31. 400 filters, 300 housing units; min cost = $5145

33. Produce 200 of each at Monaca; produce 300 commercial components and 550 domestic furnaces at Hamburg; cost = $337,750

35. I = 3 million, II = 0, III = 3 million; cost = $180,000

37. 2000 footballs, 0 soccer balls, 0 volleyballs; $60,000

CHAPTER 4 REVIEW EXERCISES

1.

2.

3.

4.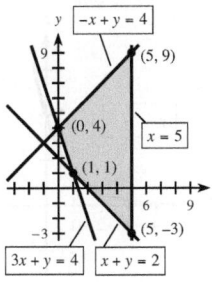

5. max = 25 at (5, 10); min = −12 at (12, 0)

6. max = 194 at (17, 23); min = 104 at (8, 14)

7. max = 140 at (20, 0); min = −52 at (20, 32)

8. min = 115 at (5, 7); no max exists, f can be made arbitrarily large

9. $f = 66$ at (6, 6)

10. $f = 43$ at (7, 9)

11. $f = 300$ at any point on the segment joining (0, 60) and (50, 40)

12. $g = 24$ at (3, 3)   **13.** $g = 84$ at (64, 4)

14. $f = 76$ at (12, 8)   **15.** $f = 75$ at (15, 15)

16. $f = 168$ at (12, 7)   **17.** $f = 260$ at (60, 20)

18. $f = 360$ at (40, 30)   **19.** $f = 80$ at (20, 10)

20. $f = 640$ on the line between (160, 0) and (90, 70)

21. no solution

22. $g = 32$ at $y_1 = 2, y_2 = 3$

23. $g = 20$ at $y_1 = 4, y_2 = 2$

24. $g = 7$ at $y_1 = 1, y_2 = 5$

25. $g = 1180$ at $y_1 = 80, y_2 = 20$

26. $f = 165$ at $x = 20, y = 21$

27. $f = 54$ at $x = 6, y = 5$

28. $f = 270$ at (5, 3, 2)

29. $g = 140$ at $y_1 = 0, y_2 = 20, y_3 = 20$

30. $g = 1400$ at $y_1 = 0, y_2 = 100, y_3 = 100$

31. $f = 156$ at $x = 15, y = 2$

32. $f = 31$ at $x = 4, y = 5$

33. $f = 4380$ at (40, 10, 0, 0)

34. $f = 900$ at $x_1 = 25, x_2 = 50, x_3 = 25, x_4 = 0$

35. $g = 2020$ at $x_1 = 0, x_2 = 100, x_3 = 80, x_4 = 20$

36. $P = \$29,500$ when 110 large and 75 small swing sets are made

37. $C = \$300,000$ when factory 1 operates 30 days, factory 2 operates 25 days

38. $P = \$10,680$ at any pair of integer values on the segment joining (120, 0) and (90, 20)

39. $P = \$960$; I = 40, II = 20

40. $P = \$1260$; Jacob's ladders = 90, locomotive engines = 30

41. (a) Let x_1 = the number of 32-in LCD sets,
x_2 = the number of 42-in LCD sets,
x_3 = the number of 50-in LCD sets,
x_4 = the number of 65-in plasma sets.

(b) Maximize $P = 80x_1 + 120x_2 + 160x_3 + 200x_4$
subject to

$$
\begin{aligned}
8x_1 + 10x_2 + 12x_3 + 15x_4 &\le 1870 \\
2x_1 + 4x_2 + 4x_3 + 4x_4 &\le 530 \\
x_1 + x_2 + x_3 + x_4 &\le 200 \\
x_3 + x_4 &\le 100 \\
x_2 &\le 120
\end{aligned}
$$

(c) $x_1 = 15, x_2 = 25, x_3 = 0, x_4 = 100$;
max profit = \$24,200

42. food I = 0 oz, food II = 3 oz; $C = \$0.60$ (min)

43. cost = \$5.60; $A = 40$ lb, $B = 0$ lb

44. cost = \$85,000; $A = 20$ days, $B = 15$ days, $C = 0$ days

45. pancake mix = 8000 lb; cake mix = 3000 lb; profit = \$3550

46. Texas: 55 desks, 65 computer tables; Louisiana: 75 desks, 65 computer tables; cost = \$12,735

47. Midland: grade 1 = 486.5 tons, grade 2 = 0 tons;
Donora: grade 1 = 13.5 tons, grade 2 = 450 tons;
cost = \$271,905

CHAPTER 4 TEST

1. max = 120 at (0, 24)

2. (a)
$$
C; \left[\begin{array}{ccccccc|c}
1 & 2 & 0 & 1 & 0 & -3/2 & 0 & 40 \\
0 & ① & 0 & -2 & 1 & 1/2 & 0 & 15 \\
0 & 3 & 1 & -1 & 0 & 1/4 & 0 & 60 \\
\hline
0 & 0 & 0 & 4 & 0 & 6 & 1 & 220
\end{array}\right]
$$
$$-2R_2 + R_1 \rightarrow R_1 \quad -3R_2 + R_3 \rightarrow R_3$$

(b) A; pivot column is column 3, but new pivot is undefined.

(c) B; $x_1 = 40, x_2 = 12, x_3 = 0, s_1 = 0,$
$s_2 = 20, s_3 = 0; f = 170$; this solution is not optimal; the next pivot is the 3-6 entry.

3. (a)

(b)

(c)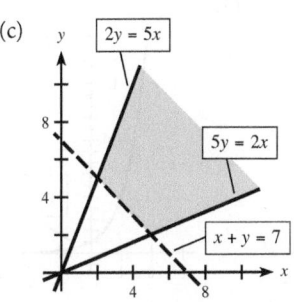

4. maximize $f = 100x_1 + 120x_2$ subject to
$$3x_1 + 4x_2 \le 2$$
$$5x_1 + 6x_2 \le 3$$
$$x_1 + 3x_2 \le 5$$
$$x_1 \ge 0, x_2 \ge 0$$

5. min $= 21$ at $(1, 8)$; no max exists, f can be made arbitrarily large

6. min $= 136$ at $(28, 52)$

7. maximize $-g = -7x - 3y$ subject to
$$x - 4y \le -4$$
$$x - y \le 5$$
$$2x + 3y \le 30$$

8. max: $x_1 = 17, x_2 = 15, x_3 = 0; f = 658$ (max)
min: $y_1 = 4, y_2 = 18, y_3 = 0; g = 658$ (min)

9. max: $= 6300$ at $x = 90, y = 0$

10. max $f = 6000$ at any point on the segment joining $(250, 150)$ and $(350, 90)$

11. max $= 1188$ at $x = 0, y = 16, z = 12$

12. If $x =$ the number of barrels of lager and $y =$ the number of barrels of ale, then maximize $P = 35x + 30y$ subject to
$$3x + 2y \le 1200$$
$$2x + 2y \le 1000$$
$P = \$16,000$ (max) at $x = 200, y = 300$ daytime

13. If $x =$ the number of day calls and $y =$ the number of evening calls, then minimize $C = 3x + 4y$ subject to
$$0.3x + 0.3y \ge 150$$
$$0.1x + 0.3y \ge 120$$
$$x \le 0.5(x + y)$$
$C = \$1850$ (min) at $x = 150, y = 350$

14. max profit $= \$15,000$ when product 1 $= 25$ tons, product 2 $= 62.5$ tons, product 3 $= 0$ tons, product 4 $= 12.5$ tons

5.1 EXERCISES

1. 3.162278

3. 0.01296525

5. 1.44225

7. 7.3891

9.

11.

13.

15.

17.

19.

21. (a) $y = 3(2.5)^{-x}$
(b) Decay. They have the form $y = C \cdot b^x$ for $0 < b < 1$ or $y = C \cdot a^{-x}$ for $a > 1$.
(c) The graphs are identical.

23. (a) and (b)
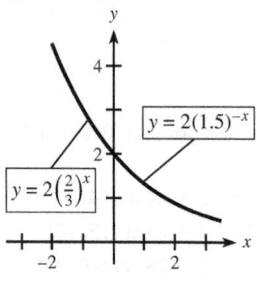

(c) $(1.5)^{-x} = \left(\dfrac{3}{2}\right)^{-x} = \left(\dfrac{2}{3}\right)^x$

25. $y = \left(\dfrac{5}{4}\right)^{-x}$

27. All graphs have the same basic shape. For larger positive values of k, the graphs fall more sharply. For positive values of k nearer 0, the graphs fall more slowly.

29. $y = f(x) + C$ is the same graph as $y = f(x)$ but shifted C units on the y-axis.

31. (a)

(b) As c changes, the y-intercept and the asymptote change.

33. $1884.54

35.

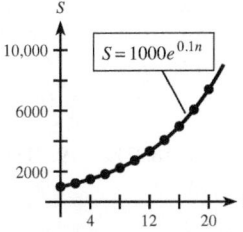

$S = 1000e^{0.1n}$

37. At time 0, the concentration is 0. The concentration rises rapidly for the first 4 minutes and then tends toward 100% as time nears 10 minutes.

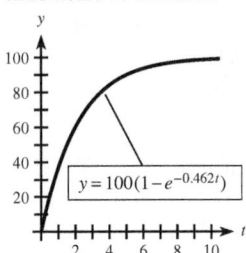

$y = 100(1 - e^{-0.462t})$

39.

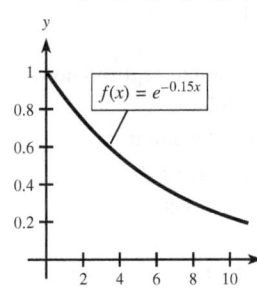

$f(x) = e^{-0.15x}$

As the TV sets age (*x* increases), the fraction of sets still in service declines.

41.

$N = 7.7(1.02)^t$

43.

$N = 7.7(1.05)^t$

45. (a) Growth; $e > 1$ and the exponent is positive for $t > 0$.

(b)

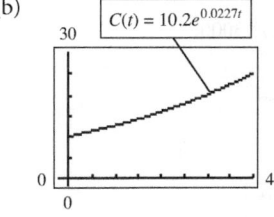

$C(t) = 10.2e^{0.0227t}$

47. (a)

(b) $y = 342.8(1.037^x)$

(c)

The model is an excellent fit to the data.

49. (a) $y = 533.6(1.065^x)$

(b) \$20,562 billion is an overestimate.   (c) 2026

51. (a)

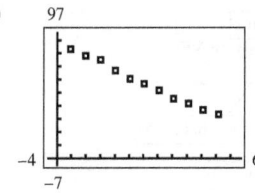

(b) $y = 95.8(0.982)^x$

(c)

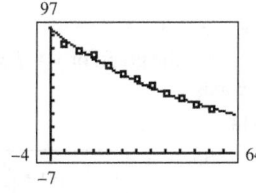

(d) about 31.24%.

53. (a) $y = 4.10(1.02^x)$ (b) growth

(c)

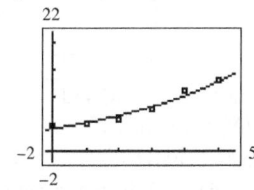

(d) 16.1 million

5.2 EXERCISES

1. $2^4 = 16$ **3.** $4^{1/2} = 2$ **5.** $x = 81$ **7.** $x = \frac{1}{4}$

9. $x = 16$ **11.** $x = 26.75$ **13.** $x \approx 2.013$

15. $\log_2 32 = 5$

17. $\log_4(\frac{1}{4}) = -1$

19. $3x + 5 = \ln(0.55); x \approx -1.866$

21.

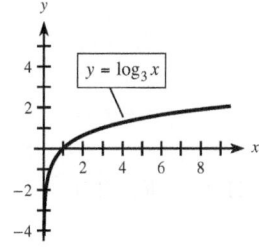

$y = \log_3 x$

23.

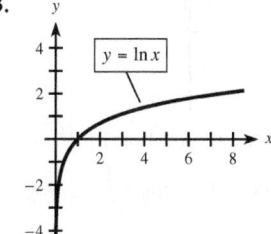

$y = \ln x$

25.

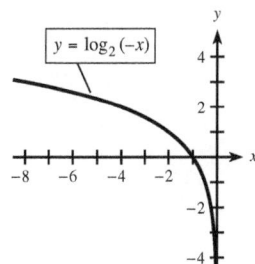

$y = \log_2(-x)$

27. (a) 3   (b) -1 **29.** x

31. -7 **33.** 3

35. (a) 4.9   (b) 0.4   (c) 12.4   (d) 0.9

37. $\log x - \log(x + 1)$

39. $\log_7 x + \frac{1}{3}\log_7(x + 4)$

41. $\ln(x/y)$

43. $\log_5[x^{1/2}(x + 1)]$

45. equivalent; Properties V and III

47. not equivalent; $\log(\sqrt[3]{8}/5)$

49. (a)

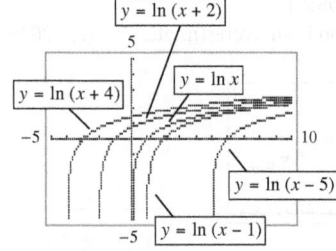

(b) For each c, the domain is $x > c$ and the vertical asymptote is at $x = c$.

(c) Each x-intercept is at $x = c + 1$.

(d) The graph of $y = f(x - c)$ is the graph of $y = f(x)$ shifted c units on the x-axis.

51. (a) 4.0875   (b) -0.1544

53.

55.

57. If $\log_a M = u$ and $\log_a N = v$, then $a^u = M$ and $a^v = N$. Therefore, $\log_a(M/N) = \log_a(a^u/a^v) = \log_a(a^{u-v}) = u - v = \log_a M - \log_a N$.

59. 63.1 times as severe   **61.** 3.2 times as severe

63. 40

65. $L = 10 \log (I/I_0)$

67. 0.1 and 1×10^{-14}

69. $\text{pH} = \log \dfrac{1}{[\text{H}^+]} = \log 1 - \log [\text{H}^+] = -\log [\text{H}^+]$

71. $\log_{1.02} 2 = 4t; t \approx 8.75$ years

73. (a)

(b) 83.6 million   (c) 2023

75. (a) $y = -13.0 + 11.9 \ln x$

(b)

A good fit.

(c) 26.1%

77. (a) $p = 11.45 + 24.22 \ln x$

(b) a good fit.   (c) 96%

5.3 EXERCISES

1. $5/3$ **3.** 2.943   **5.** 9.390   **7.** 18.971   **9.** 151.413

11. 6.679   **13.** $10^5 = 100{,}000$ **15.** 7

17. $5e^{10}$ **19.** $\dfrac{10^6}{2} = 5 \cdot 10^5$ **21.** 3

23. (a)

$f(x) = \dfrac{100}{1+e^{-x}}$

$f(x) = \dfrac{100}{1+0.25e^{-x}}$

$f(x) = \dfrac{100}{1+9e^{-x}}$

$f(x) = \dfrac{100}{1+49e^{-x}}$

(b) Different c-values change the y-intercept and how the graph approaches the asymptote.

25. (a) 2038   (b) 4.9 months

27. (a) 13.86 years   (b) $105{,}850$

29. 24.5 years   **31.** 128,402

33. $t \approx 22.7$, in 2023

35. (a) $\$4.98$ (b) 8   **37.** $\$502$

39. (a) $\$14{,}203.51$ (b) $x \approx 164.6$

41. $x \approx 56.7$, in 2027

43. (a) $\$10{,}100.31$ (b) 6.03 years

45. (a) $\$5469.03$

(b) 7 years, 9 months (approximately)

47. (a) $\$142.5$ million   (b) 35.3 years, in 2026

49. (a) $P(18) \approx 0.66$ means that in 2028, $\$1.00$ is expected to purchase 66% of what it did in 2012.

(b) $x \approx 29.3$, in 2040

51. $x \approx 993.3$; about 993 units

53. (a) 600   (b) 2119   (c) 3000

(d)

$N = 3000(0.2)^{0.6t}$

55. (a) 10   (b) 2.5 years

57. (a) 37   (b) 1.5 hours

59. (a) 52   (b) the tenth day

61. (a) 2%   (b) 20 months ($x = 19.6$)

63. (a) 0.23 km^3 (b) 5.9 years

65. (a) 160.48 million   (b) $t \approx 84.7$; in 2025

67. (a) $y = \dfrac{120}{1 + 5.25e^{-0.0637x}}$ (b) 63.9 million

(c) 120 million   (d) $x \approx 36.8$, in 2037

CHAPTER 5 REVIEW EXERCISES

1. (a) $\log_2 y = x$ (b) $\log_3 2x = y$
2. (a) $7^{-2} = \frac{1}{49}$ (b) $4^{-1} = x$

3.
4.

5.
6.

7.
8.

9.
10.

11.
12.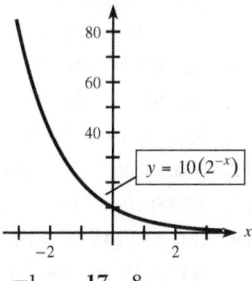

13. 0   14. 3   15. $1/2$ 16. -1 17. 8
18. 1   19. 5   20. 3.15   21. -2.7
22. 0.6   23. 5.1   24. 15.6   25. $\log y + \log z$
26. $\frac{1}{2}\ln (x+1) - \frac{1}{2}\ln x$ 27. no   28. -2
29. 5   30. 1   31. 0   32. 3.4939   33. -1.5845

34.
35.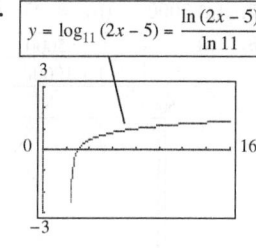

36. $x = 1.5$ 37. $x \approx 51.224$
38. $x \approx 28.175$ 39. $x \approx 40.236$
40. $x = 8$ 41. $x = 14$ 42. $x = 6$
43. Growth exponential because the general outline has the same shape as a growth exponential.
44. (a) $C(15) \approx 139.19$ means that in 2025, goods that cost $100.00 in 2012 are expected to cost $139.19.
   (b)
45. (a) \$32,627.66
   (b)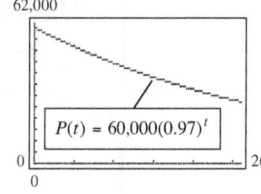
46. (a) $y = 42.1(1.04^x)$ (b)
   (c) \$239.2 thousand
47. (a) \$16,849 million
   (b)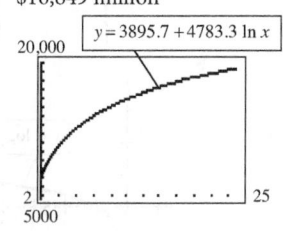
48. (a) $y = -363.3 + 166.9\ln x$
   (b) 341.1 million
   (c) $x \approx 96.9$, in 2047
49. (a) -3.9 (b) $0.14B_0$ (c) $0.004B_0$ (d) yes
50. (a) 27,441   (b) 12 weeks
51. (a) \$8731   (b) $x \approx 119.8$, about 120 units
52. (a) 47.5%   (b) $x \approx 94.6$, in 2035
53. 1366   54. 5.8 years
55. (a) \$5532.77   (b) 5.13 years
56. logistic because the graph begins like an exponential function but then grows at a slower rate

57. (a) 3000   (b) 8603   (c) 10,000

58. (a)

$$y = \frac{5000}{1 + 1000e^{-0.8x}}$$

(b) 5   (c) 4969   (d) 10 days

CHAPTER 5 TEST

1.

$y = 5^x$

2.

$y = 3^{-x}$

3.

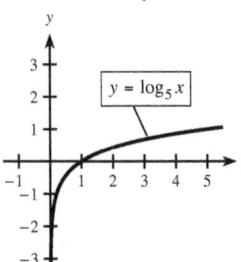

$y = \log_5 x$

4.

$y = \ln x$

5.

$y = 3^{0.5x}$

6.

$y = \ln(0.5x)$

7.

$y = e^{2x}$

8.

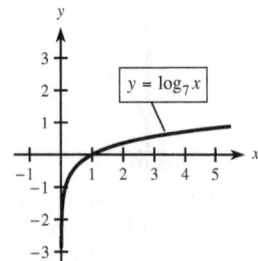

$y = \log_7 x$

9. 54.598   **10.** 0.100   **11.** 1.386

12. 1.322   **13.** $x = 7^{3.1}, x \approx 416.681$

14. $\log_3(27) = 2x; x = 1.5$ **15.** $x \approx 0.203$

16. $x = 8$ **17.** 3   **18.** x^4 **19.** 3   **20.** x^2

21. $\ln M + \ln N$ **22.** $\ln(x^3 - 1) - \ln(x + 2)$

23. $\dfrac{\ln(x^3 + 1)}{\ln 4} \approx 0.721 \ln(x^3 + 1)$

24. $x \approx 38.679$

25. decay exponential

26. (a) decay exponential
   (b) In 2030, the expected tons of CO_2 emissions per person is 14.8 tons.

27. (a) $11,943.51
   (b) $t \approx 16.0$, in 2034

28. about 6.2 months

29. (a) $37.63   (b) $x \approx 78.2$ units

30. (a) about $19,781 billion
   (b) 2024 ($t \approx 63.8$)

31. (a) $y = 63.31(1.048^x)$
   (b) 461,000
   (c) $x \approx 59.0$, in 2069

6.1 EXERCISES

1. (a) $r = 0.0625, I = 250, P = 1000, t = 4$
   (b) $P = 8000, S = 9600, I = 1600, r = 0.05, t = 4$

3. (a) $960   (b) $10,960

5. (a) $200   (b) $20,200

7. $824   **9.** $3850

11. (a) 16%   (b) 8%   **13.** (a) 5.13%   (b) 4.29%

15. $1667.49   **17.** $13,278.69   **19.** 10 years

21. pay on time

23. (a) $2120   (b) $2068.29 (nearest cent)

25. 3, 6, 9, 12, 15, 18, 21, 24, 27, 30

27. $-\frac{1}{3}, \frac{1}{5}, -\frac{1}{7}, \frac{1}{9}, -\frac{1}{11}, \frac{1}{13}$ **29.** $-1, -\frac{1}{4}, -\frac{1}{15}, 0; a_{10} = \frac{1}{20}$

31. (a) $d = 3, a_1 = 2$ (b) 11, 14, 17

33. (a) $d = \frac{3}{2}, a_1 = 3$ (b) $\frac{15}{2}, 9, \frac{21}{2}$

35. -35 **37.** 203   **39.** 2185   **41.** 1907.5

43. $-15,862.5$ **45.** 21, 34, 55   **47.** $4800

49. the job starting at $40,000 ($58,000 versus $57,600)

51. (a) $6000   (b) $9000   (c) plan II, by $3000
   (d) $20,000   (e) $27,000   (f) plan II, by $7000
   (g) plan II

6.2 EXERCISES

(Minor differences may occur because of rounding.)

1. (a) $S = 3216.87 =$ future value; principal $= 2000$; rate $= 0.02$; periods $= 24$
   (b) $P = 6049.97 =$ principal; future value $= 25,000$; rate $= 0.03$; periods $= 48$

3. (a) 8%   (b) 7   (c) 2% = 0.02   (d) 28

5. (a) 9%   (b) 5   (c) $(\frac{9}{12})\% = 0.0075$ (d) 60

7. $24,846.79   **9.** $S = \$4755.03; I = \$1555.03$

11. $13,322.91   **13.** $5583.95

15. $7309.98   **17.** $50,247.18

19. (a) $12,245.64   (b) $11,080.32
   (c) A $\frac{1}{2}$% increase in the interest rate reduces the amount required by $1165.32.

21. $50.26 more at 8%   **23.** (a) 7.55%   (b) 6.18%

25. 8% compounded monthly, 8% compounded quarterly, 8% compounded annually

27. 8.2% compounded continuously yields 8.55%. 8.4% compounded quarterly yields 8.67% and so is better.

29. The higher graph is for continuous compounding because its yield (its effective annual rate) is higher.

31. 37.02%   **33.** 3 years   **35.** 4%   **37.** $3996.02

39. (a) $2,124,876.38   (b) $480,087.44 more

41. $n \approx 20.5$; 21 quarters   **43.** $13,916.24

45.

	A	B	C
1		Future Value	(Yearly)
2	End of Year	Quarterly	Monthly
3	0	$5000.00	$5000.00
4	1	$5322.52	$5324.26
5	2	$5665.84	$5669.54
6	3	$6031.31	$6037.22
7	4	$6420.36	$6428.74
8	5	$6834.50	$6845.65
9	6	$7275.35	$7289.60
10	7	$7744.64	$7762.34
11	8	$8244.20	$8265.74
12	9	$8775.99	$8801.79
13	10	$9342.07	$9372.59

(a) from quarterly and monthly spreadsheets: after $6\frac{1}{2}$ years (26 quarters or 78 months)

(b) See the spreadsheet.

47. (a) 24, 48, 96   (b) 24, 16, $\frac{32}{3}$ (c) 32, -128, 512

49. $10(2^{12})$ **51.** $4 \cdot \left(\frac{3}{2}\right)^{15}$ **53.** $\dfrac{6(1-3^{17})}{-2}$

55. $\dfrac{3^{35}-1}{2}$ **57.** $18\left[1-\left(\frac{2}{3}\right)^{18}\right]$

59. $350,580 (approx.)   **61.** 24.4 million (approx.)

63. 35 years   **65.** 40.5 ft   **67.** $4096

69. 320,000   **71.** $7,231,366   **73.** 6; $5^6 = 15,625$

75. 305,175,780

6.3 EXERCISES

1. (a) $S = \$285,129 =$ future value; $R = 2500$; $i = 0.02$; $n = 60$

(b) $R = \$1426 =$ payment; $S = 80{,}000$; $i = 0.04$; $n = 30$

3. (a) The higher graph is $1120 per year.

(b) $R = \$1000$: $S = \$73{,}105.94$;
$R = \$1120$: $S = \$81{,}878.65$;
Difference $= \$8772.71$

5. $7328.22   **7.** $107,296.72   **9.** $1482.94

11. $n \approx 27.1$; 28 quarters   **13.** $4651.61

15. $1180.78   **17.** $41,523.18   **19.** $3787.92

21. $n \approx 17.7$; 18 quarters

23. (a) ordinary annuity   (b) $4774.55

25. (a) annuity due   (b) $3974.73

27. (a) ordinary annuity   (b) $1083.40

29. (a) ordinary annuity   (b) $1130.51

31. (a) annuity due   (b) $290,976.81

33. (a) ordinary annuity   (b) $n \approx 108.5$; 109 months

35. (a) annuity due   (b) $235.16

37. (a) annuity due   (b) $79,551.38

39. (a) ordinary annuity   (b) $795.75

41. $53,677.40

43. (a) $n \approx 35$ quarters   (b) $1,062,412 (nearest dollar)

6.4 EXERCISES

1. (a) $A_n = \$22{,}480 =$ present value; $R = 1300$; $i = 0.04$; $n = 30$

(b) $R = \$809 =$ payment; $A_n = 135{,}000$; $i = 0.005$; $n = 360$

3. $69,913.77   **5.** $2,128,391   **7.** $4595.46

9. $n \approx 73.8$; 74 quarters   **11.** $1141.81; premium

13. (a) The higher graph corresponds to 8%.

(b) $1500 (approximately)

(c) With an interest rate of 10%, a present value of about $9000 is needed to purchase an annuity of $1000 for 25 years. If the interest rate is 8%, about $10,500 is needed.

15. Ordinary annuity—payments at the end of each period
Annuity due—payments at the beginning of each period

17. $69,632.02   **19.** $445,962.23   **21.** $2145.59

23. (a) ordinary annuity   (b) $10,882.46

25. (a) annuity due   (b) $316,803.61

27. (a) ordinary annuity

(b) Taking $500,000 and $140,000 payments for the next 10 years has a slightly higher present value: $1,506,436.24.

29. (a) annuity due   (b) $146,235.06

31. (a) ordinary annuity

(b) $n \approx 1025.7$; 1026 months; about 85.5 yrs.

33. (a) annuity due   (b) $22,663.74

35. (a) ordinary annuity   (b) $11,810.24

37. (a) ordinary annuity   (b) $27,590.62

39. (a) $8629.16   (b) $9883.48

41. (a) $30,078.99   (b) $16,900   (c) $607.02

(d) $36,421.20

43. (a) $4504.85   (b) $n \approx 21.9$; 22 withdrawals

45. $25,785.99   **47.** $74,993.20   **49.** $59,768.91

51. $1317.98   **53.** $1,290,673.16

55. (a) The spreadsheet below shows the payments for the first 12 months and the last 12 months. Full payments for $13\frac{1}{2}$ years.

	A	B	C	D
1	End of Month	Acct. Value	Payment	New Balance
2	0	$100000.00	$0.00	$100000.00
3	1	$100650.00	$1000.00	$99650.00
4	2	$100297.73	$1000.00	$99297.73
5	3	$99943.16	$1000.00	$98943.16
6	4	$99586.29	$1000.00	$98586.29
7	5	$99227.10	$1000.00	$98227.10
8	6	$98865.58	$1000.00	$97865.58
9	7	$98501.70	$1000.00	$97501.70
10	8	$98135.47	$1000.00	$97135.47
11	9	$97766.85	$1000.00	$96766.85
12	10	$97395.83	$1000.00	$96395.83
13	11	$97022.40	$1000.00	$96022.40
14	12	$96646.55	$1000.00	$95646.55
⋮	⋮	⋮	⋮	⋮
154	152	$10684.71	$1000.00	$9684.71
155	153	$9747.66	$1000.00	$8747.66
156	154	$8804.52	$1000.00	$7804.52
157	155	$7855.25	$1000.00	$6855.25
158	156	$6899.81	$1000.00	$5899.81
159	157	$5938.16	$1000.00	$4938.16
160	158	$4970.25	$1000.00	$3970.25
161	159	$3996.06	$1000.00	$2996.06
162	160	$3015.53	$1000.00	$2015.53
163	161	$2028.64	$1000.00	$1028.64
164	162	$1035.32	$1000.00	$35.32
165	163	$35.55	$35.55	$0.00

(b) The spreadsheet below shows the payments for the first 12 months and the last 12 months. Full payments for almost 4 years.

	A	B	C	D
1	End of Month	Acct. Value	Payment	New Balance
2	0	$100000.00	$0.00	$100000.00
3	1	$100650.00	$2500.00	$98150.00
4	2	$98787.98	$2500.00	$96287.98
5	3	$96913.85	$2500.00	$94413.85
6	4	$95027.54	$2500.00	$92527.54
7	5	$93128.97	$2500.00	$90628.97
8	6	$91218.05	$2500.00	$88718.05
9	7	$89294.72	$2500.00	$86794.72
10	8	$87358.89	$2500.00	$84858.89
11	9	$85410.47	$2500.00	$82910.47
12	10	$83449.39	$2500.00	$80949.39
13	11	$81475.56	$2500.00	$78975.56
14	12	$79488.90	$2500.00	$76988.90
⋮	⋮	⋮	⋮	⋮
38	36	$27734.95	$2500.00	$25234.95
39	37	$25398.98	$2500.00	$22898.98
40	38	$23047.83	$2500.00	$20547.83
41	39	$20681.39	$2500.00	$18181.39
42	40	$18299.57	$2500.00	$15799.57
43	41	$15902.26	$2500.00	$13402.26
44	42	$13489.38	$2500.00	$10989.38
45	43	$11060.81	$2500.00	$8560.81
46	44	$8616.45	$2500.00	$6116.45
47	45	$6156.21	$2500.00	$3656.21
48	46	$3679.98	$2500.00	$1179.98
49	47	$1187.65	$1187.65	$0.00

6.5 EXERCISES

1. (a) the 10-year loan because the loan must be paid more quickly
   (b) the 25-year loan because the loan is paid more slowly

3. $1288.29

5. $553.42

7. $31,035.34

9.

Period	Payment	Interest
1	$39,505.48	$9000.00
2	39,505.48	6254.51
3	39,505.47	3261.92
	118,516.43	18,516.43

Period	Balance Reduction	Unpaid Balance
		$100,000.00
1	$30,505.48	69,494.52
2	33,250.97	36,243.55
3	36,243.55	0.00
	100,000.00	

11.

Period	Payment	Interest
1	$5380.54	$600.00
2	5380.54	456.58
3	5380.54	308.87
4	5380.54	156.71
	21,522.16	1,522.16

Period	Balance Reduction	Unpaid Balance
		$20,000.00
1	$4780.54	15,219.46
2	4923.96	10,295.50
3	5071.67	5,223.83
4	5223.83	0.00
	20,000.00	

13. $8852.05

15. $11,571.67

17. (a) $17,436.92
    (b) $348,738.40 + $150,000 = $498,738.40
    (c) $148,738.40

19. (a) $11,714.19
    (b) $1,405,702.80 + $250,000 = $1,655,702.80
    (c) $405,702.80

21. $8903.25

23. (a) $276,991.32
    (b) $263,575.30

25. (a) $89,120.53
    (b) $6451.45

27. (a) $168,121.30
    (b) $1286.12
    (c) $56,282.40

29. (a) $368.43; $15.57
    (b) $n \approx 57$; the 57th payment will be slightly larger
    (c) $217.80

31. (a) $12,007,827.36
    (b) $246,017.20
    (c) $n \approx 86.9$; 87 payments (rather than 100)

33. (a) The line is the total amount paid ($644.30 per month $\times$ the number of months). The curve is the total amount paid toward the principal.
    (b)

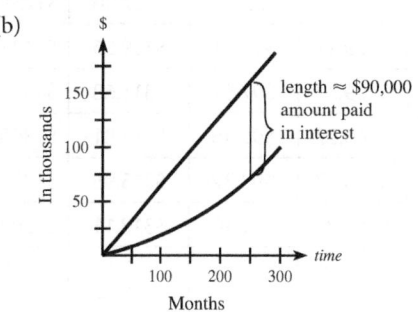

35.

	Rate	Payment	Total Interest
(a)	8%	$366.19	$2577.12
	8.5%	$369.72	$2746.56
(b)	6.75%	$518.88	$106,796.80
	7.25%	$545.74	$116,466.40
(c)	8.0%	$587.01	$131,323.60
	8.5%	$615.13	$141,446.80

37.

		Payment	Points	Total Paid
(a)	(i)	$738.99	–	$221,697
	(ii)	$722.81	$1000	$217,843
	(iii)	$706.78	$2000	$214,034

   (b) the 7% loan with 2 points

39. (a) $17,525.20
    (b) $508.76
    (c) 33.2 payments with an extra $101.16 added to the last payment
    (d) $490.16

41. The spreadsheet shows the amortization schedule for the first 12 and last 12 payments.

	A	B	C	D	E
1	Period	Payment	Interest	Bal. Reduction	Unpaid Bal.
2	0				$16700.00
3	1	$409.27	$114.12	$295.15	$16404.85
4	2	$409.27	$112.10	$297.17	$16107.68
5	3	$409.27	$110.07	$299.20	$15808.48
6	4	$409.27	$108.02	$301.25	$15507.23
7	5	$409.27	$105.97	$303.30	$15203.93
8	6	$409.27	$103.89	$305.38	$14898.55
9	7	$409.27	$101.81	$307.46	$14591.09
10	8	$409.27	$99.71	$309.56	$14281.52
11	9	$409.27	$97.59	$311.68	$13969.84
12	10	$409.27	$95.46	$313.81	$13656.03
13	11	$409.27	$93.32	$315.95	$13340.08
14	12	$409.27	$91.16	$318.11	$13021.97
	⋮	⋮	⋮	⋮	⋮
39	37	$409.27	$32.11	$377.16	$4322.49
40	38	$409.27	$29.54	$379.73	$3942.75
41	39	$409.27	$26.94	$382.33	$3560.43
42	40	$409.27	$24.33	$384.94	$3175.49
43	41	$409.27	$21.70	$387.57	$2787.91
44	42	$409.27	$19.05	$390.22	$2397.70
45	43	$409.27	$16.38	$392.89	$2004.81
46	44	$409.27	$13.70	$395.57	$1609.24
47	45	$409.27	$11.00	$398.27	$1210.97
48	46	$409.27	$8.27	$401.00	$809.97
49	47	$409.27	$5.53	$403.74	$406.24
50	48	$409.02	$2.78	$406.24	$0.00

CHAPTER 6 REVIEW EXERCISES

1. $1, \frac{1}{4}, \frac{1}{9}, \frac{1}{16}$

2. arithmetic: (a) and (c)   (a) $d = -5$ (c) $d = \frac{1}{6}$

3. 235   **4.** 109   **5.** 315

6. geometric: (a) and (b)   (a) $r = 8$ (b) $r = -\frac{3}{4}$

7. 8   **8.** $2, 391, 484\frac{4}{9}$

9. $10,880   **10.** $6\frac{2}{3}\%$ **11.** $2941.18   **12.** $4650

13. the $40,000 job ($490,000 versus $472,500)

14. (a) 40   (b) $2\% = 0.02$

15. (a) $S = P(1 + i)^n$ (b) $S = Pe^{rt}$

16. (b) monthly   **17.** $372.79   **18.** $14,510.26

19. $1616.07   **20.** $21,299.21

21. $n \approx 34.3$; 35 quarters

22. (a) 13.29%   (b) 14.21%

23. (a) 7.40%   (b) 7.47%

24. 2^{63} **25.** $2^{32} - 1$ **26.** $29,428.47

27. $6069.44   **28.** $31,194.18   **29.** $10,841.24

30. $n \approx 36$ quarters   **31.** $130,079.36   **32.** $12,007.09

33. (a) $11.828 million   (b) $161.5 million

34. $1726.85   **35.** $5390.77

36. $4053.54; discount   **37.** $n \approx 16$ half-years (8 years)

38. $88.85   **39.** $3443.61   **40.** $163,792.21

41.

Payment Number	Payment Amount	Interest	Balance Reduction	Unpaid Balance
57	$699.22	$594.01	$105.21	$94,936.99
58	$699.22	$593.36	$105.86	$94,831.13

42. (a) $401,134.67   (b) $45,596.63
(c) $22,376.50

43. $S = R\left[\dfrac{(1 + i)^n - 1}{i}\right]$ **44.** $I = Prt$

45. $A_n = R\left[\dfrac{1 - (1 + i)^{-n}}{i}\right]$ **46.** $S = P(1 + i)^n$

47. $A_n = R\left[\dfrac{1 - (1 + i)^{-n}}{i}\right]$, solved for R

48. $S = Pe^{rt}$ **49.** 16.32%   **50.** $213.81

51. (a) $1480   (b) $1601.03

52. $9319.64   **53.** 14.5 years   **54.** 79.4%

55. $381,195

56. (a) $4728.19   (b) $5398.07 (c) $1749.88
(d) 10.78%

57. $21,474.08   **58.** $12,162.06

59. Quarterly APY = 6.68%. This rate is better for the bank; it pays less interest. Continuous APY = 6.69%. This rate is better for the consumer, who earns more interest.

60. (a) $243,429.20
(b) $1825.11
(c) $n \approx 158.9$; 159 payments (rather than 180)
(d) $62,438.30

61. $32,834.69   **62.** $3,466.64

63. (a) $1185.51   (b) $355,653   (c) $171,653
(d) $\approx$ $156,366

64. (a) $95,164.21   (b) $1300.14

65. $994.08

66. Future value of IRA = $172,971.32
Present value needed = $2,321,520.10
Future value needed from deposits = $2,148,548.78
Deposits = $711.60

67. Regular payment = $64,337.43

Unpaid balance = $2,365,237.24

Number of $70,000 payments = $n \approx 46.1$

Savings $\approx$ $118,546

CHAPTER 6 TEST

1. 25.3 years (approximately) **2.** $7999.41

3. 6.87% **4.** $158,524.90 **5.** 33.53%

6. (a) $698 (b) $112,400

7. $2625 **8.** $815.47 **9.** 8.73%

10. $119,912.92 **11.** $40,552.00 **12.** $22,439.01

13. $6781.17 **14.** $n \approx 66.8$; 67 half-years

15. $116,909.12 **16.** $29,716.47

17. (a) $161,270.52 (b) $924.08 (c) $5788.80

18. $12,975.49; premium

19. (a) The difference between successive terms is always -5.5.

(b) 23.8 (c) 8226.3

20. 1000 mg (approximately)

21. (a) $145,585.54 (with the $2000);

$147,585.54 (without the $2000)

(b) $n \approx 318.8$; 319 months

Total interest = $243,738.13

(c) $n \approx 317.2$; 318 months

Total interest = $245,378.24

(d) Paying the $2000 is slightly better; it saves about $1640 in interest.

22. $1688.02

23. (a) $279,841.35 (b) $13,124.75

7.1 EXERCISES

1. (a) $\frac{2}{5}$ (b) 0 (c) 1 **3.** $\frac{1}{4}$ **5.** 1

7. (a) $\frac{3}{10}$ (b) $\frac{1}{2}$ (c) $\frac{1}{5}$ (d) $\frac{3}{5}$ (e) $\frac{7}{10}$

9. (a) $\frac{1}{13}$ (b) $\frac{1}{2}$ (c) $\frac{1}{4}$

11. {HH, HT, TH, TT}; (a) $\frac{1}{4}$ (b) $\frac{1}{2}$ (c) $\frac{1}{4}$

13. (a) $\frac{1}{12}$ (b) $\frac{1}{12}$ (c) $\frac{1}{36}$ **15.** (a) $\frac{1}{2}$ (b) $\frac{5}{12}$

17. (a) $\frac{431}{1200}$

(b) If fair, $Pr(6) = \frac{1}{6}$; $\frac{431}{1200}$ not close to $\frac{1}{6}$, so not a fair die

19. (a) 2:3 (b) 3:2 **21.** (a) $\frac{1}{21}$ (b) $\frac{20}{21}$

23. 0.46 **25.** (a) $\frac{63}{425}$ (b) $\frac{32}{425}$

27. (a) R: 0.63 D: 0.41 I: 0.51

(b) Republican

29. (a) $\frac{1}{3601}$ (b) $\frac{100}{3601}$ (c) $\frac{3500}{3601}$

(d) 30%

31. (a) 0.402 (b) 0.491 (c) 100%; yes

33. $S = \{A+, A-, B+, B-, AB+, AB-, O+, O-\}$; No. Type O+ is the most frequently occurring blood type.

35. (a) 0.04 (b) 0.96 **37.** (a) 0.13 (b) 0.87

39. 0.03 **41.** 0.75 **43.** $\frac{1}{3}$ **45.** $\frac{1}{3}$

47. 0.22; yes, 0.39 is much higher than 0.22 **49.** $\frac{3}{8}$

51. (a) no (b) {BB, BG, GB, GG} (c) $\frac{1}{2}$

53. $\frac{1}{8}$ **55.** $\frac{3}{125}$

57. $Pr(A) = 0.000019554$, or about 2.0 accidents per 100,000

$Pr(B) = 0.000035919$, or about 3.6 accidents per 100,000

$Pr(C) = 0.000037679$, or about 3.8 accidents per 100,000

Intersection C is the most dangerous.

59. (a) $\frac{557}{1200}$ (b) $\frac{11}{120}$

61. (a) boy: $\frac{1}{5}$; girl: $\frac{4}{5}$

(b) boy: 0.4946; girl: 0.5054 (c) part (b)

63. $\frac{3}{4}$ **65.** $\frac{3}{3995} \approx 0.00075$

67. Probability ≈ 0.058; odds 471 to 29

7.2 EXERCISES

1. (a) $\frac{1}{6}$ (b) $\frac{2}{3}$ **3.** (a) 0 (b) $\frac{3}{4}$ **5.** $\frac{2}{3}$

7. $\frac{2}{5}$ **9.** (a) $\frac{1}{7}$ (b) $\frac{5}{7}$ (c) $\frac{5}{7}$

11. (a) 0 (b) $\frac{3}{7}$ (c) $\frac{5}{7}$ **13.** $\frac{5}{12}$ **15.** $\frac{10}{17}$

17. $\frac{2}{3}$ **19.** (a) $\frac{1}{2}$ (b) $\frac{1}{3}$ (c) $\frac{8}{9}$ (d) $\frac{1}{9}$

21. 0.54 **23.** (a) $\frac{362}{425}$ (b) $\frac{66}{85}$

25. $\frac{17}{50}$ **27.** (a) $\frac{5}{6}$ (b) $\frac{1}{6}$

29. (a) 0.35 (b) 0.08 (c) 0.83

31. (a) 0.508 (b) 0.633 (c) 0.761

33. (a) 0.218 (b) 0.023 (c) 0.941

35. (a) $\frac{11}{12}$ (b) $\frac{5}{6}$ **37.** (a) $\frac{1}{2}$ (b) $\frac{7}{8}$ (c) $\frac{3}{4}$

39. 0.56 **41.** 0.965

43. (a) 0.72 (b) 0.84 (c) 0.61

45. $\frac{31}{40}$ **47.** 0.13

7.3 EXERCISES

1. (a) $\frac{1}{2}$ (b) $\frac{1}{13}$ **3.** (a) $\frac{1}{3}$ (b) $\frac{1}{3}$ **5.** $\frac{4}{7}$

7. (a) $\frac{2}{3}$ (b) $\frac{4}{9}$ (c) $\frac{3}{5}$ **9.** (a) $\frac{1}{4}$ (b) $\frac{1}{2}$

11. $\frac{1}{36}$ **13.** (a) $\frac{1}{8}$ (b) $\frac{7}{8}$

15. (a) $\frac{3}{50}$ (b) $\frac{1}{15}$

(c) The events in part (a) are independent because the result of the first draw does not affect the probability for the second draw.

17. (a) $\frac{4}{25}$ (b) $\frac{9}{25}$ (c) $\frac{6}{25}$ (d) 0 **19.** $\frac{5}{68}$

21. (a) $\frac{1}{5}$ (b) $\frac{3}{5}$ (c) 0 **23.** (a) $\frac{1}{17}$ (b) $\frac{13}{204}$

25. (a) $\frac{13}{17}$ (b) $\frac{4}{17}$ (c) $\frac{8}{51}$ **27.** $\frac{31}{52}$ **29.** $\frac{25}{96}$

31. $\frac{43}{50}$ **33.** $\frac{65}{87}$ **35.** $\frac{35}{435} = \frac{7}{87}$ **37.** $\frac{1}{10}$

39. $\frac{1}{144,000,000}$ **41.** 0.004292 **43.** 0.06

45. 0.045 **47.** $(0.95)^5 = 0.774$ **49.** 0.06

51. (a) 0.366 (b) 0.634

53. (a) 0.4565 (b) 0.5435

55. (a) $\left(\frac{1}{3}\right)^3 \left(\frac{1}{5}\right)^4 = \frac{1}{16,875}$

(b) $\left(\frac{2}{3}\right)^3 \left(\frac{4}{5}\right)^4 = \frac{2048}{16,875}$ (c) $\frac{14,827}{16,875}$

57. $\frac{4}{11}$; 4:7

59. (a) $\frac{364}{365}$ (b) $\frac{1}{365}$

61. (a) 0.59 (b) 0.41

7.4 EXERCISES

1. (a) $\frac{2}{5}$ (b) $\frac{1}{5}$ **3.** (a) $\frac{2}{21}$ (b) $\frac{4}{21}$ (c) $\frac{23}{35}$

5. (a) $\frac{5}{42}$ (b) $\frac{10}{21}$ (c) $\frac{4}{9}$

7. (a) $\frac{1}{30}$ (b) $\frac{1}{2}$ (c) $\frac{5}{6}$

9. (a) $\frac{6}{25}$ (b) $\frac{9}{25}$ (c) $\frac{12}{25}$ (d) $\frac{19}{25}$

11. (a) $\frac{7}{12}$ (b) $\frac{3}{13}$ (c) $\frac{19}{26}$ (d) $\frac{11}{36}$

13. $\frac{2}{3}$ **15.** $\frac{2}{3}$ **17.** 0.3095

19. (a) $\frac{81}{10,000}$ (b) $\frac{1323}{5000}$

21. (a) $\frac{6}{35}$ (b) $\frac{6}{35}$ (c) $\frac{12}{35}$

23. (a) $\frac{4}{7}$ (b) $\frac{5}{14}$ (c) $\frac{7}{10}$ (d) $\frac{16}{25}$

25. (a) 0.0015 (b) 0.006 (c) 0.627; 0.373
   (d) No. Pr(HIV($-$)|Test($+$)) = 0.373 means that 37.3% of those testing positive do not have HIV. This is too inaccurate to be effective.

27. 0.079 **29.** (a) $\frac{49}{100}$ (b) $\frac{12}{49}$

7.5 EXERCISES

1. 360 **3.** 151,200 **5.** 1

7. (a) $6 \cdot 5 \cdot 4 \cdot 3 = 360$ (b) $6^4 = 1296$ **9.** $n!$

11. $n + 1$ **13.** 16 **15.** 4950 **17.** 1 **19.** 1

21. 10 **23.** (a) 8 (b) 240 **25.** (a) 432 (b) 400

27. (a) 604,800 (b) $10^7 = 10,000,000$

29. 24 **31.** 64 **33.** 720

35. $2^{10} = 1024$ **37.** $4(_{13}C_5) = 5148$

39. 10,816,000 **41.** 30,045,015 **43.** 792

45. 210 **47.** 2,891,999,880 **49.** (a) $_{80}C_{10}$ (b) $(_{52}C_7)(_{28}C_3)$

7.6 EXERCISES

1. $\frac{1}{120}$ **3.** (a) 120 (b) $\frac{1}{120}$

5. 0.639 **7.** (a) $\frac{1}{10,000}$ (b) $\frac{1}{5040}$

9. $\frac{1}{10^6}$ **11.** 0.000048 **13.** $\frac{1}{10!} = \frac{1}{3,628,800}$

15. (a) $\frac{1}{22}$ (b) $\frac{6}{11}$ (c) $\frac{9}{22}$

17. 0.098 **19.** $\dfrac{_{90}C_{28} \cdot {}_{10}C_2}{_{100}C_{30}}$

21. (a) 0.119 (b) 0.0476 (c) 0.476

23. 0.0238 **25.** (a) 0.721 (b) 0.262 (c) 0.279

27. (a) $\frac{1}{3}$ (b) $\frac{1}{6}$ **29.** $\dfrac{_{20}C_{10}}{_{80}C_{10}} = 0.00000011$

31. (a) 0.033 (b) 0.633

33. (a) 0.0005 (b) 0.011 **35.** 0.00198

37. (a) $\frac{1}{1000} = 0.001$
   (b) 444, 446, 464, 644, 466, 646, 664, 666
   (c) $\frac{1}{8} = 0.125$

7.7 EXERCISES

1. can **3.** cannot, sum $\neq$ 1

5. cannot, not square **7.** can

9. [0.248 0.752] **11.** [0.228 0.236 0.536]

13. [0.25 0.75] **15.** [0.249 0.249 0.502]

17. $[\frac{1}{4}\ \frac{3}{4}]$ **19.** $[\frac{1}{4}\ \frac{1}{4}\ \frac{1}{2}]$

21. [0.5 0.4 0.1]; [0.44 0.43 0.13]; [0.431 0.43 0.139]; [0.4292 0.4291 0.1417]

23.
$$\begin{array}{c} \\ R \\ N \end{array} \begin{array}{cc} R & N \\ \begin{bmatrix} 0.8 & 0.2 \\ 0.3 & 0.7 \end{bmatrix} \end{array}$$
25. 0.45

27.
$$\begin{array}{c} \\ A \\ F \\ V \end{array} \begin{array}{ccc} A & F & V \\ \begin{bmatrix} 0 & 0.7 & 0.3 \\ 0.6 & 0 & 0.4 \\ 0.8 & 0.2 & 0 \end{bmatrix} \end{array}$$

29. [0.3928 0.37 0.2372]

31. $[\frac{46}{113}\ \frac{38}{113}\ \frac{29}{113}]$

33.
$$\begin{array}{c} \\ r \\ u \end{array} \begin{array}{cc} r & u \\ \begin{bmatrix} 0.7 & 0.3 \\ 0.1 & 0.9 \end{bmatrix} \end{array}; [\frac{1}{4}\ \frac{3}{4}]$$

35. $[\frac{1}{14}\ \frac{3}{14}\ \frac{5}{7}]$ **37.** $[\frac{4}{7}\ \frac{2}{7}\ \frac{1}{7}]$ **39.** $[\frac{49}{100}\ \frac{42}{100}\ \frac{9}{100}]$

CHAPTER 7 REVIEW EXERCISES

1. (a) $\frac{5}{9}$ (b) $\frac{1}{3}$ (c) $\frac{2}{9}$

2. (a) S_1 (b) $\frac{3}{4}$ (c) $\frac{1}{2}$ (d) $\frac{1}{6}$ (e) $\frac{2}{3}$

3. (a) 3:4 (b) 4:3 **4.** (a) $\frac{1}{4}$ (b) $\frac{1}{2}$ (c) $\frac{1}{4}$

5. (a) $\frac{3}{8}$ (b) $\frac{1}{8}$ (c) $\frac{3}{8}$ **6.** $\frac{2}{13}$ **7.** $\frac{16}{169}$

8. $\frac{3}{4}$ **9.** $\frac{2}{13}$ **10.** $\frac{7}{13}$ **11.** (a) $\frac{2}{9}$ (b) $\frac{2}{3}$ (c) $\frac{7}{9}$

12. (a) $\frac{2}{7}$ (b) $\frac{4}{7}$ **13.** (a) $\frac{3}{10}$ (b) $\frac{1}{2}$

14. (a) $\frac{7}{320}$ (b) $\frac{21}{320}$

15. (a) $\frac{7}{342}$ (b) $\frac{6}{19}$ **16.** $\frac{3}{14}$ **17.** $\frac{8}{15}$

18. (a) $\frac{3}{14}$ (b) $\frac{4}{7}$ (c) $\frac{3}{8}$ **19.** $\frac{49}{89}$

20. 30 **21.** 35 **22.** 26^3 **23.** 56

24. (a) not square (b) The row sums are not 1.

25. [0.76 0.24], [0.496 0.504]

26. [0.2 0.8]

27. $\frac{5}{8}$ **28.** $\frac{1}{4}$ **29.** $\frac{29}{50}$

30. $\frac{5}{56}$ **31.** $\frac{33}{56}$ **32.** $\frac{15}{22}$ **33.** 0.72

34. (a) 0.80 (b) 0.75
   (c) No. $0.224 = \text{Pr(auto)} \cdot \text{Pr(suv)} \neq \text{Pr(auto and suv)} = 0.21$
   (d) 0.40
   (e) Yes. $\text{Pr(conv)} \cdot \text{Pr(man)} = \text{Pr(conv and man)} = 0.08$

35. (a) $\frac{63}{2000}$ (b) $60/63 = 20/21$ **36.** $\frac{39}{116}$

37. (a) 0.1984 (b) $8/31 \approx 0.2581$ **38.** $4! = 24$

39. $_8P_4 = 1680$ **40.** $_{12}C_4 = 495$ **41.** $_8C_4 = 70$

42. (a) $_{12}C_2 = 66$ (b) $_{12}C_3 = 220$ **43.** 1,544,760

44. If her assumption about blood groups is accurate, there would be $4 \cdot 2 \cdot 4 \cdot 8 = 256$, not 288, unique groups.

45. $\frac{1}{24}$ **46.** $\frac{3}{500}$ **47.** $\frac{3}{1250}$

48. (a) 0.3398 (b) 0.1975 **49.** $\frac{1}{10}$

50. (a) $(_{10}C_5)(_2C_1)/_{12}C_6$
   (b) $\dfrac{(_{10}C_5)(_2C_1) + (_{10}C_4)(_2C_2)}{_{12}C_6}$

51. [0.135 0.51 0.355], [0.09675 0.3305 0.57275], [0.0640875 0.288275 0.6476375]

52. $[\frac{12}{265}\ \frac{68}{265}\ \frac{37}{53}]$

CHAPTER 7 TEST

1. (a) $\frac{4}{7}$ (b) $\frac{3}{7}$ **2.** (a) $\frac{2}{7}$ (b) $\frac{5}{7}$

3. (a) 0 (b) 1 **4.** $\frac{1}{7}$ **5.** $\frac{1}{7}$

6. (a) $\frac{2}{7}$ (b) $\frac{4}{7}$ **7.** $\frac{2}{7}$ **8.** $\frac{3}{7}$ **9.** $\frac{2}{3}$

10. $\frac{1}{17,576}$ **11.** 0.2389 **12.** (a) $\frac{1}{5}$ (b) $\frac{1}{20}$

13. (a) $\frac{3}{95}$ (b) $\frac{6}{19}$ (c) $\frac{21}{38}$ (d) 0

14. (a) 5,245,786 (b) $\frac{1}{5,245,786}$

15. (a) 2,118,760 (b) $\frac{1}{2,118,760}$

16. 0.064 **17.** (a) 0.633 (b) 0.962 **18.** 0.229

19. (a) $\frac{1}{5}$ (b) $\frac{1}{14}$ (c) $\frac{13}{14}$ **20.** $\frac{3}{14}$

21. (a) 2^{10} (b) $\dfrac{1}{2^{10}}$ (c) $\frac{1}{3}$ (d) Change the code.

22. (a) $A = \begin{bmatrix} 0.80 & 0.20 \\ 0.07 & 0.93 \end{bmatrix}$ (b) [0.25566 0.74434];
about 25.6% (c) $\frac{7}{27}$; 25.9% of market

8.1 EXERCISES

1. (a) 1/6 (b) 5/6 (c) 18 (d) 0.045
3. (a) 0.0595 (b) 0.8824
5. (a) $\frac{1}{64}$ (b) $\frac{5}{16}$ (c) $\frac{15}{64}$ (d) $\frac{57}{64}$
7. (a) $\frac{1}{6}$ (b) 0.0284 (c) 0.1122
9. (a) 0.2304 (b) 0.0102 (c) 0.3174
11. 0.0585 **13.** 0.2759
15. (a) 0.375 (b) 0.0625
17. (a) 0.035 (b) 0.706
19. (a) 0.0016 (b) 0.9984 (c) 0.9728
21. (a) 0.0729 (b) 0.5905 (c) 0.9914
23. 0.2457 **25.** 0.0007
27. (a) 0.1323 (b) 0.0308
29. (a) 0.9044 (b) 0.0914 (c) 0.0043
31. (a) 0.8683 (b) 0.2099 **33.** 0.740

8.2 EXERCISES

1.

3.

5.

7.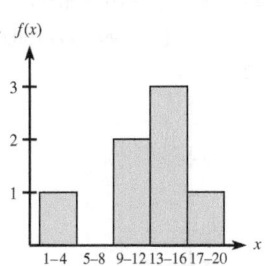

9. 3 **11.** 13 **13.** 5 **15.** 10.5
17. mode = 2, median = 4.5, mean = 6
19. mode = 17, median = 18.5, mean = 23.5
21. mode = 5.3, median = 5.3, mean = 5.32
23. 12.21, 14.5, 14.5 **25.** 9 **27.** 14
29. 4, 8.5714, 2.9277 **31.** 14, 4.6667, 2.1602
33. 2.73, 1.35 **35.** 6.75, 2.96

37. (a)

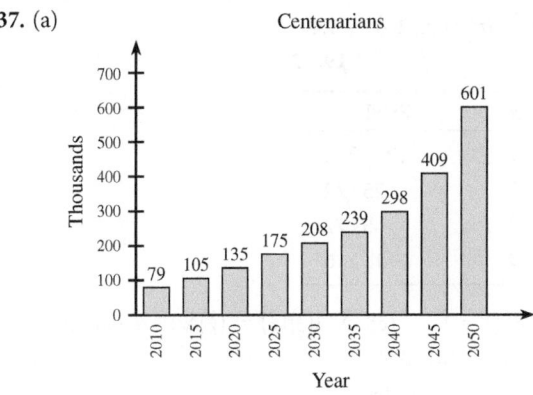

Centenarians

(b) $\bar{x} \approx 249.9; s \approx 166.5$

39.

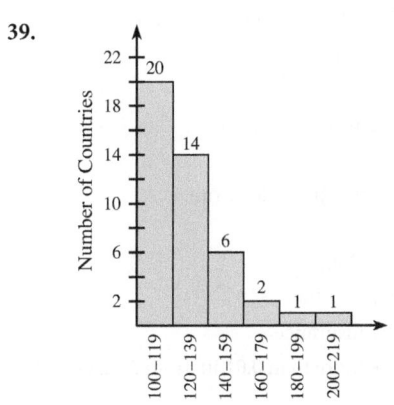

41. (a) The mean will give the highest measure.
(b) The mode will give the lowest measure.
(c) The median will give the most representative average.
43. (a) $\bar{x} \approx 63.4\%; s \approx 19.3\%$ (b) yes
45.

47. (a) $\bar{x} = 49$ thousand dollars
(b) $s \approx 3.37$ thousand dollars
49. (a) $60,000 (b) $36,000 (c) $32,000
51. (a) $23.33 (b) $5.14
53. (a) 35,434,000 (b) 13,312,000

8.3 EXERCISES

1. no; $\Pr(x) \not\geq 0$ **3.** yes; both conditions satisfied
5. yes; both conditions satisfied
7. no; $\Sigma \Pr(x) > 1$ **9.** $\frac{15}{8}$ **11.** 5
13. $\mu = \frac{13}{8}, \sigma^2 \approx 1.48, \sigma \approx 1.22$

15. $\mu = \frac{13}{3}, \sigma^2 \approx 2.22, \sigma \approx 1.49$

17. 3 **19.** 2

21. (a)

x	Pr(x)
0	125/216
1	25/72
2	5/72
3	1/216

(b) $3\left(\frac{1}{6}\right) = \frac{1}{2}$ (c) $\sqrt{3\left(\frac{1}{6}\right)\left(\frac{5}{6}\right)} = \left(\frac{1}{6}\right)\sqrt{15} \approx 0.6455$

23. (a) 42 (b) 3.55

25. (a) 30 (b) 3.464

27. 125

29. $a^6 + 6a^5b + 15a^4b^2 + 20a^3b^3 + 15a^2b^4 + 6ab^5 + b^6$

31. $x^4 + 4x^3h + 6x^2h^2 + 4xh^3 + h^4$

33. 1.85

35. TV: 37,500; personal appearances: 35,300

37. $-\$67.33$

39. Expect to lose $2 per game in the long run.

41. 100

43. E(cost with policy) = \$390;
E(cost without policy) = \$400;
save \$10 by buying the insurance

45. no; some pipes may be more than 0.01 in. from 2 in. even if average is 2 in.

47. (a) $100(0.10) = 10$ (b) $\sqrt{100(0.10)(0.90)} = 3$

49. (a) 60,000 (b) $\sqrt{24,000} \approx 154.9$ (c) 59,690

51. (a) 4 (b) 1.79

53. 2, 1.41 **55.** 300

57. (a) $\mu = 1.8;$ $\sigma \approx 1.237$
(b) 0.9078
(c) $C(x) = 208,000 + 9000x;$ \$224,200

8.4 EXERCISES

1. 0.4641 **3.** 0.2257 **5.** 0.9153 **7.** 0.1070

9. 0.0166 **11.** 0.0228 **13.** 0.8849 **15.** 0.1915

17. 0.3944 **19.** 0.3830 **21.** 0.7745 **23.** 0.9772

25. 0.0668 **27.** -1.645 **29.** -0.3

31. (a) 0.3413 (b) 0.3944 **33.** 0.9876

35. (a) 0.4192 (b) 0.0228 (c) 0.0580 (d) 0.8965

37. (a) 0.0668 (b) 0.3085 (c) 0.3830

39. (a) 0.0475 (b) 0.2033 (c) 0.5934

41. (a) 0.0228 (b) 0.1587 (c) 0.8186

43. 86 **45.** 128.7 oz **47.** 1.544

8.5 EXERCISES

1. yes **3.** no **5.** 0.0668 **7.** 0.0001

9. 0.0521 **11.** 0.0110 **13.** 0.9890

15. 0.7324 **17.** 0.3520 **19.** 0.0443

21. 0.5398 **23.** 0.7852 **25.** 0.0129

27. 0.2514 **29.** 0.0011 **31.** 0.9990

33. 0.1272; 0.4364

35. (a) 0.0038 (b) yes; students were smarter or questions were leaked **37.** 0.0166

CHAPTER 8 REVIEW EXERCISES

1. 0.0774 **2.** (a) 0.3545 (b) 0.5534

3. 0.407

4.

5. 3
6. $\frac{77}{26} \approx 2.96$
7. 3

8. $f(x)$

9. 14

10. 14

11. 14.3

12. $\bar{x} \approx 3.86; s^2 \approx 6.81; s \approx 2.61$

13. $\bar{x} = 2; s^2 \approx 2.44; s \approx 1.56$

14. 2.4 **15.** yes **16.** no; $\Sigma\text{Pr}(x) \neq 1$

17. yes **18.** no; $\text{Pr}(x) \not\geq 0$ **19.** 2

20. (a) 4.125 (b) 2.7344 (c) 1.654

21. (a) 37/12 (b) 0.9097 (c) 0.9538

22. $\mu = 4, \sigma = (2\sqrt{3})/3 \approx 1.155$ **23.** 3

24. $x^5 + 5x^4y + 10x^3y^2 + 10x^2y^3 + 5xy^4 + y^5$

25. 0.9165 **26.** 0.1498 **27.** 0.1039 **28.** 0.3413

29. 0.6826 **30.** 0.1359 **31.** 2.33 **32.** not good

33. good **34.** 0.0151 **35.** 0.9625 **36.** 0.8475

37. 0.0119 **38.** 0.297 **39.** 0.16308 **40.** 0.2048

41. (a) $(99,999/100,000)^{99,999} \approx 0.37$
(b) $1 - (99,999/100,000)^{100,000} \approx 0.63$

42. $f(x)$

43. 30.3%
44. 8.35%
45. 455
46. 3
47. \$18
48. $-\$0.50$

49. (a) 1 (b) $\left(\frac{4}{5}\right)^4$

50. (a) 0.4772 (b) 0.1359 (c) 0.0228

51. 15% **52.** 47 minutes **53.** 0.3821

54. 0.4090 **55.** 0.0262 **56.** 0.1788

CHAPTER 8 TEST

1. (a) $\frac{40}{243}$ (b) $\frac{51}{243} = \frac{17}{81}$

2. (a) 4 (b) $\mu = 4, \sigma^2 = \frac{8}{3}, \sigma = \frac{2}{3}\sqrt{6}$

3. (i) For each $x, 0 \leq \text{Pr}(x) \leq 1$ (ii) $\Sigma\text{Pr}(x) = 1$

4. 5.1

5. $\mu \approx 16.7, \sigma^2 \approx 26.61, \sigma \approx 5.16$

6. $\bar{x} \approx 21.57$, median $= 21$, mode $= 21$

7. (a) 0.4706   (b) 0.8413   (c) 0.0669

8. (a) 0.3891   (b) 0.5418   (c) 0.1210

9. 38.4   10. 0.9554   11. 0.6331

12.

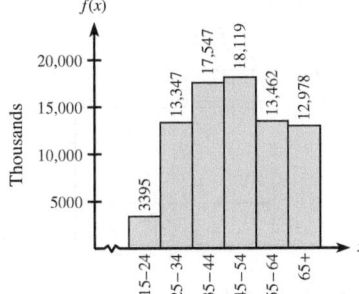

13. $\bar{x} = 48.3$, $s = 15.6$

14. (a) 38.5   (b) 60 or over; it would be lower

15. (a) 109.5   (b) increase unless a new technology replaces mobile phones

16. (a) 0.00003   (b) 30

17. 2 (1.8)   18. 5 (5.4)

19. 0 (0.054) with correct use

20. (a) 0.0158   (b) 0.0901   (c) 0.5383

21. 0.1814

22. $t \approx 0.98$ oz

9.1 EXERCISES

1. (a) 6   (b) 6

3. (a) 15   (b) does not exist

5. (a) 0   (b) 2

7. (a) does not exist (∞) (b) does not exist $(-\infty)$
(c) does not exist   (d) does not exist

9. (a) -2 (b) 0   (c) does not exist
(d) 0

11.

x	$f(x)$
0.9	-2.9
0.99	-2.99
0.999	-2.999
1.001	-3.001
1.01	-3.01
1.1	-3.1

$\lim\limits_{x \to 1} f(x) = -3$

13.

x	$f(x)$
0.9	3.5
0.99	3.95
0.999	3.995
1.001	4.995999
1.01	4.9599
1.1	4.59

$\lim\limits_{x \to 1^-} f(x) = 4$ and $\lim\limits_{x \to 1^+} f(x) = 5$. These limits differ so $\lim\limits_{x \to 1} f(x)$ does not exist

15. 2   17. -36 19. 1   21. -8

23. $2/5$ 25. 2   27. $3/2$ 29. 0   31. does not exist

33. -3 35. does not exist   37. does not exist

39. $3x^2$ 41. $\frac{1}{30}$ 43. does not exist

45. -4 47. 9

49.

a	$(1 + a)^{1/a}$
0.1	2.5937
0.01	2.7048
0.001	2.7169
0.0001	2.7181
0.00001	2.71827
$\downarrow$	$\downarrow$
0	≈ 2.718

51. (a) 2   (b) 6   (c) -8 (d) $-\frac{1}{2}$

53. (a) -6 (b) -85 (c) $-33/17$

55. $150,000

57. (a) $32 (thousands)   (b) $55.04 (thousands)

59. (a) $2800   (b) $700   (c) $560

61. (a) 1.52 units/hr   (b) 0.85 units/hr   (c) lunch

63. (a) 0; $p \to 100^-$ means the water approaches not being treated (containing 100% or all of its impurities); the associated costs of nontreatment approach zero.
(b) ∞ (c) no, because $C(0)$ is undefined

65. (a) $5081.25   (b) $5081.25   (c) $5081.25

67. $C(x) = \begin{cases} 12.76 + 15.96x & 0 \le x \le 10 \\ 172.36 + 13.56(x - 10) & 10 < x \le 120 \\ 1675 & x > 120 \end{cases}$

$\lim\limits_{x \to 10} C(x) = 172.36$

69. 11,228.00. This corresponds to the Dow Jones opening average.

71. (a) 33.7
(b) This predicts the percent of obese Americans who are severely obese as the year approaches 2040.
(c) Yes. The table shows increases of 3% to 6% per decade, and severe obesity is expected to get worse.

9.2 EXERCISES

1. (a) continuous
(b) discontinuous; $f(1)$ does not exist
(c) discontinuous; $\lim\limits_{x \to 3} f(x)$ does not exist
(d) discontinuous; $f(0)$ does not exist and $\lim\limits_{x \to 0} f(x)$ does not exist

3. continuous

5. discontinuous; $f(-3)$ does not exist

7. discontinuous; $\lim\limits_{x \to 2} f(x)$ does not exist

9. continuous

11. discontinuity at $x = -2$; $g(-2)$ and $\lim\limits_{x \to -2} g(x)$ do not exist

13. continuous   15. continuous

17. discontinuity at $x = -1$; $f(-1)$ does not exist

19. discontinuity at $x = 3$; $\lim\limits_{x \to 3} f(x)$ does not exist

21. vertical asymptote: $x = -2$;
$\lim\limits_{x \to \infty} f(x) = 0$; $\lim\limits_{x \to -\infty} f(x) = 0$; $y = 0$

23. vertical asymptotes: $x = -2$, $x = 3$;
$\lim\limits_{x \to \infty} f(x) = 2$; $\lim\limits_{x \to -\infty} f(x) = 2$; $y = 2$

25. (a) 0 (b) $y = 0$ is a horizontal asymptote.

27. (a) 1 (b) $y = 1$ is a horizontal asymptote.

29. (a) 5/3 (b) $y = 5/3$ is a horizontal asymptote.

31. (a) does not exist (∞)
(b) no horizontal asymptotes

33. (a)

$$\lim_{x \to \infty} f(x) = 0.5$$

(b) The table indicates $\lim_{x \to \infty} f(x) = 0.5$.

35. (a) $x = -1000$ (b) 1000
(c) These values are so large that experimenting with windows may never locate them.

37. $\lim_{x \to \infty} \left[\dfrac{a_n + \dfrac{a_{n-1}}{x} + \cdots + \dfrac{a_1}{x^{n-1}} + \dfrac{a_0}{x^n}}{b_n + \dfrac{b_{n-1}}{x} + \cdots + \dfrac{b_1}{x^{n-1}} + \dfrac{b_0}{x^n}} \right]$

$= \dfrac{a_n + 0 + \cdots + 0 + 0}{b_n + 0 + \cdots + 0 + 0} = \dfrac{a_n}{b_n}$

39. (a) no, not at $p = -8$ (b) yes (c) yes (d) $p > 0$

41. (a) yes, $q = -1$ (b) yes

43. (a) R/i (b) $10,000 **45.** yes, $0 \le p \le 100$

47. 100%; No, for p to approach 100% (as a limit) requires spending to increase without bound, which is impossible.

49. (a) $158.80
(b) $\lim_{x \to 100} C(x) = 38.80$; $\lim_{x \to 500} C(x) = 98.80$ (c) yes

51. (a) $m(x) = 0.591x + 43.2$; $w(x) = 0.787x + 20.9$

(b) $r(x) = \dfrac{0.591x + 43.2}{0.787x + 20.9}$

(c) $\lim_{x \to 0} r(x) \approx 2.07$ means that for years approaching 1950 there were about 2.07 men per woman in the U.S. workforce.

$\lim_{x \to 100} r(x) \approx 1.03$ means that for years approaching 2050 it is projected that there will be 1.03 men per woman in the U.S. workforce.

(d) $\lim_{x \to \infty} r(x) \approx 0.751 \approx 3/4$ means that the long-term projection is for about 3 men per 4 women in the U.S. workforce.

9.3 EXERCISES

1. (a) 6 (b) 8 **3.** (a) $\frac{10}{3}$ (b) -5

5. (a) $-3.9, -3.99$ (b) $-4.1, -4.01$ (c) -4

7. (a) 32 (b) 32 (c) $(4, 64)$

9. (a) verification (b) -8 (c) -8 (d) $(-1, 5)$

11. (a) $P(1, 1), A(3, 0)$ (b) $-\frac{1}{2}$ (c) $-\frac{1}{2}$ (d) $-\frac{1}{2}$

13. (a) $P(1, 3), A(0, 3)$ (b) 0 (c) 0 (d) 0

15. (a) $f'(x) = 10x + 6$ (b) $10x + 6; -14$ (c) -14

17. (a) $p'(q) = 4q + 1$ (b) $4q + 1; 41$ (c) 41

19. (a) 89.0072 (b) ≈ 89

21. (a) 294.0084 (b) ≈ 294

23. -31

25. (a) At A the slope is positive; at B it is negative.
(b) $-1/3$

27. $f'(4) = 7/3; f(4) = -11$ **29.** $y = 5x - 14$

31. (a) a, b, d (b) c (c) A, C, E

33. (a) A, B, C, D (b) A, D

35. (a) $f'(x) = 2x + 1$ (b) $f'(2) = 5$
(c) $y = 5x - 4$ (d)

37. (a) $f'(x) = 3x^2$ (b) $f'(1) = 3$
(c) $y = 3x + 1$ (d)

39. (a) 43 dollars per unit (b) 95.50 dollars per unit
(c) The average cost per printer when 100 to 300 are produced (a) is $43 per printer, and the average cost when 300 to 600 are produced (b) is $95.50 per printer.

41. (a) $-100/3$ (b) $-4/3$

43. AB, AC, BC. Average rate is found from the slope of a segment; AB rises most slowly; BC is steepest.

45. (a) $R'(x) = \overline{MR} = 300 - 2x$
(b) 200; the predicted increase in revenue from selling the 51st unit is about $200.
(c) 20; the predicted increase in revenue from the 141st unit is about 20 dollars.
(d) 0 (e) It changes from increasing to decreasing.

47. 200

49. (a) 100; the expected profit from the sale of the 201st car is $100.
(b) -100; the expected return from the sale of the 301st car is a loss of $100.

51. (a) 1.039
(b) If humidity changes by 1%, the heat index will change by about 1.039°F.

53. (a) Marginal revenue is given by the slope of the tangent line, which is steeper at 300 smart phones. Hence marginal revenue is greater for 300 smart phones.
(b) Marginal revenue predicts the revenue from the next unit sold. Hence, the 301st item brings in more revenue because the marginal revenue for 300 smart phones is greater than for 700.

9.4 EXERCISES

1. $y' = 0$ **3.** $f'(t) = 1$

5. $y' = -8 + 4x = 4x - 8$ **7.** $f'(x) = 12x^3 - 6x^5$

9. $y' = 50x^4 - 9x^2 + 5$ **11.** $w'(z) = 7z^6 - 18z^5$

13. $g'(x) = 24x^{11} - 30x^5 + 36x^3 + 1$

15. (a) 30 (b) 30 **17.** (a) 6 (b) 6

19. $y' = -5x^{-6} - 8x^{-9} = -5/x^6 - 8/x^9$

21. $\dfrac{dz}{dt} = 11t^{8/3} - \dfrac{7}{2}t^{3/4} - \dfrac{1}{2}t^{-1/2}$

$\qquad = 11\sqrt[3]{t^8} - \dfrac{7}{2}\sqrt[4]{t^3} - \dfrac{1}{2\sqrt{t}}$

23. $f'(x) = -4x^{-9/5} - \dfrac{8}{3}x^{-7/3}$

$\qquad = \dfrac{-4}{\sqrt[5]{x^9}} - \dfrac{8}{3\sqrt[3]{x^7}}$

25. $g'(x) = \dfrac{-15}{x^6} - \dfrac{8}{x^5} + \dfrac{2}{\sqrt[3]{x^2}}$

27. $y = -7x + 10$ **29.** $y = 3$

31. $(1, -1), (5, 31)$ **33.** $(0, 9), (3, -18)$

35. (a) $-1/2$ (b) -0.5000 (to four decimal places)

37. (a) $f'(x) = 6x^2 + 5$ $f'(2) = 29$

(b) 29.000002 verifies the answer

39. (a) $h'(x) = -30x^{-4} + 4x^{-7/5} + 2x$

$\qquad = \dfrac{-30}{x^4} + \dfrac{4}{\sqrt[5]{x^7}} + 2x$ $h'(-1) = -36$

(b) -36.000102 verifies the answer

41. (a) $y = 8x - 3$

(b) (c) yes

$y = 3x^2 + 2x$ $y = 8x - 3$

43. (a) $f'(x) = -2 - 2x$

(b)

$f(x) = 8 - 2x - x^2$

$f'(x) = -2 - 2x$

(c) $f'(x) = 0$ at $x = -1$; $f'(x) > 0$ for $x < -1$;

$\quad f'(x) < 0$ for $x > -1$

(d) $f(x)$ has a maximum when $x = -1$.

$\quad f(x)$ rises for $x < -1$.

$\quad f(x)$ falls for $x > -1$.

45. (a) $f'(x) = 3x^2 - 12$

(b)

$f'(x) = 3x^2 - 12$

$f(x) = x^3 - 12x - 5$

(c) $f'(x) = 0$ at $x = -2$ and $x = 2$

$\quad f'(x) > 0$ for $x < -2$ and $x > 2$

$\quad f'(x) < 0$ for $-2 < x < 2$

(d) $f(x)$ has a maximum when $x = -2$, a minimum when

$\quad x = 2$

$\quad f(x)$ rises when $x < -2$ and when $x > 2$

$\quad f(x)$ falls when $-2 < x < 2$

47. (a) 40; the expected change in revenue from the 301st unit is about \$40

(b) -20; the expected change in revenue from the 601st unit is about -20 dollars

49. $\dfrac{dq}{dM} = \dfrac{3k}{4M^{1/4}}$

51. (a) -4; if the price changes to \$26, the quantity demanded will change by approximately -4 units

(b) $-\frac{1}{2}$; if the price changes to \$101, the quantity demanded will change by approximately $-\frac{1}{2}$ unit

53. (a) $\overline{C}'(x) = (-4000/x^2) + 0.1$ (b) 200

(c) $C'(200) = \overline{C}(200) = 95$

55. (a) -1200

(b) If the impurities change from 10% to 11%, then the cost decreases by about \$1200.

57. (a) $WC = 45.0625 - 29.3375s^{0.16}$

(b) -0.31

(c) At 15° F, if the wind speed changes by $+1$ mph (to 26 mph), then the wind chill will change by approximately -0.31°F.

59. (a) $y = 0.0682x^2 + 1.76x + 96.0$

(b) \$2.57 per year

(c) $\dfrac{dy}{dx} = 0.1364x + 1.76$

(d) $\left.\dfrac{dy}{dx}\right|_{x=10} = 3.124$; about \$3.12 per year

(e) \$126.81

61. (a) $P(t) = -0.0000738t^3 + 0.0102t^2 + 2.20t + 163$

(b) $P'(t) = -0.0002214t^2 + 0.0204t + 2.20$

(c) 2000: $P'(50) \approx 2.67$ means that for 2001, the U.S. population will rise by about 2.67 million people. 2025: $P'(75) \approx 2.48$ means that for 2026, the U.S. population is expected to rise by about 2.48 million people.

9.5 EXERCISES

1. $\dfrac{ds}{dt} = 7t^6 - 4t^3 + 3t^2$

3. $\dfrac{dy}{dx} = (3x^7 + 4)(48x^5 - 24x^3) + (8x^6 - 6x^4 - 9)(21x^6)$

$\qquad = 312x^{12} - 198x^{10} - 189x^6 + 192x^5 - 96x^3$

5. $y' = (7x^6 - 5x^4 + 2x^2 - 1)(36x^8 + 21x^6 - 10x + 3)$

$\qquad + (4x^9 + 3x^7 - 5x^2 + 3x)(42x^5 - 20x^3 + 4x)$

7. $(\sqrt[5]{x} - 2\sqrt[4]{x} + 1)(3x^2 - 5) + (x^3 - 5x - 7)\left(\dfrac{1}{5\sqrt[5]{x^4}} - \dfrac{1}{2\sqrt[4]{x^3}}\right)$

9. (a) 40 (b) 40

11. $\dfrac{dp}{dq} = \dfrac{2q^2 - 2q - 6}{(2q - 1)^2}$

13. $\dfrac{dy}{dx} = \dfrac{4x^5 - 4x^3 - 16x}{(x^4 - 2x^2 + 5)^2}$

15. $\dfrac{dz}{dx} = 2x + \dfrac{2x - x^2}{(1 - x - 2x^2)^2}$

17. $\dfrac{dp}{dq} = \dfrac{2q + 1}{\sqrt[3]{q^2}(1 - q)^2}$

19. $y' = \dfrac{2x^3 - 6x^2 - 8}{(x - 2)^2}$

21. (a) $\frac{3}{5}$ (b) $\frac{3}{5}$ **23.** $y = 44x - 32$

25. $y = \frac{10}{3}x - \frac{10}{3}$ **27.** 104

29. 1.3333 (to four decimal places)

31. (a) $f'(x) = 3x^2 - 6x - 24$

Graph of both $f'(x)$ and numerical derivative of $f(x)$

(b) Horizontal tangents (c)
where $f'(x) = 0$;
at $x = -2$ and $x = 4$

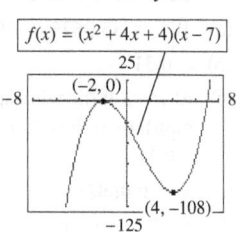

33. (a) $y' = \dfrac{x^2 - 4x}{(x - 2)^2}$

Graph of both y' and the numerical derivative of y

(b) Horizontal tangents where $y' = 0$; at $x = 0$ and $x = 4$

(c)

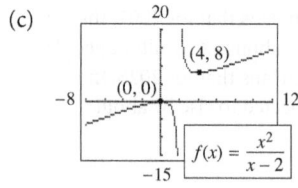

35. (a) $f'(x) = \dfrac{20x}{(x^2 + 1)^2}$ (b)

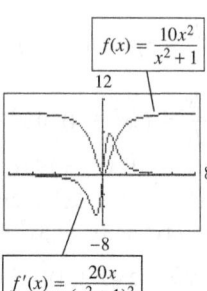

(c) $f' = 0$ at $x = 0$
$f' > 0$ for $x > 0$
$f' < 0$ for $x < 0$

(d) f has a minimum at $x = 0$.
f is increasing for $x > 0$.
f is decreasing for $x < 0$.

37. $f'(x) = \lim\limits_{h \to 0} \dfrac{\dfrac{u(x + h)}{v(x + h)} - \dfrac{u(x)}{v(x)}}{h}$

$= \lim\limits_{h \to 0} \dfrac{u(x + h)v(x) - u(x)v(x + h)}{h \cdot v(x)v(x + h)}$

$= \lim\limits_{h \to 0} \dfrac{u(x + h)v(x) - u(x)v(x) + u(x)v(x) - u(x)v(x + h)}{h \cdot v(x)v(x + h)}$

$= \lim\limits_{h \to 0} \dfrac{v(x)\left[\dfrac{u(x + h) - u(x)}{h}\right] - u(x)\left[\dfrac{v(x + h) - v(x)}{h}\right]}{v(x)v(x + h)}$

$= \dfrac{v(x)u'(x) - u(x)v'(x)}{[v(x)]^2}$

39. $C'(p) = 810{,}000/(100 - p)^2$

41. $R'(49) \approx 30.00$ The expected revenue from the sale of the next unit (the 50th) is about \$30.

43. $R'(5) = -50$ As the group changes by 1 person (to 31), the revenue will drop by about \$50.

45. $S = 1000x - x^2$

47. $\dfrac{dR}{dn} = \dfrac{r(1 - r)}{[1 + (n - 1)r]^2}$

49. (a) $P'(6) \approx 0.045$ During the next (7th) month of the campaign, the proportion of voters who recognize the candidate will change by about 0.045, or 4.5%.

(b) $P'(12) \approx -0.010$ During the next (13th) month of the campaign, the proportion of voters who recognize the candidate will drop by about 0.010, or 1%.

(c) It is better for $P'(t)$ to be positive—that is, to have increasing recognition.

51. (a) $f'(20) \approx -0.79$

(b) At 0°F, if the wind speed changes by 1 mph (to 21 mph), the wind chill will change by about −0.79°F.

53. (a) $B'(t) = (0.01t + 3)(0.0476t - 9.79)$
$+ (0.01)(0.0238t^2 - 9.79t + 3100)$

(b) $B'(70) \approx 1.42$ means that in 2020 the number of beneficiaries will be changing at the rate of about 1.42 million per year.

(c) [2010, 2020]: 1.55
[2020, 2030]: 1.39
[2010, 2030]: 1.47

The average rate over [2020, 2030] is best but is still off by almost 0.03 million per year.

55. (a) $p'(t) = \dfrac{2154.06}{(1.38t + 64.1)^2}$

(b) 2005: $p'(55) \approx 0.110$; 2020: $p'(70) \approx 0.083$

(c) $p'(55)$ means that in 2005, the percent of women in the workforce was changing about 0.110 percentage points per year. $p'(70)$ predicts the rate in 2020 will be about 0.083 percentage points per year.

9.6 EXERCISES

1. **(a)** $\dfrac{dy}{du} = 3u^2, \dfrac{du}{dx} = 2x, \dfrac{dy}{dx} = 3u^2 \cdot 2x = 6x(x^2 + 1)^2$

   (b) $\dfrac{dy}{du} = 4u^3, \dfrac{du}{dx} = 8x - 1, \dfrac{dy}{dx} = 4u^3(8x - 1)$

   $= 4(8x - 1)(4x^2 - x + 8)^3$

3. $f'(x) = 20(3x^5 - 2)^{19}(15x^4) = 300x^4(3x^5 - 2)^{19}$

5. $h'(x) = 6(x^5 - 2x^3 + 5)^7(5x^4 - 6x^2)$
   $= 6x^2(5x^2 - 6)(x^5 - 2x^3 + 5)^7$

7. $s'(t) = 5 - 9(2t^4 + 7)^2(8t^3) = 5 - 72t^3(2t^4 + 7)^2$

9. $g'(x) = -2(x^4 - 5x)^{-3}(4x^3 - 5) = \dfrac{-2(4x^3 - 5)}{(x^4 - 5x)^3}$

11. $f'(s) = -12(2s^5 + 1)^{-5}(10s^4) = \dfrac{-120s^4}{(2s^5 + 1)^5}$

13. $g'(x) = -\dfrac{3}{4}(2x^3 + 3x + 5)^{-7/4}(6x^2 + 3)$

    $= \dfrac{-3(6x^2 + 3)}{4(2x^3 + 3x + 5)^{7/4}}$

15. $y' = \dfrac{1}{2}(3x^2 + 4x + 9)^{-1/2}(6x + 4)$

    $= \dfrac{3x + 2}{\sqrt{3x^2 + 4x + 9}}$

17. $y' = \dfrac{66}{9}(x^3 - 7)^5(3x^2) = 22x^2(x^3 - 7)^5$

19. $\dfrac{dz}{dw} = \dfrac{15(3w + 1)^4 - 3}{7}$

21. (a) and (b) 96,768   23. (a) and (b) 2

25. $y = 3x - 5$ 27. $9x - 5y = 2$

29. (a) $f'(x) = 6x(x^2 - 4)^2$

   (b)

   (c) $x = 0, x = 2$
   $x = -2$

   (d) $(0, -52),$
   $(2, 12),$
   $(-2, 12)$

   Graph of both $f'(x)$ and numerical derivative of $f(x)$

   (e)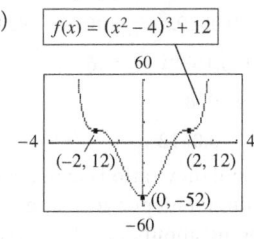

31. (a) $f'(x) = 8x(1 - x^2)^{1/3}$

   (b)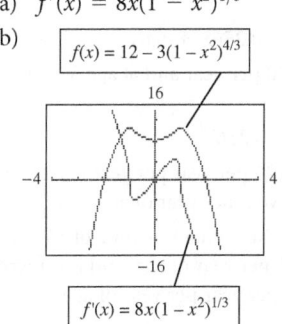

(c) $f'(x) = 0$ at $x = -1, x = 0, x = 1$
   $f'(x) > 0$ for $x < -1$ and $0 < x < 1$
   $f'(x) < 0$ for $-1 < x < 0$ and $x > 1$

(d) $f(x)$ has a maximum at $x = -1$ and $x = 1$, a minimum
   at $x = 0$.
   $f(x)$ is increasing for $x < -1$ and $0 < x < 1$.
   $f(x)$ is decreasing for $-1 < x < 0$ and $x > 1$.

33. (a) $y' = 2x^2$ (b) $y' = -2/x^4$

   (c) $y' = 2(2x)^2$ (d) $y' = \dfrac{-18}{(3x)^4}$

35. 120 in./sec

37. $1499.85 (approximately); if a 101st unit is sold, revenue will
   change by about $1499.85

39. (a) -0.114 (approximately)

   (b) If the price changes by $1, to $22, the weekly sales volume
   will change by approximately -0.114 thousand units.

41. (a) $-$3.20 per unit

   (b) If the quantity demanded changes from 49 to 50 units,
   the change in price will be about $-$3.20.

43. $\dfrac{dy}{dx} = \left(\dfrac{8k}{5}\right)(x - x_0)^{3/5}$

45. $\dfrac{dp}{dq} = -100(2q + 1)^{-3/2} = \dfrac{-100}{(2q + 1)^{3/2}}$

47. $\dfrac{dK_c}{dv} = 8(4v + 1)^{-1/2} = \dfrac{8}{\sqrt{4v + 1}}$

49. (a) $658.75. If the interest rate changed from 6% to 7%, the
   amount of the investment would change by about $658.75.

   (b) $2156.94. If the interest rate changed from 12% to 13%, the
   amount of the investment would change by about $2156.94.

51. (a) $A'(t) = 99.9(0.1t + 1)^2 - 366(0.1t + 1) + 451$

   (b) 2012: $A'(12) \approx 129.3$; 2020: $A'(20) \approx 252.1$ These
   mean that total U.S. national health care expenditures
   were changing at the rate of about $129.3 billion per year
   in 2012 and about $252.1 billion per year in 2020.

   (c) The average rate from 2018 to 2022 is $259.8 billion per year.

53. (a) 2015: $G'(15) \approx 925$; 2025: $G'(25) \approx 1510$ These mean
   that the rate of change of the GDP was about $925 billion
   per year in 2015 and will be about $1510 billion per year
   in 2025.

   (b) 1465 (billion per year)

   (c) 2020: $G'(20) \approx 1090$. The answer from part (b) is not a
   good approximation to $G'(20)$.

9.7 EXERCISES

1. 0   3. $4(-4x^{-5}); -16/x^5$

5. $15x^2 + 4(-x^{-2}); 15x^2 - 4/x^2$

7. $(x^2 - 2)1 + (x + 4)(2x); 3x^2 + 8x - 2$

9. $\dfrac{u^2(3u^2) - (u^3 + 1)(2u)}{(u^2)^2}; (u^3 - 2)/u^3$

11. $(3x^2 - 4)(x^3 - 4x)^9$

13. $\dfrac{5}{3}x^3[3(4x^5 - 5)^2(20x^4)] + (4x^5 - 5)^3(5x^2);$
    $5x^2(4x^5 - 5)^2(24x^5 - 5)$

15. $(x - 1)^2(2x) + (x^2 + 1)2(x - 1);$
    $2(x - 1)(2x^2 - x + 1)$

17. $\dfrac{(x^2 + 1)3(x^2 - 4)^2(2x) - (x^2 - 4)^3(2x)}{(x^2 + 1)^2}$;

$\dfrac{2x(x^2 - 4)^2(2x^2 + 7)}{(x^2 + 1)^2}$

19. $3[(q + 1)(q^3 - 3)]^2[(q + 1)3q^2 + (q^3 - 3)1]$;
$3(4q^3 + 3q^2 - 3)[(q + 1)(q^3 - 3)]^2$

21. $4[x^2(x^2 + 3x)]^3[x^2(2x + 3) + (x^2 + 3x)(2x)]$;
$4x^2(4x + 9)[x^2(x^2 + 3x)]^3 = 4x^{11}(4x + 9)(x + 3)^3$

23. $4\left(\dfrac{2x - 1}{x^2 + x}\right)^3\left[\dfrac{(x^2 + x)2 - (2x - 1)(2x + 1)}{(x^2 + x)^2}\right]$;

$\dfrac{4(-2x^2 + 2x + 1)(2x - 1)^3}{(x^2 + x)^5}$

25. $(8x^4 + 3)^2 3(x^3 - 4x)^2(3x^2 - 4) +$
$(x^3 - 4x)^3 2(8x^4 + 3)(32x^3)$;
$(8x^4 + 3)(x^3 - 4x)^2(136x^6 - 352x^4 + 27x^2 - 36)$

27. $\dfrac{(4 - x^2)\frac{1}{3}(x^2 + 5)^{-2/3}(2x) - (x^2 + 5)^{1/3}(-2x)}{(4 - x^2)^2}$;

$\dfrac{2x(2x^2 + 19)}{3\sqrt[3]{(x^2 + 5)^2}(4 - x^2)^2}$

29. $(x^2)\frac{1}{4}(4x - 3)^{-3/4}(4) + (4x - 3)^{1/4}(2x)$;
$(9x^2 - 6x)/\sqrt[4]{(4x - 3)^3}$

31. $(2x)\frac{1}{2}(x^3 + 1)^{-1/2}(3x^2) + (x^3 - 1)^{1/2}(2)$;
$(5x^3 + 2)/\sqrt{x^3 + 1}$

33. (a) $F_1'(x) = 12x^3(x^4 + 1)^4$

(b) $F_2'(x) = \dfrac{-12x^3}{(x^4 + 1)^6}$

(c) $F_3'(x) = 12x^3(3x^4 + 1)^4$

(d) $F_4'(x) = \dfrac{-300x^3}{(5x^4 + 1)^6}$

35. $dP/dx = 90(3x + 1)^2$

37. (a) $59,900 per camper

(b) An 11th camper sold would change revenue by about $59,900.

39. $dC/dy = 1/\sqrt{y + 1} + 0.4$

41. $dV/dx = 144 - 96x + 12x^2$

43. -1.6; This means that from the 9th to the 10th week, sales are expected to decrease by about $1600.

45. (a) 2010: $373/year; 2020: $583/year

(b) In 2020, per capita health care expenditures are expected to change at the rate of $583 per year.

(c) $621/year is a fairly good approximation of the instantaneous rate.

9.8 EXERCISES

1. $f''(x) = 180x^8 - 360x^3 - 72x$ **3.** $g''(x) = 6x - 2x^{-3}$

5. $d^2y/dx^2 = 6x + \frac{1}{4}x^{-3/2}$ **7.** $d^3y/dx^3 = 60x^2 - 96$

9. $f''(x) = 1008x^6 - 720x^3$ **11.** $d^3y/dx^3 = -6/x^4$

13. $d^2y/dx^2 = 20x^3 + \frac{1}{4}x^{-3/2}$ **15.** $f'''(x) = \frac{3}{8}(x + 1)^{-5/2}$

17. $d^4y/dx^4 = 0$ **19.** $f^{(4)}(x) = -15/(16x^{7/2})$

21. $y^{(4)} = 24(4x - 1)^{-5/2}$ **23.** $f^{(6)}(x) = -2(x + 1)^{-3}$

25. 26   **27.** 16.0000 (to four decimal places)

29. 0.0004261

31. (a) $f'(x) = 3x^2 - 6x$ $f''(x) = 6x - 6$

(b)

(c) $f''(x) = 0$ at $x = 1$
$f''(x) > 0$ for $x > 1$
$f''(x) < 0$ for $x < 1$

(d) $f'(x)$ has a minimum at $x = 1$.
$f'(x)$ is increasing for $x > 1$.
$f'(x)$ is decreasing for $x < 1$.

(e) $f''(x) < 0$ (f) $f''(x) > 0$.

33. $a = 0.12$ m/sec^2

35. -0.02 dollars/unit per unit

37. (a) $\dfrac{dR}{dm} = mc - m^2$ (b) $\dfrac{d^2R}{dm^2} = c - 2m$

(c) second

39. (a) 0.0009 (approximately)

(b) When 1 more unit is sold (beyond 25), the marginal revenue will change by about 0.0009 thousand dollars per unit, or $0.90 per unit.

41. (a) $S' = \dfrac{-3}{(t + 3)^2} + \dfrac{36}{(t + 3)^3}$ (b) $S''(15) = 0$

(c) After 15 weeks, the rate of change of the rate of sales is zero because the rate of sales reaches a minimum value.

43. (a) $W'(t) \approx 0.0447t^{1.11}$ (b) $W''(t) \approx 0.0497t^{0.11}$

(c) $W(50) \approx 81.5, W'(50) \approx 3.44$, and $W''(50) \approx 0.0764$. These mean that in 2025 the average annual wage is expected to be $81,500 and changing at a rate of about $3440 per year. Also that rate is expected to be changing about $76.40 per year per year.

45. (a) $R(x) = -0.000190x^3 + 0.0519x^2 - 4.06x + 192$

(b) $R'(x) = -0.000570x^2 + 0.1038x - 4.06$

(c) $R''(x) = -0.00114x + 0.1038$

(d) $R'(90) \approx 0.665; R''(90) \approx 0.0012$

In 2040, the economic dependency ratio is expected to be changing at a rate of about 0.665 per year, and this rate is expected to be changing about 0.0012 per year per year.

47. (a) $f'(x) = 0.002592x^2 - 0.256x + 6.61$

(b) At age 25: about $1830 per year and at age 55: about $371 per year

(c) $f''(x) = 0.005184x - 0.256$

(d) At age 25: about $-$126 per year per year of age and at age 55: about $29 per year per year of age

(e) The rate of change in the median income of 55-year-old workers is about $371 per year per year of age, and it is increasing at a rate of about $29 per year per year of age.

9.9 EXERCISES

1. (a) $\overline{MR} = 4$
   (b) The sale of each additional item brings in $4 of revenue at all levels of production.

3. (a) $6200; this is revenue from the sale of 100 units.
   (b) $R'(x) = 64 - 0.04x$
   (c) $60; Revenue will increase by about $60 if a 101st item is sold and by about $180 if 3 additional units past 100 units are sold.
   (d) Actual revenue from the sale of the 101st item is $59.98.

5. (a) $R(x) = 120x - 0.4x^2$ (in hundreds of dollars)
   (b) 10,000 subscribers ($x = 100$); $R = $800,000$
   (c) Lower the price per month.
   (d) $\overline{MR} = R'(x) = 120 - 0.8x$; when $p = 80, x = 100$
   $\overline{MR}(100) = 40$ means that if the number of customers increased from 100 to 101 (hundred), the revenue would increase by about 40 (hundred dollars), or $4000. This means the company should try to increase subscribers by lowering its monthly charge.

7. (a)
   (b) $x = 1800$
   (c) $32,400

9. $\overline{MC} = 8$
11. $\overline{MC} = 13 + 2x$
13. $\overline{MC} = 3x^2 - 12x + 24$
15. $\overline{MC} = 27 + 3x^2$

17. (a) $10; the cost will increase by about $10.
    (b) $11

19. $46; the cost will increase by about $46. For 3 additional units, the cost will increase by about $138.

21.

23. (a) The 101st item costs more. The tangent line slope is greater at $x = 100$ than at $x = 500$, and the slope of the tangent line gives the marginal cost and predicts the cost of the next item.
    (b) More efficient. As x increases, the slopes of the tangents decrease. This means that the costs of additional items decrease as x increases.

25. $\overline{MP} = 5$; This means that for each additional unit sold, profit changes by $5.

27. (a) $5600
    (b) $\overline{MP} = 20 - 0.02x$
    (c) 10; profit will increase by about $10 if a 501st unit is sold.
    (d) 9.99; the sale of the 501st item results in a profit of $9.99.

29. (a) $P(x) = R(x) - C(x)$, so profit is the distance between $R(x)$ and $C(x)$ (when $R(x)$ is above $C(x)$). $P(100) < P(700) < P(400)$; $P(100) < 0$, so there is a loss when 100 units are sold.

   (b) This asks us to rank $\overline{MP}(100)$, $\overline{MP}(400)$, and $\overline{MP}(700)$. Because $\overline{MP} = \overline{MR} - \overline{MC}$, compare the slopes of the tangents to $R(x)$ and $C(x)$ at the three x-values. Thus $\overline{MP}(700) < \overline{MP}(400) < \overline{MP}(100)$. $\overline{MP}(700) < 0$ because $C(x)$ is steeper than $R(x)$ at $x = 700$. At $x = 100$, $R(x)$ is much steeper than $C(x)$.

31. (a) $A < B < C$. Amount of profit is the height of the graph. There is a loss at A.
    (b) $C < B < A$. Marginal profit is the slope of the tangent to the graph. Marginals (slopes) are positive at all three points.

33. (a)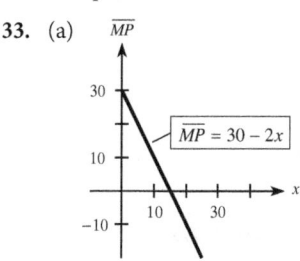
    (b) 15 hundred units
    (c) 15 hundred units
    (d) $25 thousand

35. 700
37. $9000

CHAPTER 9 REVIEW EXERCISES

1. (a) 2   (b) 2
2. (a) 0   (b) 0
3. (a) 2   (b) 1
4. (a) 2   (b) does not exist
5. (a) does not exist   (b) 2
6. (a) does not exist   (b) does not exist
7. 55
8. 0
9. -2
10. 4/5
11. $\frac{1}{2}$
12. $\frac{1}{5}$
13. no limit
14. 0
15. 4
16. no limit
17. 3
18. no limit
19. $6x$
20. $1 - 4x$
21. -14
22. 5
23. (a) yes   (b) no
24. (a) yes   (b) no
25. 2
26. no limit
27. 1
28. no
29. yes
30. yes
31. discontinuity at $x = 5$
32. discontinuity at $x = 2$
33. continuous
34. discontinuity at $x = 1$
35. (a) $x = 0, x = 1$ (b) 0   (c) 0
36. (a) $x = -1, x = 0$ (b) $\frac{1}{2}$ (c) $\frac{1}{2}$
37. $-2; y = -2$ is a horizontal asymptote.
38. $0; y = 0$ is a horizontal asymptote.
39. 7
40. true
41. false
42. $f'(x) = 6x + 2$
43. $f'(x) = 1 - 2x$
44. $[-1, 0]$; the segment over this interval is steeper.
45. (a) no   (b) no
46. (a) yes   (b) no
47. (a) -5.9171 (to four decimal places)   (b) -5.9
48. (a) $4.9/3$ (b) 7
49. about $-1/4$
50. B, C, A: $B < 0$ and $C < 0$; the tangent line at $x = 6$ falls more steeply than the segment over $[2, 10]$.
51. $20x^4 - 18x^2$
52. $90x^8 - 30x^5 + 4$
53. 1
54. $1/(2\sqrt{x})$
55. 0
56. $-4/(3\sqrt[3]{x^4})$
57. $\dfrac{-1}{x^2} + \dfrac{1}{2\sqrt{x^3}}$
58. $\dfrac{-3}{x^3} - \dfrac{1}{3\sqrt[3]{x^2}}$
59. $y = 15x - 18$
60. $y = 34x - 48$
61. (a) $x = 0, x = 2$ (b) $(0, 1) (2, -3)$

(c)

$f(x) = x^3 - 3x^2 + 1$

(0, 1)

(2, –3)

62. (a) $x = 0, x = 2, x = -2$

(b) $(0, 8)$ $(2, -24)(-2, -24)$

(c)

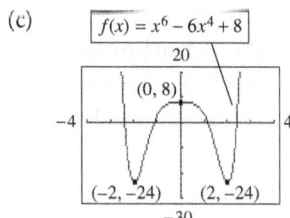

$f(x) = x^6 - 6x^4 + 8$

(0, 8)

$(-2, -24)$ $(2, -24)$

63. $9x^2 - 26x + 4$ 64. $21x^6 + 4x^3 + 27x^2$

65. $\dfrac{15q^2}{(2q^3 + 1)^2}$ 66. $\dfrac{1 - 3t}{[2\sqrt{t}(3t + 1)^2]}$ 67. $\dfrac{9x + 2}{2\sqrt{x}}$

68. $\dfrac{5x^6 + 2x^4 + 20x^3 - 3x^2 - 4x}{(x^3 + 1)^2}$

69. $(9x^2 - 24x)(x^3 - 4x^2)^2$

70. $6(30x^5 + 24x^3)(5x^6 + 6x^4 + 5)^5$

71. $72x^3(2x^4 - 9)^8$ 72. $\dfrac{-(3x^2 - 4)}{2\sqrt{(x^3 - 4x)^3}}$

73. $2x(2x^4 + 5)^7(34x^4 + 5)$ 74. $\dfrac{-2(3x + 1)(x + 12)}{(x^2 - 4)^2}$

75. $36[(3x + 1)(2x^3 - 1)]^{11}(8x^3 + 2x^2 - 1)$

76. $\dfrac{3}{(1 - x)^4}$ 77. $\dfrac{(2x^2 - 4)}{\sqrt{x^2 - 4}}$ 78. $\dfrac{2x - 1}{(3x - 1)^{4/3}}$

79. $y'' = \frac{-1}{4}x^{-3/2} - 2$ 80. $y'' = 12x^2 - 2/x^3$

81. $\dfrac{d^5y}{dx^5} = 0$ 82. $\dfrac{d^5y}{dx^5} = -30(1 - x)$

83. $\dfrac{d^3y}{dx^3} = -4(x^2 - 4)^{-3/2}$ 84. $\dfrac{d^4y}{dx^4} = \dfrac{2x(x^2 - 3)}{(x^2 + 1)^3}$

85. (a) $400,000   (b) $310,000   (c) $90,000

86. (a) $70,000; this is fixed costs.

(b) $0; $x = 1000$ is break-even.

87. (a) $140 per unit

(b) $\overline{C}(x) \to \infty$; the limit does not exist.

88. (a) $C(x) \to \infty$; the limit does not exist. As the number of units produced increases without bound, so does the total cost.

(b) $60 per unit. As more units are produced, the average cost of each unit approaches $60.

89. The average annual percent change of (a) elderly men in the workforce is 0.0825 percentage points per year and of (b) elderly women in the workforce is 0.0775 percentage points per year.

90. (a) Annual average rate of change of percent of elderly men in the workforce:

1970–1980: -0.78 percentage points per year

2030–2040: -0.23 percentage points per year

(b) Annual average rate of change of percent of elderly women in the workforce:

1970–1980: -0.16 percentage points per year

2030–2040: -0.16 percentage points per year

91. (a) $x'(10) = -1$ means that if price changes from $10 to $11, the number of units demanded will change by about -1.

(b) $x'(20) = -\frac{1}{4}$ means that if price changes from $20 to $21, the number of units demanded will change by about $-\frac{1}{4}$.

92. $h(100) \approx 4.15$; $h'(100) \approx 0.08$ means that when the updraft speed is 100 mph, the hail diameter is about 4.15 inches (softball-sized) and changing at the rate of 0.08 inch per mph of updraft.

93. The slope of the tangent at A gives $\overline{MR}(A)$. The tangent line at A is steeper (so has greater slope) than the tangent line at B. Hence, $\overline{MR}(A) > \overline{MR}(B)$, so the $(A + 1)$st unit will bring more revenue.

94. $R'(10) = 1570$. Raised. An 11th rent increase of $30 (and hence an 11th vacancy) would change revenue by about $1570.

95. (a) $P(20) = 23$ means productivity is 23 units per hour after 20 hours of training and experience.

(b) $P'(20) \approx 1.4$ means that the 21st hour of training or experience will change productivity by about 1.4 units per hour.

96. $\dfrac{dq}{dp} = \dfrac{-p}{\sqrt{0.02p^2 + 500}}$

97. $x'(10) = \frac{1}{6}$ means if price changes from $10 to $11, the number of units supplied will change by about $\frac{1}{6}$.

98. $s''(t) = a = -2t^{-3/2}$; $s''(4) = -0.25$ ft/sec/sec

99. $P'(x) = 70 - 0.2x$; $P''(x) = -0.2$

$P'(300) = 10$ means that the 301st unit brings in about $10 in profit.

$P''(300) = -0.2$ means that marginal profit $(P'(x))$ is changing at the rate of -0.2 dollars per unit per unit.

100. (a) $\overline{MC} = 6x + 6$ (b) 186

(c) If a 31st unit is produced, costs will change by about $186.

101. $C'(4) = 53$ means that a 5th unit produced would change total costs by about $53.

102. (a) $\overline{MR} = 40 - 0.04x$ (b) $x = 1000$ units

103. $\overline{MP}(10) = 48$ means that if an 11th unit is sold, profit will change by about $48.

104. (a) $\overline{MR} = 80 - 0.08x$ (b) 72

(c) If a 101st unit is sold, revenue will change by about $72.

105. $\dfrac{120x(x + 1)}{(2x + 1)^2}$ 106. $\overline{MP} = 4500 - 3x^2$

107. $\overline{MP} = 16 - 0.2x$

108. (a) C: Tangent line to $R(x)$ has smallest slope at C, so $\overline{MR}(C)$ is smallest and the next item at C will earn the least revenue.

(b) B: $R(x) > C(x)$ at both B and C. Distance between $R(x)$ and $C(x)$ gives the amount of profit and is greatest at B.

(c) A: $\overline{MR}$ greatest at A and $\overline{MC}$ least at A, as seen from the slopes of the tangents. Hence $\overline{MP}(A)$ is greatest, so the next item at A will give the greatest profit.

(d) C: $\overline{MC}(C) > \overline{MR}(C)$, as seen from the slopes of the tangents. Hence $\overline{MP}(C) < 0$, so the next unit sold reduces profit.

CHAPTER 9 TEST

1. $\frac{3}{4}$ 2. $-8/5$ 3. $9/8$ 4. does not exist

5. (a) $f'(x) = \lim\limits_{h \to 0} \dfrac{f(x + h) - f(x)}{h}$

   (b) $f'(x) = 6x - 1$

6. $x = 0, x = 8$

7. $\dfrac{dB}{dW} = 0.523$ 8. $p'(t) = 90t^9 - 42t^6 - 17$

9. $\dfrac{dy}{dx} = \dfrac{99x^2 - 24x^9}{(2x^7 + 11)^2}$

10. $f'(x) = (3x^5 - 2x + 3)(40x^9 + 40x^3) +$
    $(4x^{10} + 10x^4 - 17)(15x^4 - 2)$

11. $g'(x) = 9(10x^4 + 21x^2)(2x^5 + 7x^3 - 5)^{11}$

12. $y' = 2(8x^2 + 5x + 18)(2x + 5)^5$

13. $f'(x) = \dfrac{6}{\sqrt{x}} + \dfrac{20}{x^3}$

14. $\dfrac{d^3y}{dx^3} = 6 + 60x^{-6}$

15. (a) $y = -15x - 5$ (b) $(4, -90), (-2, 18)$
16. -15 17. (a) 2   (b) does not exist   (c) -4
18. $g(-2) = 8$; $\lim\limits_{x \to -2^-} g(x) = 8$, $\lim\limits_{x \to -2^+} g(x) = -8$

    $\therefore \lim\limits_{x \to -2} g(x)$ does not exist and $g(x)$ is not continuous at $x = -2$.

19. (a) $\overline{MR} = R'(x) = 250 - 0.02x$

    (b) $R(72) = 17{,}948.16$ means that when 72 units are sold, revenue is \$17,948.16.
    $R'(72) = 248.56$ means that the expected revenue from the 73rd unit is about \$248.56.

20. (a) $P(x) = 50x - 0.01x^2 - 10{,}000$

    (b) $\overline{MP} = 50 - 0.02x$

    (c) $\overline{MP}(1000) = 30$ means that the predicted profit from the sale of the 1001st unit is approximately \$30.

21. 104

22. (a) -5 (b) -1 (c) 4   (d) does not exist
    (e) 2   (f) $3/2$ (g) $-4, 1, 3, 6$
    (h) $-4, 3, 6$
    (i) $f'(-2) <$ average rate over $[-2, 2] < f'(2)$

23. (a) $2/3$ (b) -4 (c) $2/3$

24. (a) B: $R(x) > C(x)$ at B, so there is profit. Distance between $R(x)$ and $C(x)$ gives the amount of profit.

    (b) A: $C(x) > R(x)$

    (c) A and B: slope of $R(x)$ is greater than the slope of $C(x)$. Hence $\overline{MR} > \overline{MC}$ and $\overline{MP} > 0$.

    (d) C: Slope of $C(x)$ is greater than the slope of $R(x)$. Hence $\overline{MC} > \overline{MR}$ and $\overline{MP} < 0$.

10.1 EXERCISES

1. (a) $(1, 5)$ (b) $(4, 1)$ (c) $(-1, 2)$
3. (a) $(1, 5)$ (b) $(4, 1)$ (c) $(-1, 2)$
5. (a) $3, 7$ (b) $3 < x < 7$ (c) $x < 3, x > 7$
   (d) 7 (e) 3
7. (a) $x = 0, x = 4$
   (b)
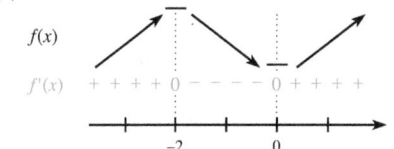
   min: $(4, -58)$; max: $(0, 6)$
9. (a) $x = -2, x = 0$
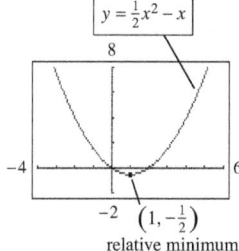
   (b) max: $(-2, 5)$; min: $(0, -11)$
11. (a) max: $(-1, 6)$; min: $(1, 2)$
    (b) $dy/dx = 3x^2 - 3$; $x = 1, x = -1$
    (c) $(1, 2), (-1, 6)$
    (d) yes
13. (a) HPI: $(-1, -3)$
    (b) $dy/dx = 3x^2 + 6x + 3$; $x = -1$
    (c) $(-1, -3)$
    (d) yes
15. (a) $\dfrac{dy}{dx} = x - 1$ (e)
    (b) $x = 1$
    (c) $\left(1, -\dfrac{1}{2}\right)$
    (d) decreasing: $x < 1$
    increasing: $x > 1$

    $y = \frac{1}{2}x^2 - x$
    $(1, -\frac{1}{2})$ relative minimum

17. (a) $dy/dx = x^2 + x - 2$
    (b) $x = -2, x = 1$ (c) $\left(-2, \frac{13}{3}\right), \left(1, -\frac{1}{6}\right)$
    (d) increasing: $x < -2$ and $x > 1$
    decreasing: $-2 < x < 1$
    (e)

    $y = \frac{x^3}{3} + \frac{x^2}{2} - 2x + 1$
    $\left(-2, \frac{13}{3}\right)$ relative maximum
    $\left(1, -\frac{1}{6}\right)$ relative minimum

19. (a) $\dfrac{dy}{dx} = \dfrac{2}{3x^{1/3}}$ (b) $x = 0$ (c) $(0, 0)$
    (d) decreasing: $x < 0$
    increasing: $x > 0$

(e)

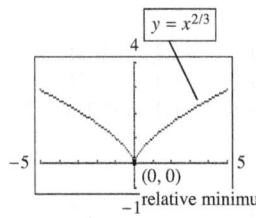

21. (a) $f'(x) = 0$ at $x = -\frac{1}{2}$

$f'(x) > 0$ for $x < -\frac{1}{2}$

$f'(x) < 0$ for $x > -\frac{1}{2}$

(b) $f'(x) = -1 - 2x$ verifies these conclusions.

23. (a) $f'(x) = 0$ at $x = 0, x = -3, x = 3$

$f'(x) > 0$ for $-3 < x < 3, x \neq 0$

$f'(x) < 0$ for $x < -3$ and $x > 3$

(b) $f'(x) = \frac{1}{3}x^2(9 - x^2)$ verifies these conclusions.

25. HPI $\left(1, \frac{4}{3}\right)$

no max or min

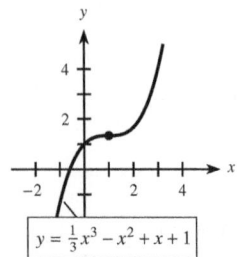

27. $(-6, 128)$ rel max;

$\left(4, -38\frac{2}{3}\right)$ rel min

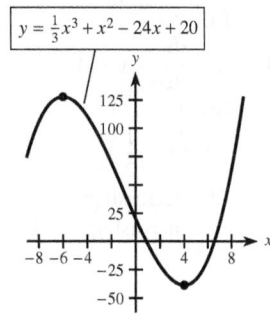

29. $(-1, 3)$ rel max;

$(1, -1)$ rel min;

HPI $(0, 1)$

31. $(1, 1)$ rel max;

$(0, 0), (2, 0)$ rel min

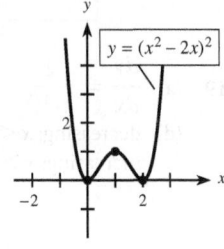

33. $(3, 4)$ rel max;

$(5, 0)$ rel min; HPI $(0, 0)$

35. $(0, 0)$ rel max;

$(2, -4.8)$ rel min

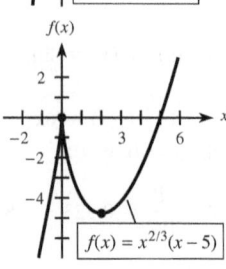

37. $(50, 300,500), (100, 238,000)$

$0 \leq x \leq 150, 0 \leq y \leq 301,000$

39. $(0, -40,000), (60, 4,280,000)$

$-20 \leq x \leq 90, \quad -500,000 \leq y \leq 5,000,000$

41. $(0, 2)$

$(0.1, 1.99975)$

$-0.1 \leq x \leq 0.2$

$1.9997 \leq y \leq 2.0007$

43. critical values: $x = -1, x = 2$

$f(x)$ increasing for $x < -1$

and $x > 2$

$f(x)$ decreasing for

$-1 < x < 2$

rel max at $x = -1$; rel min at

$x = 2$

45. critical values: $x = 0, x = 3$

$f(x)$ increasing for $x > 3$

$f(x)$ decreasing for $x < 3, x \neq 0$

rel min at $x = 3$; HPI at $x = 0$

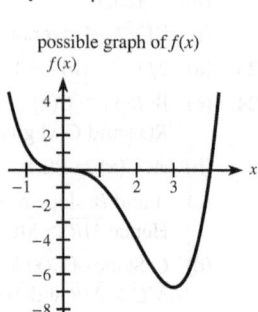

47. Graph on left is $f(x)$; on right is $f'(x)$ because $f(x)$ is increasing when $f'(x) > 0$ (i.e., above the x-axis) and $f(x)$ is decreasing when $f'(x) < 0$ (i.e., below the x-axis).

49. decrease for $t \geq 0$

51. (a) $2 \pm \sqrt{13}$ (d)
   (b) $2 + \sqrt{13} \approx 5.6$
   (c) $0 \leq t < 2 + \sqrt{13}$

53. (a) $x = 5$ (b) $0 < x < 5$
   (c) increasing for $x > 5$

55. (a) at $x = 150$, increasing; at $x = 250$, changing from increasing to decreasing; at $x = 350$, decreasing
   (b) increasing for $x < 250$ (c) 250 units

57. (a) $t = 6$ (b) 6 weeks

59. (a) 10   (b) January 1

61. $x \approx 21.1$; in 2022, the model will achieve a maximum of 9.04 billion subscriberships

63. (a) $y = -0.000487x^3 - 0.162x^2 + 19.8x + 388$
   (b) 912 million in 2020 (at $x \approx 49.9$)

65. (a) $M(t) = 0.0000889t^3 - 0.0111t^2 + 0.237t + 11.5$
   (b) relative maximum at $(12.6, 12.9)$; relative minimum at $(70.7, 4.2)$
   (c) No. The years corresponding to the critical points are 2023 and 2081. Despite the fact that the model is an excellent fit to the data given, it is unrealistic for the model to be accurate for more than 40 years beyond the data set.

10.2 EXERCISES

1. (a) concave down   (b) concave up
3. (a) concave up   (b) concave down
5. (a, c) and (d, e)   **7.** (c, d) and (e, f)   **9.** c, d, e
11. concave up when $x > 2$; concave down when $x < 2$;
   POI at $x = 2$
13. concave up when $x < -2$ and $x > 1$
   concave down when $-2 < x < 1$
   points of inflection at $x = -2$ and $x = 1$
15. no points of inflection;
   $(2, -2)$ min

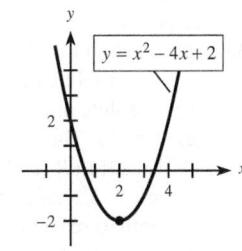

17. $\left(1, \frac{10}{3}\right)$ max; $(3, 2)$ min;
   $\left(2, \frac{8}{3}\right)$ point of inflection

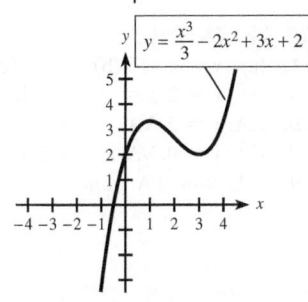

19. $(0, 0)$ rel max; $(2\sqrt{2}, -64)$, $(-2\sqrt{2}, -64)$ min; points of inflection: $(2\sqrt{6}/3, -320/9)$ and $(-2\sqrt{6}/3, -320/9)$

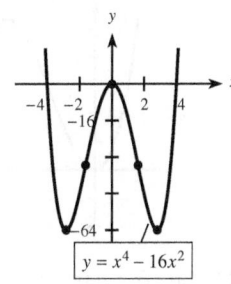

21. $(-2, 64)$ rel max; $(2, -64)$ rel min; points of inflection: $(-\sqrt{2}, 39.6)$, $(0, 0)$, and $(\sqrt{2}, -39.6)$

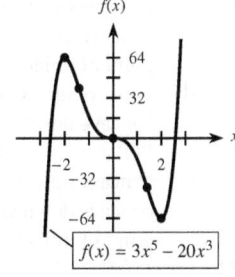

23. $(1, -3)$ min; points of inflection: $(-2, 7.6)$ and $(0, 0)$

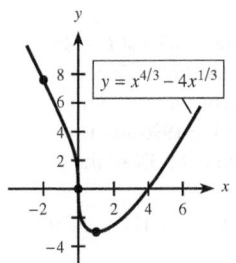

25. (a) $f''(x) = 0$ when $x = 1$
   $f''(x) > 0$ when $x < 1$
   $f''(x) < 0$ when $x > 1$
   (b) rel max for $f'(x)$ at $x = 1$; no rel min
   (c)

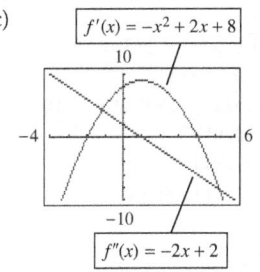

27. (a) concave up when $x < 2$; concave down when $x > 2$
   (b) point of inflection at $x = 2$
   (c)

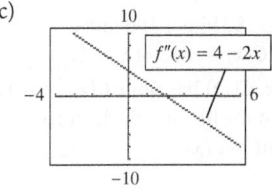

(d) possible graph of $f(x)$

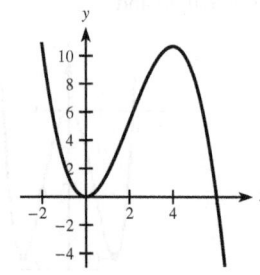

29. (a) G (b) C (c) F (d) H (e) I
31. (a) concave up when $x < 0$
    concave down when $x > 0$
    point of inflection at $x = 0$
   (b) concave up when $-1 < x < 1$
    concave down when $x < -1$ and $x > 1$
    POI at $x = -1$ and $x = 1$
   (c) concave up when $x > 0$
    concave down when $x < 0$
    point of inflection at $x = 0$
33. (a) $P'(t)$ (b) B (c) C
35. (a) C (b) right   (c) yes
37. (a) in an 8-hour shift, max when $t = 8$ (b) 4 hr
39. (a) 9 days   (b) 15 days
41. (a) $(15.9, 100.3)$, $(49.7, 85.3)$
   (b) max $= 100.3$ at $t = 15.9$; min $= 85.3$ at $t = 49.7$.
    These mean that over the years 1985 to 2035,
    the energy use per capita reached a maximum
    of 100.3% of the 1995 use during 1996 and is
    expected to reach a minimum of 85.3% of the
    1995 use during 2030.
43. (a) $y = -0.000102x^3 + 0.00884x^2 + 1.43x + 57.9$
   (b) $x = 28.9$, during 1979
45. (a) $C(t) = 0.342t^3 - 6.83t^2 + 105t + 1330$
   (b) POI at $t = 6.66$, $C(t) = 1827$. These costs increase
    at a decreasing rate until $t = 6.66$ (in 2012) and
    increase at an increasing rate afterward.

10.3 EXERCISES

1. min -6 at $x = 2$, max $3.\overline{481}$ at $x = -2/3$
3. min -1 at $x = -2$, max 2 at $x = -1$
5. min $= -2185$ at $x = -10$, max $= 1575$ at $x = 10$
7. (a) $x = 1800$ units, $R = \$32,400$
   (b) $x = 1500$ units, $R = \$31,500$
9. $x = 20$ units, $R = \$24,000$ 11. 85 people
13. $p = \$95$, $R = \$451,250$
15. (a) max $= \$2100$ at $x = 10$
   (b) $\overline{R}(x) = \overline{MR}$ at $x = 10$
17. $x = 50$ units, $\overline{C} = \$43$
19. $x = 90$ units, $\overline{C} = \$18$
21. 10,000 units ($x = 100$), $\overline{C} = \$216$ per 100 units
23. $\overline{C}(x)$ has its minimum and $\overline{C}(x) = \overline{MC}$ at $x = 5$.
25. (a) A line from $(0, 0)$ to $(x, C(x))$ has slope $C(x)/x = \overline{C}(x)$;
    this is minimized when the line has the least rise—that is,
    when the line is tangent to $C(x)$.
   (b) $x = 600$ units

27. $x = 80$ units, $P = \$280,000$
29. $x = 10\sqrt{15} \approx 39$ units, $P \approx \$71,181$ (using $x = 39$)
31. $x = 1000$ units, $P = \$39,700$
33. $\$860$ 35. $x = 600$ units, $P = \$495,000$
37. (a) 60   (b) $\$570$ (c) $\$9000$
39. (a) 1000 units   (b) $\$8066.67$ (approximately)
41. 2000 units priced at $\$90$/unit; max profit is $\$90,000$/wk
43. (a) $R(x) = 2x - 0.0004x^2$
    $P(x) = 1.8x - 0.0005x^2 - 800$
   (b) $p = \$1.28$, $x = 1800$, $P(1800) = \$820$
   (c) $p = \$1.25$, $x = 1875$, $P(1875) = \$817.19$
    Coastal would still provide sodas; profits are almost
    the same.
45. (a) B (b) B (c) B (d) $\overline{MR} = \overline{MC}$
47. (a) $y = 0.000256x^3 - 0.0280x^2 + 1.64x + 2.09$
   (b) $(36.5, 37.1)$
   (c)

The *rate* of change of the number of beneficiaries was
decreasing until 1987, after which the rate has been increasing. Hence, since 1987, the number of beneficiaries has been
increasing at an increasing rate.
49. (a) about mid-May
   (b) just after September 11, when the terrorists' planes
    crashed into the World Trade Center and the Pentagon
51. (a) 16.5
   (b) 1.9

10.4 EXERCISES

1. (a) $x_1 = \$25$ million, $x_2 = \$13.846$ million
   (b) $\$38.846$ million
3. 100 trees   5. (a) 5   (b) 237.5   7. $\$50$
9. $m = c$ 11. 1 week   13. $t = 8, p = 45\%$
15. 240 ft   17. 300 ft $\times$ 150 ft
19. 20 ft long, $6\frac{2}{3}$ ft across (dividers run across)
21. 4 in. $\times$ 8 in. $\times$ 8 in. high   23. 30,000
25. 12,000   27. $x = 2$ 29. 3 weeks from now
31. 25 plates
33. (a) 2034 (at $t = 23.3$); max $R = 27.8$ billion barrels. This is
    the absolute maximum.
   (b) absolute min: $(1, 19.5)$
   (c) $t = 3.2$. The rate reaches its maximum at $t = 3.2$
    (in 2014); $R''(t)$ changes from positive to negative
    at $t = 3.2$. After this, $R(t)$ increases at a decreasing rate
    until its maximum.

10.5 EXERCISES

1. (a) $x = 2$ (b) 1   (c) 1   (d) $y = 1$
3. (a) $x = 2, x = -2$ (b) 3   (c) 3   (d) $y = 3$
5. HA: $y = 2$; VA: $x = 3$
7. HA: $y = 0$; VA: $x = -2, x = 2$
9. HA: none; VA: none

11. HA: $y = 2$; VA: $x = 3$
no max, min, or points of
inflection

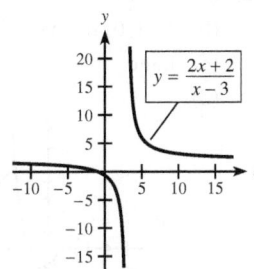

13. VA: $x = 0$;
$(-2, -4)$ rel max;
$(2, 4)$ rel min

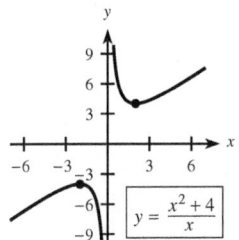

15. VA: $x = -1$; HA: $y = 0$;
$(0, 0)$ rel min; $(2, 4)$ rel max

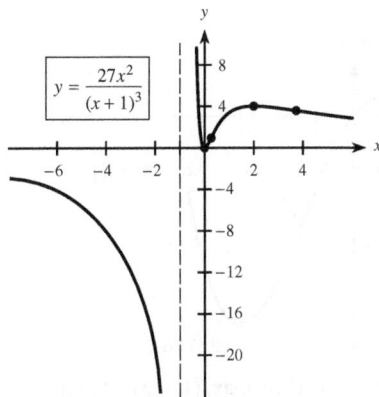

17. HA: $y = 0$; $(1, 8)$ rel max;
$(-1, -8)$ rel min

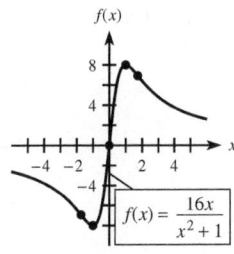

19. HA: $y = 0$; VA: $x = 1$;
$\left(-1, -\frac{1}{4}\right)$ rel min;
point of inflection: $\left(-2, -\frac{2}{9}\right)$

21. VA: $x = 3$;
$(2, -1)$ rel max;
$(4, 7)$ rel min

23. HA: $y = 0$; VA: $x = 0$; $(2, 0)$ rel min; $(3, 1)$ rel max;
points of inflection: $(1.87, 0.66)$, $(4.13, 0.87)$

25. (a) HA: approx. $y = -2$; VA: approx. $x = 4$
(b) HA: $y = -\frac{9}{4}$ VA: $x = \frac{17}{4}$

27. (a) HA: approx. $y = 2$;
VA: approx. $x = 2.5$, $x = -2.5$
(b) HA: $y = \frac{20}{9}$, VA: $x = \frac{7}{3}$, $x = -\frac{7}{3}$

29. $f(x) = \dfrac{x + 25}{x^2 + 1400}$

(a)

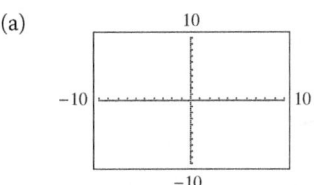

(b) HA: $y = 0$; rel min $(-70, -0.0071)$;
rel max $(20, 0.025)$

(c) x: -500 to 400
y: -0.01 to 0.03

31. $f(x) = \dfrac{100(9 - x^2)}{x^2 + 100}$

(a)

(b) HA: $y = -100$;
rel max $(0, 9)$

(c) x: -75 to 75
y: -120 to 20

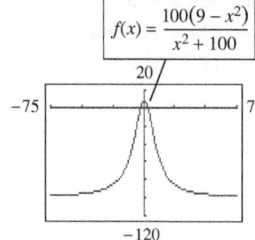

$f(x) = \dfrac{100(9 - x^2)}{x^2 + 100}$

33. $f(x) = \dfrac{1000x - 4000}{x^2 - 10x - 2000}$

(a)

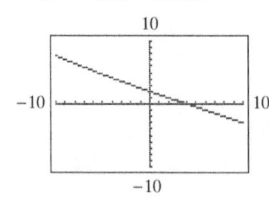

(b) HA: $y = 0$;
VA: $x = -40$,
$x = 50$; no max
or min

(c) x: -200 to 200
y: -200 to 200

$f(x) = \dfrac{1000x - 4000}{x^2 - 10x - 2000}$

35. (a) none　(b) $C \geq 0$　(c) $p = 100$　(d) no

37. (a)

$R(t) = \dfrac{50t}{t^2 + 36}$

(6, 4.17) Max

(b) 6 weeks
(c) 22 weeks after its release

39. (a) yes, $x = -1$
(b) no; domain is $x \geq 5$
(c) yes, $y = -58.5731$
(d) At $0°F$, as the wind speed increases, there is a limiting wind chill of about $-58.6°F$. This is meaningful because at high wind speeds, additional wind probably has little noticeable effect.

41. (a) $P = C$　(b) C　(c) $P' = 0$　(d) 0

43. (a) 57.0
(b) The model predicts that in the long run, 57% of workers will be female.
(c) No. Vertical asymptote is only at $t \approx -46.4$.
(d) $p(t) > 0$ for $t > 0$ and $p(t)$ never exceeds 100, so the model is never inappropriate.

45. (a) No. Barometric pressure can drop off the scale (as shown), but it cannot decrease without bound. In fact, it must always be positive.
(b) Google "storm of the century, March 1993."

CHAPTER 10 REVIEW EXERCISES

1. $(0, 0)$ max　　**2.** $(2, -9)$ min　　**3.** HPI $(1, 0)$

4. $\left(1, \frac{3}{2}\right)$ max, $\left(-1, -\frac{3}{2}\right)$ min

5. (a) $\frac{1}{3}, -1$
(b) $(-1, 0)$ rel max, $\left(\frac{1}{3}, -\frac{32}{27}\right)$ rel min
(c) none
(d)

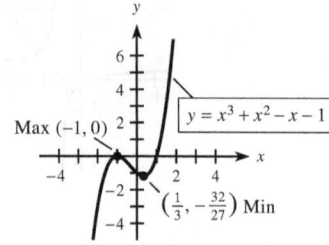

$y = x^3 + x^2 - x - 1$

Max $(-1, 0)$

$\left(\frac{1}{3}, -\frac{32}{27}\right)$ Min

6. (a) $3, 0$　(b) $(3, 27)$ max　(c) $(0, 0)$
(d)

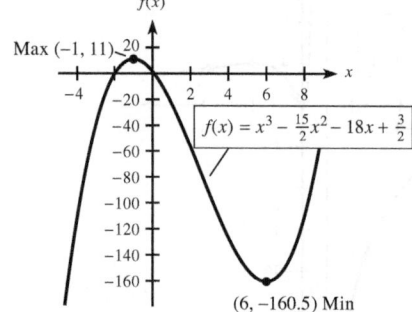

$f(x) = 4x^3 - x^4$

$(3, 27)$ Max

$(0, 0)$ HPI

7. (a) $-1, 6$
(b) $(-1, 11)$ rel max, $(6, -160.5)$ rel min
(c) none
(d)

Max $(-1, 11)$

$f(x) = x^3 - \frac{15}{2}x^2 - 18x + \frac{3}{2}$

$(6, -160.5)$ Min

8. (a) $0, \pm 1$　(b) $(-1, 1)$ rel max, $(1, -3)$ rel min
(c) $(0, -1)$　(d)

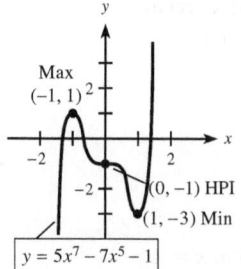

Max $(-1, 1)$

$(0, -1)$ HPI

$(1, -3)$ Min

$y = 5x^7 - 7x^5 - 1$

9. (a) 0　(b) $(0, -1)$ min　(c) none
(d)

$y = x^{2/3} - 1$

$(0, -1)$ Min

Vertical tangent

10. (a) $0, 1, 4$
(b) $(0, 0)$ rel min, $(1, 9)$ rel max, $(4, 0)$ rel min
(c) none

(d)

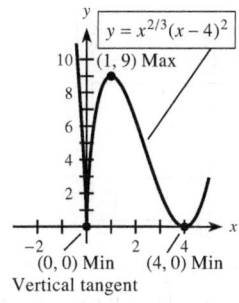

$y = x^{2/3}(x-4)^2$

(1, 9) Max

(0, 0) Min   (4, 0) Min
Vertical tangent

11. concave up
12. concave up when $x < -1$ and $x > 2$; concave down when $-1 < x < 2$; points of inflection at $(-1, -3)$ and $(2, -42)$
13. $(-1, 15)$ rel max; $(3, -17)$ rel min; point of inflection $(1, -1)$
14. $(-2, 16)$ rel max; $(2, -16)$ rel min; point of inflection $(0, 0)$

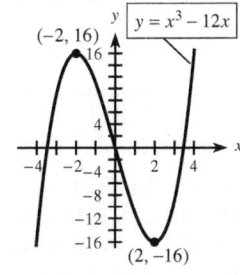

$y = x^3 - 12x$
$(-2, 16)$
$(2, -16)$

15. $(1, 4)$ rel max; $(-1, 0)$ rel min; points of inflection:

$$\left(\frac{1}{\sqrt{2}}, 2 + \frac{7}{4\sqrt{2}}\right), (0, 2), \text{ and } \left(-\frac{1}{\sqrt{2}}, 2 - \frac{7}{4\sqrt{2}}\right)$$

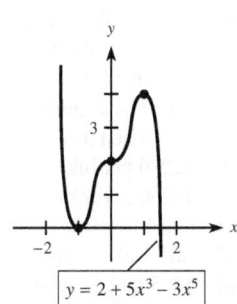

$y = 2 + 5x^3 - 3x^5$

16. (a) $(0, 0)$ absolute min; $(140, 19,600)$ absolute max
    (b) $(0, 0)$ absolute min; $(100, 18,000)$ absolute max
17. (a) $(50, 233,333)$ absolute max; $(0, 0)$ absolute min
    (b) $(64, 248,491)$ absolute max; $(0, 0)$ absolute min
18. (a) $x = 1$ (b) $y = 0$ (c) 0 (d) 0
19. (a) $x = -1$ (b) $y = \frac{1}{2}$ (c) $\frac{1}{2}$ (d) $\frac{1}{2}$
20. HA: $y = \frac{3}{2}$; VA: $x = 2$
21. HA: $y = -1$; VA: $x = 1, x = -1$
22. (a) HA: $y = 3$; VA: $x = -2$
    (b) no max or min (c)

$y = \frac{3x}{x+2}$

23. (a) HA: $y = 0$; VA: $x = 0$
    (b) $(4, 1)$ max (c)

$(4, 1)$ Max

$y = \frac{8(x-2)}{x^2}$

24. (a) HA: none; VA: $x = 1$
    (b) $(0, 0)$ rel max; $(2, 4)$ rel min
    (c)

$(0, 0)$ Max $(2, 4)$ Min

$y = \frac{x^2}{x-1}$

25. (a) $f'(x) > 0$ for $x < \frac{2}{3}$ (approximately) and $x > 2$
        $f'(x) < 0$ for about $\frac{2}{3} < x < 2$
        $f'(x) = 0$ at about $x = \frac{2}{3}$ and $x = 2$
    (b) $f''(x) > 0$ for $x > \frac{4}{3}$
        $f''(x) < 0$ for $x < \frac{4}{3}$
        $f''(x) = 0$ at $x = \frac{4}{3}$
    (c)

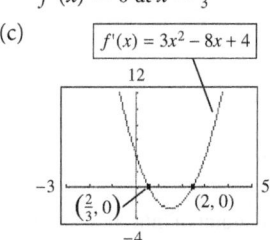

$f'(x) = 3x^2 - 8x + 4$
$\left(\frac{2}{3}, 0\right)$ $(2, 0)$

    (d)

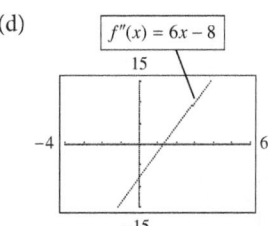

$f''(x) = 6x - 8$

26. (a) $f'(x) > 0$ for about $-13 < x < 0$ and $x > 7$
        $f'(x) < 0$ for about $x < -13$ and $0 < x < 7$
        $f'(x) = 0$ at about $x = 0, x = -13, x = 7$
    (b) $f''(x) > 0$ for about $x < -8$ and $x > 4$
        $f''(x) < 0$ for about $-8 < x < 4$
        $f''(x) = 0$ at about $x = -8$ and $x = 4$
    (c)

$f'(x) = 0.01x^3 + 0.06x^2 - 0.96x + 0.08$
$(-13.3, 0)$
$(0.8, 0)$ $(7.2, 0)$

(d) $f''(x) = 0.03x^2 + 0.12x - 0.96$

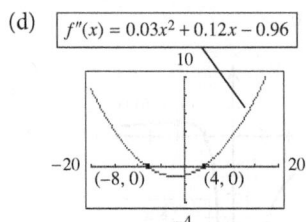

(−8, 0) (4, 0)

27. (a) $f(x)$ increasing for $x < -5$ and $x > 1$
$f(x)$ decreasing for $-5 < x < 1$
$f(x)$ has rel max at $x = -5$, rel min at $x = 1$
(b) $f''(x) > 0$ for $x > -2$ [where $f'(x)$ increases]
$f''(x) < 0$ for $x < -2$ [where $f'(x)$ decreases]
$f''(x) = 0$ for $x = -2$

(c) $f(x) = \dfrac{x^3}{3} + 2x^2 - 5x$

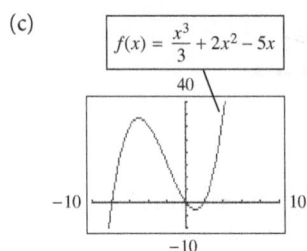

(d) $f''(x) = 2x + 4$

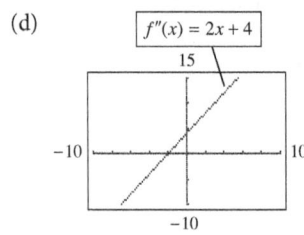

28. (a) $f(x)$ increasing for $x < 6$, $x \neq 0$
$f(x)$ decreasing for $x > 6$
$f(x)$ has rel max at $x = 6$, point of inflection at $x = 0$
(b) $f''(x) > 0$ for $0 < x < 4$
$f''(x) < 0$ for $x < 0$ and $x > 4$
$f''(x) = 0$ at $x = 0$ and $x = 4$

(c) $f(x) = 2x^3 - \dfrac{x^4}{4}$

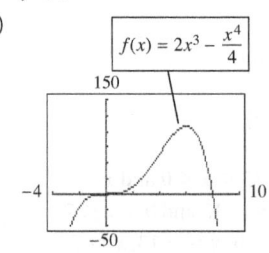

(d) $f''(x) = 12x - 3x^2$

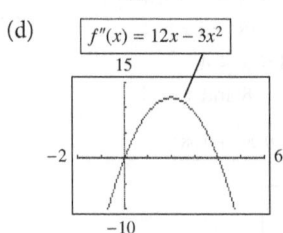

29. (a) $f(x)$ is concave up for $x < 4$.
$f(x)$ is concave down for $x > 4$.
$f(x)$ has point of inflection at $x = 4$.

(b) $f(x) = 2x^2 - \dfrac{x^3}{6}$

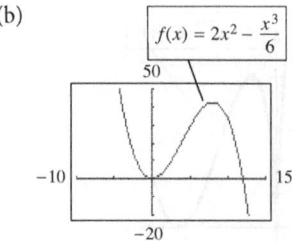

30. (a) $f(x)$ is concave up for $-3 < x < 2$.
$f(x)$ is concave down for $x < -3$ and $x > 2$.
$f(x)$ has points of inflection at $x = -3$ and $x = 2$.

(b) $f(x) = 3x^2 - \dfrac{x^3}{6} - \dfrac{x^4}{12}$

31. $x = 5$ units, $\overline{C} = \$45$ per unit
32. (a) $x = 1600$ units, $R = \$25,600$
(b) $x = 1500$ units, $R = \$25,500$
33. $P = \$54,000$ at $x = 100$ units   34. $x = 300$ units
35. $x = 150$ units   36. $x = 7$ units
37. $x = 500$ units when $\overline{MP} = 0$ and changes from positive to negative.
38. 30 hours
39. (a) $I = 60$. The point of diminishing returns is located at the point of inflection (where bending changes).
(b) $m = f(I)/I = $ the average output
(c) The segment from $(0, 0)$ to $y = f(I)$ has maximum slope when it is tangent to $y = f(I)$, close to $I = 70$.
40. $\$2080$ per bike
41. $\$2760$ per bike
42. $\$93,625$ at 325 units
43. (a) 150   (b) $\$650$
44. $\$208,490.67$ at 64 units
45. $x = 1000$ mg   46. 10 A.M.
47. 325 in 2022   48. 20 mi from A, 10 mi from B
49. 4 ft × 4 ft   50. $8\frac{3}{4}$ in. × 10. in.
51. 500 mg
52. (a) $x \approx 9.3$; during 2010
(b) point of inflection
53. 24,000
54. (a) vertical asymptote at $x = 0$
(d) $\overline{C}(x)$

$\overline{C}(x) = \dfrac{4500}{x} + 120 + 0.05x$

minimum (300, 150)

55. (a) 3%
(b) $y = 38$. The long-term market share approaches 38%.

CHAPTER 10 TEST

1. max $(-3, 3)$; min $(-1, -1)$; POI $(-2, 1)$

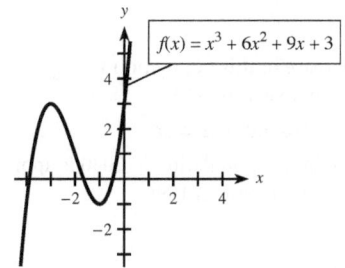

$f(x) = x^3 + 6x^2 + 9x + 3$

2. max $(3, 17)$; HPI $(0, -10)$; POI $(2, 6)$

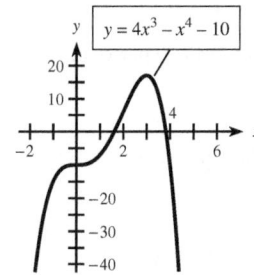

$y = 4x^3 - x^4 - 10$

3. max $(0, -3)$;
min $(4, 5)$;
vertical asymptote $x = 2$

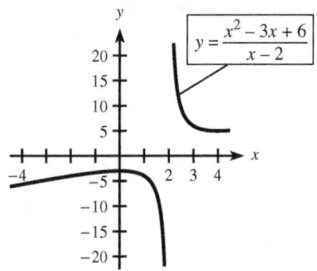

$y = \dfrac{x^2 - 3x + 6}{x - 2}$

4. $\left(-\dfrac{1}{\sqrt{2}}, 0\right)$ and $\left(\dfrac{1}{\sqrt{2}}, \infty\right)$

5. $(0, 2)$, HPI; $\left(-\dfrac{1}{\sqrt{2}}, 3.237\right), \left(\dfrac{1}{\sqrt{2}}, 0.763\right)$

6. max $(-1, 4)$; min $(1, 0)$
7. max 67 at $x = 8$; min -122 at $x = 5$
8. horizontal asymptote $y = 200$; vertical asymptote $x = -300$
9.
Point	f	f'	f''
A	−	+	−
B	+	−	0
C	+	0	+

10. (a) 2   (b) $x = -3$
    (c) $y = 2$
11. local max at $(6, 10)$
12. (a) relative minimum: $(8.7, 19.6)$; relative maximum: $(51.5, 39.0)$
    (b) The point $(8.7, 19.6)$ means that when $t = 8.7$ (during 1999), the aged dependency ratio reached a minimum of 19.6 aged individuals per 100 individuals ages 20–64. The point $(51.5, 39.0)$ means that when $t = 51.5$ (during 2042), the aged dependency ratio is expected to reach a maximum of 39.0 aged individuals per 100 individuals ages 20–64.

13. (a) $x = 7200$ (b) $518,100   14. 100 units
15. $250   16. $\frac{10}{3}$ cm   17. 28,000 units
18. (a) $y = -0.0000700x^3 + 0.00567x^2 + 0.863x + 16.0$
    (b) $x \approx 27.0$; during 1977
    (c) x-coordinate of the point of inflection

11.1 EXERCISES

1. $f'(x) = 4/x$ 3. $y' = 1/x$
5. $y' = 4/x$ 7. $f'(x) = \dfrac{4}{4x + 9}$
9. $y' = \dfrac{4x - 1}{2x^2 - x} + 3$ 11. $dp/dq = 2q/(q^2 + 1)$
13. (a) $y' = \dfrac{1}{x} - \dfrac{1}{x - 1} = \dfrac{-1}{x(x - 1)}$
    (b) $y' = \dfrac{-1}{x(x - 1)}; \ln\left(\dfrac{x}{x - 1}\right) = \ln(x) - \ln(x - 1)$
15. (a) $y' = \dfrac{2x}{3(x^2 - 1)}$
    (b) $y' = \dfrac{2x}{3(x^2 - 1)}; \ln(x^2 - 1)^{1/3} = \frac{1}{3}\ln(x^2 - 1)$
17. (a) $y' = \dfrac{4}{4x - 1} - \dfrac{3}{x} = \dfrac{-8x + 3}{x(4x - 1)}$
    (b) $y' = \dfrac{-8x + 3}{x(4x - 1)}$;
    $\ln\left(\dfrac{4x - 1}{x^3}\right) = \ln(4x - 1) - 3\ln(x)$
19. $\dfrac{dp}{dq} = \dfrac{2q}{q^2 - 1} - \dfrac{1}{q} = \dfrac{q^2 + 1}{q(q^2 - 1)}$
21. $\dfrac{dy}{dt} = \dfrac{2t}{t^2 + 3} - \dfrac{1}{2}\left(\dfrac{-1}{1 - t}\right) = \dfrac{3 + 4t - 3t^2}{2(1 - t)(t^2 + 3)}$
23. $\dfrac{dy}{dx} = \dfrac{3}{x} + \dfrac{1}{2(x + 1)} = \dfrac{7x + 6}{2x(x + 1)}$
25. $y' = 1 - \dfrac{1}{x}$ 27. $y' = (1 - \ln x)/x^2$
29. $y' = 8x^3/(x^4 + 3)$ 31. $y' = \dfrac{4(\ln x)^3}{x}$
33. $y' = \dfrac{8x^3\ln(x^4 + 3)}{x^4 + 3}$ 35. $y' = \dfrac{1}{x \ln 4}$
37. $y' = \dfrac{4x^3 - 12x^2}{(x^4 - 4x^3 + 1)\ln 6}$
39. rel min $(e^{-1}, -e^{-1})$

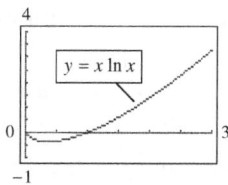

$y = x \ln x$

41. rel min $(2, 4 - 8\ln 2)$

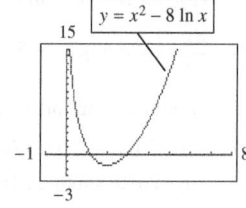

$y = x^2 - 8\ln x$

43. (a) $\overline{MC} = \dfrac{400}{2x+1}$

(b) $\overline{MC} = \dfrac{400}{401} \approx 1.0$; the approximate cost of the 201st unit is $1.

(c) $\overline{MC} > 0$. Yes

45. (a) $\overline{MR} = \dfrac{2500[(x+1)\ln(10x+10) - x]}{(x+1)\ln^2(10x+10)}$

(b) 309.67; at 100 units, selling 1 additional unit yields about $309.67.

47. (a) -5.23 (b) -1.89 (c) increasing

49. A/B **51.** $dR/dI = 1/(I\ln 10)$

53. (a) $y = -31.7 + 18.7\ln(x)$

(b) $y' = \dfrac{18.7}{x}$ (c) 0.47 percentage point per year

11.2 EXERCISES

1. $y' = 5e^x - 1$ **3.** $f'(x) = e^x - exe^{-1}$

5. $g'(x) = 50e^{-0.1x}$ **7.** $y' = 3x^2 e^{x^3}$

9. $y' = 36xe^{3x^2}$ **11.** $y' = 12x(x^2+1)^2 e^{(x^2+1)^3}$

13. $y' = 3x^2$ **15.** $y' = e^{-1/x}/x^2$

17. $y' = \dfrac{2}{x^3}e^{-1/x^2} - 2xe^{-x^2}$ **19.** $ds/dt = te^t(t+2)$

21. $y' = 4x^3 e^{x^4} - 4e^{4x}$ **23.** $y' = \dfrac{4e^{4x}}{e^{4x}+2}$

25. $y' = e^{-3x}/x - 3e^{-3x}\ln(2x)$

27. $y' = (2e^{5x} - 3)/e^{3x} = 2e^{2x} - 3e^{-3x}$

29. $y' = 30e^{3x}(e^{3x}+4)^9$ **31.** $y' = 6^x \ln 6$

33. $y' = 4^{x^2}(2x\ln 4)$

35. (a) $y'(1) = 0$ (b) $y = e^{-1}$

37. (a) $z = 0$ (b)

$y = \frac{1}{\sqrt{2\pi}}e^{-z^2/2}$

39. rel min at $x = 1, y = e$

41. rel max at $x = 0, y = -1$

43. (a) $(0.1)\,Pe^{0.1n}$ (b) $(0.1)\,Pe^{0.1}$

(c) Yes because $e^{0.1n} > 1$ for any $n \geq 1$.

45. (a) $\dfrac{dS}{dt} = -50,000e^{-0.5t}$

(b) The function is a decay exponential. The derivative is always negative.

47. $40e \approx 108.73$ dollars per unit

49. (a) $\dfrac{dy}{dt} = 46.2e^{-0.462t}$

(b) 29.107 percent per hour

51. $\dfrac{dx}{dt} = -0.0684e^{-0.38t}$

53. about $255 billion/year **55.** $\dfrac{dI}{dR} = 10^R \ln 10$

57. (a) $C'(t) = 2.51217e^{0.0271t}$

(b) 2010: about 2.51; 2025: about 3.77

(c) In 2025, the CPI is expected to change at the rate of about $3.77 per year.

59. $y' = \dfrac{98,990,100e^{-0.99t}}{(1 + 9999e^{-0.99t})^2}$

61. (a) 1.60; the rate of increase in this population was approximately 1.60 million per year in 1995.

(b) 0.808 million (808 thousand) per year

(c) The rate of increase in this population in 2040 is approximately half the rate of increase in 1995.

63. (a) $y = 0.544(1.07^x)$

(b) $y' = 0.0368(1.07^x)$

(c) 0.55 percentage point per year

65. (a) $I'(t) = 0.4464(1.014)^t$

(b) $I'(15) \approx 0.5499$; rate is about $549.90 per year.

67. (a) $y = 42.1(1.04^x)$

(b) $y' = 1.65(1.04^x)$

(c) $y'(30) \approx 5.35$ thousand dollars per year

11.3 EXERCISES

1. $\dfrac{1}{2}$ **3.** $-\dfrac{1}{2}$ **5.** $-\dfrac{5}{3}$ **7.** $-x/(2y)$

9. $-(2x+4)/(2y-3)$ **11.** $y' = -x/y$

13. $y' = \dfrac{-y}{2x-3y}$ **15.** $\dfrac{dp}{dq} = \dfrac{p^2}{4-2pq}$

17. $\dfrac{dy}{dx} = \dfrac{x(3x^3-2)}{3y^2(1+y^2)}$ **19.** $\dfrac{dy}{dx} = \dfrac{4x^3 + 6x^2y^2 - 1}{-4x^3y - 3y^2}$

21. $\dfrac{dy}{dx} = \dfrac{(4x^3 + 9x^2y^2 - 8x - 12y)}{(18y + 12x - 6x^3y + 10y^4)}$ **23.** undefined

25. 1 **27.** $y = \tfrac{1}{2}x + 1$ **29.** $y = -11x - 23$

31. $\dfrac{dy}{dx} = \dfrac{1}{2xy}$ **33.** $\dfrac{dy}{dx} = \dfrac{-y}{2x\ln x}$ **35.** $-1/x$ **37.** $\dfrac{-xy-1}{x^2}$

39. $ye^x/(1-e^x)$ **41.** -15 **43.** $\dfrac{1}{3}$ **45.** $y = 3 - x$

47. (a) $(2, \sqrt{2}), (2, -\sqrt{2})$

(b) $(2 + 2\sqrt{2}, 0), (2 - 2\sqrt{2}, 0)$

49. (a) and (b) are verifications.

(c) Yes, because $x^2 + y^2 = 4$.

51. $1/(2x\sqrt{x})$

53. max at $(0, 3)$; min at $(0, -3)$

55. $\dfrac{1}{2}$, so an additional 1 (thousand dollars) of advertising yields about $\dfrac{1}{2}$ (thousand) additional units

57. $-\dfrac{243}{128}$ hours of skilled labor per hour of unskilled labor

59. At $p = $80, q = 49$ and $\dfrac{dq}{dp} = -\dfrac{5}{16}$, which means that if the price is increased to $81, quantity demanded will decrease by approximately $\dfrac{5}{16}$ unit.

61. $-0.000436y$ **63.** $\dfrac{dH}{dT} = \dfrac{-109H - 89}{2398}$

11.4 EXERCISES

1. 36 **3.** $\dfrac{1}{8}$ **5.** $-\dfrac{24}{5}$ **7.** $\dfrac{7}{6}$

9. -5 if $z = 5, -10$ if $z = -5$

11. -80 units/sec **13.** 12π ft^2/min

15. $\dfrac{16}{27}$ in./sec   **17.** $1798/day

19. −$3/day

21. 430 units/month   **23.** 36π mm^3/month

25. $\dfrac{\frac{dW}{dt}}{W} = 3\left(\dfrac{\frac{dL}{dt}}{L}\right)$ **27.** $\dfrac{\frac{dC}{dt}}{C} = 1.54\left(\dfrac{\frac{dW}{dt}}{W}\right)$

29. $1/(4\pi)$ micrometer/day   **31.** $1/(20\pi)$ in/min

33. 0.75 ft/sec   **35.** $-120\sqrt{6}$ mph ≈ -294 mph

37. approaching at 61.18 mph   **39.** $\dfrac{1}{25}$ ft/hr

11.5 EXERCISES

1. (a) 1   (b) no change

3. (a) 84   (b) Revenue will decrease.

5. (a) $\dfrac{100}{99}$ (b) elastic   (c) decrease

7. (a) 0.81   (b) inelastic   (c) increase

9. (a) $\eta = 11.1$ (approximately)   (b) elastic

11. (a) $\eta = \dfrac{375 - 3q}{q}$

    (b) unitary: $q = 93.75$; inelastic: $q > 93.75$; elastic: $q < 93.75$

    (c) As q increases over $0 < q < 93.75$, p decreases, so elastic demand means R increases. Similarly, R decreases for $q > 93.75$.

    (d) maximum for R when $q = 93.75$; yes.

13. (a) $p = 250 - 0.125q$

    (b) $\eta = \dfrac{2000}{q} - 1$

    (c) $\eta \approx 2.33$; elastic. no

    (d) $q = 1000$; $p = \$125$; max $R = \$125,000$

15. $12/item   **17.** $t = \$350$ **19.** $115/item

21. $483 per item; $40,100   **23.** $1100/item

CHAPTER 11 REVIEW EXERCISES

1. $dy/dx = 10(6x - 1)e^{3x^2 - x}$ **2.** $y' = 12/(4x + 11)$

3. $\dfrac{dp}{dq} = \dfrac{1}{q} - \dfrac{2q}{q^2 - 1}$ **4.** $dy/dx = e^{x^2}(2x^2 + 1)$

5. $f'(x) = 10e^{2x} + 4e^{-0.1x}$

6. $g'(x) = 18e^{3x+1}(2e^{3x+1} - 5)^2$

7. $\dfrac{ds}{dx} = \dfrac{9x^{11} - 6x^3}{x^{12} - 2x^4 + 5}$ **8.** $dw/dt = 2t \ln(t^2 + 1)$

9. $dy/dx = 3^{3x - 3} \ln 3$ **10.** $dy/dx = \dfrac{1}{\ln 8}\left(\dfrac{10}{x}\right)$

11. $\dfrac{dy}{dx} = \dfrac{1 - \ln x}{x^2}$ **12.** $dy/dx = -2e^{-x}/(1 - e^{-x})^2$

13. $y = 12ex - 8e$, or $y \approx 32.62x - 21.75$

14. $y = 3x + 5$ **15.** $\dfrac{dy}{dx} = \dfrac{y}{x(10y - \ln x)}$

16. $dy/dx = ye^{xy}/(1 - xe^{xy})$ **17.** $dy/dx = 2/y$

18. $\dfrac{dy}{dx} = \dfrac{2(x + 1)}{3(1 - 2y)}$ **19.** $\dfrac{dy}{dx} = \dfrac{6x(1 + xy^2)}{y(5y^3 - 4x^3)}$

20. $d^2y/dx^2 = -(x^2 + y^2)/y^3 = -1/y^3$ **21.** 5/9

22. $\left(-2, \pm\sqrt{\frac{2}{3}}\right)$ **23.** 3/4   **24.** 11 square units/min

25. (a) $P'(t) = \dfrac{17.4}{t}$

    (b) $P(58) \approx 166.8$; $P'(58) \approx 0.3$. These mean that in 2028 this population is projected to be about 166.8 million and growing about 0.3 million (300,000) per year.

26. (a) $L'(y) = \dfrac{7.10}{y}$

    (b) $L(50) \approx 13.2$ and $L(80) \approx 16.5$. These mean that the expected number of additional years of life expectancy at age 65 is about 13.2 in 2000 and 16.5 in 2030.

    (c) $L'(50) \approx 0.14$ and $L'(80) \approx 0.09$. These mean that the number of additional years of life expectancy at age 65 is expected to change at the rate of about 0.14 year of life per year in 2000 and 0.09 year of life per year in 2030.

27. (a) $S'(n) = 120e^{0.12n}$

    (b) after 1 year: about $135.30 per year
       after 10 years: about $398.41 per year

28. (a) $D'(t) \approx 229.7e^{0.02292t}$

    (b) $D(20) \approx 15,850$ and $D'(20) \approx 363$. These mean that in 2030 total U. S. disposable income is expected to be about $15,850 billion and changing at the rate of about $363 billion per year.

29. (a) $-0.00001438A_0$ units/year

    (b) $-0.00002876A_0$ units/year   (c) less

30. $1200e \approx \$3261.94$ per unit

31. $-\$1797.36$ per year   **32.** $-1/(25\pi)$ mm/min

33. $\dfrac{48}{25}$ ft/min   **34.** $\dfrac{dS/dt}{S} = \dfrac{1}{3}\left(\dfrac{dA/dt}{A}\right)$

35. (a) 1   (b) no change

36. (a) $\dfrac{25}{12}$, elastic   (b) revenue decreases

37. (a) 1   (b) no change

38. (a)   (b) $q = 100$

    (c) max revenue at $q = 100$

    (d) Revenue is maximized where elasticity is unitary.

39. yes

40. $t = \$1466.67, T \approx \$58,667$

41. $t = \$880, T = \$3520$

CHAPTER 11 TEST

1. $y' = 15x^2 e^{x^3} + 2x$

2. $y' = \dfrac{12x^2}{x^3 + 1}$

3. $y' = \dfrac{12x^3}{x^4 + 1}$

4. $f'(x) = 20(3^{2x}) \ln 3$

5. $\dfrac{dS}{dt} = e^{t^4}(4t^4 + 1)$

6. $y' = \dfrac{e^{x^3+1}(3x^3 - 1)}{x^2}$

7. $y' = \dfrac{3 - 12 \ln x}{x^5}$

8. $g'(x) = \dfrac{8}{(4x + 7) \ln 5}$

9. $y' = \dfrac{-3x^3}{y}$

10. $-\frac{3}{2}$

11. $y' = \dfrac{-e^y}{xe^y - 10}$

12. $\$1349.50$ per week

13. $\eta = 3.71$; decreases

14. -0.05 unit per dollar

15. 586 units per day

16. (a) $y' = 31.1585e^{0.0505t}$

(b) 2010: $y'(10) \approx 51.6$ billion dollars per year

2020: $y'(20) \approx 85.5$ billion dollars per year

17. $\$540$

18. (a) $y = -12.97 + 11.85 \ln x$

(b) $y' = \dfrac{11.85}{x}$

(c) $y(25) \approx 25.2$ means that the model estimates about 25.2% of the U.S. population will have diabetes in 2025. $y'(25) \approx 0.474$ predicts that in 2025 the percent of the U.S. population with diabetes will be changing by about 0.474 percentage point per year.

19. (a) $P'(t) = 1.078(0.9732^t) \cdot \ln(0.9732) \approx -0.02928(0.9732^t)$

(b) $P(18) \approx 0.661$ and $P'(18) \approx -0.018$. These mean that in 2028 the purchasing power of $1 is expected to be about 66.1% of what it was in 2012 and is expected to be decreasing about 1.8% per year.

12.1 EXERCISES

1. $x^4 + C$ **3.** $\frac{1}{7}x^7 + C$ **5.** $\frac{1}{8}x^8 + C$

7. $2x^4 + C$ **9.** $27x + \frac{1}{14}x^{14} + C$

11. $3x - \frac{2}{5}x^{5/2} + C$ **13.** $\frac{1}{5}x^5 - 3x^3 + 3x + C$

15. $13x - 3x^2 + 3x^7 + C$

17. $2x + \frac{4}{3}x\sqrt{x} + C$ **19.** $\frac{24}{5}x\sqrt[4]{x} + C$

21. $-5/(3x^3) + C$ **23.** $\frac{3}{2}\sqrt[3]{x} + C$

25. $\dfrac{1}{4}x^4 - 4x - \dfrac{1}{x^5} + C$

27. $\dfrac{1}{10}x^{10} + \dfrac{1}{2x^2} + 3x^{2/3} + C$

29. $2x^8 - \frac{4}{3}x^6 + \frac{1}{4}x^4 + C$ **31.** $-1/x - 1/(2x^2) + C$

33.

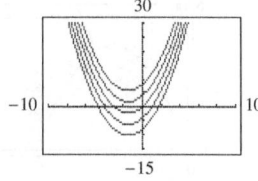
$f(x) = x^2 + 3x + C$
$(C = -8, -4, 0, 4, \text{ and } 8)$

35. $f(x) = 18x^8 - 35x^4$ **37.** $\int \left(5 - \frac{1}{2}x\right)dx$

39. $\int (3x^2 - 6x)\, dx$ **41.** $R(x) = 30x - 0.2x^2$

43. $R(50) = \$22,125$

45. $P(t) = \frac{1}{4}t^4 + \frac{4}{3}t^3 + 6t$

47. (a) $x = t^{7/4}/1050$ (b) 0.96 ton

49. (a) $\overline{C}(x) = x/4 + 100/x + 390$ (b) $\$416$ per unit

51. (a) $E(t) = 0.910t^3 - 25.3t^2 + 549t + 4560$

(b) $\$12,700$ per person

53. (a) The wind chill temperature decreases because

$\dfrac{dt}{dw} < 0$ for $w > 0$.

The rate increases because $\dfrac{d^2t}{dw^2} > 0$ for $w > 0$.

(b) $t = 48.12 - 27.2w^{0.16}$

55. (a) $t \approx 63.1$; in 2024

(b) $P(t) = -0.0000729t^3 + 0.0138t^2 + 1.98t + 181$

(c) 348 million

12.2 EXERCISES

1. $du = 10x^4\, dx$ **3.** $dp = (7 - 6q^{1/2})\, dq$

5. (a) Power Rule cannot be used; need x^3 as a factor of du

(b) $\dfrac{1}{8}(5x^3 + 11)^8 + C$

7. $\frac{1}{4}(x^2 + 3)^4 + C$ **9.** $\frac{1}{5}(5x^3 + 11)^5 + C$

11. $\frac{1}{3}(3x - x^3)^3 + C$ **13.** $\frac{1}{28}(7x^4 + 12)^4 + C$

15. $\frac{1}{4}(4x - 1)^7 + C$ **17.** $-\frac{1}{6}(4x^6 + 15)^{-2} + C$

19. $\frac{1}{10}(x^2 - 2x + 5)^5 + C$ **21.** $-\frac{1}{8}(x^4 - 4x + 3)^{-4} + C$

23. $\frac{7}{6}(x^4 + 6)^{3/2} + C$ **25.** $\frac{3}{8}x^8 + \frac{6}{5}x^5 + \frac{3}{2}x^2 + C$

27. $10.8x^{10} - 12x^6 + 6x^2 + C$ **29.** $\frac{2}{9}(x^3 - 3x)^{3/2} + C$

31. $\dfrac{-1}{[10(2x^5 - 5)^3]} + C$ **33.** $\dfrac{-1}{[8(x^4 - 4x)^2]} + C$

35. $\frac{2}{3}\sqrt{x^3 - 6x^2 + 2} + C$ **37.** $f(x) = 70(7x - 13)^9$

39. (a) $f(x) = \frac{1}{8}(x^2 - 1)^4 + C$

(b)

$f(x) = \frac{1}{8}(x^2 - 1)^4 + C$
$(C = -5, 0, 5)$

41. (a) $F(x) = \frac{15}{4}(2x - 1)^{2/5} + C$ (c) $x = \frac{1}{2}$

(b)   (d) vertical

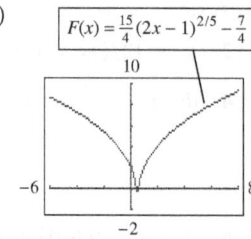
$F(x) = \frac{15}{4}(2x - 1)^{2/5} - \frac{7}{4}$

43. $\displaystyle \int \dfrac{8x(x^2 - 1)^{1/3}}{3}\, dx$

45. (b) $\dfrac{-7}{3(x^3 + 4)} + C$

(d) $\int (x^2 + 5)^{-4}\, dx$ (Many answers are possible.)

47. $R(x) = \dfrac{15}{2x + 1} + 30x - 15$

49. 3720 bricks

51. (a) $s = 10\sqrt{x + 1}$ (b) 50

53. (a) $A(t) = 100/(t + 10) - 1000/(t + 10)^2$

  (b) 2.5 million

55. 7400

57. (a) $f(x) = \dfrac{-505}{0.743x + 6.97} + 36.2$

  (b) 23.7%

59. (a) $p(t) = 56.19 - \dfrac{1561}{1.38t + 64.1}$

  (b)

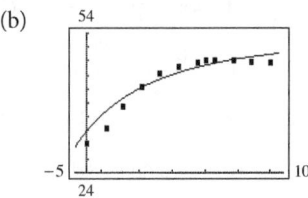

  (c) The model is a good fit to the data.

12.3 EXERCISES

1. $e^{3x} + C$ **3.** $-e^{-x} + C$ **5.** $10,000e^{0.1x} + C$

7. $-1200e^{-0.7x} + C$ **9.** $\frac{1}{12}e^{3x^4} + C$

11. $-\frac{3}{2}e^{-2x} + C$ **13.** $\frac{1}{18}e^{3x^6 - 2} + C$

15. $\frac{1}{4}e^{4x} + 6/e^{x/2} + C$

17. $\ln|x^3 + 4| + C$ **19.** $\frac{1}{4}\ln|4z + 1| + C$

21. $\frac{3}{4}\ln|2x^4 + 1| + C$ **23.** $\frac{2}{5}\ln|5x^2 - 4| + C$

25. $\ln|x^3 - 2x| + C$ **27.** $\frac{1}{3}\ln|z^3 + 3z + 17| + C$

29. $\frac{1}{3}x^3 + \ln|x - 1| + C$ **31.** $x + \frac{1}{2}\ln|x^2 + 3| + C$

33. $f(x) = h(x)$, $\int f(x)\, dx = g(x)$

35. $F(x) = -\ln|3 - x| + C$

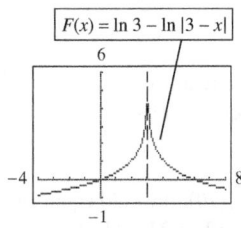

37. $f(x) = 1 + \dfrac{1}{x}$; $\displaystyle\int\left(1 + \dfrac{1}{x}\right) dx$

39. $f(x) = 5e^{-x} - 5xe^{-x}$; $\int (5e^{-x} - 5xe^{-x})\, dx$

41. (c) $\frac{1}{3}\ln|x^3 + 3x^2 + 7| + C$ (d) $\frac{5}{8}e^{2x^4} + C$

43. $1030.97 **45.** $n = n_0 e^{-Kt}$ **47.** 55

49. (a) $S = Pe^{0.1n}$ (b) $\approx$ 7 years

51. (a) $p = 95e^{-0.491t}$ (b) $\approx$ 90.45

53. (a) $l(t) = 8.66 + 14.9 \ln(t + 20)$

  (b) The model is a very good fit to the data.

  (c) 80.6 years

55. (a) Yes. The rate is an exponential that is always positive. Hence the function is always increasing.

  (b) $C(t) = 80.39e^{0.0384t} + 0.6635$

  (c) $C(35) \approx 308.91$; $C'(35) \approx 11.84$

   For 2025, the model predicts that the CPI will be $308.91 and will be changing at a rate of about $11.84 per year.

12.4 EXERCISES

1. $C(x) = x^2 + 100x + 200$

3. $C(x) = 2x^2 + 2x + 80$

5. $C(x) = 140x + 0.1x^{3/2} + 10,900$; $FC = 10,900$

7. (a) $x = 3$ units is optimal level

  (b) $P(x) = -4x^2 + 24x - 200$

  (c) loss of $164

9. (a) profit of $3120 (b) 896 units

11. (a) $\overline{C}(x) = \frac{6}{x} + \frac{x}{6} + 8$ (b) $10.50

13. (a) and (b)

  (c) Maximum profit is $114.743 thousand at $x = 200$ thousand units.

15. $C(y) = 0.80y + 7$

17. $C(y) = 0.3y + 0.4\sqrt{y} + 8$

19. $C(y) = 2\sqrt{y + 1} + 0.4y + 4$

21. $C(y) = 0.7y + 0.5e^{-2y} + 5.15$

23. $C(y) = 0.85y + 5.15$

25. $C(y) = 0.8y + \ln(y + 1) + 12$

27. $C(y) = 0.8y + \dfrac{2\sqrt{3y + 7}}{3} + 4.24$

29. (a) $C(y) = 0.00845y^2 + 0.617y + 2.43$

  (b) $C(y) = 0.00844y^2 + 0.617y + 2.43$

  (c) The functions are nearly identical; linear function

12.5 EXERCISES

1. $4y - 2xy' = 4x^2 - 2x(2x) = 0$ ✔

3. $2y\, dx - x\, dy = 2(3x^2 + 1)\, dx - x(6x\, dx) = 2\, dx$ ✔

5. $y = \frac{1}{2}e^{x + 1} + C$ **7.** $y^2 = 2x^2 + C$

9. $y^3 = x^2 - x + C$ **11.** $y = e^{x - 3} - e^{-3} + 2$

13. $y = \ln|x| - \dfrac{x^2}{2} + \dfrac{1}{2}$ **15.** $\dfrac{y^2}{2} = \dfrac{x^3}{3} + C$

17. $\dfrac{1}{2x^2} + \dfrac{y^2}{2} = C$ **19.** $\dfrac{1}{x} + y + \dfrac{y^3}{3} = C$

21. $\dfrac{1}{y} + \ln|x| = C$ **23.** $x^2 - y^2 = C$

25. $y = C(x + 1)$ **27.** $x^2 + 4\ln|x| + e^{-y^2} = C$

29. $3y^4 = 4x^3 - 1$

31. $2y = 3x + 4xy$ or $y = \dfrac{3x}{2 - 4x}$

33. $e^{2y} = x^2 - \dfrac{2}{x} + 2$ **35.** $y^2 + 1 = 5x$

37. $y = Cx^k$

39. (a) $x = 10,000e^{0.06t}$ (b) $10,618.37; $13,498.59

  (c) 11.55 years

41. $P = 100,000e^{0.05t}$; 5% **43.** $\approx$ 8.4 hours

45. $y = \dfrac{32}{(p + 8)^{2/5}}$ **47.** $\approx$ 23,100 years

49. $x = 6(1 - e^{-0.05t})$

51. $x = 20 - 10e^{-0.025t}$

53. $V = 1.86e^{2 - 2e^{-0.1t}}$

55. $V = \dfrac{k^3 t^3}{27}$

57. $t \approx 4.5$ hours

59. (a) $E(t) = 18.5e^{0.0164t}$

(b)

The model looks similar, except at the right end, where it rises more sharply than the graph of the data.

61. (a) $P(t) = 80,000e^{-0.05t}$ (b) $37,789.32

CHAPTER 12 REVIEW EXERCISES

1. $\frac{1}{7}x^7 + C$

2. $\frac{2}{3}x^{3/2} + C$

3. $3x^4 - x^3 + 2x^2 + 5x + C$ **4.** $\frac{7}{5}x^5 - \frac{14}{3}x^3 + 7x + C$

5. $\frac{7}{6}(x^2 - 1)^3 + C$ **6.** $\frac{1}{18}(x^3 - 3x^2)^6 + C$

7. $\frac{3}{8}x^8 + \frac{24}{5}x^5 + 24x^2 + C$ **8.** $\frac{5}{63}(3x^3 + 7)^7 + C$

9. $\frac{1}{3}\ln|x^3 + 1| + C$ **10.** $\dfrac{-1}{3(x^3 + 1)} + C$

11. $\frac{1}{2}(x^3 - 4)^{2/3} + C$ **12.** $\frac{1}{3}\ln|x^3 - 4| + C$

13. $\dfrac{1}{2}x^2 - \dfrac{1}{x} + C$

14. $\frac{1}{3}x^3 + \frac{1}{2}x^2 - 2x - \ln|x - 1| + C$

15. $\frac{1}{3}e^{y^3} + C$ **16.** $\frac{1}{39}(3x - 1)^{13} + C$

17. $\frac{1}{2}\ln|2x^3 - 7| + C$ **18.** $\dfrac{-5}{4e^{4x}} + C$

19. $x^4/4 - e^{3x}/3 + C$ **20.** $\frac{1}{2}e^{x^2 + 1} + C$

21. $\dfrac{-3}{40(5x^8 + 7)^2} + C$ **22.** $-\frac{7}{2}\sqrt{1 - x^4} + C$

23. $\frac{1}{4}e^{2x} - e^{-2x} + C$ **24.** $x^2/2 + 1/(x + 1) + C$

25. (a) $\frac{1}{10}(x^2 - 1)^5 + C$ (b) $\frac{1}{22}(x^2 - 1)^{11} + C$

(c) $\frac{3}{16}(x^2 - 1)^8 + C$ (d) $\frac{3}{2}(x^2 - 1)^{1/3} + C$

26. (a) $\ln|x^2 - 1| + C$ (b) $\dfrac{-1}{x^2 - 1} + C$

(c) $3\sqrt{x^2 - 1} + C$ (d) $\frac{3}{2}\ln|x^2 - 1| + C$

27. $y = C - 92e^{-0.05t}$

28. $y = 64x + 38x^2 - 12x^3 + C$

29. $(y - 3)^2 = 4x^2 + C$ **30.** $(y + 1)^2 = 2\ln|t| + C$

31. $e^y = \dfrac{x^2}{2} + C$ **32.** $y = Ct^4$

33. $3(y + 1)^2 = 2x^3 + 75$

34. $x^2 = y + y^2 + 4$ **35.** $28,800   **36.** 472

37. $P(t) = 400[1 - 5/(t + 5) + 25/(t + 5)^2]$

38. $p = 1990.099 - 100,000/(t + 100)$

39. (a) $y = -60e^{-0.04t} + 60$ (b) 23%

40. $R(x) = 800\ln(x + 2) - 554.52$

41. (a) $1000   (b) $C(x) = 3x^2 + 4x + 1000$

42. 80 units, $440

43. $C(y) = \sqrt{2y + 16} + 0.6y + 4.5$

44. $C(y) = 0.8y - 0.05e^{-2y} + 7.85$ **45.** $W = CL^3$

46. (a) $\ln|P| = kt + C_1$ (b) $P = Ce^{kt}$

(c) $P = 50,000e^{0.1t}$ (d) The interest rate is $k = 0.10 = 10\%$.

47. ≈ 10.7 million years   **48.** $x = 360(1 - e^{-t/30})$

49. $x = 600 - 500e^{-0.01t}$; ≈ 161 min

CHAPTER 12 TEST

1. $2x^3 + 4x^2 - 7x + C$ **2.** $11x - \dfrac{x^4}{2} + C$

3. $\dfrac{5x^3}{3} - 5x + C$ **4.** $4x + \frac{2}{3}x\sqrt{x} + \frac{1}{x} + C$

5. $\dfrac{(7 + 2x^3)^{10}}{10} + C$ **6.** $\dfrac{(4x^3 - 7)^{10}}{24} + C$

7. $-\frac{1}{6}(3x^2 - 6x + 1)^{-2} + C$ **8.** $e^x + 5\ln|x| - x + C$

9. $\dfrac{\ln|2s^4 - 5|}{8} + C$ **10.** $-10,000e^{-0.01x} + C$

11. $\dfrac{5}{8}e^{2y^4 - 1} + C$

12. $x^2 - x + \dfrac{1}{2}\ln|2x + 1| + C$

13. $6x^2 - 1 + 5e^x$ **14.** $\dfrac{1}{9}x^3 - \dfrac{5}{8}x + C$

15. $y = x^4 + x^3 + 4$ **16.** $y = \frac{1}{4}e^{4x} + \frac{7}{4}$

17. $y = \dfrac{4}{C - x^4}$ **18.** 157,498

19. $P(x) = 450x - 2x^2 - 300$

20. $C(y) = 0.78y + \sqrt{0.5y + 1} + 5.6$

21. (a) $x = 100e^{-0.00693t}$ (b) about 332 days

22. $x = 16 - 16e^{-t/40}$

13.1 EXERCISES

1. 7 square units   **3.** 7.25 square units

5. 3 square units   **7.** 11.25 square units

9. $S_L(10) = 4.08$; $S_R(10) = 5.28$

11. Both equal 14/3.

13. It would lie between $S_L(10)$ and $S_R(10)$. It would equal 14/3.

15. 3   **17.** 42   **19.** -5 **21.** 180   **23.** 11,315

25. $3 - \dfrac{3(n + 1)}{n} + \dfrac{(n + 1)(2n + 1)}{2n^2} = \dfrac{2n^2 - 3n + 1}{2n^2}$

27. (a) $S = (n - 1)/n$ (b) 9/10   (c) 99/100

(d) 999/1000   (e) 1

29. (a) $S = \dfrac{(n + 1)(2n + 1)}{6n^2}$

(b) $77/200 = 0.385$ (c) $6767/20,000 \approx 0.3384$

(d) $667,667/2,000,000 \approx 0.3338$ (e) $\frac{1}{3}$

31. $\dfrac{20}{3}$

33. (a) 8696 square units

(b) This represents the total per capita out-of-pocket expenses for health care between 2013 and 2021.

35. There are approximately 90 squares under the curve, each representing 1 second by 10 mph, or

$$1\,\text{sec} \times \dfrac{10\,\text{mi}}{1\,\text{hr}} \times \dfrac{1\,\text{hr}}{3600\,\text{sec}} = \dfrac{1}{360}\,\text{mile}.$$

The area under the curve is approximately $90\left(\frac{1}{360}\,\text{mile}\right) = \frac{1}{4}\,\text{mile}$.

37. 1550 square feet

39. 292 square units. This represents the total sulphur dioxide emissions (in millions of short tons) from electricity generation from 2015 to 2025.

13.2 EXERCISES

1. 18   **3.** 2   **5.** 60   **7.** 16   **9.** 0   **11.** 98

13. $12\sqrt[3]{25}$ **15.** 2   **17.** $-\frac{1}{10}$ **19.** 12,960   **21.** 0

23. 0   **25.** $\frac{49}{3}$ **27.** $e^3/3 - 1/3$ **29.** 4   **31.** $\frac{8}{3}(1 - e^{-8})$

33. (a) $\frac{1}{6}\ln(112/31) \approx 0.2140853$ (b) 0.2140853

35. (a) $\frac{3}{2} + 3\ln 2 \approx 3.5794415$ (b) 3.5794415

37. (a) A, C (b) B

39. (a) $\int_0^4 (2x - \frac{1}{2}x^2)dx$ (b) $16/3$

41. (a) $\int_{-1}^0 (x^3 + 1)\, dx$ (b) $3/4$

43. $\frac{1}{6}$ **45.** $\frac{1}{2}(e^9 - e)$

47. $\int_0^a g(x)\, dx > \int_0^a f(x)\, dx$; more area under $g(x)$

49. same absolute values, opposite signs

51. -6 **53.** 0   **55.** (a) $450,000   (b) $450,000

57. (a) $5390   (b) $2450

59. $20,405.39

61. 4146 represents the total million metric tons of CO_2 emissions from 2010 to 2020.

63. 0.04 cm³   **65.** 1222 (approximately)

67. 0.1808

69. (a) 0.5934   (b) 0.1733   (c) 0.764

71. (a) 0.5078   (b) 0.619

73. (a) $G(t) = -0.157t^2 - 0.196t + 133$
(b) 1267.9; the total amount of gasoline (1267.9 billion gallons) used by motor vehicles in the United States from 2014 to 2024.

13.3 EXERCISES

1. (a) $\int_0^2 (4 - x^2)\, dx$ (b) $\frac{16}{3}$

3. (a) $\int_1^8 [\sqrt[3]{x} - (2 - x)]\, dx$ (b) 28.75

5. (a) $\int_1^2 [(4 - x^2) - (\frac{1}{4}x^3 - 2)]\, dx$ (b) $131/48$

7. (a) $(-1, 1), (2, 4)$ (b) $\int_{-1}^2 [(x + 2) - x^2]\, dx$
(c) $9/2$

9. (a) $(0, 0), (\frac{5}{2}, -\frac{15}{4})$
(b) $\int_0^{5/2} [(x - x^2) - (x^2 - 4x)]\, dx$ (c) $\frac{125}{24}$

11. (a) $(-2, -4), (0, 0), (2, 4)$
(b) $\int_{-2}^0 [(x^3 - 2x) - 2x]\, dx + \int_0^2 [2x - (x^3 - 2x)]\, dx$
(c) 8

13. $\frac{28}{3}$ **15.** $\frac{1}{4}$ **17.** $\frac{16}{3}$ **19.** $\frac{1}{3}$ **21.** $\frac{37}{12}$

23. $4 - 3\ln 3$ **25.** $\frac{8}{3}$ **27.** 6   **29.** 0   **31.** $-\frac{4}{9}$

33. $11.8\overline{3}$

35. average profit $= \dfrac{1}{x_1 - x_0}\displaystyle\int_{x_0}^{x_1} [R(x) - C(x)]\, dx$

37. (a) $1402 per unit   (b) $535,333.33

39. (a) 102.5 units   (b) 100 units

41. (a) 40.05 million/year   (b) 69.93 million/year

43. 147 mg

45. Black: 0.479; Hispanic: 0.459
The income distribution for Black households is more unequal than it is for Hispanic households.

47. 1980: 0.383; 2015: 0.454
2015 shows more income distribution inequality than 1980.

49. $G = \dfrac{p - 1}{p + 1}$

13.4 EXERCISES

1. $126,205.10   **3.** $346,664 (nearest dollar)

5. $506,000 (nearest thousand)

7. $18,660 (nearest dollar)

9. $82,155 (nearest dollar)

11. $PV = \$2,657,807$ (nearest dollar), $FV = \$3,771,608$ (nearest dollar)

13. $PV = \$190,519$ (nearest dollar), $FV = \$347,147$ (nearest dollar)

15. Gift Shoppe, $151,024; Wine Boutique, $141,093. The gift shop is a better buy.

17. $83.33   **19.** $161.89   **21.** $(5, 56)$; $83.33

23. $11.50   **25.** $204.17   **27.** $2766.67

29. $17,839.58   **31.** $133.33   **33.** $2.50

35. $103.35

13.5 EXERCISES

1. formula 5: $\frac{1}{8}\ln |(4 + x)/(4 - x)| + C$

3. formula 11: $\frac{1}{3}\ln [(3 + \sqrt{10})/2]$

5. formula 14: $w(\ln w - 1) + C$

7. formula 12: $\frac{1}{3} + \frac{1}{4}\ln\left(\frac{3}{7}\right)$

9. formula 13: $\frac{1}{8}\ln\left|\dfrac{v}{3v + 8}\right| + C$

11. formula 7: $\frac{1}{2}[7\sqrt{24} - 25\ln(7 + \sqrt{24}) + 25\ln 5]$

13. formula 16: $\dfrac{(6w - 5)(4w + 5)^{3/2}}{60} + C$

15. formula 3: $\frac{1}{2}(5^{x^2})\log_5 e + C$

17. formula 1: $\frac{1}{3}(13^{3/2} - 8)$

19. formula 9: $-\frac{5}{2}\ln\left|\dfrac{2 + \sqrt{4 - 9x^2}}{3x}\right| + C$

21. formula 10: $\frac{1}{3}\ln |3x + \sqrt{9x^2 - 4}| + C$

23. formula 15: $\frac{3}{4}\left[\ln |2x - 5| - \dfrac{5}{2x - 5}\right] + C$

25. formula 8: $\frac{1}{3}\ln |3x + 1 + \sqrt{(3x + 1)^2 + 1}| + C$

27. formula 6: $\frac{1}{4}[10\sqrt{109} - \sqrt{10} + 9\ln(10 + \sqrt{109}) - 9\ln(1 + \sqrt{10})]$

29. formula 2: $-\frac{1}{6}\ln |7 - 3x^2| + C$

31. formula 8: $\frac{1}{2}\ln |2x + \sqrt{4x^2 + 7}| + C$

33. $2(e^{\sqrt{2}} - e) \approx 2.7899$

35. $\frac{1}{32}[\ln(9/5) - 4/9] \approx 0.004479$

37. $3391.10

39. (a) $C = \frac{1}{2}x\sqrt{x^2 + 9} + \frac{9}{2}\ln |x + \sqrt{x^2 + 9}| + 300 - \frac{9}{2}\ln 3$
(b) $314.94

41. $3882.9 thousand

13.6 EXERCISES

1. $\frac{1}{3}xe^{3x} - \frac{1}{9}e^{3x} + C$ **3.** $\frac{1}{3}x^3\ln x - \frac{1}{9}x^3 + C$

5. $\dfrac{104\sqrt{2}}{15}$ **7.** $-(1 + \ln x)/x + C$ **9.** 1

11. $\dfrac{x^2}{2}\ln(2x-3) - \dfrac{1}{4}x^2 - \dfrac{3}{4}x - \dfrac{9}{8}\ln(2x-3) + C$

13. $\frac{1}{5}(q^2-3)^{3/2}(q^2+2) + C$ **15.** 282.4

17. $-e^{-x}(x^2+2x+2) + C$ **19.** $(9e^4+3)/2$

21. $\frac{1}{4}x^4\ln^2 x - \frac{1}{8}x^4\ln x + \frac{1}{32}x^4 + C$

23. $\frac{2}{15}(e^x+1)^{3/2}(3e^x-2) + C$ **25.** II; $\frac{1}{2}e^{x^2} + C$

27. IV; $\frac{2}{3}(e^x+1)^{3/2} + C$ **29.** I; $-5e^{-4} + 1$

31. \$2794.46   **33.** \$34,836.73   **35.** 0.264

37. 166 million

13.7 EXERCISES

1. 1/5   **3.** 2   **5.** 1/e   **7.** diverges   **9.** diverges

11. 10   **13.** diverges   **15.** diverges   **17.** 0

19. 0   **21.** 0.5   **23.** 1/(2e)   **25.** $\frac{3}{2}$

27. $\int_{-\infty}^{\infty} f(x)\,dx = 1$ **29.** $c = 1$ **31.** $c = \frac{1}{4}$

33. 20

35. area $= \frac{8}{3}$

37. $\int_0^\infty Ae^{-rt}\,dt = A/r$

39. \$2,400,000

41. \$700,000

43. (a) 0.368   (b) 0.018

45. (a) 0.147   (b) 0.383

47. (a) 0.75   (b) 0.375   (c) 0.5

49. (a) $500\left[\dfrac{e^{-0.03b} + 0.03b - 1}{0.0009}\right]$

  (b) The amount approaches ∞.

13.8 EXERCISES

1. $h = \frac{1}{2}; x_0 = 0, x_1 = \frac{1}{2}, x_2 = 1, x_3 = \frac{3}{2}, x_4 = 2$

3. $h = \frac{1}{2}; x_0 = 1, x_1 = \frac{3}{2}, x_2 = 2, x_3 = \frac{5}{2}, x_4 = 3, x_5 = \frac{7}{2}, x_6 = 4$

5. $h = 1; x_0 = -1, x_1 = 0, x_2 = 1, x_3 = 2, x_4 = 3, x_5 = 4$

7. (a) 9.13   (b) 9.00   (c) 9   (d) Simpson's

9. (a) 0.51   (b) 0.50   (c) $\frac{1}{2}$ (d) Simpson's

11. (a) 5.27   (b) 5.30   (c) 5.33   (d) Simpson's

13. (a) 3.283   (b) 3.240

15. (a) 0.743   (b) 0.747

17. (a) 7.132   (b) 7.197   **19.** 7.8   **21.** 10.3

23. 119.58 (\$119,580)   **25.** \$32,389.76

27. \$14,133.33   **29.** 1222.35 (1222 units)

31. (a)

x	0	0.2	0.4	0.6	0.8	1
$L_a - L_b$	0	0.005	0.009	0.021	0.042	0

  (b) 0.031
  (c) positive; 1990

33. (a) Yes   (b) Simpson's   (c) 1586.67 ft²

CHAPTER 13 REVIEW EXERCISES

1. 212   **2.** $\dfrac{3(n+1)}{2n^2}$ **3.** $\frac{91}{72}$ **4.** 1   **5.** 1

6. 14   **7.** $\frac{248}{5}$ **8.** $-\frac{205}{4}$ **9.** $\frac{825}{4}$ **10.** $\frac{4}{13}$

11. -2 **12.** $\frac{1}{6}\ln 47 - \frac{1}{6}\ln 9$ **13.** $\frac{9}{2}$

14. $\ln 4 + \frac{14}{3}$ **15.** 190/3   **16.** $\frac{1}{2}\ln 2$

17. $(1-e^{-2})/2$ **18.** $(e-1)/2$ **19.** 95/2

20. 36   **21.** $\frac{1}{4}$ **22.** $\frac{1}{2}$

23. $\frac{1}{2}x\sqrt{x^2-4} - 2\ln|x + \sqrt{x^2-4}| + C$

24. $2\log_3 e$ **25.** $\frac{1}{2}x^2(\ln x^2 - 1) + C$

26. $\frac{1}{2}\ln|x| - \frac{1}{2}\ln|3x+2| + C$

27. $\frac{1}{6}x^6\ln x - \frac{1}{36}x^6 + C$

28. $-e^{-2x}(x^2/2 + x/2 + 1/4) + C$

29. $2x\sqrt{x+5} - \frac{4}{3}(x+5)^{3/2} + C$

30. 3   **31.** diverges   **32.** -100

33. $\frac{5}{3}$ **34.** $-\frac{1}{2}$ **35.** $c = 50$

36. (a) $\frac{8}{9} \approx 0.889$ (b) 1.004   (c) 0.909

37. 3.135   **38.** 3.9

39. (a) $n = 5$ (b) $n = 6$ **40.** \$28,000

41. (a) $1 - e^{-2.8} \approx 0.939$ (b) 0.668

42. \$1297.44   **43.** \$76.60

44. 1969: 0.3737; 2000: 0.4264; more equally distributed in 1969

45. \$1,621,803   **46.** (a) \$403,609   (b) \$602,114

47. (a) $(7, 6)$ (b) \$7.33   **48.** \$24.50

49. \$217.42   **50.** \$10,066 (nearest dollar)

51. \$86,557.41

52. $C(x) = 3x + 30(x+1)^2\ln(x+1) - 15(x+1)^2 + 2015$

53. (a) 0.165   (b) 0.301

54. \$4000 thousand, or \$4 million

55. \$197,365   **56.** \$480,000 hundred, or \$48,000,000

CHAPTER 13 TEST

1. 3.496 (approximately)

2. (a) $5 - \dfrac{n+1}{n}$ (b) 4

3. $\int_0^6 (12 + 4x - x^2)\,dx; 72$

4. (a) 4   (b) 3/4   (c) $\frac{5}{4}\ln 5$ (d) 7
  (e) 0; limits of integration are the same
  (f) $\frac{5}{6}(e^2-1)$

5. (a) $3xe^x - 3e^x + C$ (b) $\dfrac{x^2}{2}\ln(2x) - \dfrac{x^2}{4} + C$

6. -8

7. (a) $x[\ln(2x) - 1] + C$
  (b) $\dfrac{2(9x+14)(3x-7)^{3/2}}{135} + C$

8. 16.089

9. (a) \$4000   (b) \$16,000/3

10. (a) \$961.18 thousand   (b) \$655.68 thousand
  (c) \$1062.5 thousand

11. 125/6

12.

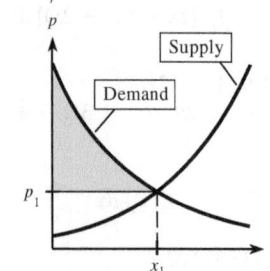

13. Before, 0.446; After, 0.19. The change decreases the difference in income.

14. (a) About 20.92 billion barrels
  (b) About 2.067 billion barrels per year

15. About 2.9666   **16.** 6800 ft²

14.1 EXERCISES

1. $\{(x, y): x \text{ and } y \text{ are real numbers}\}$
3. $\{(x, y): x \text{ and } y \text{ are real numbers and } y \neq 0\}$
5. $\{(x, y): x \text{ and } y \text{ are real numbers and } 2x - y \neq 0\}$
7. $\{(p_1, p_2): p_1 \text{ and } p_2 \text{ are real numbers and } p_1 \geq 0\}$
9. -2 11. $\frac{5}{3}$ 13. 2500 15. 36 17. 3
19. $\frac{1}{25}\ln(12)$ 21. $\frac{13}{3}$
23. $6640.23; the amount that results when $2000 is invested for 20 years
25. 34 mph
27. Max: $S \approx 112.5°F; A \approx 107.1°F$
Min: $S \approx 87.4°F; A \approx 74.7°F$
29. (a) $752.80; when $90,000 is borrowed for 20 years at 8%, the monthly payment is $752.80.
(b) $1622.82; when $160,000 is borrowed for 15 years at 9%, the monthly payment is $1622.82.
31. (a) $x = 4$ (b) $y = 2$
(c)
33. (a) 37,500 units
(b) $30(2K)^{1/4}(2L)^{3/4} = 30(2^{1/4})(2^{3/4})K^{1/4}L^{3/4} = 2[30K^{1/4}L^{3/4}]$
(c)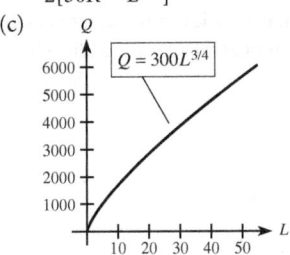
35. (a) 7200 units (b) 5000 units 37. $284,000

14.2 EXERCISES

1. $\frac{\partial z}{\partial x} = 4x^3 - 10x + 6$ $\frac{\partial z}{\partial y} = 9y^2 - 5$
3. $z_x = 3x^2 + 8xy$ $z_y = 4x^2 + 12y$
5. $\frac{\partial f}{\partial x} = 9x^2(x^3 + 2y^2)^2$ $\frac{\partial f}{\partial y} = 12y(x^3 + 2y^2)^2$
7. $f_x = 2x(2x^2 - 5y^2)^{-1/2}$ $f_y = -5y(2x^2 - 5y^2)^{-1/2}$
9. $\frac{\partial C}{\partial x} = -4y + 20xy$ $\frac{\partial C}{\partial y} = -4x + 10x^2$
11. $\frac{\partial Q}{\partial s} = \frac{2(t^2 + 3st - s^2)}{(s^2 + t^2)^2}$ $\frac{\partial Q}{\partial t} = \frac{3t^2 - 4st - 3s^2}{(s^2 + t^2)^2}$
13. $z_x = 2e^{2x} + \frac{y}{x}$ $z_y = \ln x$
15. $\frac{\partial f}{\partial x} = \frac{y}{xy + 1}$ $\frac{\partial f}{\partial y} = \frac{x}{xy + 1}$ 17. 2
19. 7 21. -19
23. (a) 0 (b) $-2xz + 4$ (c) $2y$ (d) $-x^2$

25. (a) $8x_1 + 5x_2$ (b) $5x_1 + 12x_2$ (c) 1
27. (a) 2 (b) 0 (c) 0 (d) $-30y$
29. (a) $2y$ (b) $2x - 8y$ (c) $2x - 8y$ (d) $-8x$
31. (a) $2 + y^2e^{xy}$ (b) $xye^{xy} + e^{xy}$
(c) $xye^{xy} + e^{xy}$ (d) x^2e^{xy}
33. (a) $1/x^2$ (b) 0 (c) 0 (d) $2 + 1/y^2$
35. -6 37. (a) $\frac{188}{4913}$ (b) $\frac{-188}{4913}$ 39. $2 + 2e$
41. 0 43. (a) $24x$ (b) $24x$ (c) 0
45. (a) For a mortgage of $100,000 and an 8% interest rate, the monthly payment is $771.82.
(b) The rate of change of the payment with respect to the interest rate is $66.25. That is, if the rate goes from 8% to 9% on a $100,000 mortgage, the approximate increase in the monthly payment is $66.25.
47. (a) If the number of items sold per week changes by 1, the most economical order quantity should also increase.
$$\frac{\partial Q}{\partial M} = \sqrt{\frac{K}{2Mh}} > 0$$
(b) If the weekly storage costs change by 1, the most economical order quantity should decrease.
$$\frac{\partial Q}{\partial h} = -\sqrt{\frac{KM}{2h^3}} < 0$$
49. 23.912; If brand 2 is held constant and brand 1 is increased from 100 to 101 liters, approximately 24,000 additional insects will be killed.
51. (a) $2xy^2$ (b) $2x^2y$
53. $\frac{\partial Q}{\partial K} = 100$; If labor hours are held constant at 5832 and K changes by $1 (thousand) to $730,000, Q will change by about 100 units. $\frac{\partial Q}{\partial L} = 25$; If capital expenditures are held constant at $729,000 and L changes by 1 hour (to 5833), Q will change by about 25 units.
55. (a) $\frac{\partial WC}{\partial s} = 0.16s^{-0.84}(0.4275t - 35.75)$
(b) At $t = 10, s = 25, \frac{\partial WC}{\partial s} \approx -0.34$
This means that if wind speed changes by 1 mph (from 25 mph) while the temperature remains at 10°F, the wind chill temperature will change by about $-0.34°F$.

14.3 EXERCISES

1. (a) $105
(b) $C_x = 3$ means total costs would change by $3 if labor costs changed by $1 and raw material costs stayed the same.
3. (a) $C_x = 2 + y/50$ (b) $C_y = 4 + x/50$
5. (a) $C_x = 25.78 (b) $C_y = 74.80
7. (a) If y remains at 10, the expected change in cost for a 9th unit of X is about $36.
(b) If x remains at 8, the expected change in cost for an 11th unit of Y is about $19.
9. (a) $\sqrt{y^2 + 1}$ dollars per unit
(b) $xy/\sqrt{y^2 + 1}$ dollars per unit
11. (a) $1200y/(xy + 1)$ dollars per unit
(b) $1200x/(xy + 1)$ dollars per unit
13. (a) $\sqrt{y/x}$ (b) $\sqrt{x/y}$
15. (a) $\ln(y + 1)/(2\sqrt{x})$ (b) $\sqrt{x}/(y + 1)$

17. $z = 1092$ crates (approximately)

19. $z_x = 3.6$; If 500 acres are planted, the approximate change in productivity from a 301st hour of labor is 3.6 crates.

21. (a) $z_x = \dfrac{240y^{2/5}}{x^{2/5}}$

(b)

(c) $z_y = \dfrac{160x^{3/5}}{y^{3/5}}$

(d)

(e) Both z_x and z_y are positive, so increases in both capital investment and work-hours result in increases in productivity. However, both are decreasing, so such increases have a diminishing effect on productivity.

23. $q_1 = 188$ units; $q_2 = 270$ units

25. any values for p_1 and p_2 that satisfy $6p_2 - 3p_1 = 100$ and that make q_1 and q_2 nonnegative, such as $p_1 = \$10$, $p_2 = \$21\frac{2}{3}$

27. (a) -3 units per dollar (b) -2 units per dollar
(c) -6 units per dollar (d) -5 units per dollar
(e) complementary

29. (a) -50 units per dollar
(b) $600/(p_B + 1)^2$ units per dollar
(c) $-400/(p_B + 4)^2$ units per dollar
(d) $400/(p_A + 4)^2$ units per dollar
(e) competitive

31. (a) Competitive; as the price of one type of car declines, demand for the other declines
(b) (i) $q_{NEW} = 2600 - p_{NEW}/30 + p_{USED}/15$
$q_{USED} = 750 - 0.25\,p_{USED} + 0.0125\,p_{NEW}$
(ii) Since the mixed partials are both positive (1/15 and 0.0125), the products are competitive.

14.4 EXERCISES

1. max$(0, 0, 9)$
3. min$(-2, 0, 4)$
5. saddle$(-2, -3, 16)$
7. min $(1, -2, 0)$
9. saddle$(1, -3, 8)$
11. max$(12, 24, 456)$
13. min$(-8, 6, -52)$
15. saddle$(0, 0, 0)$; min$(2, 2, -8)$
17. $\hat{y} = 5.7x - 1.4$
19. $x = 5000, y = 128$; $P = \$25,409.60$
21. $x = \frac{20}{3}, y = \frac{10}{3}$; $W \approx 1926$ lb
23. $x = 28, y = 100$; $P = 5987.84$ tons
25. $x = 20$ thousand, $y = 30$ thousand; $P = \$1900$ thousand
27. length $= 100$ in., width $= 100$ in., height $= 50$ in.
29. $x = 15$ thousand, $y = 24$ thousand; $P = \$295$ thousand
31. (a) eat-in $= 2400$; take-out $= 3800$
(b) eat-in @ $\$3.60$; take-out @ $\$3.10$; max profit $= \$12,480$
(c) Change pricing; more profitable

33. (a) $\hat{C} = 0.885y + 0.413$
(b)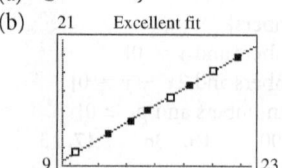
(c) $\$21.0$ billion
(d) $m = 0.885$; means that for each additional dollar of disposable personal income, 0.885 of it is spent.

35. (a) $\hat{y} = 0.0625x + 6.19$, x in years past 2000, $\hat{y}$ in billions
(b) 7.75 billion
(c) World population is changing about 0.0625 billion persons per year past 2000.

14.5 EXERCISES

1. 18 at $(3, 3)$ **3.** 35 at $(3, 2)$ **5.** 32 at $(4, 2)$
7. -28 at $\left(3, \frac{5}{2}\right)$ **9.** 15 at $(5, 3)$
11. 3 at $(1, 1, 1)$ **13.** 1 at $(0, 1, 0)$
15. $x = 2, y = 2$
17. $x = 40, y = \frac{40}{3}$

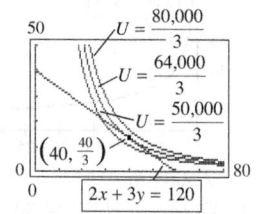

19. (a) $x = 400, y = 400$
(b) $-\lambda = 1.6$; means that each additional dollar spent on production results in approximately 1.6 additional units produced.
(c)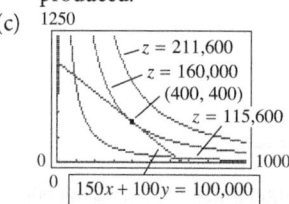

21. $x = 900, y = 300$; 900 units at plant X, 300 units at plant Y
23. $x = \$10,003.33, y = \$19,996.67$
25. length $= 100$ cm, width $= 100$ cm, height $= 50$ cm

CHAPTER 14 REVIEW EXERCISES

1. $\{(x, y): x$ and y are real numbers and $y \neq 2x\}$
2. $\{(x, y): x$ and y are real numbers with $y \geq 0$ and $(x, y) \neq (0, 0)\}$
3. -5 **4.** 896,000
5. $15x^2 + 6y$ **6.** $24y^3 - 42x^3y^2$
7. $z_x = 8xy^3 + 1/y$; $z_y = 12x^2y^2 - x/y^2$
8. $z_x = x/\sqrt{x^2 + 2y^2}$; $z_y = 2y/\sqrt{x^2 + 2y^2}$
9. $z_x = -2y/(xy + 1)^3$; $z_y = -2x/(xy + 1)^3$
10. $z_x = 2xy^3 e^{x^2y^3}$; $z_y = 3x^2y^2 e^{x^2y^3}$
11. $z_x = ye^{xy} + y/x$; $z_y = xe^{xy} + \ln x$
12. $z_x = y$; $z_y = x$ **13.** -8 **14.** 8
15. (a) $2y$ (b) 0   (c) $2x - 3$ (d) $2x - 3$

16. (a) $18xy^4 - 2/y^2$ (b) $36x^3y^2 - 6x^2/y^4$
    (c) $36x^2y^3 + 4x/y^3$ (d) $36x^2y^3 + 4x/y^3$

17. (a) $2e^{y^2}$ (b) $4x^2y^2e^{y^2} + 2x^2e^{y^2}$
    (c) $4xye^{y^2}$ (d) $4xye^{y^2}$

18. (a) $-y^2/(xy + 1)^2$ (b) $-x^2/(xy + 1)^2$
    (c) $1/(xy + 1)^2$ (d) $1/(xy + 1)^2$

19. $\max(-8, 16, 208)$

20. saddles at $(2, -3, 38)$ and $(-2, 3, -38)$; min at $(2, 3, -70)$; max at $(-2, -3, 70)$

21. 80 at $(2, 8)$

22. 11,664 at $(6, 3)$

23. (a) $x^2y = 540$ (b) 3 units

24. (a) $46,204
    (b) When the monthly contribution is $250 and the interest rate is 7.8%, the accumulated value is about $143,648.
    (c) When the contribution is $250, if the interest rate changed from 7.8% to 8.8%, the approximate change in the account would be $17,770.
    (d) $A_R \approx 574.59$ means that with an interest rate of 7.8%, if the monthly contribution changed from $250 to $251, the approximate change in the accumulated value would be $574.59.

25. (a) 8.996 thousand, or $8996
    (b) 0.009; means that when the benefits are paid for 20 years, if the account value changes from 1000 to 1001 (thousand dollars), the monthly benefit increases by about 0.009 (thousand), or $9.
    (c) -0.161; means that when the account value is $1,000,000, if the duration of benefits changes from 20 to 21 years, the monthly benefit decreases by about $161.

26. (a) If selling price is fixed, more dollars spent for advertising will increase sales.
    (b) If advertising dollars are fixed, an increase in the selling price will decrease sales.

27. (a) 280 dollars per unit of x
    (b) $2400/7$ dollars per unit of y

28. $\partial Q/\partial K = 81.92$ means that when capital expenditures increase by $1000 (to $626,000) and work-hours remain at 4096, output will change by about 8192 units; $\partial Q/\partial L = 37.5$ means that when labor hours change by 1 (to 4097) and capital expenditures remain at $625,000, output will change by about 3750 units.

29. (a) -2 (b) -6 (c) complementary

30. competitive

31. $x = 20, y = 40; P = 2000

32. 200 units at plant I; 1500 units at plant II

33. $x = 10, y = 4$

34. (a) $x = 1000, y = 500$
    (b) $-\lambda \approx 3.17$; means that each additional dollar spent on production results in approximately 3 additional units.
    (c)

35. (a) $\hat{y} = 2375x + 39{,}630$ (b) $75,255

36. (a) $\hat{y} = 0.736x + 28.4$
    (b) $m = 0.736$ means that for every 1000 women entering the workforce, about 736 men are entering it.

CHAPTER 14 TEST

1. (a) all pairs (x, y) with $y < x^2$ (b) 14

2. $z_x = 5 + 10y(xy + 1)^4$ $z_y = -18y + 10x(xy + 1)^4$
    $z_{xx} = 40y^2(xy + 1)^3$ $z_{yy} = -18 + 40x^2(xy + 1)^3$
    $z_{xy} = z_{yx} = 10(5xy + 1)(xy + 1)^3$

3. $(0, 2)$, a relative minimum; $(4, -6)$ and $(-4, -6)$, saddle points

4. (a) $1625 thousand
    (b) 73.11; means that if capital investment increases from $10,000 to $11,000, the approximate change in monthly production value will be $73.11 thousand, if labor hours remain at 1590.
    (c) 0.56; means that if labor hours increase by 1 to 1591, the approximate change in monthly production value will be $0.56 thousand, if capital investment remains at $10,000.

5. (a) When $94,500 is borrowed for 25 years at 7%, the monthly payment is $667.91.
    (b) If the percent goes from 7% to 8%, the approximate change in the monthly payment is $60.28, if the loan amount remains at $94,500 for 25 years.
    (c) Negative. If the loan amount remains at $94,500 and the percent remains at 7%, increasing the time to pay off the loan will decrease the monthly payment, and vice versa.

6. $8xy\, e^{x^2y^2}(x^2y^2 + 1)$

7. Find $\dfrac{\partial q_1}{\partial p_2}$ and $\dfrac{\partial q_2}{\partial p_1}$ and compare their signs. Both positive means competitive. Both negative means complementary. These products are complementary.

8. $x = $7, y = $11; P = 5065

9. $x = 200, y = 100$

10. (a) $\hat{y} = 0.241x + 5.78$
    (b) The fit is excellent.
    (c) 16.6%

Index